# WRITERS' AND ARTISTS' YEARBOOK 1990

D0766066

# Writers' & Artists' Yearbook

# 1990

## EIGHTY-THIRD YEAR OF ISSUE

*A directory for writers, artists, playwrights,
writers for film, radio and television,
photographers and composers*

A & C BLACK · LONDON

©1990 A & C BLACK (PUBLISHERS) LIMITED
35 BEDFORD ROW, LONDON WC1R 4JH

All rights reserved. No part of this publication
may be reproduced, stored in a retrieval system,
or transmitted, in any form or by any means,
electronic, mechanical, photocopying, recording
or otherwise, without the prior permission in writing of
A. & C. Black (Publishers) Limited.

A. & C. Black (Publishers) Limited has used its
best efforts in collecting and preparing material
for inclusion in the *Writers' and Artists' Yearbook
1990*. It does not assume, and hereby disclaims,
any liability to any party for any loss or
damage caused by errors or omissions in the
*Writers' and Artists' Yearbook 1990*, whether such
errors or omissions result from negligence,
accident or any other cause.

A CIP catalogue record for this book
is available from the British Library.

Typeset, printed and bound in Great Britain by
BPCC Hazell Books Ltd
Member of BPCC Ltd
Aylesbury, Bucks, England

# Contents

## PART ONE: Markets

### Articles, reports, short stories

### Books

### Poetry

## Scripts for theatre, radio, television and film

## Illustration and design

## Photography

# PART TWO: General Information

## Publishing practice

## Preparation of materials, resources

See also PICTURE RESEARCH section

## Societies and prizes

# Preface

This 83rd annual edition of *Writers' & Artists' Yearbook* has been completely updated and revised. The book is arranged to form two main parts with fourteen clearly-defined sections.

*The first part* provides *Markets* for articles, books, scripts, poetry, illustrations, photographs, picture research and music.

*The second part* offers *General information*, with articles on many practical and legal matters of importance to writers and artists, together with lists of resources.

Cross-references to material in other sections has been included where this may be of relevance.

Annual revision of *Writer's & Artists' Yearbook* ensures that the directory sections are carefully checked by the relevant editor, publishing house or agent. All addresses, requirements, rates of payment and other details are therefore up to date at the time of going to press. All the other sections of the book are carefully revised by reference to the original source.

This 1990 edition includes three significant articles: a new and detailed review of the markets for poetry in *Poetry Publishing Today*, a brief survey of the future of broadcasting in *Writing for Broadcasting in the Nineties* and an outline of the new Copyright, Designs and Patents Act. An extended index makes for easier and more rapid reference.

**Vanity publishing** Every edition of the *Yearbook* in recent years has contained a strong warning that the author who pays for the publication of his work is almost invariably making an expensive mistake. It has been suggested that several distinguished poets have found it necessary to underwrite their first books in order to establish themselves, and in this respect the cautionary note on 'vanity publishing' on page 247 has been mildly modified; but unhappily there still is ample evidence that an emphatic general warning is necessary.

It should be repeated, too, that the publishers of the *Yearbook* cannot provide an advisory service, and that to rely on an out-of-date edition is to invite inevitable difficulties and disappointments.

Because users of the reference sections will frequently need to know the new telephone codes which come into operation in May 1990, a full list of codes appears at the end of the *Yearbook* immediately *after* the index.

# PART ONE
# Markets

# Articles, reports and short stories

## SUBMITTING MATERIAL

More than seven hundred titles are included in the United Kingdom newspapers and magazines section of the *Yearbook,* almost all of them offering opportunities to the writer. Some 200 leading Commonwealth and South African titles are also included, and while some of these have little space for freelance contributions, many of them will always consider outstanding work. Many do not appear in our lists because the market they offer for the freelance writer is either too small or too specialised, or both. It is impossible to include all such publications in the *Yearbook,* for the benefit of only a small proportion of its purchasers, without substantially increasing its price. Those who wish to offer contributions to technical, specialist or local journals are likely to know their names and can ascertain their addresses; before submitting a manuscript to any such periodical they are advised to write a preliminary letter to its editor.

Magazine editors frequently complain to us about the unsuitability of many manuscripts submitted to them. Not only are the manuscripts unsuitable, but no postage is sent for their return. In their own interests, writers and others are advised to *enclose postage for the return of unsuitable material.*

Before submitting manuscripts, writers should study carefully the editorial requirements of a magazine; not only for the subjects dealt with, but for the approach, treatment, style and length. Obvious though these comments may be to the practised writer, the beginner would be spared much disappointment by studying the markets more carefully (but should not expect editors to send free specimen copies of their magazines). An article or short story suitable for *Woman's Realm* is unlikely to appeal to the readers of *The Spectator.* The importance of studying the market cannot be over-emphasised. It is an editor's job to know what readers want, and to see that they get it. Thus freelance contributions must be tailored to fit a specific market; subject, theme, treatment, length, etc., must meet the editor's requirements.

A number of magazines and newspapers will accept and pay for letters to the editor, paragraphs for gossip columns and brief filler paragraphs. For a list of these see the **Classified Index** at the end of this section. This index provides only a rough guide to markets and must be used with discrimination. For lists of recent mergers, changes of title, and terminations, also see end of this section.

A list of British magazine publishers, with their addresses, follows the Classified Index.

Writers and artists, and others, are advised not to accept from editors less than a fair price for their work, and to ascertain exactly what rights they are being asked to dispose of when an offer is made.

It has always been our aim to obtain and publish the rates of payment offered for contributions by newspapers and magazines. Certain journals of the highest standard and reputation are reluctant, for reasons that are understandable, to state a standard rate of payment, since the value of a contribution may be dependent not upon length but upon the standing of the writer or of the information given. Many periodicals when giving a rate of payment indicate that it is the 'minimum rate'; others, in spite of efforts to extract more precise information from them, prefer to state 'usual terms' or 'by arrangement'.

**The Society of Authors** makes the following additional suggestions for submitting freelance contributions to newspapers and magazines (see also Typescripts under **Preparation of Materials, Resources**).

*General points:*

1. Keep copies of all material and correspondence and a note of telephone conversations.
2. Confirm any oral arrangements (whether made on the telephone or face-to-face) in writing immediately.
3. Make clear to the editor, in the letter accompanying your MSS or on its cover sheet, what rights you are offering. As a rule, offer only First British Serial Rights.
4. Enclose a stamped addressed envelope for the return of your manuscript.
5. Don't wait for more than five weeks before you ask for a decision or the return of your manuscript, but don't start making enquiries until the editor has had it for a fortnight—unless, of course, it is highly topical material.
6. When your piece is accepted make sure that there is a letter (either from or to the editor) confirming the rate of payment and the probable date of publication. Aim for payment on acceptance even though most magazines will insist on paying on publication. As publication is sometimes considerably delayed, make it clear that you wish to be paid by a specified date even if your article has not been published by then.
7. If you are asked to rewrite your piece as a condition of acceptance, ensure that the request is confirmed in writing and that you will be paid even if the material is not used.

*Commissioned articles:*

1. Agree the fee or rate of payment at the outset, specify the rights offered, and ask for payment on delivery.
2. If payment is to be made on publication, make it clear that your fee will become due in any event if the article has not been published by a specified date.

**Writing for markets outside the UK** The lists of overseas newspapers and magazines contain only a selection of those journals which offer some market for the freelance. To print, and to keep up to date, a complete list for each English-speaking country would increase the extent and cost of the *Yearbook* quite disproportionately to the value of such enlargement. The overseas market for stories and articles is small and editors often prefer their fiction to have a local setting.

The larger newspapers and magazines buy many of their stories, as the smaller papers buy general articles, through one or other of the well-known syndicates, and a writer may be well advised to send printed copies of stories he has had published at home to an agent for syndication overseas.

Most of the big newspapers depend for news on their own staffs and the press agencies. The most important papers have permanent representatives in Britain who keep them supplied, not only with news of especial interest to the country concerned, but also with regular summaries of British news and with articles on events of particular importance. While many overseas newspapers and magazines have a London office, it is usual for MSS from freelance contributors to be submitted to the headquarters' editorial office overseas.

When sending MSS abroad it is important to remember to enclose International Reply Coupons; these can be exchanged in any foreign country for stamps representing the minimum postage payable on a letter sent from that country to this country.

# List of Newspapers and Magazines

## UNITED KINGDOM

**Aberdeen Evening Express,** R. J. Williamson, Lang Stracht, Aberdeen AB9 8AF   *tel* (0224) 690222   *telex* 73133 Jnlsab G   *fax* (0224) 685738.
20p. D. Lively evening paper reading. *Payment:* by arrangement. *Illustrations:* mainly half-tone.

**(Aberdeen) The Press and Journal** (1748), Harry Roulston, Lang Stracht, Aberdeen AB9 8AF   *tel* (0224) 690222. London Office: Pemberton House (Third Floor), East Harding Street, EC4A 3AS   *tel* 01-353 9131.
23p. D. Contributions of Scottish interest. *Payment:* by arrangement. *Illustrations:* half-tone.

**Accountancy** (1889), Brian O'Kane, 40 Bernard Street, London WC1N 1LD   *tel* 01-628 7060.
£2.25. M. Articles on accounting, taxation, financial, legal and other subjects likely to be of professional interest to accountants in practice or industry, and to top management generally. *Payment:* £92 per page. *Illustrations:* half-tone and colour. Cartoons.

**Accountancy Age** (1969), Robert Bruce, VNU Business Publications, VNU House, 32-34 Broadwick Street, London W1A 2HG   *tel* 01-439 4242   *telex* 23918 VNU G   *fax* 01-437 7001.
£1.50. W. Articles of accounting, financial and business interest. *Payment:* by arrangement. *Illustrations:* colour and b&w photos; freelance assignments commissioned; *payment:* NUJ rates.

**The Accountant's Magazine** (1897), official journal of The Institute of Chartered Accountants of Scotland, Winifred N. Elliott, M.A., 27 Queen Street, Edinburgh EH2 1LA   *tel* 031-225 5673   *telex* 727530   *fax* 031-225 3813.
£1.85. M. (£20.00 p.a.). Articles on accounting, auditing, company law, finance, taxation, topical subjects, management, investment. *Length:* 1000-2500 words. *Payment:* by arrangement. *Illustrations:* line, half-tone, colour.

**Accounting World** (formerly **Administrative Accountant**) (1920), Garry Carter, The Publishing Dimension Ltd., 11, St. Mark's Road, Windsor, Berkshire SL4 3BD   *tel* (0753) 830909   *fax* (0753) 830034. Journal of The Institute of Financial Accountants and The International Association of Book-keepers, Burford House, 44 London Road, Sevenoaks, Kent TN13 1AS   *tel* (0732) 458080.
£18.00 p.a. M. Articles on accounting, management, company law, data processing, information technology, pensions, factoring, investment, insurance, fraud prevention and general business administration. *Length:* 1000-2000 words. *Payment:* by arrangement. *Illustrations:* offset litho (mono or colour).

**Achievement,** World Trade House, 145 High Street, Sevenoaks, Kent TN13 1XJ   *tel* (0732) 458144.

£1.50. M. Lively articles relating to British business achievements in international project management. *Illustrations:* first-class photographs. *Payment:* by arrangement.

**Acumen** (1985), Patricia Oxley, 6 The Mount, Higher Furzeham, Brixham, South Devon TQ5 8QY   *tel* (08045) 51098.
£5 p.a. Bi-annual (Apr/Oct). Poetry, literary articles, interviews with poets on poetry. *Payment:* by negotiation. *Illustrations:* line drawings; *payment:* by negotiation. Send *sae* with submissions.

**Administrator** (1971), official journal of The Institute of Chartered Secretaries and Administrators, Susan Grayling, 16 Park Crescent, London W1N 4AH   *tel* 01-580 4741   *fax* 01-323 1132.
£2.00. M. (£20.00 p.a. post free). Practical and topical articles 750-1600 words (occasionally longer) on law, finance, and personnel-orientated problems and development affecting company secretaries and other senior administrators in business, nationalised industries, local and central government and other institutions in Britain and overseas. Most articles commissioned from leading administrators. *Payment:* by arrangement. *Illustrations:* line and half-tone, only by special commission.

**Aeromodeller** (1935), Geoff Clarke, Argus Specialist Publications Ltd., P.O. Box 35, Hemel Hempstead, Hertfordshire HP2 4SS   *tel* (0442) 41221   *fax* (0442) 216429.
£1.95. M. Articles and news concerning model aircraft and radio control of model aircraft. Suitable articles and first-class photographs by outside contributors are always considered. *Length:* 750-2000 words, or by arrangement. *Illustrations:* photographs and line drawings to scale.

**Aeroplane Monthly** (1973), Richard R. Riding, Prospect Magazines, Reed Business Publishing Ltd., Prospect House, 9-13 Ewell Road, Cheam, Surrey SM1 4QQ   *tel* 01-661 4554   *telex* 892084.
£1.50. M. Articles relating to historical aviation. *Length:* up to 2500 words. *Illustrations:* half-tone, line, colour. *Payment:* £35 per 1000 words; photographs £8.00 minimum; colour £40 minimum.

**African Business** (1978), Linda Van Buren, P.O. Box 261, Carlton House, 69 Great Queen Street, London WC2B 5BN   *tel* 01-404 4333   *telex* 8811757 Araby G   *fax* 01-404 5336.
£1.20. M. Articles on business, economic and financial topics of interest to businessmen, ministers, officials concerned with African affairs. *Length:* 400 to 750 words; shorter coverage 100 to 400 words. *Payment:* £70 per 1000 words. *Illustrations:* line, half-tone.

**Agenda,** William Cookson and Peter Dale, 5 Cranbourne Court, Albert Bridge Road, London SW11 4PE   *tel* 01-228 0700.
£14.00 p.a. (£18 for Libraries and Institutions). Q. Poetry and criticism. *Payment:* £12.00 per poem or per page of poetry. *Illustrations:* half-tone. Contributors should study the journal before submitting MSS with an sae.

**Air Pictorial,** Kristall Productions, 71b Maple Road, Surbiton, Surrey KT6 4AG   *tel* 01-399 9656.
£1.35. M. Journal with wide aviation coverage. Many articles commissioned, and the Editor is glad to consider competent articles exploring fresh ground or presenting an individual point of view on technical matters. *Payment:* £18.00 per 1000 words. *Illustrations:* half-tones and line; new photographs of unusual or rare aircraft considered.

**Albion** (1977), David Goss, 33 Millstream Close, Hitchin, Hertfordshire SG4 0DA.
£5.00 p.a. 3 p.a. Devoted to the work of the private presses worldwide and to every aspect of the history and practice of letterpress printing and the arts of the book. Contributions always welcome by discussion with the Editor. *Payment:* by arrangement. *Illustrations:* line, half-tone.

**Amateur Gardening** (1884), G. Clarke, Westover House, West Quay Road, Poole, Dorset BH15 1JG  *tel* (0202) 680586  *fax* (0202) 674335.
55p. W. Articles up to 700 words about any aspect of gardening. *Payment:* by arrangement. *Illustrations:* half-tone, colour.

**Amateur Photographer** (1884), George Hughes, Prospect House, 9-13 Ewell Road, Cheam, Surrey SM1 4QQ  *tel* 01-661 4449.
£1.00. W. Original articles of pictorial or technical interest, preferably illustrated with either photographs or diagrams. Good instructional features especially sought. *Length preferred:* (unillustrated) 400 to 800 words: articles up to 1500 words; (illustrated) 2 to 4 pages. *Payment:* monthly, at rates according to usage. *Illustrations* unaccompanied by text will be considered for covers or feature illustrations; please indicate if we can hold on file.

**Amateur Stage** (1946), Charles Vance, 83 George Street, London W1H 5PL  *tel* 01-486 1732, 01-486 7930  *fax* 01-224 2215.
£1.00. M. Articles on all aspects of the amateur theatre, preferably practical and factual. *Length:* 600-2000 words. *Payment:* nominal. *Illustrations:* photographs and line drawings, *payment* for which varies.

**Ambit** (1959), Dr Martin Bax, 17 Priory Gardens, Highgate, London N6 5QY  *tel* 01-340 3566.
£2.50. Q. Poems, short stories, criticism. *Payment:* by arrangement. *Illustrations:* line and half-tone.

**Angler's Mail,** Roy Westwood, IPC Magazines Ltd, King's Reach Tower, Stamford Street, London SE1 9LS  *tel* 01-261 5778.
53p. W. Features and news items about sea, coarse and game fishing. *Length:* 650 to 800 words. *Payment:* by arrangement. *Illustrations:* half-tone, colour, line and wash drawings (Web offset litho printing).

**Angling Times** (1953), Neil Pope, EMAP Pursuit Publishing Ltd, Bretton Court, Bretton, Peterborough PE3 8DZ  *tel* Peterborough (0733) 266222, (0733) 264666  *fax* (0733) 265515.
43p. W. Articles, pictures, news stories, on all forms of angling. *Illustrations:* colour, half-tone, line.

**Animal World,** Elizabeth Winson, RSPCA, Causeway, Horsham, Sussex RH12 1HG  *tel* Horsham (0403) 64181.
30p. Q. Fiction and factual articles concerning animals and animal welfare. *Length:* 350-1000 words. All MSS must be typewritten. *Readership:* young people between 5 and 17. *Payment:* according to value. *Illustrations:* mainly colour transparencies and black and white photographs.

**Annabel** (D. C. Thomson & Co., Ltd.), 80 Kingsway East, Dundee DD4 8SL, and 185 Fleet Street, London EC4A 2HS.
80p. M. Colour gravure monthly for the modern woman with wide interests. Personal experience stories, biographical stories of well-known personalities, family and parenthood topics, fashion, cookery, knitting, fiction. Art *illustrations* and photographs in full colour and black-and-white. *Payment:* on acceptance.

**Antique Clocks** (1978), Argus Specialist Publications Ltd. Editorial address: Hunter Communications, P.O. Box 233, Edinburgh EH6 7BD    *tel* 031-554 5660    *fax* 031-554 5665.
£2.25. M. Well researched articles on antique clocks and their makers, clock repair and restoration, and in general anything of interest to knowledgeable horologists. Sundials, barometers and associated scientific instruments are minority interests of Antique Clocks readers. *Length:* 1500-3000 words. *Payment:* £30 per 1000 words, £5 per black and white photograph, £8 per colour print/transparency. *Illustrations:* line, half-tone, colour. No cartoons.

**The Antique Collector** (1930), David Coombs, Eagle House, 50 Marshall Street, London W1V 1LR    *tel* 01-439 5000    *fax* 01-439 5177.
£2.50. M. Authoritative and fully illustrated information for those interested in extending their knowledge and enjoyment of all aspects of antiques and art. *Illustrations:* fine black and white and colour photographs.

**The Antique Dealer & Collectors Guide,** Philip Bartlam, IPC Magazines Ltd., King's Reach Tower, Stamford Street, London SE1 9LS    *tel* 01-261 6894.
£1.60. M. Articles on antique collecting and art. *Length:* up to 1500 words. *Payment:* £68 per 1000 words. *Illustrations:* half-tone and colour.

**Antiques Folio** (incorporating **Antiques**) (1963), Tony Keniston, Old Rectory, Hopton Castle, Craven Arms, Shropshire SY7 0QJ    *tel* (05474) 464.
10p. Q. Articles on antiques and of interest to antique dealers and serious collectors. *Length:* 300 to 600 words. *Payment:* on merit. *Illustrations:* line and half-tone.

**Apollo** (1925) (Apollo Magazine Ltd.), Anna Somers Cocks, 22 Davies Street, London W1Y 1LH    *tel* 01-629 3061.
£4.00. M. Knowledgeable articles of about 2500 words on art, ceramics, furniture, armour, glass, sculpture, and any subject connected with art and collecting. *Payment:* by arrangement. *Illustrations:* colour and half-tone.

**The Aquarist and Pondkeeper** (1924), John Dawes, Dog World Ltd, 9 Tufton Street, Ashford, Kent TN23 1QN    *tel* (0233) 621877    *fax* (0233) 45669.
£1.10. M. Illustrated authoritative articles by professional and amateur biologists, naturalists and aquarium hobbyists on all matters concerning life in and near water. *Length:* about 1500 words. *Payment:* by arrangement. *Illustrations:* photographs, line, colour.

**The Architects' Journal** (1895), Colin Davies, R.I.B.A., 9 Queen Anne's Gate, London SW1H 9BY    *tel* 01-222 4333    *fax* 01-222 5196.
£1.00. W. Articles (mainly technical) on architecture, planning and building accepted only with prior agreement of synopsis. *Payment:* by arrangement. *Illustrations:* photographs and drawings.

**Architectural Design** (1930), Dr Andreas C. Papadakis, Academy Group Ltd, 42 Leinster Gardens, London W2 3AN    *tel* 01-402 2141    *telex* 896928 Academ G    *fax* 01-723 9540.
£45.00 p.a. 6 double issues. International magazine comprising an extensively illustrated thematic profile presenting architecture and critical interpretations of architectural history, theory and practice. *Payment:* by arrangement. *Illustrations:* drawings and photographs, colour, half-tone, line (colour preferred). Uncommissioned articles not accepted.

**Architectural Review** (1896), Peter Davey, 9 Queen Anne's Gate, Westminster, London SW1H 9BY    *tel* 01-222 4333    *telex* 8953505    *fax* 01-222 5196.

£4.25. M. Contains articles (up to 3000 words in length) on architecture and the allied arts. Must be thoroughly qualified writers. *Payment:* by arrangement. *Illustrations:* photographs, drawings, etc.

**Arena** (1986), Nick Logan, The Old Laundry, Ossington Buildings, London W1   *tel* 01-935 8232   *fax* 01-935 2237.
£1.50. Bi-M. Profiles, articles on a wide range of subjects intelligently treated; art, architecture, politics, sport, business, music, film, design, media, fashion. *Length:* up to 3000 words. *Payment:* £80-£90 per 1000 words. *Illustrations:* black-and-white and colour photographs.

**Argo** (incorporating **Delta**) (1979), Hilary Davies and David Constantine, Argo Publishing Co., Museum of Modern Art, 30 Pembroke Street, Oxford OX1 1BP.
£1.75. (£6.00 p.a.) 3 p.a. Poetry, short stories, translations of poetry, extracts from unpublished novels. S.a.e. essential. No unsolicited reviews. *Payment:* £3.00 per contributor. *Illustrations:* line, half-tone.

**Army Quarterly & Defence Journal** (1829), Publisher/Editor: T. D. Bridge, Research Director: Major-General H. M. Tillotson, 1 West Street, Tavistock, Devon PL19 8DS   *tel* (0822) 613577/612785   *fax* (0822) 612785.
£32 p.a. Q. Articles on a wide range of defence issues, historical and current, and UN forces affairs; also diary, book reviews. *Length:* 1000-6000 words. *Payment:* by arrangement. *Illustrations:* b&w photos, line drawings, maps; *payment:* by arrangement. *Preliminary letter preferred.*

**Art & Craft** (1946), Eileen Lowcock, Scholastic Publications (Magazines) Ltd., Marlborough House, Holly Walk, Leamington Spa, Warwickshire CV32 4LS   *tel* (0926 81) 3910   *telex* 312138 Spls G.
£1.30. M. Articles to offer fresh, creative ideas of a practical nature, based on sound art practice, for the infant/junior school teacher. Articles by experts on traditional crafts. *Illustrations:* colour and black-and-white line drawings. *Payment:* by arrangement.

**Art & Design** (1985), Dr Andreas C. Papadakis, Academy Group Ltd., 42 Leinster Gardens, London W2 3AN   *tel* 01-402 2141   *telex* 896928 Academ G   *fax* 01-723 9540.
£35.00 p.a. 6 double issues. International magazine covering the whole spectrum of the arts, with particular emphasis on New Art. Feature articles, exhibition reviews/previews, book reviews, product news. *Payment:* by arrangement. *Illustrations:* line, half-tone, colour (colour preferred). Uncommissioned articles not accepted.

**Art Book Review** (1982), Eric Shanes, 7 Cumberland Road, London W3 6EX   *tel* 01-992 7985.
£2.50 Q. Articles on art history; book reviews. *Payment:* £5.00 per 100 words. *Illustrations:* colour and half-tone.

**The Artist** (1931), Sally Bulgin, Caxton House, 63-65 High Street, Tenterden, Kent TN30 6BD   *tel* (05806) 3673.
£1.35. M. Practical and appreciative articles on all aspects of the visual arts. *Payment:* by arrangement. *Illustrations:* line, half-tone, colour.

**The Artist's & Illustrator's Magazine** (1986), David Mills, 4th Floor, 4 Brandon Road, London N7 9TP   *tel* 01-609 2177   *telex* 299656 Cii G   *fax* 01-700 4985.
£1.50 M. Mainly technical and practical articles on all the artistic media. *Length:* 1500 to 2000 words. *Payment:* £80 per 1000 words. *Illustrations:* colour photographs.

**Artrage,** Black Arts Quarterly (1982), Julian Brutus, 28 Shacklewell Lane, London E8 2EZ    *tel* 01-254 7275.
£1.50. Q. Black literature, performing arts and media arts, including arts reviews, interviews, poetry. *Length/payment:* 500-1000 words, £30; 1000-1800 words, £50-£80. *Illustrations:* half-tone, line.

**Arts Review** (1949), Starcity Ltd., 69 Faroe Road, London W14 0EL    *tel* 01-603 7530 and 8533.
£1.95. (£39.00 p.a.) F. Art criticism and reviews. Commissioned work only. *Illustrations:* half-tone and line; colour.

**The Author** (1890), Derek Parker, 84 Drayton Gardens, London SW10 9SB    *tel* 01-373 6642    *telegraphic address* Auctoritas, London.
£3.00. Q. Organ of The Society of Authors. Commissioned articles from 1000 to 2000 words on any subject connected with the legal, commercial or technical side of authorship. *Payment:* by arrangement. (Little scope for the freelance writer: a preliminary letter is advisable.)

**Autocar and Motor** (1895), Bob Murray, Haymarket Publishing Ltd, 38-42 Hampton Road, Teddington, Middlesex TW11 0JE    *tel* 01-977 8787    *telex* 8952440    *fax* 01-977 0517.
95p. W. All aspects of cars, motoring and motor industries. Articles, general, practical, competition and technical. *Payment:* varies; mid-month following publication. *Illustrations:* tone, line (litho) and colour. Press day news: Friday.

**Back Street Heroes** (1983), Steven Myatt, P.O. Box 28, Altrincham, Cheshire WA15 8SH    *tel* 061-928 3480    *fax* 061-941 6897.
£1.40. M. Custom motorcycle features plus informed lifestyle pieces. Biker fiction. *Payment:* by arrangement. *Illustrations:* half-tone, colour. Cartoons.

**Balance** (1935), Julie Apfel, The British Diabetic Association, 10 Queen Anne Street, London W1M 0BD    *tel* 01-323 1531    *fax* 01-637 3644.
85p. Bi-M. Articles on diabetes or related topics. *Length:* 1000-2000 words. *Payment:* £60.00 per 1000 words. *Illustrations:* line, half-tone, colour.

**Ballroom Dancing Times** (1956), Alex Moore, Editorial Adviser, Mary Clarke, Executive Editor, Clerkenwell House, 45-47 Clerkenwell Green, London EC1R 0BE    *tel* 01-250 3006.
60p. M. Dealing with ballroom dancing from every aspect, but chiefly from the serious competitive, teaching and medal test angles. Well informed freelance articles are occasionally used, but only after preliminary arrangements. *Payment:* by arrangement. *Illustrations:* web offset; action photographs preferred.

**The Banker** (1926), Gavin Shreeve, 102-8 Clerkenwell Road, London EC1M 5SA    *tel* 01-251 9321    *telex* 23700 Finbi G    *fax* 01-251 4686.
£3.50. M. Articles on capital markets, trade finance, bank analysis and top 1000 listings. *Illustrations:* half-tones of people, charts, tables.

**Banking World** (1983), Garth Hewitt, 3rd Floor, Greater London House, Hampstead Road, London NW1 7QQ    *tel* 01-822 3630    *telex* 922488 Bureau G (ref: HWY)    *fax* 01-383 7570.
£2.50. M. Commissioned articles on developments in retail banking world wide. *Length:* 200-2000 words. *Payment:* by arrangement. *Illustrations:* line, half-tone.

**Baptist Times** (1855), Geoffrey Locks, 4 Southampton Row, London WC1B 4AB    *tel* 01-405 5516    *fax* 01-831 1972.
28p. W. Religious or social affairs matter, 800 words. *Payment:* by arrangement. *Illustrations:* half-tone.

**BBC Wildlife Magazine,** Rosamund Kidman Cox, Broadcasting House, White-ladies Road, Bristol BS8 2LR    *tel* (0272) 732211.
£1.50. M. Popular but scientifically accurate articles about wildlife and conservation (national and international), some linked by subject to BBC tv and radio programmes. Two news sections for short, topical biological and environmental stories. *Length:* 1000-2000 words. *Payment:* £150 per article. *Illustrations:* top-quality colour and black-and-white photographs.

**The Beano** (D. C. Thomson & Co. Ltd.), Courier Place, Dundee DD1 9QJ, and 185 Fleet Street, London EC4A 2HS.
22p. W. Picture paper for young folk. Comic strip series, 11-22 pictures. *Payment:* on acceptance.

**Beano Library** (D. C. Thomson & Co. Ltd.), Courier Place, Dundee DD1 9QJ and 185 Fleet Street, London EC4A 2HS.
32p. 2 per month. Extra-long comic adventure stories featuring well-known characters from the weekly Beano publication.

**Beano Puzzle Library** (D. C. Thomson & Co. Ltd.) Courier Place, Dundee DD1 9QJ and 185 Fleet Street, London EC4A 2HS.
32p. M. 64 pages of puzzles, word-games and teasers featuring the well known characters from the weekly Beano, Dandy, Topper and Beezer publications.

**Bedfordshire Magazine** (1947), Betty Chambers, 50 Shefford Road, Meppershall, Shefford SG17 5LL    *tel* Hitchin (0462) 813363.
£1.25. Q. Articles of Bedfordshire interest, especially history and biography. *Length:* up to 1500 words. *Payment:* £1.05 per 1000 words. *Illustrations:* line and half-tone.

**The Beezer** (D. C. Thomson & Co. Ltd.), Courier Place, Dundee DD1 9QJ, and 185 Fleet Street, London EC4A 2HS.
26p. W. Comic strips for boys and girls. Approx. 10 pictures per single page story and 18 pictures per double page story. Promising artists encouraged. *Payment:* on acceptance.

**Bella** (1987), Jackie Highe, Shirley House, 25 Camden Road, London NW1 9LL    *tel* 01-284 0909.
32p. W. General interest magazine for women. Practical articles on fashion and beauty, health, cooking, home, travel. Short stories up to 2000 words. *Payment:* by arrangement. *Illustrations:* half-tone, line including cartoons, colour.

**Best** (1987), Sally Pearce, 10th Floor, Portland House, Stag Place, London SW1E 5AU    *tel* 01-245 8847    *fax* 01-245 8825.
40p. W. Short stories, articles, celebrity interviews, features. *Length:* from small columns to 2-page features. *Payment:* £35 for small articles; £400 for 1-page articles. *Illustrations:* line, half-tone, colour. Cartoons.

**Bicycle Action** (1984), Graeme Gibson, Muddy Fox Publications, 95 Manor Farm Road, Wembley, Middlesex HA0 1BY    *tel* 01-998 8711    *telex* 27421 Muddy G    *fax* 01-991 5963.
£1.20. M. Racing, touring, mountain bikes; emphasis on leisure aspects of cycling. *Payment:* by arrangement.

**Birmingham Evening Mail** (1870), I. Dowell, Colmore Circus, Birmingham B4 6AX    *tel* 021-236 3366    *telex* 337552. London Office: 19-21 Tudor Street, EC4Y 0AL    *tel* 01-353 0811.
17p. D. Ind. Features of topical Midland interest considered. *Length:* 400-800 words.

**The Birmingham Post,** P. Saunders, P.O. Box 18, 28 Colmore Circus, Birmingham B4 6AX  *tel* 021-236 3366  *telex* 337552. London Office: 19-21 Tudor Street, EC4Y 0LA  *tel* 01-353 0811.
22p. D. Authoritative and well-written articles of industrial, political or general interest are considered, especially if they have relevance to the Midlands. *Length:* up to 1000 words. *Payment:* by arrangement.

**Blue Jeans** (D. C. Thomson & Co., Ltd.), Courier Place, Dundee DD1 9QJ  *tel* 23131; and 185 Fleet Street, London EC4A 2HS  *tel* 01-242 5086.
32p. W. Colour gravure magazine for teenage girls. Photo love stories. True experience text stories up to 3000 words. Pop features and pin-ups. General teen interest features. Fashion and beauty. *Illustrations:* pop and boy/girl transparencies and black and whites, photo story photography, humorous illustrations. *Payment:* on acceptance.

**Blue Jeans Photo Novels** (D. C. Thomson & Co., Ltd.), Courier Place, Dundee DD1 9QJ  *tel* (0382) 23131, and 185 Fleet Street, London EC4A 2HS.
32p. Four per month. Teenage stories in photo story form. Approx 120 frames. Scripts required. *Payment:* on acceptance.

**Boards** (1982), Jeremy Evans, 196 Eastern Esplanade, Southend-on-Sea, Essex SS1 3AB  *tel* (0702) 582245  *fax* (0702) 588434.
£1.50. 9 p.a. (Monthly during summer, bi-monthly during winter). Articles, photographs and reports on all aspects of windsurfing and boardsailing. *Payment:* by arrangement. *Illustrations:* line, half-tone, colour.

**Bolton Evening News** (1867), Chris Walder, Newspaper House, Churchgate, Bolton, Greater Manchester BL1 1DE  *tel* (0204) 22345  *telegraphic address* Newspapers, Bolton.
20p. D. and W. Articles, particularly those with South Lancashire appeal. *Length:* up to 700 words. *Illustrations:* photographs; considered at usual rates. *Payment:* on 15th of month following date of publication.

**The Book Collector** (1952) (incorporating **Bibliographical Notes and Queries**), Editorial Board: Nicolas Barker (Editor), A. Bell, J. Commander, T. Hofmann, D. McKitterick, Stephen Weissman, The Collector Ltd., 68 Neal Street, London WC2H 9PA  *tel.* 01-379 5416.
£20.00 p.a. ($35.00), postage extra. Q. Articles, biographical and bibliographical, on the collection and study of printed books and MSS. *Payment:* by arrangement.

**Book News From Wales**—see **Llais Llyfrau**.

**Books Magazine** (1987), Matthew Bray, 43 Museum Street, London WC1A 1LY  *tel* 01-404 0304  *fax* 01-242 0762.
£1.20. M. Reviews, features, interviews with authors. *Payment:* negotiable. *Illustrations:* line, half-tone, colour.

**The Bookseller** (1858), Louis Baum, J. Whitaker and Sons Ltd., 12 Dyott Street, London WC1A 1DF  *tel* 01-836 8911  *fax* 01-836 6381.
£61.00 p.a. W. The journal of the publishing and bookselling trades. While outside contributions are always welcomed, most of the journal's contents are commissioned. *Length:* about 1000 to 1500 words. *Payment:* by arrangement.

**Brewing & Distilling International** (1865), Bruce Stevens, 52 Glenhouse Road, Eltham, London SE9 1JQ  *tel* 01-859 4300  *fax* 01-859 5813.
M. Devoted to the interests of brewers, maltsters, hop growers, barley growers, distillers, soft drinks manufacturers, bottlers and allied traders, circulating in over 80 countries. Contributions (average 1000 words) accepted are technical and marketing articles written by authors with a special knowledge of the

subjects dealt with. *Illustrations:* line drawings, photographs. *Payment:* by arrangement.

**Bridge International** (1926), Alan Hiron, 13 Queens Road, Wimbledon, London SW19 8NG    *tel* 01-947 6143    *telex* 8814338    *fax* 01-947 6149.
£19.95 p.a. M. Articles on bridge. *Payment:* by arrangement. *Illustrations:* line, half-tone.

**Bristol Evening Post** (1932), B. Jones, Temple Way, Bristol BS99 7HD    *tel* Bristol 260080.
18p. D. Articles up to 600 words with strong West-country interest. *Payment:* at recognised rates.

**La Brita Esperantisto** (Journal of the Esperanto Association de Britujo) (1905), W. Auld, 140 Holland Park Avenue, London W11 4UF    *tel* 01-727 7821.
95p. (£5.50 p.a.). M. Articles in Esperanto, by arrangement, on the applications of the International Language, Esperanto, to education, commerce, travel, international affairs, scouting, radio, television, literature, linguistics, etc. *Illustrations:* photos by arrangement. *Payment:* by arrangement.

**British Book News** (1940), Jennifer Creswick, The British Council, 65 Davies Street, London W1Y 2AA    *tel* 01-930 8466    *telex* 8952201 Bricon G    *fax* 01-493 5035. Subscriptions: Journal Dept, Basil Blackwell, 108 Cowley Road, Oxford OX4 1JF.
£24.50 p.a. (£33 for institutions; overseas rates on application). M. High quality articles on the book trade, book surveys, company profiles and reviews of new journals. *Length:* up to 2000 words. *Payment:* by arrangement.

**British Chess Magazine** (1881), B. Cafferty, 9 Market Street, St. Leonards-on-Sea, East Sussex TN38 0DQ    *tel* (0424) 424009    *fax* (0424) 435439.
£1.60. (£19.20 p.a. post free). M.

**The British Deaf News** (1955), Mrs Irene Hall, The British Deaf Association, 38 Victoria Place, Carlisle CA1 1HU    *tel* (0228) 48844 (Voice), (0228) 28719 (DCT).
40p. M. (£6.48 p.a.) Articles, news items, letters dealing with deafness. *Payment:* by arrangement. *Illustrations:* line and half-tone.

**The British Journal of Photography** (1854), Chris Dickie, 244–249 Temple Chambers, Temple Avenue, London EC4Y 0DT    *tel* 01-583 6463    *fax* 01-353 6867.
60p. W. Articles on professional, commercial and press photography, and on the more advanced aspects of amateur, technical, industrial, medical, scientific and colour photography. *Payment:* by arrangement. *Illustrations:* in line, half-tone, colour.

**British Journal of Special Education,** Official Journal of the National Council for Special Education. Margaret Peter, 12 Hollycroft Avenue, London NW3 7QL    *tel* 01-794 7109.
£14.00 p.a. (£28.00 Inland Institutions). Q. Articles by specialists on the education of the physically, mentally and emotionally handicapped, including the medical, therapeutic and sociological aspects of special education. *Length:* about 2000 to 3000 words. *Payment:* by arrangement. *Illustrations:* half-tone and line.

**British Medical Journal** (1840), Stephen Lock, M.A., M.D., M.SC., F.R.C.P., British Medical Association House, Tavistock Square, London WC1H 9JR    *tel* 01-387 4499.
£3.50. W. Medical and related articles.

**British Printer** (1888), Andrew Parker, Maclean Hunter House, Chalk Lane, Cockfosters Road, Barnet, Herts. EN4 0BU   *tel* 01-975 9759.
£35.00 p.a. M. Articles on technical and aesthetic aspects of printing processes and graphic reproduction. *Payment:* by arrangement. *Illustrations:* offset litho from photographs, line drawings and diagrams.

**British-Soviet Friendship** (formerly **Russia To-day**) (1927), 36 St. John's Square, London EC1V 4JH   *tel* 01-253 4161.
30p. M. An illustrated magazine on British-Soviet relations. Good photographs and well-informed news items and articles up to 900 words (on Soviet Union and British-Soviet relations). *Payment:* for articles and photographs only by special arrangement.

**Broadcast,** Marta Wohrle, 100 Avenue Road, London NW3 3TP   *tel* 01-935 6611   *telex* 299973 Aether G.
95p. (£48.00 p.a.). W. News and authoritative articles designed for all concerned with the British broadcast and non-broadcast industries, and with programmes and advertising on television, radio, video, cable, satellite, business. *Payment:* by arrangement.

**Brownie,** Official Magazine of The Girl Guides Association, Lynn Hurdwell, 17-19 Buckingham Palace Road, London SW1W 0PT   *tel* 01-834 6242.
50p. F. Short articles for Brownies (girls 7-10 years). Serials with Brownie background (500-800 words per instalment). Puzzles, "Things to make", etc. *Payment:* £26.60 per 1000 words. *Illustrations:* line and half-tone.

**Budgerigar World** (1982), Gerald S. Binks, Tanglewood, Knowle Grove, Virginia Water, Surrey GU25 4JB   *tel* Wentworth (09904) 3250.
£1.60 (subscription £20.00 p.a.). M. Articles about exhibition budgerigars. *Payment:* by arrangement. *Illustrations:* half-tone, colour.

**Building** (1842), Graham Rimmer, Builder House, 1 Millharbour, London E14 9RA   *tel* 01-537 2222   *telex* 927110 and 25212 Builda G.
90p. W. A magazine covering the entire professional, industrial and manufacturing aspects of the building industry. Articles on architecture and techniques at home and abroad considered, also news and photographs. *Payment:* by arrangement.

**The Building Societies Gazette** (1869), Neil Madden, Franey & Co., Ltd., South Quay Plaza, 183 Marsh Wall, London E14 9FS   *tel* 01-538 5386.
£2.25 (£29.25 p.a. pre-paid). M. Articles on all aspects of building society management, housing finance, retail financial services. *Length:* up to 2000 words. *Average payment:* £125.00 per 1000 words. *Illustrations:* line and half-tone.

**Built Environment,** Professor Peter Hall, Alexandrine Press, P.O. Box 15, 51 Cornmarket Street, Oxford OX1 3EB   *tel* (0865) 724627.
£9.50. Q. (£32.50 p.a.). Articles about architecture, planning and the environment. *Length:* 1000 to 5000 words. *Payment:* by arrangement. *Illustrations:* photographs and line. A preliminary letter is advisable.

**Bulletin of Hispanic Studies** (1923), Department of Hispanic Studies, The University, P.O. Box 147, Liverpool L69 3BX   *tel* 051-709 6022, ext. 3056. Published by the Liverpool University Press, P.O. Box 147, Liverpool L69 3BX.
£30.00 p.a. (institutions); £16 p.a. (individual). Q. Specialist articles on the languages and literatures of Spain, Portugal and Latin America, written in English, Spanish, Portuguese, Catalan or French. *Payment:* none.

**Bunty** (D. C. Thomson & Co. Ltd.), Courier Place, Dundee DD1 9QJ, and 185 Fleet Street, London EC4A 2HS.

26p. W. Picture-story paper for young girls of school age. Vividly told stories in picture-serial form, 16-18 frames in each 2 page instalment; 23-24 frames in each 3-page instalment. Comic strips and features. *Payment:* on acceptance. Special encouragement to promising scriptwriters and artists.

**Bunty Library** (D. C. Thomson & Co. Ltd.), Courier Place, Dundee DD1 9QJ, and 185 Fleet Street, London EC4A 2HS.
32p. M. Stories told in pictures for schoolgirls; 64 pages (about 140 line drawings). Ballet, school, adventure, theatre, sport. Scripts considered; promising artists and script-writers encouraged. *Payment:* on acceptance.

**Burlington Magazine** (1903), Caroline Elam, 6 Bloomsbury Square, London WC1A 2LP   *tel* 01-430 0481   *fax* 01-242 1205.
£7.00. M. Deals with the history and criticism of art. Average *length* of article, 500 to 3000 words. The Editor can use only articles by those who have special knowledge of the subjects treated and cannot accept MSS compiled from works of reference. Book and exhibition reviews and an illustrated monthly Calendar section. No verse. *Illustrations:* almost invariably made from photographs.

**Buses** (1949), Stephen Morris, Terminal House, Station Approach, Shepperton, Middlesex TW17 8AS   *tel* (0932) 228950   *fax* (0932) 232366.
£1.15. M. Articles of interest to both road passenger transport operators and bus enthusiasts. *Illustrations:* colour transparencies, half-tone, line maps. *Payment:* on application. Preliminary inquiry essential.

**Business** (1986), Stephen Fay, 234 Kings Road, London SW3 5UA   *tel* 01-351 7351   *telex* 914549 Intmag G   *fax* 01-351 2794.
£2.00. M. Business and finance articles. *Payment:* £200 per 1000 words. *Illustrations:* photographs, graphics, colour.

**Business Credit and Hire Purchase Journal,** Quaintance & Co. (Publishers) Ltd., 46 Bridge Street, Godalming, Surrey GU7 1HH   *tel* (04868) 27333.
£35.00 p.a. Bi-M. Articles on any aspect of credit, preferably by contributors with practical or professional experience. *Length:* 1500 to 2500 words. *Payment:* by arrangement. *Illustrations:* half-tone or line.

**Business Scotland** (1947), Sandra Brown, Peebles Publishing Group, Bergius House, Clifton Street, Glasgow G3 7LA   *tel* 041-331 1022   *fax* 041-331 1395.
Controlled circulation. M. Features, profiles and news items relevant to business advertisers. *Payment:* by arrangement.

**Buster** (1960), Greater London House, Hampstead Road, London NW1 7QQ   *tel* 01-383 7156.
30p. W. Juvenile comic. Comedy characters in picture strips. For boys and girls ages 6 to 12. Full colour, 2 colour, and black and white.

**Butterfly News** (1985), Simon Regan, Lodmoor Country Park, Greenhill, Weymouth, Dorset DT4 7SX   *tel* (0305) 776300.
25p. Bi-M. Hard news stories about butterflies, insects, conservation. *Payment:* £25 to £50 per 1000 words. *Illustrations:* black-and-white, colour.

**Cage and Aviary Birds** (1902), Brian Byles, Prospect House, 9-13 Ewell Road, Cheam, Sutton, Surrey SM1 4QQ   *tel* 01-661 4491   *fax* 01-661 0887.
60p. W. Practical articles on aviculture. First-hand knowledge only. *Payment:* by arrangement. *Illustrations:* line, photographs, colour.

**Campaign,** Christine Barker, 22 Lancaster Gate, London W2 3LY   *tel* 01-402 4200   *fax* 01-402 7885.
£1.00. W. News and articles covering the whole of the mass communications field, particularly advertising in all its forms, marketing and the media. Features

should not exceed 2000 words. News items also welcome. Press day, Wednesday. *Payment:* by arrangement.

**Camping & Walking** (1961), Philip Pond, Link House, Dingwall Avenue, Croydon CR9 2TA   *tel* 01-686 2599   *telex* 947709 Linkho G   *fax* 01-760 0973.
£1.20. M. Articles based on real camping experiences and walks, all aspects, illustrated with photographs; also camp site reports. *Length:* 600-1500 words average. *Payment:* by arrangement. *Illustrations:* line, half-tone, colour.

**Candour** (1953), R. de Bounevialle, Forest House, Liss Forest, Hants GU33 7DD   *tel* (0730) 892109.
50p. M. Politico-economic articles with a national and Commonwealth appeal. *Length:* 1200-1500 words. *Payment:* £5 per 1000 words.

**Car** (1962), Gavin Green, 97 Earls Court Road, London W8 6QH   *tel* 01-370 0333   *fax* 01-373 7544.
£2.00. M. Top-grade journalistic features on car driving, car people and cars. *Length:* 1000-2500 words. *Payment:* £150 per 1000 words minimum. *Illustrations:* black-and-white and colour photographs to professional standard.

**Car Mechanics,** Mike Penny, Audit House, Field End Road, Eastcote, Ruislip, Middlesex HA4 9LT   *tel* 01-868 4499.
£1.30. M. Practical articles on car maintenance and repair for the technical motorist with limited facilities. *Length:* average 1500 words of hard fact. *Payment:* by arrangement. *Illustrations:* line and half-tone. *Preliminary letter outlining the article is necessary.*

**Caravan Magazine** (1933), Barry Williams, Link House, Dingwall Avenue, Croydon CR9 2TA   *tel* 01-686 2599   *telex* 947709 Linkho G   *fax* 01-760 0973.
£1.30. M. Lively articles based on real experience of touring caravanning, especially if well illustrated by photographs. General countryside or motoring material not wanted. *Payment:* by arrangement.

**Caring** (1982), Charles Lloyd, Stanley House, 9 West Street, Epsom, Surrey KT18 7RL   *tel* Epsom (03727) 41411.
£1.00. M. Factual and informative articles aimed at the disabled, carers and the elderly. *Length:* up to 1200 words. *Payment:* by arrangement. *Illustrations:* line, half-tone.

**Cat World** (1981), Joan Moore, 10 Western Road, Shoreham-by-Sea, West Sussex BN43 5WD   *tel* (0273) 462000.
£1.20. M. Bright, lively articles on any aspect of cat ownership. Articles on breeds of cats and veterinary articles by acknowledged experts only. No unsolicited fiction. *Payment:* by arrangement. *Illustrations:* mono, colour.

**Catholic Gazette** (1910), Fr. Seamus O'Boyle, 114 West Heath Road, London NW3 7TX   *tel* 01-458 3316.
60p. M. Articles concerned with evangelisation and the Christian life. *Length:* up to 1500 words. *Payment:* by arrangement. *Illustrations:* line, half-tone; cartoons.

**The Catholic Herald,** Peter Stanford, Herald House, Lambs Passage, Bunhill Row, London EC1Y 8TQ   *tel* 01-588 3101   *telex* 8813473, Cather G   *fax* 01-256 9728.
35p. W. An independent newspaper covering national and international affairs from a Catholic Christian viewpoint as well as Church news. Articles 600 to 1100 words. *Payment:* by arrangement. *Illustrations:* photographs of Catholic and Christian interest.

**Catholic Pictorial** (1961), Norman Cresswell, Media House, Mann Island, Pier Head, Liverpool L3 1DQ *tel* 051-236 2191 *fax* 051-236 2216.
30p. W. News and photo features (maximum 1000 words plus illustration) *strictly* of Lancashire Catholic interest only. Has a strongly social editorial and is a trenchant tabloid. *Payment:* £1 per 100 words. News: on merit.

**Cencrastus: Scottish & International Literature, Arts and Affairs** (1979), Raymond J. Ross, 34 Queen Street, Edinburgh EX2 1JX *tel* 031-226 5605.
£1.50. Q. Articles, short stories, poetry. *Payment:* by arrangement. *Illustrations:* line, half-tone.

**Certified Accountant,** Leon Hopkins, Certified Accountant (Publications) Ltd., Westgate House, Spital Street, Dartford, Kent DA1 2EQ *tel* (0322) 79131 *fax* (0322) 20628.
£1.20. M. Articles of accounting and financial interest.

**Chapman** (1969), Joy Hendry, 80 Moray Street, Blackford, Perthshire PH4 1QF *tel* 031-557 2207.
£1.80 (subscription £7.00 p.a.). Q. Poetry, short stories, reviews, articles on Scottish culture. *Payment:* £8.00 per page. *Illustrations:* line, half-tone.

**Chat** (1986), Terry Tavner, 195 Knightsbridge, London SW7 1RE *tel* 01-589 8877.
28p. W. Tabloid weekly for women; no fiction. *Length:* up to 500 words. *Payment:* by arrangement. *Illustrations:* half-tone, colour.

**Cheshire Life** (1934), Jane Fickling, Town & County Magazines, The Custom House, 70 Watergate Street, Chester CH1 2LF *tel* (0244) 45226.
£1.00. M. Articles of county interest only. No fiction. *Length:* 800-1500 words. *Payment:* £50.00 per 1000 words minimum. *Illustrations:* line and half-tone, 4-colour positives. Photographs of news value and definite Cheshire interest.

**Child Education** (1924), Gill Moore, Scholastic Publications Ltd., Marlborough House, Holly Walk, Leamington Spa, Warwickshire CV32 4LS *tel* Southam (0926) 813910 *telex* 312138 Spls G.
£1.25. M. For teachers, pre-school staff, nursery nurses and parents concerned with children aged 3-8. Articles by specialists on practical teaching ideas and methods, child development, education news. *Length:* 1000 to 2000 words. *Payment:* by arrangement. Profusely illustrated with photographs and line drawings; also large pictures in full colour. Also **Infant Projects** (formerly Child Education Special) (1978). Mary-Jane Wilkins. £1.20. Bi-M.

**The China Quarterly,** Brian Hook, School of Oriental and African Studies, Thornhaugh Street, Russell Square, London WC1H 0XG *tel* 01-637 2388 *telex* 291829 Soasp *fax* 01-436 3844.
£5.50. Q. (£20.00 p.a.). Articles on Contemporary China. *Length:* 8000 words approx. *Payment:* on specially commissioned articles only.

**Choice** (1974), Annette Brown, Apex House, Oundle Road, Peterborough PE2 9NP *tel* (0733) 555123 *fax* (0733) 312025.
£1.20. M. Commissioned articles on financial and investment advice, State benefits, pensions and health for newly retired or about to retire. *Length:* up to 750 words inc. fact panels. *Payment:* by arrangement. *Illustrations:* colour and b&w photos of 55–65-year-olds, at leisure, second career, with young people, etc.; *payment:* £25 colour, £10 b&w.

**Christian Herald** (1866), 96 Dominion Road, Worthing, West Sussex BN14 8JP *tel* (0903) 821082 *fax* (0903) 821081.

35p. W. A conservative, evangelical paper aimed at families. News and 'it really happened', well *illustrated* if possible; poetry and readers' recipes. *No* general interest articles or short stories. *Payment:* none, or modest.

**Christian Week** (Interdenominational Weekly) (1969), 11 Carteret Street, London SW1H 9DJ	*tel* 01-222 3464	*fax* 01-222 5414.
30p. W. Emphasis on news features for Evangelical Free Church market. Mostly commissioned feature articles. *Length:* 1000 words maximum. *Payment:* c. £25.00 per 1000. *Illustrations:* photographs and line drawings.

**Church of England Newspaper** (1828), 11 Carteret Street, London SW1H 9DJ	*tel* 01-222 3464	*fax* 01-222 5414.
30p. W. The newspaper contains Anglican news and articles relating the Christian faith to everyday life. Study of paper desirable. Evangelical basis; mostly commissioned articles. *Length:* 1000 words maximum. *Payment:* c. £25.00 per 1000. *Illustrations:* photographs and line drawings.

**Church News** (1948), Canon Rhodes, College Gate House, Bury St. Edmunds, Suffolk IP33 1NN	*tel* (0284) 753530.
£3.25 p.a. M. An Illustrated Church magazine inset. Articles of popular Church interest (500 to 800 words); occasional short stories and verse. *Illustrations:* photographs and line drawings of religious and ecclesiastical subjects. *Payment:* by arrangement.

**Church Times** (1863), John Whale, 7 Portugal Street, London WC2A 2HP.
25p. W. Articles on ecclesiastical and social topics are considered. Usual *length:* 750 to 1500 words. No verse or fiction. *Payment:* £25.00 per 1000 words minimum. *Illustrations:* news photographs.

**Classic Cars** Tony Dron, Prospect House, 9-13 Ewell Road, Cheam, Surrey SM1 4QQ	*tel* 01-661 4411	*telex* 892084 Bisprs G	*fax* 01-770 7091.
£1.90. M. Specialist articles on older cars. *Length:* from 1000 to 4000 words (subject to prior contract). *Payment:* by negotiation. *Illustrations:* half-tone and colour.

**Classical Music** (1976), Graeme Kay, 241 Shaftesbury Avenue, London WC2H 8EH	*tel* 01-836 2383	*telex* 264675	*fax* 01-528 7991.
£1.00. F. News, opinion, features on classical music and general arts matters. *Payment:* from £50 per 1000 words. *Illustrations:* half-tone, colour covers.

**Climber and Hill Walker** (1962), Cameron McNeish, The Plaza Tower, The Plaza, East Kilbride, Glasgow G74 1LW	*tel* (03552) 46444.
£1.40. M. Articles on all aspects of mountaineering and hill walking in Great Britain and abroad and on related subjects. *Length:* 1500 to 2500 words, preferably illustrated. *Payment:* according to merit. *Illustrations:* colour, half-tone, line. Study of magazine essential.

**Club Secretary** (1953), Jane Burt, UTP House, 33-35 Bowling Green Lane, London EC1R 0DA	*tel* 01-837 1212	*fax* 01-278 4003.
£21.00 p.a. M. Features, news, drink news, catering news, legal and financial advice as a guide to the successful management of clubs. *Payment:* by arrangement. *Illustrations:* line and half-tone.

**Coin & Medal News** (1964), John W. Mussell, Token Publishing Ltd., Crossways Road, Grayshott, Hindhead, Surrey GU26 6HF	*tel* (0428) 737242.
£1.20. M. Articles of high standard on coins, tokens, paper money and medals. *Length:* up to 2000 words. *Payment:* by arrangement.

**Coin Monthly** (1966), Rita Smith, Sovereign House, Brentwood, Essex CM14 4SE  *tel* (0277) 219876.
£1.50. M. Articles on all aspects of numismatics. *Length:* 1500 to 2000 words. *Payment:* £10.00 per 1000 words. *Illustrations:* half-tone.

**Commando** (D. C. Thomson & Co. Ltd.), Albert Square, Dundee DD1 9QJ  *tel* (0382) 23131 and 185 Fleet Street, London EC4A 2HS.
32p. Eight each month. Fictional war stories of World War II told in pictures. Scripts should be of about 135 pictures. Synopsis required as an opener. Send for details. New writers encouraged. *Payment:* on acceptance.

**Commercial Motor** (1905), Brian Weatherley, Reed Business Publishing Ltd, Quadrant House, The Quadrant, Sutton, Surrey SM2 5AS  *tel* 01-661 3302/3303.
85p. W. *Payment:* varies for articles (technical and road transport only), maximum length 2000 words, drawings and photographs.

**Community Care** (1974), Terry Philpot, Carew House, Wallington, Surrey SM6 0DX  *tel* 01-661 4861.
£1.00. W. Articles of professional interest to local authority and voluntary body social workers, managers, teachers and students. *Length:* 800 to 1500 words. *Payment:* at current rates. *Illustrations:* half-tone and line. Preliminary letter advisable.

**Company** (1978), Gill Hudson, National Magazine House, 72 Broadwick Street, London W1V 2BP  *tel* 01-439 5000.
£1.00. M. Articles on a wide variety of subjects, relevant to young, independent women. Most articles commissioned. *Payment:* usual magazine rate.

**Computing** (1973) Sarah Underwood, 32-34 Broadwick Street, London W1A 2HG  *tel* 01-439 4242  *fax* 01-437 8985.
£70.00 p.a. W. Features and news items on the computer industry and on applications and implications of computers and microelectronics. *Length:* up to 1800 words. *Payment:* £110 per 1000 words. *Illustrations:* half-tone, line.

**Construction Weekly** (incorporating **Construction Plant & Equipment** and **Civil Engineering**), Simon Murray, Morgan-Grampian (Construction Press) Ltd, 30 Calderwood Street, London SE18 6QH  *tel* 01-855 7777  *telex* 896238  *fax* 01-854 8058.
Controlled circulation. Contains news of construction matters, in-depth technical articles of current interest to civil engineers, contractors and manufacturers of plant and equipment. *Length:* 1000-2000 words. *Payment:* by arrangement. *Illustrations:* line drawings, charts, graphs and colour pictures relating to articles. *A preliminary letter is essential.*

**Contemporary Review** (incorporating the **Fortnightly**) (1866), Betty Abel, 61 Carey Street, London WC2A 2JG  *tel* 01-831 7791.
£1.50. M. Independent, but slightly left of centre. A review dealing with all questions of the day, chiefly politics, theology, history, literature, travel, poetry, the arts. A great part of the matter is commissioned, but there is scope for freelance specialists. Articles submitted should be typewritten and should be about 2000 to 3000 words. If refused, articles are returned, *if sae is enclosed*. *Payment:* £5.00 per page (500 words), 2 complimentary copies. Intending contributors should study journal before submitting MSS.

**Control & Instrumentation** (1958), Brian J. Tinham, B.Sc., C.Eng., M.Inst.M.C. (Morgan-Grampian (Process Press) Ltd.), 30 Calderwood Street, Woolwich, London SE18 6QH  *tel* 01-855 7777.

£36.00 p.a. M. Authoritative main feature articles on measurement, automation, control systems, instrumentation, and data processing. Also export, business and engineering news. *Payment:* according to value. *Length of articles:* 750 words for highly technical pieces. 1000 to 2500 words main features. *Illustrations:* half-tone and photographs and drawings of equipment using automatic techniques, control engineering personalities.

**Cosmetic World News** (1949), M. A. Murray-Pearce, Caroline Marcuse, 130 Wigmore Street, London W1H 0AT    *tel* 01-486 6757-8    *telex* 817133    *fax* 01-487 5436.
£56.00 p.a. M. International news magazine of perfumery, cosmetics and toiletries industry. World-wide reports, photo-news stories, articles (500-1000 words) on essential oils and new cosmetic raw materials, and exclusive information on industry's companies and personalities welcomed. *Payment:* by arrangement. Minimum 10p per word. *Illustrations:* black-and-white and colour photographs or colour separations.

**Cosmopolitan** (1972), Linda Kelsey, National Magazine House, 72 Broadwick Street, London W1V 2BP    *tel* 01-439 5000    *fax* 01-437 6886.
£1.00. M. Short stories, articles. Commissioned material only. *Payment:* by arrangement.

**Country,** The Magazine of the Country Gentlemen's Association (1901), Jeanne Griffiths, Telepress Ltd., 361a Upper Richmond Road West, London SW14 8QN    *tel* 01-392 1499    *fax* 01-878 0341.
£25.00 p.a. M. Authoritative articles of general interest, plus some on country matters. *Length:* 500 to 1000 words. *Payment:* by arrangement.

**Country Homes & Interiors** (1986), Vanessa Berridge, King's Reach Tower, Stamford Street, London SE1 9LS    *tel* 01-261 6434.
£1.60 M. Articles on property, country homes, interior designs. *Payment:* £150 per 1000 words. *Illustrations:* half-tone, colour.

**Country Life** (1897), Jenny Greene, King's Reach Tower, Stamford Street, London SE1 9LS    *tel* 01-261 7058.
£1.30. W. An illustrated journal, chiefly concerned with British country life, social history, architecture and the fine arts, natural history, agriculture, gardening and sport. *Length of articles:* about 700, 1000 or 1250 words; short poems are also considered. *Payment:* according to merit. Press day, Thursday. *Illustrations:* mainly photographs.

**Country Living** (1985), Francine Lawrence, 72 Broadwick Street, London W1V 2BP    *tel* 01-439 5000.
£1.30. M. Well written features or news items on all aspects of country living. *Payment:* by arrangement. *Illustrations:* line, half-tone, colour.

**Country Quest,** Ray Bower, North Wales Newspapers, Business Park, Mold, Clwyd    *tel* (0352) 700022.
90p. M. Illustrated articles on matters relating to countryside of Wales and border counties. *Length:* 500 to 1500 words. No fiction. Illustrated work preferred. *Payment:* by arrangement. *Illustrations:* half-tone and line.

**The Countryman** (1927), Christopher Hall, Sheep Street, Burford, Oxford OX8 4LH    *tel* (099 382) 2258.
£1.50. Q. Every department of rural life and progress except field sports. Party politics and sentimentalising about the country barred. Copy must be trustworthy, well-written, brisk, cogent and light in hand. Articles up to 1500 words. Good paragraphs and notes, first-class poetry and skilful sketches of life and character from personal knowledge and experience. Dependable natural

history based on writer's own observation. Really good matter from old unpublished letters and MSS. *Payment:* £40.00 per 1000 words and upwards according to merit. *Illustrations:* black-and-white photographs and drawings, but all must be exclusive and out of the ordinary, and bear close scrutiny. Humour welcomed if genuine.

**Country-Side** (1905), Dr. David Applin, P.O. Box 87, Cambridge CB1 3UP. £10.00 p.a. Q. Official organ of the British Naturalists' Association (B.N.A.), the national body for naturalists. Original observations on wild life and its protection, and on natural history generally, but not on killing for sport. *Payment:* not usually made. *Illustrations:* photographs, drawings. *Preliminary letter* or study of magazine advisable.

**The Courier and Advertiser** (1816 and 1801), (D. C. Thomson & Co. Ltd.), 7 Bank Street, Dundee DD1 9HU *tel* Dundee 23131 *telex* DCThom 76380 *fax* (0382) 27159; and 185 Fleet Street, London EC4A 2HS *tel* 01-242 5086.
22p. D. Independent.

**Coventry Evening Telegraph,** Geoffrey Elliott, Corporation Street, Coventry CV1 1FP *tel* (0203) 633633.
20p. D. Illustrated articles of topical interest, those with a Warwickshire interest particularly acceptable. *Maximum length:* 600 words.

**Creative Camera** (1968), Peter Turner, CC Publishing, Battersea Arts Centre, Old Town Hall, Lavender Hill, London SW11 5TF *tel* 01-924 3017.
£1.95. M. Illustrated articles and pictures dealing with creative photography, sociology of, history of and criticism of photographs. Book and Exhibition reviews. Arts Council supported. *Payment:* by arrangement. *Illustrations:* black-and-white; colour.

**The Cricketer International** (1921), Christopher Martin-Jenkins, 29 Cavendish Road, Redhill, Surrey RH1 4AH *tel* (0737) 772221 *fax* (0737) 771720.
£1.40. M. Articles on cricket at any level. *Payment:* £50 per 1000 words. *Illustrations:* line, half-tone, colour.

**The Criminologist** (1966), East Row, Little London, Chichester, West Sussex PO19 1PG.
Controlled circulation. £30.00 p.a. post free. Q. Specialised material designed for an expert and professional readership. Covers nationally and internationally criminology, the police, forensic science, the law, penology, sociology and law enforcement. Articles, up to 2000 words, by those familiar with the journal's style and requirements are welcomed. *A preliminary letter* with a brief résumé is preferable. *Payment:* is wholly governed by the nature and quality of manuscripts. *Illustrations:* line and photographs.

**Critical Quarterly** (1959), Editorial Board: C. B. Cox, Maureen Duffy, Colin MacCabe, Department of English, The University, Manchester M13 9PL *tel* 061-275 3145.
£14.50 p.a., Institutions £19.50 p.a. Q. Fiction, poems, literary criticism. *Length:* 2000-5000 words. *Payment:* by arrangement. Interested contributors should study magazine before submitting MSS.

**CTN (Confectioner, Tobacconist, Newsagent),** Michael Eaton, Reed Business Publishing, Quadrant House, The Quadrant, Sutton, Surrey SM2 5AS *tel* 01-661 8290.
45p. W. (£40.00 p.a.). Trade news and brief articles illustrated when possible with photographs or line drawings. Must be of live interest to retail confectioner-tobacconists and newsagents. *Length:* Articles 600-800 words. *Payment:*

news lineage rates, minimum of £6.50 per 100 words, articles at negotiated rates.

**Cue International,** Patricia MacKay, Cue International Publishing Ltd, Blanchard Works, Kangley Bridge Road, Sydenham, London SE26 5AQ    *tel* 01-659 2300    *fax* 01-659 3153.
£1.75 (£10.50 p.a.). Bi-M. The magazine of international design, technology and business for the performing arts and entertainment industry—theatre, opera, dance, film, television, clubs and concerts. *Length:* 1000-2000 words, usually illustrated. *Payment:* varies. *Illustrations:* line, half-tone, colour.

**Cumbria** (1951), Hilary Gray, Dalesman Publishing Company Ltd., Clapham, via Lancaster LA2 8EB    *tel* Clapham (046 85) 225.
50p. M. Articles of genuine rural interest concerning Lakeland. Short *length* preferred. *Payment:* according to merit. *Illustrations:* line drawings and first-class photographs.

**Custom Car** (1970), Link House, Dingwall Avenue, Croydon CR9 2TA    *tel* 01-686 2599    *telex* 947709 Linkho G.
£1.20. *Payment:* by arrangement. *Length:* by arrangement.

**Cycling** (1891), Martin Ayres, Prospect House, 9-13 Ewell Road, Cheam, Surrey SM1 4QQ    *tel* 01-661 4300    *fax* 01-642 6006.
80p. W. Racing, touring, technical, articles not exceeding 2000 words. Topical photographs with a cycling interest also considered. *Payment:* by arrangement.

**Daily Express,** Nicholas Lloyd, Ludgate House, 245 Blackfriars Road, London SE1 9UX    *tel* 01-928 8000    *cables* Lon Express    *telex* 21841/21842    *fax* 01-633 0244; Great Ancoats Street, Manchester M60 4HB    *tel* 061-236 2112.
22p. D. Exclusive news: striking photographs. Leader page articles, 600 words; facts preferred to opinions. *Payment:* according to value.

**Daily Mail** (1896) (Now incorporating **News Chronicle** and **Daily Sketch**), Sir David English, Northcliffe House, 2 Derry Street, London W8 5TT    *tel* 01-938 6000    *fax* 01-937 3193.
22p. D. Highest payments for good, exclusive news. Leader page articles, 500-800 words average. Ideas for these welcomed. Exclusive news photographs always wanted.

**Daily Mirror** (1903), R. Stott, Holborn Circus, London EC1P 1DQ    *tel* 01-353 0246.
22p. D. Top payment for exclusive news and news pictures. Few articles from freelances used, but ideas bought. Send only a synopsis. 'Unusual' pictures and those giving a new angle on the news are welcomed.

**Daily Record,** Editor-in-Chief: E. J. Laird, Anderston Quay, Glasgow    *tel* 041-248 7000    *telex* 778277. London: 33 Holborn, EC1P 1DQ    *tel* 01-353 0246.
22p. D. Web offset with full colour facilities. Topical articles of from 300 to 700 words. Exclusive stories of Scottish interest and exclusive photographs.

**Daily Star** (1978), Brian Hitchen, Ludgate House, 245 Blackfriars Road, London SE1 9UX    *tel* 01-928 8000    *cables* Lon Express    *telex* 21841/21842    *fax* 01-633 0244.
20p. D. Hard news exclusives, commanding substantial payment. Major interviews with big-star personalities; short features; series based on people rather than things; picture features. *Payment:* short features: £75-£100; full page £250-£300; double page £400-£600. Otherwise by negotiation. *Illustrations:* line, half-tone; cartoons.

**The Daily Telegraph** (1855), Max Hastings, Peterborough Court at South Quay, 181 Marsh Wall, London E14 9SR *tel* 01-538 5000 *telex* 22874/5/6.
32p, Sat. 35p. D. Independent. Articles on a wide range of subjects of topical interest considered. Preliminary letter and synopsis required. *Length:* 700–1000 words. *Payment:* by arrangement.

**Dairy Farmer,** David Shead, Wharfedale Road, Ipswich IP1 4LG *tel* Ipswich (0473) 43011 *fax* (0473) 240501.
Controlled circulation. M. Authoritative articles dealing in practical, lively style with dairy farming. Topical controversial articles invited. Well-written, illustrated accounts of new ideas being tried on dairy farms are especially wanted. *Length:* normally up to 1500 words. *Payment:* by arrangement. *Illustrations:* half-tone, line, colour.

**Dairy Industries International** (1936), Pauline Russell, 33-35 Bowling Green Lane, London EC1R 0DA *tel* 01-837 1212.
£42.00 post free (UK). M. Covers the entire field of milk processing, the manufacture of products from liquid milk, and ice cream. Articles relating to dairy plant, butter and cheese making, ice cream making, new product developments and marketing, etc. *Payment:* by arrangement. *Illustrations:* glossy prints and indian ink diagrams.

**The Dalesman** (1939), David Joy, Dalesman Publishing Company Ltd., Clapham, via Lancaster LA2 8EB *tel* Clapham (046 85) 225.
55p. M. Articles and stories of genuine rural interest concerning Yorkshire; but no fiction. Short *length* preferred. *Payment:* according to merit. *Illustrations:* line drawings and first-class photographs preferably featuring people.

**Dance & Dancers** (1950), John Percival, 248 High Street, Croydon CR0 1NF *tel* 01-681 7817 *fax* 01-688 9573.
£1.75. M. Specialist features, reviews on modern/classical dance, dancers. *Length:* up to 2000 words. *Payment:* by arrangement. *Illustrations:* line, half-tone; colour covers.

**Dancing Times** (1910), Editor: Mary Clarke, Editorial Adviser: Ivor Guest, Clerkenwell House, 45-47 Clerkenwell Green, London EC1R 0BE *tel* 01-250 3006.
£1.10. M. Dealing with ballet and stage dancing, both from general, historical, critical and technical angles. Well informed freelance articles are occasionally used, but only after preliminary arrangements. *Payment:* by arrangement. *Illustrations:* web offset, occasional line, action photographs always preferred.

**The Dandy** (D. C. Thomson & Co. Ltd.), Courier Place, Dundee DD1 9QJ, and 185 Fleet Street, London EC4A 2HS.
22p. W. Comic strips for boys and girls. 10-12 pictures per single page story, and 18-20 pictures per 2 page story. Promising artists encouraged. *Payment:* on acceptance.

**Dandy Cartoon Library** (D. C. Thomson & Co. Ltd.), Courier Place, Dundee DD1 9QJ and 185 Fleet Street, London EC4A 2HS.
32p. M. 64 pages of jokes and gags in cartoon form featuring the well known characters from the weekly Beano, Dandy, Topper and Beezer publications.

**Dandy Library** (D. C. Thomson & Co. Ltd.), Courier Place, Dundee DD1 9QJ and 185 Fleet Street, London EC4A 2HS.
32p. 2 per month. Extra-long comic adventure stories featuring well-known characters from the weekly Dandy publication. 'Guest appearances' by characters from weeklies Topper and Beezer publications.

**Darts World** (1972), Tony Wood, World Magazines Limited, 2 Park Lane, Croydon, Surrey CR9 1HA   *tel* 01-681 2837.
£1.00 M. Articles and stories with darts theme. *Payment:* £40 to £50 per 1000 words. *Illustrations:* half-tone. Cartoons.

**Day by Day** (1963), Patrick Richards, Woolacombe House, 141 Woolacombe Road, Blackheath, London SE3 8QP   *tel* 01-856 6249. Published by The Loverseed Press.
48p. M. Articles and news on non-violence and social justice. Reviews of art, books, films, plays, musicals and opera. Cricket reports. Occasional poems and very occasional short stories in keeping with editorial viewpoint. *Payment:* £2 per 1000 words. No *illustrations* required.

**Debbie Library** (D. C. Thomson & Co. Ltd.), Courier Place, Dundee DD1 9QJ, and 185 Fleet Street, London EC4A 2HS.
32p. M. Stories told in pictures, for schoolgirls; 64 pages (about 140 line drawings). Adventure, animal, mystery, school, sport. Scripts considered; promising script-writers and artists encouraged. *Payment:* on acceptance.

**Dental Update** (1973), Andrew Baxter, Update-Siebert Publications Ltd., Friary Court, 13-21 High Street, Guildford, Surrey GU1 3DX   *tel* (0483) 502125   *telex* 859500 Ref S/054   *fax* (0483) 301441.
£28.00 p.a. (students £20.00 p.a.) 10 p.a. Clinical articles, clinical quizzes. *Payment:* £50-£100 per 1000 words. *Illustrations:* line, colour.

**Derbyshire Life and Countryside** (1931), Lodge Lane, Derby DE1 3HE   *tel* (0332) 47087-8-9   *fax* (0332) 290688.
75p. M. Articles, preferably illustrated, about Derbyshire life, people, and history. *Length:* 800-1000 words. Short stories set in Derbyshire accepted, but verse not used. *Payment:* according to nature and quality of contribution. *Illustrations:* photographs of Derbyshire subjects.

**Design** (1949), Marion Hancock, Design Council, 28 Haymarket, London SW1Y 4SU   *tel* 01-839 8000.
£2.75. M. Articles on industrial design and design management. *Payment:* by arrangement.

**Designers' Journal** (1985), Alastair Best, 9 Queen Anne's Gate, London SW1H 9BY   *tel* 01-222 4333   *fax* 01-222 5196.
£2.00. M. Articles on new developments in interior design, new products, technical innovation and practice guidance. *Payment:* by arrangement. *Illustrations:* photographs, drawings.

**Devon Life** (1965), Jan Beart-Albrecht, Finance House, Barnfield Road, Exeter, Devon EX1 1QR   *tel* (0392) 216766   *fax* (0392) 71050.
£1.00. M. Articles and stories about nature, people, life in Devon. *Length:* 1000 words. *Payment:* by arrangement. *Illustrations:* line, photos.

**The Dickensian,** Margaret Reynolds, PH.D., Dickens House, 48 Doughty Street, London WC1N 2LF.
£9.00 p.a. (£11.00 UK institutional. Overseas: £10.00 individual; £13.00 institutional; plus airmail postage £4.00). 3 times a year. Published by The Dickens Fellowship. Welcomes articles on all aspects of Dickens' life, works and character. *Payment:* none.

**Digests** with one or two exceptions are not included since they seldom use original material, but reprint articles previously published elsewhere and extracts from books. But see **The Reader's Digest.**

**Dirt Bike Rider** (1981), Peter Donaldson, Bushfield House, Orton Centre, Peterborough PE2 0UW  *tel* (0733) 237111.
£1.25. M. Features, track tests, coverage on all aspects of off road motorcycling. *Length:* up to 1000 words. *Payment:* £80 per 1000 words. *Illustrations:* colour, half-tone.

**Disability Now** (1957), Mary Wilkinson, The Spastics Society, 12 Park Crescent, London W1N 4EQ  *tel* 01-636 5020  *fax* 01-436 2601.
£6 p.a. (£10 for organisations/overseas). M. Topical, authoritative articles of interest to people with a wide range of disabilities, carers and professionals; also arts and book reviews. Contributions from people with disabilities particularly welcome. *Length:* up to 1000 words. *Payment:* £50 per 1000 words. *Illustrations:* b&w news photos, cartoons; *payment:* by arrangement. *Preliminary letter or phone call desirable.*

**Diver** (1953), Bernard Eaton, 40 Grays Inn Road, London WC1X 8LR  *tel* 01-405 0224.
£1.50. M. Articles on sub aqua diving and underwater developments. *Length:* 1500 to 2000 words. *Payment:* by arrangement. *Illustrations:* line and half-tone, colour.

**DIY Today** (1983), Wendy Biggs, Sovereign House, Brentwood, Essex CM14 4SE  *tel* (0277) 219876.
£1.95. M. Articles on DIY subjects. *Length:* 1500 words with illustrations. *Payment:* £25.00 per 1000 words. *Illustrations:* line, half-tone.

**Do It Yourself** (1957), John McGowan, Link House, Dingwall Avenue, Croydon CR9 2TA  *tel* 01-686 2599  *telex* 947709 Linkho G.
£1.20. M. Authoritative articles on every aspect of do-it-yourself in the house, garden, workshop and garage. Leaflet describing style requirements available on request. *Payment:* by arrangement. *Length:* up to 1000 words unless negotiated. Press 3 months ahead.

**Dog & Country** (1897), Edward Askwith, Gilbertson & Page Ltd., P.O. Box 321, Welwyn Garden City, Herts. AL7 1LF  *tel* (0707) 371105.
£1.10. Q. (£5.00 p.a.). Informative articles of from 300 to 1000 words on angling, shooting, dogs, conservation, and natural history. *Payment:* by arrangement. *Illustrations:* camera-ready art work, monochrome only.

**Dorset County Magazine** (1967), John Newth, Trinity Lane, Wareham, Dorset BH20 4LN  *tel* (0929) 551264.
£1. M. Articles (500–1500 words), photographs (colour or black and white) and line drawings with a *specifically* Dorset theme.

**The Downside Review,** Dom Daniel Rees, Downside Abbey, Stratton on the Fosse, nr. Bath, Somerset BA3 4RH  *tel* Stratton-on-the-Fosse (0761) 232 295.
£4.00. Q. (£15.00 p.a.). Articles and book reviews on theology, metaphysics, mysticism and modernism and monastic and church history. *Payment:* not usual.

**DR The Fashion Business** (formerly **Drapers Record**) (1887), Sally Bain, International Thomson Publishing Ltd., 100 Avenue Road, London NW3 3TP  *tel* 01-935 6611  *telex* 299973 ITP LM G  *fax* 01-722 4920.
£1.00. W. Editorial aimed at fashion retailers, large and small. No unsolicited material. *Payment:* by negotiation. *Illustrations:* colour and b&w; photographs, drawings and cartoons.

**Driver** (1987), Tom Boswell, The Liberty Publishing Company Ltd, Chichester House, 145A London Road, Kingston upon Thames, Surrey KT2 6NH   *tel* 01-541 5700, 01-541 3684   *telex* 927329   *fax* 01-541 3732.
£1. M. Motoring-related articles. *Length:* up to 1000 words. *Payment:* £145 per 1000 words, or by arrangement. *Illustrations:* colour transparencies, b&w photos; *payment:* by arrangement.

**Dundee Evening Telegraph and Post** (D. C. Thomson & Co. Ltd.), Bank Street, Dundee DD1 9HU   *tel* Dundee 23131   *telex* DCThom 76380; and 185 Fleet Street, London EC4A 2HS   *tel* 01-242 5086.
20p. D.

**Early Music** (1973), Nicholas Kenyon, Oxford University Press, Ely House, 37 Dover Street, London W1X 4AH   *tel* 01-493 9376.
£7.00 (£24.00 p.a.). Q. Lively, informative and scholarly articles on aspects of medieval, renaissance, baroque and classical music. *Payment:* £20 per 1000 words. *Illustrations:* line, half-tone; colour on cover.

**Early Times** (1988), Robert Dunkley, The Brighton Business Centre, 95 Ditchling Road, Brighton, East Sussex BN1 4SB   *tel* (0273) 675374   *fax* (0273) 692081.
38p. W. Serious weekly newspaper for children. News and features of interest to 8-17 year olds. *Payment:* by arrangement. *Illustrations:* line, half-tone.

**Eastern Daily Press** (1870), L. Sear, Prospect House, Rouen Road, Norwich NR1 1RE   *tel* (0603) 628311   *telex* 975276 Ecnnch G   *fax* (0603) 612930. London Office: Temple Chambers, Temple Avenue, EC4Y 0DT   *tel* 01-583 0375.
26p. D. Independent. Limited market for articles of East Anglian interest not exceeding 900 words.

**Eastern Evening News** (1882), Peter Ware, EEN, Prospect House, Rouen Road, Norwich NR1 1RE   *tel* (0603) 628311   *telex* 975276 Ecnnch G   *fax* (0603) 612930. London Office: Temple Chambers, Temple Avenue, EC4Y 0DT   *tel* 01-583 0379.
20p. D. Independent. Interested in news-based features, material for advert features and cartoons. *Length:* up to 500 words. *Payment:* NUJ or agreed rates.

**The Ecologist,** Edward Goldsmith, Worthyvale Manor Farm, Camelford, Cornwall PL32 9TT   *tel* (0840) 212711.
£3.00. 6 issues p.a. Articles and news stories on economic, social and environmental affairs from an ecological standpoint. *Length:* 1000 to 3000 words. *Payment:* by arrangement. *Illustrations:* line and half-tone. Magazine should be studied for level and approach.

**Economic Journal** (1891), John D. Hey, Department of Economics, University of York, York YO1 5DD   *tel* (0904) 433575.
£60.50 p.a. (Free to members). Q. The organ of the Royal Economic Society. The kind of matter required is economic theory, applied economics and the development of economic thinking in relation to current problems. *Payment:* none. Statistical and economic diagrams. Reviews of new books and other publications.

**Economica** (1921. New Series, 1934), Editors: Dr. F. A. Cowell, Dr. D. C. Webb, London School of Economics and Political Science, Houghton Street, London WC2A 2AE   *tel* 01-405 7686, ext. 3087.
£22.50 p.a. (U.K.), £31.00 or $62.00 (Overseas). Individuals: £12.50 (U.K.), £12.50 or $25.00 (Overseas). Q. A learned journal covering the fields of economics, economic history and statistics.

**The Economist** (1843), 25 St. James's Street, London SW1A 1HG  *tel* 01-839 7000.
£1.40. W. Articles staff-written.

**Edinburgh Evening News,** Terry Quinn, 20 North Bridge, Edinburgh EH1 1YT  *tel* 031-225 2468  *fax* 031-225 7302.
20p. D. Independent. Features on current affairs, preferably in relation to our circulation area. Women's talking points, local historical articles; subjects of general interest.

**Edinburgh Review** (1969), Peter Kravitz, 22 George Square, Edinburgh EH8 9LF  *tel* 031-667 1011, ext. 2412  *fax* 031-667 7938.
£4.95. Q. (£16 p.a.) Fiction, clearly written articles on Scottish and international cultural and philosophical ideas. *Payment:* by arrangement.

**Education** (1903), George Low, 21-27 Lamb's Conduit Street, London WC1N 3NJ  *tel* 01-242 2548  *fax* 01-831 2855.
£1.10. W. Special articles on educational administration, all branches of education; technical education; universities; school building; playing fields; environmental studies; physical education; school equipment; school meals and health; teaching aids. *Length:* 1000 to 1200 words. *Payment:* by arrangement. *Illustrations:* photographs and drawings.

**Education and Training** (1959), Derek Bradley, 8 Holmwood Avenue, South Croydon, Surrey CR2 9HY  *tel* 01-657 1247  *telex* 51317 Mcbuni G  *fax* (0274) 547143.
£5.00. Bi-M. (£25.95 p.a.) Authoritative articles of 1000-2000 words on all aspects of further education, commercial and industrial training. *Payment:* by arrangement. *Illustrations:* offset litho.

**Electrical Review** (1872), T. C. J. Cogle, B.SC. (ENG.), M.I.C.E., F.I.E.E., Reed Business Publishing, Quadrant House, Sutton, Surrey SM2 5AS  *tel.* 01-661 3113  *telex* 892084 Reedbp G.
£1.50. F. Technical and business articles on electrical and control engineering; outside contributions considered. Electrical news welcomed. *Illustrations:* photographs and drawings.

**The Electrical Times** (1891), G. A. Jack, Reed Business Publishing, Quadrant House, The Quadrant, Sutton, Surrey SM2 5AS  *tel* 01-661 3138  *telex* 892084 Reedbp G.
£2.25. M. Technical articles about 1000 to 1500 words, with illustrations as necessary. *Payment:* by arrangement. *Illustrations:* line, half-tone.

**Elle (UK)** (1985), Maggie Alderson, Rex House, 4-12 Lower Regent Street, London SW1Y 4PE  *tel* 01-930 9050.
£1.20. M. Commissioned material only. *Payment:* by arrangement. *Illustrations:* colour.

**Embroidery,** The Embroiderers' Guild, P.O. Box 42B, East Molesey, Surrey KT8 9BB  *tel* 01-943 1229.
£1.50. Q. (£6.75 p.a.). Articles on historical and contemporary embroidery by curators and artists. Exhibition and book reviews. Saleroom report. Diary of events. *Payment:* by arrangement. *Illustrations:* line, half-tone, colour.

**Encounter** (1953), Melvin J. Lasky and Richard Mayne, 43-44 Great Windmill Street, London W1V 7PA  *tel* 01-434 3063.
£1.50. 10 p.a. Reportage, stories, poems. *Length:* 3000-5000 words. *Payment:* £10 per 1000. Interested contributors should study magazine before submitting MSS; s.a.e. essential for return if unsuitable.

**The Engineer** (1856), John Pullin, 30 Calderwood Street, London SE18 6QH    *tel* 01-855 7777.
£2.50. W. (£60.00 p.a.). Outside contributions paid for if accepted.

**Engineering** (1866), Richard Wood, Design Council, 28 Haymarket, London SW1Y 4SU    *tel* 01-839 8000.
£2.00. M. Contributions considered on all aspects of engineering, particularly design. *Payment:* by arrangement. Photographs and drawings used.

**Engineering Materials and Design,** Kevin O'Toole, Reed Business Publishing, Quadrant House, The Quadrant, Sutton, Surrey SM2 5AS    *tel* 01-661 3174    *telex* 892084 Reedbp G    *fax* 01-661 8924.
Controlled circulation. Technical articles on engineering design and on materials and components. *Payment:* by arrangement. *Length:* from 1000 words. *Illustrations:* line and half-tone.

**English Historical Review** (1886), Dr. P. H. Williams, Dr. R. J. W. Evans, Academic Dept., Longman Group U.K. Ltd., Burnt Mill, Harlow, Essex CM20 2JE    *tel* (0279) 26721.
£42.00 p.a. Q. High-class scholarly articles (such as are usually found in quarterlies), documents, and reviews or short notices of books. Contributions are not accepted unless they supply original information and should be sent direct to Dr. P. H. Williams, Editor, E.H.R., New College, Oxford OX1 3BN. Books for review should be sent to Dr. R. J. W. Evans, Editor, E.H.R., Brasenose College, Oxford OX1 4AJ. *Payment:* none.

**Entomologist's Monthly Magazine** (1864), K. G. V. Smith, Gem Publishing Co., Brightwood, Bell Lane, Brightwell cum Sotwell, Wallingford, Oxon OX10 0QD    *tel* (0491) 33882.
£22.00 p.a. 3 times p.a. Articles on all orders of insects and terrestrial arthropods, foreign and British. *Payment:* none.

**Envoi** (1957), Anne Lewis-Smith, Pen Ffordd, Newport, Dyfed SA42 0QT    *tel* (0239) 820285.
£6 p.a. 3 p.a. New poetry and reviews. Poetry Competitions. Editorial panel of 30 who criticise each poem sent in (with s.a.e.) at no charge.

**ES Magazine** (1987), Tim Willis, Northcliffe House, 2 Derry Street, London W8 5EE    *tel* 01-938 6000.
Free with The Evening Standard. M. Feature ideas, not exclusively about London. *Payment:* by negotiation. *Illustrations:* all types.

**Essentials** (1988), Gillian de Bono, GE Magazines Ltd, 31-39 Earlham Street, London WC2H 9LD    *tel* 01-379 4044    *telex* 929414 Gepub    *fax* 01-836 0280.
90p. M. Features on fashion, health and beauty, cookery; also short stories, 2000-3000 words. *Payment:* by negotiation. *Illustrations:* colour.

**Essex Countryside** (1952), Carol Boatman, Essex Countryside Ltd., Wenden Court, Wendens Ambo, Saffron Walden, Essex CB11 4LB.
95p. M. Articles of county interest. *Length:* approximately 1000 words. *Illustrations:* half-tone and line.

**European Plastics News** (1929), Tim Tunbridge, Reed Business Publishing, Quadrant House, The Quadrant, Sutton, Surrey SM2 5AS    *tel* 01-661 3292    *telex* 892084    *fax* 01-661 8924.
£10.00. (£58.00 p.a.) M. Technical articles dealing with plastics and allied subjects. *Length:* depending on subject. *Payment:* by arrangement. *Illustrations:* half-tone blocks 120 screen, line.

**The European Racehorse,** Andrew Caulfield, 19 Clarges Street, London W1Y 7PG *tel* 01-493 7353 *fax* 01-409 3578.
£6.00. March, June, September, November. Preliminary letter essential. Articles on breeding of racehorses and ancillary subjects by recognised experts.

**Evangelical Quarterly** (1929), Prof. I. H. Marshall, Department of New Testament, King's College, Aberdeen AB9 2UB. Published from Paternoster House, 3 Mount Radford Crescent, Exeter, Devon EX2 4JW *tel* (0392) 50631.
£2.60. Q. An international review of Bible and theology in defence of the historic Christian faith. Articles on the defence or exposition of Biblical theology as exhibited in the great Reformed Confessions. *Payment:* none.

**Evening Chronicle** (Newcastle), Graeme Stanton, Newcastle Chronicle and Journal Ltd., Thomson House, Groat Market, Newcastle upon Tyne NE99 1BO *tel* (091) 232-7500. London: Thomson Regional Newspapers, Pemberton House, East Harding Street, EC4A 3AS *tel* 01-353 9131.
20p. D. News, photographs and features covering almost every subject which is of interest to readers in Tyne and Wear, Northumberland and Durham. *Payment:* according to value.

**Evening Post,** 395 High Street, Chatham, Kent ME4 4PG *tel* Medway (0634) 830600.
16p. Monday to Friday. Local news covering the Medway towns, Gravesend, Dartford, Swale and Maidstone. Also national news. Paper with emphasis on news and sport, plus regular feature pages. *Illustrations:* line and half-tone.

**Evening Post** (Reading) (1965), Trevor Wade, 8 Tessa Road, Reading RG1 8NS *tel* Reading (0734) 575833 *fax* (0734) 599363.
18p. D. Topical articles based on current news. *Length:* 800 to 1200 words. *Payment:* based on lineage rates. *Illustrations:* half-tone.

**The Evening Standard** (1827), John Leese, Northcliffe House, 2 Derry Street, London W8 5EE *tel* 01-938 6000.
20p. D. Independent. Articles of general interest considered, 1500 words or shorter; also news, pictures and ideas.

**Everyday Electronics** (1971), Mike Kenward, Wimborne Publishing Ltd., 6 Church Street, Wimborne, Dorset BH21 1JH *tel* (0202) 881749.
£1.40. M. Constructional and theoretical articles aimed at the student and hobbyist. *Length:* 1000-5500 words. *Payment:* £55-£90 per 1000 words depending on type of article. *Illustrations:* line and half-tone.

**Everywoman** (1985), Barbara Rogers, 34 Islington Green, London N1 8DU *tel* 01-359 5496.
£1.00. M. Features, especially news features. Study of magazine essential; covering note should state which section a piece is for. *Payment:* for commissions, by arrangement. *Illustrations:* line, half-tone; cartoons.

**Exchange and Mart** (1868), Link House, 25 West Street, Poole, Dorset BH15 1LL *tel* Poole (0202) 671171 *telex* 417109.
75p. W. No editorial matter used.

**The Face** (1980), Nick Logan, The Old Laundry, Ossington Buildings, Moxon Street, London W1 *tel* 01-935 8232.
£1.50. M. Articles on music, fashion, films, popular youth culture. *Payment:* £100.00 per 1000 words. *Illustrations:* half-tone, colour.

**Faith and Freedom: A Journal of Progressive Religion** (1947), Manchester College, Oxford. Editor: Peter B. Godfrey, B.A., 41 Bradford Drive, Ewell, Epsom, Surrey KT19 0AQ *tel* 01-393 9122.

£7.00 p.a., 3 issues (April, July, Oct.). Articles on philosophy and religion from free, non-dogmatic point of view, 3000 to 5000 words. *Payment:* none.

**Family Circle**, King's Reach Tower, Stamford Street, London SE1 9LS	*tel* 01-261 5000.
70p. 13 p.a. Practical, medical and human interest material. *Length:* minimum 650 words. *Payment:* NUJ rates or above.

**Family Law** (1971), Miles McColl, Elizabeth Walsh, 21 St. Thomas Street, Bristol BS1 6JS	*tel* (0272) 230600	*telex* 449119. *DX:* 78161 Bristol	*fax* (0272) 230063.
£50.00 p.a. M. Articles dealing with all aspects of the Law as it affects the Family, written from a legal or socio- legal point of view. *Length:* 1000 words plus. *Payment:* £15.00 per 1000 words, or by arrangement. No *illustrations*.

**Fantasy Tales** (1977), Stephen Jones and David A. Sutton, Robinson Publishing, 11 Shepherd House, Shepherd Street, London W1Y 7LD	*tel* 01-493 1064	*telex* 28905 Mon Ref G Ref 778.
99p. Bi-annual (Spring/Autumn). All types of fantasy and horror short stories. *Payment:* by negotiation. *Illustrations:* line drawings—commissioned only, but examples of artwork welcomed. *Sae* essential. MSS submissions to: David A. Sutton, 194 Station Road, Kings Heath, Birmingham B14 7TE; artwork submissions to: Stephen Jones, 130 Park View, Wembley, Middlesex HA9 6JU.

**Farmers Weekly** (1934), Ted Fellows, Reed Business Publishing Ltd, Carew House, Wallington, Surrey SM6 0DX	*tel* 01-661 4701.
60p. W. Articles on agriculture from freelance contributors will be accepted subject to negotiation.

**Farming News** (1983), Marcus Oliver, Morgan Grampian, plc, 30 Calderwood Street, London SE18 6QH	*tel* 01-855 7777	*telex* 896238	*fax* 01-854 6795.
£1.00. W. (£45 p.a.) News, business, technical and leisure articles; crosswords, features. *Payment:* NUJ freelance rates. *Illustrations:* half-tone, colour; cartoons.

**Fashion Forecast** (1946), Suzanne Turower, 33 Bedford Place, London WC1B 5JX	*tel* 01-637 2211	*telex* 8954884	*fax* 01-637 2248.
£22.00 in U.K. and Europe, £32.00 airmail including **Fashion Buyers Diary**, **Hosiery Forecast** and **Sportswear Forecast**. Twice p.a. (March, September). Factual articles on fashions and accessories with forecast trend. *Length:* 800 to 1000 words. *Illustrations:* half-tone and line.

**Fashion Weekly** (1959), Eric Musgrave, 1st Floor, 26-28 Bartholomew Square, London EC1V 3QH	*tel* 01-490 1994	*fax* 01-490 1868.
£1.00 (subscription £45 p.a.). W. Business and product paper for clothing retailers, manufacturers and distributors. *Payment:* by arrangement. *Illustrations:* line, half-tone, colour.

**Fear** (1988), John Gilbert, Newsfield Ltd, Research House, Fraser Road, Perivale, Middlesex UB6 7AQ	*tel* 01-997 8567	*fax* 01-991 5557.
£2.50. Bi-M. Fantasy, horror and science fiction short stories; also interviews, articles, news items, book and film reviews. *Length:* 1500-4000 words. *Payment:* 1st-time fiction £50 per 1000 words; fiction/articles £70 per 1000 words. *Illustrations:* in colour, half-tone and line. Cartoons considered; *payment:* £10-£20. *Sae* essential.

**The Field** (1853), (incorporating **Land and Water** and **The Country Gentleman**), 6 Sheet Street, Windsor, Berks. SL4 1BG	*tel* (0753) 856061.

£1.50. M. Specific, topical and informed features on the British countryside and country pursuits, including natural history, field sports, gardening and farming. Overseas subjects considered but opportunities for such articles are limited. No fiction or children's material. Articles, *length* 800-2000 words, by outside contributors considered. *Payment:* on merit. *Illustrations:* colour photographs of a high standard.

**Film Monthly,** Ken Ferguson, Argus Specialist Publications, Argus House, Boundary Way, Hemel Hempstead HP2 7ST *tel* (0442) 66551 *telex* 827797 *fax* (0442) 66998.
£1.30. M. Features on the film, video and TV scene. Stamped addressed envelope to be enclosed for return of MS. if not suitable. *Payment:* by arrangement.

**Films & Filming,** Kathryn Kirby, 8 Primrose Mews, Sharpleshall Street, London NW1 8YL *tel* 01-586 8591 *fax* 01-586 1549.
£1.75. M. Articles on contemporary cinema, preferably with illustrations. *Payment:* by arrangement. *Illustrations:* line, half-tone.

**Filtration & Separation** (1964), R. Feather, Uplands Press Ltd., 38 Mount Pleasant, London WC1X 0AP *tel* 01-833 0392 *telex* 261177.
£6.00. Bi-M. Articles on the design, contruction and application of filtration and separation equipment and dust control and air cleaning equipment for all industrial purposes; articles on filtration and separation and dust control and air cleaning operations and techniques in all industries. *Payment:* by arrangement. *Illustrations:* line and half-tone.

**Financial Decisions** (1984), Mary Bogan, VNU Business Publications, VNU House, 32-34 Broadwick Street, London W1A 2HG *tel* 01-439 4242 *telex* 23918 VNU G *fax* 01-437 7001.
£2 (free to finance directors). M. Features on financial and strategic management issues. *Length:* 1500-2000 words. *Payment:* £120-£150 per 1000 words. *Illustrations:* colour and b&w photos, line drawings; *payment:* photos, variable; line, £250-£300.

**Financial Times** (1888), Sir Geoffrey Owen, Number One, Southwark Bridge, London SE1 9HL *tel* 01-873 3000.
45p. D. Articles of financial, commercial, industrial and economic interest. *Length:* 800-1000 words. *Payment:* by arrangement.

**Financial Weekly** (1979), Tom Lloyd, 14 Greville Street, London EC1 *tel* 01-405 2622.
£1.40. W. Financial, industrial and business features. Interviews and profiles. *Payment:* £100 per 1000 words. *Illustrations:* line, half-tone and colour.

**The Fine Art Trade Guild Journal,** 192 Ebury Street, London SW1W 8UP *tel* 01-730 3220.
Distributed to members only; £2.00 extra copies. Q. For the promotion and improvement of all aspects of the Fine Art Trade. *Length* of articles 2000 words maximum, with good illustrations. *Payment:* by arrangement.

**Fitness** (1984), Antony Jacobson, 40 Bowling Green Lane, London EC1R 0NE *tel* 01-278 0333 *telex* 267247 *fax* 01-833 3199.
£1.50. M. Articles on all aspects of fitness. *Payment:* by arrangement. *Illustrations:* line, half-tone, colour; cartoons.

**Flight International** (1909), A. Winn, Reed Business Publishing, Quadrant House, The Quadrant, Sutton, Surrey SM2 5AS *tel* 01-661 3882 *telex* 892084 Reedbp G *fax* 01-661 3840.
£1.35. W. Deals with aviation in all its branches. Articles operational and technical, illustrated by photographs, engineering cutaway drawings, also

news, paragraphs, reports of lectures, etc. *Payment:* varies; cheques month following publication. *Illustrations:* tone, line, two- and four-colour. News press days: Friday, Monday.

**Football Picture Story Library,** D. C. Thomson & Co. Ltd., Courier Place, Dundee DD1 9QJ and 185 Fleet Street, London EC4A 2HS.
32p. Two each month. Football stories for boys told in pictures.

**Forensic Photography,** incorporating **Medico-Legal Photography** (1972), 87 London Street, Chertsey, Surrey KT16 8AN   *tel* (0932) 562933.
£10.00 p.a. Q. Though this journal goes only to subscribers and is not sold through retail channels, the editor is always interested in articles (illustrated or not) concerned with photographic techniques slanted to the professional and concerned with any aspect of the journal's title. *Payment:* by arrangement. *Illustrations:* line or half-tone.

**Freelance Market News**—see **Freelance Press Services** in **Editorial, Literary and Production Services.**

**Freelance Writing & Photography** (1965), Victoria House, Victoria Road, Hale, Cheshire WA15 2BP   *tel* 061-928 5588.
£1.95. Q. (£7.50 p.a.). Articles, short stories, essays, reviews, interviews, market news for the freelance writer and photographer. *Length:* articles 500 to 1500 words; stories 2000 words maximum. *Payment:* by arrangement. *Illustrations:* line, half-tone. No work will be considered unless accompanied by s.a.e.

**The Friend** (1843), David Firth, Drayton House, 30 Gordon Street, London WC1H 0BQ   *tel* 01-387 7549. Publishing: Headley Brothers Ltd., Ashford Kent.
50p. W. A Quaker weekly paper. Matter of interest to the Society of Friends, devotional or general, considered from outside contributors. No fiction. 1200 words maximum length. *Payment:* none.

**Fresh Produce Journal** (1895), Andrew Clayton, 430 Market Towers, New Covent Garden, Nine Elms Lane, London SW8 5NN   *tel* 01-720 8822 and 622 6677   *telex* 915149 Frtjnl G.
90p. W. Articles dealing with above trades on the marketing aspects of production but particularly importing, distribution and post-harvest handling; articles should average 500-700 words. *Payment:* by arrangement. *Illustrations:* half-tone.

**Garden News** (1958), Adam Pasco, Bushfield House, Orton Centre, Peterborough PE2 0UW   *tel* (0733) 237111.
45p. W. Gardening news and human features on gardeners and their methods of success. *Payment:* £25.00 per 1000 words. Higher rate for good short pieces and suited to our style. *Illustrations:* line, half-tone and colour.

**Gas World** (1884), Victoria Thomas, Benn Publications Ltd., Sovereign Way, Tonbridge, Kent TN9 1RW   *tel* (0732) 364422   *telex* 95162 Benton G   *fax* (0732) 361534.
£4.20. M. (£44.00 p.a.). Full news coverage and technical articles on all aspects of engineering and management in the gas industry. *Length:* up to 1800 words. Pictures and news items of topical interest are paid for at standard rates. *Payment:* by arrangement.

**Gay Times** (1982), John Marshall, 283 Camden High Street, London NW1 7BX   *tel* 01-482 2576.

£1.20. M. Full news and review coverage of all aspects of homosexual life. Short stories and feature articles. *Length:* up to 2000 words. *Payment:* by arrangement. *Illustrations:* line and half-tone; cartoons.

**Gemmological Newsletter** (1969), Michael O'Donoghue, 7 Hillingdon Avenue, Sevenoaks, Kent TN13 3RB   *tel* (0732) 453503.
£6.50 p.a. 30 p.a. (Oct.--July). Articles about minerals, gemstones, man-made crystals, lapidary and jewellery making. *Length:* up to 800 to 1000 words. *Payment:* by arrangement. *Illustrations:* line and half-tone.

**Geographical Journal** (1893), B. H. Farmer, Royal Geographical Society, Kensington Gore, London SW7 2AR   *tel* 01-589 5466   *telex* 933669   *fax* 01-581 9918.
£12.00 (post free). 3 p.a. (£32.00 p.a.). Papers read before the Royal Geographical Society and papers on all aspects of geography or exploration. *Length:* max. 3500 words. *Payment:* for reviews. *Illustrations:* photographs, maps and diagrams.

**The Geographical Magazine,** Mark Ausenda, 27 Kensington Court, London W8 5DN   *tel* 01-937 3535   *telex* 8953616   *fax* 01-937 2262.
£1.40. M. Informative, readable, well-illustrated, authentic articles, from 1500 to 2000 words in length, dealing with people and their environment in all parts of the world; modern geography in all its aspects; kindred subjects such as hydrology, meteorology, communications, civil engineering, space, etc.; man's control of the environment in which he lives, works and plays; travel, exploration, research; plant and animal life in their relationship with mankind. A *preliminary* letter is recommended. *Payment:* from £50.00 per 1000 words. *Illustrations:* of highly technical and artistic quality. Photographs unaccompanied by articles may be considered. *Payment:* colour, from £12.00 upwards, covers by negotiation; black and white, from £5.00 upwards, depending on size of reproduction.

**Geological Magazine** (1864), Dr. C. P. Hughes, Professor I. N. McCave, Dr. N. H. Woodcock, Cambridge University Press, The Edinburgh Building, Shaftesbury Road, Cambridge CB2 2RU   *tel* (0223) 312393.
£82.00 p.a., £91.00 p.a. overseas. Bi-M (January, etc.). Original articles on all earth science topics containing the results of independent research by experts and amateurs. Also reviews and notices of current geological literature, correspondence on geological subjects—illustrated. *Length:* variable. *Payment:* none.

**Gifts International,** Vhairi Cotter, Benn Publications Ltd., Sovereign Way, Tonbridge, Kent TN9 1RW   *tel* (0732) 364422   *telex* 95132 Benton G.
£30.00 p.a., £40.00 p.a. overseas. M. News of gift industry—products, trends, shops. *Articles:* retailing, exporting, importing, manufacturing, crafts (U.K. and abroad). *Payment:* by agreement. *Illustrations:* products, news, personal photographs.

**Girl,** IPC Magazines Ltd., 27th Floor, King's Reach Tower, Stamford Street, London SE1 9LS   *tel* 01-261 6312.
50p. W. A colour photo-story and feature magazine for pre-teen girls and early teens. Stories always commissioned.

**Girl About Town Magazine** (1973), Claire Gillman, 141-3 Drury Lane, Covent Garden, London WC2B 5TS   *tel* 01-836 4433   *fax* 01-836 3156.
Free. W. Articles of general interest to London women. *Length:* about 1000 words. *Payment:* by arrangement. *Illustrations:* line, half-tone, colour.

**Glasgow Evening Times** (1876), George McKechnie, 195 Albion Street, Glasgow G1 1QP  *tel* 041-552 6255; London Office: 1 Jerome Street, London E1 6NJ  *tel* 01-377 0890  *telex* 779818  *fax* 041-553 1355.
22p. D.

**Glasgow Herald** (1783), Arnold Kemp, 195 Albion Street, Glasgow G1 1QP  *tel* 041-552 6255  *fax* 041-552 2288. London: 1 Jerome Street, E1 6NJ  *tel* 01-377 0890.
27p. D. Independent. Articles up to 1000 words.

**Gloucestershire Life,** Bill Charlton, Town & County Magazines, 10th Floor, St. Lawrence House, Broad Street, Bristol BS1 2EX  *tel* (0272) 291069.
£1.00. M. Articles of interest to the county dealing with people in the news, personalities who live in the area; projects concerning individuals and communities; historical articles. *Length:* 800 to 1000 words. *Payment:* by arrangement. Photographs also by arrangement. *Illustrations:* preference given to articles accompanied by good photographs.

**Golf Illustrated Weekly,** Neil Elsey, Advance House, 37 Millharbour, Isle of Dogs, London E14 9TX  *tel* 01-538 1031  *fax* 01-537 2053.
£1.00. W. News, tournament reports and articles on golf and of interest to golfers. *Payment:* by arrangement. *Illustrations:* photographs of golfers and golf courses.

**Golf Monthly** (1911), Malcolm Campbell, Hamilton House, 3/4 Claremont Terrace, Glasgow G3 7XR  *tel* 041-332 2828.
£1.40. M. Original articles on golf considered (not reports). *Payment:* by arrangement. *Illustrations:* half-tone, colour.

**Golf World** (1962), Robert Green, Advance House, 37 Millharbour, Isle of Dogs, London E14 9TX  *tel* 01-538 1031.
£1.75. M. Expert golf instructional articles, 500-3000 words; general interest articles, personality features 500-3000 words. Little fiction. *Payment:* by negotiation. *Illustrations:* line, half-tone, colour.

**Good Housekeeping** (1922), Noëlle Walsh, National Magazine House, 72 Broadwick Street, London W1V 2BP  *tel* 01-439 7144.
£1.10. M. Articles of 1000-2500 words from qualified writers are invited on topics of interest to intelligent women. Domestic subjects covered by staff writers. Short stories and humorous articles also used. *Payment:* good magazine standards. *Illustrations:* mainly commissioned.

**The Good Ski Guide** (1980), John Hill, 1-2 Dawes Court, 93 High Street, Esher, Surrey KT10 9QD  *tel* (0372) 69799  *telex* 8951417 Letron G.
£2.50. Q. Factual articles on all aspects of skiing. *Payment:* £100 per 1000 words. *Illustrations:* colour slides/prints. *Payment:* £200 for cover; £50 inside page.

**GQ** (1988), Paul Keers, Vogue House, Hanover Square, London W1R 0AD  *tel* 01-499 9080  *telex* 27338 Volon G  *fax* 01-493 1345.
£1.80. M. Articles relating to the lifestyle of the successful, stylish man. *Payment:* by arrangement. *Illustrations:* b&w and colour photographs, line drawings, cartoons; *payment:* by arrangement.

**Gramophone,** Christopher Pollard, 177-179 Kenton Road, Harrow, Middx HA3 0HA  *tel* 01-907 4476.
£1.10. M. Outside contributions are occasionally used. Features on recording artists, technical articles, and articles about gramophone needs. 1000 to 1500 words preferred. *Payment:* by arrangement. *Illustrations:* line and half-tone.

**Granta** (1889; new series 1979), Bill Buford, 44A Hobson Street, Cambridge CB1 1NL *tel* (0223) 315290. Published in association with Penguin Books U.K., Ltd.
£4.95. Q. Original fiction and cultural journalism. *Length:* determined by content. *Payment:* by arrangement. *Illustrations:* photographs.

**The Great Outdoors** (1978), Peter Evans, The Plaza Towers, The Plaza, East Kilbride, Glasgow G74 1LW *tel* (03552) 46444.
£1.30. (£15.50 p.a.). M. Articles on walking or camping in specific areas, preferably illustrated. *Length:* 1500-2000 words. *Payment:* by arrangement. *Illustrations:* line, half-tone and colour.

**The Grocer** (1861), A. de Angeli, 5-7 Southwark Street, London SE1 1RQ *tel* 01-407 6981 *telex* 8812648 *fax* 01-378 6781.
25p. W. This journal is devoted entirely to the trade. Contributions accepted are articles or news or illustrations of general interest to the grocery and provision trades. *Payment:* by arrangement.

**The Grower** (1923), Peter Rogers, 50 Doughty Street, London WC1N 2LS *tel* 01-405 0364.
73p. W. News and practical articles on commercial horticulture, preferably illustrated. *Payment:* by arrangement. *Illustrations:* photographs, line drawings.

**The Guardian** (1821), Peter Preston, 119 Farringdon Road, London EC1R 3ER *tel* 01-278 2332 *telex* 8811746/7/8 Guardn G; 164 Deansgate, Manchester M60 2RR *tel* 061-832 7200.
30p. D. Independent. The paper takes few articles from outside contributors except on its specialist pages. Articles should not normally exceed 1200 words in length. *Payment:* from £126.95 per 1000 words. *Illustrations:* news and features photographs.

**Guiding,** Official Organ of the Girl Guides Association, Nora Warner, 17-19 Buckingham Palace Road, London SW1W 0PT *tel* 01-834 6242.
75p. M. Articles of interest to women of all ages, with special emphasis on youth work and the Guide Movement. *Length:* 500-1500 words. *Payment:* £26.60 per 1000 words. *Illustrations:* line and half-tone.

**Hampshire—The County Magazine,** Dennis Stevens, 74 Bedford Place, Southampton SO1 2DF *tel* (0703) 223591 and 333457.
70p. M. Factual articles concerning all aspects of Hampshire and Hampshire life, past and present. *Length:* 500-1500 words. *Payment:* £10 per 1000 words. *Illustrations:* photographs and line drawings.

**Harpers & Queen** (1929), Sally O'Sullivan, National Magazine House, 72 Broadwick Street, London W1V 2BP *tel* 01-439 7144.
£2.20. M. Features, fashion, beauty, art, theatre, films, travel, interior decoration, mainly commissioned. *Illustrations:* line, wash, full colour and two- and three-colour, and photographs.

**Health & Efficiency International** (1900), Kate Sturdy, 2nd Floor, 67-73 Worship Street, London EC2A 2DU *tel* 01-377 5122.
£1.50. M. Articles on nudist/naturist/social matters. Naturist travel features. *Length:* from 1000 to 1500 words. *Payment:* £40 per 1000 words. *Illustrations:* line, half-tone, colour transparencies, colour prints, cartoons.

**Health Education Journal** (1943), Public Affairs Division, Health Education Authority, Hamilton House, Mabledon Place, London WC1H 9TX *tel* 01-631 0930 *fax* 01-387 3550.

£10.00 p.a. Q. Matter on mental and physical health, health education and social well-being; reports of surveys of people's knowledge of health: educational method and material; nutrition; educational psychology and preventive psychiatry. Book reviews. *Length:* 1500 to 3000 words. *Payment:* none. *Illustrations:* camera ready artwork.

**Heredity: An International Journal of Genetics** (1947), P. D. S. Caligari, Department of Agricultural Botany, University of Reading, Whiteknights, Reading RG6 2AS.
£72.00 (U.K.), £75.00 (overseas) (two volumes each of three parts yearly). Research and review articles in genetics of 1000 to 15,000 words with summary and bibliography. Book reviews and abstracts of conferences. *Payment:* none. *Illustrations:* line, half-tone and colour.

**Here's Health,** Victory House, Leicester Place, London WC2H 7NB *tel* 01-437 9011 *telex* 266400 *fax* 01-494 0497.
95p. M. Articles on healthy eating, nutrition, alternative medicine, organic gardening, natural beauty, conservation. *Length:* 750-1800 words. *Payment:* on publication. Preliminary letter essential.

**Hertfordshire Countryside** (1946), George Seward, Beaumonde Publications Ltd., 4 Mill Bridge, Hertford, Herts. SG14 1PY *tel* (0992) 553571.
75p. M. Articles of county interest, 1000 words. *Illustrations:* line and half-tone.

**The Heythrop Journal** (1960), Rev. Dr. Joseph A. Munitiz, Heythrop College, University of London, 11 Cavendish Square, London W1M 0AN *tel* 01-580 6941.
£3.50 including postage. Q. (individuals £13.50 p.a.; U.S.A. $35.00; institutions £20.00 p.a.; U.S.A. $48.00). Articles (5000-8000) in: philosophy, theology speculative and positive, scripture, canon law, church relations, moral and pastoral psychology, of general interest but of technical merit. *Payment:* Authors receive 24 offprints.

**Hi!** (D.C. Thomson & Co. Ltd.), 2 Albert Square, Dundee DD1 9QJ *tel* (0382) 23131. London Office: 185 Fleet Street, EC4A 2HS *tel* 01-242 5086/8.
32p. W. 32 pages of features, photo stories and picture stories, with 75% colour. Aimed at trendy 10-14 year-olds. *Payment:* on acceptance.

**Hi-Fi News & Record Review** (1956), Steve Harris, Link House, Dingwall Avenue, Croydon CR9 2TA *tel* 01-686 2599 *telex* 947709 Linkho G *fax* 01-760 0973.
£1.60. M. Articles on all aspects of high quality sound recording and reproduction; also extensive record review section and supporting musical feature articles. Audio matter is essentially technical, but should be presented in a manner suitable for music lovers interested in the nature of sound. *Payment:* by arrangement. *Length:* 2000 to 3000 words. *Illustrations:* line and/or half-tone; cartoons.

**Higher Education Quarterly** (1946), Michael Shattock, Basil Blackwell Ltd., 108 Cowley Road, Oxford OX4 1JF *tel* (0865) 791100.
Q. Articles on higher education policy, national and international. *Length:* 2000 to 6000 words. *Payment:* 6 copies of issue.

**History** (1916), Professor W. A. Speck, M.A., D.PHIL. Editorial: School of History, The University of Leeds, Leeds LS2 9JT *tel* (0532) 333587. Business: 59A Kennington Park Road, London SE11 4JH *tel* 01-735 3901.
£9.50 for Historical Ass. Members; £20.00 p.a. non-members. 3 p.a. Published by the Historical Association. Historical articles and reviews by experts.

*Length:* usually up to 8000 words. *Payment:* none. *Illustrations:* only exceptionally.

**History Today** (1951), Gordon Marsden, 83-84 Berwick Street, London W1V 3PJ *tel* 01-439 8315.
£1.80. M. History in the widest sense—political, economic, social, biography, relating past to present; World history as well as British. *Length:* articles 3500 words; shorter news/views pieces 600-1200 words. *Payment:* by agreement. *Illustrations:* from prints and original photographs. Please do not send original material until publication is agreed.

**Home and Country** (1919), Penny Kitchen, 39 Eccleston Street, London SW1W 9NT *tel* 01-730 0307.
40p. M. Some of the material published relates to the activities of the National Federation of Women's Institutes for England and Wales, whose official journal it is, but articles of general interest to women, particularly country women, of 800 to 1200 words are considered. *Payment:* by arrangement. *Illustrations:* photographs and drawings.

**Home and Family** (1954), Sue Steel, The Mothers' Union, The Mary Sumner House, 24 Tufton Street, London SW1P 3RB *tel* 01-222 5533.
30p. Q. Short articles related to Christian family life. *Payment:* approx. £5.00 to £15.00 per 1000 words. *Illustrations:* line and half-tone.

**Home Words** (1870) P.O. Box 44, Guildford, Surrey GU1 1XL *tel* (0483) 33944.
M. An illustrated C. of E. magazine inset. Articles of popular Christian interest (400 to 800 words) with relevant photographs.

**Homes and Gardens** (1919), Amanda Evans, King's Reach Tower, Stamford Street, London SE1 9LS *tel* 01-261 5000.
£1.35. M. Articles of general interest to intelligent women and men. *Length:* articles, 900-3000 words. *Payment:* generous, but exceptional work required. *Illustrations:* all types.

**Horse and Hound,** M. A. Clayton, King's Reach Tower, Stamford Street, London SE1 9LS *tel* 01-261 6315.
85p. W. Special articles, news items, photographs, on all matters appertaining to horses, hunting.

**Horse & Pony** (1980), Sarah Haw, EMAP Pursuit Publishing Ltd., Bretton Court, Bretton, Peterborough PE3 8DZ *tel* (0733) 264666 *fax* (0733) 265515.
72p. F. All material relevant to young people with equestrian interests. *Payment:* on value to publication rather than length. *Illustrations:* colour, black and white, with a strong story line.

**Horse and Rider** (1959), Managing Editor: Kate Austin, Editor: Janet Evans, 296 Ewell Road, Surbiton, Surrey KT6 7AQ *tel* 01-390 8547 *fax* 01-390 8696.
£1.10. M. A sophisticated magazine covering all forms of equestrian activity at home and abroad. Good writing and technical accuracy essential. *Length:* 1000 to 1600 words. *Payment:* by arrangement. *Illustrations:* photographs and drawings, the latter usually commissioned.

**Horticulture Week,** S. Gunn, 38-42 Hampton Road, Teddington, Middlesex TW11 0JE *tel* 01-977 8787.
70p. W. (£45.00 p.a.). A practical horticultural journal for the nursery and garden centre trade, landscape industry and public parks and sports ground staff. Outside contributions considered and, if accepted, paid for. *Length:* 500 to 1500 words. No fiction. *Payment:* by arrangement. *Illustrations:* colour, halftone and line.

**Hortus** (1987), David Wheeler, The Neuadd, Rhayader, Powys LD6 5HH   *tel* (0597) 810227.
£22.00 p.a. Q. Articles on decorative horticulture: plants, gardens, history, design, literature, people. *Length:* up to 10,000 words. *Payment:* by arrangement. *Illustrations:* line, half-tone and wood-engravings.

**Hospitality** (1980), Consultant Editor: Miles Quest, 35 Albemarle Street, London W1X 3FB   *tel* 01-629 4320   *telex* 291852   *fax* 01-491 4880. Official magazine of the Hotel Catering & Institutional Management Association.
£2.00. M. Articles for a management readership on food, accommodation services and related topics in hotels, restaurants, educational establishments, the health service, industrial situations, educational and other institutions. *Illustrations:* photographs, line. *Payment:* by arrangement.

**House & Garden,** Robert Harling, Vogue House, Hanover Square, London W1R 0AD   *tel* 01-499 9080   *telex* 27338 Volon G.
£2.00. M. Articles (always commissioned), on subjects relating to domestic architecture, interior decorating, furnishing, gardening, household equipment.

**House Builder,** Phillip Cooke, 82 New Cavendish Street, London W1M 8AD   *tel* 01-580 5588.
£4.00. M. A technical journal for those engaged in house and flat construction and the development of housing estates. The Official Journal of the House-Builders Federation, National House Building Council and New Homes Marketing Board. Articles on design, construction, and equipment of dwellings, estate planning and development, and technical aspects of house-building. *Length:* articles 500 words and upwards, preferably with illustrations. *Preliminary letter* advisable. *Payment:* by arrangement. *Illustrations:* photographs, plans, constructional details.

**Ideal Home** (1920), Terence Whelan, King's Reach Tower, Stamford Street, London SE1 9LS   *tel* 01-261 6474.
£1.20. M. Specialised home subjects magazine, and articles usually commissioned. Contributors advised to study editorial content before submitting material. *Payment:* according to material. *Illustrations:* usually commissioned.

**The Illustrated London News** (1842), James Bishop, Laurence House, 91–93 Southwark Street, London SE1 0HX   *tel* 01-928 2111   *fax* 01-620 1594.
£2.00. 6 p.a. A magazine dealing chiefly with London and the UK, travel, environment and the quality of life. Interesting articles accepted; but most material commissioned. *Payment:* usual rates; special rates for exclusive material.

**Impact of Science on Society** (1950), Howard Moore, Unesco, 31 rue François-Bonvin, Paris 75015   *tel* 33(1) 4568-4144/49   *telegraphic address* Unesco, Paris   *telex* 204461 Paris   *fax* 33(1) 43 06 11 22.
96p. Q. Articles and original studies on the social, political, economic, cultural aspects of science and technology. A *preliminary letter* to the Editor is requested. *Length:* 4500 words. *Payment:* up to £250 on acceptance. *Illustrations:* photographs, tables, graphs and drawings. Intending contributors are advised to study the magazine.

**In Britain** (1930), Bryn Frank, British Tourist Authority, Thames Tower, Black's Road, London W6 9EL   *tel* 01-846 9000   *telex* 21231 Btaadm G.
£1.25. M. (£17.50 p.a.). Features magazine about places to see and things to do in Britain. Short pieces (150 words) sometimes accepted.

**The Independent** (1986), Andreas Whittam Smith, 40 City Road, London EC1Y 2DB   *tel* 01-253 1222.

30p, Sat. 40p. D. (Mon.-Sat.). Occasional freelance contributions; preliminary letter advisable. *Payment:* by arrangement.

**The Independent Magazine** (1988), Alexander Chancellor, 40 City Road, London EC1Y 2DB   *tel* 01–253 1222   *fax* 01–962 0016.
Free with newspaper. W. Profiles and illustrated articles of topical interest; *all material commissioned. Length:* 500–3000 words. *Payment:* by arrangement. *Illustrations:* cartoons; commissioned colour and b&w photos; *payment:* by arrangement. *Preliminary study of the magazine essential.*

**Index on Censorship** (1972), Sally Laird, 39c Highbury Place, London N5 1QP   *tel* 01-359 0161.
£1.80 (£18.00 p.a.). 10 p.a. Articles up to 5000 words dealing with political censorship, book reviews 750-1500 words. *Payment:* Articles £42 per 1000 words, book reviews £21.

**The Indexer** (1958), Journal of the Society of Indexers, American Society of Indexers, Australian Society of Indexers, and Indexing & Abstracting Society of Canada. Hazel Bell, 139 The Ryde, Hatfield, Herts. AL9 5DP   *tel* Hatfield (070-72) 65201.
Free to members (subscription £15.00 p.a. from Journal Subscriptions Officer, 16 Coleridge Close, Hitchin, Herts. SG4 0QX). 2 p.a. Articles of interest to professional indexers, authors, publishers, documentalists. *Payment:* none.

**An Indian Bookworm's Journal** (1987), Pyare Shivpuri, Institute of India Studies, 45 Museum Street, London WC1A 1LR   *tel* 01-405 7226/3784.
£1.00. Q. Articles and news pieces about books with specific interest for the Indian subcontinent. *Payment:* by arrangement. *Illustrations:* line, including cartoons; half-tone. Preliminary letter preferred.

**Industrial Participation** (1884), Anthony Barry, 85 Tooley Street, London SE1 2QZ   *tel* 01-403 6018.
£20.00 p.a. U.K., £30.00 p.a. overseas, post free. Q. Journal of the Industrial Participation Association. Articles on participation and involvement in industry, employee shareholding, joint consultation, the sharing of information, labour-management relations, workers participation, and kindred industrial subjects from the operational angle, with emphasis on the practice of particular enterprises, usually written by a member of the team involved, whether manager or workers, and with a strong factual background. *Length:* up to 3500 words. *Payment:* £80 per 1000 words.

**Information & Library Manager** (1981), MCB University Press, 62 Toller Lane, Bradford, West Yorkshire BD8 9BY   *tel* (0274) 499821.
£39.95 p.a. 6 p.a. Information and library professional articles. *Illustrations:* line. *Payment:* none.

**Information and Software Technology** (1959), Butterworth Scientific Ltd., P.O. Box 63, Westbury House, Bury Street, Guildford, Surrey GU2 5BH   *tel* (0483) 300966   *telex* 859556 Scitec G.
£10.00. 10 issues p.a. (£95.00 p.a., $114.00 overseas). Papers on software design and development and the application of information processing in large organisations, especially multinationals. *Length:* 5000 words. *Payment:* by arrangement. *Illustrations:* half-tone and line.

**The Inquirer** (1842), Keith Gilley, 1-6 Essex Street, London WC2R 2HY   *tel* 01-240 2384.
25p. F. A journal of news and comment for Unitarians and religious liberals. Articles up to 750 words of general religious, social, cultural and international interest. Articles should be liberal and progressive in tone. *Payment:* none.

**Insurance Brokers' Monthly** (1950), Brian Susman, 7 Stourbridge Road, Lye, Stourbridge, West Midlands DY9 7DG  *tel* Lye (0384) 895228.
£2.00. M. Articles of technical and non-technical interest to insurance brokers and others engaged in the insurance industry. Occasional articles of general interest to the City, on finance, etc. *Length:* 1000 to 1500 words. *Payment:* from £14.50 per 1000 words on last day of month following publication. Authoritative material written under true name and qualification receives highest payment. *Illustrations:* line and half-tone, 100-120 screen. Cartoons with strong insurance interest.

**InterMedia** (1970), Rod McShane, International Institute of Communications, Tavistock House South, Tavistock Square, London WC1H 9LF  *tel* 01-388 0671  *telex* 24578 IIC LDN  *fax* 01-380 0623.
£30.00 p.a. 5 issues p.a.; Institutions: £50 p.a. International journal concerned with policies, events, trends and research in the field of communications. *Preliminary letter* essential. *Payment:* by arrangement. *Illustrations:* black-and-white line.

**International Affairs** (1922), Royal Institute of International Affairs, Chatham House, 10 St James's Square, London SW1Y 4LE  *tel* 01-930 2233.
£5.00. Q. (£22.00 p.a.; £26.00 p.a. overseas). Serious long-term articles on international affairs and reviews of books. *Length:* average 7000 words. *Illustrations:* none. *Payment:* by arrangement. *A preliminary letter is advisable.*

**International Broadcast Engineer,** David Kirk, International Trade Publications Ltd, Queensway House, 2 Queensway, Redhill, Surrey RH1 1QS  *tel* Redhill (0737) 768611  *telex* 948669 Topjnl G  *fax* Redhill (0737) 760564.
£47.00 p.a. Bi-M. An independent journal devoted to the design, manufacture and operation of professional television and radio broadcast equipment. Circulates to over 144 countries and international aspect is stressed. Preliminary letter essential. *Illustrations:* line and half-tone. *Payment:* by arrangement.

**International Construction,** A. J. Peterson, Carew House, Wallington, Surrey SM6 0DX  *tel* 01-661 3500  *telex* 892084 Reed Bpg  *fax* 01-661 4804.
M. Articles dealing with new techniques of construction, applications of construction equipment and use of construction materials in any part of the world. *Length:* maximum 1500 words plus illustrations. *Payment:* from £65.00 per 1000 words minimum, plus illustrations. *Illustrations:* half-tone, line, colour. Some two-colour line illustrations can be used.

**Interzone** (1982), David Pringle, 124 Osborne Road, Brighton BN1 6LU  *tel* (0273) 504710.
£1.95. Bi-M. (£11.00 p.a.). Science-fiction short stories. *Length:* 2000 to 6000 words. *Payment:* by arrangement. *Illustrations:* line, half-tone, colour.

**Inverness Courier** (1817), Stuart Lindsay, P.O. Box 13, 9-11 Bank Lane, Inverness IV1 1QW  *tel* (0463) 233059.
15p. Bi-W. Short articles (no stories or verses) of Highland interest. *Payment:* by arrangement. No *illustrations.*

**Investors Chronicle,** Gillian O'Connor, Greystoke Place, Fetter Lane, London EC4A 1ND  *tel* 01-405 6969.
£1.20. W. The leading British journal for investment and personal finance. Occasional outside contributions for surveys are accepted. *Payment:* by negotiation.

**Iron** (1973), Peter Mortimer, 5 Marden Terrace, Cullercoats, North Shields, Tyne & Wear NE30 4PD  *tel* Tyneside (091) 2531901.

£2.00, inc. postage. 3 p.a. Poems; short stories up to 6000 words. *Payment:* £10.00 per page. *Illustrations:* line, half-tone.

**IS** (formerly **Industrial Society**), (1918), Anna Smith, The Industrial Society, 17-23 Southampton Row, London WC1B 5HA *tel* 01-839 4300. £10.00 p.a., £15.00 p.a. overseas. Q. Articles, news items, photographs on people management in industry and commerce in five inter-related areas: effective leadership, productive management-union relations and participation, practical communication, relevant conditions of employment and working environment and the development of young employees. *Length:* 1000-2000 words. *Payment:* by arrangement. *Illustrations:* half-tones and line drawings.

**Jackie** (D. C. Thomson & Co. Ltd.), Courier Place, Dundee DD1 9QJ *tel* 23131; and 185 Fleet Street, London EC4A 2HS *tel* 01-242 5086. 35p. W. Colour gravure magazine for teenage girls. Complete photo love stories. Type stories up to 2000 words dealing with young romance. Pop features and pin-ups. General features of teen interest---emotional, astrological, humorous. Fashion and beauty advice. *Illustrations:* transparencies, colour illustrations for type stories. *Payment:* on acceptance.

**Jane's Defence Weekly** (1984), Peter Howard, Sentinel House, 163 Brighton Road, Coulsdon, Surrey CR3 2NX *tel* 01-763 1030 *telex* 916907 Janes G *fax* 01-763 1005. £72.00 p.a. W. Defence news, military, political, industrial; analysis or briefing articles. *Length:* up to 1500 words. *Payment:* £90 per 1000 words. *Illustrations:* line, half-tone, colour.

**Jazz Journal International** (1948), Eddie Cook (Publisher and Editor-in-Chief), Jazz Journal Ltd., 113-117 Farringon Road, London EC1R 3BT *tel* 01-278 0631, 01-278 0637. £1.50. M. Articles on jazz. Record reviews. *Payment:* by arrangement. *Illustrations:* photographs.

**Jewish Chronicle** (1841), Geoffrey Paul, 25 Furnival Street, London EC4A 1JT *tel* 01-405 9252. 30p. W. Authentic and exclusive news stories and articles of Jewish interest from 500 to 1500 words are considered. There are weekly children's, women's and teenage sections. *Payment:* by arrangement. *Illustrations:* of Jewish interest, either topical or feature.

**Jewish Quarterly** (1953), Colin Shindler, P.O. Box 1148, London NW5 2AZ *tel* 01-485 4062. £2.95. Q. (£10.00 p.a.). Articles of Jewish interest, literature, history, music, politics, poetry, book reviews, fiction. *Length:* 2000-3000 words. *Illustrations:* half-tone.

**Jewish Telegraph** (1950), Paul Harris, Telegraph House, 11 Park Hill, Bury Old Road, Prestwich, Manchester M25 8HH *tel* 061-740 9321 *fax* 061-740 9325. 4a Roman View, Leeds LS8 2LW *tel* (0532) 695044. 2a Westgate Road, Wavertree, Liverpool L15 5BA *tel* 051-734 3911. 16p. W. Non-fiction articles of Jewish interest, especially humour. Exclusive Jewish news stories and pictures, international, national and local. *Length:* 1000-1500 words. *Payment:* by arrangement. *Illustrations:* half-tone and line.

**The Journal,** Christopher Cox, Thomson House, Groat Market, Newcastle upon Tyne NE1 1ED *tel* Newcastle 091-2327500. London Office: Pemberton House, 3rd Floor, East Harding Street, EC4A 3AS *tel* 01-353 9131. 20p. D. Independent.

**Journal of the Royal College of General Practitioners** (founded as the Journal of the College of General Practitioners in 1954), Dr. E. G. Buckley, F.R.C.G.P., 8 Queen Street, Edinburgh EH2 1JE   *tel* 031-225 7629.
£70.00 p.a. (£75 outside UK). M. Articles relevant to general medical practice. *Payment:* none. *Illustrations:* half-tone and colour.

**Journalist,** Tim Gopsill, N.U.J., Acorn House, 314 Gray's Inn Road, London WC1X 8DP   *tel* 01-278 7916   *telex* 892384.
30p. (£7.50 p.a., £10 p.a. abroad) M. Newspaper of the National Union of Journalists. Relating to journalism, trade unionism and general conditions in the newspaper industry. Mainly contributed by members, and outside written contributions not paid.

**Judy** (D. C. Thomson & Co. Ltd.), Courier Place, Dundee DD1 9QJ, and 185 Fleet Street, London EC4A 2HS.
26p. W. Picture-story paper for schoolgirls. Stories in pictures (mainly line drawings) as serials or series, 8-9 frames per page. Also interesting features written to appeal to girls of school age. *Payment:* on acceptance. Encouragement to young artists and writers of promise.

**Judy Library** (D. C. Thomson & Co. Ltd.), Courier Place, Dundee DD1 9QJ, and 185 Fleet Street, London EC4A 2HS.
32p. M. Stories told in pictures, for schoolgirls; 64 pages (about 140 line drawings). Ballet, school, adventure, theatre, sport. Scripts considered; promising artists and script-writers encouraged. *Payment:* on acceptance.

**Jump** (1987), Diane James, 27 Cowper Street, London EC2A 4AP   *tel* 01-251 4232   *fax* 01-251 1610.
£1.45. M. Full-colour magazine aimed at 4-8 year olds. Games, puzzles, stories, poems, things to make, features and competitions. *Payment:* by arrangement. *Illustrations:* colour photographs and full-colour artwork.

**Junior Bookshelf,** Marsh Hall, Thurstonland, Huddersfield HD4 6XB   *tel* Huddersfield (0484) 661811.
£1.50. Six issues p.a. (£7.20 inland, £9.00 overseas p.a.). Articles on children's books and authors. *Length:* about 1200 to 1500 words.

**Junior Education** (1977), Terry Saunders, Scholastic Publications Ltd., Marlborough House, Holly Walk, Leamington Spa, Warwickshire CV32 4LS   *tel* (0926) 81 3910   *telex* 312138 Spls G   *fax* (0926) 883331 Schol Pub.
£1.25. M. For teachers, educationalists and students concerned with children aged 7-12. Articles by specialists on practical teaching ideas and methods, plus in-depth coverage and debate on current issues in education. *Length:* 800 to 1200 words. *Payment:* by arrangement. *Illustrated* with photographs and line drawings; includes colour poster. **Junior Projects** (1982), Mary Jane Wilkins, £1.20. Bi-M. Project-based magazine for teachers of 7-12 year olds. Includes 12 pages of project notes on a different theme each issue. Photocopiable material and posters form an integral part of the practical cross-curricular activities outlined.

**Just Seventeen** (1983), Beverly Hillier, 52-55 Carnaby Street, London W1V 1PF   *tel* 01-437 8050   *fax* 01-494 0851 ext. 2748.
50p. W. Articles of interest to girls aged between 12 and 18. Fashion, beauty, pop, and various features. Short stories up to 1500 words. Quizzes. *Payment:* £110 per 1000 words. *Illustrations:* line, half-tone, colour; cartoons.

**Justice of the Peace** (1837), N. A. McKittrick, LL.B., Little London, Chichester, West Sussex PO19 1PG   *tel* (0243) 775552.

£98.00 p.a., inc. postage. W. Articles on magisterial law and associated subjects including children and young persons, criminology, medico-legal matters, penology, police, probation (length preferred, under 1400 words). Short reports of conferences, meetings, etc. *Payment:* articles minimum £6.50 per column except when otherwise commissioned. *Preliminary letter welcomed although not essential.*

**Karate and Oriental Arts Magazine** (1966), Paul H. Crompton, 102 Felsham Road, London SW15 1DQ  *tel* 01-780 1063.
95p. Bi-M. Accounts of eastern dancing, body development, body training systems: yoga, karate, fencing, etc. Photographs of men and women with brief notes on same. *Payment:* £20.00 per 1000 words. *Illustrations:* half-tones, line.

**Kent** (The Journal of the Men of Kent and Kentish Men), Clifford W. Russell, F.R.S.A., 193 White Horse Hill, Chislehurst, Kent BR7 6DH  *tel* 01-857 7509. Free to members. Q. Articles referring to County of Kent or former Kent people of interest. *Length:* maximum 500 to 600 words. *Payment:* modest, by arrangement. *Illustrations:* photographs and line.

**Kent Messenger,** Messenger House, New Hythe Lane, Larkfield, Kent ME20 6SG  *tel* (0622) 77880. London Office: Suite 511 International Press Centre, 76 Shoe Lane, London EC4A 3JB.
30p. Friday. Articles of special interest to Kent particularly Maidstone and Mid-Kent areas. *Payment:* state price. *Illustrations:* line and half-tone.

**The Lady** (1885), Joan L. Grahame, 39-40 Bedford Street, Strand, London WC2E 9ER  *tel* 01-379 4717.
48p. W. British and foreign travel, countryside, human-interest, animals, cookery, historic-interest and commemorative articles (a preliminary letter is advisable for articles dealing with anniversaries). *Length:* 800-1500 words. Viewpoint: 800 words. *Payment:* by arrangement, averaging £42.00 per 1000 words for first British Serial Rights only, plus varying *payments* for *illustrations* (drawings, mono photographs).

**Lancashire Evening Post,** C. S. Kendall, Oliver's Place, Fulwood, Preston PR2 4ZA  *tel* (0772) 54841  *fax* (0772) 563288, (0772) 204939.
19p. D. Topical articles on all subjects. Area of interest Wigan to Lake District and coast. 600 to 900 words. *Payment:* by arrangement. *Illustrations:* half-tones and line blocks.

**Lancashire Evening Telegraph** (1886), Peter Butterfield, New Telegraph House, High Street, Blackburn, Lancashire BB1 1HT  *tel* (0254) 63588.
19p. D. Will consider general interest articles, such as holidays, property, motoring, finance, etc.

**Lancashire Life,** J. A. F. Sheard, Town & County Magazines, Oyston Mill, Strand Road, Preston PR1 8UR  *tel* (0772) 722022  *fax* (0772) 736496.
£1.00. M. Quality features and photographic material of national and regional interest. *Payment:* by negotiation.

**Lancashire Magazine** (1977), Winston Halstead, Barclays Bank Chambers, Sowerby Bridge, Yorkshire HX6 2DX  *tel* Halifax (0422) 839643 and 839633.
70p. Bi-M. Articles about people, life and character of all parts of Lancashire. *Length:* 1500 words. *Payment:* £20-£30 approx. per published page. *Illustrations:* line and half-tone.

**Lancet** (1823), Gordon Reeves, F.R.C.P., F.R.C.PATH., 46 Bedford Square, London WC1B 3SL  *tel* 01-436 4981  *telex* 291785  *fax* 01-436 7550.
£2.75. W. Mainly for medical profession and medical scientists.

**Land & Liberty** (1894), Fred Harrison, 177 Vauxhall Bridge Road, London SW1V 1EU  *tel* 01-834 4266.
80p. (£5.00 p.a.) Bi-M. Articles on land economics, land taxation, land prices, land speculation as they relate to housing, the economy, production, politics. *Length:* up to 3000 words. *Payment:* by arrangement. *Illustrations:* half-tone. Study of journal essential.

**Learned Publishing** (1988), (Successor to **ALPSP Bulletin**), Hazel K. Bell, 139 The Ryde, Hatfield, Herts. AL9 5DP  *tel* (070 72) 65201.
£50.00 p.a. Free to members. Q. Articles regarding publishing/learned societies. *Length:* 1000–5000 words. *Payment:* none. *Illustrations:* line, half-tone.

**Leisure Management** (1981), Liz Terry, Dicestar Ltd, 40 Bancroft, Hitchin, Herts. SG5 1LA  *tel* (0462) 31385  *fax* (0462) 33909.
£30 p.a. (on subscription). M. Articles on the development of leisure, recreation, tourism, entertainment, sports, hotels, heritage and countryside matters. Unsolicited manuscripts, cartoons, news and ideas welcomed. *Length:* up to 1500 words. *Payment:* by arrangement. *Illustrations:* colour and b&w photos, cartoons.

**The Leisure Manager** (1985), official journal of The Institute of Leisure and Amenity Management, Judy Richardson, Victoria House, 25 High Street, Over, Cambridgeshire CB4 5NB  *tel* (0954) 30940  *fax* (0954) 31886.
£30.00 p.a. M. Articles on amenity, leisure, parks, entertainment, recreation and sports management. *Payment:* by arrangement. *Illustrations:* line, half-tone.

**Leisure Painter** (1966), Irene Briers, 63–65 High Street, Tenterden, Kent TN30 6BP  *tel* (05806) 3315.
£1.20. M. Instructional articles on painting and fine arts. *Payment:* £50 per 1000 words. *Illustrations:* line, half-tone, colour, original artwork.

**The Library** (1889), M. J. Jannetta, British Library, Humanities & Social Sciences, Collection Development, Great Russell Street, London WC1B 3DG *tel* 01-636 1544. Oxford University Press for the Bibliographical Society.
£10.00. (£32.00 p.a.) Q. Articles up to 15,000 words as well as shorter Notes, embodying original research on subjects connected with bibliography. *Payment:* none. *Illustrations:* half-tone and line.

**Library Review** (1927), Holmes McDougall Bookselling, 30 Clydeholm Road, Clydeside Industrial Estate, Glasgow G14 0BJ  *tel* 041-954 2271.
£26.00 p.a. Q. Concerned with information transfer, conservation and exploitation. Papers of 2500-5000 words considered. Line *illustrations.* Publication of contributions accepted, after referring, is regarded as conferring distinction to which *payment* is irrelevant.

**Life and Work: Record of the Church of Scotland,** 121 George Street, Edinburgh EH2 4YN  *tel* 031-225 5722.
25p. M. Articles and news not exceeding 1200 words. *Illustrations:* photographs and line. Seldom uses poems or stories. Study the magazine. *Payment:* up to £30.00 per 1000 words, or by arrangement.

**The Linguist,** Dr. J. L. Kettle-Williams, The Institute of Linguists, 24A Highbury Grove, London N5 2EA  *tel* 01-359 7445.
£3.50. Bi-M. (£17.00 p.a.). Articles of interest to professional linguists in translating, interpreting and teaching fields. Articles usually contributed, but *payment* by arrangement. All contributors have special knowledge of the subjects with which they deal. *Length:* 3000-3500 words. *Illustrations:* line.

**The Listener,** Peter Fiddick, Listener Publications Ltd, 199 Old Marylebone Road, London NW1 5QS *tel* 01-258 3581 *fax* 01-724 8071.
£1.00. W. Articles on media and arts. Poetry. Most articles are commissioned. *Payment:* market rates. *Illustrations:* colour, half-tone and line.

**The Literary Review** (1979), Auberon Waugh, 51 Beak Street, London W1R 3LF *tel* 01-437 9392.
£1.40. M. (£15.00 p.a.). Reviews, articles of cultural interest, interviews, profiles, short stories. *Length:* stories 2000 words maximum, articles and reviews 800-1500 words. *Payment:* £25.00 per 1000 words. *Illustrations:* line. Material mostly commissioned.

**(Liverpool) Daily Post** (1855), John Griffith, P.O. Box 48, Old Hall Street, Liverpool L69 3EB *tel* 051-227 2000.
18p. D. Independent. Takes articles of general interest and topical features of special interest to North West England and North Wales. *Payment:* month following publication: according to value. News and feature photographs used. No verse or fiction.

**Liverpool Echo,** Chris Oakley, P.O. Box 48, Old Hall Street, Liverpool L69 3EB *tel* 051-227 2000.
18p. D. Independent. Articles of up to 600-800 words of local or topical interest. *Payment:* according to merit; special rates for exceptional material. This newspaper is connected with, but independent of, the **Liverpool Daily Post.** Articles not interchangeable.

**Living** (1967), Olwen Rice, IPC Magazines Ltd, King's Reach Tower, Stamford Street, London SE1 9LS *tel* 01-261 5000.
£1.00. M. General interest and human interest features; law, money, health, leisure, home, food, fashion and beauty. *Payment:* by arrangement.

**Llais Llyfrau/Book News From Wales** (1964), Islwyn Ffowc Elis, Welsh Books Council, Castell Brychan, Aberystwyth, Dyfed SY23 2JB *tel* (0970) 624151 *fax* (0970) 625385.
£3.00 p.a. Q. Articles in Welsh and English on authors and their books, Welsh publishing; reviews and book lists. Mainly commissioned. *Payment:* by arrangement.

**The Local Council Review** (The Official Journal of the National Association of Local Councils), Valerie Shepard, B.A., M.A.I.E., 38 Franklin Avenue, Tadley, Basingstoke, Hants RG26 6ET *tel* (07356) 5682.
£3.40 p.a. post free. Q. Articles on the law and practice of local government in relation to parish, town and community councils in England and Wales. *Length:* 400-1000 words. *Illustrations:* black and white photographs, drawings.

**Local Government Chronicle** (1855), Paul Keenan, 122 Minories, London EC3N 1NT *tel* 01-623 2530 *telex* 945828.
£1.10. W. Articles relating to financial, legal and administrative work of the local government officer. *Payment:* by arrangement. *Illustrations:* half-tone, cartoons.

**Local Government Review** (until 1971, part of **Justice of the Peace,** 1837). Barry Rose, Little London, Chichester, West Sussex PO19 1PG *tel* (0243) 775552.
£120 p.a. including postage. W. Articles on local government law and practice, including administration, finance, environmental health, town and country planning, rating and valuation (*length* preferred, 1200-1400 words). Short reports of Conferences, Meetings, etc. *Payment:* articles minimum £4.50 per column except where otherwise commissioned. *Preliminary letter welcomed although not essential.*

**The Local Historian** (formerly **The Amateur Historian**), (1952). Dr. Philip Morgan, Department of Adult & Continuing Education, The University, Keele ST5 5BG   *tel* (0782) 621111. British Association for Local History, Shopwyke Hall, Chichester, West Sussex PO20 6BQ.
£2.75. Q. (£8.50 p.a. post free). Articles, popular in style but based on knowledge of research, covering methods of research, sources and background material helpful to regional, local and family historians—histories of particular places, people or incidents *not* wanted. *Length:* maximum 4000 words. *Payment:* none. *Illustrations:* line and photographs.

**London Magazine: A Review of the Arts** (1954), Alan Ross, 30 Thurloe Place, London SW7 2HQ   *tel* 01-589 0618.
£1.75. (£2.50 double issue). M. (£15.00 p.a.). Poems, stories, literary memoirs, critical articles, features on art, photography, sport, theatre, cinema, music, architecture, events, reports from abroad, drawings. Self-addressed envelope necessary. *Payment:* by arrangement.

**London Review of Books** (1979), Karl Miller, Tavistock House South, Tavistock Square, London WC1H 9JZ   *tel* 01-388 6751   *fax* 01-383 4792.
£1.40. Bi-M. Features, essays, short stories, poems. *Payment:* by arrangement. *Illustrations:* line and half-tone.

**London Traveletter** (1984), Clark C. Siewert, Siewert Publications Ltd., Box 662, London W10 6EQ   *tel* 01-960 2424.
£2.50. 11 p.a. (£20.00 p.a.). Articles on travel, discoveries and unusual places to visit or stay at in Britain; American oriented. *Length:* 500 to 1000 words. *Payment:* by arrangement. No *illustrations*.

**Love Story** (1987), Veronica Dunn, 12-18 Paul Street, London EC2A 4JS   *tel* 01-247 8233   *telex* 8951167   *fax* 01-377 9709.
95p. M. General interest features and short romantic stories, up to 4000 words; may be sad, wistful, as well as happy ending. *Payment:* from £25.00 per 1000 words, depending on author/strength of story. *Illustrations:* colour and b&w line drawings; colour photos for cover.

**Loving** (1970), Lorna Read, IPC Magazines Ltd., King's Reach Tower, Stamford Street, London SE1 9LS   *tel* 01-261 5000.
85p. M. General romantic fiction stories. Can be first or third person, male or female viewpoint, for 18-30 market. Do not accept uncommissioned features material, but unsolicited stories welcome. Send *sae* for authors' guidelines. *Length:* 1000-5000 words. *Payment:* by arrangement.

**Magazine Week** (1988), Tony Loynes, 244–249 Temple Chambers, Temple Avenue, London EC4Y 0DT   *tel* 01-583 6463   *telex* 931110 Bplon G   *fax* 01-353 6867.
50p. W. Articles and news stories relating to magazine publishing. *Payment:* £100 per 1000 words. *Illustrations:* half-tone, line, including cartoons.

**Mail on Sunday** (1982), Stewart Steven, Northcliffe House, 2 Derry Street, London W8 5TT   *tel* 01-938 6000.
50p. W. Articles. *Payment:* by arrangement. *Illustrations:* line and half-tone. Includes colour supplement.

**Making Better Movies** (1985), Bob Tomalski, Oasis Publishing, Media House, Boxwell Road, Berkhamsted, Herts. HP4 3ET   *tel* (0442) 876191.
£1.95. M. Articles on home video and home movie-making. Articles from freelance contributors particularly welcome. *Length:* 1000 to 2500 words. *Payment:* by arrangement. *Illustrations:* line, half-tone, colour.

**Making Music** (1986), Paul Colbert, 20 Bowling Green Lane, London EC1R 0BD   *tel* 01-251 1900   *telex* 299049 Utpres G   *fax* 01-278 4003.
£8.00 p.a. M. Technical, musicianly and instrumental features. *Length:* 500 to 1000 words. *Payment:* £70 per 1000 words. *Illustrations:* Colour; mono cartoons.

**Manchester Evening News,** Michael Unger, 164 Deansgate, Manchester M60 2RD   *tel* 061-832 7200.
20p. D. Feature articles of up to 1000 words, topical or general interest and illustrated where appropriate, should be addressed to the Features Editor. *Payment:* on acceptance.

**Mandy** (D. C. Thomson & Co. Ltd.), Courier Place, Dundee DD1 9QJ, and 185 Fleet Street, London EC4A 2HS.
26p. W. Picture-story paper for schoolgirls. Serials and series in line drawings. 2 and 3 page instalments, 8-9 frames per page. Editorial co-operation offered to promising scriptwriters. *Payment:* on acceptance.

**Mandy Library** (D. C. Thomson & Co. Ltd.), Courier Place, Dundee DD1 9QJ, and 185 Fleet Street, London EC4A 2HS.
32p. M. Stories told in pictures, for schoolgirls; 64 pages (about 140 line drawings). Adventure, animal, mystery, school, sport. Scripts considered; promising script-writers and artists encouraged. *Payment:* on acceptance.

**Manx Life** (1971), Ian Faulds, Trafalgar Press Ltd, 14 Douglas Street, Peel, Isle of Man   *tel* (0624) 843881.
75p. M. Factual articles on historical or topical aspects of the social, commercial, agricultural or cultural activities and interests of the Isle of Man. *Payment:* £20.00 per 1000 words on publication or by arrangement. *Illustrations:* black and white, half-tone and line.

**Margin** (1986), Robin Magowan, 20 Brook Green, London W6 7BL   *tel* 01-602 2471.
£3. Q. Literature and ideas: non-fiction mainly, stories, poems. *Payment:* £15 per page. *Illustrations:* b&w photos, line drawings, cartoons; *payment:* as above, plus expenses. *Sae* essential.

**Market Newsletter** (1965), John Tracy, Focus House, 497 Green Lanes, London N13 4BP   *tel* 01-882 3315.
£28.00 p.a. M. Current information on editorial requirements of interest to writers and photographers.

**Masonic Square** (1975), B. P. Hutton, Terminal House, Shepperton, Middlesex TW17 8AS   *tel* Walton-on-Thames (0932) 228950 and 222211.
£1.10. Q. (£5.00 p.a.). Biographies, history, symbolism, news items all relevant to Freemasonry or affiliated subjects. *Length:* 1000 to 1500 words. *Illustrations:* black and white, line and half-tone.

**Mayfair** (1966), Kenneth H. Bound, 6 Great James Street, London WC1N 3DA   *tel* 01-242 1593.
£1.75. M. Masculine interest, well-researched features of 3000 to 4000 words. Short humorous articles. Up-beat, pacey reader-identifying short stories. Particularly receptive to highly anecdotal features on events, characters, nostalgia. *Payment:* £75.00 per 1000 words or by arrangement. *Illustrations:* colour transparencies to illustrate highly visual feature ideas.

**Media Week** (1985), Steven Buckley, 20-22 Wellington Street, London WC2E 7DD   *tel* 01-379 5155   *fax* 01-240 7764.
£1.00. W. News and analysis of U.K. and international advertising media. *Illustrations:* colour, half-tone.

**Melody Maker,** Allan Jones, IPC Magazines Ltd., King's Reach Tower, Stamford Street, London SE1 9LS *tel* 01-261 5463 *fax* 01-260 6037.
55p. W. Technical, entertaining and informative articles on rock and pop music. *Payment:* by arrangement. *Illustrations:* half-tone and line.

**Men Only** (published by Paul Raymond: 1971), Nevile Player, 2 Archer Street, London W1V 7HE *tel* 01-734 9191.
£1.50. M. Erotic fiction. Humour. Glamour photography. *Payment:* by arrangement.

**Methodist Recorder** (1861), Michael Taylor, 122 Golden Lane, London EC1Y 0TL *tel* 01-251 8414.
30p. W. Methodist and Free Church newspaper; ecumenically involved. Limited opportunities for freelance contributors. *A preliminary letter* is advised.

**Military Modelling,** Kenneth M. Jones, Argus Specialist Publications Ltd., P.O. Box 35, Hemel Hempstead, Herts. HP2 4SS *tel* (0442) 41221 *fax* (0442) 216429.
£1.20. M. Articles on military modelling. *Length:* up to 2000 words. *Payment:* by arrangement. *Illustrations:* line, half-tone, colour.

**Millennium—Journal of International Studies** (1971), Charles Armstrong, Kathleen Newland, London School of Economics and Political Science, Houghton Street London WC2A 2AE *tel* 01-405 7686 ext. 2407-8.
£5.00. 3 times a year (£13.00 p.a.). Serious articles on International Studies; original research work published, as well as topical articles on all aspects of international affairs. *Length:* 4500-8000 words (in triplicate with abstract). *Payment:* none. No *illustrations*.

**Mind** (1876), Dr Simon Blackburn, Pembroke College, Oxford OX1 1DW.
£11.00 p.a. Q. A review of philosophy intended for those who have studied and thought on this subject. Articles from about 5000 words. Shorter discussion notes. Critical notices and reviews. *Payment:* none.

**Mobile & Holiday Homes** (1960), Anne Webb, Link House, Dingwall Avenue, Croydon CR9 2TA *tel* 01-686 2599 *telex* 947709 Linkho G *fax* 01-760 0973.
£1.30. M. Informative articles on residential mobile homes and holiday static caravans---personal experience articles, site features, news items. No preliminary letter. *Payment:* by arrangement. *Illustrations:* photographs, half-tone and line.

**Model Boats** (1964), John L. Cundell, Argus Specialist Publications Ltd., P.O. Box 35, Hemel Hempstead, Herts. HP2 4SS *tel* (0442) 41221 *fax* (0442) 216429.
£1.30. M. Articles, drawings, plans, sketches of model boats. *Payment:* £25 per page; plans £80. *Illustrations:* line, half-tone.

**Model Engineer** (1898), Ted Jolliffe, Argus Specialist Publications Ltd., P.O. Box 35, Hemel Hempstead, Herts. HP2 4SS *tel* (0442) 41221 *fax* (0442) 216429.
£1.10. 2 p.m. Detailed description of the construction of models, small workshop equipment, machine tools and small electrical and mechanical devices; articles on small power engineering, mechanics, electricity, workshop methods, clocks and experiments. *Payment:* up to £25 per page. *Illustrations:* half-tone and line drawings, occasional 4-colour facility.

**Model Railways** (1971), Dave Lowery, Argus Specialist Publications Ltd., P.O. Box 35, Hemel Hempstead, Herts. HP2 4SS *tel* (0442) 41221 *fax* (0442) 216429.

£1.10. M. Descriptive articles on model railways and prototype railways suitable for modelling. Articles covering all aspects of construction, planning, electrical wiring, experimental model railway engineering, and operation of model layouts. *Payment:* by arrangement. *Illustrations:* photographs, line.

**Modelling and Miniature Crafts** (1983), Susan Cleeve, Guild of Master Craftsman Publications Ltd, 166 High Street, Lewes, East Sussex BN7 1XU   *tel* (0273) 477374   *fax* (0273) 478606.
£4.95. Bi-annual (Jan/June). Articles, of any length, on models (e.g. metal, wood, scratchbuilt) or miniatures of any scale. Book reviews. *Payment:* £30 per 1000 words. *Illustrations:* colour transparencies and b&w photos; *payment:* by negotiation.

**Modern Churchman** (1911), The Modern Churchpeople's Union, The School House, Leysters, Leominster, Hereford HR6 0HS   *tel* (056 887) 271.
£1.30. Q. Covers contemporary and pastoral theology, ethics, politics, current affairs. *Length:* 1500 to 3500 words. Contributions voluntary.

**Modern Language Review** (1905), Modern Humanities Research Association, King's College, Strand, London WC2R 2LS.
£38.50 p.a. (U.K.), £46.00 overseas; $92.00 (U.S.A.). Q. Contains articles and reviews of a scholarly or specialist character on English, Romance, Germanic and Slavonic languages and literatures. *Payment:* none, but offprints are given.

**Modern Languages** (Journal of the Modern Language Association) (1905), Alan Smalley, B.A., F.I.L., 10 Holt Park Way, Leeds LS16 7QR   *tel* (0532) 679258 (home), (0532) 759061 ext. 293 (work). *Central Office:* M.L.A., Regents College, Inner Circle, Regent's Park, London NW1 4NS   *tel* 01-486 0750.
£2.50 (£10.00 p.a.). Q. All aspects of modern language study, linguistic, pedagogic, and literary. *Payment:* none.

**Modus,** Geoffrey Thompson, Official Journal of the National Association of Teachers of Home Economics Ltd., Hamilton House, Mabledon Place, London WC1H 9BJ   *tel* 01-387 1441   *fax* 01-383 7230.
£2.13. 8 p.a. (£17.00 p.a.). Articles on the teaching of home economics, including textiles, nutrition, and social and technical background information for teachers. *Length:* up to 1500 words. *Payment:* by arrangement. *Illustrations:* line and half-tone. Most articles for teachers and educationists.

**Money Week** (1987), Nick Morgan, EMAP Business Information Ltd, Meed House, 21 John Street, London WC1N 2BP   *tel* 01-404 5513   *fax* 01-405 6639.
Free. W. Any articles of interest to independent financial advisers, e.g. Financial Services Act, life insurance, pensions. *Length:* up to 1000 words. *Payment:* £150 per 1000 words. *Illustrations:* in half tone.

**The Month** (1864), John McDade, S.J., 114 Mount Street, London W1Y 6AH   *tel* 01-491 7596.
£1.00. M. A Christian review of Christian thought, and world affairs, with arts and literary section, edited by the Jesuit Fathers. *Length:* up to 3000 words. *Payment:* by arrangement. *Illustrations:* photographs. A preliminary letter is desirable.

**Morning Star** (formerly **Daily Worker,** 1930), Tony Chater (The Morning Star Co-operative Society Ltd.), 74 Luke Street, London EC2A 4PY   *tel* 01-739 6166   *telex* 916463   *telegraphic address* Morsta Telex, London   *fax* 01-739 5463.
30p. D. Articles of general interest. *Illustrations:* photos, cartoons and drawings.

**Mother** (1936), Sarah Touquet, 12-18 Paul Street, London EC2A 4JS   *tel* 01-247 8233.
80p. M. Articles on subjects of interest to parents of young children. *Length:* 1500 words. *Payment:* by arrangement. *Illustrations:* photographs and sketches.

**Motor Boat & Yachting** (1904), Tom Willis (Reed Business Publishing), Quadrant House, Sutton, Surrey SM2 5AS   *tel* 01-661 3098   *fax* 01-643 2144.
£1.70. M. General interest as well as specialist motor boating material welcomed. Features up to 2000 words considered on all aspects, sea-going and on inland waterways. *Payment:* varies. *Illustrations:* photographs (mostly colour and transparencies preferred) and line.

**Motor Caravan Magazine** (1985), Paul Carter, Link House Magazines Ltd., Link House, Dingwall Avenue, Croydon CR9 2TA   *tel* 01-686 2599   *telex* 947709 Linkho G.
£1.30. M. Practical features, touring features (home and abroad). *Length:* up to 1500 words. *Payment:* £35-£40 per page. *Illustrations:* line, half-tone, colour.

**Motor Cycle News** (1955), Malcolm Gough, P.O. Box 11, Huxloe Place, High Street, Kettering, Northants. NN16 8SS   *tel* (0536) 81651   *telex* 3215710 MCN G   *fax* (0536) 513582.
58p. W. Features (up to 1000 words), photographs and news stories of interest to motor cyclists.

**Motorcaravan and Motorhome Monthly** (1966 as Motor Caravan and Camping), John Hunt, 8 Swan Meadow, Pewsey, Wilts. SN9 5HW   *tel* (0672) 62574.
£1.20. M. Articles including motorcaravan travel in the U.K. and D.I.Y. *Payment:* from £10 per printed page. *Illustrations:* line, half-tone, colourprint.

**Municipal Review and AMA News** (1930), a journal of urban and local government affairs published by the Association of Metropolitan Authorities. Peter Smith, 35 Great Smith Street, London SW1P 3BJ   *tel* 01-222 8100   *fax* 01-222 0878.
£9.00 p.a. including postage. (£18.00 overseas.) M. (10 issues p.a.). Articles on the current urban local government scene.

**Museums Journal** (1901), The Museums Association, 34 Bloomsbury Way, London WC1A 2SF   *tel* 01-404 4767.
£5.00. (Free to members; £30.00 p.a. individuals; £48.00 p.a. institutions.) M. Articles and news items on museum and art gallery policy, administration, research, architecture and display, notes on technical developments and conservation, book reviews. *Length:* 500 to 2500 words. *Payment:* by negotiation. *Illustrations:* half-tone, line, colour.

**Music and Letters** (1920), Editorial: Dr. Nigel Fortune, Dr. John Whenham, Department of Music, Barber Institute of Fine Arts, University of Birmingham, Birmingham B15 2TS   *tel* 021-414 3726. For other matters: Journals Production, Oxford University Press, Walton Street, Oxford OX2 6DP.
£8.00. Q. Scholarly articles, up to 10,000 words, on musical subjects, neither merely topical nor purely descriptive. Technical, historical, and research matter preferred. *Payment:* none. *Illustrations:* music quotations and plates.

**Music & Musicians** (1952), Christopher James, 4th Floor, Centro House, Mandela Street, London NW1 0DU   *tel* 01-387 3848   *fax* 01-388 8532.
£1.50. M. Long and short features, previews, reviews about music and musicians. *Payment:* by arrangement.

**The Music Review** (1940), A. F. Leighton Thomas, Glyneithin, Burry Port, Dyfed SA16 0TA. Other matters: Black Bear Press, King's Hedges Road, Cambridge CB4 2PQ.
£12.50. Q. (£39.00 p.a.). Articles from 1500 to 8000 words dealing with any aspect of standard or classical music (no jazz). *Payment:* small, by arrangement.

**Music Teacher** (1908), Marianne Barton, Rhinegold Publishing Ltd., 241 Shaftesbury Avenue, London WC2H 8EH    *tel* 01-836 2384    *fax* 01-528 7991.
£1.25. M. Provides information and articles for both school and private music teachers. *Length:* articles 1250 or 2700 words. *Payment:* by arrangement. Articles and illustrations must have a teacher, as well as a musical, interest.

**Music Week** (1959), David Dalton, Greater London House, Hampstead Road, London NW1 7QZ    *tel* 01-387 6611.
£1.90. W. (£65.00 p.a.). News and features on all aspects of producing, manufacturing, marketing and retailing music. *Payment:* NUJ rates.

**Musical Opinion** (1877), Denby Richards, 2 Princes Road, St. Leonards-on-Sea, East Sussex TN37 6EE    *tel* (0424) 715167.
£1.80. M. Suggestions for contributions of musical interest, scholastic, educational, anniversaries, ethnic, and relating to the organ world. Record, opera, festival, book, music reviews. All editorial matter must be commissioned. *Payment:* on publication. *Illustrations:* b&w photographs.

**Musical Times** (1844), Eric Wen, 8 Primrose Mews, 1a Sharpleshall Street, London NW1 8YL    *tel* 01-586 8591.
£1.40. M. Musical articles, reviews, 150 to 2500 words. *Payment:* by arrangement. *Illustrations:* photographs and music. Intending contributors are advised to study recent numbers of the journal.

**My Story,** Geoff Kemp, P.O. Box 94, London W4 2ER    *tel* 01-995 0590.
85p. M. Confessions type stories, aimed at marrieds; age group 20-30. *Length:* 3000 words. *Payment:* £14.00 per 1000 words.

**My Weekly** (1910) (D. C. Thomson & Co. Ltd.), 80 Kingsway East, Dundee DD4 8SL, and 185 Fleet Street, London EC4A 2HS.
28p. W. Serials, from 30,000 to 80,000 words, suitable for family reading. Short complete stories of 1500 to 5000 words with humorous, romantic or strong emotional theme. Articles on prominent people and on all subjects of feminine interest. All contributions should make their appeal to the modern woman. *No preliminary letter* required. *Payment:* on acceptance. *Illustrations:* colour and black and white.

**My Weekly Story Library,** D. C. Thomson & Co. Ltd., Courier Place, Dundee DD1 9QJ    *tel* Dundee 23131.
32p. 4 per month. 35,000 to 37,500-word romantic stories aimed at the postteenage market. *Payment:* by arrangement; competitive for the market. No *illustrations*.

**National Builder** (1921), Michael Harnett, 82 New Cavendish Street, London W1M 8AD    *tel* 01-580 5588    *telegraphic address* Natbuild, Westcent, London    *fax* 01-631 3872.
£1.50. M. The official journal of the Building Employers Confederation. Articles on building and constructional methods, management techniques, materials and machinery used in building. Articles, 750-1000 words, preferably with *illustrations*. *Preliminary letter* advisable. *Payment:* by arrangement.

**Natural World** (1981), The Magazine of the Royal Society for Nature Conservation, Linda Bennett, 91-93 Southwark Street, London SE1 0HY   *tel* 01-928 2111.
Membership subscription. 3 p.a. Short articles on nature conservation; contributors normally have special knowledge of subjects on which they write. *Length:* up to 1500 words. *Payment:* by arrangement. *Illustrations:* line, half-tone, colour.

**Naturalist** (1875), M. R. D. Seaward, M.SC., PH.D., D.SC., The University, Bradford BD7 1DP   *tel* (0274) 733466, ext. 8540.
£12.00 p.a. Q. Original papers on British Natural History subjects of all kinds relating to this country to include various aspects of geology, archaeology and environmental science; length immaterial. *Payment:* none. *Illustrations:* photographs and line drawings.

**Nature** (1869), John Maddox (Macmillan Magazines Ltd.), Little Essex Street, London WC2R 3LF   *tel* 01-836 6633   *telex* 262024.
£1.95. W. Devoted to scientific matters and to their bearing upon public affairs. All contributors of articles have specialised knowledge of the subjects with which they deal. *Illustrations:* half-tone and line.

**Nautical Magazine** (1832), L. Ingram-Brown, F.INST.S.M.M., M.B.I.M., M.R.I.N., Brown, Son & Ferguson Ltd., 4-10 Darnley Street, Glasgow G41 2SD   *tel* 041-429 1234   *telegraphic address* Skipper, Glasgow.
£20.64 p.a. including postage; 3 years £61.50. M. Articles relating to nautical and shipping profession, from 1500 to 2000 words, also translations. *Payment:* by arrangement. No *illustrations*.

**Navy International,** Anthony J. Watts, Hunters Moon, Hogspudding Lane, Newdigate, Nr. Dorking, Surrey RH5 5DS   *tel* (0306) 77442.
£28.50 p.a. M. Geo-political, strategic and technical articles on current world naval affairs. *Length:* 1500-2000 words. *Payment:* £60 per 1000 words. *Illustrations* used.

**New Beacon** (1930) (as **Beacon,** 1917), Ann Lee, R.N.I.B., 224 Great Portland Street, London W1N 6AA   *tel* 01-388 1266   *fax* 01-388 2034.
50p. M. (£5.65 p.a.). Authoritative articles on all aspects of blind welfare. *Length:* from 500 words. *Payment:* £15.00 per 1000 words: *Illustrations:* half-tone, colour. Also Braille edition (£3.00 p.a.).

**New Blackfriars** (1920), The English Dominicans (Rev. John Orme Mills, O.P.), Blackfriars, Oxford OX1 3LY   *tel* Oxford (0865) 278414.
£1.20 net. M. (£12.00 p.a.) A critical review, surveying the field of theology, philosophy, sociology and the arts, from the standpoint of Christian principles and their application to the problems of the modern world. Incorporates *Life of the Spirit. Length:* 2500 to 6000 words. *Payment:* by arrangement.

**New Hi-Fi Sound** (1983), George Entwistle, Haymarket Publishing Ltd., 10-12 The Causeway, Teddington, Middlesex TW11 0HE   *tel* 01-943 5533.
£1.60. M. Articles by professional contributors on audio equipment and related subjects by arrangement with editor. *Payment:* by arrangement. *Illustrations:* line, half-tone and colour transparencies. *Preliminary letter* essential.

**New Library World** (1898), MCB University Press, 62 Toller Lane, Bradford, West Yorkshire BD8 9BY   *tel* (0274) 499821.
£49.95 p.a. M. Professional and bibliographical articles. *Illustrations. Payment:* by arrangement.

**New Musical Express,** Alan Lewis, 25th Floor, King's Reach Tower, Stamford Street, London SE1 9LS   *tel* 01-261 5000.

55p. W. Authoritative articles and news stories on the world's rock and movie personalities. *Length:* by arrangement. *Payment:* by arrangement. *Illustrations:* action photos with strong news-angle of recording personalities. *Preliminary letter or phone call* desirable.

**New Scientist,** Michael Kenward, Holborn Publishing Group, King's Reach Tower, Stamford Street, London SE1 9LS *tel* 01-261 5000 *fax* 01-261 6464 *Electronic mailbox:* Telecom Gold/Dialcom: 83:NSM005.
£1.20. W. Authoritative articles of topical importance on all aspects of science and technology are considered. *Length:* 1000 to 3000 words. Preliminary letter or telephone call is desirable. Short items from specialists also considered for *Science, This Week, Forum* and *Technology.* Intending contributors should study recent copies of the magazine. *Payment:* varies but average £100 per 1000 words. *Illustrations:* line and half-tone, colour.

**New Socialist** (1981), Nigel Williamson and John Willman, The Labour Party and Fabian Society, 11 Dartmouth Street, London SW1H 9BN *tel* 01-976 7129 *fax* 01-976 7153.
£1.20. Bi-M. (£6.50 UK individuals, £11.00 overseas individuals, £14.00 UK multi-reader institutions, £21.50 overseas multi-reader institutions). The Labour Party's journal of discussion and ideas. *Payment:* NUJ freelance rates. *Illustrations:* b&w photographs, cartoons; *payment:*NUJ freelance rates.

**New Statesman & Society** (1988), Foundation House, Perseverance Works, 38 Kingsland Road, London E2 8DQ *tel* 01-739 3211.
£1.20. W. Interested in news and analysis of current political and social issues at home and overseas, plus book reviews and coverage of the arts, seen from the perspective of the British Left. *Length:* strictly according to the value of the piece. *Payment:* basic £77.50 per 1000 words.

**New Theatre Quarterly** (1985; as **Theatre Quarterly** 1971), Clive Barker, Simon Trussler, Great Robhurst, Woodchurch, Ashford, Kent TN26 3TB.
£5.00 (individual subs. £12.50 p.a.) Q. Articles, documentation, reference material covering all aspects of live theatre. An informed, factual and serious approach essential. Preliminary discussion and synopsis desirable. *Payment:* by arrangement. *Illustrations:* line, half-tone.

**The New Welsh Review** (1988), Belinda Humfrey, Peter J. Foss, Department of English, St David's University College, Lampeter, Dyfed SA48 7ED *tel* (0570) 423523.
£2.50. Q. Articles, short stories, poetry; plus reviews, interviews and profiles. Especially, but not exclusively, concerned with Welsh literature in English. *Length:* (articles) up to 4000 words; short poems preferred. *Payment:* £7-£12 per page prose; £12-£20 per poem. *Illustrations:* half-tone, line; colour cover; *payment:* £10-£20.

**New Woman** (1988), Frankie McGowan, King's House, 8–10 Haymarket, London SW1Y 4BP *tel* 01-839 8272 *fax* 01-839 7939.
£1.00. M. Features up to 3000 words. Welcomes unsolicited articles; enclose *sae* for return. *Payment:* at or above NUJ rates. *Illustrated.*

**New World,** United Nations Association, 3 Whitehall Court, London SW1A 2EL *tel* 01-930 2931 *telex* 24973 Wwbc UK G.
30p. 6 p.a.

**News of the World** (1843), Patricia Chapman, 1 Virginia Street, London E1 9BH *tel* 01-782 4000 *fax* 01-583 9504.
30p. W.

**Nikki** (1985), (D. C. Thomson & Co. Ltd.), 2 Albert Square, Dundee DD1 9QJ *tel* (0382) 23131. London Office: 185 Fleet Street, EC4A 2HS *tel* 01-242 5086/8.
28p. W. Picture stories and features for schoolgirls 7-12 years. *Payment:* on acceptance.

**19** (1968), Maureen Rice, IPC Magazines Ltd, King's Reach Tower, Stamford Street, London SE1 9LS *tel* 01-261 6360.
85p. M. A glossy fashion and general interest magazine for young women aged 17 to 22 including beauty, music and social features of strong contemporary interest.

**Ninth Decade** (1983), Editorial Board: Tony Frazer, Ian Robinson, Robert Vas Dias, 12 Stevenage Road, London SW6 6ES *tel* 01-736 5059, 01-607 7270.
£6 p.a. 3 p.a. Fiction, poetry, critical essays. *Length:* up to 4000 words. *Payment:* none, but two complimentary copies of magazine. *Illustrations:* mostly line drawings, 2-colour on cover; *payment:* as above. *Preliminary study of magazine essential.* Send *sae* with all submissions.

**The Northern Echo** (1870), Allan Prosser, P.O. Box 14, Priestgate, Darlington, Co. Durham DL1 1NF *tel* (0325) 381313 *fax* (0325) 380539.
18p. D. Articles of interest to North-East and North Yorkshire; *all material commissioned.* Literary broadsheet pull-out published quarterly. *Length:* 800–1000 words. *Payment:* by negotiation. *Illustrations:* in colour, half-tone and line; mostly commissioned; *payment:* by negotiation. *Preliminary study of the newspaper advisable.*

**Nottingham Evening Post** (1878), Forman Street, Nottingham NG1 4AB *tel* Nottingham (0602) 482000.
22p. D. Will consider material on local issues.

**Number One** (1983), Colin Irwin, IPC Magazines, King's Reach Tower, 28th Floor, Stamford Street, London SE1 9LS *tel* 01-261 5000 *fax* 01-261 6034.
47p. W. Interviews and articles on pop stars, for the teenage market. *Payment:* by negotiation. *Illustrations:* colour and b&w photos, occasional cartoons; *payment:* by negotiation.

**Numbers** (1986), Editorial Board: John Alexander, Alison Rimmer, Peter Robinson, Clive Wilmer, 6 Kingston Street, Cambridge CB1 2NU *tel* (0223) 353425.
£4.50. Bi-annual (Spring/Autumn). Poetry only. No *illustrations.* Send unsolicited material, including *sae*, to: 57 Norwich Street, Cambridge CB2 1ND.

**Numismatic Chronicle** (1839), c/o Dr. A. M. Burnett, Department of Coins and Medals, British Museum, London WC1B 3DG.
£24 per annual volume. The Journal of the Royal Numismatic Society. Articles on coins and medals. Memoirs relating to coins and medals are unpaid, and contributions should reach a high standard of quality.

**Nursery World,** Sue Hubberstey, The School House Workshop, 51 Calthorpe Street, London WC1X 0HH *tel* 01-837 7224.
65p. W. For all grades of nursery and child care staff, nannies, foster parents and all concerned with the care of expectant mothers, babies and young children. Authoritative and informative articles, 750-1500 words, and photographs, on all aspects of child welfare, from 0-7 years, in the U.K.

Practical ideas and leisure crafts. *No* short stories. *Payment:* by arrangement. *Illustrations:* line and half-tone.

**Nursing Times and Nursing Mirror** (1905), Macmillan Magazines Ltd., 4 Little Essex Street, London WC2R 3LF *tel* 01-379 0970.
65p. W. Articles of clinical interest, nursing education and nursing policy. Illustrated articles not longer than 1500 words. Contributions from other than health professionals rarely accepted. Press day, Friday.

**The Observer** (1791), Donald Trelford, Chelsea Bridge House, Queenstown Road, London SW8 4NN *tel* 01-627 0700 *telegraphic address* Observer, London, SW8 *telex* 888963 Obs Ldn *fax* 01-627 5570/1/2.
60p. W. Independent. Some articles and illustrations commissioned.

**The Observer Colour Magazine** (1964), Angela Palmer, Chelsea Bridge House, Queenstown Road, London SW8 4NN *tel* 01-627 0700 *telegraphic address* Observer, London, SW8 *telex* 888963 Obs Ldn *fax* 01-627 5570/1/2.
Free with newspaper. W. Articles on all subjects. *Illustrations:* also accepted. *Payment:* by arrangement.

**Opera,** Rodney Milnes, 1A Mountgrove Road, London N5 2LU *tel* 01-359 1037 *fax* 01-354 2700. Seymour Press Ltd., Windsor House, 1270 London Road, London SW16 4DH.
£1.65. 13 issues a year. Articles on general subjects appertaining to opera; reviews; criticisms. *Length:* up to 2000 words. *Payment:* by arrangement. *Illustrations:* photographs and drawings.

**Options** (1982), Jo Foley, IPC, King's Reach Tower, Stamford Street, London SE1 9LS *tel* 01-261 5000.
£1.00. M. Articles only of 1000 to 3000 words. Mostly commissioned. *Payment:* by arrangement.

**Orbis** (1968), Mike Shields, 199 The Long Shoot, Nuneaton, War. CV11 6JQ *tel* (0203) 327440.
£12.00 p.a. Q. Poetry, short stories (up to 1000 words), literary criticism, letters. Annual competition for rhymed poetry. *Payment:* by arrangement. *Illustrations:* line.

**The Organ** (1921), D. Carrington, 84 Park View Road, Lytham St. Annes, Lancashire FY8 4JF *tel* (0253) 737859.
£2.25. Q. Articles, 4000 to 5000 words, relating to the organ, historical, technical, and artistic. Reviews of music, records. *Payment:* small. *Illustrations:* half-tone and line.

**Other Poetry** (1978), Evangeline Paterson, 2 Stoneygate Avenue, Leicester LE2 3HE *tel* (0533) 703159.
£6.00 p.a. 3 p.a. Poetry. *Payment:* token £2 per poem.

**Outdoor Action,** Laura McCaffrey, Haymarket Magazines Ltd., 38-42 Hampton Road, Teddington, Middlesex TW11 0JE *tel* 01-977 8787.
£1.25. M. U.K. and foreign touring features and general outdoor interest articles, including all outdoor pursuits, with a lightweight or backpacking bias, by arrangement with editor. *Payment:* by arrangement. *Illustrations:* half-tone, colour. *Preliminary letter* essential.

**Outposts Poetry Quarterly** (1943), Roland John, 22 Whitewell Road, Frome, Somerset BA11 4EL *tel* Frome (0373) 66653. *Founder:* Howard Sergeant, M.B.E.

£2.50. Q (£8.00 p.a.). Poems, essays and critical articles on poets and their work. Poetry competitions. *Payment:* by arrangement.

**Parents** (1976), Daphne Metland, Victory House, Leicester Place, London WC2H 7QP   *tel* 01-437 9011.
£1.00. M. Articles on pregnancy, childbirth, general family health, food, fashion, child upbringing and marital relations. Preliminary letter essential. Commissioned features only. *Payment:* in accordance with national magazine standards; by arrangement. *Illustrations:* black-and-white half-tones or colour.

**Parents Voice** (1950), Alan Leighton, Royal Society for Mentally Handicapped Children and Adults, 123 Golden Lane, London EC1Y 0RT   *tel* 01-253 9433   *fax* 01-251 2547.
£4.40 p.a. Q. Journal of MENCAP. Contributions on the subject of mental handicap considered. *Payment:* none. *Illustrations:* photographs.

**Parks & Sports Grounds** (1935), 61 London Road, Staines, Middlesex TW18 4BN   *tel* (0784) 461326   *fax* (0784) 466307.
£23.00 p.a. M. Articles on the design, construction, maintenance and management of parks, sports grounds, golf courses, open spaces and amenity areas. Any aspect of outdoor recreation. *Length:* 750-2000 words. *Payment:* from £55.00 per 1000 words. *Illustrations:* line, half-tone. Cartoons.

**Peace News** for nonviolent revolution (1936), 8 Elm Avenue, Nottingham NG3 4GF   *tel* (0602) 503587 and 5 Caledonian Road, London N1 9DX   *tel* 01-837 9795.
50p. F. Political articles based on nonviolence in every aspect of human life. *Payment:* none. *Illustrations:* line, half-tone.

**Penthouse Magazine,** The International Magazine for Men (1965), Northern & Shell plc., The Northern & Shell Building, P.O. Box 381, Mill Harbour, London E14 9TW   *tel* 01-987 5090.
£2.50. M. Serious and light articles on sex, motoring, star interviews. *Length:* 3000 words. *Payment:* by arrangement. *Illustrations:* colour and b&w photographs, but by commission only.

**The People,** Wendy Henry, Holborn Circus, London EC1P 1DQ   *tel* 01-353 0246   *telex* 27286   *fax* 01-822 3405/3684.
35p. W. A Sunday paper for all classes of readers. Features, single articles and series considered. Pictures should be supplied with contributions if possible. Features should be of deep human interest, whether the subject is serious or light-hearted. The first investigative newspaper, the People is particularly noted for its exposures of social evils, criminal activities, financial and other rackets and bureaucratic malpractices, in the public interest. Very strong sports following. Exclusive news and news-feature stories also considered. *Payment:* rates high, even for tips that lead to published news stories.

**People's Friend** (1869), (D. C. Thomson & Co. Ltd.), 80 Kingsway East, Dundee DD4 8SL, and 185 Fleet Street, London EC4A 2HS.
28p. W. An illustrated weekly appealing to women of all ages and devoted to their personal and home interests. Serial and complete stories of strong romantic and emotional appeal—serials of 60,000-70,000 words, completes of 1500-3500 words. Stories for children considered. Knitting, fashions and cookery are especially featured. *Illustrations:* colour and black and white. No *preliminary letter* is required. *Payment:* on acceptance.

**People's Friend Library,** D. C. Thomson & Co. Ltd., 80 Kingsway East, Dundee DD4 8SL.
 60p. 2 per month. 50,000 to 55,000 word family and romantic stories aimed at 30 plus age groups. *Payment:* by arrangement. No illustrations.

**Performance Car** (1983), Jesse Crosse, AGB Specialist Publications Ltd., Audit House, Field End Road, Eastcote, Ruislip, Middlesex HA4 9LT *tel* 01-868 4499.
 £1.80. M. Articles, 2000 to 3000 words on all aspects of cars. *Payment:* by arrangement. *Illustrations:* half-tone, colour.

**Performance Tuning & Sports Car** (1981), Ian Ward, CW Editorial Ltd., 538 Ipswich Road, Slough, Berks. SL1 4EQ *tel* (0753) 820161.
 £1.95. M. Articles on all aspects of tuned cars. *Length:* 1500 to 2500 words. *Payment:* by arrangement. *Illustrations:* line, half-tone.

**Personal Computer World** (1977), Derek Cohen, 32-34 Broadwick Street, London W1A 2HG *tel* 01-439 4242 *telex* 23918 VNU G.
 £1.30. M. Articles about computers. *Length:* 2000-5000 words. Reviews. *Payment:* from £94.00 per 1000 words. *Illustrations:* line, half-tone.

**Personnel Management,** Journal of the Institute of Personnel Management, Susanne Lawrence, Personnel Publications Ltd., 1 Hills Place, London W1R 1AG *tel* 01-734 1773 *telex* 21714 Printn G *fax* 01-734 1773 ext. 30.
 £3.00. M. (£35.00 p.a.). Features and news items on recruitment and selection, training and development; wage and salary administration; industrial psychology; employee relations; labour law; welfare schemes, working practices and new practical ideas in personnel management in industry and commerce. *Length:* up to 3000 words. *Payment:* by arrangement. *Illustrations:* photographers and illustrators should contact Art Editor.

**The Pharmaceutical Journal** (1841), D. Simpson, M.R.PHARM.S., 1 Lambeth High Street, London SE1 7JN *tel* 01-735 9141 *telegraphic address* and *cables* Pharmakon, London SE1 *fax* 01-735 7629.
 90p. W. The official journal of the Royal Pharmaceutical Society of Great Britain. Articles of 1000 words on any aspect of pharmacy may be submitted. *Payment:* by arrangement. *Illustrations:* half-tone, colour.

**Photo Answers,** Steve Bavister, EMAP, Bushfield House, Orton Centre, Peterborough PE2 0UW *tel* (0733) 237111.
 £1.30. M. Magazine appealing to everyone interested in photography. Little opportunity for freelance writers, but always interested in seeing quality photographs. *Payment:* upwards of £25.00 per published page, colour or mono. *Illustrations:* print, slide, line, half-tone.

**Photography** (1945), Tom Ang, Argus Specialist Publications, Argus House, Boundary Way, Hemel Hempstead HP2 7ST *tel* (0442) 66551 *fax* (0442) 66998.
 £1.50. M. Articles on photographers, the uses of photography and topical subjects such as the media, advertising and contemporary issues such as the environment. Important showcase for documentary photojournalism and historical photographs. Aimed at anyone with an interest in photography. *Length:* according to subject. *Payment:* by arrangement. *Illustrations:* world-class photography or with very strong story only.

**Physiotherapy** (Journal of the Chartered Society of Physiotherapists), Jill Whitehouse, 14 Bedford Row, London WC1R 4ED *tel* 01-242 1941.

£3.25. M. Articles on physiotherapy and related subjects, technical items and news regarding activities of members of the Society. Contributions welcomed from physiotherapists and doctors. *Length:* 2000 words (average). *Payment:* £15 per published page for technical and medical articles. *Illustrations:* photographs and line.

**Pig Farming,** M. C. Looker, Farming Press Ltd., Wharfedale Road, Ipswich IP1 4LG   *tel* Ipswich (0473) 43011   *fax* (0473) 240501.
£18.00 p.a. M. Practical, well-illustrated articles on all aspects of pig production required, particularly those dealing with new ideas in pig management, feeding and housing. *Length:* 1000 to 2000 words. *Payment:* by arrangement. *Illustrations:* colour, half-tone or line.

**Pilot** (1968), James Gilbert, 88 Burlington Road, New Malden, Surrey KT4 3NT   *tel* 01-949 3462   *fax* 01-336 1129.
£1.40. M. Feature articles on general aviation in private and business flying. *Payment:* £80 to £300 per article on acceptance. *Illustrations:* line, half-tone, colour. *Payment:* £20 for each photograph used.

**Planet** (1970-9; relaunched 1985), Ned Thomas, John Barnie, Gwen Daves, P.O. Box 44, Aberystwyth, Dyfed   *tel* (0970) 611255.
£2.00. 6 p.a. (£10.00 p.a.). Short stories, poems, topical articles on Welsh current affairs, politics and society; articles on minority cultures throughout the world. New literature in English. *Length* of articles: 1000 to 3500 words. *Payment:* £40.00 per 1000 words for prose; £20.00 minimum per poem. *Illustrations:* line, half-tone. Cartoons.

**Plays and Players,** Natasha Curry, 248 High Street, Croydon CR0 1NF   *tel* 01-681 7817.   *fax* 01-688 9573.
£1.75. M. Articles and photos on world theatre. *Payment:* by arrangement. *Illustrations:* line, photographs.

**PN Review,** formerly **Poetry Nation** (1973), Michael Schmidt, Michael Freeman, 208 Corn Exchange Buildings, Manchester M4 3BQ   *tel* 061-834 8730.
£2.75 (£16.50 p.a.). Q. Poems, essays, reviews, fiction, translations. *Payment:* by arrangement.

**Poetry Durham** (1982), David Hartnett, Michael O'Neill, Gareth Reeves, School of English, University of Durham, Elvet Riverside, New Elvet, Durham DH1 3JT   *tel* (091) 374 2730.
£4.50 p.a. (£8.00 for 2 years). 3 p.a. Poems and review essays on contemporary poetry. *Payment:* on publication.

**Poetry Nottingham** (1941), Howard Atkinson, Christine Michael, Claire Piggott, 21 Duncombe Close, Nottingham NG3 3PH   *tel* (0602) 584207.
£1.50. Q. Poems. *Length:* not more than 50 lines. *Payment:* none, but complimentary copy of magazine. *Illustrations:* line.

**Poetry Review,** Peter Forbes, 21 Earls Court Square, London SW5 9DE   *tel* 01-373 7861-2.
£12.00 p.a. (Institutions, schools and libraries £17.00 p.a.) Q. Poems, features and reviews. Send no more than six poems with s.a.e. Preliminary study of the magazine is essential. *Payment:* £10-£15 per poem.

**Poetry Wales** (1965), Mike Jenkins, 26 Andrew's Close, Heolgerrig, Merthyr Tudful CF48 1SS, Cymru/Wales   *tel* (0685) 76726.
£1.95 (£8.00 p.a. inc. postage). Q. Poems mainly in English and mainly by Welsh people or resident: other contributors (and Welsh poetry) also published. Articles on Welsh literature in English and in Welsh, as well as

on poetry from other countries. Special features; reviews on poetry and wider matters. *Payment:* by arrangement.

**Police Journal** (1928), R. W. Stone, Q.P.M., Little London, Chichester, West Sussex PO19 1PG *tel* (0243) 787841 *fax* (0243) 779278.
£37.50 p.a. Q. Articles of technical or professional interest to the Police Service throughout the world. *Payment:* by negotiation. *Illustrations:* half-tone.

**The Political Quarterly** (1930), Basil Blackwell Ltd., 108 Cowley Road, Oxford OX4 1JF *tel* (0865) 791100. Editors: Colin Crouch (Trinity College, Oxford OX1 3BH *tel* (0865) 279879 and 279900 *fax* (0865) 279911) and David Marquand (University of Salford, Salford M5 4WT *tel* 061-761 5843). Literary Editor: James Cornford. Books for review to be sent to: James Cornford, 28 Bedford Square, London WC1B 3EG.
£6.25. Q. £33.50 p.a. A journal devoted to topical aspects of national and international politics and public administration; it takes a progressive, but not a party, point of view. *Payment:* average. £50.00 per article. *Length:* average 4000 words.

**Pony** (1949), Managing Editor: Kate Austin, 296 Ewell Road, Surbiton, Surrey KT6 7AQ *tel* 01-390 8547 *fax* 01-390 8696.
85p. M. Lively articles and short stories with a horsy theme aimed at young readers in the 10 to 18 year-old age group. Technical accuracy and young, fresh writing essential. *Length:* up to 1600 words. *Payment:* by arrangement. *Illustrations:* drawings (commissioned) and interesting photographs.

**Popular Crafts,** Kym Wagner, Argus Specialist Publications, Argus House, Boundary Way, Hemel Hempstead, Herts. HP2 7ST *tel* (0442) 66551.
£1.50. M. Factual articles on crafts in general; embroidery, dressmaking, knitting, toymaking, pottery, weaving, lacemaking. *Payment:* by arrangement. *Illustrations:* transparencies and half-tones.

**Port of London,** Port of London Authority, Trident House, Tilbury Docks, Tilbury, Essex RM18 7EH *tel* (0375) 855477 *telex* 995562 *fax* (0375) 855478.
£1.00. Q. The magazine of the Port of London Authority. Articles up to 2500 words considered, semi-technical, historical or having bearing on trade and commerce of London essential. *Preliminary letter* essential. *Payment:* £65 per 1000 words. *Illustrations:* half-tone, line, colour.

**The Post** (1920), J. Jacques, UCW House, Crescent Lane, Clapham, London SW4 9RN *tel* 01-622 9977 *telex* 913585 *fax* 01-720 6853.
Free to members. M. The journal of the Union of Communication Workers. Articles on postal, telephone and telegraph workers in the UK and abroad and on other questions of interest to a Trade Union readership. *Length:* 1000 words or less. *Payment:* by arrangement. *Illustrations:* line and half-tone occasionally.

**Poultry World,** John Farrant, The Farmers Publishing Group, Carew House, Wallington, Surrey SM6 0DX *tel* 01-661 3500.
£1.10. M. Articles on commercial poultry breeding, production, marketing and packaging. News of international poultry interest. *Payment:* by arrangement. Line and photographic illustrations.

**Power Farming,** Ian G. Marshall, The Farmers Publishing Group, Carew House, Wallington, Surrey SM6 0DX *tel* 01-661 4843.
£1.10. M. Articles concerning all aspects of farm equipment, its use and management. General engineering in its application to machinery maintenance.

*Length:* up to 1500 words. Short practical workshop hints welcomed. *Payment:* by arrangement. *Illustrations:* photographs, drawings.

**The Powys Review** (1977), Belinda Humfrey, Dept. of English, Saint David's University College, Lampeter, Dyfed SA48 7ED   *tel* (0570) 422351 and 422018.
£3.50. Twice yearly. Articles and reviews on the writings of John Cowper Powys, T. F. Powys and Llewelyn Powys, and on related subjects and literature, especially of the period since 1890. *Payment:* £4.00 per 750 words. *Illustrations:* line, photographs.

**PR Week** (1984), Peter Yeo, Haymarket Marketing Publications, 32 Lancaster Gate, London W2 3LP   *tel* 01-706 1212.
£40.00 p.a. W. News and features on public relations. *Length:* approx. 800 words. *Payment:* £100 per 1000 words. *Illustrations:* half-tone.

**Practical Boat Owner** (1967), George Taylor, Westover House, West Quay Road, Poole, Dorset BH15 1JG   *tel* (0202) 680593.
£1.65. M. Articles of up to 2000 words in length, about practical matters concerning the boating enthusiast. *Payment:* by negotiation. *Illustrations:* photographs or drawings.

**Practical Computing,** Ian Stobie, Room L309, Quadrant House, The Quadrant, Sutton, Surrey SM2 5AS   *tel* 01-661 3633.
£1.90. M. Articles on business and professional microcomputing. *Length:* 1000 to 2500 words. *Payment:* from £50 per page. *Illustrations:* line.

**Practical Electronics** (1964), John Becker, 193 Uxbridge Road, London W12 9RA   *tel* 01-743 8888.
£1.25. M. Constructional and theoretical articles. *Length:* 1000-5500 words. *Payment:* £55-£90 per 1000 words depending upon type of article. *Illustrations:* line and half-tone.

**Practical Fishkeeping** (1966), Nick Fletcher, EMAP Pursuit Publishing Ltd, Bretton Court, Bretton, Peterborough PE3 8DZ   *tel* (0733) 264666.
£1.25. M. Practical experiences in fishkeeping and informative interviews with people of special standing in this field. *Payment:* by arrangement. *Illustrations:* line, half-tone, occasional colour.

**Practical Gardening** (1959), M. Wyatt, EMAP, Bushfield House, Orton Centre, Peterborough PE2 0UW   *tel* (0733) 237111   *fax* (0733) 231137.
£1.25. M. 500 to 1000 words on practical gardening subjects, particularly if oriented towards ideas for garden improvement, and well illustrated. *Payment:* from £70 per 1000 words. *Illustrations:* line, half-tone, colour.

**Practical Householder** (1955), David Bridle, Greater London House, Hampstead Road, London NW1 7QQ   *tel* 01-388 3171.
£1.10. M. Articles about 1500 words in length, about practical matters concerning home improvement. *Payment:* according to subject. *Illustrations:* line and half-tone.

**Practical Motorist** (1934), Denis Rea, Unit 8, Forest Close, Ebblake Industrial Estate, Verwood, Wimborne, Dorset BH21 6DQ   *tel* (0202) 823581.
£1.20. M. Practical articles on upkeep, servicing and repair and customising and performance improvements of all makes of cars, also practical hints and tips. *Payment:* according to merit. *Illustrations:* black and white, colour prints or transparencies and line drawings.

**Practical Photography** (1959), Richard Hopkins, EMAP, Bushfield House, Orton Centre, Peterborough PE2 0UW   *tel* (0733) 237111.

£1.50. M. Features on any aspect of photography with practical bias. *Payment:* from £50 per 1000 words. *Illustrations:* line, half-tone, colour; *payment:* from £10 black and white or colour.

**Practical Wireless** (1932), G. Arnold, PW Publishing Ltd., Enefco House, The Quay, Poole, Dorset BH15 1PP   *tel* (0202) 678558   *fax* (0202) 666244. 48p. M. Articles on the practical and theoretical aspects of domestic and amateur radio and communications. Constructional projects. *Illustrations:* photographs, line drawings and wash half-tone for offset litho. *Payment:* from £60 to £70 per 1000 words, plus extra for illustrations.

**Practical Woodworking,** Alan Mitchell, King's Reach Tower, Stamford Street, London SE1 9LS   *tel* 01-261 6602. £1.30. M. Articles of a practical nature covering any aspect of woodworking. Articles on tools, joints or timber technology. *Illustrations.*

**The Practitioner** (1868), Howard Griffiths, Morgan-Grampian (Professional Press) Ltd., 30 Calderwood Street, London SE18 6QH   *tel* 01-855 7777. £5.00. M. (£36.00 p.a., Overseas $88). Articles of interest to GPs and vocational trainees, and others in the medical profession.

**Prediction** (1936), Jo Logan, Link House, Dingwall Avenue, Croydon CR9 2TA   *tel* 01-686 2599   *telex* 947709 Linkho G. 95p. M. Articles on all occult subjects. *Length:* 2000 words maximum. *Payment:* by arrangement. *Illustrations:* Litho; full-colour cover.

**Prep School,** Anne Kiggell, 103 Palewell Park, London SW14 8JJ   *tel* 01-876 0368. £6.00 p.a. 3 p.a. by subscription. The journal of the Preparatory School world: the magazine of IAPS and SATIPS. Articles of educational interest covering ages 4-13. *Length:* about 1000 words. *Illustrations:* line, half-tone. *Payment:* by arrangement.

**Priests & People,** Revd. B. W. Bickers, M.A., Christ's & Notre Dame College, Woolton Road, Liverpool L16 8ND   *tel* 051-722 7331. £16.25 p.a. M. A journal of information, dialogue and research for Christians of English-speaking countries. *Length* and *payment* by arrangement.

**Prima** (1986), Portland House, Stag Place, London SW1E 5AU   *tel* 01-245 8700. 85p. M. Articles on fashion, crafts, health and beauty, cookery for women, features. *Illustrations:* half-tone, colour.

**Printing World** (1878), Eric Bignell, Benn Publications Ltd, Benn House, Sovereign Way, Tonbridge, Kent TN9 1RW   *tel* (0732) 364422   *fax* (0732) 361534. £1.40. W. (£43.00 p.a.). Commercial, technical, financial and labour news covering all aspects of the printing industry in the UK and abroad. Outside contributions. *Payment:* by arrangement. *Illustrations:* half-tone, line, colour.

**Private Eye** (1962), Ian Hislop, 6 Carlisle Street, London W1V 5RG   *tel* 01-437 4017   *fax* 01-437 0705. 50p. F. Satire. *Payment:* by arrangement. *Illustrations:* black and white, line.

**The Professional Nurse** (1985), Elizabeth M. Horne, Austen Cornish Publishers Ltd., Austen Cornish House, Walham Grove, London SW6 1QW   *tel* 01-381 6301.

£22.50 p.a. M. Articles of interest to the professional nurse. *Length:* Articles: 2500 to 3000 words; Factsheets: 1400 words; letters: 250-500 words. *Payment:* by arrangement. *Illustrations:* line, colour, half-tone.

**Prospice** (1973), J. C. R. Green, Roger Elkin, Prospice Publishing Ltd, P.O. Box 18, Buxton, Derbyshire SK17 6YP *tel* (0298) 72471 *fax* (0298) 72402.
£3.95 single copy (£12.50 p.a. subscription). Q. Poetry, including groups of or long sequences of poems, short fiction. Also essays, reviews and work in translation. Contributions welcomed, but must be accompanied by an *sae.* *Payment:* by negotiation. *Illustrations:* interested in photo-sequences of art/experimental nature only; *payment:* by negotiation.

**Publishing News** (1979), Fred Newman, 43 Museum Street, London WC1A 1LY *tel* 01-404 0304.
80p. W. Articles and news items on books and publishers. *Payment:* £60 to £80 per 1000 words. *Illustrations:* half-tone.

**Pulse,** Howard Griffiths, Morgan-Grampian (Professional Press) Ltd., Morgan-Grampian House, 30 Calderwood Street, Woolwich, London SE18 6QH *tel* 01-855 7777 *fax* 01-855 2406.
£68.00 p.a. W. Articles and photographs of direct interest to G.P.s. Purely clinical material can only be accepted from medically-qualified authors. *Length:* up to 750 words. *Payment:* £100 average. *Illustrations:* black and white, and colour photographs.

**Punch** (1841), David Thomas, 245 Blackfriars Road, London SE1 9UY *tel* 01-921 5900.
£1.00. W. Many features commissioned, but unsolicited contributions actively encouraged—short or long, just make it funny. Maximum article *length:* 1000 words; minimum *payment:* £120.00; topical material preferred. Cartoons and illustrations welcome, *payment* by arrangement, and all submissions *must* be accompanied by an sae.

**Quaker Monthly** (1921), Carol Gardiner, Quaker Home Service, Friends House, Euston Road, London NW1 2BJ *tel* 01-387 3601.
42p. M. (£6.80 p.a.). Articles, poems, reviews, expanding the Quaker approach to the spiritual life. Writers should be members or attenders of a Quaker meeting. *Illustrations:* line, half-tone. *Payment:* none.

**Quarterly Journal of Medicine** (1907), *Publisher:* Oxford University Press, Walton Street, Oxford OX2 6DP. *Executive Editor:* Dr. J. M. Holt, John Radcliffe Hospital, Oxford OX3 9DU *tel* (0865) 817348 *fax* (0865) 741357.
£10.00. M. (£84 p.a., overseas £105 p.a.). Devoted to the publication of original papers and critical reviews dealing with clinical medicine. *Payment:* none.

**Radio Control Models and Electronics** (1960), David Boddington, Argus Specialist Publications Ltd., P.O. Box 35, Hemel Hempstead, Herts. HP2 4SS *tel* (0442) 41221 *fax* (0442) 216429.
£1.10. M. Well illustrated articles on topics related to radio control. *Payment:* £30.00 per published page. *Illustrations:* line, half-tone. Cartoons.

**Radio Times** (The Journal of the BBC), Nicholas Brett, BBC Enterprises, 35 Marylebone High Street, London W1M 4AA *tel* 01-580 5577.
40p. W. Articles support and enlarge BBC Television and Radio programmes, and are, therefore, on every subject broadcast. *Length:* from 600

to 2500 words. *Payment:* by arrangement. *Illustrations:* in colour and black and white; photographs, graphic designs, or drawings.

**Railway Gazette International,** Richard Hope, Reed Business Publishing Ltd., Quadrant House, The Quadrant, Sutton, Surrey SM2 5AS   *tel* 01-661 3739   *telex* 892084 Reedbp G   *fax* 01-661 3738.
£5.00. M. Deals with management, engineering, operation and finance of railways world wide. Articles of practical interest on these subjects are considered and paid for if accepted. Illustrated articles, of 1000 to 3000 words, are preferred. A *preliminary letter* is desirable.

**Railway Magazine** (1897), Prospect House, 9-13 Ewell Road, Cheam, Surrey SM1 4QQ   *tel* 01-661 4480.
£1.50. M. An illustrated magazine dealing with all railway subjects; not fiction. Articles from 1500 to 2000 words accompanied by photographs. A *preliminary letter* is desirable. No verse. *Payment:* by arrangement. *Illustrations:* colour transparencies, half-tone and line.

**Railway World** (founded as **Railways** 1939), Handel Kardas, Terminal House, Station Approach, Shepperton TW17 8AS   *tel* (0932) 228950.
£1.40. M. Articles on railway and allied matters. *Length:* 500 to 3000 words. *Payment:* by arrangement. *Illustrations:* line, half-tone and colour.

**Reader's Digest,** Russell Twisk (The Reader's Digest Association Ltd.), 25 Berkeley Square, London W1X 6AB   *tel* 01-629 8144.
£1.40. M. Original anecdotes—£150 for up to 300 words—are required for humorous features.

**Red Tape** (1911), Barry A. Reamsbottom, Civil and Public Services Association, 160 Falcon Road, Clapham Junction, London SW11 2LN   *tel* 01-924 2727   *fax* 01-924 1847.
11 per year. Subscription rate for non-members: £4.00 p.a. + £2.00 (inland), £5.00 (overseas) postage. Well-written articles on Civil Service, trade union and general subjects considered. *Length:* 750 to 1400 words. Also photographs and humorous drawings of interest to Civil Servants. *Illustrations:* line and half-tone.

**Reform** (1972), Norman Hart, 86 Tavistock Place, London WC1H 9RT   *tel* 01-837 7661.
50p. M. Published by United Reformed Church. Articles of religious or social comment. *Length:* 600-1000 words. *Illustrations:* full colour, half-tone and line subjects. *Payment:* by arrangement.

**Report** (Journal of the Assistant Masters and Mistresses Association), Editorial: 7 Northumberland Street, London WC2N 5DA   *tel* 01-930 6441   *fax* 01-930 1359.
£8.00 p.a., overseas £12.00 p.a. 8 p.a. Features, articles, comment, news about primary, secondary and further education; no poems. *Payment:* £60 per 1000 words (minimum).

**Retail Attraction,** Jay Myers, AGB Business Publications Ltd., Audit House, Field End Road, Eastcote, Ruislip, Middlesex HA4 9LT   *tel* 01-868 4499   *telex* 926726 AGB Pub G   *fax* 01-429 3117.
£24.00 p.a. post free. Bi-M. (£4.00 per copy.) Reviews, retail business orientated articles, features and news, preferably illustrated, of shop and store premises design, display, planning, construction and fitting, services and lighting. *Length:* 750-1250 words (or longer by arrangement), or short paragraphs; features by arrangement. *Payment:* by arrangement. *Illustrations:* photographs, plans and sketches.

**The Rialto** (1984), Michael Mackmin, John Wakeman, 32 Grosvenor Road, Norwich, Norfolk NR2 2PZ    *tel* (0603) 666455.
£2.10 3 p.a. (£6.00 p.a.). Poetry and criticism. *Illustrations:* line. *Payment:* by arrangement. Sae essential.

**Road Racer Magazine** (1986), Julian Ryder, London House, 42 Upper Richmond Road West, London SW14 8DD    *tel* 01-876 0102    *fax* 01-392 1132.
£1.40. M. Profiles, history, technical articles, short fiction concerning motorcycle road racing. *Payment:* £95 per 1000 words. *Illustrations:* line, half-tone, colour.

**Romance**, Geoff Kemp, P.O. Box 94, London W4 2ER    *tel* 01-995 0590.
85p. M. Confessions stories aimed at, and about, pre-marrieds; 16-20 age group. *Length:* 3000 to 4000 words. *Payment:* £14.00 per 1000 words.

**The Round Table** (1910), The Commonwealth Journal of International Affairs, Peter Lyon, Institute of Commonwealth Studies, University of London, 27-28 Russell Square, London WC1B 5DS    *tel* 01-580 5876    *fax* 01-255 2160.
£39 p.a. Q. Appropriate articles. *Payment:* £10 per 1000 words. No *illustrations*.

**Running Magazine** (1979), Nick Troop, 67-71 Goswell Road, London EC1V 7EN    *tel* 01-250 1881.
£1.30. M. Articles on jogging, running and fitness. *Payment:* by arrangement. *Illustrations:* line, half-tone, colour.

**RUSI Journal** (Journal of the Royal United Services Institute for Defence Studies), Ian Smart, Whitehall, London SW1A 2ET    *tel* 01-930 5854.
£5.50. Q. Articles on international security, the military sciences, defence technology and procurement, and military history; also book reviews and correspondence. *Length:* 2000-4500 words. *Illustrations:* b&w photographs, maps and diagrams. *Payment:* £12.50 per printed page upon publication.

**Safety Education** (1966; founded 1937 as **Child Safety**; 1940 became **Safety Training**), Ian Edginton, Royal Society for the Prevention of Accidents, Cannon House, The Priory Queensway, Birmingham B4 6BS    *tel* 021-200 2461.
£3.45 p.a. 3 p.a. Articles on every aspect of safety for children and in particular articles on the teaching of road, home, water and leisure safety by means of established subjects on the school curriculum. All ages. *Illustrations:* line, half-tone and colour.

**Saga Magazine** (1984), Paul Bach, The Saga Building, Middelburg Square, Folkestone, Kent CT20 1AZ    *tel* (0303) 47523    *telex* 966331    *fax* (0303) 48622.
85p (£8.90 p.a. on subscription). 10 p.a. Articles relevant to interests of 60+ age group, and profiles of celebrities in same age group. *Length:* up to 1800 words. *Payment:* negotiable, approx. £200 per 1200 words. *Illustrations:* colour transparencies, commissioned colour artwork; *payment:* £120 per page and pro rata.

**Sandwell Evening Mail** (1975), Ian Dowell, Shaftesbury House, 402 High Street, West Bromwich    *tel* 021-553 7221. London office: Clan House, 19-21 Tudor Street, EC4Y 0DJ    *tel* 01-353 0811.
18p. D. Independent. Features of topical West Midland interest considered. *Length:* 400-800 words.

**Satellite Times** (1988), John D. Bryant, Satellite House, 85-89 Church Road, Crystal Palace, London SE19 2TA    *tel* 01-653 9933    *fax* 01-653 3291.

£1.20. M. Television personality articles and interviews, sports articles, crosswords, competitions. *Payment:* by negotiation. *Illustrations:* in colour, b&w and line. Cartoons and TV-related illustrations, e.g. stars' caricatures, considered; *payment:* by negotiation.

**Scale Models International,** Kelvin Barber, Argus Specialist Publications Ltd., P.O. Box 35, Hemel Hempstead, Herts. HP2 4SS *tel* (0442) 41221 *fax* (0442) 216429.
£1.25. M. Articles on scale models. *Length:* up to 2500 words. *Payment:* £30 per page. *Illustrations:* line, half-tone, colour.

**School Librarian** (1937), Editor: Sheila Ray; Review Editor: Keith Barker, The School Library Association, Liden Library, Barrington Close, Liden, Swindon, Wilts. SN3 6HF *tel* (0793) 617838.
£25.00 p.a. post free. Q. Official journal of the School Library Assoc. (free to members). Reviews of books from pre-school to young adult age range with articles on authors and illustrators; also articles on school library organisation, use and skills. *Length:* 3200 words maximum. *Payment:* by arrangement.

**Science Progress,** Professor J. M. Ziman, F.R.S., Professor P. J. B. Slater, Professor Patricia H. Clarke, F.R.S., (Blackwell Scientific Publications Ltd.), Osney Mead, Oxford OX2 0EL *tel* (0865) 40201.
£12.00. Q. (£47.50 p.a.). Articles of 5000 to 10,000 words suitably illustrated on scientific subjects, written so as to be intelligible to workers in other branches of science. *Payment:* £1.50 per printed page. *Illustrations:* line and half-tone.

**Scoop** (1988), Ian Drew, Planagraphic Printers, 153 Praed Street, London W2 1RL *tel* 01-437 2659 *fax* 01-437 0845.
40p. W. Articles of interest to children aged 9-14; also cartoons, puzzles, readers' jokes and letters. *Length:* up to 500 words. *Payment:* by arrangement. *Illustrations:* b&w photos (occasional colour), line drawings, cartoons.

**Scootering** (1985), Gareth Brown, P.O. Box 69, Altrincham, Cheshire WA15 8SJ *tel* 061-941 3296.
£1.25. 13 p.a. Custom, racing and vintage scooter features, plus technical information. Music features and related lifestyle pieces. *Payment:* by arrangement. *Illustrations:* half-tone, colour.

**The Scorpion** (1981), Michael E. Walker, Schnellweiderstraße 50, 5000-Cologne-80, Rheinland, W. Germany.
£1.50-£3.00. Bi-annual. Each issue deals with a particular subject related to problems of culture. A magazine in defence of European culture. *Preliminary letter essential. Payment:* £5-£30 per article. *Illustrations:* line, half-tone.

**Scotland on Sunday** (1988), Andrew Jaspan, North Bridge, Edinburgh EH1 1YT *tel* 031-225 2468 *telex* 72255 *fax* 031-220 2443.
40p. W. Also **Scotland on Sunday Magazine** (1989).

**The Scots Magazine** (1739), (D. C. Thomson & Co. Ltd.), Bank Street, Dundee DD1 9HU *tel* Dundee (0382) 23131.
75p. M. Articles on all subjects of Scottish interest. Short stories, poetry, but must be Scottish. *Payment:* varies according to quality. *Illustrations:* colour and black and white photographs, and drawings.

**Scotsman** (1817), Magnus Linklater, 20 North Bridge, Edinburgh EH1 1YT *tel* 031-225 2468 *fax* 031-225 7302.

30p. D. Independent. Considers articles, 800-1000 words, on political, economic and general themes, which add substantially to current information. Prepared to commission topical and controversial series from proved authorities. *Illustrations:* outstanding news pictures.

**Scottish Educational Journal,** 46 Moray Place, Edinburgh EH3 6BH    *tel* 031-225 6244.
50p. 8 p.a., plus Specials. Published by the Educational Institute of Scotland.

**The Scottish Farmer** (1893), Angus MacDonald, The Plaza Tower, The Plaza, East Kilbride, Glasgow G74 1LW    *tel* (03552) 46444.
65p. W. Articles on agricultural subjects. *Length:* 1000-1500 words. *Payment:* by arrangement. *Illustrations:* line and half-tone.

**Scottish Field** (1903), Joe Stirling, George Outram & Co. Ltd (Magazine Division), The Plaza Tower, The Plaza, East Kilbride, Glasgow G74 1LW    *tel* (03552) 46444.
£1.30. M. (£16.75 p.a.) Will consider all material with a Scottish link and good photographs. *Payment:* above average rates.

**Scottish Historical Review** (Company of Scottish History, Ltd.), Dr A. Grant and Dr I. G. C. Hutchison, Distributed by Aberdeen University Press, Farmers Hall, Aberdeen AB9 2XT    *tel* (0224) 630724    *fax* (0224) 643286.
£15.00 p.a. (£18.00 through booksellers). 2 p.a. Contributions to the advancement of knowledge in any aspect of Scottish history. *Length:* up to 8000 words. *Payment:* none; contributors are given offprints. *Illustrations:* line and half-tone.

**Scottish Home and Country** (1924), Stella Roberts, 42A Heriot Row, Edinburgh EH3 6ES    *tel* 031-225 1934.
40p. M. Articles on crafts, cookery, travel, personal experience, village histories, country customs, DIY, antiques, farming; humorous rural stories; fashion, health, books. *Illustrations:* half-tone. *Length:* up to 1000 words, preference being given to those accompanied by photographs, etc.

**Scouting,** David Easton, The Scout Association, Baden-Powell House, Queens Gate, London SW7 5JS    *tel* 01-584 7030    *fax* 01-581 9953.
90p. M. The National Magazine of The Scout Association. Ideas, news, views, features and programme resources for Leaders and Supporters. Training material, accounts of Scouting events and articles of general interest with Scouting connections. *Illustrations:* photographs---action shots preferred rather than static posed shots for use with articles or as fillers or cover potential. *Payment:* on publication by arrangement.

**Screen International,** Editor-in-Chief: Peter Noble; Editor: Nick Roddick, 6-7 Great Chapel Street, London W1V 4BR    *tel* 01-734 9452 and 437 5741    *telex* 27261 Screen G    *fax* 01-434 1898.
£1.25. W. International news and features on every aspect of films, television and associated media. *Length:* variable. *Payment:* by arrangement.

**Sea Angler** (1973), Melvyn Russ, EMAP Pursuit Publishing Ltd., Bretton Court, Bretton, Peterborough PE3 8DZ    *tel* (0733) 264666.
£1.25. M. Topical articles on all aspects of sea-fishing around the British Isles. *Payment:* by arrangement. *Illustrations:* line, half-tone and colour.

**Sea Breezes** (1919), C. H. Milsom, 202 Cotton Exchange Building, Old Hall Street, Liverpool L3 9LA    *tel* 051-236 3935.

£1.35. M. Factual articles on ships and the sea past and present, preferably illustrated. *Length:* up to 4000 words. *Payment:* by arrangement. *Illustrations:* colour, half-tone, line.

**Secrets** (D. C. Thomson & Co. Ltd.), Courier Place, Dundee DD1 9QJ, and 185 Fleet Street, London EC4A 2HS.
26p. W. Complete stories of 1500 to 4000 words, with mainly romantic interest to appeal to women of most ages. Serials, 5000-word instalments. *No preliminary letter required. Payment:* on acceptance.

**Secrets Story Library** (D. C. Thomson & Co. Ltd.), Courier Place, Dundee DD1 9QJ, and 185 Fleet Street, London EC4A 2HS.
32p. M. 64 pages. Exciting and romantic stories in text.

**She** (1955), Editor-in-Chief: Joyce Hopkirk, National Magazine House, 72 Broadwick Street, London W1V 2BP  *tel* 01-439 7144.
£1.00. M. Articles 500 to 1000 words on all subjects except fashion and beauty; controversial, factual, medical, relating to women. First person experiences. Picture features welcome. *Payment:* NUJ freelance rates. *Illustrations:* photos.

**Ship & Boat International** (incorporating **Small Craft**), Richard White, Royal Institution of Naval Architects, 10 Upper Belgrave Street, London SW1X 8BQ  *tel* 01-235 4622  *telex* 265844 Sinai G  *fax* 01-245 6959.
£39.00 p.a. M. Technical articles on the design, construction and operation of all types of specialised small ships and workboats. *Length:* 500-1500 words. *Payment:* by arrangement. *Illustrations:* line and half-tone, photographs and diagrams.

**Ships Monthly** (1966), Robert Shopland, Waterway Productions Ltd., Kottingham House, Dale Street, Burton-on-Trent DE14 3TD  *tel* (0283) 64290.
£1.40. M. Illustrated articles of maritime interest---both mercantile and naval, preferably of 20th century ships. Well-researched, factual material only. No short stories or poetry. 'Notes for Contributors' available. Mainly commissioned material; preliminary letter essential. *Payment:* by arrangement. *Illustrations:* half-tone and line, colour transparencies.

**Shooting Times and Country Magazine** (1882), Jonathan Young, Burlington Publishing Co. Ltd., 10 Sheet Street, Windsor, Berks. SL4 1BG  *tel* (0753) 856061.
85p. W. Articles on fieldsports especially shooting, and on related natural history and countryside topics. *Length:* up to 1000 words. *Payment:* by arrangement. *Illustrations:* photographs, drawings, colour transparencies.

**The Short Wave Magazine** (1937), Dick Ganderton, G8VFH, Enefco House, The Quay, Poole, Dorset BH15 1PP  *tel* (0202) 678558.
£1.45. M. (£17.00 p.a.). Technical and semi-technical articles, 500 to 20,000 words, dealing with design, construction and operation of radio receiving equipment. *Payment:* £52.00 per page. *Illustrations:* line and half-tone.

**Sight and Sound** (1932), Penelope Houston (published by the British Film Institute), 21 Stephen Street, London W1P 1PL  *tel* 01-255 1444.
£1.80. Q. Topical and critical articles on the cinema of any country. Highly specialised articles only occasionally. 1000 to 5000 words. *Payment:* by arrangement. *Illustrations:* relevant photographs.

**The Sign** (1905), Chansitor Publications Ltd, St Mary's Works, St Mary's Plain, Norwich, Norfolk NR3 3BH  *tel* (0603) 615995.

5p. M. Leading national inset for C. of E. parish magazines. Unusual b&w. photos, drawings considered. *Payment:* by arrangement. Items should bear the author's name and address; return postage essential.

**Signal,** Approaches to Children's Books (1970), Nancy Chambers, Lockwood, Station Road, South Woodchester, Stroud, Gloucestershire GL5 5EQ   *tel* Amberley (0453 87) 3716 or 2208.
£2.50. Three p.a. (£7.50 p.a.). Articles on any aspect of children's books or the children's book world. *Length:* no limit but average 2500-3000 words. *Payment:* £2.50 per printed page. *Illustrations:* line occasionally.

**Signature** (1953), Mary Ratcliffe, 7-11 St. Johns Hill, London SW11 1TE   *tel* 01-228 3344.
£1.75. 9 p.a. Articles on travel, food and wine. *Payment:* by arrangement. No unsolicited manuscripts accepted.

**Singles Magazine** (1977), Lorraine Furneaux, 23 Abingdon Road, London W8 6AH   *tel* 01-938 1011.
£1.00. M. Articles of interest to single people. *Length:* up to 2000 words. *Payment:* by arrangement. *Illustrations:* line and half-tone.

**Ski Magazine,** Skyline Publications, Sunseeker House, West Quay Road, Poole, Dorset BH15 1JF   *tel* (0202) 665616   *fax* (0202) 684841.
£1.50. 6 p.a. Articles, instructive and informative on all aspects of skiing and resorts in all parts of the world. Winter travel articles, news items. *Length:* 1000 words, illustrations preferred. *Payment:* by arrangement. *Illustrations:* black and white photographs and colour transparencies.

**Slimmer Magazine** (1972), Judith Wills, Stirling Publishing Group, P.O. Box 839, 86-88 Edgware Road, London W2 2YW   *tel* 01-258 0066.
85p. Bi-M. Articles of interest to people interested in health, nutrition, slimming. *Length:* 500 to 1500 words. *Payment:* £10 per 100 words (s.a.e. essential).

**Slow Dancer** (1977), John Harvey, Flat 4, 1 Park Valley, Nottingham NG7 1BS   *tel* (0602) 414948.
£2. Annual (Oct). Poetry, some short stories. *Payment:* none, but 3 complimentary copies of magazine. *Illustrations:* in b/w photos. *Preliminary study of the magazine essential.* Reading period for submissions 1 Nov–30 Apr; send US poetry submissions to: Alan Brooks, Box 3010, RFD 1, Lubec, Maine 04652, USA.

**Smallholder** (1985), Liz Wright, Hook House, Hook Road, Wimblington, March, Cambs. PE15 0QL   *tel* (0354) 740719, (0366) 501035.
£1.20. M. Articles of relevance to small farmers about livestock and crops; items relating to the countryside considered. *Payment:* £10.00 per 1000 words. *Illustrations:* line, half-tone.

**Smash Hits,** Richard Lowe, 52–55 Carnaby Street, London W1V 1PF   *tel* 01-437 8050   *fax* 01-494 0851.
52p. F. News items on pop stars, puzzles. *Payment:* £100 per page. *Illustrations:* colour photos, cartoons: *payment:* £100.

**Snooker Scene** (1971), Clive Everton, Cavalier House, 202 Hagley Road, Edgbaston, Birmingham B16 9PQ   *tel* 021-454 2931.
90p. M. News and articles about snooker. *Payment:* by arrangement. *Illustrations:* photographs.

**Social and Liberal Democrats News,** Mike Harskin, 4 Cowley Street, London SW1P 3NB   *tel* 01-222 7999   *fax* 01-222 7904.

50p. W. (£20.00 p.a.). The official newspaper of the Social and Liberal Democrats. News, political and social features. *Payment:* none.

**Sociological Review**, Managing Editors: John Eggleston, Ronald Frankenberg, Gordon Fyfe, University of Keele, Keele, Staffs. ST5 5BG   *tel* Newcastle under Lyme (0782) 621111 Ext. 3620.
£32.00 p.a. (Institutions £46.00 p.a.) including Monograph. Q. Articles of 8000 to 10,000 words treating social subjects in a scientific way. *Payment:* none. *Illustrations:* line.

**The Solicitors Journal** (1857), 21-27 Lamb's Conduit Street, London WC1N 3NJ   *tel* 01-242 2548.
£1.15. W. Articles, preferably by practising solicitors on subjects of practical interest. *Length:* up to 2000 words.

**Somerset & Avon Life** (incorporating **Bristol Illustrated**) (1975), Heidi Best, St. Lawrence House, Broad Street, Bristol BS1 2EX   *tel* (0272) 291069   *fax* (0272) 225633.
£1.00. M. Feature articles of local and general interest. *Length:* 1200 words. *Payment:* by arrangement. *Illustrations:* half-tone, colour.

**Songwriting and Composing** (1986), Magazine of the Society of International Songwriters and Composers, Roderick Glyn Jones, 12 Trewartha Road, Praa Sands, Penzance, Cornwall TR20 9ST   *tel* (0736) 762826.
Free to members. Q. Short stories, articles, letters relating to songwriting, publishing, recording and the music industry. *Payment:* negotiable upon content £5-£40. *Illustrations:* line, half-tone.

**South,** the business magazine of the developing world (1980), Raana G. Noman, Rex House, 1st Floor, 4-12 Regent Street, London SW1Y 4TS   *tel* 01-930 8411   *cables* Thirdworld, London SW1   *telex* 8814201 Trimed G   *fax* 01-930 0980.
£1.25. M. News—economic, political, commodity, business relating to the Third World. *Payment:* approx. £100 per 1000 words. *Illustrations:* half-tone; some colour.

**Spaceflight** (1956), Prof. G. V. Groves, 27-29 South Lambeth Road, London SW8 1SZ   *tel* 01-735 3160. Published by The British Interplanetary Society.
£1.25. (Free to members). M. Articles up to 2500 words dealing with topics of astronomy, space and astronautics. *Illustrations:* colour, line, half-tone. *Payment:* none.

**Spare Rib,** 27 Clerkenwell Close, London EC1R 0AT   *tel* 01-253 9792 and 251 1773.
90p. M. (£12.00 p.a.). Women's liberation magazine; features, news, reviews, fiction, poetry, cartoons by women about women. Welcomes contributions on health, parenting, young women. *Illustrations:* black and white.

**The Spectator** (1828), Charles Moore, 56 Doughty Street, London WC1N 2LL   *tel* 01-405 1706   *telex* 27124   *fax* 01-242-0603.
£1.20. W. Articles of a suitable character will always be considered. *Payment:* rate depends upon the nature and length of the article.

**Speech and Drama** (1951), Dr. Paul Ranger, 4 Fane Road, Old Marston, Oxford OX3 0SA   *tel* (0865) 728304.
£5.00 p.a. 2 p.a. Specialist articles only. *Length:* 1500-2000 words. Photographs welcome. Covers theatre, drama and all levels of education relating to speech and drama. Preliminary abstract of 300 words. *Payment:* none, complimentary copy.

**Spiritualist Gazette** (1972), Tom Johanson, S.A.G.B. Ltd., 33 Belgrave Square, London SW1X 8QB   *tel* 01-235 3351.
£4.30 p.a. M. Spiritualism, healing, life after death and allied subjects. *Payment:* none.

**Spoken English** (1968), English Speaking Board (International), 32 Norwood Avenue, Southport, Merseyside PR9 7EG   *tel* (0704) 231366.
£10.00 p.a., 3 times p.a. Articles on all aspects of oral English and drama at all levels of education and of a serious nature. Overseas as well as U.K. *Length:* from 1000 words.

**The Sport** (1988), Peter Grimsditch, 19 Great Ancoats Street, Manchester M60 4BT   *tel* 061-236 4466   *telex* 665058 TSport   *fax* 061-236 4535.
25p. W. Factual stories and series. *Length:* up to 1000 words per episode. *Payment:* £30-£1000. *Illustrations:* b&w and colour photographs, cartoons; *payment:* £30-£1000.

**Sport and Leisure** (1949), Andrew Shields, The Sports Council, 16 Upper Woburn Place, London WC1H 0QP   *tel* 01-388 1277   *fax* 01-383 5740.
£2.00. 6 p.a. Articles on various sports, physical education, sports politics, the leisure boom, sponsorship, buildings, equipment and outdoor activities. *Length:* 500-1200 words. *Payment:* £85.00 per 1000 words. *Illustrated.* Sports photographers encouraged; black and white photographs.

**The Sporting Life,** Monty Court (Odhams Newspapers Ltd.), Orbit House, 1 New Fetter Lane, London EC4A 1AR   *tel* 01-353 0246   *telex* 263403   *fax* 01-583 3885/6.
40p. D.

**Squash World** (1986), Larry Halpin, Dennis Fairey Publishing Ltd, Chiltern House, 184 High Street, Berkhamsted, Herts. HP4 3AP   *tel* (0442) 874947   *fax* (0442) 863152.
£1.20. 9 p.a. Articles on players, events, equipment, clothing, sponsorship. *Payment:* by arrangement. *Illustrations:* half-tone, colour.

**The Stage and Television Today** (1880), Peter Hepple, Stage House, 47 Bermondsey Street, London SE1 3XT   *tel* 01-403 1818.
35p. W. Original and interesting articles on professional stage and television topics may be sent for the Editor's consideration, 500-800 words.

**Stamp Lover** (1908), Publisher: National Philatelic Society, British Philatelic Centre, 107 Charterhouse Street, London EC1M 6PT   *tel* 01-251 5040. Editor: Peter Collins.
£1.00. 6 p.a. Original articles on stamps and postal history. *Payment:* by arrangement. *Illustrations:* photographs, half-tone and line.

**Stamp Magazine** (1934), Richard West, Link House, Dingwall Avenue, Croydon CR9 2TA   *tel* 01-686 2599   *telex* 947709 Linkho G.
£1.35. M. Informative articles and exclusive news items on stamp collecting and postal history. *No preliminary letter. Payment:* by arrangement. *Illustrations:* photographs, half-tone and line.

**Stamp Monthly,** Hugh Jefferies, Stanley Gibbons Publications Ltd., 5 Parkside, Ringwood, Hants BH24 3SH   *tel* (04254) 2363.
£1.25. M. (£19.75 p.a.). Articles on philatelic topics. Previous reference to the editor advisable. *Length:* 500 to 2500 words. *Payment:* by arrangement, £17.00 per 1000 words and up. *Illustrations:* photographs.

**Stamps** (1979), Lesley Yates-Newman, CGB Publishing, Newspaper House, Tannery Lane, Penketh, Cheshire WA5 2UD *tel* (092572) 4234 *fax* (092572) 2617.
£1.30. M. Stamps. *Payment:* £40 per 1000 words. *Illustrations:* line, half-tone.

**Stand Magazine** (1952), Jon Silkin, Lorna Tracy, Lynn Evans, 179 Wingrove Road, Newcastle on Tyne NE4 9DA *tel* (091) 273 3280 and 281 2614.
£2.30 (inc. p&p). Q. (£7.95 p.a.). Poetry, short stories, drama, translations, literary criticism, art. *Payment:* £30.00 per 1000 words of prose; £30.00 per poem; s.a.e. for return.

**The Star** (1887), M. Corner, York Street, Sheffield S1 1PU *tel* (0742) 767676 *fax* (0742) 753551.
18p. D. Well-written articles of local character. *Length:* about 800 words. *Payment:* by negotiation. *Illustrations:* topical photographs, line drawings, graphics.

**Star Love Stories** (D. C. Thomson & Co. Ltd.), Albert Square, Dundee DD1 9QJ *tel* (0382) 23131, and 185 Fleet Street, London EC4A 2HS.
32p. 2 each month. Romantic and emotional stories told in pictures. Scripts should be about 135 pictures. Synopsis required as an opener. *Payment:* on acceptance.

**Starblazer Library** (D. C. Thomson & Co. Ltd.), Courier Place, Dundee DD1 9QJ, and 185 Fleet Street, London EC4A 2HS.
32p. M. 64 pages. Fantasy fiction picture story adventure for boys.

**Street Machine** (1979) Clive Househam, AGB Specialist Publications Ltd., Audit House, Field End Road, Eastcote, Ruislip, Middlesex HA4 9LT *tel* 01-868 4499.
£1.35. M. Articles on all cars and bodywork, 2000 to 3000 words. *Payment:* by arrangement. *Illustrations:* line, half-tone, colour.

**Stride** (1980), Rupert M. Loydell, 37 Portland Street, Newtown, Exeter, Devon EX1 2EG.
£3. Q. Short stories, poems, interviews and reviews. *Length:* 500-1500 words. *Payment:* none, but two complimentary copies of magazine. *Illustrations:* b&w photos, line drawings, original art; *payment:* as above.

**Studies in Comparative Religion,** Perennial Books Ltd., Pates Manor, Bedfont, Middlesex TW14 8JP *tel* 01-890 2790.
£3.95. Q. Comparative religion, metaphysics, traditional studies, eastern religions, mysticism, holy places, etc. *Length:* 2000-4000 words.

**Studio International** (1893), Michael Spens, Medical Tribune Group, Tower House, Southampton Street, London WC2E 7LS *tel* 01-379 6005 *fax* 01-379 6737.
£5.00. Q. An international magazine dealing with the contemporary fine arts and design. *Remarks:* only *illustrated* articles and notes accepted. A *preliminary letter* is desirable. *Payment:* by arrangement. *Illustrations:* reproductions of paintings, sculpture, drawings, engravings, applied art.

**Studio Sound** (1959), Keith Spencer-Allen, Link House, Dingwall Avenue, Croydon CR9 2TA *tel* 01-686 2599 *telex* 947709 Linkho G *fax* 01-760 0973.
£2.00. M. Articles on all aspects of professional sound recording. Technical and operational features on the functional aspects of studio equipment: general features on studio affairs. *Length:* widely variable. *Payment:* by arrangement. *Illustrations:* line and half-tone.

**The Sun** (1969), Kelvin MacKenzie, News Group Newspapers Ltd., Virginia Street, London E1 9XP  *tel* 01-782 4000  *telegraphic address* Sunnews, London  *telex* 262135 Sunews.
22p. D.

**Sunday Express** (1918), Robin Morgan, Ludgate House, 245 Blackfriars Road, London SE1 9UX  *tel* 01-928 8000  *cables* Lon Express  *telex* 21841/21842  *fax* 01-633 0244.
50p. W. Exclusive news stories, photographs, personality profiles and features of controversial or lively interest. *Length:* 800 to 1000 words. *Payment:* top rates.

**Sunday Express Magazine,** Dee Nolan, Ludgate House, 245 Blackfriars Road, London  SE1  9UX  *tel* 01-928  8000  *cables* Lon  Express  *telex* 21841/21842  *fax* 01-633 0244.
Free with newspaper. W. General interest features. *Length:* 1500 words. *Payment:* from £150 per 1000 words. *Illustrations:* colour, half-tone, artwork.

**Sunday Magazine** (1981), Colin Jenkins, 214 Gray's Inn Road, London WC1X 8EZ  *tel* 01-782 7000  *telex* 297918 KRM G  *fax* 01-782 7373.
Free with News of the World. W. Freelance writers' ideas and material always welcomed. *Payment:* by arrangement.

**Sunday Mail,** E. Noel Young, Anderston Quay, Glasgow G3 8DA  *tel* 041-242 3403. London Office: 33 Holborn Circus, EC1P 1DQ.
32p. W. Exclusive stories and pictures (in colour if possible) of national and Scottish interest. *Payment:* above average.

**Sunday Mercury,** J. K. Bradbury, Colmore Circus, Birmingham B4 6AZ  *tel* 021-236 3366  *telex* 337552  *fax* 021-233 3958.
30p. W. News specials or features of Midland interest. *Illustrations:* colour, b&w. Special rates for special matter.

**Sunday Mirror** (1915), Eve Pollard, 33 Holborn, London EC1P 1DQ  *tel* 01-353 0246.
35p. W. Concentrates on human interest news features, social documentaries, dramatic news and feature photographs. Ideas, as well as articles, bought. *Payment:* high, especially for exclusives.

**Sunday Post** (D. C. Thomson & Co. Ltd.), 144 Port Dundas Road, Glasgow G4 0HZ, Courier Place, Dundee DD1 9QJ, and 185 Fleet Street, London EC4A 2HS  *tel* (Glasgow) 041-332 9933; (Dundee) (0382) 23131; (London) 01-404 0199.
32p. W. Human interest, topical, domestic, and humorous articles and exclusive news; and short stories up to 2000 words. *Illustrations:* humorous drawings. *Payment:* on acceptance.

**Sunday Sport** (1986), Drew Robertson, 3rd Floor, Marten House, 39-47 East Road, London N1 6AH  *tel* 01-251 2544  *telex* 269277 Ssport  *fax* 01-608 1979.
35p. W. Also **Friday Sport** (1989), 25p. W.

**The Sunday Sun** (1919), Jim Buglass, Thomson House, Groat Market, Newcastle NE1 1ED  *tel* 091-2327500.
30p. W. Immediate topicality and human sidelights on current problems are the keynote of the Sun's requirements. Particularly welcomed are special features of family appeal and news stories of special interest to the North of England. Photographs used to illustrate articles. *Length:* 500 to 1200

words. *Payment:* normal lineage rates, or by arrangement. *Illustrations:* photographs and line.

**Sunday Telegraph,** Max Hastings, Peterborough Court at South Quay, 181 Marsh Wall, London E14 9SR   *tel* 01-538 5000.
45p. W.

**The Sunday Times** (1822), Andrew Neil, 1 Pennington Street, London E1 9XW   *tel* 01-782 5640.
60p. W. Special articles by authoritative writers on politics, literature, art, drama, music, finance and science, and topical matters. *Payment:* top rate for exclusive features. *Illustrations:* first-class photographs of topical interest and pictorial merit very welcome; also topical drawings.

**Sunday Times Magazine,** Philip Clarke, 214 Gray's Inn Road, London WC1X 8EZ   *tel* 01-782 7000   *telegraphic address* Sunday Times, London, E1.
Free with paper. W. Articles and pictures. *Payment:* £150 per 1000 words. *Illustrations:* colour photographs; *payment* £150 per page.

**SuperBike,** Tony Middlehurst, Link House Magazines Ltd., Link House, Dingwall Avenue, Croydon CR9 2TA   *tel* 01-686 2599   *telex* 947709 Link-ho G.
£1.20. M. Motorcycle touring stories; drag racing; motorcycle fiction. *Payment:* by arrangement. *Illustrations:* half-tone, colour.

**The Tablet** (1840), John Wilkins, 48 Great Peter Street, London SW1P 2HB   *tel* 01-222 7462   *fax* 01-222 4967.
80p. W. The senior Catholic weekly. Religion, philosophy, politics, society, the arts. Freelance work welcomed. Articles should not exceed 1500 words. *Payment:* by arrangement.

**The Tatler** (1709), Emma Soames, Vogue House, Hanover Square, London W1R 0AD   *tel* 01-499 9080.
£1.80. 10 issues p.a. Smart society magazine favouring sharp articles, profiles, fashion and the arts. *Illustrations:* colour, black and white, but all arranged by the journal.

**Telegraph Weekend Magazine** (1964), Nigel Horne, Peterborough Court at South Quay, 181 Marsh Wall, London E14 9SR   *tel* 01-538 5000   *telegraphic address* Teleweek London.
Free with Sat. paper. W. Short profiles (about 1600 words), articles of topical interest. *Payment:* by arrangement. *Illustrations:* all types. *Payment for illustrations:* by arrangement, dependent on the feature requirements. *Preliminary study of the magazine essential.*

**Television** (1950), IPC Magazines Ltd., King's Reach Tower, Stamford Street, London SE1 9LS   *tel* 01-261 5752.
£1.50. M. Articles on the technical aspects of domestic tv and video equipment, especially servicing; long-distance television; constructional projects; satellite tv; video recording; teletext and viewdata; test equipment. *Payment:* by arrangement. *Illustrations:* photographs and line drawings for litho.

**Tempo,** Calum MacDonald, Boosey & Hawkes, Music Publishers, Ltd., 295 Regent Street, London W1R 8JH   *tel* 01-580 2060.
£1.50. Q. (£7.50 p.a.). Authoritative articles about 2000 to 4000 words on contemporary music. *Payment:* by arrangement. *Illustrations:* music type, occasional photographic or musical supplements.

**Tennis** (1979), Charles Elder, Sunseeker House, West Quay Road, Poole, Dorset BH15 1JF   *tel* (0202) 665616   *fax* (0202) 684841.
£1.20. 9 p.a. Articles on any aspect of tennis, preferably player- or coach-oriented. Technical articles also considered. *Payment:* by arrangement. *Illustrations:* half-tone and colour of a superior quality.

**Tennis World,** Alastair McIver, Dennis Fairey Publishing Ltd, Chiltern House, 184 High Street, Berkhamsted, Herts. HP4 3AP   *tel* (0442) 874947   *fax* (0442) 863152.
£1.40. 10 times p.a. Tournament reports, topical features, personality profiles, instructional articles. *Length:* 600 to 1500 words. *Payment:* by arrangement. *Illustrations:* colour, black and white, line.

**Theology** (1920), Peter Coleman, Diocesan House, Palace Gate, Exeter EX1 1HX   *tel* (0392) 73509.
£1.75. Bi-M. Articles and reviews on theology, ethics, Church and Society. *Length:* up to 3500 words. *Payment:* by arrangement.

**Third Way** (1977), Tim Dean, 2 Chester House, Pages Lane, London N10 1PR   *tel* 01-883 0372.
£1.50. 12 issues p.a. Aims to present a biblical perspective on a wide range of current issues, e.g. sociology, politics, education, economics, industry and the arts. *Payment:* for articles: on publication.

**This Caring Business** (1985), Michael J. Monk, 7 Harlequin Gardens, St. Leonards-on-Sea, East Sussex TN37 7PF   *tel* (0424) 751366.
£18.00 p.a. M. Specialist contributions relating to the commercial aspects of health and residential care, including hospitals. *Payment:* £75 per 1000 words. *Illustrations:* half-tone, line.

**This England** (1968), Roy Faiers, P.O. Box 52, Cheltenham, Gloucestershire GL50 1HT   *tel* (0242) 577775.
£2.35. Q. Articles on towns, villages, traditions, customs, legends, crafts of England; stories of people. *Length:* 250 to 2000 words. *Payment:* £20 per page and pro rata. *Illustrations:* line, half-tone, colour.

**Tick-Tock,** D. C. Thomson & Co. Ltd, Albert Square, Dundee DD1 9QJ   *tel* (0382) 23131, and 185 Fleet Street, London EC4A 2HS.
£1.45. Bi-M. Picture stories, comic strips and 'early learning' features, specially for young children. Promising writers and artists encouraged. *Payment:* on acceptance. *Illustrations:* drawings in line or colour for litho.

**Time Out 20/20** (1989), Don Atyeo, Tower House, Southampton Street, London WC2E 7HD   *tel* 01-836 4411   *fax* 01-836 7118.
£1.50. M. Reports and reviews on arts and entertainment. *Length:* 800-6000 words. *Payment:* £140 per 1000 words. *Illustrations:* colour and b&w transparencies and photographs; *payment:* approx. £100.00.

**The Times** (1785), Charles Wilson, 1 Pennington Street, London E1 9XN   *tel* 01-782 5000   *telex* 262141.
30p. D. Independent. Outside contributions considered from (1) experts in subjects of current interest: (2) writers who can make first-hand experience or reflection come readably alive. *Length:* best up to 1200 words. *No preliminary letter* is required.

**The Times Educational Supplement,** Priory House, St. John's Lane, London EC1M 4BX   *tel* 01-253 3000   *telex* 244460 TTSupp   *fax* 01-608 1599.

65p. W. Articles on education written with special knowledge or experience. News items. Books, arts and equipment reviews. *Illustrations:* suitable photographs and drawings of educational interest.

**Times Educational Supplement Scotland** (1965), Willis Pickard, 37 George Street, Edinburgh EH2 2HN *tel* 031-220 1100 *fax* 031-220 1616.
65p. W. Articles on education, preferably 1100 words, written with special knowledge or experience. News items about Scottish educational affairs. *Illustrations:* line and half-tone.

**Times Higher Education Supplement** (1971), Peter Scott, Priory House, St. John's Lane, London EC1M 4BX *tel* 01-253 3000 *telex* 24460 *fax* 01-608 1599.
75p. W. Articles on higher education written with special knowledge or experience or articles dealing with academic topics. News items. *Illustrations:* suitable photographs and drawings of educational interest.

**The Times Literary Supplement,** Jeremy Treglown, Priory House, St. John's Lane, London EC1M 4BX *tel* 01-253 3000 *telex* 24460 TTSupp *fax* 01-608 1599.
£1.10. W. Will consider poems for publication, literary discoveries and articles, particularly of an opinionated kind, on literary and cultural affairs.

**Titbits** (1881), Leonard Holdsworth, Caversham Communications, 2 Caversham Street, London SW3 4AH *tel* 01-351 4995.
60p. M. Human interest articles; also show business, pop stars and medical. No fiction. *Payment:* £8 per 100 words. *Illustrations:* colour transparencies and photos, cartoons; *payment:* (colour only) cartoons £15, all others at magazine rates.

**Today** (1986), David Montgomery, 70 Vauxhall Bridge Road, London SW1V 2RP *tel* 01-630 1300 *telex* 919925 *fax* 01-630 6839 Group 2/3.
22p. D. Feature and news-type articles. *Length:* 300 to 3000 words. *Payment:* by arrangement. *Illustrations:* line, half-tone, colour.

**Today Magazine** (1955), John Oakes, 37 Elm Road, New Malden, Surrey KT3 3HB *tel* 01-942 9761 *fax* 01-949 2313.
£1.00. M. Aimed at everyone with leadership responsibility at any level in their local church. Major features designed to present a non-party view of biblical Christianity and to provide practical help for leaders. Emphasis on issues and current affairs as well as news and down-to-earth advice.

**Today's Golfer** (1988), W. M. C. Robertson, EMAP Pursuit Publishing Ltd., Bretton Court, Bretton, Peterborough PE3 8DZ *tel* (0733) 264666 *fax* (0733) 265515.
£1.50. M. Features and articles on golf. *Payment:* £100 per 1000 words. *Illustrations:* line, photographs, colour.

**Today's Guide,** Official Monthly of the Girl Guides Association, Diana Wallace, 17-19 Buckingham Palace Road, London SW1W 0PT *tel* 01-834 6242.
50p. M. Articles of interest to Guides (aged 10-15) and general interest topics. Serials and short stories with Guiding background (800 words per instalments). Cartoons. *Payment:* £26.60 per 1000 words. *Illustrations:* line, and half-tone.

**Together** (1956), Church House Publishing, Church House, Great Smith Street, London SW1P 3NZ *tel* 01-222 9011. Editor: Mrs. Pamela Egan, The National Society, Church House, Great Smith Street, London SW1P 3NZ.

60p. 9 issues p.a. Short, practical or topical articles dealing with all forms of children's Christian education or concerned with the development and psychology of children. *Illustrations:* half-tone and line. *Length:* up to 1200 words. *Payment:* by arrangement.

**The Topper** (D. C. Thomson & Co. Ltd.), Courier Place, Dundee DD1 9QJ, and 185 Fleet Street, London EC4A 2HS.
26p. W. All-picture paper for children. Comic strip series, in sets of 6-20 pictures each. Special encouragement to promising artists. *Payment:* on acceptance.

**Town and Country Planning** (Journal of the Town and Country Planning Association), 17 Carlton House Terrace, London SW1Y 5AS *tel* 01-930 8903-5.
£40.50. M. Informative articles on town and country planning, regional planning, land use, new towns, green belts, countryside preservation, industrial, business and social life in great and small towns, environment in general and community development. *Length:* 1000 words. *Payment:* none. *Illustrations:* photographs and drawings.

**Toy Trader** (1908), Jon Salisbury, Turret-Group plc, 177 Hagden Lane, Watford, Herts. WD1 8LN *tel* (0923) 228577 *telex* 9419706 *fax* (0923) 221346.
£34.00 p.a. M. A trade journal specialising in anything to do with games and toys circulating to manufacturers and retailers. *Length:* by negotiation. *Payment:* by negotiation.

**Transport** (1980), David Robinson, Chartered Institute of Transport, 80 Portland Place, London W1N 4DP *tel* 01-636 9952 *fax* 01-637 0511.
Free to Institute members; subscription rate on application. 10 p.a. Articles on all types/aspects of transport. *Length:* 1000-2000 words. *Payment:* £100 per 1000 words. *Illustrations:* b&w photos, line drawings, cartoons.

**Traveller** (1970), Wexas Ltd., 45 Brompton Road, London SW3 1DE *tel* 01-581 4130 *telegraphic address* Wexas London SW3 *telex* 297155 Wexas G *fax* 01-589 8418.
£25.56 p.a. 3 p.a. Features on independent travel of all kinds but specialising in long-haul and off beat destinations with first class photographs. Articles giving useful tips on particular aspects of travel, country and city reports providing an insight and factual information of use to other travellers. Articles not strictly on travel but of related interest also welcomed. *Length:* 1000 to 2000 words. *Payment:* rates and leaflet giving full details of requirements available; s.a.e. required. *Illustrations:* line, half-tone, colour; maps.

**Treasure Hunting** (1977), Rita Smith, Sovereign House, Brentwood, Essex CM14 4SE *tel* (0277) 219876.
£1.60. M. Stories of interesting finds. Articles on all aspects of treasure hunting with or without a detector. *Payment:* £15.00 per 1000 words. *Illustrations:* half-tone, colour.

**The Trefoil,** Myra Street, Official Journal of the Trefoil Guild, C.H.Q., The Girl Guides Association, 17-19 Buckingham Palace Road, London SW1W 0PT *tel* 01-828 7610.
Q. Articles on the activities of The Guild and of Guiding in the UK and overseas and on the work of voluntary organisations. *Length:* not more than 1400 words. Photographs. No fiction. *Payment:* by arrangement.

**Tribune,** Editor: Phil Kelly; Reviews Editor: Paul Anderson, 308 Gray's Inn Road, London WC1X 8DY *tel* 01-278 0911.

50p. W. Political, literary, with Socialist outlook. Informative articles (about 800 words), news stories (250-300 words), some poetry. No unsolicited reviews or fiction. *Payment:* by arrangement. *Illustrations:* cartoons and photographs.

**Trout and Salmon** (1955), Sandy Leventon, EMAP Pursuit Publishing Ltd, Bretton Court, Bretton Centre, Peterborough PE3 8DZ *tel* (0733) 264666 *telex* 32157 *fax* (0733) 265515.
£1.50. M. Articles of good quality with strong trout or salmon angling interest. *Length:* 400 to 2000 words, accompanied if possible by photographs. *Payment:* by arrangement. *Illustrations:* line, half-tone, colour transparencies.

**True Romances,** Managing Editor: Veronica Dunn, Argus Consumer Publications, 12-18 Paul Street, London EC2A 4JS *tel* 01-247 8233.
80p. M. First-person stories with strong love interest. Aimed at young, lively reader, 16-19, first love, boyfriends, at college, first job. *Length:* 1500 to 5000 words. *Payment:* by arrangement, on acceptance.

**True Story,** Managing Editor: Veronica Dunn, Argus Consumer Publications, 12-18 Paul Street, London EC2A 4JS *tel* 01-247 8233.
80p. M. First-person stories with strong love interest. Traditional attitudes, young couples, 20-24, living together, early marriage, problems, etc. *Length:* 1500 to 5000 words. *Payment:* by arrangement, on acceptance.

**TV Guide** (1989), Ian Birch, 214 Gray's Inn Road, London WC1X 8EZ *tel* 01-782 7000 *fax* 01-782 7887.
40p. W. News, views and previews on TV programmes and personalities. No unsolicited articles or illustrations accepted. *Payment:* fee, by arrangement, for commissioned work.

**TV Times,** Richard Barber, 247 Tottenham Court Road, London W1P 0AU *tel* 01-323 3222 *fax* 01-580 3986.
40p. W. Features with an affinity to ITV and Channel Four programmes and personalities and television generally. *Length:* from 500 words or by arrangement. *Photographs:* only those of outstanding quality. *Payment:* by arrangement.

**Twinkle** (D. C. Thomson & Co. Ltd.), Albert Square, Dundee DD1 9QJ, and 185 Fleet Street, London EC4A 2HS.
28p. W. Picture stories, features and comic strips, specially for little girls. Drawings in line or colour for gravure. *Payment:* on acceptance. Special encouragement to promising writers and artists.

**The Unesco Courier** (1948), Adel Rifaat, Unesco, P.O.Box 5738, 7 Place de Fontenoy, Paris 75700 *tel* 45 68 47 13 *telegraphic address* Unesco, Paris.
£5.25 p.a. Monthly in 33 language editions. Illustrated feature articles in the fields of science, culture, education and communication; promotion of international understanding; human rights; first-hand accounts of ways of life in other lands. *Length:* 2000 words. *Illustrations:* colour and black-and-white photographs, drawings, graphs, maps.

**The Universe** (1860), Tom Murphy, 33-39 Bowling Green Lane, London EC1R 0AB *tel* 01-278 7321 *fax* 01-278 7320 *telegraphic address* Unicredo London.
35p. W. A newspaper and review for Catholics. News stories, features and photographs on all aspects of Catholic life required. MSS should not be submitted without *sae. Payment:* by arrangement.

**The Use of English,** Roger Knight, School of Education, 21 University Road, Leicester LE1 7HF *Publishers:* Scottish Academic Press Ltd., 33 Montgomery Street, Edinburgh EH7 5JX    *tel* 031-556-2796.
3 issues p.a. (£11.75 p.a. institutions; £8.50 p.a. individuals). For teachers in all fields of English in Great Britain and overseas. *Length:* usually up to 3500 words. *Payment:* none.

**The Vegan** (1946), Barry Kew, The Vegan Society, 33-35 George Street, Oxford OX1 2AY    *tel* (0865) 722166.
75p. Q. Articles on animal rights, nutrition, cookery, agriculture, Third World, health. *Length:* approx. 1500 words. *Payment:* by arrangement. *Illustrations:* photographs, cartoons, line drawings—foods, animals, livestock sysems, crops, people, events. Colour for cover.

**The Vegetarian,** Bronwen Humphreys, Parkdale, Dunham Road, Altrincham, Cheshire WA14 4QG    *tel* 061-928 0793.
£1.00. Bi-M. Articles on animal welfare, nutrition, world food problems, vegetarian and alternative lifestyles. Interviews with vegetarian celebrities. *Payment:* by arrangement. *Illustrations:* photographs and line drawings of foods, crops, relevant events, nature studies; colour for cover.

**Verse** (1984), Robert Crawford, David Kinloch, Henry Hart, Department of English, University of St. Andrews, St. Andrews, Fife KY16 9AL    *tel* (0334) 76161 ext. 471.
£1.50. 3 p.a. Poems in English, Scots, or translation; critical pieces on contemporary poetry.

**Victor** (D. C. Thomson & Co. Ltd.), Courier Place, Dundee DD1 9QJ, and 185 Fleet Street, London EC4A 2HS.
26p. W. Vigorous, well-drawn stories in pictures (line drawings) for boys and young men. War, adventure, sport. Instalments 2, 3, or 4 pages; 8 to 9 frames per page. *Payment:* on acceptance.

**Video Week** (1983), Steve Hurst, United Magazines, Greater London House, Hampstead Road, London NW1 7QZ    *tel* 01-387 6611    *telex* 299485 Music G.
£1.95. (Controlled circulation.) W. News and features on all aspects of producing, manufacturing, marketing and retailing video software programmes; also cable and satellite TV, video games and computer software. *Payment:* NUJ rates.

**Vogue,** Elizabeth Tilberis, Vogue House, Hanover Square, London W1R 0AD    *tel* 01-499 9080    *telex* 27338 Volon G.
£2.00. M. Fashion, beauty, health, decorating, art, theatre, films, literature, music, travel, food and wine. Articles from 1000 words.

**The Voice** (1982), Steve Pope, 370 Coldharbour Lane, London SW9 8PL    *tel* 01-737 7377    *fax* 01-274 8994.
38p. W. News stories, general and arts features of interest to black readers. *Payment:* £80 per 1000 words. *Illustrations:* colour and b&w photos, cartoons; *payment:* £20-£35.

**Voice of the Arab World Intelligence Report** (1972), Claud Morris, 15A Lowndes Street, London SW1X 9EY    *tel* 01-235 5966.
£12.00. Q. (£40.00 p.a.). M. Background intelligence reports on the Press, media, Parliament with specific reference to Middle East. *Length:* 500 to 1500 words. *Payment:* £150 per 1000 words. *Illustrations:* none. Write for specimen copy.

**Wales on Sunday** (1989), John Humphries, Thomson House, Cardiff CF1 1WR *tel* (0222) 223333 *fax* (0222) 342462. London Office: Pemberton House, East Harding Street, London EC4A 3AS *tel* 01-353 9131.
50p. Sunday. Independent. General interest articles suitable for use in a national Sunday newspaper which offers comprehensive news, features, arts and entertainments coverage at a weekend, plus a particular focus on events from Wales.

**War Cry** (1879), Published by The Salvation Army. Major Robert Street, 101 Queen Victoria Street, London EC4P 4EP *tel* 01-236 5222 *fax* 01-236 3491.
15p. W. (£18.25 p.a. UK). Voluntary contributions, mostly by Salvationists. Puzzles. *Illustrations:* line and photographs.

**Warwickshire and Worcestershire Life** (including **West Midlands**), D. J. N. Green, 27 Waterloo Place, Leamington Spa, Warwickshire CV32 5LF *tel* (0926) 422003 and 422372 *fax* (0926) 334050. A member of the Town & County Magazines Group.
90p. M. Articles of interest in the counties concerned based on first-hand experience dealing with work, customs and matters affecting urban and rural life. *Length:* 500 to 1500 words. *Payment:* by arrangement. Photographs also by arrangement. *Illustrations:* preference given to articles accompanied by good photographs relating to subject.

**Waterways World** (1972), Hugh Potter, Waterway Productions Ltd., Kottingham House, Dale Street, Burton-on-Trent, Staffordshire DE14 3TD *tel* (0283) 64290 and 42721.
£1.40. M. Feature articles on all aspects of inland waterways in Britain and abroad, including historical material. Factual and technical articles preferred. No short stories or poetry. *Payment:* by arrangement. *Illustrations:* black and white photographs, colour, line.

**Weekend,** Grant Lockhart, New Carmelite House, London EC4Y 0JA *tel* 01-353 6000.
40p. W. Factual articles appealing to men and women, true-life dramas, human interest, show business (500 to 1000 words). *Payment:* by arrangement. *Illustrations:* mono and colour photographs, cartoons.

**Weekend Guardian,** supplement of Saturday edition of The Guardian, Alan Rusbridger, 119 Farringdon Road, London EC1R 3ER *tel* 01-278 2332 *telex* 8811746/7/8 Guardn G; 164 Deansgate, Manchester M60 2RR *tel* 061-832 7200.
Free with paper. W. Features on books, book trade, 'domestic' subjects, 'new age' (alternative health, etc.), travel and leisure pursuits; also good reportage on social or political subjects. *Payment:* £120 per 1000 words. *Illustrations:* half-tone and line; *payment:* apply for rates.

**The Weekly News** (D. C. Thomson & Co. Ltd.), Courier Place, Dundee DD1 9QJ *tel* (0382) 23131; 139 Chapel Street, Manchester M3 6AA *tel* 061-834 2831-7; 144 Port Dundas Road, Glasgow G4 0HZ *tel* 041-332 9933; and 185 Fleet Street, London EC4A 2HS *tel* 01-242 5086.
26p. W. Real-life dramas of around 2000 words told in the first person. Non-fiction series with lively themes or about interesting people. Keynote throughout is strong human interest. Joke sketches. *Payment:* on acceptance.

**WES Journal** formerly **PNEU Journal** (1890), Hugh Boulter, M.A., World-wide Education Service, Strode House, 44-50 Osnaburgh Street, London NW1 3NN	*tel* 01-387 9228	*telex* 263250 Telex G (PNE 118).
£7.50 p.a. 3 times p.a. Journal of the World-wide Education Service. Articles on education, psychology, teaching methods and children's activities within the age-range 3-14. Feature articles preferably related to children or parents whose children have been taught with the help of WES. *Length:* 1000-2000 words. *Payment:* by arrangement.

**West Africa,** Ad'Obe Obe, 43-45 Coldharbour Lane, London SE5 9AR	*tel* 01-737 2946	*telex* 892420 West Af G	*fax* 01-978 8334.
£1.00. W. A weekly summary of West African news, with articles on political, economic and commercial matters, and on all matters of general interest affecting West Africa. Also book reviews. Covers Ghana, Nigeria, Sierra Leone, The Gambia, French-speaking African States, former Portuguese West Africa, Liberia and Zaire. Articles about 1200 words. *Payment:* as arranged. *Illustrations:* half-tone.

**Western Mail** (1869), John Humphries, Thomson House, Cardiff CF1 1WR	*tel* (0222) 223333. London Office: Pemberton House, East Harding Street, London EC4A 3AS	*tel* 01-353 9131.
22p. D. Independent. Articles of political, industrial, literary or general and Welsh interest are considered. *Payment:* according to value. Special fees for exclusive news. Topical general news and feature pictures.

**The Western Morning News** (1860), Colin Davison, 65 New George Street, Plymouth PL1 1RE	*tel* (0752) 266626.
20p. D. Articles of 600 to 900 words, plus illustrations, considered on West Country subjects.

**Which Computer** (1977), Clive Couldwell, 67 Clerkenwell Road, London EC1R 5BH	*tel* 01-430 1200.
£1.75. M. Will consider proposals for equipment reviews and general features about business computing. *Payment:* £115 per 1000 words. *Illustrations:* line, half-tone, colour. *Preliminary letter essential.*

**Wisden Cricket Monthly** (1979), David Frith, 6 Beech Lane, Guildford, Surrey GU2 5ES	*tel* (0483) 32573.
£1.30. M. Cricket articles of general interest. *Length:* 1000 maximum. *Payment:* by arrangement. *Illustrations:* half-tone, colour.

**(Wolverhampton) Express and Star** (1874), Keith Parker, Queen Street, Wolverhampton WV1 3BU	*tel* (0902) 313131. London: Chronicle House, 72-78 Fleet Street, London EC4Y 1HY.
20p. D. Open to consider topical contributions up to 750 words with or without illustrations. *Payment:* by arrangement.

**Woman** (1937), David Durman, IPC Magazines Ltd, King's Reach Tower, Stamford Street, London SE1 9LS	*tel* 01-261 5000.
37p. W. Practical articles of varying length on all subjects of interest to women. No unsolicited fiction. *Payment:* by arrangement. *Illustrations:* colour transparencies, photographs, sketches.

**Woman and Home** (1926), Sue Dobson, IPC Magazines Ltd, King's Reach Tower, Stamford Street, London SE1 9LS	*tel* 01-261 5423.
85p. M. Centres on the personal and home interests of the lively-minded woman with or without career and family. Articles dealing with leisure pursuits, crafts, gardening, dressmaking and fashion, needlework and knitting. Things to make and buy for the home. Features on people and places.

Fiction: serial stories 3 to 6 instalments, and complete stories from 2000 to 7000 words in *length*, some romantic interest. *Illustrations:* photographs and sketches for full-colour and mono reproduction.

**The Woman Journalist,** Organ of the Society of Women Writers and Journalists (1894), Jocelyn Glegg, 300 Hills Road, Cambridge CB2 2QG.
Free to members. 3 p.a. Short articles of interest to professional writers. *Payment:* none.

**Woman's Journal** (1927), Deirdre Vine, IPC Magazines Ltd, King's Reach Tower, Stamford Street, London SE1 9LS *tel* 01-261 6622 *fax* 01-261 7061.
£1.10. M. A magazine devoted to the looks and lives of intelligent women. Contents include short stories of literary merit (3000 words maximum); interviews and articles (1000-2500 words) dealing in depth with topical subjects and personalities; fashion, beauty and health, food and design. *Illustrations:* full colour, line and wash, first-rate photographs.

**Woman's Own,** Bridget Rowe, IPC Magazines Ltd, King's Reach Tower, Stamford Street, London SE1 9LS *tel* 01-261 5474.
37p. W. Appealing to modern women of all ages, all classes, predominantly in the 20-35 age group. No unsolicited fiction accepted except for annual short story competition. Good, original feature ideas welcome from show business to human interest and sociological issues. *Illustrations:* in full colour and mono. Original knitting, crochet, craft designs, interior decorating and furnishing ideas, fashion. Please address work to relevant department editor.

**Woman's Realm** (1958), Ann Wallace, IPC Magazines Ltd, King's Reach Tower, Stamford Street, London SE1 9LS *tel* 01-261 6033.
33p. W. Lively general interest weekly magazine specialising in service to women with growing families. Articles on personalities, topical subjects, cookery, fashion, beauty, home. Short stories of 1000 to 4000 words; serials of 20,000-60,000 words. *Payment:* by arrangement. *Illustrations:* four-colour and two-colour drawings; photographs in colour and monotone.

**Woman's Story Magazine** (1956), Managing Editor: Veronica Dunn, 12-18 Paul Street, London EC2A 4JS *tel* 01-247 8233.
85p. M. Short stories with realistic characterisation and strong romantic woman-interest plot. *Length:* 1000-3000 words. *Payment:* by arrangement, on acceptance.

**Woman's Weekly** (1911), Judith Hall, IPC Magazines Ltd, King's Reach Tower, Stamford Street, London SE1 9LS *tel* 01-261 6131 *fax* 01-261 6322.
34p. W. A lively, family-interest magazine. Two serials, averaging 6000 words each instalment of strong romantic interest, and one short story of 2000 to 4000 words of general interest. Personality features with photographs. Important biographies, and memoirs of celebrities. *Payment:* by arrangement. *Illustrations:* full colour and mono fiction illustrations, small sketches and photographs.

**Woman's World** (1977), Kerry MacKenzie, IPC Magazines Ltd, King's Reach Tower, Stamford Street, London SE1 9LS *tel* 01-261 5000 *fax* 01-261 6772.
85p. M. A wide-ranging magazine for women, covering all aspects of a woman's world and her interests today. Celebrity interviews, offbeat anecdotal features, light-hearted human interest stories using case histories,

cartoons, humorous and thought-provoking articles on man-woman and family relationships; fashion, beauty, cookery, home, competitions; short stories. *Illustrations:* full colour, line and wash, photographs.

**Woodworker,** John Hemsley, Argus Specialist Publications, Argus House, Boundary Way, Hemel Hempstead HP2 7ST *tel* (0442) 66551 *telex* 827797 *fax* (0442) 66998.
£1.40. M. For the craft and professional woodworker. Practical illustrated articles on cabinet work, carpentry, wood polishing, wood turning, wood carving, rural crafts, craft history, antique and period furniture; also wooden toys and models; timber procurement, conditioning, seasoning; tool, machinery and equipment reviews. *Payment:* by arrangement. *Illustrations:* line drawings and photographs.

**Work Study,** Keith Hammond (Sawell Publications, Ltd.), 127 Stanstead Road, London SE23 1JE *tel* 01-699 6792 *telegraphic address* Sawells, London.
£2.40 including postage. M. (£15.00 p.a. post £6.00). Authoritative articles about all aspects of Work Study, i.e. Motion and Time study, methods, engineering, process control, scientific management, incentive schemes and business efficiency. *Length:* 1000 to 2000 words. *Payment:* by arrangement. *Illustrations:* half-tone and line.

**Workbox** (1984), Audrey Babington, 40 Silver Street, Wiveliscombe, Nr Taunton, Somerset TA4 2NY *tel* (0984) 24033.
£1.25. Mar, June and Sept. Features, of any length, on all aspects of needle-crafts. *Payment:* by agreement. *Illustrations:* good b&w photos and colour transparencies; also line drawings; *payment:* by agreement. Send *sae* with enquiries and submissions.

**World Bowls** (1954), *Publisher:* G. K. Browne, P.O. Box 17, East Horsley, Surrey KT24 5JU *tel* (0372) 59319.
£1.00. M. Unusual features, fiction and news about all codes of bowling. *Payment:* by arrangement. *Illustrations:* half-tone, colour.

**World Development,** Pergamon Press plc, Headington Hill Hall, Oxford OX3 0BW *tel* (0865) 64881.
DM850 p.a. M. The multi-disciplinary international journal devoted to the study and promotion of world development.

**World Fishing** (1952), Nortide Ltd., Nortide House, Stone Street, Faversham, Kent ME13 8PG *tel* (0795) 536536 *telex* 965770 Wfmag *fax* (0795) 530244.
£29 p.a. M. The International Journal of commercial fishing. Technical and management emphasis on catching, processing, farming and marketing of fish and related products. Fishery operations and vessels covered world wide. *Length:* 1000 to 2000 words. *Payment:* by arrangement. *Illustrations:* Photographs and diagrams for litho reproduction.

**World Magazine** (incorporating **Environment Now**) (1987), Mark Ausenda, Hyde Park Publications, 27 Kensington Court, London W8 5DN *tel* 01-937 3535 *telex* 8953616 G *fax* 01-937 21262.
£1.80. M. People, places, wildlife and the environment. *Length:* 1500 to 2000 words. *Payment:* £70 per published page including pictures. *Illustrations:* colour slides—advise use of either Kodachrome 25 or 64, or Fuji 50; prefer 35 mm.

**World Outlook,** The Baptist Men's Movement. Editor: M. E. Putnam, 61 Hempstead Lane, Potten End, Berkhamsted, Herts. HP4 2RZ   *tel* (0442) 865245.
£2.50 p.a. Q. Articles on Christian ethics and world questions. *Length:* 1000 to 1200 words. *Illustrated.*

**The World Today** (1945), Christopher Cviic, The Royal Institute of International Affairs, Chatham House, 10 St. James's Square, London SW1Y 4LE   *tel* 01-930 2233   *fax* 01-839 3593.
£1.80. M. Objective and factual articles on current questions of international affairs. *Length:* about 3500 words. *Payment:* £25 each article.

**World War Investigator** (1988), Derek Bingham, 194 Muswell Hill Broadway, London N10 3SA   *tel* 01-883 3252.
£1.65. M. Factual articles on World War II. *Length:* 600 to 3000 words. *Payment:* by arrangement. *Illustrations:* half-tone, colour.

**The World's Children** (1920), the magazine of The Save the Children Fund, Sharon Welch (Editorial Director), Mary Datchelor House, 17 Grove Lane, London SE5 8RD   *tel* 01-703 5400.
£5.00 p.a. Q. Articles on child welfare topics related to Save the Children's areas of interest. *Length:* 500 words. *Payment:* by arrangement. Photographs for cover and article illustration.

**Writers' Monthly** (1984), Joanne Mallabar, 18-20 High Road, Wood Green, London N22 6DN   *tel* 01-888 1242.
£2.50 (£29.50 p.a.). M. Articles and features of interest to the freelance writer. *Payment:* £35 per 1000 words. *Illustrations:* black and white.

**Writing** (1959), Barbara Horsfall, 87 Brookhouse Road, Farnborough, Hants GU14 0BU. Designed to inform and entertain.
£1.70. 3 p.a. (£4.50 p.a. UK; $6.00 per issue overseas, inc. postage). Articles and short stories, approx. 300–1000 words. Verse up to 30 lines. All aspects of 'How to' articles by experienced writers considered. Content of interest to freelance writers, poets, creative writing groups, with special rates and encouragement for the latter. Regular book reviews. *Sae* essential for enquiries and submissions. *Payment:* small, except abroad—copies of magazine sent in lieu, when MSS published.

**Writing Women** (1981), Jo Alberti, Gillian Allnutt, Linda Anderson, Cynthia Fuller, Margaret Wilkinson, 7 Cavendish Place, Newcastle upon Tyne NE2 2NE.
£2.00. 3 p.a. Poems, short stories, critical articles. *Payment:* £10.00 per poem or per 1000 words.

**Y Faner** (Banner and Times of Wales), (1843), Hafina Clwyd, County Press, Bala, Gwynedd LL23 7PG   *tel* (0678) 520262.
75p. W. National weekly news review in Welsh; articles of economic, literary and political interest. Non-party. *Length:* 1000 words. *Payment:* minimum £7 per article. *Illustrations:* line and photographs.

**Yachting Monthly** (1906), Andrew Bray, Room 2209, King's Reach Tower, Stamford Street, London SE1 9LS   *tel* 01-261 6040.
£1.65. M. Technical articles, up to 2250 words, on all aspects of seamanship, navigation, the handling of sailing craft, and their design, construction and equipment. Well-written narrative accounts, up to 3000 words, of cruises in yachts. *Payment:* quoted on acceptance. *Illustrations:* black-and-white, colour transparencies, line or wash drawings.

**Yachting World** (1894), Dick Johnson, Prospect Magazines, Reed Business Publishing, Quadrant House, The Quadrant, Sutton, Surrey SM2 5AS   *tel* 01-661 3864.
£1.80. M. Practical articles of an original nature, dealing with sailing and boats, 1500 to 2000 words. *Payment:* varies. *Illustrations:* black and white prints and colour transparencies, or drawings.

**Yachts and Yachting** (1947), Peter Cook, 196 Eastern Esplanade, Southend-on-Sea, Essex SS1 3AB   *tel* (0702) 582245.
£1.25. F. Short articles which should be technically correct. *Payment:* by arrangement. *Illustrations:* line and half-tone; occasional colour.

**Yorkshire Evening Press** (1882), Richard Wooldridge (York and County Press), 76–78 Walmgate, York YO1 2TL   *tel* (0904) 653051. London Office: Newspaper House, 8-16 Great New Street, EC4   *tel* 01-353 1030.
20p. Articles of Yorkshire or general interest, humour, personal experience of current affairs. *Length:* 500-1500 words. *Payment:* by arrangement. *Illustrations:* half-tone and line.

**Yorkshire Gazette and Herald Series,** P. A. Austin-Clarke, 76–78 Walmgate, York YO1 2TL   *tel* (0904) 653051   *fax* (0904) 611488.
16p. W. Stories and pictures of local interest. *Payment:* varies. *Illustrations:* colour, half-tone and line.

**Yorkshire Life** (1947), Patrick O'Neill, P.O. Box 362, 51 Burley Road, Leeds LS3 1LR   *tel* (0532) 426644   *fax* (0532) 425412. A publication of Zabaxe Ltd.
90p. M. Topics of Yorkshire interest, with or without photographs. Humour and topical subjects treated from a Yorkshire angle especially required. *Length:* 200-500 words and 800 to 1500 words. *Payment:* varies. *Illustrations:* colour, tone or line.

**Yorkshire Post** (1754), John Edwards, Wellington Street, Leeds LS1 1RF   *tel* 432701. London Office: 23-27 Tudor Street, EC4   *tel* 01-583 9199.
27p. D. Conservative. Authoritative and well-written articles elucidating new topics or on topical subjects of general, literary or industrial interests are preferred. *Length:* 800 words. *Payment:* by arrangement. Contributions to *People*, a column about personalities in the news, are welcomed. *Illustrations:* photographs and frequent pocket cartoons (single column width), topical wherever possible.

**Yorkshire Riding Magazine** (1964), Winston Halstead, Barclays Bank Chambers, Sowerby Bridge, Yorkshire HX6 2DX   *tel* (0422) 839633 and 839643.
70p. Bi-M. Articles exclusively about people, life and character of the three Ridings of Yorkshire. *Length:* up to 1500 words. *Payment:* approx. £25.00 per published page. *Illustrations:* line and half-tone.

**You** (1982), Nicholas Gordon, New Carmelite House, Carmelite Street, London EC4Y 0JA   *tel* 01-353 6000   *telex* 28301 Ldm   *fax* 01-353 2602.
Free with Mail on Sunday. W. Features on all subjects. *Length:* 1000-2500 words. *Payment:* by arrangement. *Illustrations:* line, half-tone, colour photographs, generally commissioned.

**The Young Soldier** (1881), Major Caroline Croly, The Salvation Army's children's newspaper; 101 Queen Victoria Street, London EC4P 4EP   *tel* 01-236 5222, Ext. 2284   *fax* 01-236 3491.
15p. W. Stories, pictures, cartoon strips, puzzles etc., often on Christian themes. *Payment:* usual. *Illustrations:* half-tone, line and two-colour line.

**Your Computer** (1981), John Brissenden, Greencoat House, Francis Street, London SW1P 1DG  *tel* 01-834 1717  *fax* 01-828 0270.
£1.35. M. Articles and news about computers. *Payment:* £75 per printed page. *Illustrations:* line, half-tone, colour.

# Africa

## KENYA

**Daily Nation,** Group Managing Editor: George Mbugguss; Managing Editor: Mwangi Wangethi, P.O. Box 49010, Nairobi  *tel* 337691.
K. Sh. 4.00. D. News, features, etc. Pictures.

**East African Agricultural & Forestry Journal** (1935), J.O. Mugah, P.O. Box 30148, Nairobi  *tel* Karuri 32880.
£18.00 p.a. Q. Papers on agriculture, forestry and applied sciences. *Length:* 100 to 125 pages.

**East African Medical Journal** (1923), E. G. Kasili, M.B., CH.B., M.D., P.O. Box 41632, Nairobi  *tel* 724711, 726073.
£65.00 p.a. M. Medical articles, preferably on tropical medicine, case reports, etc. *Illustrations:* Photographs.

**The Standard,** P.O. Box 30080, Nairobi  *tel* 540280  *telex* 24032 Newstad KE.
K.Sh. 3.00 daily; K.Sh. 3.40 Sunday. D. News and topical articles of East African interest.

**Swara** (1978), The Magazine of the East African Wild Life Society, Shereen Karmali, P.O. Box 20110, Nairobi  *tel* 27047  *telex* 22153 Funga KE  *fax* 254-2-729612.
£15.00 p.a. 6 p.a. Articles on wildlife, conservation and natural beauty of East Africa. *Payment:* by arrangement. *Illustrations:* Photographs, colour and black and white; line drawings occasionally.

## NIGERIA

**Monthly Life** (1984) West African Book Publishers Ltd., Ilupeju Industrial Estate, P.O. Box 3445, Lagos, Nigeria  *tel* 900760-4  *telex* 26144 Presac NG.
UK: Magazine Production Ltd., 13 Southgate Street, Winchester, Hampshire SO23 9DZ  *tel* (0962) 60444  *telegraphic address* Hambleside, Winchester  *telex* 477357.
N.2.00 M. Features, human interest stories, short stories with a West African setting. *Illustrations:* line drawings, cartoons, colour and black & white photographs—West African subjects. *Payment:* by arrangement.

## SUDAN

**Sudanow,** Fath el Rahman Mahgoub, Ministry of Culture and Information, P.O. Box 2651, Khartoum  *tel* 77913  *telex* 22418 and 22419.
£S1.50 M. News stories, business stories, book reviews, travelogues—all about the Sudan. *Payment:* £S30 per column. *Illustrations:* line, half-tone.

## TANZANIA

**The Daily News,** J. M. Mapunda, P.O. Box 9033, Dar es Salaam  *tel* 25318  *telex* 41071.
2½p. D.

**Sunday News,** Box 9033, Dar es Salaam  *tel* 29881.
4p. W.

## UGANDA

**Eastern Africa Journal of Rural Development,** Department of Agricultural Economics, Makerere University, P.O. Box 7062, Kampala.

**The New Vision,** P.O. Box 9815, Kampala  *tel* 235209  *telex* 62072 Vision.
100 shillings. D. News, topical features, news pictures.

**Weekly Topic** (1979), Wafula Oguttu, P.O. Box 1725, Kampala  *tel* 233834/231798/257513  *telex* 62106.
200 shillings. W. Non-sectarian, non-provocative, general interest articles. *Length:* up to 1000 words. *Payment:* 4000 shillings per article. *Illustrations:* b&w photos, line drawings, cartoons; *payment:* 2000 shillings per illustration.

## ZIMBABWE

**The Chronicle** (1894), Geoff Nyarota, P.O. Box 585, Bulawayo  *tel* 65471.
15c. D. (not Sunday). Topical articles.

**The Farmer,** Modern Farming Publications (1928), Myfanwy van Hoffen, Agriculture House, Moffat Street, P.O. Box 1622, Harare  *tel* 708245-6.
$45 p.a. W. Official journal of the Commercial Farmers Union. Articles on all aspects of agriculture. *Payment:* by arrangement. *Illustrations*.

**The Herald** (1891), T. A. G. Sithole, P.O. Box 396, Harare  *tel* 795771  *telegraphic address* Manherald, Harare.
17c. D. Topical articles of news value. *Payment:* varies, depends on length, content and news value. *Illustrations:* bromides, colour.

**Hotel & Catering Gazette,** P.O. Box 66070, Kopje, Harare  *tel* 738-722.
Free. Controlled circ. M. Articles dealing with hotel and catering management. *Payment:* $20.00 per 1000 words.

**Mahogany,** Gill Beach, P.O. Box UA589, Harare  *tel* Harare 705412  *telex* 4748 ZW.
60c. F. Articles concerning events and personalities; standard women's magazine formula. Average *length:* 1500 words. *Payment:* by arrangement. *Illustrations:* line, half-tone, colour.

**The Manica Post,** A. Hamiwe, P.O. Box 960, Mutare  *tel* 61212.
16c. W. Non-fiction articles only. *Length:* up to 500 words. *Payment:* by arrangement. *Illustrations:* half-tone.

**Prize Africa** (1973), Tinos Calfinos Guvi, P.O. Box UA189, Harare  *tel* 705411  *telex* 4748ZW.
41c. M. Political reports, features and biographies, love, crime, thriller short stories. *Payment:* Short story (approx. 2000 words) $30, two-part serial (maximum) $50. *Illustrations:* line, half-tone, colour.

**The Sunday Mail** (1935), S. Mpofu, P.O. Box 396, Harare  *tel* 795771  *telegraphic address* Manherald, Harare.
20c. W. Topical articles of news value. *Payment:* varies, depends on length, content and news value. *Illustrations:* bromides, colour.

**The Sunday News** (1930), Lawrence Chikuwira, P.O. Box 585, Bulawayo  *tel* 65471.
14c. W. Topical articles.

## AUSTRALIA

*Newspapers are listed under the towns in which they are published.*

**(Adelaide) Advertiser** (1858), Piers Akerman, 121 King William Street, Adelaide 5000   *tel* (08) 218-9218   *telex* 82101   *fax* (08) 231 1147. London: 3rd Floor, Allen House, 70 Vauxhall Bridge Road, SW1V 2RP   *tel* 01-834 9405   *fax* 01-828 6090 (news), 01-828 5833 (syndications)   *telex* 267297.
40c., Sat. 70c. D. The only morning daily in S. Australia. Descriptive and news background material, 400-800 words, preferably with pictures.

**(Adelaide) News** (1923), R. G. Holden, The News (South Australia) Pty Ltd., 112 North Terrace, Adelaide   *tel* 231-0351.
25c. D. One feature page open for topical articles. *Length:* preferably 600-750. *Payment:* by arrangement. *Illustrated* articles preferred.

**(Adelaide) Sunday Mail** (1912), K. Sullivan, 121 King William Street, Adelaide 5000   *tel* 218-9218   *fax* 212-6264.

**Australasian Dirt Bike,** Andrew Clubb, P.O. Box 696, Brookvale, Sydney, N.S.W. 2100   *tel* 02-938 4155.
$3.50. M. Tests and reports of off-road bikes and equipment, news and features of interest to off-road enthusiasts. *Payment:* by arrangement.

**Australasian Sporting Shooter,** Ray Galea, Yaffa Publishing Group, 17-21 Bellevue Street, Surry Hills, N.S.W. 2010   *tel* 02-281 2333   *telex* AA 121887.
$2.75. All aspects of game shooting, collecting, antiques, archery (associated with hunting), pistol shooting, clay target shooting, reloading, ballistics and articles of a technical nature. *Payment:* by arrangement.

**The Australian,** Frank Devine, G.P.O. Box 4245, Sydney, N.S.W. 2000   *tel* 288 3000.
50c. Will consider topical articles from freelance writers. *Length:* up to 1500 words. *Payment:* by arrangement.

**Australian Angler's Fishing World,** Ron Calcutt, Yaffa Publishing Group Pty. Ltd., 17-21 Bellevue Street, Surry Hills, N.S.W. 2010   *tel* 281 2333   *telex* AA 121887   *fax* 281 2750.
$3.25. M. All aspects of rock, surf, stream, deep sea and game fishing, with comprehensive sections on gear, equipment and boats. *Payment:* by arrangement.

**Australian Bookseller & Publisher** (1921), John Nieuwenhuizen, D. W. Thorpe, 20-24 Stokes Street, Port Melbourne 3207   *tel* 03-645 1511   *telex* AA 39476   *fax* 03-645 3981. UK agent: J. Whitaker & Sons.

**The Australian Financial Review,** Gerard Noonan, 235-243 Jones Street, Broadway, Sydney 2001. London: 12 Norwich Street, EC4A 1BH   *tel* 01-353-9321. New York: Suite 2401, 1500 Broadway, N.Y. 10036   *tel* 212-398 9494.
90c. D. (except Saturday & Sunday). Investment business and economic news and reviews; government and politics, production, banking, commercial, and Stock Exchange statistics; company analysis. General features in Friday *Weekend Review* supplement.

**Australian Flying,** Lawr Cohen, Yaffa Publishing Group, 17-21 Bellevue Street, Surry Hills, N.S.W. 2010   *tel* 281-2333   *telex* AA 121887   *fax* 281-2750. London: Robert Logan, 64 The Mall, Ealing, W5   *tel* 01-579 4836.
$3.25. 6 times p.a. Appeals to light and medium aircraft owners, as well as those directly and indirectly associated with the aircraft industry. *Payment:* by arrangement.

**Australian Historical Studies,** John Rickard, Monash University, Clayton, Victoria 3168.
$30.00 p.a. Twice yearly. *Length:* 8000 words maximum. *Payment:* none. *Illustrations:* tables and maps.

**The Australian Home Beautiful** (1913), A. Fawcett, 32 Walsh Street, West Melbourne 3003.
M. Deals with home building, interior decoration, furnishing, gardening, cookery, etc. Short articles with accompanying photographs with Australian slant accepted. *Preliminary* letter advisable. *Payment:* higher than Australian average.

**Australian House and Garden** (1948), Publisher: Richard Walsh, 54 Park Street, Sydney, New South Wales 2000.
$3.20. M. Factual articles dealing with interior decorating, home design, gardening, wine, food. *Payment:* by arrangement. *Illustrations:* line, half-tone, colour. Preliminary letter essential.

**The Australian Journal of Politics and History,** J. A. Moses, Department of History, University of Queensland Press, St. Lucia, Queensland 4067   *tel* 377 2265.
$36.00; US $40.00, UK £24.00 p.a. inc. postage. 3 a year. Australian, Commonwealth, Asian, S.W. Pacific, and international articles. Special feature: regular surveys of Australian Foreign Policy and State and Commonwealth politics. *Length:* 8000 words max. *Payment:* none. *Illustrations:* line, only when necessary.

**Australian Mining,** Meng Yap, Thomson Publications Australia, 47 Chippen Street, Chippendale, N.S.W. 2008   *tel* 699-2411. *postal address* P.O. Box 65, Chippendale, N.S.W. 2008.
$48.00 p.a. in Australia.

**Australian Outlook,** Dr. John Ravenhill, Dept. of Government, University of Sydney, N.S.W. 2006   *tel* (02) 692 3090   *telex* AA 74261 Unipur   *fax* (02) 692 4202.
$26.00 p.a. in Australia and New Zealand; $35.00 p.a. in other countries. 3 times p.a. Scholarly articles on international affairs. *Length:* 4000 to 7000 words. *Payment:* none.

**The Australian Quarterly** (1929), Dr. Elaine Thompson, Dr. Hugh Pritchard, Australian Institute of Political Science, 3rd Floor, 149 Castlereagh Street, Sydney, N.S.W. 2000   *tel* 02-264 8923.
$20.00 p.a.; $25.00 overseas. Q. Articles of high standard on politics, law, economics, social issues, etc. *Length:* 3500 words preferred. *Payment:* none.

**The Australian Women's Weekly** (Australian Consolidated Press, Ltd.), 54 Park Street, Sydney, N.S.W. 2000.
$2.50. M. Fiction and features. *Length:* fiction 1000 to 10,000 words. Features 750 to 2500 words plus colour or black-and-white photographs. *Payment:* according to length and merit. *Fiction illustrations:* sketches by own artists and freelances.

**(Brisbane) Courier Mail,** G. Chamberlin, (Queensland Newspapers Pty. Ltd.), Campbell Street, Bowen Hills, Brisbane 4006   *tel* 07-252-6011   *fax* 07-252-6696.
30c. D. Occasional topical special articles required, 1000 words.

**(Brisbane) Sunday Mail,** D. A. Houghton, G.P.O. Box No. 130, Brisbane, Queensland, 4001.

60c. W. Anything of general interest. Up to 1500 words. *Illustrations:* line, photographs, black and white, and colour. *Payment:* by arrangement. Rejected MSS. returned if postage enclosed.

**Catholic Weekly,** R. F. Robinson (Catholic Press Newspaper Co. Pty., Ltd.), Freeman House, 397 Riley Street, Surry Hills 2010, N.S.W    *tel* 2114499    *fax* 02-281 2187.
$1.00. W. Christian newspaper and review magazine of general interest. *Length:* up to 1000 words. *Payment:* standard rates. *Illustrations:* half-tone.

**Cleo** (1972), Lisa Wilkinson, 54 Park Street, Sydney 2000, N.S.W    *tel* 282-8617    *fax* (02) 267-2150.
$2.95. M. Articles up to 3000 words, short quizzes. *Payment:* Articles $200 per 1000 words. *Illustrations:* colour, half-tones.

**The Countryman,** Russell C. Raymond, 219 St. Georges Terrace, Perth 6000    *tel* 482-3301    *telegraphic address* Westralian Perth.
50c. W. Agriculture, farming or country interest features and service columns. *Payment:* standard rates. *Illustrations:* line and half-tone.

**Current Affairs Bulletin** (1942), Dr. Bob Howard, CAB, 72 Bathurst Street, Sydney, N.S.W. 2000    *tel* 264-5726.
$3.00. $35.00 p.a. ($50.00 overseas). M. Authoritative well-documented articles on all national and international affairs: politics, economics, science, the arts, business and social questions. *Length:* 3000-5000 words. *Payment:* by arrangement. *Illustrations:* line, half-tone.

**Dolly** (1970), Caroline Lees, 54 Park Street, Sydney, N.S.W. 2001    *tel* (02) 282 8000    *fax* (02) 267 2150.
$2.40. M. Features on fashion, health and beauty, personalities, social issues and how to cope with growing up, etc. *Length:* not less than 1750 words. *Payment:* by arrangement.

**Electronics Australia** (incorporating **Radio, Television and Hobbies**) (1939), J. Rowe, Box 227, Waterloo, N.S.W. 2017    *tel* (02) 693 6620    *telex* AA 74488    *fax* (02) 693 9997 or 693 9935.
$3.50. M. Articles on technical television and radio, hi-fi, popular electronics, microcomputers and avionics. *Length:* up to 2000 words. *Payment:* by arrangement. *Illustrations:* line, half-tone.

**Geo,** Australasia's Geographical Magazine (1978), Alfredo Roces, 372 Eastern Valley Way, Willoughby, New South Wales 2068    *tel* (02) 406-9222    *fax* (02) 406-6919.
$5.95. Q. ($23.80 p.a.). Non-fiction articles on wild life and natural history. *Length:* 1500 to 3000 words. *Payment:* $400 to $1,200 by arrangement. *Illustrations:* photographs, colour transparencies.

**Herald of the South** (1925), Editorial Board: Andrew Gash, Jennifer Lemon, Keith McDonald (Sec.), Aflatoon Payman, Kaye Vessey, G.P.O. Box 283, Canberra, A.C.T. 2601    *tel* (09)337 9525 (Sec.).
$20 p.a. (on subscription). Q. Baha'i magazine with particular emphasis on religious approach to unity. Features, fiction and non-fiction. *Length:* up to 3500 words. *Payment:* by negotiation. *Illustrations:* colour and b&w photos; *payment:* by negotiation.

**Labor News,** Steve Harrison, Peter Kelly, F.I.A., 51-65 Bathurst Street, Sydney, 2000, New South Wales    *tel* (612) 264-2877    *telex* 176770    *fax* (612) 261-1701.
Bi-M. Official Journal Federated Ironworkers' Association of Australia.

**(Launceston) Examiner,** Michael Courtney, Box 99A, P.O. Launceston, Tasmania, 7250   *tel* 315111   *telegraphic address* Examiner, Launceston, Tasmania   *telex* 58511   *fax* 003-320 300.
35c. D.

**(Melbourne) Age,** C. Burns (David Syme & Co., Ltd.), 250 Spencer Street, Melbourne, Victoria 3000   *tel* 6004211   *telex* 30331, 30376, 30449 *fax* 6707514. London: The London International Press Centre, 76 Shoe Lane, London EC4A 3JB.
40c., (Sat. 60c.) D. Independent liberal morning daily. Room occasionally for outside matter. An illustrated weekend magazine and literary review is published on Saturday. Accepts occasional freelance material.

**(Melbourne) Australasian Post,** Southdown Press, 32 Walsh Street, West Melbourne 3003.
$1.60. W. Opening for casual contributions of topical factual illustrated articles. All contributions must have Australian interest. General appeal. *Payment:* average $300 per 500 words plus $50 (minimum) per picture.

**(Melbourne) Herald,** Bruce Baskett, 44-74 Flinders Street, Melbourne   *tel* 652-1111.
40c. D. Evening broadsheet; articles with or without illustrations. *Length:* up to 750 words. *Payment:* on merit. *Illustrations:* half-tone and line.

**(Melbourne) Sun News Pictorial** (1922), Colin Duck, 44-74 Flinders Street, Melbourne, 3000.
40c. D. Freelance articles with or without illustrations. *Payment:* on merit.

**Modern Boating** (1965), 180 Bourke Road, Alexandria, N.S.W. 2015   *tel* (02) 693 6666   *telex* AA 74488.
$3.25. M. Articles on all types of boats and boating. *Payment:* $80-$150 per 1000 words. *Illustrations:* half-tone and colour.

**New Idea** (1902), Mrs D. Boling, 32 Walsh Street, Melbourne, Victoria 3001   *tel* 320 7000.
$1.20. W. General interest woman's magazine; news stories, features, fashion, services, short stories of general interest to women of all ages. *Length:* stories, 500 to 4000 words: articles, 1000 to 2000 words. *Payment:* on acceptance. Minimum $150.00 per 1000 words.

**The Newcastle Herald** (1858), J. A. Allan, P.O. Box 510G, 28-30 Bolton Street, Newcastle, 2300, N.S.W   *tel* 049-263-222.
40c. D. (Monday to Saturday). Travel articles up to 800 words. *Payment:* up to $50 per 1000 words.

**Overland,** S. Murray-Smith, P.O. Box 249, Mt. Eliza, Victoria 3930   *tel* 03-787 1545.
$5.00. Q. Literary and general. Australian material preferred. *Payment:* by arrangement. *Illustrations:* line and half-tone.

**People Magazine** (National weekly news-pictorial), D. Naylor, 54 Park Street, Sydney, N.S.W. 2000   *tel* 282 8000   *fax* 267 2150.
$1.70. W. Mainly people stories, but good documentary subjects needed. Photographs depicting exciting happenings, candid camera pictures of events affecting Australians, glamour and show business, modern-living features, and complete series of any subject such as unusual occupations, rites, customs. *Payment:* highest Australian scale.

**(Perth) Daily News** (1840), Jack Harrison, 120 Roe Street, Northbridge, Perth 6000   *tel* 427 1400   *fax* 227 7351.

40c. D. (Evening). Accepts special articles on subjects of outstanding interest. *Payment:* according to merit. *Illustrations:* half-tone, line.

**(Perth) Sunday Times** (1897), 34 Stirling Street, Perth, 6000, Western Australia *tel* 326-8326.
80c. W. Topical articles to 800 words. *Payment:* on acceptance.

**(Perth) The West Australian** (1833), R. E. Cronin, 219 St. Georges Terrace, Perth, 6000 *tel* 482-3111 *fax* 324-1416 or 322 7353 *telegraphic address* Westralian, Perth.
50c. M.-F., 60c. Sat. D. Articles and sketches about people and events in Australia and abroad. *Length:* 300-700 words. *Payment:* Award rates or better. *Illustrations:* line or half-tone.

**Poetry Australia** (1964), John Millett, South Head Press, Market Place, Berrima, 2577 N.S.W *tel* 048-771421.
$27 p.a. Q. Previous unpublished new poetry, and criticism. *Payment:* $5 to $40 per poem depending on length.

**Quadrant,** Editors: Peter Coleman, Roger Manne, 115 Clarence Street, Sydney 2000. *postal address* Box C344, Clarence Street P.O., Sydney, 2000, New South Wales *tel* 262-4830 *fax* 262-4831.
$4.00. M. Articles, short stories, verse, etc. *Prose length:* 2000-5000 words. *Payment:* minimum $80 articles, $60 stories, $40 reviews, $30 poems.

**Reader's Digest** (Australian and New Zealand editions), Hugh Vaughan-Williams, 26-32 Waterloo Street, Surry Hills, N.S.W., 2010 *tel* 690-6111 *telegraphic address* Readigest, Sydney *fax* 699-8165.
$2.45. M. Articles on Australia and New Zealand subjects by commission only. No unsolicited manuscripts accepted. *Length:* 2500 to 3000 words. *Payment:* $1000-$3000 per article. Brief filler paragraphs, $50 to $200. *Illustrations:* half-tone, colour.

**The Sun,** M. E. Quirk, G.P.O. Box 222, Brisbane, Queensland 4001 *tel* 07-253 3333. 40c. D.

**Sunday Sun,** D. Houghton, 367 Brunswick Street, Fortitude Valley, Brisbane, Queensland 4006 *tel* 07-253 3274.
40c. W.

**The Sun-Herald** (Sunday edition of **The Sydney Morning Herald**), David Hickie, G.P.O. Box 506, Sydney, 2001. London: 12 Norwich Street, London EC4A 1BH *tel* 01-353 9321.
60c. W. Topical articles to 1000 words; sections on politics, social issues, show business, finance and fashion. *Payment:* by arrangement.

**(Sydney) Bulletin** (1880), David Dale, 54 Park Street, Sydney, N.S.W *tel* 282-8200. London: Australian Consolidated Press, 112 Westbourne Park Road, W2 *tel* 01-229 3916. New York: Australian Consolidated Press, Lesa Tinker, 25 Van Dam Street, New York, N.Y. 10022 *tel* 212-627 7050.
$2.20. W. Concerned mainly with reporting Australia to Australians, or the world from an Australian aspect. *Payment:* by arrangement.

**(Sydney) Daily Mirror** (1941), 2 Holt Street, Sydney, 2010, N.S.W *tel* 02-288 3000.
40c. D. Accept modernly written feature articles and series of Australian or world interest. *Length:* 1000-2000 words. *Payment:* according to merit/length.

**(Sydney) Daily Telegraph** (News Limited), J. Hartigan, 2 Holt Street, Surry Hills, 2010, N.S.W *tel* 02-288 3000 *fax* 288 2300.
40c. D.

**The Sydney Morning Herald** (1831), J. H. Alexander, P.O. Box 506, Sydney 2001. London: 12 Norwich Street, London, EC4A 1BH   *tel* 01-353 9321.
50c. D. Saturday edition has pages of literary criticism and also magazine articles, plus glossy colour magazine. Topical articles 600 to 4000 words. *Payment:* varies, but minimum $100.00 per 1000 words. *Illustrations:* all types.

**What's On Video** (1983), Peter Barrett, P.O. Box 12, Rockdale, N.S.W. 2216   *tel* 587 7165.
$26 p.a. M. Star interviews, linked with video movies. *Length:* up to 1000 words. *Payment:* AJA freelance rates. *Illustrations:* half-tone.

**Woman's Day,** Nene King, 54-58 Park Street, Sydney 2000   *tel* (02) 282-8000   *fax* (02) 267-2150.
$1.40. W. National women's magazine; news, show business, fiction, fashion, general articles, cookery, home economy.


# CANADA

*Newspapers are listed under the towns in which they are published.*

**The Atlantic Advocate,** H. P. Wood, P.O. Box 3370, Fredericton, New Brunswick, E3B 5A2   *tel* 452 6671.
$2.00. M. Non-fiction and short stories, focus must be on Atlantic Provinces. *Length:* up to 1500 words. *Payment:* up to 10 cents per word. *Illustrations:* line and half-tone.

**The Beaver,** Christopher Dafoe (Hudson's Bay Co.), 450 Portage Avenue, Winnipeg, Manitoba R3C 0E7.
$18.00 p.a., foreign $24.00 p.a. Bi-M. Articles, historical and modern in the sphere of Hudson's Bay Company's activities and Canadian history. *Length:* 1500 to 5000 words, with illustrations. *Payment:* on acceptance, about 10 cents a word. *Illustrations:* photographs or drawings. Black and white and colour.

**Broadcaster** (1942), Lynda Ashley, 7 Labatt Avenue, Toronto, Ontario, M5A 3P2   *tel* 416-363-6111   *fax* 416-861-9564.
$3.00 ($25.00 p.a.). M. Articles pertaining to broadcasting. *Length:* 500 to 1500 words. *Payment:* minimum $150.

**Canadian Author and Bookman,** 121 Avenue Road, Suite 104, Toronto, Ontario, M5R 2G3.
$12.50 p.a. $17.50 p.a. overseas. Q. Published by Canadian Authors Association. Interested in an international view on writing techniques, profiles, interviews, freelance opportunities for Canadian writers. *Query only. Payment:* $30 per printed page.

**Canadian Aviation** (1928), Hugh Whittington (Maclean-Hunter, Ltd.), 777 Bay Street, Toronto, Ontario, M5W 1A7   *tel* 416-596-5789   *fax* 416-596-5810.
London: EDP Press Associates, Hemingford Grey, Huntingdon, Cambs. PE18 9DF   *tel* (0480) 63073.
$35 (Gt. Britain) p.a. M. Stories with a Canadian angle, on civil or military aviation. *Payment:* $250 to $700. *Photographs:* from $25.

**The Canadian Forum,** John Hutcheson, 70 The Esplanade, Toronto, Ontario, M5E 1R2   *tel* 416-364-2431.
$2.00, $18.00. p.a. 10 issues p.a. Articles on public affairs and the arts. *Length:* up to 2500 words. *Payment:* $100 per article. *Illustrations:* line and photographs.

**Canadian Interiors,** Dean Shalden, The Maclean Hunter Building, 777 Bay Street, Toronto, M5W 1A7    *tel* 416-596-5976    *telegraphic address* Macpub.
$33.00 p.a. 8 issues p.a. ($69 elsewhere). Articles on all aspects of interior design; also technical and business articles. *Payment:* $100-$400 per article. *Illustrations:* half-tone and colour.

**Canadian Literature** (1959), W. H. New, 2029 West Mall, University of British Columbia, Vancouver, B.C., V6T 1W5    *tel* 604-228-2780.
$7.50. Q. Articles on Canadian writers and writing in English and French. *Length:* up to 5000 words. *Payment:* $5.00 per printed page.

**Chatelaine,** 777 Bay Street, Toronto, M5W 1A7    *tel* 416-596-5425.
$2.00. M. Articles with woman's slant used; Canadian angle preferred. *Payment:* on acceptance; from $1000.

**The Dalhousie Review,** Dr. Alan Andrews, Dalhousie University Press Ltd., Sir James Dunn Building, Suite 314, Halifax, N.S., B3H 3J5    *tel* 902-424-2541.
$5.00 (plus postage). Q. ($15.00 p.a., $21.50 p.a. overseas; or $36.00 for 3 years; $42.50 for 3 years overseas). Articles on literary, political, historical, educational and social topics; fiction; verse; book reviews. *Length:* prose, normally not more than 5000 words; verse, preferably less than 40 words. *Payment:* $1 per printed page for fiction; $3 for 1st poem, $2 for each subsequent poem (per issue). Contributors receive two copies of issue and 15 offprints of their work. Usually not more than two stories and about 10 or 12 poems in any one issue.

**The Fiddlehead** (1945), Michael Taylor, Room 317, Old Arts Building, University of New Brunswick, P.O. Box 4400, Fredericton, N.B., E3B 5A3    *tel* 506-453-3501.
$5.00. Q. Reviews, poetry, short stories. *Payment:* $10.00 per printed page (approx.). *Illustrations:* line and photographs.

**The Hamilton Spectator** (1846), Publisher, Gordon Bullock, 44 Frid Street, Hamilton, L8N 3G3    *tel* 416-526-3333.
35 cents. Monday to Friday; $1.00 Saturday. Articles of general interest, political analysis and background; interviews, stories of Canadians abroad. *Length:* 800 maximum. *Payment:* rate varies.

**Journal of Canadian Studies,** Michael Peterman, Robert Campbell, Trent University, Peterborough, Ontario, K9J 7B8.
$18.00 p.a. (Institutions: $35.00 p.a.). Q. Major academic review of Canadian studies. Articles of general as well as scholarly interest on history, politics, literature, society, arts. *Length:* 2000-10,000 words.

**Maclean's Magazine,** Kevin Doyle, Maclean Hunter Building, 777 Bay Street, 7th Floor, Toronto, M5W 1A7    *tel* 416-596-5386    *telex* 065-24196    *fax* 416-596-7730. London: Suite 701, 25 St. James's Street, SW1.
$2.00. W. News magazine articles of interest to Canadian readers, 500 to 3000 words. *Payment:* by arrangement. *Illustrations:* on assignment.

**The Malahat Review** (1967), Constance Rooke, University of Victoria, P.O. Box 1700, Victoria, British Columbia V8W 2Y2    *tel* 604-721 8524.
$15.00 p.a.; Overseas $20.00 p.a. Q. Short stories, poetry, short plays, reviews, some graphics and critical essays. *Payment:* Prose: $40.00 per 1000 words; Poetry: $20.00 per page or per poem. *Illustrations:* half-tone.

**Performing Arts in Canada Magazine** (1961), Patricia Michael, 263 Adelaide Street West, 5th Floor, Toronto, Ontario, M5H IY2    *tel* 416-971-9516.
$8.00 p.a., $14.00 p.a. outside Canada. Q. Feature articles on Canadian theatre, music, dance and film artists and organisations; technical articles on

scenery, lighting, make-up, costumes, etc. *Length:* 1000 to 2000 words. *Payment:* $150 to $250, one month after publication. *Illustrations:* black-and-white photographs, colour slides.

**Quebec Chronicle Telegraph** (1764), Karen Macdonald, Quebec Chronicle-Telegraph Inc., 22 rue Ste-Anne, Quebec City, Quebec G1R 3X3 *tel* 418-692-0056.
40 cents. W. Covers local events within English community in Quebec City. Some feature articles.

**Quill & Quire** (1935), Valerie Thompson, 56 The Esplanade, Suite 213, Toronto, Ontario, M5E 1A7 *tel* 416-364-3333.
$50.00 p.a. (in the UK). 12 issues p.a. Articles of interest about the Canadian book trade. *Payment:* from $100. *Illustrations:* line, half-tone.

**Reader's Digest,** Alexander Farrell, 215 Redfern Avenue, Montreal, Quebec, H3Z 2V9 *tel* 514-934-0751.
$2.25. M. Original articles on all subjects of broad general appeal, thoroughly researched and professionally written. Outline or query *only. Length:* 3000 words approx. *Payment:* from $2500.00 Also previously published material. *Illustrations:* colour, half-tone, line.

**(Toronto) The Globe and Mail** (1844), A. Roy Megarry, Publisher; William Thorsell, Editor-in-Chief, 444 Front Street West, Toronto, Ontario, M5V 2S9. London: 164-167 Temple Chambers (2nd Floor), Temple Avenue, London, EC4Y 0EA *tel* 01-353-5795.
35c. Mon-Fri; $1.00. Sat. D.

**Toronto Life** (1967), Marq de Villiers, 59 Front Street East, Toronto, Ontario, M5E 1B3 *tel* 416-364-3333.
$2.50. M. Articles, profiles on Toronto and Torontonians. *Illustrations:* line, half-tone, colour.

**Toronto Star** (1892), One Yonge Street, Toronto, M5E 1E6 *tel* 367-2000. London: Level 4A, P.O. Box 495, Virginia Street, E1 9XY *tel* 01-833 0791.
30 cents. D. ($1.00 Saturday, 75 cents Sunday.)

**(Vancouver) Province** (1898), Robert McMurray, 2250 Granville Street, Vancouver, V6H 3G2 *tel* 732-2484 *fax* 732-2720.
50 cents. M.-F. 75 cents Sunday.

**Vancouver Sun,** Nicholas Hills, Editor; Frank Rutter, Editor of Editorial Pages; Bruce Hutchison, Editor Emeritus, 2250 Granville Street, Vancouver, V6H 3G2, B.C *tel* 604-732-2111 *fax* 604-732-2323. London: Southam News, 8 Bouverie Street, 4th Floor, London, EC4Y 8AX *tel* 01-583 7322.
50 cents. D. Fri, Sat. 75 cents (not Sunday). Rates depending on arrangements. Very little outside contribution.

**Wascana Review** (1966), Joan Givner, c/o English Department, University of Regina, Regina, Sask., S4S 0A2.
$7.00 p.a. Overseas: $8.00 p.a. Semi-annual. Criticism, short stories, poetry, reviews. *Length:* prose, not more than 6000 words; verse, up to 100 lines. *Payment:* $3 per page for prose; $10 per printed page for verse; $3.00 per page for reviews. Contributors also receive two free copies of the issue. Manuscripts from freelance writers welcome.

**Winnipeg Free Press** (1872), John Dafoe, 300 Carlton Street, Winnipeg, Manitoba R3C 3C1 *tel* 943-9331.
25 cents, $1.00 Saturday. D. Some freelance articles. *Payment:* $100.

## THE REPUBLIC OF IRELAND AND NORTHERN IRELAND

**Africa - St. Patrick's Missions,** Rev. Brendan Cooney, St. Patrick's, Kiltegan, Co. Wicklow *tel* (0508) 73233.
25p. (£4.00 p.a.) 9 times p.a. Articles of general interest. *Length:* up to 1500 words. *Payment:* £25 per article. *Illustrations:* All kinds.

**Aspect Magazine** (1982), John O'Neill, P.O. Box 15, New Road, Greystones, Co. Wicklow *tel* 01-875514.
75p. M. Hard business stories relevant to Irish readers. *Length:* up to 1000 words. *Payment:* by arrangement. *Illustrations:* half-tone.

**(Belfast) News Letter** (1737), Sam Butler, 51-59 Donegall Street, Belfast, BT1 2GB *tel* (0232) 244441.
25p. D. Unionist.

**Belfast Telegraph** (1870), 124–144 Royal Avenue, Belfast BT1 1EB *tel* (0232) 321242 *telex* 74269 *fax* (0232) 242287.
24p. D. Any material relating to Northern Ireland. *Payment:* by negotiation.

**Books Ireland** (1976), Jeremy Addis, 11 Newgrove Avenue, Dublin 4 *tel* (01) 692185 *fax* (01) 688242.
75p. £9.00 p.a. (M. except January and August). Reviews of Irish interest and Irish-author books, articles of interest to librarians, booksellers and readers. *Length:* 800 to 1400 words. *Payment:* £24 per 1000 words.

**Caritas** (1934). Published by the Hospitaller Order of St. John of God in Ireland. Editorial Office: St. Augustine's, Carysfort Avenue, Blackrock, Co. Dublin *tel* 885518.
Q. A magazine of Christian concern. Articles and features on mental and physical health concerning family and community well-being. Scripts of 1200 to 1500 words on children and youth, personal and case histories, biographies, religious and general interest. Poems not normally accepted. *Payment:* £15 to £60. Photos, illustrations and appropriate cartoons paid for separately. Send 2 International Reply Coupons for return of MSS.

**Church of Ireland Gazette** (1885, New Series 1963), Rev. Canon C. W. M. Cooper, 48 Bachelor's Walk, Lisburn, Co. Antrim, BT28 1XN *tel* (0846) 675743.
20p. W. Church news, articles of religious and general interest. *Length:* 600 to 1000 words. *Payment:* according to length and interest.

**Commercial Transport** (1970), Bridget Gavin, Rathcoole, Co. Dublin *tel* 589211.
£1.00 M. Articles relating to transport on land, sea and air. *Payment:* £50 to £60 per 1000 words. *Illustrations:* line, half-tone, colour.

**Cyphers** (1975), Leland Bardwell, Pearse Hutchinson, Eiléan Ní Chuilleanáin, Macdara Woods, 3 Selskar Terrace, Dublin 6 *tel* 978866.
£1.35. 2 to 3 p.a. Poems, fiction, articles on literary subjects, translations. *Payment:* £7 per page (verse), £5 per page (prose).

**East Cork News,** Peter Doyle, 25 Michael Street, Waterford *tel* (051) 74951.
40p. W. News articles. *Payment:* by arrangement. *Illustrations:* line and half-tone (web offset).

**Evening Herald, Dublin,** Michael Brophy, Middle Abbey Street, Dublin 1 *tel* 731666.
35p. D. Articles. *Payment:* by arrangement. *Illustrations:* line, half-tone.

**Evening Press** (1954), Sean Ward, Burgh Quay, Dublin 2   *tel* 713333   *telex* 93752   *fax* 713097.
40p. D. News items, articles. *Payment:* NUJ rates.

**Fortnight.** An Independent Review for Northern Ireland (1970), Robin Wilson, 7 Lower Crescent, Belfast BT7 1NR   *tel* (0232) 232353.
80p. M. Current affairs analysis, investigative reporting, opinion pieces, cultural criticism, poems, short stories of Northern Irish interest. *Payment:* £10 to £30 per article. *Illustrations:* line, half-tone. Cartoons.

**The Furrow** (1950), Rev. Ronan Drury, St. Patrick's College, Maynooth, Co. Kildare   *tel* 286215.
£1.25. M. Religious, pastoral, theological, social articles. *Length:* 4000 words. *Payment:* average £10 per page (450 words). *Illustrations:* line or half-tone.

**The Honest Ulsterman,** Robert Johnstone, Ruth Hooley, 102 Elm Park Mansions, Park Walk, London SW10 0AP.
£1.00. 3 p.a. Poetry, short stories, critical articles. *Payment:* by arrangement.

**Hotel and Catering Review,** Frank Corr, Jemma Publications Ltd., 22 Brookfield Avenue, Blackrock, Co. Dublin   *tel* Dublin 886946   *telex* 90169.
£15 p.a. M. Short news and trade news pieces. *Length:* approx. 200 words. Features. *Payment:* £50 per 1000 words. *Illustrations:* half-tone and cartoons.

**Image** (1974), Jane McDonnell, 22 Crofton Road, Dun Laoghaire, Co. Dublin *tel* 01-808415   *fax* 01-808309.
£1.20. M. Short stories of a high literary standard and of interest to women. *Length:* up to 3000 words. Interviews with actors, writers, etc. Human interest stories. *Payment:* by arrangement.

**In Dublin** (1976), John Doyle, 15 Lower Baggot Street, Dublin 2   *tel* 615555   *fax* 615302.
95p. Fortnightly. Articles, reviews, current affairs, arts and entertainment. *Length:* 200-5000 words. *Payment:* £50 per 1000 words. *Illustrations:* line, half-tone; cartoons.

**Ireland of the Welcomes,** Irish Tourist Board, Baggot Street Bridge, Dublin 2   *tel* Dublin 765871.
£1.25. Bi-M. Irish items with cultural, sporting or topographical background designed to arouse interest in Irish holidays. *Length:* 1200 to 1800 words. *Payment:* by arrangement. *Illustrations:* scenic and topical. Preliminary letter preferred. Mostly commissioned.

**Ireland's Own** (1902), Austin Channing, North Main Street, Wexford   *tel* 053-22155.
35p. W. Short stories (1500 to 2000 words); romances in particular, but with an Irish background; articles of interest to Irish readers at home and abroad (1000 to 3000 words); general and literary articles (1000 to 2500 words). Special issues for Christmas and St. Patrick's Day. Jokes, funny stories, riddles, always welcome. Suggestions for new features considered. *Payment:* varies according to quality, originality and length. Serials of novel length, preliminary letter advisable, enclosing synopsis and s.a.e., payment by arrangement. *Illustrations:* no restriction (web off-set).

**Irish Business** (1975), Frank FitzGibbon, 128 Lower Baggot Street, Dublin 2   *tel* 619236.
£1.20. (£13.00 p.a.) M. Topical articles on finance, banking, economics. *Length:* 900 to 1500 words. *Payment:* by arrangement. *Illustrations:* line, half-tone.

**Irish Independent,** Vincent Doyle, Independent House, 90 Middle Abbey Street, Dublin 1   *tel* 731666.
55p. D. Special articles on topical or general subjects. *Length:* 700 to 1000 words. *Payment:* Editor's estimate of value.

**Irish Journal of Medical Science** (1st series 1832, 6th series January 1926, Volume 158, 1989), Royal Academy of Medicine, 6 Kildare Street, Dublin 2   *tel* 767650.
£3.00. M. (Subscription Great Britain and Ireland £36.00 post free; overseas £42.00 post free). Official Organ of the Royal Academy of Medicine in Ireland. Original contributions in medicine, surgery, midwifery, public health, etc.; reviews of professional books, reports of medical societies, etc. *Illustrations:* half-tone, line and colour.

**Irish Medical Times,** Dr. John O'Connell, 15 Harcourt Street, Dublin 2   *tel* 757461.
£1.00. W. Medical articles, also humorous articles with medical slant. *Length:* 850-1000 words. *Payment:* £60 per 1000 words. *Illustrations:* line and half-tone.

**The Irish News and Belfast Morning News** (1855), J. J. Fitzpatrick, Managing Editor, 113-117 Donegall Street, Belfast BT1 2GE   *tel* 322226   *fax* 231282.
20p. D. Articles of historical and topical interest. *Payment:* by arrangement.

**Irish Press,** Hugh Lambert, Burgh Quay, Dublin 2   *tel* 713333.
50p. D. Topical articles about 1000 words. *Payment:* by arrangement. *Illustrations:* topical photographs.

**Irish Times,** Conor Brady, 11-15 D'Olier Street, Dublin 2   *tel* Dublin 792022   *telex* 93639   *fax* 793910.
60p. D. Mainly staff-written. Specialist contributions (800 to max. 2000 words) by commission on basis of ideas submitted. *Payment:* at editor's valuation. *Illustrations:* photographs and line drawings.

**IT Magazine,** Noelle Campbell-Sharp, The Village Centre, Ballybrack Village, Co. Dublin   *tel* 826411.
£1.00. M. (£14.50 p.a.). Fashion and social magazine; beauty, interiors, health books, wine and cookery, art, theatre, cinema, television, music, motoring, knitting and special monthly interviews. *Length:* 700 to 1500 words. *Payment:* by arrangement. *Illustrations:* half-tone.

**Krino** (1986), Gerald Dawe, Avril Forrest, Aodan MacPoilin, Glenrevagh, Corrandulla, Co. Galway.
£3.50. 2 p.a. Poetry; fiction; critical prose mostly on commissioned basis. *Payment:* none, but complimentary copies of the magazine. *Illustrations:* line, half tone.

**The Nationalist and Munster Advertiser** (1890), Brendan Long, Queen Street, Clonmel, Co. Tipperary   *tel* 052-22211.
50p. W. Requirements by arrangement. *Payment:* £22 per 1000 words. *Illustrations:* artwork.

**Poetry Ireland** (1981), Micheal O'Siadhail, 44 Upper Mount Street, Dublin 2.
£3.00. Q. Poetry, short lyric and sections from long poems, articles and reviews. *Payment:* by arrangement.

**Portadown Times & Craigavon News** (1859), David Armstrong, 38A High Street, Portadown, BT62 1HY   *tel* (0762) 336111.
38p. W. Articles. *Payment:* NUJ rates.

**Reality** (1936), Rev. K. H. Donlon, Redemptorist Publications, Orwell Road, Rathgar, Dublin 6   *tel* Dublin 961488 and 961688.

60p. M. Illustrated magazine for christian living. Articles on all aspects of modern life, including family, youth, religion, leisure. Illustrated articles black and white photos only. Short stories. *Length:* 1000-1500 words. *Payment:* by arrangement; average £20.00 per 1000 words.

**The Songwriter** (1967), James D. Liddane, International Songwriters Association Ltd., Limerick City	*tel* 061 28837.
Available to members only as part of membership fee. 4 times a year. Articles on song writing and interviews with music publishers and recording company executives. *Length:* 400-5000 words. *Payment:* from £40 per page and by arrangement. *Illustrations:* photographs.

**Studies** An Irish quarterly review (1912), Rev. Brian Lennon, s.j., 35 Lower Leeson Street, Dublin 2	*tel* 766785.
£3.00. Q. A general review of social comment, literature, history, the arts. Articles written by specialists for the general reader. Critical book reviews. *Length:* 3500 words. Preliminary letter.

**Sunday Independent,** Aengus Fanning, Independent House, 90 Middle Abbey Street, Dublin, 1	*tel* 731333	*fax* 720304, 731787.
55p. W. Special articles. *Length:* according to subject. *Payment:* at Editor's valuation; good. *Illustrations:* topical or general interest.

**Sunday Life** (1988), Edmund Curran, 124 Royal Avenue, Belfast BT9 1EB *tel* 331133	*telex* Belfast 74269	*fax* 248968.
35p. W. Items of interest to Northern Ireland Sunday tabloid readers. *Payment:* by arrangement. *Illustrations:* colour and b&w.

**Sunday News** (1965), Ken Reid, 51-67 Donegall Street, Belfast, BT1 2GB	*tel* (0232) 244441.
30p. W. General topical articles of 500 words. *Payment:* by arrangement. *Illustrations:* line and half-tone.

**The Sunday Press,** Michael Keane, Burgh Quay, Dublin, 2	*tel* Dublin 713333	*telegraphic address* Sceala, Dublin	*telex* 93752	*fax* 713097.
60p. W. Articles of general interest. *Length:* 1000 words. *Illustrations:* line and half-tone.

**Theatre Ireland Magazine** (1982), David Grant, 16b Adelaide Park, Belfast BT9 6FX	*tel* (0232) 451368 and 669989.
£1.75. Q. Articles, photographs, practical information, reference material on all aspects of live theatre, international as well as of Irish interest. *Length:* 1000 to 3000 words. *Payment:* by arrangement. *Illustrations:* colour and black and white.

**Waterford News & Star,** Peter Doyle, 25 Michael Street, Waterford	*tel* (051) 74951.
60p. W. News articles. *Payment:* by arrangement. *Illustrations:* line and half-tone (web-offset).

**Woman's Way** (1963), Celine Naughton, J. S. Publications, 126 Lower Baggot Street, Dublin 2	*tel* 608264	*fax* 619486.
60p. W. Short stories, light romance, career, holiday, 2000 to 3000 words. *Payment:* £30.00 to £50.00. Articles of interest to women. *Illustrations:* half-tone, line and colour.

**The Word** (1936), Rev. Brother Paul Hurley, s.v.d., (The Word Press, Hadzor, Droitwich), Divine Word Missionaries, Maynooth, Co. Kildare	*tel* Dublin 286391.

40p. M. A Catholic illustrated magazine for the family. Illustrated articles of general interest up to 1000 words and good picture features. *Payment:* by arrangement. *Illustrations:* photographs and large colour transparencies.

## NEW ZEALAND

*Newspapers are listed under the towns in which they are published.*

**(Auckland) New Zealand Herald** (1863), P. J. Scherer, P.O. Box 32, Auckland *tel* 795-050  *fax* 366-1568. London: Ludgate House, 107 Fleet Street, EC4  *tel* 01-353 2686.
35c. D. Topical and informative articles 800 to 1100 words. *Payment:* minimum $50-$150. *Illustrations:* half-tone blocks (65 screen).

**Auckland Star** (1870), Judy McGregor (Auckland Star Ltd.), P.O. Box 1409, Auckland  *tel* 797-626.
40c. Monday to Friday.

**(Christchurch) The Press,** E. B. Lock, Private Bag, Christchurch  *tel* (03) 790-940  *fax* (03) 654-702.
40c. D. Articles of general interest not more than 1000 words. *Payment:* by arrangement. Extra for photographs and line drawings.

**(Christchurch) The Star** (1868), I. H. Reddington (New Zealand Newspapers, Ltd.), Kilmore Street, Christchurch  *tel* 797-100  *telex* NZ 4871  *fax* (03) 660-180.
40c. D. Topical articles.

**(Dunedin) Otago Daily Times** (1861), G. T. Adams, P.O. Box 181, Dunedin. London: 107 Fleet Street, EC4A 2AN  *tel* 01-353 2686.
40c. D. Any articles of general interest up to 1000 words, but preference is given to New Zealand writers. Topical illustrations and personalities. *Payment:* current New Zealand rates.

**The Gisborne Herald** (1874), Iain Gillies, P.O. Box 1143, 64 Gladstone Road, Gisborne  *tel* 82099  *telegraphic address* Herald, Gisborne.
12c. D. Topical features of local interest. *Length:* 1000 to 1500 words. *Payment:* by arrangement. *Illustrations:* bromides.

**Hawke's Bay Herald Tribune** (result of merger between Hawke's Bay Herald (1857), Hastings Standard (1896) and Hawke's Bay Tribune (1910)), J. E. Morgan, P.O. Box 180, Karamu Road, Hastings  *tel* 85-155  *fax* 070-85668.
45c. D. Limited requirements. *Payment:* $30+ for articles, $10+ for photographs. *Illustrations:* web offset.

**(Invercargill) The Southland Times** (1862), P. M. Muller, P.O. Box 805, Invercargill  *tel* (021) 81-909  *telegraphic address* Times, Invercargill  *telex* NZ 5254  *fax* (021) 84-237.
40c. D. Articles of up to 1500 words on topics of Southland interest. *Payment:* by arrangement. *Illustrations:* colour, line and half-tone.

**Islands,** Robin Dudding, 4 Sealy Road, Torbay, Auckland 10  *tel* 4039007.
$11. Q. ($33 p.a.; overseas: $16.50 single issue, $39.60 p.a.). Short stories, verse, criticism, reviews. No limits to *length.* Most critical work commissioned or prior letter preferred. *Payment:* about $1200 divided among contributors to a single issue. *Illustrations:* usually commissioned.

**Kiwi Rider Magazine,** Box 20241, Glen Eden, Auckland  *tel* 09-818-8715.
$2.50. F. Reports, interviews, road tests about motor cycles. *Payment:* from $25.00. *Illustrations:* photos, technical drawings.

**Landfall** (1947), Editorial Board: Mark Williams, Hugh Lauder, Iain Sharp, Judith Baker, The Caxton Press, P.O. Box 25-088, Christchurch   *tel* 668516. $38.50 p.a. ($42.00 p.a. overseas). Q. Literary and general material by N.Z. writers considered of any length. Illustrates the work of N.Z. painters, sculptors, architects, photographers. *Payment:* by arrangement.

**Management** (Profile Publishing), Box 5544, Auckland   *tel* (09) 784-475   *fax* (09) 780-244.
$5.00. M. Articles on the practice of management skills and techniques, individual and company profiles, coverage of trends and topics of interest to the manager. A New Zealand/Australian angle or application preferred. *Length:* 2000 words. *Payment:* by arrangement; minimum 23c. per word. *Illustrations:* photographs, line drawings.

**(Napier) The Daily Telegraph** (1871), K. R. Hawker, P.O. Box 343, Napier   *tel* (070) 354-488   *fax* 356-786.
50c. D. Limited market for features. *Payment:* $20 upwards per 1000 words; $10 a picture. *Illustrations:* line and half-tone; colour.

**The Nelson Evening Mail,** D. J. Mitchell, P.O. Box 244, 15 Bridge Street, Nelson   *tel* 87-079.
40c. D. Features, articles on New Zealand subjects. *Length:* 500-1000 words. *Payment:* up to $60 per 1000 words. *Illustrations:* half-tone, colour.

**(New Plymouth) The Daily News** (1857), D. Garcia, P.O. Box 444, New Plymouth   *tel* 80559   *fax* (067) 86849.
45c. D. Articles preferably with a Taranaki connection. *Payment:* by negotiation. *Illustrations:* half-tone.

**New Zealand Farmer,** Hugh Stringleman, N.Z. Rural Press Ltd., P.O. Box 4233, 540 Great South Road, Greenlane, Auckland 5   *tel* (9) 591-124   *fax* (9) 599-589.
F. Authoritative, simply-written articles on new developments in livestock husbandry, grassland farming, cropping, farm machinery, marketing. *Length:* 500 words. *Payment:* according to merit.

**New Zealand Gardener,** Communication Associates Ltd., Private Bag, Petone *tel* 058-34495.
$1.75. M. Topical articles on gardening and gardeners, new plants and methods of cultivation, new products of horticultural interest, home workshop projects for the home and garden. Authoritative articles by specialists but general interest articles by freelance writers. *Payment:* $50 per 1000 words. *Illustrations:* $10 per print on publication; $15 per colour slide, $50 for cover shots.

**The New Zealand Listener** (1939), Bob Edlin (acting editor), P.O. Box 3140, Wellington   *tel* 741-200.
$1.30. W. Topical features of New Zealand and international interest: also features related to television and radio programmes. *Length:* up to 2500 words. *Illustrations:* colour and black and white. *Payment:* from $300.00 per 1000 words, or by arrangement.

**New Zealand Woman's Weekly** (1932), Jenny Lynch, NZ Magazines (Wilson & Horton), Private Bag, Dominion Road, Auckland 3   *tel* 688-177   *telex* NZ 21731   *fax* 609-128.
$1.70. W. Pictorial features. Illustrated articles of general, family, world interest, particularly with a New Zealand slant. *Length:* articles 750-1750. *Payment:* by arrangement. *Illustrations:* black-and-white, colour.

**N.Z. Engineering** (1946), L. W. McEldowney, B.A., Engineering Publications Co. Ltd., P.O. Box 12241, Wellington   *tel* (04) 739-444   *fax* (04) 732-324.

$4.00. M. Articles of interest to New Zealand engineers, not necessarily technical. Preliminary letter essential. *Payment:* by arrangement.

**N.Z. Truth** (News Media Ownership Ltd.), Hedley Mortlock, Glenside Crescent, Auckland, P.O. Box 1327 *tel* 794780.
£1.00. W. Bold investigative reporting, exposés. *Length:* 500-1000 words, preferably accompanied by photographs. *Payment:* about $50 per 500 words, extra for photographs.

**Sea Spray** (1945), Shane Kelly, Private Bag 9, Parnell, Auckland *tel* 398-292 *fax* 396-361.
$3.30. M. Feature material and photographs on pleasure boating concerning New Zealanders, power or sail. Technical and how-to articles. *Payment:* $100 per 1000 words. *Illustrations:* line, half-tone, colour.

**Sunday Star** (1986), Jenny Wheeler (Auckland Star Ltd.), P.O. Box 1409, Auckland *tel* 797-626.
90c. Sunday.

**The Timaru Herald,** B. R. Appleby, P.O. Box 46, Bank Street, Timaru *tel* 44-129.
40c. D. Topical articles. *Payment:* by arrangement. *Illustrations:* screened bromides.

**(Wellington) The Evening Post** (1865), R. S. Neville, P.O. Box 3740, Willis Street, Wellington *tel* 740-444 *fax* 740-237. *London Office* N.Z. Associated Press, 107 Fleet Street, EC4A 2AN *tel* 01-353 2686.
10c. D. General topical articles, 600 words. *Payment:* N.Z. current rates or by arrangement. News illustrations.

## SOUTH AFRICA

*Newspapers are listed under the towns in which they are published.*

**Argus South African Newspapers.**
**The Argus,** Cape Town, 50c. D.; **Weekend Argus** (Sat.), R1.00; **The Star,** Johannesburg, 50c. D.; **The Sunday Star,** Johannesburg, R1.80; **The Daily News,** Durban, 50c. D.; **Sunday Tribune,** Durban, R1.50; **Pretoria News,** 50c, D; **The Diamond Fields Advertiser,** Kimberley, 50c. D. Accepts articles of general and South African interest. *Payment:* in accordance with an Editor's assessment. Contributions should be addressed to the Foreign Editor, Argus South African Newspapers Ltd., 32-33 Hatton Garden, London EC1N 8DL *tel* 01-831 0882 *fax* 01-831 2339, and not direct.

**Bona,** Republican Press (Pty) Ltd., P.O. Box 32083, Mobeni 4060, Natal *tel* Durban 422041 *telegraphic address* Keur Durban. UK: Suite 438-439 High Holborn House, 52-54 High Holborn, London WC1V 6RB *tel* 01-831 2965. R1.20. M. Articles on fashion, cookery, sport, music of interest to black people. *Length:* up to 3000 words. *Payment:* by arrangement. *Illustrations:* line, half-tone, colour.

**(Cape Town) Cape Times** (1876), J. C. Viviers, Newspaper House, St. George's Street, Cape Town *tel* 021-2084911. *Postal address:* P.O. Box 11, Cape Town 8000. London Office: 1st Floor, 32-33 Hatton Garden, London EC1N 8DL *tel* 01-405 3742.
50c. D. Contributions must be suitable for daily newspaper and must not exceed 800 words. *Illustrations:* photographs of outstanding South African interest.

**Car** (1957), David Trebett, P.O. Box 180, Howard Place, 7450 *tel* 53-1391, *telegraphic address* Confrere   *telex* 526 933   *fax* 533333.
R2.23 + GST. M. New car announcements with pictures and full colour features of motoring interest. *Payment:* by arrangement. *Illustrations:* half-tone and colour.

**(Durban) Natal Mercury** (1852), J. O. McMillan, Natal Newspapers (Pty.) Ltd., Devonshire Place, Durban, 4001   *tel* 319331.
40c. D. (except Sunday). Serious background news and inside details of world events. *Length:* 700 to 900 words. *Illustrations:* photographs of general interest.

**Fair Lady,** Liz Butler (National Magazines), P.O. Box 1802, Cape Town 8000 *tel* 254878   *telegraphic address* Ladyfair. London:   *tel* 01-823-5308.
R1.95. F. Fashion, beauty, articles and stories for women including showbiz, travel, humour. *Length:* articles up to 2000 words; short stories approx. 3000 words; short novels and serialisation of book material. *Payment:* on quality rather than length—by arrangement.

**Farmer's Weekly** (1911), M. Fisher, P.O. Box 32083, Mobeni 4060, Natal   *tel* Durban 422041. U.K.: Suite 438-439 High Holborn House, 52-54 High Holborn, London WC1V 6RB   *tel* 01-831 2965.
R1.50. W. Articles, generally illustrated, up to 1000 words in length dealing with all aspects of practical farming and research with particular reference to conditions in Southern Africa. *Payment:* according to merit. *Illustrations:* continuous-tone, full colour and line. Includes women's section which accepts articles suitably illustrated, on subjects of interest to women. *Payment:* according to merit.

**Femina Magazine,** Jane Raphaely, Associated Magazines, Box 3647, Cape Town 8000. UK: Suite 438-439 High Holborn House, 52-54 High Holborn, London WC1V 6RB   *tel* 01-831 2965.
R2.00. M. For young married women and those who would like to be. Humour, good fiction, personalities, real-life drama, medical breakthroughs, popular science. *Payment:* by arrangement. *Illustrations:* half-tone, line, colour.

**Garden and Home,** Margaret Wasserfall, Republican Press (Pty.) Ltd., P.O. Box 32083, Mobeni 4060, Natal   *tel* Durban 422041   *telegraphic address* Keur, Durban. U.K.: Suite 438-439 High Holborn House, 52-54 High Holborn, London WC1V 6RB   *tel* 01-831 2965.
R2.80. M. Well illustrated articles on gardening, suitable for Southern Hemisphere. Articles for home section on furnishings, flower arrangement, food. *Payment:* by arrangement. *Illustrations:* half-tone and colour.

**(Johannesburg) Sunday Times,** Tertius Myburgh, P.O. Box 1090, Johannesburg 2000   *tel* 710-2600. London: South African Morning Newspapers Ltd., 135 Fleet Street, EC4   *tel* 01-353 4473.
R1.80. Every Sunday. Illustrated articles of political or human interest, from a South African angle if possible. Maximum 1000 words long and two or three photographs. Shorter essays, stories, and articles of a light nature from 500 to 750 words. *Payment:* average rate £100.00 a column. *Illustrations:* photographic (colour or black and white) and line.

**Living and Loving** (1970), Angela Still, Republican Press (Pty.) Ltd., P.O. Box 32083, Mobeni 4060, Natal   *tel* Durban 422041   *telegraphic address* Keur Durban. U.K.: Suite 438-439 High Holborn House, 52-54 High Holborn, London WC1V 6RB   *tel* 01-831 2965.

R2.00. M. Romantic fiction, 1500 to 4000 words. Articles dealing with first person experiences; baby, family and marriage, medical articles up to 3000 words. *Payment:* by merit.

**Natal Witness** (1846), R. S. Steyn, 244 Longmarket Street, Pietermaritzburg, Natal 3201 *tel* 0331-942011 *telex* 6-43385 SA *fax* 0331-940468.
50c. D. Accepts topical articles. *Length:* 500 to 1000 words. *Payment:* Average of R50 per 1000 words. All material should be submitted direct to the Editor in Pietermaritzburg.

**Personality,** J. Gardiner, Republican Press (Pty.) Ltd., P.O. Box 32083, Mobeni 4060, Natal *tel* Durban 422041 *telegraphic address* Keur, Durban. U.K.: Suite 438-439 High Holborn House, 52-54 High Holborn, London WC1V 6RB *tel* 01-831 2965.
R1.50. W. Illustrated. Primarily an entertainment-oriented magazine but also a market for articles about people and places, preferably with South African angle. Strong news features and/or photojournalism. 1000-4000 words, with b/w and colour photographs. Short stories 1500-5000 words. *Payment:* by arrangement. *Illustrations:* usually commissioned.

**(Port Elizabeth) Eastern Province Herald,** P.O. Box 1117, Port Elizabeth 6000 *tel* 523470. London: 1st Floor, 32-33 Hatton Garden, London EC1N 8DL *tel* 01-405 3742.
25c. D. Contributions from 700 to 1500 words considered. *Payment:* £6.00 per 700 words minimum. *Illustrations:* topical photographs.

**Scope,** D. Mullany, Republican Press (Pty.) Ltd., P.O. Box 32083, Mobeni 4060, Natal *tel* Durban 422041 *telegraphic address* Keur, Durban. U.K.: Suite 438-439 High Holborn House, 52-54 High Holborn, London WC1V 6RB *tel* 01-831 2965.
R2.00. F. Strong news features, well illustrated, about people and places in all parts of the world. *Length:* up to 4000 words. Short stories 1500 to 5000 words, serials from 20,000 words. *Illustrations:* half-tone, colour.

**South African Yachting, Power Waterski & Sail** (1957), Neil Rusch, P.O. Box 3473, Cape Town 8000 *tel* 461-7472 *fax* (021) 461-3758.
R3.50. M. Articles on yachting, boating or allied subjects. *Payment:* R6.00 per 100 words. *Illustrations:* half-tone and line. Colour covers.

**Southern Cross,** P.O. Box 2372, 8000 Cape Town *tel* 455007 *telegraphic address* Catholic.
50c. W. The national English language Catholic weekly. Catholic news reports, world and South African. 1000-word articles, cartoons of Catholic interest acceptable from freelance contributors. *Payment:* 30c. per column cm. for all copy used. *Illustrations:* photographs, R2.50 per column width.

**World Airnews,** Tom Chalmers, P.O. Box 35082, Northway, Durban 4065 *tel* (031) 84-1319.
£12.50. M. Aviation news and features with an African angle. *Payment:* £75 per 1000 words. *Illustrations:* photographs, £25 each (conditional).

**Your Family,** Angela Waller-Paton, Republican Press (Pty.) Ltd., P.O. Box 32083, Mobeni 4060, Natal *tel* Durban 422041 *telegraphic address* Keur, Durban. U.K.: Suite 438-439 High Holborn House, 52-54 High Holborn, London WC1V 6RB *tel* 01-831 2965.
R2.00. M. Cookery, knitting, crochet and homecrafts. Short fiction, family drama, happy ending. *Payment:* by arrangement. *Illustrations:* continuous tone, colour and line.

## UNITED STATES OF AMERICA

Because of the difficulties in providing an up-to-date list of US journals, the *Yearbook* does not contain a detailed list; instead we refer readers who are particularly interested in the US market to: *Writer's Market*, an annual guidebook giving editorial requirements and other details of over 4,000 US markets for freelance writing, published by **Writer's Digest Books**, 1507 Dana Avenue, Cincinnati, Ohio 45207 ($24.00, plus $3.00 postage and handling); *The Writer's Handbook*, a substantial volume published by **The Writer Inc,** 120 Boylston Street, Boston, Mass. 02116 ($27.50 plus $5.00 handling and postage). It contains 100 chapters, each written by an authority in his field, giving practical instruction on a wide variety of aspects of freelance writing and including details of 2200 markets, payment rates and addresses. Also publishes books on writing fiction, non-fiction, poetry, articles, plays, etc.

**The Writer Inc.** also publish a monthly magazine *The Writer* ($31 per year) which contains articles of instruction on all writing fields, lists of markets for manuscripts and special features of interest to freelance writers everywhere.

**Writer's Digest Books** also publish the monthly magazine *Writer's Digest* ($25 per year) and the annual directories, *Novel and Short Story Writer's Market, Children's Writer's and Illustrator's Market, Poet's Market,* and many other books on creating and selling writing.

For availability in the UK details may be obtained from:

**Freelance Press Services,** 5-9 Bexley Square, Salford, Manchester M3 6DB   *tel* 061-832 5079.

SUBMISSION OF MSS

When submitting MSS to US journals send your covering letter with the MS together with any illustrations, stamped return envelope or International Reply Coupons. Make clear what rights are being offered for sale for some editors like to purchase MSS outright, thus securing world copyright, i.e. the traditional British market as well as the US market. MSS should be sent direct to the US office of the journal and not to any London office.

In many cases it is far better to send a preliminary letter giving a rough outline of your article or story. Enclose International Reply Coupons for reply. Most magazines will send a leaflet giving guidance to authors.

# Recent Magazine Changes

The following changes of title, mergers, and terminations of publication of magazines listed in the *Yearbook* have recently taken place.

Because of the proliferation of technical journals, and the limited market in most of these for freelance contributions, a considerable number of the most specialist of such publications which were previously listed in the *Yearbook* now no longer appear.

## CHANGES OF NAME AND MERGERS

Antiques now Antiques Folio (incorporating Antiques)
Bristol Illustrated merged with Somerset & Avon Life
The British Esperantist now La Brita Esperantisto
Caring for Disabled now Caring
Celebrity merged with Weekly News
Civil Engineering now Construction Weekly
 (incorporating Construction Plant & Equipment
 and Civil Engineering)
Climber now Climber and Hill Walker
Clocks now Antique Clocks
Dorset—The County Magazine now Dorset County
 Magazine
Drapers Record now DR The Fashion Business
Fruit Trades Journal now Fresh Produce Journal
Gloucestershire and Avon Life now Gloucestershire Life
Golf Illustrated now Golf Illustrated Weekly
Health Educational Journal now Health Education Journal
Leadership Today now Today Magazine
Living Magazine now Living
Patches merged with Blue Jeans
Photoplay now Film Monthly
SLR Photography now Photo Answers
Voice of the Arab World now Voice of the Arab World
 Intelligence Report
World War II Investigator now World War Investigator

## MAGAZINES CEASED PUBLICATION

Designer
Dorset Tatler
Drama
Fiction
Look Now
Popular Caravan
Practical Model Railways
Proteus
Teacher
Today's Selling World
Women's Review

# Classified Index of Magazines

*\*Commonwealth, Irish and South African Journals*

This index can be only a broad classification. It should be regarded as a pointer to possible markets, and should be used with discrimination.

## SHORT STORIES

This list does not include the women's journals requiring short stories, *see* WOMEN'S MAGAZINES; *see also* LITERARY

| | | |
|---|---|---|
| Ambit | Iron | Prospice |
| *Atlantic Advocate (Can.) | *Islands (N.Z.) | *Quadrant (Aus.) |
| Christian Herald | *(Johannesburg) Sunday Times | *Reality (Ire.) |
| Company | (S.A.) | Romance |
| Encounter | *Landfall (N.Z.) | *Scope (S.A.) |
| Essentials | Literary Review | Scots Magazine |
| Fantasy Tales | London Magazine | Slow Dancer |
| Fear | Loving | Stand |
| *Fiddlehead (Can.) | *Malahat Review (Can.) | Stride |
| Good Housekeeping | *Monthly Life (Nigeria) | Sunday Post |
| Granta | My Story | True Romances |
| *Honest Ulsterman | Ninth Decade | *Wascana Review (Can.) |
| Interzone | *Personality (S.A.) | *Your Family (S.A.) |
| *Ireland's Own | *Prize Africa (Zimbabwe) | |

## LONG COMPLETE STORIES

From 8000 words upwards (*See also under* WOMEN'S MAGAZINES)

| | | |
|---|---|---|
| *Landfall (N.Z.) | My Weekly Story Library | Peoples Friend Library |

## SERIALS

(*See also entries under* WOMEN'S MAGAZINES)

| | | |
|---|---|---|
| *Ireland's Own | Secrets | Weekly News |
| People's Friend | | |

## CARTOONS

(*See also* FOR YOUNG PEOPLE: HUMOROUS AND PICTURE PAPERS)

| | | |
|---|---|---|
| Accountancy | Eastern Evening News | Just Seventeen |
| Annabel | Everywoman | Leisure Management |
| Back Street Heroes | Fear | Local Government Chronicle |
| Bella | Fitness | Magazine Week |
| Best | *Fortnight (Ire.) | Margin |
| *Caritas (Ire.) | Gay Times | *Monthly Life (Nigeria) |
| Catholic Gazette | Health & Efficiency | Morning Star |
| Catholic Pictorial | Hi-Fi News | New Statesman & Society |
| Celebrity | *Hotel and Catering Review | Parks & Sports Grounds |
| Countryman | (Ire.) | Planet |
| Coventry Evening Telegraph | The Independent Magazine | Private Eye |
| Daily Star | Indian Bookworm's Journal | Punch |
| Disability Now | Insurance Brokers Monthly | Radio Control Models |
| DR The Fashion Business | *In Dublin (Ire.) | Red Tape |
| Early Times | *Ireland's Own | Satellite Times |

Scouting
Smash Hits
*Southern Cross (S.A.)
The Sport
Sunday Post
Titbits

Today's Guide
Transport
Traveller
Tribune
Vegan

The Voice
Weekend
Woman and Home
Yorkshire Post
Young Soldier

## HUMOUR

Annabel
Custom Car
Dundee Evening Telegraph
    and Post
Good Housekeeping

Hi-Fi News
*Ireland's Own
Jewish Telegraph
Private Eye
Punch

*Reality (Ire.)
Signature
Sunday Post
Weekend

## LETTERS TO THE EDITOR

Annabel
Art & Craft
*Australian Home Beautiful
*Australian Woman's Weekly
Autocar and Motor
Banking World
Best
British Deaf News
Choice
*Commercial Transport (Ire.)
Countryman
Daily Express
Devon Life
Do It Yourself
Family Circle
Film Monthly
Freelance Writing &
    Photography

*The Furrow (Ire.)
Garden News
Good Housekeeping
Good Ski Guide
Ideal Home
Jewish Telegraph
Living
*Living and Loving (S.A.)
Motor Caravan Magazine
Mother
New Woman
19
Outdoor Action
Practical Gardening
Practical Householder
Practical Photography

Professional Nurse
Saga
Satellite Times
She
Singles Magazine
*Songwriter (Ire.)
Stamps
Street Machine
Sunday Mail
True Story
Weekly News
Woman
Woman's Own
Woman's Realm
*Woman's Way (Ire.)
Woman's Weekly

## GOSSIP PARAGRAPHS

Aberdeen Press and
    Journal
Angler's Mail
Angling Times
Architectural Review
Art & Design
*Aspect Magazine (Ire.)
*Auckland Star (N.Z.)
Baptist Times
Birmingham Evening Mail
Bristol Evening Post
British Deaf News
Campaign
*(Cape Town) Cape Times
    (S.A.)
Catholic Herald
Catholic Pictorial
Cheshire Life
Christian Week
Church of England Newspaper
Coin Monthly
*Commercial Transport (Ire.)

Computing
Cosmetic World News
Country Homes & Interiors
Countryman
Coventry Evening Telegraph
Cricketer International
CTN
Daily Mail
Devon Life
Diver
Do It Yourself
DR The Fashion Business
Early Music
Eastern Evening News
Edinburgh Evening News
Education and Training
Engineering
Evening Chronicle
Evening Standard
The Face
Fashion Weekly
The Field

Financial Weekly
Fitness
*Fortnight (Ire.)
Freelance Writing &
    Photography
Garden News
Gas World
Gemmological Newsletter
Golf Monthly
Guiding
Hi-Fi News and Record
    Review
Horse & Pony
Hortus
The Independent
*In Dublin (Ire.)
Insurance Brokers' Monthly
*Irish Business
Jewish Telegraph
Just Seventeen
Justice of the Peace
Lancashire Evening Telegraph

Literary Review
Magazine Week
Making Better Movies
Making Music
Melody Maker
*(Melbourne) Australasian Post
The Mirror
Model Boats
Mother
PR Week
Parents
Penthouse
Popular Crafts
Poultry World
Power Farming
Printing World
Private Eye
Radio Times
Satellite Times

Scoop
Scotland on Sunday
Scottish Field
Somerset & Avon Life
*Songwriter (Ire.)
*Southern Cross (S.A.)
Sport and Leisure
Stage and Television Today
Studio International
Sunday Express
*Sunday Life (Ire.)
Sunday Times
*(Sydney) Bulletin
*Timaru Herald (N.Z.)
Time Out 20/20
Times
Times Educational
    Supplement

Times Educational
    Supplement Scotland
Times Higher Education
    Supplement
Treasure Hunting
Universe
*Weekly Topic (Uganda)
West Africa
Western Mail
Western Morning News
Woman's Realm
*Woman's Way (Ire.)
World Bowls
Writers' Monthly
Yachts and Yachting
Yorkshire Life
Yorkshire Post

## BRIEF FILLER PARAGRAPHS

Aberdeen Press and Journal
Aeroplane Monthly
African Business
Air Pictorial
Angler's Mail
Angling Times
Annabel
Architectural Design
Architectural Review
Art & Design
*Auckland Star (N.Z.)
*Australian Home Beautiful
Autocar and Motor
Balance
Baptist Times
Best
Birmingham Evening Mail
British Deaf News
Budgerigar World
Building
*(Cape Town) Cape Times (S.A.)
Catholic Herald
Catholic Pictorial
Cheshire Life
Christian Herald
Christian Week
Church of England
    Newspaper
Classical Music
Coin Monthly
*Commercial Transport (Ire.)
Cosmetic World News
Countryman
Cricketer International
CTN
Cue International
Daily Star
Daily Telegraph
Dairy Industries International

Devon Life
Do It Yourself
DR The Fashion Business
Early Music
Eastern Evening News
Edinburgh Evening News
Education and Training
Electrical Review
*Electronics Australia
Engineering
Evening Standard
The Face
*Farmer's Weekly (S.A.)
Fashion Forecast
Fashion Weekly
Fear
Fitness
Freelance Writing &
    Photography
*The Furrow (Ire.)
Garden News
Gas World
Gay Times
Gemmological Newsletter
Golf Illustrated Weekly
Golf Monthly
Guiding
Hi-Fi News and Record
    Review
Homes and Gardens
Horticulture Week
Hortus
*Hotel and Catering Review
    (Ire.)
*Image (Ire.)
*In Dublin (Ire.)
*Irish Business
Jane's Defence Weekly
Jewish Telegraph

Just Seventeen
Lancashire Evening
    Telegraph
Literary Review
Liverpool Echo
Local Government Chronicle
Magazine Week
Making Better Movies
Manx Life
Masonic Square
Melody Maker
Model Boats
Model Engineer
Modelling and Miniature
    Crafts
Motor Boat & Yachting
Nautical Magazine
New Musical Express
*New Zealand Gardener
Penthouse
Pilot
Pony
Popular Crafts
Poultry World
Practical Fishkeeping
Printing World
Private Eye
Radio Times
Reader's Digest
Safety Education
Satellite Times
Scoop
Scotland on Sunday
She
Ship and Boat International
Singles Magazine
Snooker Scene
Somerset & Avon Life
*Songwriter (Ire.)

*Southern Cross (S.A.)
Spare Rib
The Sport
Sport and Leisure
Sunday Express
*Sunday Life (Ire.)
Sunday Sun
Sunday Times
*(Sydney) Bulletin
Tennis World

*Theatre Ireland Magazine
*Timaru Herald (N.Z.)
Times Educational
  Supplement
Times Educational
  Supplement Scotland
Times Higher Education
  Supplement
Town and Country Planning
Treasure Hunting

Universe
Vegan
Waterways World
Woman's Realm
World Bowls
World Fishing
Writers' Monthly
Yachting Monthly
Yachts and Yachting
Yorkshire Post

## *Women's Magazines*

### Fiction, Home, Fashions, Children, Beauty Culture

Annabel
*Australian Women's Weekly
Bella
Best
*Bona (S.A.)
Chat
*Chatelaine (Can.)
Company
Cosmopolitan
Country Living
Edinburgh Evening News
Elle (UK)
Essentials
Everywoman
*Fair Lady (S.A.)
Family Circle
*Femina (SA)
Girl About Town
Good Housekeeping
Harpers & Queen
Home and Country
Home Words

Homes and Gardens
*Image (Ire.)
*IT Magazine (Ire.)
Just Seventeen
Lady
Living
*Living and Loving (S.A.)
Love Story
*Mahogany (Zimbabwe)
Mother
My Weekly
*New Idea (Aus.)
New Woman
*New Zealand Woman's
  Weekly
19
Nursery World
Options
Parents
People's Friend
Prima
Scottish Home and Country

Secrets
She
Singles Magazine
Spare Rib
Sunday Post
True Romances
True Story
Vogue
Weekend
Woman
Woman and Home
*Woman's Day (Aus.)
Woman's Journal
Woman's Own
Woman's Realm
Woman's Story Magazine
*Woman's Way (Ire.)
Woman's Weekly
Woman's World
World's Children
*Your Family (S.A.)

## *Men's Magazines*

### (*See also* AVIATION, SPORT, etc.)

Arena
Country
Gay Times
GQ

Masonic Square
Mayfair
Men Only

Penthouse
Signature
Singles Magazine

## *For Young People*

### PERIODICALS

Beano Puzzle Library
Beezer

Blue Jeans
Blue Jeans Photo Novels

Brownie
Bunty

Bunty Library
Commando
*Dolly (Aus.)
Early Times
Horse & Pony
Jackie

Jump
Junior Bookshelf
Just Seventeen
Number One
Pony
Scoop

Scouting
Star Love Stories
Tick-Tock
Today's Guide
Topper
Victor

## HUMOROUS AND PICTURE PAPERS

The Beano
Beano Library
Beezer
Bunty
Buster
Commando
The Dandy
Dandy Cartoon Library

Dandy Library
Debbie Library
Football Picture Story Library
Girl
Hi!
Judy
Judy Library

Mandy
Mandy Library
Nikki
Star Love Stories
Starblazer Library
Today's Guide
Twinkle

## SOME JOURNALS WHICH CONTAIN A CHILDREN'S PAGE OR COLUMN

Birmingham Evening Mail
Church Times
Coventry Evening Telegraph
Driver

*Ireland's Own
Jewish Chronicle
*Melbourne Age (Aus.)
Nursery World

People's Friend
Sunday Post
Woman

# *Subject Articles*

## ADMINISTRATION AND LAW

Administrator
Banking World
Contemporary Review
Country
Criminologist
Education
Family Law
Financial Decisions
Hospitality

Insurance Brokers' Monthly
Justice of the Peace
Land & Liberty
Local Council Review
Local Government Chronicle
Local Government Review
*Management (N.Z.)
Millennium
Municipal Review

Personnel Management
Police Journal
Political Quarterly
Post
Red Tape
Sociological Review
Solicitors' Journal
Work Study

## ADVERTISING, DESIGN, PRINTING & PUBLISHING

*(See also under* LITERARY*)*

Albion
Arena
*Australian Bookseller &
   Publisher
Campaign
*Canadian Interiors
Design
Designers' Journal

Exchange & Mart
The Face
Indexer
Interior Design
InterMedia
Journalist
Learned Publishing

Magazine Week
Market Newsletter
Media Week
PR Week
Publishing News
Studio International
World of Interiors

## AGRICULTURE AND GARDENING

Amateur Gardening
Country
Country Life
Countryman
*Countryman (Aus.)

Country-Side
Dairy Farmer
*Eastern African Agricultural
   & Forestry Journal
   (Kenya)

*East African Journal of
   Rural Development
   (Uganda)
*The Farmer (Zimbabwe)
Farmer's Weekly

*Farmer's Weekly (S.A.)
Farming News
Field
Fresh Produce Journal
*Garden and Home (S.A.)
Garden News

Grower
Horticulture Week
Hortus
*New Zealand Farmer
*New Zealand Gardener
Pig Farming

Poultry World
Power Farming
Practical Gardening
Scottish Farmer
Smallholder
Town and Country Planning

## ARCHITECTURE AND BUILDING

Architects' Journal
Architectural Design
Architectural Review
Building
Building Societies' Gazette
Built Environment
Burlington Magazine
Construction Weekly
Contemporary Review

Country Homes & Interiors
Country Life
Design
Designers' Journal
Education
Homes and Gardens
House & Garden
House Builder
Ideal Home

International Construction
Local Historian
Municipal Review
Museums Journal
National Builder
Retail Attraction
Studio International
Town and Country Planning

## ART AND COLLECTING

*(See also under* PHILATELY*)*

Antique Clocks
Antique Collector
Antique Dealer & Collectors
    Guide
Antiques Folio
Apollo
Art Book Review
Art & Design
Artist

Artist's & Illustrator's
    Magazine
Arts Review
Burlington Magazine
Coin & Medal News
Coin Monthly
Contemporary Review
Country Life
Creative Camera

Design
Fine Art Trade Guild Journal
Gemmological Newsletter
Illustrated London News
Leisure Painter
Museums Journal
Numismatic Chronicle
Studio International

## AVIATION

Aeromodeller
Aeroplane Monthly
Air Pictorial
*Australian Flying

*Canadian Aviation (Can.)
Flight International
Pilot

Spaceflight
Transport
*World Airnews (S.A.)

## BLIND AND DEAF-BLIND

Published by the Royal National Institute for the Blind (see **United Kingdom Book Publishers**)

Braille Chess Magazine
Braille Journal of
    Physiotherapy
Braille Music Magazine
Braille Radio Times
Braille Rainbow
Braille TV Times
Channels of Blessing
Crusade Messenger
Daily Bread
Diane
Fleur de Lys

Gleanings
"Law Notes" Extracts
Light of the Moon
Monthly Announcements
Moon Magazine
Moon Messenger
Moon Newspaper
Moon Rainbow
National Braille Mail
New Beacon (in Braille and
    letterpress)

Nuggets
Physiotherapists' Quarterly
Piano Tuners' Quarterly
Portland Magazine
Roundabout
School Magazine
Scripture Union Daily Notes
Tape Record
Theological Times
Torch
Trefoil Trail

## CINEMA AND FILMS

Campaign
Film Monthly
Films & Filming

International Broadcast
    Engineer
Making Better Movies

New Statesman & Society
Screen International
Sight and Sound

Speech and Drama
Stand

Studio Sound
Time Out 20/20

*What's on Video (Aus.)

## COMPUTERS

Computing
Personal Computer World

Practical Computing
Which Computer?

Your Computer

## ECONOMICS, ACCOUNTANCY AND FINANCE

Accountancy
Accountancy Age
Accountant's Magazine
Accounting World
African Business
*Aspect Magazine (Ire.)
*Australian Financial Review
Banker
Banking World
Building Societies Gazette
Business
Business Credit

Business Scotland
Certified Accountant
Choice
Contemporary Review
Dairy Industries
Economic Journal
Economica
Economist
Financial Decisions
Financial Times
Financial Weekly

Grower
Insurance Brokers Monthly
Investors Chronicle
*Irish Business
Land & Liberty
Local Government Chronicle
Money Week
New Statesman & Society
*Studies (Ire.)
Tribune
West Africa

## EDUCATION

Amateur Stage
Art & Craft
La Brita Esperantisto
British Journal of Special
  Education
Child Education
Education
Education and Training
Guiding
Health Education Journal
Higher Education Quarterly
IS
Junior Bookshelf
Junior Education
Linguist
Local Historian
Modern Language Review

Modern Languages
Modus
Month
Mother
Municipal Review
Museums Journal
Music Teacher
New Blackfriars
New Statesman & Society
Nursery World
Parents
Parents Voice
Prep School
*Reality (Ire.)
Report
Safety Education
School Librarian

Scottish Educational Journal
Speech and Drama
Spoken English
Theology
Times Educational
  Supplement
Times Educational
  Supplement Scotland
Times Higher Education
  Supplement
Together
Tribune
Unesco Courier
Use of English
WES Journal
World's Children

## ENGINEERING AND MECHANICS

(*See also under* AGRICULTURE, ARCHITECTURE, AVIATION, MOTORING, NAUTICAL, RADIO, SCIENCE, TRADE AND COMMERCE)

*Australian Mining
Buses
Car Mechanics
Construction Weekly
Control and Instrumentation
Design
Electrical Review
Electrical Times
*Electronics Australia

Engineer
Engineering
Engineering Materials and
  Design
Everyday Electronics
Filtration & Separation
Gas World
International Construction

Model Engineer
*N.Z. Engineering
Practical Woodworking
Railway Gazette
Railway Magazine
Railway World
Spaceflight
Transport

## HEALTH, MEDICINE AND NURSING

Balance
British Deaf News

British Medical Journal
Caring

*Caritas (Ire.)
Choice

Community Care
Dental Update
Disability Now
*East African Medical Journal
  (Kenya)
Fitness
Health & Efficiency
Health Education Journal
Here's Health
Hospitality
*Irish Journal of Medical
  Science

*Irish Medical Times
Journal of the Royal College
  of General Practitioners
Lancet
Mother
New Statesman & Society
Nursery World
Nursing Times
Parents
Parents Voice
Pharmaceutical Journal
Physiotherapy

The Practitioner
Professional Nurse
Pulse
Quarterly Journal of Medicine
Running Magazine
Saga
Slimmer Magazine
This Caring Business
Vegan
Vegetarian

## HISTORY AND ARCHAEOLOGY

Albion
Bedfordshire Magazine
Coin & Medal News
Contemporary Review
Country Quest
English Historical Review

Geographical Magazine
Heythrop Journal
History
History Today
Illustrated London News
In Britain

Lancashire Life
Local Historian
Museums Journal
New Blackfriars
Scottish Historical Review
*Studies (Ire.)

## HOME

*(See also* WOMEN'S MAGAZINES)

*Australian Home Beautiful
*Australian House and Garden
*Canadian Interiors
*Caritas (Ire.)
Choice
Country Homes & Interiors
DIY Today

Do It Yourself
Embroidery
*Garden and Home (S.A.)
Home and Family
House & Garden
Ideal Home
Jewish Telegraph

Modus
Parents
Practical Householder
Safety Education
Saga
*Your Family (S.A.)

## LITERARY

*(See also under Poetry section)*

Argo
Artrage
*Australian Bookseller &
  Publisher
Author
Book Collector
*Books Ireland
Books Magazine
Bookseller
British Book News
*Canadian Author (Can.)
*Canadian Forum
*Canadian Literature
Cencrastus
Chapman
Contemporary Review
Critical Quarterly
*Dalhousie Review (Can.)
Dickensian
Edinburgh Review
Encounter
*Fiddlehead (Can.)
Freelance Writing &
  Photography
Granta

Illustrated London News
Index on Censorship
Indexer
Indian Bookworm's Journal
Information & Library
  Manager
*Islands (N.Z.)
*Journal of Canadian Studies
Journalist
Junior Bookshelf
*Landfall (N.Z.)
Learned Publishing
Library
Library Review
Literary Review
Llais Llyfrau
London Magazine
London Review of Books
*Malahat Review (Can.)
Margin
Modern Language Review
Modern Languages
New Library World
New Statesman & Society
The New Welsh Review

Orbis
Outposts Poetry Quarterly
*Overland (Aus.)
Planet
Powys Review
Prospice
Publishing News
*Quadrant (Aus.)
*Quill & Quire (Can.)
*Reality (Ire.)
The Scorpion
Signal
Spectator
Stand
*Studies (Ire.)
Times Literary Supplement
Tribune
Use of English
*Wascana Review (Can.)
Woman Journalist
Writers' Monthly
Writing
Writing Women
Y Faner

## MOTORING AND CYCLING

*Australasian Dirt Bike
Autocar and Motor
Back Street Heroes
Bicycle Action
Buses
Car
*Car (S.A.)
Car Mechanics
Caravan Magazine
Classic Cars
Commercial Motor

*Commercial Transport (Ire.)
Custom Car
Cycling
Dirt Bike Rider
Driver
*Kiwi Rider Magazine (N.Z.)
Mobile & Holiday Homes
Motor Caravan Magazine
Motor Cycle News
Motorcaravan and Motorhome
  Monthly

Performance Car
Performance Tuning & Sports
  Car
Practical Motorist
Road Racer Magazine
Scootering
Street Machine
Superbike
Transport

## MUSIC AND RECORDING

Arena
Classical Music
Early Music
The Face
Gramophone
Hi-Fi News
Jazz Journal International
Making Music
Melody Maker

Music and Letters
Music & Musicians
Music Review
Music Teacher
Music Week
Musical Opinion
Musical Times
New Hi-Fi Sound
New Musical Express

Number One
Opera
Organ
Smash Hits
*Songwriter (Ire.)
Songwriting and Composing
Studio Sound
Tempo
Time Out 20/20

## NATURAL HISTORY

*(See also under* AGRICULTURE, RURAL LIFE AND COUNTRY)

Animal World
Aquarist and Pondkeeper
BBC Wildlife Magazine
Budgerigar World
Butterfly News
Cage and Aviary Birds
Cat World
Dalesman
Dog & Country

Ecologist
Entomologist's Monthly
  Magazine
European Racehorse
*Geo (Aus.)
Geographical Magazine
Guiding
Heredity
Horse & Pony

Museums Journal
Natural World
Naturalist
Nature
Pony
Practical Fishkeeping
*Swara (Kenya)
World Magazine

## NAUTICAL AND MARINE

Diver
*Modern Boating (Aus.)
Motor Boat & Yachting
Nautical Magazine
Navy International

Port of London
Practical Boat Owner
Sea Breezes
*Sea Spray (N.Z.)
Ship & Boat International

Ships Monthly
Transport
Yachting Monthly
Yachting World
Yachts and Yachting

## PHILATELY

Stamp Lover
Stamp Magazine

Stamp Monthly

Stamps

## PHOTOGRAPHY

Amateur Photographer
British Journal of Photography
Creative Camera
Forensic Photography

Freelance Writing &
  Photography
Photo Answers

Photography
Practical Photography
Studio International

## POETRY

(*See Poetry section*)

## POLITICS

*Australian Journal of Politics
  and History
*Australian Outlook
*Australian Quarterly
Candour
China Quarterly
Contemporary Review
*Current Affairs Bulletin (Aus.)
*Fortnight (Ire.)
Illustrated London News
International Affairs

Justice of the Peace
New Blackfriars
New Statesman & Society
Peace News
Political Quarterly
*Prize Africa (Zimbabwe)
Round Table
Scorpion
Social and Liberal
  Democrats News
South

*Studies (Ire.)
*Times on Sunday (Aus.)
Town and Country Planning
Tribune
Unesco Courier
Voice of the Arab World
  Intelligence Report
West Africa
*Winnipeg Free Press (Can.)
World Development
World Today

## RADIO AND TELEVISION

Broadcast
*Broadcast (Can.)
Campaign
*Electronics Australia
Gramophone
Hi-Fi News
InterMedia
International Broadcast
  Engineer

Listener
New Statesman & Society
*New Zealand Listener
Practical Wireless
Radio Times
Satellite Times
Short-Wave Magazine
Stage and Television Today

Studio Sound
Television
Time Out 20/20
Tribune
TV Guide
TV Times
Video Week

## RELIGION AND PHILOSOPHY

Baptist Times
*Caritas (Ire.)
Catholic Gazette
Catholic Herald
Catholic Pictorial
*Catholic Weekly (Aus.)
Christian Herald
Christian Week
Church News
Church of England Newspaper
*Church of Ireland Gazette
Church Times
Contemporary Review
Day by Day
Downside Review
Evangelical Quarterly
Faith and Freedom
Friend

*The Furrow (Ire.)
*Herald of the South (Aus.)
Heythrop Journal
Home and Family
Home Words
Inquirer
Jewish Chronicle
Jewish Quarterly
Jewish Telegraph
Life and Work
Methodist Recorder
Mind
Modern Churchman
Month
New Blackfriars
Priests & People
Quaker Monthly
*Reality (Ire.)

Reform
Sign
*Southern Cross (S.A.)
Spiritualists Gazette
*Studies (Ire.)
Studies in Comparative
  Religion
Tablet
Theology
Third Way
Today Magazine
Together
Universe
War Cry
West Africa
*Word (Ire.)
World Outlook
Young Soldier

## RURAL LIFE AND COUNTRY

(*See also under* NATURAL HISTORY)

Bedfordshire Magazine
Cheshire Life

Country
Country Life

Country Quest
Countryman

Country-Side
Coventry Evening Telegraph
Cumbria
Dalesman
Derbyshire Life and
 Countryside
Devon Life
Dorset
Eastern Daily Press
Essex Countryside
The Field
Gloucestershire Life

Hampshire
Hertfordshire Countryside
In Britain
Inverness Courier
Kent
Lady
Lancashire Evening Post
Lancashire Life
Lancashire Magazine
Local Historian
Manx Life
Scots Magazine

Scottish Field
Scottish Home and Country
Shooting Times and Country
 Magazine
Somerset & Avon Life
This England
Town and Country Planning
Warwickshire and Worcester-
 shire Life
Waterways World
Yorkshire Life
Yorkshire Riding

## SCIENCE

(*See also under* AGRICULTURE, AVIATION, CINEMA, ENGINEERING, HEALTH, HISTORY,
MOTORING, NATURAL HISTORY, NAUTICAL, PHOTOGRAPHY, RADIO, SPORTS, TRAVEL)

Contemporary Review
Criminologist
Design
Geological Magazine
Heredity
Illustrated London News

Impact of Science on Society
Information and Software
 Technology
*Irish Press
Mind
Nature

New Blackfriars
New Scientist
Practical Electronics
Science Progress
Sociological Review
West Africa

## SERVICES: NAVAL, MILITARY, AIR, AND CIVIL

Air Pictorial
Army Quarterly & Defence
 Journal

Jane's Defence Weekly
Red Tape
Round Table

RUSI Journal
World War Investigator

## SPORTS, GAMES, HOBBIES AND PASTIMES

(*See also under* AGRICULTURE, ART, AVIATION, CINEMA, HOME, MEN'S MAGAZINES,
MOTORING, MUSIC, NATURAL HISTORY, NAUTICAL, PHILATELY, PHOTOGRAPHY, RADIO,
THEATRE, TRAVEL, WOMEN'S MAGAZINES)

Aeromodeller
Anglers' Mail
Angling Times
*Australasian Sporting Shooter
*Australian Angler's Fishing
 World
Boards
Bridge International
British Chess Magazine
Camping & Walking
Climber and Hill Walker
Club Secretary
Cricketer International
Darts World
Dog & Country
Edinburgh Evening News
European Racehorse
The Field
Gemmological Newsletter
Golf Illustrated Weekly
Golf Monthly
Golf World
Good Ski Guide

Great Outdoors
Guiding
Horse and Hound
Horse and Rider
In Britain
Karate
Leisure Management
Leisure Manager
Military Modelling
Model Boats
Model Engineer
Model Railways
Modelling and Miniature
 Crafts
Outdoor Action
Parks & Sports Grounds
Popular Crafts
Radio Control Models
Railway World
Running Magazine
Scale Models International
Scottish Field
Scouting

Sea Angler
Shooting Times
Ski Magazine
Snooker Scene
*South African Yachting,
 Power Waterski & Sail
Sport and Leisure
Sporting Life
Squash World
Tennis
Tennis World
Today's Golfer
Trout and Salmon
Wisden Cricket Monthly
Woodworker
*Word (Ire.)
Workbox
World Bowls
World Fishing
Yachting Monthly
Yachting World
Yachts and Yachting

## THEATRE, DRAMA AND DANCING

*(See also under* CINEMA, MUSIC)

Amateur Stage
Ballroom Dancing Times
*Canadian Forum
Celebrity
Contemporary Review
Cue International
Dance & Dancers
Dancing Times
Illustrated London News

In Britain
*In Dublin
Karate
*Landfall (N.Z.)
New Statesman & Society
New Theatre Quarterly
*Performing Arts in Canada
Plays & Players

Radio Times
*Reality (Ire.)
Speech and Drama
Stage and Television Today
*Theatre Ireland Magazine
Time Out 20/20
Tribune
TV Times

## TRADE AND COMMERCE

*(See also under* ARCHITECTURE, ADVERTISING, AGRICULTURE, CINEMA, ECONOMICS, ENGINEERING, MOTORING)

Achievement
Bookseller
Brewing & Distilling
 International
British Printer
Business Credit
Cosmetic World News
CTN
Dairy Industries International
DR The Fashion Business
European Plastics News

Fashion Forecast
Fashion Weekly
Fresh Produce Journal
Gifts International
Grocer
Hospitality
*Hotel & Catering Gazette
 (Zimbabwe)
*Hotel and Catering Review
 (Ire.)
Industrial Participation

Information and Software
 Technology
IS
Magazine Week
PR Week
Printing World
Retail Attraction
Toy Trader
Woodworker
World Development

## TRAVEL AND GEOGRAPHY

La Brita Esperantisto
British-Soviet Friendship
Bulletin of Hispanic Studies
Caravan Magazine
Contemporary Review
*Geo (Aus.)

Geographical Journal
Geographical Magazine
Illustrated London News
In Britain
*Ireland of the Welcomes
Local Historian

London Traveletter
*Natal Witness (S.A.)
Railway World
Town and Country Planning
Traveller
World Magazine

# United Kingdom Magazine and Newspaper Publishers

The publishers included here are those who issue periodicals listed in the earlier pages of this *Yearbook*. For a fuller list of newspaper and magazine publishers, with the titles they publish, see *Willing's Press Guide*.

**Academic Press Ltd.,** 24-28 Oval Road, London NW1 7DX   *tel* 01-267 4466   *telex* 25775 Acpres G.

**Ian Allan Ltd.,** Terminal House, Station Approach, Shepperton, Surrey TW17 8AS   *tel* (0932) 228950   *telex* 929806 Iallan G   *fax* (0932) 232366.

**The Architectural Press Ltd** (1902), 9 Queen Anne's Gate, London SW1H 9BY   *tel* 01-222 4333   *telex* 8953505   *fax* 01-222 5196.

**Argus Consumer Publications,** 12-18 Paul Street, London EC2A 4JS   *tel* 01-247 8233.

**Argus Specialist Publications Ltd.,** Argus House, Boundary Way, Hemel Hempstead, Herts. HP2 7ST   *tel* (0442) 66551   *fax* (0442) 66998.

**Associated Magazines Ltd.,** Carmelite House, Carmelite Street, London EC4 0JA   *tel* 01-353 6000.

**Baillière Tindall** (1826), (a division of **Harcourt Brace Jovanovich Ltd**), 24-28 Oval Road, London NW1 7DX   *tel* 01-267 4466   *telex* 25775 Acpres G.

**Benn Publications Ltd.** (1977), Sovereign Way, Tonbridge, Kent TN9 1RW   *tel* (0732) 364422   *telex* 95132 Benton G   *fax* (0732) 361534. *Directors:* James Lear (Chairman & Managing), John Brazier (Managing—Industrial Division), Christopher Leonard-Morgan (Managing—Retail Division), Trevor Barratt, Brian Downing, John Mann, Michael Staton, Patrick Wade.

**Blackwell Scientific Publications, Ltd.** (1939), Osney Mead, Oxford OX2 0EL   *tel* (0865) 240201; 8 John Street, London WC1N 2ES   *tel* 01-404 4101; 23 Ainslie Place, Edinburgh EH3 6AJ   *tel* 031-226 7232   *telex* 83355 Medbok G   *fax* (0865) 721205.

**Cambridge University Press** (1534), The Edinburgh Building, Shaftesbury Road, Cambridge CB2 2RU   *tel* (0223) 312393   *telegraphic address* Unipress, Cambridge   *telex* 817256 Cupcam   *fax* (0223) 315052. *Publishing Director* (Journals): Richard L. Ziemacki, M.A., PH.D.

**Frank Cass & Co., Ltd.** (1958), 11 Gainsborough Road, London E11 1RS   *tel* 01-530 4226   *telegraphic address* Simfay, London   *telex* 897719 Cass G   *fax* 01-530 7795. *Directors:* Frank Cass (Managing), A. E. Cass, M. P. Zaidner.

**The Condé Nast Publications, Ltd** (1916), Vogue House, Hanover Square, London W1R 0AD   *tel* 01-499 9080   *telegraphic address* Volon, London   *telex* 27338 Volon G. *Directors:* Daniel Salem (Chairman), R. S. Hill (Managing), W. G. Stanford, B. Tims, M. J. M. Garvin, D. J. Montgomery, C. Bourne, Richard A. Shortway, S. Boler, P. Stuart, S. Quinn.

**EMAP Pursuit Publishing Ltd.,** Bretton Court, Bretton, Peterborough PE3 8DZ   *tel* (0733) 264666   *fax* (0733) 265515.

**Express Newspapers plc,** Ludgate House, 245 Blackfriars Road, London SE1 9UX   *tel* 01-928 8000   *cables* Lon Express   *telex* 21841/21842   *fax* 01-633 0244.

**Haymarket Publishing Group Ltd,** 22 Lancaster Gate, London W2 3LY *tel* 01-402 4200; 30 Lancaster Gate, London W2 3LP *tel* 01-402 4200 *fax* 01-258 1873.

**IPC Magazines Ltd.,** King's Reach Tower, Stamford Street, London SE1 9LS *tel* 01-261 5000 *telex* 915748 Magdiv G.

**Jane's Information Group,** 163 Brighton Road, Coulsdon, Surrey CR3 2NX *tel* 01-763 1030 *telex* 916907 *fax* 01-763 1005.

**Justice of the Peace Ltd.,** Little London, Chichester, West Sussex PO19 1PG *tel* (0234) 775552 *fax* (0243) 779174.

**Link House Magazines Ltd.,** Dingwall Avenue, Croydon CR9 2TA *tel* 01-686 2599 *telex* 947709 Linkho G. *Directors:* B. Downing (Chairman), P. J. Cosgrove (Managing), D. G. Shuard, A. P. Swinburne, C. K. Gamm, C. D. Jakes.

**Macmillan Magazines Ltd.,** 4 Little Essex Street, London WC2R 3LF *tel* 01-836 6633 *telex* 262024 Macmil G. *Chairman:* N. G. Byam Shaw; *Directors:* R. Barker (Managing), Miss M. Waltham, J. Barnes, T. Tamsett, R. Hartgill.

**Mirror Group Newspapers Ltd.,** Holborn Circus, London EC1P 1DQ *tel* 01-353 0246 *telex* 27286/7 Mirror G *fax* 01-822 3405 and 3864.

**Morgan-Grampian plc,** 30 Calderwood Street, London SE18 6QH *tel* 01-855 7777.

**The National Magazine Co., Ltd.,** National Magazine House, 72 Broadwick Street, London W1V 2BP *tel* 01-439 5000 *telex* 263879 Natmag G *fax* 01-437 6886.

**Numismatic Publishing Company,** Sovereign House, Brentwood, Essex CM14 4SE *tel* (0277) 219876.

**Pergamon Press** (1948), Headington Hill Hall, Oxford OX3 0BW *tel* (0865) 64881 *telegraphic address* Pergapress, Oxford *telex* 83177.

**Polystyle Publications Limited,** 159-161 Camden High Street, London NW1 7JY *tel* 01-482 3202 *telex* 927472 Kings G *fax* 01-482 1826. Children's books and periodicals.

**Profile Books Ltd,** 138 New Road, Ascot, Berkshire SL5 8QH *tel* (0344) 883004.

**Reed Business Publishing Group,** Quadrant House, The Quadrant, Sutton, Surrey SM2 5AS *tel* 01-661 3500 *telex* 892084 Reedbp G *fax* 01-661 2071 *ad doc* DX 45550 Sutton 3.

**Regional Magazines Ltd.,** Finance House, Barnfield Road, Exeter EX1 1QR *tel* (0392) 216766 *fax* (0392) 71050; 9th Floor, St. Lawrence House, Broad Street, Bristol BS1 2EX *tel* (0272) 291069. County magazines.

**Sawell Publications, Ltd.,** 127 Stanstead Road, London SE23 1JE *tel* 01-699 6792 *fax* 01-699 1753.

**Scholastic Publications Ltd.,** Marlborough House, Holly Walk, Leamington Spa, Warwickshire CV32 4LS *tel* (0926 81) 3910 *telex* 312138 Spls G *fax* (0926) 883331 Schol Pub.

**The Scout Association,** Baden-Powell House, Queen's Gate, London SW7 5JS *tel* 01-584 7030 *fax* 01-581 9953 *telegraphic address* Scouting, London. *General Editor:* David Easton.

**Scripture Union** (1867), Scripture Union House, 130 City Road, London EC1V 2NJ *tel* 01-782 0013 *fax* 01-782 0014. Christian Publishers and Booksellers.

**Taylor & Francis, Ltd.,** 4 John Street, London WC1N 2ET *tel* 01-405 2237-9.

**Thomson-Leng Publications,** Dundee DD1 9QJ *tel* 23131 *telegraphic address* Courier, Dundee *telex* 76380. London: 185 Fleet Street, London EC4A 2HS *tel* 01-242 5086 *telegraphic address* Courier, London EC4.

**Times Newspapers Ltd.,** Virginia Street, London E1 9BD *tel* 01-481 4100 *telex* 262141.

**Town & County Magazines,** Oyston Publications plc, Oyston Mill, Strand Road, Preston PR1 8UR *tel* (0772) 722022 *fax* (0772) 736496.

**United Trade Press Ltd.,** UTP House, 33-35 Bowling Green Lane, London EC1R 0DA *tel* 01-837 1212 *telex* 299049 Utpres G *fax* 01-278 4003.

**J. Whitaker & Sons Ltd.,** 12 Dyott Street, London WC1A 1DF *tel* 01-836 8911 *fax* 01-836 2909. *Directors:* Peter Allsop, Louis Baum, R. F. Baum, Richard Hunt, Alan Mollison, T. E. Sweetman, David Whitaker, Sally Whitaker.

**Whitehall Press Ltd.,** Earl House, Maidstone, Kent ME14 1PE *tel* (0622) 59841 *telex* 965204 Whpres G *fax* (0622) 675734.

**John Wright Ltd.** (1825), P.O. Box 63, Westbury House, Bury Street, Guildford GU2 5AW *tel* (0483) 300966. *Managing Director:* A. Pearce, *Editorial Director:* D. J. Kingham.

# Syndicates, News and Press Agencies

In their own interests writers and others are strongly advised to make preliminary enquiries before submitting MSS, and to ascertain terms of work. Commission varies. The details given in the following entries should be noted carefully in respect of syndication, as many news and press agencies do not syndicate articles.

**Academic File** (1985), Centre for Near East, Asia and Africa Research (NEAR), Ground Floor, 172 Castelnau, London SW13 9DH   *tel* 01-741 5878   *telex* 940 12777 Near G   *fax* 01-741 5671. *Editor:* S. Rizvi. Feature and photo syndication with special reference to Middle East, North Africa and Asia.

**Advance Features,** 35 Cantelupe Road, East Grinstead, West Sussex RH19 3BE   *tel* (0342) 328562. *Managing Editor:* Peter Norman. Supplies text and visual services to the regional press in Britain and newspapers overseas. Editorial for advertising supplements on consumer and commercial themes. Instructional graphic panels on a variety of subjects. Text services (weekly); 'agony' columns (teenagers and general), property, careers, women's page editorial, general interest series, family finance, business editorial, daily and weekly crosswords. Legal and business articles for the specialist press. Daily and weekly cartoons for the regional press (not single cartoons).

**Ameuropress,** *Postal address:* P.O. Box 3535, Buenos Aires 1000, Argentina. Located at: Av. Libertador 5560-8°B, Buenos Aires 1426 *tel* 786-4851   *cables* Ameuropres. *Director:* José Gregorio Rîos. Illustrated features to newspapers and magazines world-wide. Specialising in Latin American subjects including travel, human interest stories, hobbies, science, animal features. Regularly supplying women's material including cookery, beauty, fashion, interior decorating, glamour. Also stock colour library for advertising, calendars and illustrations. Undertakes assignments for Latin American subjects.

**Aries Press Features,** P.O. Box 14235, Lyttelton 0140, Transvaal, South Africa *tel* Pretoria 629103. *Director:* Major J. W. Lamb. Well written features suitable for newspaper reading for world-wide syndication. *Payment:* by arrangement.

**The Associated Press Ltd.** (News Department), The Associated Press House, 12 Norwich Street, London EC4A 1BP   *tel* 01-353 1515   *telegraphic address* Associated Londonpsy.

**The Associated Press** (of America), London Office: The Associated Press House, 12 Norwich Street, London EC4A 1BP   *tel* 01-353 1515.

**Australasian News & Press Services (D. J. Varney & Associates** 1964), Box T 1834, G.P.O., Perth, W. Australia 6001   *tel* 293-1455. Australian correspondents and representatives for the international media. Services provided: features and news for colour photo magazines. Articles for consumer, trade, technical and professional journals. Trade news summaries and newsletters. Full range of professional public relations and market research services available including film, television and stage writing, production and talent services.

**Australian Associated Press** (1935), John Coomber, (*Chief Correspondent, London,*) 85 Fleet Street, London EC4Y 1EH   *tel* 01-353 0153-4   *telex* 24661   *fax* 01-583 3563. News service to the Australian, New Zealand and Pacific Island press, radio and television.

**BIPS—Bernsen's International Press Service, Ltd.,** 9 Paradise Close, Eastbourne, East Sussex BN20 8BT   *tel* (0323) 28760. *Editor:* Emile L. Habets. Specialise in photo-features, both black and white and colour. Want human interest, oddity, gimmicky, popular mechanical, scientific, medical, etc., material suitable for marketing through own branches (London, San Francisco, Paris, Hamburg, Milan, Stockholm, Amsterdam (for Benelux), Helsinki) in many countries. Give full information, well researched. Willing to syndicate, but prefer to assign free-lances either on BIPS' ideas or photographer's ideas. Buy outright and pay on acceptance. Query with picture story ideas. Syndicate written features, preferably illustrated. Send s.a.e. for 4-page *Guidelines for Photo-Journalists*.

**Bulls Presstjänst AB,** Tulegatan 39, Box 6519, 113 83 Stockholm, Sweden   *tel* 23 40 20   *telex* 19 482   *cables* Pressbull   *fax* 158010. **Bulls Pressedienst GmbH,** Eysseneckstrasse 50, 6000 Frankfurt am Main 1, Western Germany   *tel* 59 04 18   *telex* 412117   *cables* Pressbull   *fax* 596 22 67. **Bulls Pressetjeneste A/S,** Ebbels Gate 3, N-0183, Oslo, Norway   *tel* 20 56 01   *fax* 204978   *cables* Bullpress. **Bulls Pressetjeneste,** Vesterbrogade 14B, 1620 Copenhagen V, Denmark   *tel* 21 37 27   *telex* 19385   *cables* Pressbull   *fax* 21 14 05. **Bulls Finska Försäljnings AB,** Itäinen Teatterikuja 1 A 23, Box 1019, SF-001 01 Helsinki, Finland   *tel* 62 90 37   *telex* Bullsfin 121 394   *fax* 607602. *Market:* Newspapers, magazines and weeklies in Sweden, Denmark, Norway, Finland, Iceland, Germany, Austria and German-speaking Switzerland. *Syndicates:* dramatic and human interest picture stories; topical and well-illustrated background articles and series; photographic features dealing with science, people, personalities, glamour; condensations and serialisations of best-selling fiction and non-fiction, cartoons, comic strips, merchandising..

**The Canadian Press** (1919), Jim Sheppard (Chief Correspondent), The Associated Press House, 12 Norwich Street, London EC4A 1EJ   *tel* 01-353 6355. London Bureau of the national news agency of Canada.

**Capital Press Service,** 2 Long Cottage, Church Street, Leatherhead, Surrey KT22 8EJ   *tel* (0372) 377451. *Directors:* M. Stone, E. W. Stone. *News Editor:* Nicholas Miller. Stories of trade, commerce and industry for trade papers in this country and abroad. Interested in tobacco, confectionery, air-cargo affairs and business travel (including hotels, luggage, guides, new routes via air, sea, road and train) for U.K. and U.S. journals.

**Caters News Agency, Ltd.,** 191 Corporation Street, Birmingham B4 6RP   *tel* 021-236 9001   *telegraphic address* Copy, Birmingham. *Managing Director:* R. P. Blyth. Collection of news and pictures throughout Midlands. Representatives of Overseas, National and Provincial Press.

**Central Press Features,** 131 Aldersgate Street, London EC1A 4JA   *tel* 01-600 4502   *telegraphic address* Features, London, EC1. Supplies every type of feature to newspapers and other publications in 50 countries. Included in over 100 daily and weekly services are columns on international affairs, politics, sports, medicine, law, finance, computers, video, motoring, science, women's and children's features, strips, crosswords, cartoons and regular 6-12 article illustrated series of international human interest; also editorial material for advertising features.

**Compass News Features** (1984), 16 Boulevard Royal, 2449 Luxembourg   *tel* (352) 274-94   *telex* 3187 Compa Lu   *fax* (352) 27498. *Managing Editor:* Gerard Loughran. News features and graphics agency specializing in subjects relating to the developing world.

**J. W. Crabtree and Son** (1919), 36 Sunbridge Road, Bradford BD1 2AA *tel* 732937 (Office); 637312 (Home). News, general, trade and sport; information and research for features undertaken.

**The Daily Telegraph Syndication,** Ewan Mcnaughton Associates, Alexandra Chambers, 6 Alexandra Road, Tonbridge, Kent TN9 2AA *tel* (0732) 771116 *fax* (0732) 771160. News, features, cartoon-strips, photography, book serialisation. World-wide distribution and representation.

**Europa-Press,** Sveavägen 47, 4th Floor, Box 6410, S-113 82, Stockholm, Sweden *tel* 34 94 35 *cables* Europress *telex* 12359 Eupress S *fax* 34 80 79. *Managing Director:* Sven Berlin. Market: Newspapers, magazines and weeklies in Sweden, Denmark, Norway and Finland. Syndicates: High quality features of international appeal such as topical articles, photo-features, black and white and colour, women's features, short stories, serial novels, non-fiction stories and serials with strong human interest, crime articles, popular science, cartoons, comic strips.

**Europress Features (UK),** 18 St. Chads Road, Didsbury, near Manchester M20 9WH *tel* 061-445 2945. **Europress Features (USA),** Sarah Johns, 142 Hartford Street, San Francisco, California 94105 *tel* 415-558-9270. Representation of newspapers and magazines in Europe, Australia, United States. Syndication of top-flight features with exclusive illustrations—human interest stories—showbusiness personalities. 30-35% commission on sales of material successfully accepted; 40% on exclusive illustrations.

**The Exchange Telegraph Co., Ltd.,** Extel House, 298 Regents Park Road, London N3 2LZ *tel* 01-346 0200. Graham J. S. Wilson (*Chairman*), Stuart Hall (*Managing Director*), Keith R. Smith (*Secretary*).

**Features International,** Tolland, Lydeard St. Lawrence, Taunton TA4 3PS *tel* (0984) 23014 *cables* Deadline, Taunton *fax* (0984) 23901. *Editorial Director:* Anthony Sharrock. Syndicates features to magazines and newspapers throughout the world. The agency produces a wide range of material—mainly from freelance sources—including topical articles, women's features and weekly columns. Distributes directly to all English-language countries. Agents throughout the Common Market countries, Scandinavia, Japan, the Americas and Eastern Europe. Buys copy outright and welcomes story ideas. Sae essential.

**Gemini News Service,** 119 Farringdon Road, London EC1R 3DA *tel* 01-833 4141 *telex* 28604 Monref G (ref. M 3172). Derek Ingram (*Editor*). Bethel Njoku (*General Manager*). Network of correspondents and specialist writers all over the world. Some opening for freelance. Specialists in news-features of international, topical and development interest. Preferred *length* 1000-1200 words.

**Global Syndication & Literary Agency, Limited,** *President:* A. D. Fowler, 323 N. Euclid, Fullerton, California 92632, U.S.A. Interested in previously published books for possible syndication and placement of subsidiary rights. Our book reviewers always looking for non-fiction titles. U.S. postage required for return of material.

**Golconda Response Publications** (1986), 11 Vincent Gardens, Dollis Hill, London NW2 7RJ *tel* 01-450 4767 *telex* 265451/265871 Monref G ref. MAG32310 *fax* 01-208 0084. *Syndication Editor:* Martin Kelleher. Wide range of material including articles on celebrities, motoring, fashion, sport, films, books, wine, food, property, travel, antiques, derived from British and overseas sources. Specialises in electronic storage and transmission of articles. *Sae* essential.

**Graphic Syndication** (1981), 2 Angel Meadows, Odiham, Hampshire RG25 1AR *tel* (0256) 703004. *Manager:* M. Flanagan. Cartoon strips and single frames supplied to newspapers and magazines in Britain and overseas. *Terms:* 50%.

**India-International News Service,** *Head Office:* Jute House, 12 India Exchange Place, Calcutta, 700001 *tel* 20-9563, 20-6572, 45-0009 *telegraphic address* Zeitgeist. *Proprietor:* Ing H. Kothari, B.SC., D.W.P.(LOND), F.I.MECH.E., F.I.E., F.V.I., F.INST.D. 'Calcutta Letters' and Air Mail news service from Calcutta. Specialists in industrial and technical news. Public relations and publicity consultants. Publishes trade and professional journals.

**International Fashion Press Agency,** Mumford House, Mottram Road, Alderley Edge, Cheshire SK9 7JF *tel* (0625) 583537. *Directors:* P. Bentham (Managing), P. Dyson, L. C. Bentham, S. Fagette. Monitors and photographs international fashion collections and developments in textile and fashion industry, including 'state of industry', business development and diversification. Specialist writers on health, fitness, beauty and personalities. Undertakes individual commissioned features. Supplies syndicated columns and pages to press, radio and TV. (NUJ staff writers and photographers). Associate Companies specialise in Management Consultancy and PR.

**International Feature Service,** 104 rue de Laeken, 1000 Brussels, Belgium *tel* 217-03-42. *Managing Director:* Max S. Kleiter. Feature articles, serial rights, tests, cartoons, comic strips and illustrations. Handles English TV-features and books; also production of articles for merchandising.

**The International Press Agency (Pty) Ltd** (1934), P.O. Box 67, Howard Place 7450, South Africa *tel* 021-531926 *telex* 5-26837 SA *fax* 021-538789. *Manager:* Mrs T. Temple; *Editor:* Ms R. Myers. *London Office:* Mrs U. A. Barnett, PH.D. (*Managing Editor*), 19 Avenue South, Surbiton, Surrey KT5 8PJ *tel* 01-390 4414 *fax* 01-398 8723. South African agents for many leading British, American and Continental Press firms for the syndication of comic strips, cartoons, jokes, feature articles, short stories, serials, press photos for the South African market.

**Irish Features** (1986), 2 Church Drive, Glengormley, Co. Antrim, Northern Ireland BT36 6EX *tel* (02313) 44700 *telex* 265871 monref G (quoting 72 Mag 30118). Offers features material of Irish interest for international distribution, research, back-up. Video archive, extensive cuttings library based on Irish press.

**Irish International News Service,** *Editor & Managing Director:* Barry J. Hardy, P.C., 7 King's Avenue, Minnis Bay, Birchington-on-Sea, East Kent CT7 9QL *tel* (0843) 45022. News, sport, book reviews, TV, radio, photographic department; also equipment for TV films, etc.

**Knight Features** (1985), 20 Crescent Grove, London SW4 7AH *tel* 01-622 1467 *fax* 01-622 1522. *Director:* Peter Knight. *Associates:* Ann King-Hall, Caroline Figini, Robin Mackay Miller. World-wide selling of strip cartoons and major features and serialisations. Exclusive agent in U.K. for United Feature Syndicate and Newspaper Enterprise Association.

**London Express News and Feature Services,** division of **Express Newspapers plc,** Ludgate House, 245 Blackfriars Road, London SE1 9UX *tel* 01-928 8000 *cable* Lon Express *telex* 21841/21842 *fax* 01-922 7926. Strips, features, cartoons, photographs, book serialisations and rights, merchandising, etc.

**London News Service,** 68 Exmouth Market, London EC1R 4RA    *tel* 01-278 5661    *fax* 01-278 8480    *telex* 21120 quote M 1317. Worldwide Syndication of features and photographs. *Editor:* John Rodgers.

**Magazine Production Ltd** (1984), 13 Southgate Street, Winchester, Hampshire SO23 9DZ    *tel* (0962) 840088    *telegraphic address* Hambleside, Winchester *telex* 477357    *fax* (0962) 840144. *Directors:* D. R. Yellop, R. A. Jeffery, D. K. Sleap. Requirements: features, short stories, line illustrations, cartoons, colour and black and white photographs mainly for West African market. *Payment:* by arrangement.

**Maharaja Features Private Ltd.,** 5/226 Sion Road East, Bombay, 400022, India    *tel* 484776    *telex* 011-74406 Bydr In ref. DR-016. *Editor:* K. R. N. Swamy. Syndicates feature and pictorial material to newspapers and magazines in India and abroad. Specialists in well-researched articles on India by eminent authorities for publication in prestige journals throughout the world. Also topical features 1000-1500 words. *Illustrations:* Monochrome prints and colour transparencies.

**New Zealand Associated Press,** 107 Fleet Street, London EC4A 2AN    *tel* 01-353 2686.

**New Zealand Press Association,** 85 Fleet Street, London EC4P 4AJ    *tel* 01-353 7040.

**News Blitz International,** Via Cimabue 5, 00196 Rome, Italy    *tel* 36.00.620, 36.19.014, 36.01.489    *telex* 623676 Blitz I    *fax* 06 361 90 14. *President:* Vinicio Congiu. *Sales Manager:* Gianni Piccione. *Graphic Dept:* Giovanni A. Congiu. *Literary* and *Telelevision Depts:* Giovanni A. Congiu. Syndicates cartoons, comic strips, humorous books with drawings, general books, feature and pictorial material, especially high-quality nudes, environment, travels, throughout the world and Italy. Television: importation and dubbing TV series, documentaries, educational films and video for schools. Material from freelance sources required. Average rates of commission 60-40% monthly report of sales, payments on receipt of invoice.

**North West News & Sports Agency, Ltd.** (1956), 148 Meols Parade, Meols, Wirral L47 6AN    *tel* 051-632 5261. News and sports coverage, Birkenhead, Bebington, Wallasey and Wirral.

**Northpix,** 75a Bold Street, Liverpool L1 4EZ    *tel* 051-708 6044. North West and North Wales areas, news, sport, features. 24 hour wire service.

**Orion Press,** 55 1-Chome, Kanda-Jimbocho, Chiyoda-ku, Tokyo, 101, Japan    *tel* (03) 295-1402    *telegraphic address* Orionserv, Tokyo    *telex* J24447 Orionprs    *fax* (03) 295-1430. International press service.

**PA NewsFeatures** (the Feature Service of the Press Association, Ltd.), 85 Fleet Street, London EC4P 4BE    *tel* 01-353 7440. *Features Editor:* Neil Williams; *Chief NewsFeatures Editor:* David Staveley. World-wide syndication to newspapers, magazines and trade journals of regular text and strip services.

**Palach Press Ltd.,** Press and Literary agency (1976), 71 Belmont Avenue, London N17 6AX    *tel* 01-889 1074    *telex* 94012860 Plch G. *Directors:* Jan Kavan, Dr. Trevor Roberts. Czechoslovakia: current affairs, news items, political, economic and cultural information not covered by the official government agency. Also make available opposition documents, literary works by banned authors. Film and news items for TV. Publishes: *Uncensored Czechoslovakia.*

**Chandra S. Perera,** Cinetra, 437 Pethiyagoda, Kelaniya, Sri Lanka   *tel*
521885   *cables* Telecinex, Colombo   *telex* 21918/22425 Perimr Ce Attn Chandra Perera   *fax* 547884 Unique Ce Attn Chandra Perera. Press and TV news,
news films on Sri Lanka and Maldives, colour and black-and-white photo news
and features, photographic and film coverages, screen plays and scripts for TV
and films, Press clippings. Broadcasting, television and newspapers; journalistic features, news, broadcasting and TV interviews.

**Pixfeatures** (Mr. P. G. Wickman), 5 Latimer Road, Barnet, Hertfordshire   *tel*
01-449 9946 and 01-441 6246. Specialises in sale of picture features and news
to European and South African press.

**The Press Association Ltd.** (1868), I. H. N. Yates (*Chief Executive*), C. T. Webb
(*Editor-in-Chief*), R. C. Henry (*Finance Director*) 85 Fleet Street, London
EC4P 4BE   *tel* 01-353 7440   *telegraphic address* Press Association, London.
Home News Agency: Teleprinter and viewdata news, photographs, features.
Distributes world agencies' news in British Isles outside London.

**Christopher Rann & Associates Pty. Ltd.** (1977), *Proprietors:* C. F. Rann, J. M.
Jose, 182 Melbourne Street, North Adelaide, South Australia, 5006   *tel* 08-
267 2299   *fax* 08-267 5524. Former BBC, Guardian and CBS News foreign
correspondents offering full range of professional PR, press releases, special
newsletters, commercial intelligence, media monitoring. Major clients in
Australia, Britain and Scandinavia. Welcomes approaches from organisations
requiring PR representation or press release distribution.

**Reportage Bureau RBL,** Philip Laszlo, Kalevankatu 14 C, 00100 Helsinki-10,
Finland   *tel* (9)0-640 522   *cables* Reportage Helsinki   *telex* 123949 rbl sf.

**Republican Press (London),** Suite 438-439 High Holborn House, 52-54 High Holborn, London WC1V 6RB   *tel* 01-831 2965   *fax* 01-831 2549.

**Reuters Limited,** 85 Fleet Street, London EC4P 4AJ   *tel* 01-250 1122   *telex*
23222.

**Anton Rippon Press Services,** 20 Chain Lane, Mickleover, Derby DE3 5AJ   *tel*
(0332) 512379   *fax* (0332) 384235. News, sport and feature coverage of East
Midlands.

**St. Albans Crown Court News Agency,** 134 Marsh Road, Luton LU3 2NL   *tel*
(0582) 572222   *telex* 826634.

**Sandesa News Agency,** 23 Canal Row, Colombo 1, Sri Lanka   *tel* 21507. *Director:* Gamini Navaratne, B.SC.(ECON)LOND. Supplies—news, features, photographs and press cuttings to local and overseas newspapers and agencies.

**Singer Media Corporation Inc.** (a division of Media Transasia), *President:* Kurt
Singer, *Chairman:* J. S. Uberoi, 3164 Tyler Avenue, Anaheim, California
92801, USA   *tel* 714-527-5650. Use 25 features every week which are distributed to publications in 35 countries. Current needs for reprint rights (no
originals): Profiles of famous people—1-3 parts; Men's fiction; Women's fiction
(high standard only); Adventure features (which are not blood-dripping or
over-sexed); Travel articles with transparencies; Westerns—short stories and
books; modern romance books; books published by reputable publishers. 'We
accept only previously published material.' Interested in books for serial and
book rights. World-wide syndication of cartoons, strips and interviews with
celebrities.

**Solo Syndication & Literary Agency Ltd.** (1978), 49-53 Kensington High Street,
London W8 5ED   *tel* 01-376 2166   *fax* 01-938 3165   *telex* 925235 Solo G.
*Chairman:* Don Short. World-wide syndication of newspaper features, photos,

strips and book serialisations. Professional journalists only. *Commission:* 50/50. Agency represents the international syndication of the London Daily Mail group, the Guinness Book of Records strip cartoon, Guinness Books, IPC Magazines (*Woman, Woman and Home, Woman's Own, Woman's Realm, Woman's Weekly*), News Ltd. of Australia, *New Idea* and *TV Week*, Australia.

**Southern Media Services** (a division of Maximedia Pty Ltd.), P.O. Box 140, Springwood NSW 2777, Australia *tel* (047) 514967 *telex* AA 10720589 *fax* (047) 515545. *Directors:* Nic van Oudtshoorn, Daphne van Oudtshoorn. Illustrated features (colour and black and white) to newspapers and magazines in Australasia and many parts of the world. Also stock colour library. Assignments (news and feature stories, photographs) accepted at moderate rates. Syndicates freelance features and photo features in Australia and abroad, but query before submitting. Commission 50% or by arrangement.

**The Stone Syndicate** (1989), 9 Mountacre Close, London SE26 6SX *tel* 01-670 4419. *Directors:* Charles Garvie, Chancery Stone. *Requirements:* short (up to 5000 words) unconventional noir fiction, especially crime passionel, macabre, horror and fantasy. *No* novels or 'women's fiction'. *Commission:* 50/50. *Preliminary letter; sae* essential; no unsolicited manuscripts.

**Swedish Features,** Sweden, Wennerbergsgatan 10, S–105 16 Stockholm, Sweden *tel* 8-738 30 00 *telex* 17480 *fax* 8-53 28 72. *Managing Director:* Herborg Ericson. *Market:* Newspapers, magazines and weeklies in Sweden, Norway, Denmark and Finland. *Syndicates:* High quality features of international appeal such as topical articles, photo-features, black and white and colour, women's features, short stories, serial novels, non-fiction stories and serials with strong human interest, popular science, cartoons, comic strips and TV features and TV personalities.

**Syndication International, Ltd.,** 4-12 Dorrington Street, London EC1N 7TB *tel* 01-404 0004 *telex* 267503 *fax* 01-430 2437. Major UK supplier of publishing material and international rights for news pictures and text. Comprehensive photo library specialising in pop, royalty, personalities. Agents for Mirror Group Newspapers.

**Tass Agency,** Room 205 (2nd Floor), Communications House, 12-16 Gough Square, London EC4A 3JH. General news service to USSR *tel* 01-353 9831; economic and commercial news service to USSR *tel* 01-353 2661 *telex* 24201 *fax* 01-353 7732.

**Peter Tauber Press Agency** (1950), 94 East End Road, London N3 2SX *tel* 01-346 4165 *telegraphic address* Tauberpres N3. UK and worldwide syndication of exclusive big name celebrity interviews, especially interviews with their associates or ex-associates. Also unique human interest features. Commission 25%.

**THC Newsfeatures Agency** (1984), P.O. Box 9175, Ikeja, Nigeria *tel* 01-961509 *telex* 27207 Magna NG. *Directors:* Babatunde Harrison, Mrs Jemima Harrison. West African correspondents for broadcast and print media in English-speaking parts of the world. Services include special newsletters, market research, commercial and intelligence clippings. Welcomes approaches from organisations abroad requiring PR representation or press release distribution.

**TransAtlantic News Service,** 7100 Hillside Avenue, Suite 304, Hollywood, California 90046, USA *tel* 213-874-1284. News and photo agency serving the British and Foreign press. Staffed by former Fleet Street reporters, TANS supplies entertainment news, features and columns from Hollywood, and topical news in general from California. Covers all Hollywood events and undertakes commissions and assignments in all fields. Candid photos of stars at major Hollywood events a speciality.

**United Press International,** 2 Greenwich View, Millharbour, London E14 9NN   *tel* 01-538 5310 (news), 01-538 5460 (audio), 01-538 0933 (admin), 01-538 0939 (sports)   *telex* 28829   *fax* 01-538 1051.

**Universal News Services Ltd.,** Communications House, Gough Square, Fleet Street, London EC4P 4DP   *tel* 01-353 5200. *Managing Director:* Robert Simpson.

**Eric Whitehead,** Picture Agency and Library (1984), P.O. Box 33, Kendal, Cumbria LA9 4SU   *tel* (0539) 33166, and 24 hour (0860) 534767. News coverage of Lancaster to Carlisle, Lake District.

**Yaffa Newspaper Service of New Zealand,** P.O. Box 509, 10 Spencer Street, Wellington 4, New Zealand   *tel* 793 531   *fax* 797 221.

**Yaffa Syndicate Pty, Ltd.,** 17-21 Bellevue Street, Surry Hills, N.S.W. 2010. *postal address* Box 606, G.P.O. Sydney, N.S.W. 2001, Australia   *tel* 281 2333   *telex* AA 121887 Yaffa   *fax* 281 2750. Largest and oldest established Australian syndicate.

See also the **Agents** section for literary agents.

# Books

## SUBMITTING MANUSCRIPTS

Care should be taken when submitting manuscripts to book publishers. A suitable publisher should be chosen either by examining publishers' lists of publications or by looking out for the names of suitable publishers in the relevant sections in libraries and bookshops. It is a waste of time and money to send the typescript of a novel to a publisher who publishes no fiction, or poetry to one who publishes no verse, though all too often this is done. A preliminary letter is appreciated by most publishers, and this should outline the nature and extent of the typescript and enquire whether the publisher would be prepared to read it (writers have been known to send out such letters of enquiry in duplicated form, an approach not calculated to stimulate a publisher's interest). It is desirable to enclose the cost of return postage when submitting the typescript and finally it must be understood that although every reasonable care is taken of material in the publishers' possession, responsibility cannot be accepted for any loss or damage thereto.

Authors are strongly advised not to pay for the publication of their work. If a MS is worth publishing, a reputable publisher will undertake its publication at their own expense, except possibly for works of an academic nature. In this connection attention is called to the paragraphs on *Self-publishing* and *Vanity Publishing*, at the end of this section, and to the article on *Publishers' Agreements* in the **Publishing Practice** section.

## List of Book Publishers

### UNITED KINGDOM

*Members of the Publishers' Association

**\*AA Publishing** (1979), Automobile Association, Fanum House, Basingstoke, Hants RG21 2EA   *tel* (0256) 20123   *telex* 858538 Aabas G   *fax* (0256) 22575. *Distribution centre* AA Distribution Services Ltd, Dunhams Lane, Letchworth, Herts. SG6 1LF   *tel* (0462) 686241 (24 hours)   *fax* (0462) 480295   *teleordering* Aadist.

*Titles in print* 275    *No. of titles published in 1988* 95

*Managing director* John Howard, *marketing director* Brian Stelling; *editorial manager* Michael Buttler.

*Active publishing areas* travel, atlases, maps, leisure interests, including Baedeker and Egon Ronay titles. **Waymark**—leisure interests.

**Abacus**—see **Sphere Books Ltd.**

**\*Abelard-Schuman Ltd.**—subsidiary company of **Blackie Children's Books.**

**\*Abson Books** (1970), Abson, Wick, Bristol BS15 5TT    *tel* (0275-82) 2446. *Partners:* Anthea Bickerton, Pat McCormack.
English speaking glossaries, guides, West Region. Literary puzzle books. No fiction.

**\*Academic Press,** 24-28 Oval Road, London NW1 7DX    *tel* 01-267 4466    *telex* 25775 Acpres G. *Managing Director:* Joan M. Fujimoto. *Editorial Director:* Conrad Guettler.

**\*Academy Editions** (1967), a member of the Academy Group Ltd. 7-8 Holland Street, Kensington, London W8 4NA. *Editorial* 42 Leinster Gardens, London W2 3AN    *tel* 01-402 2141    *telex* 896928 Academ G    *fax* 01-723 9540. *Distribution* Tiptree Book Services, Colchester, Essex    *tel* (0621) 816362    *fax* (0621) 819011.

*Titles in print* 200    *No. of titles published in 1988* 32
*Director* Dr A. C. Papadakis; *company secretary* John Lister; *sales manager* Sheila de Vallee.

*Active publishing areas* art, architecture, crafts, design, typography, photography, fashion, urbanism, philosophy.

*Series include Architectural Design* Profiles, Architecture Monographs, *Art and Design* Profiles, Art Monographs.

**\*Acorn Editions**—imprint of **James Clarke & Co. Ltd.** Local books on East Anglia.

**Actinic Press Ltd.,** 311 Worcester Road, Malvern, Worcs. WR14 1AN    *tel* (0684) 565045. *Directors*: Leslie Smith, Audrey Smith.
Chiropody.

**\*Addison-Wesley Publishers Ltd.** (1970), Finchampstead Road, Wokingham, Berks. RG11 2NZ    *tel* (0734) 794000    *telex* 846136    *fax* (0734) 794035. *Directors:* R. Bristow, D. Hammonds (USA), P. I. Hoenigsberg, W. R. Stone (USA), N. W. White.
Educational, pure and applied sciences, engineering, computing, software, business studies, economics.

**\*Adlard Coles, Ltd**—imprint of **William Collins Sons & Co Ltd.** Sailing.

**Airlife Publishing Ltd** (1976), 101 Longden Road, Shrewsbury, Shropshire SY3 9EB    *tel* (0743) 235651    *fax* (0743) 232944.

*Titles in print* 143    *No. of titles published in 1988* 26

*Directors* Alastair Simpson (chairman and managing), Robert Pooley.

*Active publishing areas* aviation, technical and general: military, travel, local interest, country pursuits.

**\*The Alison Press,** 81 Fulham Road, London SW3 6RB    *tel* 01-581 9393    *telex* 920191    *fax* 01-589 8419. Associate of **Secker & Warburg Ltd.**
Fiction.

**Ian Allan Ltd,** Terminal House, Station Approach, Shepperton, Surrey TW17 8AS    *tel* (0932) 228950    *telex* 929806 Iallan G    *fax* (0932) 232366.
Transport: railways, aircraft, shipping, road; naval and military history; reference books and magazines; no fiction.

**\*Philip Allan Publishers Ltd**—booklist acquired by **Simon & Schuster International.**

**\*George Allen & Unwin Publishers Ltd.**—see **Unwin Hyman Ltd.**

**\*J. A. Allen & Co. Ltd** (1926), 1 Lower Grosvenor Place, Buckingham Palace Road, London SW1W 0EL    *tel* 01-834 0090 and 5606    *telegraphic address* Allenbooks, London    *telex* 28905 ref. 3810    *fax* 01-976 5836. *Managing Director:* Joseph A. Allen; *Publishing Manager:* Caroline Burt.
Specialist publishers of books on the horse and equestrianism including bloodstock breeding, racing, polo, dressage, horse care, carriage driving, breeds, veterinary and farriery. Technical books usually commissioned but willing to consider any serious, specialist MSS on the horse and related subjects. Also willing to consider exceptionally well-written horse/pony related fiction suitable for young and teenage readers.

**W. H. Allen & Co. plc,** Sekforde House, 175/9 St John Street, London EC1V 4LL    *tel* 01-490 1232    *telex* 28117 Whalen G    *fax* 01-608 3360. *Chairman:* Robert Devereux. *Directors:* Tim Hailstone (Managing), Barry Jafrato (Marketing), Bob Tanner, Vivien James (Publishing).
Biography and memoirs, current affairs, fiction, films, general, history, humour, illustrated, practical handbooks, rock music, television, theatre, true crime. Division: Allison & Busby; imprints: Nexus, Star Books, Virgin Books. Business books imprint: Mercury.

**Allison & Busby**—division of **W. H. Allen & Co. plc.** Art, biography and memoirs, crime, current affairs, economics, general, history, international fiction, literary criticism, poetry, politics, translations, writers' guides.

**\*Alphabooks Ltd.** (1978), 35 Bedford Row, London WC1R 4JH    *tel* 01-242 0946    *telex* 32524 Acblac G    *fax* 01-831 8478. *Directors:* Charles Black, David Gadsby, William Still. A subsidiary of **A. & C. Black plc.**
Ceramics, specialist horticulture, beekeeping, folk art, architecture, crafts.

**Anaya Publishers Ltd** (1988), 49 Neal Street, Covent Garden, London WC2H 9PJ    *tel* 01-836 5644    *fax* 01-836 7889. *Chairman:* Germán Sánchez Ruipérez; *Deputy Chairman:* Sue Thomson; *Managing Director:* Maggie Pearlstine; *Sales and Marketing Manager:* Nick Wells; *Associate Publisher:* Yvonne McFarlane.
Reference, health, cookery, gardening, arts and crafts, sports and leisure; also biography, humour and TV tie-ins.

**Andersen Press Ltd** (1976), Brookmount House, 62-65 Chandos Place, Covent Garden, London WC2N 4NW    *tel* 01-240 8162    *telegraphic address* Literarius, London    *telex* 261212 Lit Ldn G    *fax* 01-240 8636. *Distributor* Tiptree Book Services Ltd, Tiptree, nr Colchester, Essex    *tel* (0621) 816362    *fax* (0621) 819011. *Sales* Century Hutchinson Ltd, address as above    *tel* 01-240 3411: *home sales director* Mike Dougdale, *export sales director* David Parrish.

*Titles in print* 280        *No. of titles published in 1988* 34        *Turnover 1988* £1.6m

*Managing director/publisher* Klaus Flugge; *directors* Philip Durrance, Joëlle Flugge (company secretary); *editor* Audrey Adams; *rights* Pilar Jenkins; *accounts* Frank Stinson.

Children's picture books and fiction. International coproductions.

**Angus & Robertson (U.K.) Ltd.,** 16 Golden Square, London W1R 4BN    *tel* 01-437 9602    *telex* 897284 Arpub G    *fax* 01-434 2080    *Distribution and orders* John Bartholomew & Son Ltd, 12 Duncan Street, Edinburgh EH9 1TA    *tel* 031-667 9341    *telex* 728134 Barts G    *fax* 031-662 4282.

*Titles in print* 326        *No. of titles published in 1988* 74

*Chairman* George Barber; *managing director* Barry Winkleman; *directors* Valerie Hudson (editorial), Marion Head (rights), Helen Priday (publicity).

*Active publishing areas* biography, children's books (fiction, non-fiction), cinema, sports, crafts, travel, humour, leisure, literature, health and beauty, Australia.

**Antique Collectors Club** (1965), 5 Church Street, Woodbridge, Suffolk IP12 1DS   *tel* (0394) 385501   *telex* 987271 Antbok G   *fax* (03943) 4434. *Directors:* John Steel, Diana Steel.
Fine art, antiques, garden history, architecture.

**Anvil Press Poetry** (1968), 69 King George Street, London SE10 8PX   *tel* 01-858 2946. *Directors:* L. W. Carp, Peter Jay, Dieter Pevsner, Caroline Root, Julia Sterland.
Poetry. Submissions only with sae.

**Apple Press** (1984), The Old Brewery, 6 Blundell Street, London N7 9BH   *tel* 01-700 6700   *telex* 298844 Quarto G. Imprint of **Quarto Publishing plc**, book packagers.
Leisure, domestic and craft pursuits; cookery, gardening, fitness.

*****The Aquarian Press Ltd** (1952), Denington Estate, Wellingborough, Northants. NN8 2RQ   *tel* (0933) 440033   *telex* 311072 Thopub G.; 312511 Tpg (0933) 440512. *Directors:* David Young, Eileen Campbell.
Popular, mid-range and scholarly books on all New Age subjects including astrology, magic and occultism, the Western mystery tradition, the paranormal, tarot and divination, character analysis techniques, folklore and mythology. **Crucible** imprint: deals with the subject of transformation, focusing on religion and spirituality, psychology and psychotherapy, philosophy and esoteric thought.

*****Arena**—imprint of **Arrow Books Ltd**. Quality fiction and non-fiction.

**Argus Books Ltd.,** Argus House, Boundary Way, Hemel Hempstead, Herts. HP2 7ST   *tel* (0442) 66551   *telex* 827797   *fax* (0442) 66998.
Model engineering, general modelling, woodworking, hobbies, maritime, aviation, railways, military, crafts, electronics, amateur winemaking, home brewing.

*****Arkana**—'mind, body and spirit' list (formerly owned by Routledge) of **Penguin Books Ltd**.

*****Armada** paperbacks—imprint of **William Collins Sons & Co. Ltd.** Children's books.

*****Arms & Armour Press** (1966), Artillery House, Artillery Row, London SW1P 1RT   *tel* 01-222 7676. *Directors:* Philip Sturrock (Chairman and Managing), R. Dymott, M. R. Chapman, F. J. Roney. Imprint of **Cassell plc.**
Military subjects (tanks, ships, aircraft, small arms, etc.).

**E. J. Arnold & Son Ltd.** (1863), Parkside Lane, Dewsbury Road, Leeds LS11 5TD   *tel* (0532) 772112   *telex* 556347. *Directors:* D. W. Adam (Managing), G. Newton (Marketing), S. E. Sharp (Publishing).
Educational (primary and secondary).

*****Edward Arnold,** the academic, professional and medical publishing division of **Hodder & Stoughton Ltd.,** 41 Bedford Square, London WC1B 3DQ   *tel* 01-637 7161   *telegraphic address* Scholarly, London, WC1   *telex* 265806 Edward G. *Founded* by Edward Arnold in 1890. *Directors:* Richard Stileman (Managing), Paul Price, John Roberts, Philip Walters, Nick Dunton.
English language teaching; textbooks and advanced works in humanities, social sciences, pure and applied science, and medicine; journals.

**\*Arrow Books Ltd,** Brookmount House, 62-65 Chandos Place, Covent Garden, London WC2N 4NW *tel* 01-240 3411 *telex* 261212 Lit Ldn G *fax* 01-836 1409. Division of **Century Hutchinson Ltd.**

*Titles in print* 950 *No. of titles published in 1988* 325 *Turnover 1988* £9.8m

*Chairman* A. J. V. Cheetham; *managing director* D. Attwooll; *directors* R. M. F. Cheetham, R. Hills, P. C. K. Roche, R. L. Smith, J. Wood.

*Active publishing areas* fiction, non-fiction and children's paperbacks. No unsolicited manuscripts.

*Imprints* Arena, Beaver Books, Legend, Mysterious Press.

**\*Art Guide Publications**—imprint of **A. & C. Black (Publishers) Ltd.**

**Art Trade Press Ltd.,** 9 Brockhampton Road, Havant, Hampshire PO9 1NU *tel* (0705) 484943.
Publishers of *Who's Who in Art.*

**Ashford** (1985), 1 Church Road, Shedfield, Hants SO3 2HW *tel* (0329) 834265 *fax* (0329) 834250. *Directors:* Richard Joseph (Publishing), John Mole (Sales and Marketing), *Marketing manager:* Penny Flemons, *Senior editor:* Rebecca Skillman.
General, travel, specialist education with emphasis on field sports and nautical books.

**Ashgrove Press Ltd.** (1980), 4 Brassmill Centre, Brassmill Lane, Bath BA1 3JN *tel* (0225) 25539 *telex* 449212 Lantel G, quote Ashgrove *fax* (0225) 319137. *Directors:* Robin Campbell (Managing), William Allberry, Keith Nelson.
Health, healing and diet, complementary medicine, esoteric, self-help.

**Aslib** (The Association for Information Management) (1924), 26-27 Boswell Street, London WC1N 3JZ *tel* 01-430 2671 *telex* 23667 *fax* 01-430 0514. (For further details see entry under **Societies, Associations and Clubs.**)

**Associated University Presses**—see **Golden Cockerel Press.**

**\*The Athlone Press Ltd.** (1949), 1 Park Drive, London NW11 7SG *tel* 01-458 0888. *Directors:* Brian Southam, Doris Southam, Clive Bingley.
Archaeology, architecture, art, economics, history, medical, music, Japan, oriental, philosophy, politics, psychology, religion, science, sociology, zoology.

**Aurum Press Ltd.** (1977), 33 Museum Street, London WC1A 1LD *tel* 01-631 4596 *telex* 299557 Aurum X *fax* 01-580 2469. *Directors:* Timothy J. M. Chadwick, Michael Alcock, Sue Tarsky, Geoff Barlow.
General, illustrated and non-illustrated adult non-fiction: biography and memoirs, design, sport, film, art, travel. **Aurum Books for Children:** picture books *and* activity books for under fives, classic picture books for all ages. A member of the Really Useful Group plc.

**Avebury**—imprint of **Gower Publishing Group Ltd.** Social science research.

**Bernard Babani (Publishing) Ltd.,** The Grampians, Shepherds Bush Road, London W6 7NF *tel* 01-603 2581 and 7296 *fax* 01-603 8203. *Directors:* S. Babani, M. H. Babani, B.SC.(ENG.).
Practical handbooks on radio, electronics and computing.

**\*Bailey Bros. & Swinfen, Ltd.,** Warner House, Folkestone, Kent CT19 6PH *tel* (0303) 850501 *telegraphic address* Forenbuks, Folkestone *telex* 96328 *fax* (0303) 850162.
Education and library science, general, biography.

**\*Baillière Tindall** (1826), 24-28 Oval Road, London NW1 7DX   *tel* 01-267 4466   *telex* 25775 Acpres G. *Managing Director:* Joan M. Fujimoto, *Editor-in-Chief:* Sean Duggan.
Medical, veterinary, nursing, pharmaceutical books and journals. Agents for Iowa State University Press.

**Howard Baker Press Ltd.**, 27A Arterberry Road, Wimbledon, London SW20 8AF   *tel* 01-947 5482   *cables* Bakerbook, London. *Directors:* W. Howard Baker, I. T. Baker, H. C. I. D. Baker, J. K. Montgomerie M.A. (BARRISTER). *Company Secretary:* D. R. Ridgwell, A.C.I.S., G. P. Mann A.L.A.
General fiction and non-fiction, political science, autobiography, biography, reference, specialist facsimile editions. Preliminary letter and synopsis with s.a.e. required before submitting unsolicited MSS.

**\*Bantam** paperbacks—imprint of **Transworld Publishers Ltd.** General fiction and non-fiction; young adult titles.

**\*Bantam Little Rooster** paperbacks—imprint of **Transworld Publishers Ltd.** Children's picture books.

**\*Bantam Press** (1985), 61-63 Uxbridge Road, London W5 5SA   *tel* 01-579 2652   *telegraphic address* Transcable   *telex* 267974 Trnspb G   *fax* 01-579 5479. *Directors:* Mark Barty-King, Ursula Mackenzie. A division of **Transworld Publishers Ltd.**
Fiction, general, cookery, craft, business, crime, child care, health and diet, history, humour, military, music, paranormal, photography, politics, self-help, science, travel/adventure.

**Arthur Barker Ltd.**, 91 Clapham High Street, London SW4 7TA   *tel* 01-622 9933   *telex* 918066 Wpwnab G   *fax* 01-627 3361. *Chairman:* Lord Weidenfeld. *Directors:* David Roberts (Managing), Richard Hussey, Bud Pauling, Rose Scott, Christopher Falkus, Alan Miles. Imprint of **George Weidenfeld & Nicolson Ltd.**
Sport, humour, showbusiness biographies.

**\*Barrie & Jenkins Ltd.**, 289 Westbourne Grove, London W11 2QA   *tel* 01-727 9636   *telex* 267009   *fax* 01-229 4571. Imprint of **Century Hutchinson Publishing Ltd.**

*Titles in print* 80     *No. of titles published in 1988* 30     *Turnover* £2.5m

*Chairman* A. J. V. Cheetham; *managing director* Julian Shuckburgh; *directors* M. H. J. Agnew, Robert Christie, David Fordham, Anne Furniss, Beth Macdougall, Dallas Manderson, P. C. K. Roche, P. G. W. Snyman, Susan Wakeford.

*Active publishing areas* general fiction; general non-fiction: history, biography, travel, gardening, food and wine, health and beauty, art, design, photography, antiques and collecting, music, politics and contemporary affairs.

**\*John Bartholomew & Son Ltd.** (1826), 12 Duncan Street, Edinburgh EH9 1TA   *tel* 031-667 9341   *telex* 728134 Barts G   *fax* 031-662 4282. Cartographers, printers and publishers.
Maps, atlases, guides.

**\*B. T. Batsford Ltd.** (1843) Subsidiary of Batsford Holdings Ltd, 4 Fitzhardinge Street, London W1H 0AH   *tel* 01-486-8484   *telex* 943763 Crocom G Ref Bat   *fax* 01-487 4296   *Distribution centre* PO Box 4, Braintree, Essex CM7 7QY   *tel* (0376) 21276 (24 hr ansaphone).

*Titles in print* 1300     *No. of titles published in 1988* 150     *Turnover* £4m

*Managing director* Peter Kemmis Betty; *directors* Timothy Auger (editorial), Robert Beard (marketing & sales), John Faulder (non-executive), A. N. Finlay (finance; company secretary), R. E. Huggins (production; U.S. Sales).

*Active publishing areas* archaeology, architecture, building (Mitchell imprint), art, catering, cinema, chess, costume, countryside, travel, craft, needlecraft, history, horticulture, literary criticism, music, school library reference, social work.

**\*BBC Books**, a Division of **BBC Enterprises Ltd.**, Woodlands, 80 Wood Lane, London W12 0TT   *tel* 01-576 2000   *telex* 934678 BBCENT G   *fax* 01-749 8766.

*Titles in print* 2000     *No. of titles published in 1988* 100     *Turnover* £12.5m

*Active publishing areas* books related to television and radio programmes of all subjects.

**\*Beaver Books**—imprint of **Arrow Books Ltd.** Children's books.

**\*Bedford Square Press, National Council for Voluntary Organisations,** 26 Bedford Square, London WC1B 3HU   *tel* 01-636 4066.
Practical guides, directories and issue-based titles covering child welfare, women's and ethnic minority concerns, environmental issues, self help, community development and consumer affairs. Reference books, social planning and policy studies.

**\*Belhaven Press**—see **Pinter Publishers Ltd.**

**\*Belitha Press Ltd.** (1980), 31 Newington Green, London N16 9PU   *tel* 01-241 5566   *telex* 8950511 Oneone G ref. 32159001   *fax* 01-254 5325. *Directors:* Martin Pick, Richard Hayes, Peter Osborn, Rachel Pick (non-executive), Peter West, A.C.A.
Children's books, mostly published in series on an international co-edition basis; books about children; books for children in association with non-publishing organizations; and general books especially on Asia, preferably with potential for television tie-ins. No unsolicited TSS please. Associated film production company Inner Eye Ltd.

**\*Bell & Hyman Ltd.**—see **Unwin Hyman Ltd.**

**\*Ernest Benn Ltd.**—see **A. & C. Black plc.**

**Berkshire Books**—imprint of **Wheaton Publishers Ltd.**

**Bible Society,** Publishing Division, Stonehill Green, Westlea, Swindon, Wilts. SN5 7DG   *tel* (0793) 513713   *telex* 44283 Bibles G   *fax* (0793) 512539. *Publishing Director:* Dave Halls.
Bibles, testaments, portions and selections in English and over 200 other languages; also books on use of Bible for personal, education, church situations.

**\*Clive Bingley Ltd.** (1965), 7 Ridgmount Street, London WC1E 7AE   *tel* 01-636 7543. An imprint of **Library Association Publishing Ltd.**
Librarianship, information work, reference books.

**A. & C. Black plc** (1807), 35 Bedford Row, London WC1R 4JH   *tel* 01-242 0946   *telex* 32524 Acblac G   *fax* 01-831 8478. *Hon. Life President:* A. A. G. Black (great-grandson of founder), *Directors:* Charles Black (Chairman and Joint Managing), David Gadsby (Joint Managing), Leonard Brown, William Still (Secretary). Proprietors of A. & C. Black (Publishers) Ltd, Ernest Benn Ltd, The Dacre Press, Alphabooks Ltd, Nautical Publishing Co. Ltd, Stanford Maritime, Art Guide Publications. Acquired (1983) the publishing assets of EP Publishing Ltd.

**\*A. & C. Black (Publishers) Ltd.** (1978) A subsidiary of A. & C. Black plc.
35 Bedford Row, London WC1R 4JH    *tel* 01-242 0946    *telex* 32524 Acblac
G    *fax* 01-831 8478.    *Sales and distribution centre* Howard Road, Eaton
Socon, Huntingdon, Cambs. PE19 3EZ    *tel* (0480) 212666    *telex* 32524
Acblac    *fax* (0480) 405014.

*Titles in print* 1250    *No. of titles published in 1988* 100    *Turnover* £5m

*Chairman* Charles Black; *managing directors* Charles Black, David Gadsby;
*directors* Leonard Brown (production), Jill Coleman (children's books), Paul
Langridge (rights), William Still (company secretary), Paul White (sales).

*Active publishing areas* children's and educational books (including music) for
3–15 years; arts and crafts, calligraphy, drama (*New Mermaid* series), fishing,
nautical, reference (*Who's Who*), sport, theatre, travel (*Blue Guides*).

**\*Black Swan** paperbacks—imprint of **Transworld Publishers Ltd.** Quality fiction.

**\*Blackie & Son, Ltd.** (1809) Bishopbriggs, Glasgow G64 2NZ    *tel* 041-772
2311    *telex* 777283 Blacki G    *fax* 041-762 0897    *telegraphic address* Blackie,
Glasgow. *London Office*: 7 Leicester Place, London WC2H 7BP    *tel* 01-734
7521    *fax* 01-734 7525.

*Titles in print* 994    *No. of titles published in 1988* 130    *Turnover* £3.2m

*Chairman and managing director* R. M. Miller; *directors* J. W. G. Blackie,
Alexander D. Mitchell, Dr. A. Graeme Mackintosh, A. Rosemary Wands.

*Active publishing areas* educational (infant, primary, secondary); children's
books (fiction and non-fiction for all ages); professional, reference and text
books (biological sciences, earth sciences, chemistry, food technology, engineering, physics, mathematics, business administration).

**\*Blackie Children's Books**, 7 Leicester Place, London WC2H 7BP    *tel* 01-734
7521    *telex* 777283 Blacki G    *fax* 01-734 7525.

*Titles in print* 400    *No. of titles published in 1988* 100    *Turnover* £1.5m

*Directors:* R. M. Miller, A. D. Mitchell; children's publisher Martin West;
Katy Loffman (rights).

*Active publishing areas* children's books, novelty, picture, young fiction,
poetry.

**\*Blackstaff Press Ltd**—see Irish Book Publishers.

**\*Basil Blackwell Ltd.** (1922), 108 Cowley Road, Oxford OX4 1JF    *tel* (0865)
791100    *telex* 837022    *fax* (0865) 791347. *Directors:* Nigel Blackwell (Chairman), David Martin (Deputy Chairman), Julian Blackwell, Michael Holmes,
Per Saugman, John Davey, Terry Collins, James Nash, René Olivieri (Managing), Janet Joyce, Philip Carpenter, Charles Ashford.
Classical studies, economics, education, geography, history, industrial
relations, linguistics, literature and criticism, modern languages, and philology,
politics, psychology, social anthropology, social policy and administration,
sociology, theology, business studies, professional, law, reference, feminism,
information technology, philosophy. **NCC-Blackwell**—joint venture company.

**\*Blackwell Scientific Publications Ltd.** (1939) Osney Mead, Oxford OX2 0EL
*tel* (0865) 240201    *telex* 83355 Medbok G    *fax* (0865) 721205    *cables*
Research, Oxford    *telecom gold dialcom* 79:BSP001. *Other offices* Edinburgh,
London, Boston, Melbourne.

*Titles in print* 2000    *No. of titles published in 1988* 200    *Turnover* £17m

*Chairman* Per Saugman; *managing director* Robert Campbell; *directors* Nigel Blackwell, Keith Bowker, Terry Collins, Jonathan Conibear, Oluf Møller, John Robson, Peter Saugman, Martin Wilkinson.

*Active publishing areas* medicine, nursing, dentistry, veterinary medicine, life sciences, earth sciences, computer science, chemistry, professional.

*****Blandford Press Ltd.**, Artillery House, Artillery Row, London SW1P 1RT *tel* 01-222 7676. *Directors:* Philip Sturrock (Chairman and Managing), M. R. Chapman, F. J. Roney, Clare Howell, Stephen Lustig. Imprint of **Cassell plc.** Art, educational (infants, primary, secondary, technical), crafts, gardening, history, hobbies, juvenile, militaria, music, natural history, practical handbooks, religion, transport, humour.

**Bloodaxe Books Ltd** (1978), P.O. Box 1SN, Newcastle upon Tyne NE99 1SN *tel* 091-232 5988. *Directors:* Neil Astley, Simon Thirsk.
Poetry, literary criticism, literary biography, photography.

**Bloomsbury Publishing Ltd.** (1986) 2 Soho Square, London W1V 5DE *tel* 01-494 2111 *telex* 21323 Blooms *fax* 01-434 0151 *Distribution centre* DMS, 3 Sheldon Way, Larkfield, Maidstone, Kent ME20 6SE *tel* (0622) 882000 *telex* 965514 *fax* (0622) 718036.

*Titles in print* 250 *No. of titles published in 1988* 130

*Chairman* Nigel Newton; *directors* Nigel Newton (managing), David Reynolds (publishing), Liz Calder (publishing), Alan Wherry (marketing), Kathy Rooney (editorial), Caroline Michel (publicity), Roger Yelland (production), Nigel Batt (finance), Mike Petty (editorial), Lucy Juckes (sales), Ruth Logan (rights).

*Active publishing areas* fiction, biography, illustrated, reference, travel and current affairs in hardcover, trade paperback and mass market paperback.

*****The Bodley Head**—see **Jonathan Cape Ltd.**

*****Bowker-Saur, Ltd.** A division of the **Butterworth Group**, Borough Green, Sevenoaks, Kent TN15 8PH *tel* (0732) 884567 *telex* 95678 *fax* (0732) 884530. *Chief Executive:* Klaus G. Saur. *Managing Director:* Shane O'Neill. Bibliographies, trade and reference directories, library and information science, electronic publishing.

*****Marion Boyars Publishers Ltd.**, 24 Lacy Road, London SW15 1NL *tel* 01-788 9522. *Directors:* Marion Boyars, Arthur Boyars.
Belles-lettres and criticism, fiction, sociology, open forum series, ideas in progress series, critical appraisals series, signature series, iris series, music, travel, drama, cinema, dance, biography.

**Boydell & Brewer Ltd.** (1969), P.O. Box 9, Woodbridge, Suffolk IP12 3DF. Medieval history, literature, art history, country and sporting books. *No unsolicited MSS.*

**Brassey's Defence Publishers Ltd** (1886), 24 Gray's Inn Road, London WC1X 8HR *tel* 01-242 2363 *telex* 265871 *fax* 01-405 3194. *Directors:* Maj. Gen. Anthony J. Trythall, C.B., M.A. (Executive Deputy Chairman), Jenny Shaw, B.SC(ECON), M.A. (Publishing). Member of the **Maxwell Pergamon Publishing Corporation plc.**
Defence and national security, foreign policy, weapons technology, military affairs, military history, Soviet studies, reference.

**British ITI Publications,** 4 St. George's House, 15 Hanover Square, London W1R 9AJ *tel* 01-486 6363 *fax* 01-408 1388.

Theatre, reference, bibliography, publications for the British Centre of the International Theatre Institute and for ITI/Unesco, Paris.

**British Leisure Publications**—imprint of **Reed Information Services Ltd.** Leisure books.

*****The British Library (Publications)** (1973), Marketing & Publishing Office, Humanities & Social Sciences, 41 Russell Square, London WC1B 3DG   *tel* 01-323 7704   *telex* 21462   *fax* 01-323 7736. *Head of Marketing & Publishing:* Jane Carr. *Managers:* David Way (Publishing), Colin Wight (Sales & Retail). Bibliography, book arts, music, maps, oriental, manuscript studies, history, literature, facsimiles.

**British Media Publications**—imprint of **Reed Information Services Ltd.** Media and creative services reference books.

*****British Museum (Natural History)** (1881), Cromwell Road, London SW7 5BD   *tel* 01-938 8963 and 9365   *telex* 929437 NH Pubs G   *fax* 01-938 8709. *Head of Publications:* Clive Reynard.
Natural sciences; entomology, botany, geology, palaeontology, zoology.

*****British Museum Publications Ltd.** (1973), 46 Bloomsbury Street, London WC1B 3QQ   *tel* 01-323 1234   *telex* 28592 Bmpubs G   *fax* 01-436 7315. *Directors:* H. J. F. Campbell, Graham C. Greene, H.R.H. the Duke of Gloucester, Sir David Attenborough, Peter Bagnall, Sir Peter Harrop, K.C.B., Professor Sir Harry Hinsley, O.B.E., F.B.A., Professor Peter Lasko, H. A. Stevenson, Sir Ian Trethowan, The Rt. Hon. Lord Windlesham, C.V.O., P.C.
Art history, archaeology, numismatics, history, oriental art and archaeology, horology, children's museum-related books.

**James Brodie Ltd.** (1926), 15 Springfield Place, Lansdown, Bath BA1 5RA   *tel* (0225) 317706. *Directors:* Corinne Wimpress (Secretary), Jeremy Wimpress. Educational (primary and secondary) books, tape recordings, computer software for primary schools; and literal classical translations.

**Brown, Son & Ferguson, Ltd.** (1860), 4-10 Darnley Street, Glasgow G41 2SD   *tel* 041-429 1234 (24 hours)   *telegraphic address* Skipper, Glasgow   *fax* 041-420 1694.
Nautical books; Scottish books and Scottish plays. Scout, Cub Scout, Brownie and Guide story books.

*****Burke Publishing Co., Ltd.,** Pegasus House, 116-120 Golden Lane, London EC1Y 0TL   *tel* 01-253 2145   *telex* 975573 Burke G. *Directors:* Harold K. Starke (Chairman), Naomi Galinski (Managing).
Children's books, (fiction, non-fiction), educational (pre-school and nursery, primary, secondary).

**Burns & Oates Ltd.** (1847), Publishers to the Holy See, Wellwood, North Farm Road, Tunbridge Wells, Kent TN2 3DR   *tel* (0892) 510850   *telex* 957258 Search G   *fax* (0892) 515903. *Directors:* Charlotte de la Bedoyere, Alfred Zimmermann.
Theology, philosophy, spirituality, history, biography, literature, education and books of Catholic interest.

**Ed. J. Burrow & Co. Ltd.** (1900), Publicity House, Streatham Hill, London SW2 4TR   *tel* 01-674 1222. *Chairman:* Remo Dipré. *Managing Director:* Richard Hodges.
Guide books, street plans and maps, travel, year books, etc.

**Business Books, Ltd.** (1921), Brookmount House, 62-65 Chandos Place, Covent Garden, London WC2N 4NW   *tel* 01-240 3411   *telex* 261212 Lit Ldn G   *fax*

01-836 1409. *Directors:* A. J. V. Cheetham, I. Fallon, P. C. K. Roche, L. Shankleman. Imprint of **Century Hutchinson Ltd.**
Business, management, advertising, communication, marketing, selling, investment, financial.

**\*Butterworth & Co. (Publishers), Ltd.—see Butterworths.**

**\*Butterworth Architecture,** P.O. Box 63, Westbury House, Bury Street, Guildford, Surrey GU2 5BH *tel* (0483) 300966 *telex* 859556 Scitec G *fax* (0483) 301563.
Architecture, the environment, planning, townscape, building technology; general.

**\*Butterworth Scientific Ltd,** P.O. Box 63, Westbury House, Bury Street, Guildford, Surrey GU2 5BH *tel* (0483) 300966 *telex* 859556 Scitec G *fax* (0483) 301563.
Scientific, technical and medical.

**\*Butterworths** (1818), 88 Kingsway, London WC2B 6AB *tel* 01-405 6900, Westbury House, Bury Street, Guildford, Surrey GU2 5BH *tel* (0483) 300966 and Borough Green, Sevenoaks, Kent TN15 8PH *tel* (0732) 884567 *telex* 95678 Butwth G *telegraphic address* Butterwort, London. *Directors:* W. G. Graham (Chairman), G. R. N. Cusworth (Chief Executive), D. A. Day, D. J. Jackson, P. Kirk, A. Martin, P. J. Robinson, D. L. Summers, P. E. Cheeseman, G. Burn, E. J. Newman, K. G. Saur. *Branches overseas:* Australia, Canada, New Zealand, Singapore, USA, West Germany.
Law, taxation, accountancy, banking, medicine, science, technology, library, bibliography.

**\*John Calder (Publishers) Ltd.,** 18 Brewer Street, London W1R 4AS *tel* 01-734 3786-7. *Director:* John Calder.
European, international and British fiction and plays, art, literary, music and social criticism, biography and autobiography, essays, humanities and social sciences, European classics. Series include: Scottish Library, New Writing and Writers, Platform Books, Opera Library, Historical Perspectives. Publishers of *Gambit*, the drama magazine, and the *Journal of Beckett Studies*. No unsolicited typescripts.

**Caliban Books** (1977), 17 South Hill Park Gardens, Hampstead, London NW3 2TD *tel* 01-435 0222. *Managing Director:* Peter Razzell.
Social history, biography, history of exploration, psychology and psychotherapy, historical ethnography, sociology.

**\*Cambridge University Press** (1534) The Edinburgh Building, Shaftesbury Road, Cambridge CB2 2RU *tel* (0223) 312393 *telex* 817256 Cupram *telegraphic address* Unipress, Cambridge *fax* (0223) 315052. *U.S.A.* 32 East 57th Street, New York, N.Y., 10022. *Australia* 10 Stamford Road, Oakleigh, Melbourne, Victoria 3166.

*Titles in print* 9266    *No. of titles published in 1988* 1234

*Chief executive and Secretary of the Press Syndicate* Geoffrey A. Cass, M.A.; *deputy chief executive and university printer* Philip E. V. Allin, M.A.; *managing director (publishing division) and deputy secretary* Anthony K. Wilson, M.A.; *marketing director* David A. Knight, M.A.; *Press editorial director* Jeremy Mynott, PH.D.; *director, American branch* Alan Winter, M.A.; *director, Australian branch* Kim W. Harris.

*Active publishing areas* archaeology, art and architecture, computer science, educational (primary, secondary, tertiary), educational software, English language teaching, history, language and literature, law, mathematics, medicine, music, oriental, philosophy, reference, science (physical and biological), social sciences, theology and religion. The Bible and Prayer Book.

**Campbell Books** (1987), 96 Leonard Street, London EC2A 4RH   *tel* 01-739 2929   *telex* 262655 Groluk G   *fax* 01-739 2318. *Directors:* Rod Campbell (Joint Managing/Publisher), David Kewley (Joint Managing/Sales), Marlene Johnson (Finance/Operations), Rita Ireland (Production). Member of **The Watts Group.**
Books for children under 7.

**Canongate Publishing Ltd.** (1973), 17 Jeffrey Street, Edinburgh EH1 1DR   *tel* 031-557 5888   *telex* 72165 Canpub   *fax* 031-557 5665. *Chairman:* George Riches. *Directors:* Stephanie Wolfe Murray (Managing), Neville Moir, A. G. Y. Cowen, D. M. Phillips.
Adult general non-fiction and fiction. **Canongate Classics.** Children's books. **Kelpie** paperbacks.

*****Jonathan Cape Ltd.** (1921), 32 Bedford Square, London WC1B 3SG   *tel* 01-255 2393   *telex* 299080 Random G   *fax* 01-255 1620. Subsidiary of **Random Century.**

*Titles in print* 924     *No. of titles published in 1988* 77     *Turnover 1987* £6.7m

*Chairman* Tom Maschler; *managing director* David Godwin; *directors* Georgina Capel, Anthony Colwell, Tim Chester, Gaye Poulton, Ian Craig.

*Active publishing areas* archaeology, biography and memoirs, children's books, current affairs, drama, economics, fiction, history, philosophy, poetry, sociology, travel. Imprint: **The Bodley Head.**

**Carcanet Press Ltd.** (1969), 208 Corn Exchange Buildings, Manchester M4 3BQ   *tel* 061-834 8730. *Director:* Michael Schmidt (Mexico).
Poetry, memoirs (literary), Fyfield Books, translations, biography, fiction.

*****Cardinal**—see **Sphere Books Ltd.**

**Careers Consultants Ltd** (1970), 12-14 Hill Rise, Richmond, Surrey TW10 6UA   *tel* 01-940 5668. *Directors:* A. F. Trotman, J. L. O'Reilly.
Higher education guidance, careers, lifeskills. Subsidiary of Trotman & Co. Ltd.

**Frank Cass & Co., Ltd.** (1958), Gainsborough House, 11 Gainsborough Road, London E11 1RS   *tel* 01-530 4226   *telegraphic address* Simfay, London E11   *telex* 897719 Cass G   *fax* 01-530 7795. *Directors:* Frank Cass (Managing), A. E. Cass, M. P. Zaidner.
History, African studies, Middle East studies, economic and social history, strategic studies, international affairs, development studies, academic and law journals.

*****Cassell plc** (1848), Artillery House, Artillery Row, London SW1P 1RT   *tel* 01-222 7676   *cables* Cassellpub London   *telex* 9413701 Caspub G   *fax* 01-799 1514. *Orders to* Cassell, Stanley House, 3 Fleets Lane, Poole, Dorset BH15 3AJ   *tel* (0202) 670581   *cables* Blandpress Poole   *telex* 418304 Cassell G   *fax* (0202) 666219.

*Titles in print* 3167     *No. of titles published in 1989* 300

*Chairman and managing director* Philip Sturrock; *editorial directors* Stephen Butcher (academic and educational), Clare Howell (general non-fiction); David Holmes (Ward Lock); *sales directors* Stephen Lustig (academic and educational), Mathew Clarke (general non-fiction); *sales managers* Jonathan King (UK), John Mills (export), Liz White (ELT); *rights and permissions* Chris White.

*Active publishing areas* general, reference, religion, gardening, cookery, sport and pastimes, art and craft, natural history, education (primary, secondary, tertiary), business and professional, military, ELT.

*Imprints* Arms & Armour Press, Blandford, Cassell, Geoffrey Chapman, Mansell, Mowbray, New Orchard, Studio Vista, Tycooly, Ward Lock, Wisley Handbooks.

*Castle House Publications Ltd.* (1978), 28-30 Church Road, Tunbridge Wells, Kent TN1 1JP *tel* (0892) 39606 *fax* (0892) 39609. *Director:* D. Reinders. *Editor:* W. Wilson.
Medical.

**Catholic Truth Society** (1868), 38-40 Eccleston Square, London SW1V 1PD *tel* 01-834 4392 *telex* 295542 Pavis G. *Chairman:* Rt. Rev. Bishop Patrick Kelly, s.t.l., ph.l.; *General Secretary:* David Murphy, m.a.
General books of Roman Catholic and Christian interest, Bibles, prayer books and pamphlets of doctrinal, historical, devotional, or social interest. MSS. of 4,000 to 5,000 words or 2,500 to 3,000 words with up to six illustrations considered for publication as pamphlets.

**Caxton & English Educational Programmes International Ltd.,** 4th Floor, Headway House, 66-73 Shoe Lane, London EC4P 4AB *tel* 01-377 4600 *telex* 885233 Macdon G *fax* 01-822 3319.

**C.B.D. Research Ltd.** (1961), 15 Wickham Road, Beckenham Kent BR3 2JS *tel* 01-650 7745. *Directors:* G. P. Henderson, S. P. A. Henderson, C. A. P. Henderson.
Directories, reference books, bibliographies, guides to business and statistical information.

**Centaur Press, Ltd.** (1954), Fontwell, Arundel, West Sussex BN18 0TA *tel* Eastergate (0243) 543302. *Directors:* Jon Wynne-Tyson, Jennifer M. Wynne-Tyson, M. S. Cover, S. J. Cover, C. A. Vacher, C. G. Vacher. A preliminary letter should be sent before submitting MS.
Philosophy, environment, humane education, biography, the arts, dictionaries, reference.

**Century Hutchinson Ltd.,** Brookmount House, 62-65 Chandos Place, Covent Garden, London WC2N 4NW *tel* 01-240 3411 *telex* 261212 Lit Ldn G *fax* 01-836 1409. *Directors:* F. C. B. Bland (Chairman), A. J. V. Cheetham (Managing), P. G. W. Snyman, D. Attwooll, P. G. Brearley, J. N. M. Cheetham, J. H. Gunn, J. V. Hatch, J. M. Mottram, G. R. Rebuck, P. C. K. Roche. Holding company of the Century Hutchinson Group.

*Century Hutchinson Publishing Ltd,* Brookmount House, 62-65 Chandos Place, Covent Garden, London WC2N 4NW *tel* 01-240 3411 *telex* 261212 Lit Ldn G *fax* 01-836 1409. Division of **Century Hutchinson Ltd.**

*Titles in print* 2000    *No. of titles published in 1988* 500    *Turnover 1988* £18m

*Chairman* A. J. V. Cheetham; *managing director* P. G. W. Snyman; *directors* P. C. K. Roche, R. B. Bloomfield, R. M. F. Cheetham, R. A. Cohen, M. Dugdale, S. C. Lamb, D. A. R. Manderson, J. M. Mottram, G. R. Rebuck, R. H. Trinder, S. V. Wakeford.

*Active publishing areas* antiques and collecting, art, biography and memoirs, children's books (fiction and non-fiction, toy and picture books), dogs (care and breeding), current affairs, essays, fiction, general, history, humour, music, mysticism and meditation, oriental religion and philosophy, poetry, reference, classics, romance, sport, thrillers, travel, films, graphics, fashion, illustrated editions, cookery.

*Imprints* Arrow, Barrie & Jenkins Ltd, Benham Press (stationery items), Business Books Ltd, Century, Cresset Press (stationery items), Ebury Press Ltd, Hutchinson Children's Books, Hutchinson Education Ltd, Frederick Muller Ltd, Stanley Paul & Co., Popular Dogs Publishing Co. Ltd, Radius, Rider & Co.

**\*W. and R. Chambers Ltd** (1820), 43-45 Annandale Street, Edinburgh EH7 4AZ   *tel* 031-557 4571   *telegraphic address* Chambers, Edinburgh   *telex* 727967 Words G   *fax* 031-557 2936.

*Titles in print* 500       *Titles published in 1989* 48

*Chairman* A. S. Chambers; *managing director* W. G. Henderson; *directors* R. Thomson, J. Osborne, R. S. R. Mair.

*Active publishing areas* dictionaries and reference books; educational (primary, secondary, vocational, including mathematics and business studies); general (non-fiction); Scottish books for tourists and home market.

*Imprints* Chambers, Chambers-Cambridge, Blackie-Chambers.

**\*Chapman & Hall, Ltd.** A division of **Routledge, Chapman & Hall Ltd;** 11 New Fetter Lane, London EC4P 4EE   *tel* 01-583 9855   *telex* 263398 *telegraphic address* Elegiacs, London. *Directors:* P. Gardner (Managing), A. Watkinson (Publishing), J. Lavender (Marketing), G. McDonald (Book Production), A. J. Davies (Finance).
Science, technology, medical, professional, reference.

**\*Geoffrey Chapman Publishers**—imprint of **Cassell plc.** Academic and scholarly, biography and autobiography, children's, educational and textbooks, history, antiquarian, law, literature and criticism, music, philosophy, reference and dictionaries, religion and theology, sociology and anthropology.

**Paul Chapman Publishing Ltd** (1987), 144 Liverpool Road, London N1 1LA   *tel* 01-609 5315. *Directors:* P. R. Chapman (Managing), Marianne Lagrange (Editorial).
Business, management, accounting, finance, economics, geography, education, information technology.

**\*Chatto & Windus Ltd & The Hogarth Press Ltd** (1855 & 1917), 30 Bedford Square, London WC1B 3RP   *tel* 01-255 2393   *telex* 299080 Random G   *fax* 01-255 1620. Subsidiary of **Random Century.**

*Titles in print* 665       *No. of titles published in 1988* 107       *Turnover 1988* £4m

*Chairman* John Charlton; *managing director* Carmen Callil; *directors* Jonathan Burnham, Catherine Eccles, Barry Featherstone, Rupert Lancaster, Hilary Laurie, Nicole Paulissen, Alison Samuel.

*Active publishing areas* archaeology, art, belles-lettres, biography and memoirs, cookery, crime/thrillers, current affairs, drama, essays, fiction, history, illustrated books, poetry, politics, psychoanalysis, translations, travel, hardbacks and paperbacks.

**Church of Scotland Department of Communication**—see **Saint Andrew Press.**

**\*Churchill Livingstone** (Medical division of **Longman Group UK Ltd.**), Robert Stevenson House, 1-3 Baxter's Place, Leith Walk, Edinburgh EH1 3AF    *tel* 031-556 2424    *telex* 727511 Longman G    *fax* 031-558 1278.

*Titles in print* 1300     *No. of titles published in 1988* 217

Churchill Livingstone are the agent in Britain, Europe and Africa for the medical publications of Little, Brown.

*Managing director* Andrew Stevenson; *directors* Peter Shepherd (sales and marketing), Peter Richardson (editorial); *publishing managers* Tim Horne, Mary Law, Sally Morris; *production manager* Craig Cameron.

*Active publishing areas* medical books and journals for students, trainees and practitioners; books and journals in nursing, midwifery, physiotherapy, and other allied health disciplines.

**\*Clarendon Press**—see **Oxford University Press.**

**Robin Clark Ltd.** (1976), 27-29 Goodge Street, London W1P 1FD    *tel* 01-636 3992. *Director:* N. I. Attallah (Chairman). A member of the **Namara Group.** Fiction, biography, social history.

**\*T. & T. Clark Ltd.** (1821), 59 George Street, Edinburgh EH2 2LQ    *tel* 031-225 4703    *telex* 728134    *fax* 031-220 4260    *telegraphic address* Dictionary, Edinburgh. *Managing Director:* Geoffrey F. Green, M.A., PH.D.
Dictionaries, law, philosophy, theology.

**\*James Clarke & Co., Ltd.** (1859), P.O. Box 60, Cambridge CB1 2NT    *tel* (0223) 350865    *telex* 817114 Camcom G    *fax* (0223) 66951. *Managing Director:* Adrian Brink.
Theology, religion, educational, technical, reference books.

**\*Collets (Publishers) Ltd.**, Denington Estate, Wellingborough, Northants. NN8 2QT    *tel* (0933) 224351    *telex* 317320 Collet G    *fax* (0933) 76402. *Directors:* Dr. Eva Skelley, S. R. F. Lytton.
Politics, art, music studies, travel guides, language study materials.

**W. H. & L. Collingridge Ltd.**—imprint of **The Hamlyn Publishing Group Ltd.**
Gardening and horticulture.

**Rex Collings Ltd.** (1969), 38 King Street, Covent Garden, London WC2E 8JS    *tel* 01-836 8634    *telex* 337340 Bookps G. *Directors:* Rex Collings, Ian Coltart, Eric Agume Opia.
Children's books (12 years upwards), Africana, poetry, reference books.

**\*William Collins Sons & Co. Ltd.** (1819) General and Children's Book Publishing Offices, and Fontana, Armada and Grafton Paperback Publishing Offices, 8 Grafton Street, London W1X 3LA    *tel* 01-493 7070    *telex* 25611 Collins G    *fax* 01-493 3061. Educational and Religious Book Publishing Offices, Middlesex House, 34-42 Cleveland Street, London W1P 5FB    *tel* 01-638 8300    *telex* 21736 Gower G    *fax* 01-631 3594. *Printing and distribution offices and editorial offices* for Bibles, cartographic and reference books, Westerhill Road, Bishopbriggs, Glasgow G64 2QT    *tel* 041-772 3200.

*Titles in print* 3650     *No. of titles published in 1988* 1300     *Turnover* £118m

*Chairman* K. R. Murdoch; *directors* G. Craig, J. McAlpine, S. Land, T. Kitson.

*General Division* including General Trade Publishing; Fontana and Collins Harvill; *Reference Division* including English bilingual dictionaries, English language teaching, cartographic, reference books, home and leisure, and natural history; *Children's Division* including Fontana Lions, Dragon Books,

Dinosaur Publications and Armada paperbacks; *Collins Grafton* including Grafton Hardbacks, Grafton Paperbacks, Panther and Paladin; *Religious Division* including Bibles and liturgical; *Educational Division. Associated & subsidiary companies: Australia:* William Collins Pty Ltd; *Canada:* William Collins Sons & Co (Canada) Ltd; *New Zealand:* William Collins Publishers Ltd; *South Africa:* Collins Publishers (SA) (Pty) Ltd; *U.S.A.:* Collins Publishers Inc.

*Active publishing areas* archaeology, architecture, art, belles-lettres, Bibles, biography and memoirs, children's books (fiction, non-fiction, rewards, toy and picture, annuals), current affairs, dictionaries, directories or guide books, educational (infants, primary, secondary), essays, fiction, general history, humour, liturgical books, maps and atlases, natural history, naval and military, philosophy, practical handbooks, reference, sailing and nautical, science (history of), sports, games and hobbies, travel, theology and religion. Crime Club, Flamingo paperbacks, Fontana, Fontana Press, Fount Religious Paperbacks, Armada Children's paperbacks, Collins Harvill, Collins Willow Books, Grafton Hardbacks, Grafton Paperbacks, Grafton Trade Books, Paladin Books, Panther Books, Adlard Coles Ltd.

*\*Collins Harvill—imprint of **William Collins Sons & Co. Ltd.** Literature; literature in translation (especially Russian, Italian, French); quality thrillers.

*\*Collins Willow Books—imprint of **William Collins Sons & Co. Ltd.** Special interest.

**Columbus Books Ltd**—incorporated with **Harrap Publishing Group Ltd.**

**Conran Octopus Ltd** (1984), 37 Shelton Street, London WC2H 9HN   *tel* 01-240 6961   *telex* 296249 Conoct G   *fax* 01-836 9951. *Directors:* Alison Cathie (Managing), Mary Evans (Art), Serena Harrison (Production), Anne Dixon (Marketing), Marlis Ironmonger (Financial Controller).
Interior design, DIY, crafts and hobbies, cookery, gardening, travel, antiques, photography, cinema, health and beauty, children's books.

**Conservative Political Centre** (1945), 32 Smith Square, London SW1P 3HH   *tel* 01-222 9000   *telex* 8814563. *Director:* Alistair B. Cooke, o.B.E. Politics, current affairs.

*\*Constable & Company Limited** (1890) 10 Orange Street, London WC2H 7EG   *tel* 01-930 0801-7   *trade* 062-181 6362   *telex* 27950 ref. 830   *telegraphic address* Dhagoba, London WC2   *fax* 01-930 0802.

*Titles in print* 400      *No. of titles published in 1988* 80      *Turnover* £2.5m

*Chairman and managing director* Benjamin Glazebrook; *directors* Anthony Cheetham, Christopher Bland, R. A. A. Holt, Miles Huddleston, P. N. Marks, Richard Tomkins, Robin Baird-Smith, Jeremy Potter.

*Active publishing areas* fiction: general, thrillers, historical. General non-fiction: literature, biography, memoirs, history, politics, current affairs, food, travel and guide books, social sciences, psychology and psychiatry, counselling, social work, sociology, mass media.

**Conway Maritime Press Limited** (1972), 24 Bride Lane, Fleet Street, London EC4Y 8DR   *tel* 01-583 2412   *telex* 8814206 Popper G   *fax* 01-936 2153. *Directors:* W. R. Blackmore (Managing), D. C. Greening, Catherine V. Blackmore.
Maritime and naval history, ship modelling.

**Leo Cooper Ltd.**, 190 Shaftesbury Avenue, London WC2H 8JL   *tel* 01-836 3141   *telex* 8954961   *fax* 01-240 9247. An independent imprint of the **Octopus Publishing Group plc.**

**\*Corgi** paperbacks—imprint of **Transworld Publishers Ltd.** General fiction and non-fiction; titles for ages 10-12.

**Cornwall Books**—see **Golden Cockerel Press.**

**Cornwall Books**—imprint of **Wheaton Publishers Ltd.**

**\*Coronet**—imprint of **Hodder & Stoughton, Ltd.** Fiction and non-fiction paperbacks.

**Council for British Archaeology** (1944), 112 Kennington Road, London SE11 6RE *tel* 01-582 0494. *Director:* Henry Cleere.
British archaeology—academic; practical pocket handbooks; no general books.

**Country Life**—imprint of **The Hamlyn Publishing Group Ltd.** Non-fiction.

**Crocodile Books Ltd** (1987), 1-6 Grand Parade, Brighton, East Sussex BN2 2QB *tel* (0273) 675050 *telex* 878942 Dbcroc *fax* (0273) 675095. *Directors:* David Booth (Chairman), Sonia Birch (Managing), Karen Jankel, Michael Bond.
Children's books.

**\*Croom Helm Ltd.**—incorporated in **Routledge.**

**The Crowood Press** (1982), Crowood House, Ramsbury, Marlborough, Wiltshire SN8 2HE *tel* (0672) 20320 *telex* 449703 Telser G *fax* (0672) 20134. *Chairman:* John Dennis. *Directors:* Tom Bailey, Ken Hathaway (Managing), Rob Henderson, Sarah Somers.
Sport, equestrian, fishing, shooting and country sports, climbing and mountaineering, animal and land husbandry, gardening, dogs, health and social issues, crafts, transport.

**\*Crucible**—see **The Aquarian Press Ltd.**

**James Currey Ltd.** (1985). 54b Thornhill Square, London N1 1BE *tel* 01-609 9026 *telex* 262433 W6327 *fax* 01-609 9605. *Directors:* James Currey, Clare Currey, Keith Sambrook.
Academic studies of Africa, Caribbean, Third World: history, economics, agriculture, politics, literary criticism, sociology.

**Terrence Dalton Ltd.** (1966), Water Street, Lavenham, Sudbury, Suffolk CO10 9RN *tel* (0787) 247572 *fax* (0787) 248267. *Directors:* T. R. Dalton (Managing), T. A. J. Dalton, E. H. Whitehair.
Maritime and aeronautical history, East Anglian interest and history.

**The C. W. Daniel Company Ltd.** (1902), 1 Church Path, Saffron Walden, Essex CB10 1JP *tel* (0799) 21909 *fax* (0799) 513462. *Directors:* Ian Miller, Jane Miller.
Natural healing, homoeopathy, diet, mysticism.

**Dartmouth Publishing Co. Ltd**—associate company of **Gower Publishing Group Ltd.** International relations and international law.

**\*Darton, Longman & Todd, Ltd.** (1959), 89 Lillie Road, London SW6 1UD *tel* 01-385 2341 *telegraphic address* Librabook, London SW6. *Directors:* C. J. Ward (Managing), L. L. Kay, S. Baird-Smith.
Bibles, ethics, theology and religion, spirituality.

**Darwen Finlayson, Ltd.**—see **Phillimore & Co., Ltd.**

**\*David & Charles Publishers plc** (1960) Brunel House, Newton Abbot, Devon TQ12 4PU *tel* (0626) 61121 *telex* 42904 Books G *fax* (0626) 64463.
*Titles in print* 1000 *No. of titles published in 1988* 148 *Turnover* £10.6m

*Chairman* D. St. John Thomas; *directors* G. St. J. Thomas, N. Loasby, C. J. Holmes, L. Springfield, R. Erven, G. M. J. Richardson; *associate directors* E. Allhusen, S. Bryant, C. Sage, A. Williams.

*Active publishing areas* adult non-fiction; practical books; specialising in craft, fishing, gardening, health, music, natural history, railways, sailing, sport, travel. Preliminary letter with outline welcomed. *Authors' Guide* available on receipt of first class stamp.

*Imprint* Poplar Press Ltd.

**Christopher Davies Publishers, Ltd.** (1949), P.O. Box 403, Sketty, Swansea SA2 9BE   *tel* (0792) 48825. *Directors:* Christopher Talfan Davies, K. E. T. Colayera, D. M. Davies.

History, leisure books, sport, general, Welsh interest, Welsh dictionaries, *Triskele Books.*

**Dean's**—imprint of **The Hamlyn Publishing Group Ltd.** Children's books.

**Deloitte Haskins & Sells,** 128 Queen Victoria Street, London EC4P 4JX   *tel* 01-248 3913   *telex* 894941 Dhsldn G   *fax* 01-248 3623. *Managing Editor:* John Pepper; *Production Manager:* Gerald Smith.

Business, accounting, tax and computing.

**J. M. Dent & Sons, Ltd.** (1888), 91 Clapham High Street, London SW4 7TA   *tel* 01-622 9933   *telex* 918066 Wpwnab G   *fax* 01-627 3361   *telegraphic address* Nicobar, London, SW4. *Directors:* Lord Weidenfeld (Chairman), Malcolm Gerratt, Richard Hussey, Alan Miles, Christopher Falkus. Subsidiary of **George Weidenfeld & Nicolson Ltd.**

*Everyman's Library, Everyman's Encyclopaedia, Everyman's Reference Library, Everyman Paperbacks, Everyman Fiction, Classic Thrillers, Mastercrime, Healthright, Master Musicians.*

Archaeology, biography, children's books (fiction, non-fiction), cookery, gardening, health and nutrition, humour, military history, music, natural history, photography, reference, science fact, literary fiction, (no poetry). Preliminary letter/synopsis and s.a.e. requested before submitting MSS.

**\*André Deutsch Ltd.** (1950), 105-106 Great Russell Street, London WC1B 3LJ   *tel* 01-580 2746   *telex* 261026 Adlib G   *fax* 01-631 3253   *cables* Adlib London WC1.

*Titles in print* 650      *No. of titles published in 1988* 140

*Chairman and managing director* T. G. Rosenthal; *president and founder* André Deutsch; *directors* Penelope Buckland, Richard Fernley, Caroline Knox, Nicola Mayhew, Sara Menguc, Laura Morris, Pamela Royds, Jeffrey Sains, Anthony Thwaite, Julian Tobin, Esther Whitby; *literary adviser* Diana Athill.

*Active publishing areas* art, belles-lettres, biography and memoirs, children's books, fiction, general, history, humour, politics, travel, photography.

**Devon Books**—imprint of **Wheaton Publishers Ltd.**

**Dial Industry Publications**—imprint of **Reed Information Services Ltd.** Industrial products and services reference books.

**\*Dinosaur Publications**—imprint of **William Collins Sons & Co. Ltd.** Children's books.

**John Donald Publishers Ltd.** (1973), 138 St. Stephen Street, Edinburgh EH3 5AA   *tel* 031-225 1146. *Directors:* Gordon Angus, D. L. Morrison (Managing), J. B. Tuckwell, Fiona Morrison.

British history, archaeology, ethnology, local history, vernacular architecture, general non-fiction. **Sportsprint**—sports imprint.

**Dorling Kindersley Ltd.** (1974) 9 Henrietta Street, Covent Garden, London WC2E 8PS *tel* 01-836 5411 *telex* 8954527 Deekay G *fax* 01-836 7570.
*Titles in print* 250 *No. of titles published in 1989* 45 *Turnover* £16.6m
*Chairman* Peter Kindersley; *deputy chairman and publisher* Christopher Davis; *managing director* Richard Harman; *directors* Ruth Sandys (international sales), Mike Strong (U.K. sales), Alan Buckingham (editorial), Stuart Jackman (art), John Adams (special sales), Martyn Longly (production), Paul Sayers (finance).
*Active publishing areas* high quality books on non-fiction subjects, including health, cookery, gardening, crafts and reference; also children's non-fiction. Specialists in international co-editions.

**Dorset Books**—imprint of **Wheaton Publishers Ltd.**

**\*Doubleday (UK)** (1989), 100 Wigmore Street, London W1H 9DR *tel* 01-935 1269 *fax* 01-935 4840. *Directors:* Mark Barty-King, Marianne Velmans. A division of **Transworld Publishers Ltd.**
General fiction and non-fiction.

**Downlander Publishing** (1978), 88 Oxendean Gardens, Lower Willingdon, Eastbourne, East Sussex BN22 0RS *tel* (0323) 505814. *Patron:* Jane Gow. *President:* Nora Potter, M.B.E. *Directors:* Derek Bourne-Jones, M.A. (OXON), F.R.S.A., Hilary Bourne-Jones.
Poetry. Preliminary letter and s.a.e. essential; no unsolicited MSS.

**Dragon's World Ltd.**, Paper Tiger Books (1975), High Street, Limpsfield, Surrey RH8 0DY *tel* (0883) 715044 *fax* (0883) 716032 and 26 Warwick Way, London SW1V 1RX *tel* 01-976 8477 *fax* 01-976 8429. *Directors:* H. A. Schaafsma, C. M. A. Schaafsma.
Illustrated books of fantasy, mythology, science fiction, astrology, art and children's fantasy books, natural history, D.I.Y., hobbies.

**Richard Drew Publishing Limited** (1981), 6 Clairmont Gardens, Glasgow G3 7LW *tel* 041-333 9341 *telex* 777308. *Director:* Richard Drew.
General non-fiction, fiction, language, children's.

**Dryad,** P.O.Box 38, Northgates, Leicester LE1 9BU *tel* (0533) 510405 *telex* 341766 Dryad G *fax* (0533) 515015. *General Manager:* J. A. Green.
Dryad *500 series* full colour craft booklets, workcards, patterns.

**Gerald Duckworth & Co., Ltd.** (1898), The Old Piano Factory, 43 Gloucester Crescent, London NW1 7DY *tel* 01-485 3484. *Directors:* Ray Davies, Colin Haycraft (Chairman and Managing).
General, fiction, and academic.

**Earthscan Publications Ltd** (1987), 3 Endsleigh Street, London WC1H 0DD *tel* 01-388 2117 *telex* 261681 Eascan G *fax* 01-388 2826. *Directors:* Neil Middleton (Managing), Margaret Busby (Editorial).
Third World issues including politics, sociology, feminism, cultural questions, environment, economics, current events.

**\*East-West Publications (UK) Ltd.** (1977), Newton Works, 27-29 Macklin Street, London WC2B 5LX *tel* 01-831 6767. *Chairman:* L. W. Carp. *Editor:* B. Thompson.
General non-fiction, travel, Eastern studies, sufism. Children's imprint: **Gallery Children's Books**.

**\*Ebury Press Ltd**—imprint of **Century Hutchinson Publishing Ltd.** Cookery, health, beauty, photography, travel, transport, humour, crafts, antiques, hobbies, gardening, natural history, DIY. Publishers of books from *Good Housekeeping*, *Cosmopolitan*, *Harpers & Queen* and *She*.

**Edinburgh House Press.** All enquiries to: **Lutterworth Press,** *q.v.*

**\*Edinburgh University Press,** 22 George Square, Edinburgh, EH8 9LF   *tel* 031-667 1011   *telegraphic address* Edinpress   *telex* 727442 Unived G   *fax* 031-667 7938.
Academic and general publishers. Archaeology, Islamic studies, information technology, politics, history, visual arts, biological sciences, linguistics, literature (criticism), philosophy, medical sciences, Scottish studies. Imprint: **Polygon.**

**Educational Explorers** (1962), 11 Crown Street, Reading, Berks. RG1 2TQ   *tel* (0734) 873103. *Directors:* C. Gattegno, D. M. Gattegno.
Educational, mathematics: *Numbers in colour with Cuisenaire Rods*, languages: *The Silent Way*, literacy, reading: *Words in Colour*, Educational films.

**Element Books** (1978), The Old School House, The Courtyard, Bell Street, Shaftesbury, Dorset SP7 8BP   *tel* (0747) 51448   *fax* (0747) 51394. *Directors:* Michael Mann, Annie Walton, Jean Allen, David Bacon, Michael Butterwick.
Philosophy, mysticism, religion, psychology, complementary medicine and therapies, astrology and esoteric traditions. Also wide range of original non-fiction under **Nadder** and **Broadcast** imprints.

**Elliot Right Way Books,** Kingswood Buildings, Brighton Road, Lower Kingswood, Tadworth, Surrey KT20 6TD   *tel* Mogador (0737) 832202.
Specialist in low-price "how to" paperbacks. The *Paperfronts* range already includes cookery, family financial and legal, motoring, pets and equestrian, business, fishing, general reference, gardening, games, health and popular educational titles. New ideas considered; editorial help provided.

**Edward Elgar Publishing Ltd**—associate company of **Gower Publishing Group Ltd.** Economics.

**ELM Publications** (1977), 12 Blackstone Road, Huntingdon, Cambs. PE18 6EF   *tel* (0480) 414553. Sheila Ritchie.
Educational books and training resources. Management and business, languages and international (multi-language) conference proceedings.

**\*Elm Tree Books**—see **Hamish Hamilton Ltd.**

**\*Elsevier Science Publishers Ltd.** (1963), Crown House, Linton Road, Barking, Essex IG11 8JU   *tel* 01-594 7272   *telex* 896950 Appsci G   *telegraphic address* Elsbark, Barking   *fax* 01-594 5942. *Publishers:* H. Th. J. E. Gieskes (Managing), R. Lomax, N. Paskin.
Agriculture, architectural science, building and civil engineering, chemistry, food technology, materials science, petroleum technology, pollution, polymers, plastics technology.

**\*Encyclopaedia Britannica International Ltd.** Carew House, Station Approach, Wallington, Surrey SM6 0DA   *tel* 01-669 4355   *telex* 23866 Enbri G   *fax* 01-773 3631. *Managing Director:* Joe D. Adams.

**Enitharmon Press** (1969), 40 Rushes Road, Petersfield, Hampshire GU32 3BW   *tel* (0730) 62753. *Director:* Stephen Stuart-Smith.
Literature, especially poetry.

**\*EP Publishing Ltd**—see **A. & C. Black plc.**

**Epworth Press,** Room 195, 1 Central Buildings, London SW1H 9NR  *tel* 01-222 8010. *Editorial Committee:* Rev. John Stacey, Dr. Valerie Edden, Rev. Dr. Ivor H. Jones, Rev. Graham Slater, Rev. Michael Townsend.
Religion and Theology.

**Ethnographica** (1976), 19 Westbourne Road, London N7 8AN  *tel* 01-607 4074. *Directors:* Stuart Hamilton, Jane Hansom.
Ethnography, history, anthropology, social studies, arts and crafts; catalogues and books produced for museums, galleries and universities in U.K. and Overseas.

**Eurobook Ltd**—see **Peter Lowe (Eurobook Ltd).**

**Euromonitor Publications** (1972), 87-88 Turnmill Street, London EC1M 5QU  *tel* 01-251 8024  *telex* 21120 Monref G 2281  *fax* 01-608 3149. *Directors:* T. J. Fenwick (Managing), R. N. Senior (Chairman).
Business and commercial reference, marketing information, European and International Surveys, directories.

**Europa Publications Ltd.,** 18 Bedford Square, London WC1B 3JN  *tel* 01-580 8236  *telex* 21540 Europa G. *Directors:* C. H. Martin (Chairman), P. A. McGinley (Managing), J. P. Desmond, D. P. Easton, R. M. Hughes, P. G. C. Jackson, R. J. M. Joseph, A. G. Oliver, J. Quinney.
Directories, international relations, reference, year books, history.

**Evangelical Press of Wales** (1955), Bryntirion, Bridgend, Mid Glamorgan CF31 4DX  *tel* (0656) 55886. *Director of English publications:* Gwynn Williams. *Director of Welsh publications:* E. W. James.
Theology and religion (in English and Welsh).

*****Evans Brothers Ltd.** (1905), 2A Portman Mansions, Chiltern Street, London W1M 1LE  *tel* 01-935 7160  *telegraphic address* Byronitic, London, W1 *telex* 8811713 Evbook G  *fax* 01-487 5034. *Directors:* S. T. Pawley (Managing), D. J. Ellis (Sales & Marketing), B. O. Bolodeoku (Nigeria).
Educational books, particularly primary and secondary for Africa, the Caribbean and Hong Kong, general books for Europe and Africa; preschool and school library books for U.K.

**Exley Publications Ltd.** (1976), 16 Chalk Hill, Watford, Herts. WD1 4BN  *tel* Watford (0923) 50505  *telex* 927500  *fax* (0923) 818733. *Directors:* Richard Exley, Helen Exley.
Humour, gift books, children's biographies, anthologies for special occasions. No unsolicited MSS; s.a.e. essential.

**Eyre & Spottiswoode Publishers,** North Way, Andover, Hants SP10 5BE  *tel* (0264) 334202  *telex* 47214 Abpand  *fax* (0264) 334110. *Director:* A. J. Holder (Managing). Division of the **Octopus Group plc.**
Publishers of Bibles, prayer books and religious books.

*****Faber & Faber Ltd.** (1929) 3 Queen Square, London WC1N 3AU  *tel* 01-278 6881  *telex* 299633 Faber G  *fax* 01-278 3817  *telegraphic address* Fabbaf London WC1. *Distribution centre* Elizabeth Way, Harlow, Essex CM20 2HX  *tel* (0279) 21352  *fax* (0279) 417366.

*Titles in print* 2000    *No. of titles published in 1988* 280    *Turnover* £7.5m

*Chairman* Matthew Evans; *managing director* Matthew Evans; *directors* John Bodley (editorial), Dennis Crutcher (production), Giles de la Mare (contracts/editorial), T. E. Faber, Joanna Mackle (publicity), Robert McCrum (fiction), Peter Simpson (company secretary), Will Sulkin (non-fiction).

*Active publishing areas* archaeology, architecture, art, biography, children's books (fiction, non-fiction, picture), cookery books, current affairs, drama, fiction, films, history, literary criticism, medical and nursing, military history, music, philosophy, poetry, politics, screenplays, theatre and ballet, travel.

*Faber Paperbacks* cover many of the subjects shown above. *Art books* include the following series: Faber Monographs on pottery and porcelain, glass and silver.

**Faber & Faber (Publishers) Ltd.** (1969), 3 Queen Square, London WC1N 3AU *tel* 01-278 6881 *telex* 299633 Faber G *fax* 01-278 3817 *telegraphic address* Fabbaf, London, WC1. *Directors:* T. E. Faber (Chairman), Matthew Evans, P. W. G. DuBuisson, Simon Jenkins, John McConnell, Robin Boyle, Peter Simpson. Holding company of **Faber & Faber Ltd.**

**Fabian Society** (1884), 11 Dartmouth Street, London SW1H 9BN *tel* 01-222 8877 *fax* 01-976 7153 (also controls **NCLC Publishing Society Ltd.**). Current affairs, economics, educational, political economy, social policy.

**\*Fantail** (1988), mass market children's imprint of **Penguin Books,** 27 Wrights Lane, London W8 5TZ *tel* 01-938 2200. *Editor-in-Chief:* Adrian Sington. Teenage media books, licensed character publishing, novelties, graphic novels, film and TV tie-ins.

**Farming Press Books** (1951), 4 Friars Courtyard, 30-32 Princes Street, Ipswich, Suffolk IP1 1RJ *tel* (0473) 43011 *fax* (0473) 240501. *Manager:* Roger Smith. Agriculture, humour, veterinary.

**Filmscan Lingual House,** Longman House, Burnt Mill, Harlow, Essex CM20 2JE *tel* (0279) 26721 *telex* 81259 Longmn G *fax* (0279) 31059. *Managing Director:* T. M. Hunt. Educational video/book publishers. English Language Teaching (school and self-study material).

**\*Firefly Books**—see **Wayland (Publishers) Ltd.**

**Fishing News Books Ltd.** (1953), 1 Long Garden Walk, Farnham, Surrey GU9 7HX *tel* (0252) 726868 *telex* 859500 Sharet G (F/077). *Directors:* Vivien M. Heighway, William E. Redman. Commercial fisheries, aquaculture and allied subjects.

**\*Flamingo**—imprint of **William Collins Sons & Co. Ltd.** Paperback literary fiction; non-fiction.

**Focal Press,** P.O. Box 63, Westbury House, Bury Street, Guildford, Surrey GU2 5BH *tel* (0483) 300966 *telex* 859556 Scitec G *fax* (0483) 301563. *Publishing Director:* John Edmondson. Photography and media imprint of **Butterworths.** Professional, technical and academic books on photography, broadcasting, film, television, radio, audio visual and communication media.

**\*Fontana**—imprint of **William Collins Sons & Co Ltd.** Mass market, paperback fiction and non-fiction.

**\*Fontana Lions**—imprint of **William Collins Sons & Co. Ltd.** Paperback children's books.

**G. T. Foulis & Co. Ltd.,** Sparkford, Yeovil, Somerset BA22 7JJ *tel* North Cadbury (0963) 40635 *telex* 46212 Haynes G *fax* (0963) 40825. *Directors:* J. H. Haynes (Executive Chairman), J. Scott (Managing), R. T. Grainger, A. P. Lynch, R. J. Stagg, J. R. Clew, A. C. Haynes. Imprint of **Haynes Publishing Group.**

Motoring/motorcycling, marque and model history, practical maintenance and renovation, related biographies, motor/motorcycle sport, aircraft, nautical, aviation.

**\*W. Foulsham & Co., Ltd.** (1819), Yeovil Road, Slough, Berks. SL1 4JH   *tel* (0753) 26769   *telex* 849041 Sharet G.
General manuals, children's activity, educational, school library, popular occult, do-it-yourself, hobbies and games, sport, travel, art directories, collectibles.

**\*The Foundational Book Co. Ltd.,** Trade: P.O. Box 659, London SW3 6SJ   *tel* 01-584 1053.
Spiritual science.

**\*Foundery Press**—imprint of **Methodist Publishing House.** Ecumenical.

**\*Fount Paperbacks**—imprint of **William Collins Sons & Co. Ltd.** Religious.

**Fourth Estate Ltd** (1984), Classic House, 113 Westbourne Grove, London W2 4UP   *tel* 01-727 8993 and 243 1382. *Directors:* Victoria Barnsley, Michael Mason, John Newall, Giles O'Bryen.
Current affairs, literature, guide books, popular culture, fiction, humour, architecture, design.

**L. N. Fowler & Co. Ltd** (1880), 1201-3 High Road, Chadwell Heath, Romford, Essex RM6 4DH   *tel* 01-597 2491-2.
Astrology, healing, mental science.

**Free Association Books** (1984), 26 Freegrove Road, London N7 9RQ   *tel* 01-609 5646   *fax* 01-700 0330. *Directors:* R. M. Young, M. Arnold, L. Levidow.
Psychoanalysis and psychotherapy; political and cultural aspects of science, technology and medicine; history; biography, autobiography and memoirs.

**W. H. Freeman & Co., Ltd.** (1959), 20 Beaumont Street, Oxford OX1 2NQ   *tel* (0865) 726975   *telex* 83677 Whfrmn G   *fax* (0865) 790391. *Directors:* L. Chaput, G. Voaden, F. Fochetta, H. Morgan.
Science, technical, medicine, economics, psychology, archaeology.

**\*Freeway** paperbacks—imprint of **Transworld Publishers Ltd.** Young adult books.

**\*Samuel French Ltd.** (1830), 52 Fitzroy Street, London W1P 6JR   *tel* 01-387 9373   *fax* 01-387 2161. *Branches:* New York, Hollywood, Toronto, Sydney *q.v. Directors:* Abbott Van Nostrand (Chairman), John Hughes (Managing), John Bedding. Publishers of plays and agents for the collection of royalties.
Drama.

**David Fulton Publishers Ltd** (1987), 2 Barbon Close, Great Ormond Street, London WC1N 3JX   *tel* 01-405 5606   *telex* 934999 Txlink G   *fax* 01-831 4840.
Education, educational psychology, special education, geography, office skills and personal computing, psychiatry.

**Futura,** Headway House, 66–73 Shoe Lane, Holborn, London EC4P 4AB   *tel* 01-377 4600   *telex* 885233 Macdon G   *fax* 01-583 4407/8. Division of **Macdonald & Co. (Publishers Ltd.**
General paperback fiction and non-fiction. Imprints: Orbit, Troubadour.

**Gairm Publications,** incorporating Alex MacLaren & Sons, (1875), 29 Waterloo Street, Glasgow G2 6BZ   *tel* 041-221 1971.
Dictionaries, language books, novels, poetry, music, quarterly magazine (Gaelic only).

**\*Gallery Children's Books**—imprint of **East-West Publications (UK) Ltd.**

**Gateway Books** (1982), The Hollies, Mill Hill, Wellow, Nr Bath, Avon BA2
8QJ *tel* (0225) 835127 *telex* 449212 Lantel G ref 197 *fax* (0225) 469845 ref
197. *Publisher:* Alick Bartholomew.
Popular psychology, philosophy, alternative medicine, self help.

**The Gay Men's Press**—see **GMP Publishers Ltd.**

**Gee & Son (Denbigh) Ltd.** (1808), Chapel Street, Denbigh, Clwyd LL16 3SW
*tel* Denbigh (074 571) 2020. *Directors:* E. Evans, H. M. Lloyd, J. Williams.
Oldest Welsh publishers. Books of interest to Wales, in Welsh and English.

*****Geographia Ltd.** (1921), 105-107 Bath Road, Cheltenham, Glos. GL53
7LE *tel* (0242) 512748 *fax* (0242) 222725. *Manager:* C. J. Moore. A
division of **John Bartholomew & Son Ltd.**
Maps, guides, and atlases.

**Geographical Publications Ltd.** (1933), The Keep, Berkhamsted Place, Berkhamsted, Herts. HP4 1HQ *tel* (0442) 862981. *Directors:* A. N. Clark, G.
N. Clark, G. N. Blake, D. R. Denman. *Secretary:* G. N. Clark.
Books on geography and land affairs, both on own account and jointly with
other publishers. Publishers and general agents to World Land Use Survey
and International Geographical Union.

*****Stanley Gibbons Publications Ltd.** (1856), Parkside Industrial Estate,
Christchurch Road, Ringwood, Hants BH24 3SH *tel* (0425) 472363 *telex*
41271 Sgp Pub G *fax* (0425) 470247. *Managing Director:* S. Northcote.

**Robert Gibson & Sons Glasgow, Ltd.** (1885), 17 Fitzroy Place, Glasgow G3
7SF *tel* 041-248 5674. *Directors:* R. D. C. Gibson, R. G. C. Gibson, Dr. J.
S. McEwan, M. Pinkerton, H. C. Crawford, N. J. Crawford.
Educational.

**John Gifford Ltd.** (1937), 113-119 Charing Cross Road, London WC2H 0EB
*Directors:* R. Batty, C. Batty.
Gardening, natural history, collecting antiques.

*****Ginn & Company Ltd.** (1867) Prebendal House, Parson's Fee, Aylesbury,
Bucks. HP20 2QZ *tel* (0296) 88411 *telex* 83535 Ginn D *fax* (0296) 25487.
*Titles in print* 800 *No. of titles published in 1988* 40
*Chairman* N. Thompson; *managing director* W. P. Shepherd; *directors*
C. Bushnell-Wye, D. J. Miller, N. G. Hall.
*Active publishing areas* educational (pre-school to age 12).

*****Mary Glasgow Publications Ltd.** (1956), Avenue House, 131–133 Holland Park
Avenue, London W11 4UT *tel* 01-603 4688 *telex* 311890 Mgpubs *fax* 01-
602 5197. *Directors:* A. S. Brode (Chairman), P. St C. Proctor (Joint Managing), J. N. Samsom (Joint Managing), D. Raggett, L. K. Upton, W. D.
Antrobus.
Modern languages: French, Spanish, German, and English as a foreign language; language magazines and readers, courses, films, filmstrips, tapes;
geography and social studies at primary and secondary level.

**GMP Publishers Ltd** (1979), P.O. Box 247, London N17 9QR *tel* 01-365
1545 *fax* 01-365 1252. *Directors:* Aubrey Walter, David Fernbach, Richard
Dipple.
**The Gay Men's Press** imprint: modern, pop, historical/literary fiction, biography and memoir, art, photography, history, humour, drama, film, health,
social/political questions, gay verse, lit crit; *Gay Modern Classics* (reprints
of gay fiction/non-fiction from past 100 years). Also **Heretic Books**, *qv.*

**Godfrey Cave Associates Ltd.** (1975), 42 Bloomsbury Street, London WC1B 3QJ *tel* 01-636 9177 *telex* 266945 Macrol G *fax* 01-636 9091 *telegraphic address* Godave London WC1. *Directors:* John Maxwell, Geoffrey Howard. General non-fiction, reprints, remainders.

**Golden Cockerel Press,** 25 Sicilian Avenue, London WC1A 2QH *tel* 01-405 7979. *Directors:* Michael Wright, Thomas Yoseloff (USA). Imprints: **Associated University Presses**—literary criticism, art, music, history, film, theology, philosophy, Jewish studies, politics, sociology; **Cornwall Books**—antiques, history, sport, film, general.

**\*Victor Gollancz Ltd.** (1927), 14 Henrietta Street, London WC2E 8QJ *tel* 01-836 2006 *telex* 265033 Vgbook G *fax* 01-379 0934. *Directors:* Livia Gollancz, Stephen Bray, David Burnett, Jane Blackstock, Chris Kloet, Elizabeth Dobson, Malcolm Edwards, Joanna Goldsworthy, Liz Knights, Andrew Kay. Biography and memoirs, children's books, current affairs, fiction, crime fiction, science fiction, fantasy and macabre, history, music, mountaineering, natural history, sociology, travel. In association with Peter Crawley: Master Bridge Series, historical architecture, cookery, general.

**Gomer Press** (1892), J. D. Lewis & Sons Limited, Gomer Press, Llandysul, Dyfed SA44 4BQ *tel* (055 932) 2371 *fax* (055 932) 2591 *telegraphic address* Gomerian, Llandysul. *Directors:* J. Huw Lewis, John H. Lewis. Books in Welsh: biography, local history.

**Gower Publishing Group Ltd.** (1967), Gower House, Croft Road, Aldershot, Hampshire GU11 3HR *tel* (0252) 331551. *Managing Director:* N. A. E. Farrow. Practical management and business reference, library science, engineering, industrial technology. Academic monographs on the social sciences. Reference and scholarly works in art, architecture, music, humanities. Imprints: Avebury, Dartmouth Publishing Co. Ltd, Edward Elgar Publishing Ltd, Scolar Press, Technical Press Ltd, Wildwood House Ltd.

**\*Grafton Books Ltd.**—imprint of **William Collins Sons & Co. Ltd.** Fiction and non-fiction.

**\*Graham & Trotman Ltd.** (1972), Sterling House, 66 Wilton Road, London SW1V 1DE *tel* 01-821 1123 *telegraphic address* Infobooks London *telex* 298878 Gramco G *fax* 01-630 5229. *Directors:* A. M. W. Graham, S. Willcox, F. W. B. Van Eysinga, D. Dissel, G. Monkhorst, P. le Bosquet. International business, international law, finance and banking.

**\*Grapevine**—see **Thorsons Publishers Ltd.**

**Green Print**—see **Merlin Press, Ltd.**

**Gresham Books,** The Gresham Press, P.O. Box 61, Henley-on-Thames, Oxfordshire RG9 3LQ *tel* (073 522) 3789. *Chief Executive:* Mrs. M. V. Green. Music technique, hymn books, wood engraving.

**Charles Griffin & Co., Ltd.** (1820), 16 Pembridge Road, London W11 3HL *tel* 01-229 1825. Imprint of the Edward Arnold Division of **Hodder & Stoughton Ltd.** Scientific and technical, notably statistics.

**Grisewood & Dempsey Ltd.** (1973) Elsley House, 24-30 Great Titchfield Street, London W1P 7AD *tel* 01-631 0878 *telex* 27725 *fax* 01-323 4694. Publishing imprint: *Kingfisher Books. Distributors* AA Publishing, Fanum House, Basingstoke, Hants RG21 2EA *tel* (0256) 491515 *telex* 858538 *fax* (0256) 22575.

*Titles in print* 299 *No. of titles published in 1988* 70 *Turnover (1988)* £6m

*Managing director* Daniel Grisewood; *directors* J. M. Bourgois, Librairie Nathan S. A., Margaret Barrett (accounts, company secretary), Jane Olliver (publishing), John Richards (production), John Grisewood (editorial), Henryk Wesloowski (sales and marketing).

*Active publishing areas* children's books (poetry and fiction, history, general reference, popular non-fiction, paperbacks, picture books); natural history, reference.

**\*Guinness Publishing Ltd.** (1954), 33 London Road, Enfield, Middlesex EN2 6DJ *tel* 01-367 4567 *telex* 23573 Gbrldn G *fax* 01-367 5912 *cables* Mostest Enfield.
General reference books.

**Gwasg Gee—see Gee & Son (Denbigh) Ltd.**

**Peter Halban Publishers Ltd** (1986), 42 South Molton Street, London W1Y 1HB *tel* 01-491 1582 *fax* 01-629 5381. *Directors* Martine Halban, Peter Halban.
General fiction and non-fiction; history and biography; Judaica and Middle East.

**Robert Hale Ltd.** (1936) Clerkenwell House, 45-47 Clerkenwell Green, London EC1R 0HT *tel* 01-251 2661 *telex* 23353 Nurbks G *fax* 01-251 0584 *telegraphic address* Barabbas, London EC1. *Distribution centre* 4 Vestry Road, Vestry Trading Estate, Sevenoaks, Kent TN14 5EL *tel* (0732) 459852.

*Titles in print* 1530     *No. of titles published in 1988* 347

*Managing director* John Hale; *directors* Eric Restall (production), Robert Kynaston (financial), Martin Kendall (marketing), Betty Weston (rights).

*Active publishing areas* adult general non-fiction and fiction.

**\*Hamish Hamilton Ltd.** (1931) 27 Wrights Lane, London W8 5TZ *tel* 01-938 3388 *telex* 917181/2 Hamish G *fax* 01-937 8704 *cables* Hamisham, London. Imprint of the **Penguin Group**.

*Titles in print* 1200     *No. of titles published in 1988* 197     *Turnover* £6m

*Publishing director* Andrew Franklin; *directors* Jane Nissen, Trevor Glover, John Rolfe, John Webster, Peter Tummons, Nigel Sisson.

*Active publishing areas* belles-lettres, biography and memoirs, children's books (fiction, non-fiction), current affairs, drama, fiction, general, history, humour, music, political, theatre and ballet, travel. **Elm Tree Books:** entertainment, cookery, crafts, sports, hobbies, natural history, literary reference.

**The Hamlyn Publishing Group Ltd.** (1947), Michelin House, 81 Fulham Road, London SW3 6RB *tel* 01-581 9393 *telex* 920191 *fax* 01-589 8419. *Directors:* P. Hamlyn, I. Irvine, D. Freeman. Parent Company: **Octopus Publishing Group plc**.

**Hammond, Hammond & Co., Ltd**—incorporated with **Barrie & Jenkins**.

**Hampshire Books**—imprint of **Wheaton Publishers Ltd.**

**Patrick Hardy Books** (1982), P.O. Box 60, Cambridge CB1 2NT *tel* (0223) 350865 *telex* 817114 Camcom G *fax* (0223) 66951. An imprint of **Lutterworth Press**.
Children's fiction.

**\*Harper & Row, Ltd.**, Middlesex House, 34-42 Cleveland Street, London W1P 5FB   *tel* 01-636 8300   *telex* 21736 Gower G   *fax* 01-631 3594.
Medical, nursing. Markets **Gower Medical Publishing** titles.

**Harrap Publishing Group Ltd**, Chelsea House, 26 Market Square, Bromley, Kent BR1 1NA   *tel* 01-313 3484   *telex* 28673 Consol G   *fax* 01-313 0702. *Distribution centre* Tiptree Book Services Ltd, Church Road, Tiptree, Colchester, Essex CO5 0SR   *tel* (0621) 816362   *telex* 99487 Consol Book Co   *fax* (0621) 819011.

*Titles in print* 200

*Directors* N. W. Berry (chairman), E. R. Dobby (managing), J.-L. Barbanneau (deputy manager), M. Hughes (deputy managing), J.-M. Bourgois.

*Active publishing areas* dictionaries, reference, self-study language courses, travel and maps.

**\*Harvester Wheatsheaf** (1969), 16 Ship Street, Brighton, East Sussex BN1 1AD.   *tel* (0273) 723031   *telex* 877101 Olship   *fax* (0273) 820718. *Editorial Director:* Robert Bolick. Division of **Simon & Schuster International Group.** History, English literature, philosophy, psychology, women's studies, cognitive science, economics, politics.

**\*Harvey Miller Publishers** (1968), 20 Marryat Road, London SW19 5BD   *tel* 01-946 4426   *telex* 9312 1303 39 (HM G)   *BTG:* 84:DDS 2017. *Directors:* H. I. Miller, E. Miller.
Art history, medical atlases.

**J. H. Haynes & Co. Ltd.** (trading as **Haynes Publishing Group**), Sparkford, Yeovil, Somerset BA22 7JJ   *tel* North Cadbury (0963) 40635   *telex* 46212 Haynes G   *fax* (0963) 40825. *Directors:* J. H. Haynes (Executive Chairman), J. Scott (Managing), P. J. Bishop, J. R. Clew, A. C. Haynes, A. P. Lynch, R. J. Stagg, P. B. Ward, R. T. Grainger.
Car and motorcycle owners workshop manuals, car handbooks/servicing guides, do-it-yourself books, aircraft, trains, nautical.

**Haynes Publishing Group**—see **J. H. Haynes & Co. Ltd.**

**Headline Book Publishing plc** (1986) Headline House, 79 Great Titchfield Street, London W1P 7FN   *tel* 01-631 1687   *telex* 268326 Headln G   *fax* 01-631 1958.

*Titles in print* 300      *No. of titles published in 1988* 160      *Turnover 1988* £3.5m

*Chairman* The Earl of Donoughmore (non-executive); *managing director* Tim Hely Hutchinson; *directors* Sue Beavan (production), Jeremy Dawson, Sue Fletcher (editorial), Paul Coley (financial), Sian Thomas (sales and publicity), Christopher Weston.

*Active publishing areas* fiction, biography, humour, food and wine, design, music, cinema, TV and film tie-ins, hardbacks and both trade and mass-market paperbacks.

**Health Science Press**—imprint of **The C. W. Daniel Company Ltd.** Homeopathy.

**\*William Heinemann Ltd,** Michelin House, 81 Fulham Road, London SW3 6RB   *tel* 01-581 9393   *telex* 920191   *fax* 01-589 8437. Subsidiary of **Octopus Publishing Group plc.**

*No. of titles published in 1988* 80      *Turnover* £5m

*Directors:* Helen Fraser (publisher), Amanda Conquy, Laura Longrigg, Claudia Zeff, Peter Kilborn, Annie Garwood, Piers Russell-Cobb, W. Roger Smith, Martin Cowell.

*Active publishing areas* art, biography and memoirs, belles-lettres, fiction, history, humour, travel.

**\*Heinemann Educational**—division of **Heinemann Educational Books Ltd.**

**\*Heinemann Educational Books, Ltd.** Halley Court, Jordan Hill, Oxford OX2 8EJ *tel* (0865) 311366 *telex* 837292 HEBOX G *fax* (0865) 310043. *Directors:* N. Thompson (Chairman), David Fothergill (Managing), Bob Osborne (Managing, Heinemann Educational), Mike Esplen (Managing, Heinemann International), Stephen Ashton, Paul Berry, David Boggiano (Secretary), Richard Gale, Yvonne De Henseler, Paul Lewis, Kay Symons, Vicky Unwin. Subsidiary of **Octopus Publishing Group plc**.

African studies, African writers, biology, chemistry, physics, mathematics, English, drama, history, geography, economics, business studies, home economics, modern languages, education, primary, English as a foreign language.

**\*Heinemann International**—division of **Heinemann Educational Books Ltd.**

**\*Heinemann Newnes**—imprint of **Heinemann Professional Publishing Ltd.**

**\*Heinemann Professional Publishing Ltd,** Halley Court, Jordan Hill, Oxford OX2 8EJ *tel* (0865) 311366 *telex* 837292 HEBOX G *fax* (0865) 310043. *Directors:* Nicolas Thompson (Chairman), Douglas Fox (Managing), David Boggiano (Finance), Peter Dixon, Kathryn Grant, Tom McGorry (Sales). Subsidiary of **Octopus Publishing Group plc**.

Business and management, catering and hotel management, vocational subjects, technology and engineering, medical and nursing, Made Simple books.

**\*Heinemann Young Books,** 38 Hans Crescent, London SW1 0LZ *tel* 01-581 9393 *telex* 920191 *fax* 01-823 9406. *Publisher:* Ingrid Selberg. Member of **Octopus Publishing Group plc**.

Quality fiction, picture books and poetry for pre-school to mid-teens age range; some non-fiction for under-elevens.

**\*Christopher Helm Publishers Ltd.,** Imperial House, 21-25 North Street, Bromley, Kent BR1 1SD *tel* 01-466 6622 *telex* 265833 Chrish G *fax* 01-290 0281. *Distribution centre* A. & C. Black, Howard Road, Eaton Socon, Huntingdon, PE19 3EZ *tel* (0480) 212666 *telex* 32524 Acblac *fax* (0480) 405014 *telegraphic address* Biblos, Huntingdon.

*Titles in print* 150 *No. of titles published in 1988* 51

*Chairman* Christopher Helm; *deputy chairman* John Munro; *directors* Amanda Halstead, Jo Hemmings (editorial), Robert Kirk (marketing), Phil Hartley (finance), Darina Williams (production), Bruce Ackerman, Richard Burns, Robert Kiernan.

*Active publishing areas* natural history and ornithology, gardening and botany, travel, wine and food, cinema, theatre, music, current affairs, politics, history, cricket.

**\*Her Majesty's Stationery Office,** *Head Office*, St. Crispins, Duke Street, Norwich NR3 1PD *tel* (0603) 622211 *telex* 97301. *Distribution and order point:* P.O. Box 276, London SW8 5DT *tel* 01-873 0011 *telex* 297138. *Government Bookshops* (retail): 49 High Holborn, WC1V 6HB *tel* 01-837 0011; 9-21 Princess Street, Manchester, M60 8AS *tel* 061-834 7201; 71 Lothian Road, Edinburgh, EH3 9AZ (wholesale and retail) *tel* 031-228 4181; 258 Broad Street, Birmingham, B1 2HE *tel* 021-643 3740; Southey House, Wine Street, Bristol, BS1 2BQ *tel* (0272) 264306; 80 Chichester Street, Belfast, BT1 4JY *tel* (0232) 238451.

Archaeology, architecture, art, current affairs, directories or guide books, educational (primary, secondary, technical, university), general, history, naval and military, practical handbooks, reference, science, sociology, year books.

As the Government Publisher, **HMSO** publishes only material sponsored by Parliament, Government Departments and other official bodies. Consequently it cannot consider unsolicited work submitted by private citizens.

**\*Herbert Press Ltd.** (1972), 46 Northchurch Road, London N1 4EJ    *tel* 01-254 4379    *telex* 8952022 Ctytel G. *Directors:* David Herbert, Brenda Herbert.
Art, architecture, design, crafts, art nostalgia, fashion and costume, natural history, archaeology, biography, illustrated non-fiction.

**Heretic Books** (1982), P.O. Box 247, London N17 9QR    *tel* 01-365 1545    *fax* 01-365 1252. *Directors:* David Fernbach, Aubrey Walter.
Ecology, animal liberation, green politics, third world.

**Nick Hern Books** (1988), 87 Vauxhall Walk, London SE11 5HJ    *tel* 01-739 0909    *telex* 8955572 Walker G    *fax* 01-587 1123. *Publisher:* Nick Hern. *Managers:* Jackie Bodley (Editorial), Diane Petherick (Sales). Division of **Walker Books Ltd.**
Theatre, plays.

**\*Adam Hilger,** Techno House, Redcliffe Way, Bristol, BS1 6NX    *tel* (0272) 297481    *telex* 449149 Instp G    *fax* (0272) 294318.
Physics and physics-related science and technology; general science books.

**Hilmarton Manor Press** (1964), Calne, Wilts. SN11 8SB    *tel* Hilmarton (0249 76) 208.
Fine art, photography, antiques, visual art.

**\*Hippo Books** (1980), 10 Earlham Street, London WC2H 9RX    *tel* 01-240 5753    *telex* 264604 Sbslon G    *fax* 01-240 6927. *Managing Director:* J. E. Cox. Imprint of **Scholastic Publications Ltd.**
Children's paperbacks—fiction and non-fiction.

**Hippopotamus Press** (1974), 22 Whitewell Road, Frome, Somerset BA11 4EL    *tel* Frome (0373) 66653. *Editors:* Roland John, Anna Martin.
Poetry, essays, criticism. Publishes *Outposts Poetry Quarterly.* Poetry submissions from new writers welcome.

**Hobsons Publishing plc** (1974), Bateman Street, Cambridge CB2 1LZ    *tel* (0223) 354551    *telex* 81546 Hobcam G    *fax* (0223) 323154. *Directors:* Adrian Bridgewater (Managing), Stephen Bartlett (Finance), Robert Baker, Roger Dalzell. Careers guidance, PSIE, science, business studies. Publishers under licence to CRAC—Careers Research & Advisory Centre.

**\*Hodder & Stoughton Ltd.,** a subsidiary of Hodder & Stoughton Holdings Ltd., Mill Road, Dunton Green, Sevenoaks, Kent TN13 2YA    *tel* (0732) 450111    *telex* 95122 Hodder G    *fax* (0732) 450134    *cables* Expositor Sevenoaks    *Editorial offices* Hodder & Stoughton, 47 Bedford Square, London WC1B 3DP    *tel* 01-636 9851    *fax* 01-631 5248    *telegraphic address* Expositor.

*Titles in print* 6546        *No of titles published in 1988* 899        *Turnover (1988–89)* £45.131m

*Executive chairman* Philip Attenborough; *deputy chairman* Mark Hodder-Williams; *joint managing directors* Michael Attenborough, Richard Morris; *director* Eric Major (trade publishing); *company secretary* Anthony Brown; *divisional directors* Tom Biggs-Davison (trade marketing), Adrian Bourne (paperbacks), David Grant (children's books), Brian Steven (educational), Jim McEwen (trade sales), J. A. G. Wilson (production).

*Active publishing areas* general, fiction, religious, children's (hardback and paperback) schoolbooks, academic, medical, vocational, ELT, see also: **Edward Arnold.**

\***The Hogarth Press Ltd**—see **Chatto & Windus Ltd. & The Hogarth Press Ltd.**

\***Holmes McDougall Ltd.**, Allander House, 137-141 Leith Walk, Edinburgh EH6 8NS *tel* 031-554 9444 *cables* Educational Edinburgh *telex* 727508 Holmes G *fax* 031-554 4051.
Educational (infant, primary and secondary).

\***Holt, Rinehart & Winston,** 24-28 Oval Road, London NW1 7DX *tel* 01-267 4466 *telex* 25775 Acpres G. *Managing Director:* Joan M. Fujimoto.
Educational books (school, college, university) in all subjects.

**Ellis Horwood Ltd.** (1973) Market Cross House, Cooper Street, Chichester, West Sussex PO19 1EB *tel* (0243) 789942 *telex* 86516 Elwood G *fax* (0243) 778855 *cables* Horwood Chichester. *Directors:* Ellis Horwood, M.B.E. (Chairman), Clive Horwood, F. M. Horwood, J. Gillison, Sue Horwood.
Chemical science and engineering, computer science, artificial intelligence, cognitive science, cybernetics, engineering, environmental science, mathematics, medical science, physics, water science, food science, space science and space technology, aquaculture and fisheries support, biomedicine, applied science and industrial technology, information technology, biochemistry, robotics, metallurgy, geology, entomology, corrosion science, energy and fuel science, polymer science, inorganic, organic, photo and physical chemistry.

**Hugo's Language Books** (1864), Old Station Yard, Marlesford, Woodbridge, Suffolk IP13 0AG *tel* (0728) 746546 *fax* (0728) 746236.
Hugo's language books and courses; distributors for 'Fishing' titles.

\***Hulton Educational Publications Ltd**—merged with **Stanley Thornes (Publishers) Ltd.**

\***C. Hurst & Co. (Publishers) Ltd** (1967), 38 King Street, London WC2E 8JT *tel* 01-240 2666, (night) 01-852 9021. *Director:* Christopher Hurst.
Geographical 'area studies' covering contemporary history, politics, political economy, social studies, religion, autobiography.

\***Hutchinson Children's Books Ltd.**, Brookmount House, 62-65 Chandos Place, Covent Garden, London WC2N 4NW *tel* 01-240 3411 *telex* 261212 Lit Ldn G. *Directors:* A. J. V. Cheetham (Chairman), P. C. K. Roche (Managing), R. M. F. Cheetham, J. M. Mottram. Imprint of **Century Hutchinson Ltd**.
Children's books, fiction and non-fiction, picture books.

\***Hutchinson & Co. (Publishers) Ltd.**—see **Century Hutchinson Publishing Ltd.**

\***Hutchinson Education**—list acquired by **Stanley Thornes Ltd.**

**Institute of Physics,** Techno House, Redcliffe Way, Bristol BS1 6NX *tel* (0272) 297481 *telex* 449149 Instp G *fax* (0272) 294318.
Physics-related journals and conference proceedings.

\***International Textbook Co. Ltd.**, a member of **The Blackie Group,** Bishopbriggs, Glasgow G64 2NZ *tel* 041-772 2311 *telex* 777283 Blacki G *fax* 041-762 0897.
Imprints: International Textbook Company; Leonard Hill; Surrey University Press. *Directors:* Dr. Graeme Mackintosh, Michael Miller.
Professional, reference and text books in engineering, hotel and tourism management, business administration, food technology, chemistry, physics, biological sciences.

**\*Inter-Varsity Press,** 38 De Montfort Street, Leicester LE1 7GP    *tel* (0533) 551700    *fax* (0533) 555672.
Theology and religion.

**Arthur James Ltd.** (1935), 1 Cranbourne Road, London N10 2BT    *tel* 01-883 1831, 883 2201, 883 8307 and (0386) 446566    *fax* (0386) 446566 and 01-883 8307. *Directors:* D. M. Duncan, Jillian Tallon.
Religion, sociology, psychology.

**Jane's Information Group,** 163 Brighton Road, Coulsdon, Surrey CR3 2NX    *tel* 01-763 1030    *telex* 916907    *fax* 01-763 1005. *Managing Director:* Michael Goldsmith.
Military, aviation, naval, non-fiction, reference.

**Herbert Jenkins Ltd**—incorporated with **Barrie & Jenkins.**

**Jewish Chronicle Publications,** 25 Furnival Street, London EC4A 1JT    *tel* 01-405 9252    *telex* 01 940 11415. *Executive Director:* M. Weinberg. Agents for Jewish Publications Society of America, Ktav, New York; Behrman House, New York; Keter, Jerusalem; Sepher-Hermon, New York.
Theology and religion, reference; *Jewish Year Book, Jewish Travel Guide.*

**\*Johnson Publications Ltd.** (1946), 130 Wigmore Street, London W1H 0AT    *tel* 01-486 6757    *telex* 266504    *fax* 01-487 5436. *Directors:* M. A. Murray-Pearce, Z. M. Pauncefort.
Belles-lettres, biography and memoirs, current affairs, economics, history, law, political economy, sociology, travel, medical, philosophy; perfumery. Return postage should be sent with unsolicited manuscripts.

**Jordan & Sons Ltd.** (1836), 21 St. Thomas Street, Bristol, BS1 6JS    *tel* (0272) 230600    *telex* 449119    *fax* (0272) 230063. *DX:* 78161 Bristol. *Publishing Director:* Richard Hudson.
Law, particularly company and family (including the *Family Law Journal*), company administration, business, finance, loose-leaf services.

**\*Michael Joseph Ltd.** (1935), 27 Wrights Lane, London W8 5TZ    *tel* 01-937 7255    *telex* 917181/2    *fax* 01-937 8704. Imprint of the **Penguin Group.**

*Titles in print* 383    *No. of titles published in 1988* 106    *Turnover 1988* £12.3m

*Publishing director* Susan Watt; *directors* Jenny Dereham, Nellie Flexner (U.S.A.), Trevor Glover, Roger Houghton, John Lyon, John Rolfe, Ruth Salazar, Nigel Sisson, Peter Tummons, John Webster.

*Active publishing areas* belles-lettres, biography and memoirs, current affairs, fiction, general, history, humour, illustrated books (including **Mermaid** trade paperbacks).

**The Journeyman Press Ltd**—imprint of **Pluto Publishing Ltd.** Socialist, feminist fiction, poetry, drama, art, graphics, biography, social history, politics, philosophy.

**Kelly's Directories**—imprint of **Reed Information Services Ltd.** Industrial, commercial and business directories.

**Kelpie Books**—see **Canongate Publishing Ltd.**

**Kenyon-Deane Ltd.,** 311 Worcester Road, Malvern, Worcs. WR14 1AN    *tel* (0684) 565045. *Directors:* Leslie Smith, Audrey Smith.
Plays and drama textbooks. Specialists in plays for women.

***William Kimber & Co. Ltd** (1950), Denington Estate, Wellingborough, North-ants. NN8 2RQ *tel* (0933) 440033 *telex* 311072 Thopub G *fax* (0933) 440512. *Directors:* D. J. Young (Managing), M. L. Hawkesworth, D. C. J. Palmer, J. G. Rivers, P. A. Winslow, F.C.A. Imprint of **Thorsons Publishing Group Ltd.**
Naval, military, aviation, biography, memoirs, fiction.

**Kingfisher Books.** The publishing imprint of **Grisewood & Dempsey Ltd.** Elsley House, 24-30 Great Titchfield Street, London W1P 7AD *tel* 01-631 0878 *telegraphic address* Greatbooks, London *telex* 27725 *fax* 01-323 4694.
Children's books and general non-fiction.

***Kingsway Publications Ltd.**, 1 St Anne's Road, Eastbourne, East Sussex BN21 3UN *tel* (0323) 410930 *fax* (0323) 411970. *Directors:* Ray Bodkin, Geoffrey J. Booker, Tony Collins, Nigel Coltman, Richard Herkes, Gilbert W. Kirby (Chairman), David Nickalls, Gavin H. Reid, Geoffrey P. Ridsdale (Managing). Religious books.

***Kluwer Law Publishers**—imprint of **Kluwer Publishing**. Law.

***Kluwer Publishing** (1972), Croner House, London Road, Kingston-upon-Thames, Surrey KT2 6SY *tel* 01-549 1455. *Directors:* A. S. Brode, P. Sefton, C. Hilton-Childs. Subsidiary of Croner Publications Ltd.
Law, taxation, finance, insurance, business management, medicine, farming, loose-leaf information services, books, databases, conferences.

***Knight**—imprint of **Hodder & Stoughton Ltd.** Children's paperbacks.

**Charles Knight Publishing,** Tolley House, 2 Addiscombe Road, Croydon, Surrey CR9 5AF *tel* 01-686 9141 *fax* 01-686 3155. *Business Publisher:* M. G. Pomel. *Managing Editor:* S. C. Cotter. Member of the **Benn Group.**
Looseleaf legal works on local government, offshore oil industry, construction industry, and technical subjects.

***Kogan Page Ltd.** (1967), 120 Pentonville Road, London N1 9JN *tel* 01-278 0433 *telex* 263088 Kogan G *fax* 01-837 6348.

*Titles in print* 900 *No. of titles published in 1988* 180 *Turnover* £3.2m

*Managing director* Philip Kogan; *directors* Piers Burnett and Pauline Goodwin (editorial), Tom Davy (sales and marketing), Peter Chadwick (production), Praba Kan (financial), Ben Kogan.
*Active publishing areas* computer science and information technology, manufacturing management and technology, education, training, educational and training technology, journals, business and management, human resource management, transport and distribution, marketing, sales, advertising and PR, finance and accounting, directories, small business, careers and vocational, personal finance.

**Kompass Publishers**—imprint of **Reed Information Services Ltd.** Industrial and commercial products reference books.

***Ladybird Books Ltd.** (1924) Beeches Road, Loughborough, Leicestershire LE11 2NQ *tel* (0509) 268021 *telex* 341347 Ldbird G *fax* (0509) 234672 *telegraphic address* Ladybird, Loughborough.

*Titles in print* 930 *No. of titles published in 1988* 131 *Turnover* £14m

*Chairman* T. J. Rix; *managing director* M. P. Kelley; *directors* M. G. Banks, P. H. Bagnall, D. P. Collington, B. D. L. Cotton, M. H. Gabb, R. Smith, A. T. Warren, J. D. Williamson, M. G. P. Wymer.

*Active publishing areas* children's books, general and educational (infants, primary, junior and secondary).

**\*Allen Lane, The Penguin Press,** academic hardcover imprint of **Penguin Books,** 27 Wrights Lane, London W8 5TZ  *tel* 01-938 2200.
Non-fiction titles of academic and intellectual interest, principally but not exclusively the humanities.

**Lawrence & Wishart, Ltd.,** 144A Old South Lambeth Road, London SW8 1XX  *tel* 01-820 9281  *telegraphic address* Interbook, London, SW8  *fax* 01-587 0469. *Directors:* R. Simon, J. Skelley, S. Davison, S. Sedley, S. Hayward, E. Munro, N. Temple, W. Norris, J. Taylor, J. Rodrigues.
Current affairs, economics, history, socialism and Marxism, literary criticism, philosophy, political economy, sociology, biography.

**\*Legend**—imprint of **Arrow Books Ltd.** Science fiction and fantasy.

**\*Leicester University Press** (1951), Fielding Johnson Building, University of Leicester, University Road, Leicester LE1 7RH  *tel* (0533) 523333  *telex* 347250  *fax* (0533) 522200. *Publisher:* Alec McAulay. Division of **Pinter Publishers.**
Academic books, especially in history (including English local history and urban history), archaeology, politics and international relations, defence studies, English and foreign literature.

**Lennard Publishing,** Musterlin House, Jordan Hill Road, Oxford OX2 8AP  *tel* (0865) 311075  *fax* (0865) 310562. *Directors:* George J. Riches, K. A. A. Stevenson, R. L. Brown, C. R. Sawford, D. M. Phillips, A. G. Y. Cowen. Division of **Lennard Books Ltd,** member of the Musterlin Group plc.
Biography, memoirs, heritage, gardening, cookery, wine, humour, photography; general non-fiction.

**\*Charles Letts (Holdings) Ltd.** (1796), Diary House, Borough Road, London SE1 1DW  *tel* 01-407 8891  *telex* 884498 Letts G. *Directors:* A. A. Letts (Chairman), J. M. Letts, T. R. Letts, R. W. Aitken, J. W. B. Gibbs, W. J. Swords (Managing). **Charles Letts & Co. Ltd.** wholly owned publishing subsidiary.
Diary and book publishers and manufacturers.

**Lewis Masonic** (1870), Terminal House, Shepperton TW17 8AS  *tel* Walton-on-Thames (0932) 228950  *telex* 929806 Iallan G. *Managing Director:* D. I. Allan.
Masonic books. *Masonic Square Magazine.*

**\*H. K. Lewis & Co. Ltd.** (1844), 136 Gower Street, London WC1E 6BS  *tel* 01-387 4282  *telex* 22607 Hklmed G  *telegraphic address* Publicavit, London, WC1. *Directors:* G. W. Edwards, R. D. Spence, J. L. Haynes, P. Belch.
Science, medical.

**John Libbey & Co. Ltd.** (1979), 13 Smiths Yard, Summerley Street, London SW18 4HR  *tel* 01-947 2777  *telex* 94013503 John G  *fax* 01-947 2664. *Directors:* John Libbey, G. Cahn.
Medical: nutrition, obesity, epilepsy, neurology, diabetes, biological psychiatry.

**\*Library Association Publishing Ltd** (1981), 7 Ridgmount Street, London WC1E 7AE  *tel* 01-636 7543  *telex* 21897 Laldn G  *fax* 01-636 3627. *Chairman:* E. M. Broome, O.B.E., F.L.A.; *Deputy Chairman:* G. Cunningham, B.A., B.SC. (ECON); *Directors:* Mrs E. A. L. Esteve-Coll, B.A., A.L.A., C. Ellis, M.A. (Managing), C. Bingley, M.A., F.L.A., S. A. Brewer, M.A., A.L.A., F.B.I.M., J. Cameron, M.A., K. Crawshaw, B.A., D.L.I.S., A.L.A., D. E. House, B.A., M.I.INF.SC., A.L.A., R. A. McKee, B.A., M.A., PH.D., A.L.A., R. G. Surridge, M.A., F.R.S.A., F.L.A., A. G. D. White, F.L.A.
Bibliographies, directories, reference works, library science.

**\*Lion Publishing plc** (1972), Peter's Way, Sandy Lane West, Littlemore, Oxford OX4 5HG   *tel* (0865) 747550   *telex* 837161 Lion G   *fax* (0865) 747568.
*Directors:* David Alexander, Pat Alexander, Tony Wales, Mark Beedell, Robin Keeley, Denis Cole.
Reference, paperbacks, illustrated children's books, educational, gift books, religion and theology; all reflecting a Christian position.

**Little, Brown and Company (U.K.) Ltd** (1988), Beacon House, 30 North End Road, London W14 0SH   *tel* 01-603 1456   *fax* 01-603 0503. *Directors:* Terry Melia (Managing), Ian Sinclair, Robert Hyde. A subsidiary of **Little, Brown and Company**, Boston, USA.
Art, photography, gardens, travel, crafts, some children's.

**\*Liverpool University Press** (1901), Robin Bloxsidge (Acting Secretary and Publisher), P.O. Box 147, Liverpool L69 3BX   *tel* 051-794 2231/7 (7 lines) *telex* 627095 Unilpl G   *fax* 051-708 6502.
Academic and scholarly books in a range of disciplines. Special interests: literature, social, political, economic and ancient history, archaeology, philosophy and the natural sciences, medicine, veterinary science and urban and regional planning.

**London & International Publishers Ltd** (1984), 49 St. James's Street, London SW1A 1JT   *tel* 01-499 5042   *fax* 01-629 4435. *Directors:* Shaie Selzer, Klaus Boehm, J. A. Miller, N. R. Reynolds, Prof. John M. **Stopford**, L. Viney, P. W. Durrance (Secretary).
Publishing under The Stock Exchange Press in finance, investment, the securities industry; sports and leisure under Sportsworld imprint.

**\*Longman Group UK Ltd** (1724), 5 Bentinck Street, London W1M 5RN   *tel* 01-935 0121   *telegraphic address* Longman, London, W1. Longman House, Burnt Mill, Harlow, Essex CM20 2JE   *tel* (0279) 26721   *fax* (0279) 31059   *telex* 81259 Longmn G   *telegraphic address* and   *cables* Longman, Harlow. T. J. Rix (Chairman), M. G. P. Wymer (Deputy Chairman), P. Kahn (Chief Executive—Publishing). *Directors:* R. G. B. Duncan, M. P. Kelley, C. J. Rea, J. D. Williamson (Finance), J. Osborne, J. M. Little, P. Blackburn, P. Warwick. Associated Companies (*qv.*) in India, Australia, New Zealand, Uganda, Kenya, Zimbabwe, Hong Kong, Japan, Malaysia, Nigeria, The Caribbean, South Africa, U.S.A., Canada, Singapore, Botswana, Lesotho, Swaziland, Italy, Spain, Greece, France, Netherlands, West Germany, Egypt.
Atlases, audio-visual aids, children's, school, further education, university, scholarly, undergraduate, post-graduate, academic, scientific and technical, legal, financial, business education, dictionaries, reference, English language teaching, directories, learned journals; micro computer software, videos. Africana (including African studies and African and Caribbean literature.) Medical—see **Churchill Livingstone.** Preliminary letter recommended before submitting MSS.

**\*Longman Law Tax and Finance,** 21-27 Lamb's Conduit Street, London WC1N 3NJ   *tel* 01-242 2548   *telex* 295445 Lawtax G   *fax* 01-831 8119. *Directors:* L. W. Herbert (Managing), R. E. M. Baynes, A. R. Wells, M. G. Smith, E. A. O. Bramwell, J. D. Williamson, J. E. Robinson.
Books and professional journals on law, business, taxation, pensions, insurance, government contracting, finance and accountancy.

**Peter Lowe (Eurobook Ltd)** (1968), P.O. Box 52, Wallingford, Oxon OX10 0XU   *tel* (086732) 8333   *fax* (086732) 8263. *Directors:* P. S. Lowe, R. Lowe. Illustrated general information books, natural history, gardening, books for children (not small picture books), young people and adults.

**Lund Humphries Publishers Ltd.**, 16 Pembridge Road, London W11 3HL   *tel* 01-229 1825   *telex* 8950511. *Directors:* Clive Bingley, Charlotte Burri, Lionel Leventhal, John Taylor.
Art, architecture, graphic art and design, Arabic language.

*****Lutterworth Press** (1799), P.O. Box 60, Cambridge CB1 2NT   *tel* (0223) 350865   *telex* 817114 Camcom G   *fax* (0223) 66951. Subsidiary of **James Clarke & Co. Ltd**.
The arts, biography and memoirs, children's books (fiction, non-fiction, rewards), craft, educational, gardening, general, history, leisure, philosophy, practical, science, sociology, theology and religion.

*****Macdonald & Evans (Publications) Ltd.**—see **Pitman Publishing**.

**Macdonald & Co. (Publishers) Ltd**, 66–73 Shoe Lane, Holborn, London EC4P 4AB   *tel* 01-377 4600   *telex* 885233 Macdon G   *fax* 01-583 4407/8. *Distribution centre* Purnell Book Centre, Paulton, Avon   *tel* (0761) 413301.

*Titles in print* 2123     *No. of titles published in 1988* 675     *Turnover* £30m

*Managing director* N. Webb; *directors* A. Samson (general; Queen Anne Press, Optima), S. Snape (illustrated books).

*Active publishing areas* hardback and paperback fiction, general non-fiction and illustrated books.

*Divisions* Futura, Macdonald, Optima, Queen Anne Press, Sphere.

**Macdonald Children's Books/Macdonald Educational,** Wolsey House, Wolsey Road, Hemel Hempstead, Herts. HP2 4SS   *tel* (0442) 231900   *fax* (0442) 214467. *Children's Publisher:* Philippa Stewart. Division of **Simon & Schuster Ltd.**
Educational and information books; picture books and fiction for children from pre-school to teenage.

*****McGraw-Hill Book Company (U.K.) Ltd.**, McGraw-Hill House, Shoppenhangers Road, Maidenhead, Berkshire SL6 2QL   *tel* (0628) 23432   *telex* 848484 Mchill G   *fax* (0628) 35895   *telegraphic address* McGraw-Hill, Maidenhead.

*Titles in print* 419     *No. of titles published in 1988* 60     *Turnover* £6.4m

*Managing director* Stephen White; *director* Ian Oldham (financial).

*Active publishing areas* technical, scientific, professional reference, medical.

**Macmillan Publishers, Ltd.** (book holding company, a subsidiary of **Macmillan Ltd**), 4 Little Essex Street, London WC2R 3LF   *tel* 01-836 6633   *telex* 262024 Macbsk G   *fax* 01-379 4204   *telegraphic address* Publish, London WC2. Brunel Road, Houndmills, Basingstoke, Hants. RG21 2XS   *tel* (0256) 29242   *telex* 858493 Macbsk G   *fax* (0256) 479476. *Foreign Cables:* Publish, London; Publish, Basingstoke. *Chairman:* A. D. A. Macmillan, The Second Earl of Stockton. *Directors:* N. G. Byam Shaw (Managing), R. Barker, B. J. Davies, A. Gordon Walker, A. R. Soar, M. J. Barnard, G. R. U. Todd. *Imprint:* **Macmillan Children's Books.** *Publishing Director:* M. Wace.
Children's fiction and non-fiction.
*Operating Subsidiaries:*

**Macmillan Education Ltd,** Brunel Road, Houndmills, Basingstoke, Hants. RG21 2XS  *tel* (0256) 29242. *Chairman:* A. Soar; *Directors:* J. E. Jackman (Managing), R. Balkwill, D. Knight, P. Murby, Prof. J. J. Thompson, C. R. Harrison, T. S. Creed, R. Jones-Parry, R. Parry, S. Kennedy, J. Winckler. Primary, secondary and college level educational books and visual aids.

**The Macmillan Press Ltd,** 4 Little Essex Street, London WC2R 3LF  *tel* 01-836 6633. *Chairman:* A. Soar; *Directors:* C. Paterson (Managing), T. M. Farmiloe, J. F. K. Ashby, A. Gordon, H. Holt, D. Knight.
Academic, scientific and technical works, learned journals, economics and world affairs, publishers of The Statesman's Year-Book, and other reference works.

**Macmillan London Ltd,** 4 Little Essex Street, London WC2R 3LF  *tel* 01-836 6633. *Chairman:* N. G. Byam Shaw; *Directors:* F. Rubinstein (Managing), Roland Philips, M. Wace, M. J. Neild, A. P. Sisman, H. Hale, F. Blake, R. H. Hartgill, A. Kay, A. Martin.
General literature, biography, fiction and children's books.

*Allied and Subsidiary Companies:* Macmillan Magazines Ltd., Macmillan Publishers Group Administration Ltd., Macmillan Distribution Ltd., Macmillan Production Ltd., Macmillan Accounts and Administration Ltd., Gill & Macmillan, Ltd., *(Eire)*, Macmillan India, Ltd., St. Martin's Press Inc., *(USA)*, Macmillan Nigeria Publishers Ltd., The Macmillan Co. of Australia Pty., Ltd., Macmillan Publishers (Hong Kong), Ltd., Macmillan Southeast Asia Pte. Ltd., Macmillan Shuppan K.K., Japan, Hospital and Social Service Publications Ltd., Globe Book Services Ltd., Macmillan Publishers (UK) Ltd., Nature America Inc. *(USA)*, Macmillan Kenya (Publishers) Ltd., The Macmillan Company of New Zealand Ltd., Macmillan Boleswa Publishers (Pty) Ltd. *(Swaziland)*, Editorial Macmillan de Mexico SA de CV, The College Press (Pvt) Ltd *(Zimbabwe)*, Grove's Dictionaries of Music Inc. *(USA)*, Macmillan Publishers (Malaysia) SB, Macmillan Publishers (China) Ltd *(Hong Kong)*, Pan Books Ltd.

**Julia MacRae Books** (1979), a division of **Walker Books Ltd,** 87 Vauxhall Walk, London SE11 5HJ  *tel* 01-793 0909  *telex* 8955572  *fax* 01-587 1123. *Director:* Julia MacRae (Managing).
Children's books, music and general non-fiction.

**Magi Publications** (1987), 55 Crowland Avenue, Hayes, Middlesex UB3 4JP  *tel* 01-387 0610, 01-388 9832  *fax* 01-383 5003. *Directors:* M. S. Bhatia, A. S. Bhatia, G. F. Chester.
Dual-language multicultural children's books.

**Mainstream Publishing Co. (Edinburgh) Ltd** (1978), 7 Albany Street, Edinburgh EH1 3UG  *tel* 031-557 2959  *fax* 031-556 8720. *Directors:* Bill Campbell, Peter MacKenzie.
Literature, fiction, biography, history, politics, sport, alternative medicine, current affairs, popular paperbacks, art, photography, architecture.

**Mammoth**—see **Mandarin Paperbacks.**

**\*Manchester University Press** (1912), Oxford Road, Manchester M13 9PL  *tel* 061-273 5530, 5539  *telex* 666517 Uniman G  *fax* 061-274 3346.
Works of academic scholarship: literary criticism, cultural studies, history, politics, economics, medical. General books on North of England, specialises in international law, non-linear science, Spanish, Italian, German and French texts; social anthropology, sociology, African studies, special education. Texts at sixth form and student levels.

**\*Mandala**—see **Unwin Hyman Ltd.**

**Mandarin Paperbacks** (1989), Michelin House, 81 Fulham Road, London SW3 6RB *tel* 01-581 9393 *telex* 920191 *fax* 01-589 8450. *Publisher:* John Potter. *Directors:* Max Eilenberg (Editorial), Elsbeth Lindner (Editorial), Martin Cowell (Sales & Marketing).
Paperback fiction, crime/thriller, humour, romance, TV tie-in, military, biography, business; imprints: **Mandarin, Minerva.** Children's fiction and non-fiction paperbacks; imprint: **Mammoth.**

**\*Mansell Publishing Ltd.** (1966), Artillery House, Artillery Row, London SW1P 1RT *tel* 01-222 7676 *telex* 9413701 Caspub G *fax* 01-799 1514. *Director:* J. E. Duncan (Managing). Imprint of **Cassell plc.**
Bibliographies in all academic subject areas and monographs in urban and regional planning, Islamic studies, librarianship, history.

**Marshall Cavendish Books Ltd.** (1969), 58 Old Compton Street, London W1V 5PA *tel* 01-734 6710 *telex* 23880 Marcar G. *Directors:* Lim Chin Geok (Chief Executive), Reg Wright (Publishing), Sarah Dixon (Production).
Cookery, crafts, gardening, do-it-yourself, general non-fiction.

**Marshall Pickering Holdings Ltd** (1928), Middlesex House, 34-42 Cleveland Street, London W1P 5FB *tel* 01-636 8300 *telex* 21736 *fax* 01-631 3594. *Managing Director:* Ron Chopping.
Theology, music, popular religions, illustrated, children's, wide range of Christian books.

**Marshall Pickering Ltd**—imprint of **Marshall Pickering Holdings Ltd.** Christian books.

**Martin Books,** Fitzwilliam House, 32 Trumpington Street, Cambridge CB2 1QY *tel* (0223) 66733 *telex* 818454 Wfpubl G *fax* (0223) 461428. Imprint of **Simon & Schuster International Group.**
Cookery, gardening and other popular subjects.

**Martin Brian & O'Keeffe, Ltd.** (1971), 78 Coleraine Road, Blackheath, London SE3 *tel* 01-858 5164. *Director:* Timothy O'Keeffe.
General literature including biography, fiction, history, travel, science, economics and poetry.

**Martin Robertson & Co. Ltd.**—now merged with **Basil Blackwell Ltd.**

**\*Kenneth Mason Publications, Ltd.** (1958), 12a North Street, Emsworth, Hampshire PO10 7DQ *tel* (0243) 377977 *fax* (0243) 378194. *Directors:* Kenneth Mason, M. A. Mason, P. A. Mason.
Nautical, football, slimming and patent licensing. No poetry. Technical journals, high court law reports.

**Maxwell Pergamon Publishing Corporation plc,** Headington Hill Hall, Oxford OX3 0BW *tel* (0865) 64881 *telex* 83177 *fax* (0865) 60285. *Directors:* I. R. Maxwell (Chairman), Kevin Maxwell (Chief Executive), Martin Heller, Gilbert Richards, William Davis, James Mann, Brian Gilbert, Andrew Zielinski, Alan Stephens (Secretary). *Divisions:* Pergamon Press plc, Macdonald Publishing Group, Pergamon Orbit Infoline.

**Meadowfield Press Ltd.** (1976), I.S.A. Building, Dale Road Industrial Estate, Shildon, Co. Durham DL4 2QZ *tel* Bishop Auckland (0388) 773065. *Directors:* Dr. J. G. Cook, M. Cook, J. A. Verdon, A. M. Creasey.
Microbiology, zoology, archaeology, botany, biology.

**Medici Society Ltd.,** 34-42 Pentonville Road, London N1 9HG *tel* 01-837 7099.

Publishers of the Medici Prints, greeting cards and other colour reproductions of Old Masters and Modern Artists.
Art, nature and children's books. Preliminary letter requested.

**Melrose Press Ltd.** (1969), 3 Regal Lane, Soham, Ely, Cambridgeshire CB7
5BA    *tel* Ely (0353) 721091    *telegraphic address* Melropres Ely    *telex*
81584 Mpibc G    *fax* (0353) 721839. *Directors:* Ernest Kay, R. A. Kay, J. M.
Kay, B. J. Wilson, N. S. Law, C. Emmett, F.C.A., V. A. Kay.
International biographical reference works, including *International Authors
& Writers Who's Who.*

**Mercury Books**—imprint of **W. H. Allen & Co. plc.** Business books.

**Merehurst Ltd.** (1982), Ferry House, 51/57 Lacy Road, Putney, London SW15
1PR    *tel* 01-780 1177    *telex* 296616 Mhurst G    *fax* 01-780 1714.

*Titles in print* 137        *No. of titles published in 1988* 40        *Turnover* £3.5m

*Managing director* Carole Saunders, *directors* Glynis Watts (deputy managing), Liz Allen (production and publishing), Stuart Binns (sales and marketing), Gary Chapman (publicity), Shirley Patton (editorial).

*Active publishing areas* animal and pet care, aviculture, business, cake decorating, cookery, crafts and hobbies, floristry, graphic art, natural history, reference, travel.

**Merlin Press, Ltd.,** 10 Malden Road, London NW5 3HR    *tel* 01-267 3399.
*Directors:* M. W. Eve, Jon Carpenter, Norman Franklin.
Incorporates **Green Print**, publishing books on green politics and the environ-
ment. Politics, economics, history, philosophy. Publishers of *The Socialist
Register.* Distributors for **Augustus M. Kelley** (USA). *No unsolicited mss,
please.*

*****Mermaid**—see **Michael Joseph Ltd.**

**Merrow Publishing Company Limited** (1951), I.S.A. Building, Dale Road
Industrial Estate, Shildon, Co. Durham DL4 2QZ    *tel* Bishop Auckland
(0388) 773065. *Directors:* J. G. Cook, M. Cook, J. A. Verdon, A. M. Creasey.
Textiles, plastics, popular science, scientific.

**Methodist Church, Division of Education and Youth,** 2 Chester House, Pages
Lane, Muswell Hill, London N10 1PR    *tel* 01-444 9845.
Theology and religion.

*****Methodist Publishing House** (1773), 20 Ivatt Way, Peterborough PE3 7PG    *tel*
(0733) 332202    *fax* (0733) 331201.
Hymn and service books. **Foundery Press:** ecumenical titles.

*****Methuen & Co., Ltd.**—incorporated in **Routledge.**

*****Methuen Children's Books,** 38 Hans Crescent, London SW1X 0LZ    *tel* 01-581
9393    *telex* 920191    *fax* 01-823 9406. *Publisher:* Rona Selby. *Rights Manager:* Kate Wilson. Member of **Octopus Publishing Group plc.**
Children's books (picture, fiction, non-fiction, for young children to early
teens).

*****Methuen London,** Michelin House, 81 Fulham Road, London SW3 6RB    *tel*
01-581 9393    *telex* 920191    *fax* 01-589 8419. *Directors:* Geoffrey Strachan
(Publishing), Elsbeth Lindner (Fiction), Ann Mansbridge (Non-fiction),
Pam Edwardes (Drama), Anne Nicholson (Rights).
General fiction, biography and memoirs, history, current affairs, topogra-
phy, humour. Performing arts under **Methuen Drama** imprint. Please write

with synopsis before submitting MSS. A member of the **Octopus Publishing Group plc.**

**Michelin Tyre plc** (1989), Davy House, Lyon Road, Harrow, Middlesex HA1 2DQ   *tel* 01-861 2121   *telex* 919071   *fax* 01-863 0680. *Head of Tourism Department:* D. C. Brown. *Sales Manager:* J. E. Addison.
Tourist guides, maps and atlases, hotel and restaurant guides.

**Milestone Publications** (1967), 62 Murray Road, Horndean, Hants PO8 9JL   *tel* (0705) 597440   *fax* (0705) 591975. *Directors:* Nicholas J. Pine (Managing), D. M. Pine, Lynda J. Pine, V. Amis, T. D. G. Harland.
Heraldic china, antique porcelain, business, economics.

**J. Garnet Miller Ltd.** (1951), 311 Worcester Road, Malvern, Worcestershire WR14 1AN   *tel* (0684) 565045. *Directors:* Leslie Smith, Audrey Smith.
Drama, theatre.

**\*Mills & Boon (Publishers) Ltd.** (1908) Eton House, 18-24 Paradise Road, Richmond, Surrey TW9 1SR   *tel* 01-948 0444   *telex* 24420 Milbon G   *fax* 01-940 5899.

*Titles in print* 600      *No. of titles published in 1988* 560      *Turnover* £15m

*Chairman* J. T. Boon, C.B.E.; *managing director* R. J. Williams; *directors* A. W. Boon, B. C. J. Rogers (financial), M. N. Saraceno (production), R. Hedley (export sales), F. Whitehead (editorial), N. Peters (direct marketing), H. Walton (retail marketing), G. Howe (paperback sales); *managers* S. Lomax (export), C. Stevens (sales operations).

*Active publishing areas* romantic fiction in paperback and hardback.

**Minerva**—see **Mandarin Paperbacks**.

**Mitchell Beazley Ltd.**, Artists House, 14-15 Manette Street, London W1V 5LB   *tel* 01-439 7211   *telex* 24892 MB Book G   *fax* 01-734 0389. *Directors:* Janice Mitchell, Duncan Baird (Managing), Jack Tresidder, Ian Irvine (Chairman), Paul Hamlyn, Tony Cobb, Nicolas Thompson. Holding company controlling Mitchell Beazley International Ltd., Mitchell Beazley Encyclopaedias Ltd., Mitchell Beazley London Ltd. Subsidiary of **Octopus Publishing Group plc.**

**Mitchell Beazley Encyclopaedias Ltd.**, Artists House, 14-15 Manette Street, London W1V 5LB   *tel* 01-439 7211   *telex* 24892 MB Book G   *fax* 01-734 0389. *Directors:* Duncan Baird (Managing), Janice Mitchell, Nicolas Thompson.
International reference books and encyclopaedias.

**Mitchell Beazley International Ltd.** (1969), Artists House, 14-15 Manette Street, London W1V 5LB   *tel* 01-439 7211   *telex* 24892 MB Book G   *fax* 01-734 0389. *Directors:* Duncan Baird (Managing), Tony Cobb, David Hight, Janice Mitchell, Malcolm Saunders, Jack Tresidder, Douglas Holford, Nicolas Thompson.
Astronomy, astrology, atlases, cookery, family reference books, gardening, history and culture, educational books for children, natural history, photography, pocket books, sex education, wine.

**Mitchell Beazley London Ltd.**, Artists House, 14-15 Manette Street, London W1V 5LB   *tel* 01-439 7211   *telex* 24892 MB Book G   *fax* 01-734 0389. *Directors:* Duncan Baird (Managing), David Hight, Nicolas Thompson.
UK and Commonwealth publishers of all Mitchell Beazley Group titles.

**Moorland Publishing Co. Ltd.** (1972), Moor Farm Road, Ashbourne, Derby-shire DE6 1HD　*tel* (0335) 44486　*telex* 377106 Chacom G MPC　*fax* (0335) 46397. *Directors:* Dr J. A. Robey (Chairman and Production Direc-tor), C. L. M. Porter (Managing), Mrs J. A. Cundy (Administration), John Whitby (Sales), J. Angell.
Travel, collecting, countryside, gardening, sport, railways.

**Morgan-Grampian Books** (1977), Royal Sovereign House, 40 Beresford Street, Woolwich, London SE18 6BQ　*tel* 01-855 7777　*telex* 896238　*fax* 01-316 0512. *General Manager:* Glen Wilders.
Directories for the travel trade and engineering industries.

**The Mothers' Union** (1876), 24 Tufton Street, London SW1P 3RB　*tel* 01-222 5533.
Religious, educational and social subjects connected with marriage and the family; religious books for adults and children; quarterly magazine *Home and Family*.

**\*Mowbray**—imprint of **Cassell plc**. Religion and theology.

**Frederick Muller Ltd**—imprint of **Century Hutchinson Ltd**. Biography and autobiography, cinema, fiction, history, humour.

**Muller, Blond & White Ltd.**—see **Frederick Muller Ltd.**

**\*John Murray (Publishers) Ltd.** (1768) 50 Albemarle Street, London W1X 4BD　*tel* 01-493 4361　*telex* 21312 Murray G　*fax* 01-499 1792　*telegraphic address* Guidebook, London, W1.

*Titles in print* 900　　*No. of titles published in 1988* 60

*Chairman* John R. Murray (general books marketing); *managing director* Nich-olas Perren; *directors* Grant McIntyre (general editorial), John G. Murray C.B.E.; Keith Nettle (educational editorial), Judith Reinhold (educational marketing); *company secretary* John Roberts; *managers* Philip Powell (distri-bution), Lorraine Abraham (production), Sarah Fulford (rights).

*Active publishing areas* general: art and architecture, biography, autobiogra-phy, fiction, letters and diaries, travel, exploration and guidebooks, Middle East, Asia, India and sub-continent, general history, health education, avi-ation, craft and practical.
Educational: biology, chemistry, physics, business studies, economics, man-agement and law, English, geography and environmental studies, history and social studies, mathematics, modern languages, technical subjects. Also self teaching in all subjects in *Success Studybook* series.

**Mysterious Press**—imprint of **Arrow Books Ltd**. Crime and detective fiction

**\*National Christian Education Council** (incorporating **Hillside Publishing** and **International Bible Reading Association**), Robert Denholm House, Nutfield, Redhill RH1 4HW　*tel* Nutfield Ridge (0737) 82411　*fax* (0737) 822116.
Books on all aspects of Christian education. Material for children's work in the Church, also R.E. and M.E. material for day schools. Activity, visual and resource material, religious drama and religious music.

**\*Nautical Publishing Co. Ltd**—imprint of **A. & C. Black (Publishers) Ltd.**

**\*Thomas Nelson & Sons, Ltd.** (1798), Nelson House, Mayfield Road, Walton-on-Thames, Surrey KT12 5PL　*tel* Walton-on-Thames (0932) 246133　*telex* 929365 Nelson G　*telegraphic address* Thonelson, Walton-on-Thames　*fax* (0932) 246109/254260. Subsidiary in Hong Kong. *Directors:* M. E. Thompson

(Managing), M. J. Givans, Brian Snaith, G. Taylor, John Tuttle, Pamela Bowen, Barry Hinchmore.

Educational (infant, primary, secondary), school atlases and dictionaries, English language teaching world-wide, educational books for Africa, Caribbean and S.E. Asia.

**New Beacon Books** (1966), 76 Stroud Green Lane, London N4 3EN *tel* 01-272 4889. *Directors:* John La Rose, Sarah White, Michael La Rose, Janice Durham.

Small specialist publishers: general non-fiction, fiction, poetry, critical writings, mainly concerning the Caribbean, Africa, Afro-America, Black Europe.

**New Cavendish Books** (1973), 3 Denbigh Road, London W11 2SJ *tel* 01-229 6765 *telex* 8951182 Gecoms G *fax* 01-792 0027. **White Mouse Editions Ltd.** (1979).

Specialist books for the collector.

***New English Library, Ltd.** (1957), Mill Road, Dunton Green, Sevenoaks, Kent TN13 2YA *tel* (0732) 450111 *cables* Expositor, Sevenoaks *telex* 95122 *fax* (0732) 460134. *Directors:* P. J. Attenborough, M. F. Attenborough, R. F. M. Morris, E. P. Major.

Fiction and non-fiction.

***New Holland Publishers**, 37 Connaught Street, London W2 2AZ *tel* 01-258 0204 *telex* 995448 Tythan G *fax* 01-262 6184.

Illustrated books on home design, crafts, gardening, cookery, natural history.

***New Orchard**—imprint of **Cassell plc**. Antiques and collecting, children's, cookery, wines and spirits, gardening, history and antiquarian, illustrated and fine editions, military and war, natural history, reference and dictionaries, transport, travel and topography.

**Newnes Technical Books**—now **Heinemann Newnes**.

**Newnes**—imprint of **The Hamlyn Publishing Group Ltd.** Maps and non-fiction.

**Nexus**—imprint of **W. H. Allen plc**.

***NFER-NELSON Publishing Co. Ltd** (1981), Darville House, 2 Oxford Road East, Windsor, Berkshire SL4 1DF *tel* (0753) 858961 *telex* 937400 Onecom G ref. 24966001 *fax* (0753) 856830.

Educational, occupational and psychological tests and assessments, educational research.

**Robert Nicholson Publications Ltd.** (1967), 16 Golden Square, London W1R 4BN *tel* 01-437 9602 *telex* 897284 Arpub *fax* 01-434 2080. *Director:* B. Winkleman (Managing).

Maps and guides.

**James Nisbet & Co., Ltd.** (1810), 78 Tilehouse Street, Hitchin, Herts. SG5 2DY *tel* (0462) 438331. *Directors:* Miss E. M. Mackenzie-Wood, Mrs. R. M. Mackenzie-Wood, A. D. M. Hill, Mrs. A. A. C. Bierrum.

Dictionaries, educational (infants, primary, secondary).

**The Nonesuch Press Ltd.**—see **Reinhardt Books Ltd.**

**The Normal Press** (1889), 25 Vicarage Lane, Upper Hale, Farnham, Surrey GU9 0PG. *Director:* L. W. Cradwick. Educational.

**Northcote House Publishers Ltd** (1985), Harper & Row House, Estover Road, Plymouth, Devon PL6 7PZ *tel* (0752) 705251 *telex* 45635 Hardis G *fax*

(0752) 777603. *Directors:* R. E. Ferneyhough, B. R. W. Hulme, M. W. Beevers F.C.A.
Business and professional text and reference books, accountancy, banking, economics, computer studies, data processing, management, marketing, international business reference and specialist dictionaries, travel, police and social studies, How-To books, dance, peace studies, revision aids. Exclusive distributors for a number of American and European publishers.

**W. W. Norton & Company** (1980), 37 Great Russell Street, London WC1B 3NU *tel* 01-323 1579 *telex* 21879 Attn GAI *telegraphic address* Gavia, London WC1 *fax* 01-436 4553. *Directors:* Alan Cameron (Managing), Donald Lamm (USA), Victor Schmalzer (USA), Eric Swenson (USA), Lord Bullock, F.B.A.
History, biography, current affairs, sailing, English and American literature, economics, music, psychology, science.

**Octopus Publishing Group plc** (1971), Michelin House, 81 Fulham Road, London SW3 6RB *tel* 01-581 9393 *telex* 920191 *fax* 01-589 8419. *Directors:* Paul Hamlyn (Chairman), Ian Irvine (Chief Executive), Richard Charkin, Peter Cheeseman, Mark Radcliffe, Nicolas Thompson, Derek Freeman, Paul Richardson.
*Subsidiaries:* Hamlyn Publishing Group, William Heinemann Ltd, Secker & Warburg, Octopus Group, Brimax Books Ltd, Ginn & Co., Mitchell Beazley Ltd, George Philip Ltd, Heinemann Educational Books Ltd, Heinemann Professional Publications Ltd.

**The Oleander Press** (1960), 17 Stansgate Avenue, Cambridge CB2 2QZ *tel* (0223) 244688 *telegraphic address* Oleander. *Managing Director:* P. Ward.
Language, literature, Libya, Arabia and Middle East, Indonesia and Far East, Cambridgeshire, travel, medical history, reference. Preliminary letter required before submitting MSS.; please send s.a.e. for reply.

**\*Oliver & Boyd,** a Division of **Longman Group UK, Ltd.,** Longman House, Burnt Mill, Harlow, Essex CM20 2JE *tel* (0279) 26721 *fax* (0279) 31059 *telex* 81259 Longman G. *Director:* Chris Kington (Divisional Managing).
Educational material for primary and secondary schools; Scottish school books.

**\*Omnibus Press/Music Sales Ltd** (1976), 8/9 Frith Street, London W1V 5TZ *tel* 01-434 0066 *telex* 21892 Msldn G *fax* 01-439 2848. *Directors:* Robert Wise (Managing—Music Sales Group), Frank Warren (Omnibus Press).
Rock music biographies, books about music.

**Open Books Publishing Limited** (1974), Beaumont House, New Street, Wells, Somerset BA5 2LD *tel* (0749) 77276. *Directors:* P. Taylor (Managing), C. Taylor.
Academic and general non-fiction; education, child development, medicine, human behaviour, local history.

**\*Open University Press** (1977), 12 Cofferidge Close, Stony Stratford, Milton Keynes, Bucks. MK11 1BY *tel* (0908) 566744 *fax* 260012. *Directors:* P. S. Wright (Managing), J. Skelton (Publishing), B. P. Clarke (Financial).
Earth sciences, education, health studies, history, life sciences, literature, music, politics, popular culture, psychology, sociology, social policy, technology, women's studies.

**Optima** (1987), 66-73 Shoe Lane, Holborn, London EC4P 4AB   *tel* 01-377 4600   *telex* 885233 Macdon G   *fax* 01-583 4407/8. *Directors:* Harriet Griffey, Terry Jackson. Division of **Macdonald & Co. (Publishers) Ltd.**
Health, alternative medicine, women's studies, the environment, popular psychology, self-help.

**Orbit**—imprint of **Futura**. Science fiction and fantasy paperbacks.

*****Orchard Books** (1985), 96 Leonard Street, London EC2A 4RH   *tel* 01-739 2929   *telex* 262655 Groluk G   *fax* 01-739 2318. *Directors:* David Kewley (Chairman/Sales), Judith Elliott (Managing/Publisher), Marlene Johnson (Finance/Operations), Rita Ireland (Production). Division of **The Watts Group**.
Children's picture books, fiction, poetry, novelty books.

**Osprey Publishing, Ltd.** (1968), 59 Grosvenor Street, London W1X 9DA   *tel* 01-493 5841   *telex* 27278   *fax* 01-491 3803.
Aviation, automotive, military, yachting, sport. See also **George Philip Ltd.**

**Outposts Publications** (1956), 72 Burwood Road, Walton-on-Thames, Surrey KT12 4AL   *tel* Walton-on-Thames 240712. *Founder:* Howard Sergeant, M.B.E. *Director:* Jean Sergeant. Poetry.

*****Peter Owen Ltd.**, 73 Kenway Road, London SW5 0RE   *tel* 01-373 5628 and 370 6093   *fax* 01-373 6760. *Director:* Peter L. Owen (Managing).
Art, belles-lettres, biography and memoirs, fiction, general, theatre.

**Oxford Illustrated Press Ltd.**, Sparkford, Yeovil, Somerset BA22 7JJ   *tel* (0963) 40635   *telex* 46212 Haynes G   *fax* (0963) 40825. *Editorial:* The Gables, Newington, Oxford OX9 8AH   *tel* Oxford (0865) 890026. *Directors:* J. H. Haynes (Executive Chairman), J. Scott (Managing), A. P. Lynch, Jane Marshall (Editorial), R. J. Stagg, A. C. Haynes. Imprint of **Haynes Publishing Group**.
Well-illustrated non-fiction books, sport, leisure and travel guides, car books, art books, general.

**Oxford Publishing Company** (1976). Sparkford, Yeovil, Somerset BA22 7JJ   *tel* (0963) 40635   *telex* 46212 Haynes G   *fax* (0963) 40825. *Chairman:* J. H. Haynes. *Editor:* P. Nicholson. Imprint of **Haynes Publishing Group**.
Railway transport.

*****Oxford University Press** (1478), Walton Street, Oxford OX2 6DP   *tel* (0865) 56767   *telex* 837330 Clarpress   *fax* (0865) 56646   *cables* Clarendon Press.
*Oxford Distribution centre* Oxford University Press Distribution Services, Saxon Way West, Corby, Northants NN18 9ES   *tel* (0536) 741519   *fax* (0536) 746337   *telex* 34313 Oxpres G   *cables* Oxonian Corby.

*Titles in print* 11355 *No. of titles published in 1988* 1474 *Turnover* £110m

*Chief Executive and Secretary to the Delegates* Sir Roger Elliott; *Deputy Secretary and Finance Director* W. R. Andrewes; Art and Reference Division: *managing director* Ivon Asquith; *directors* Simon Wratten (sales and marketing, and dictionary publishing), B. Townsend (production); head of UK sales: George Taylor, head of international rights and permissions: Anthony Mulgan. Science, Medical and Journals Division: *managing director* John Manger, *marketing director* Kate Jury. Education Division: *managing director* Peter Mothersole; *sales director* Martin Cuss. ELT Division: *managing director* vacant; *sales director* David Stewart.
*Branches or offices* in New York, Toronto, Melbourne, Auckland, Delhi, Bombay, Calcutta, Madras, Karachi, Lahore, Cape Town, Johannesburg, Durban, Nairobi, Dar es Salaam, Kuala Lumpur, Singapore, Hong Kong,

Taipei, Tokyo, Beijing; *ELT Offices* in Buenos Aires, St. Philip, Rio de Janiero, São Paulo, Kyoto, Montesson (France), Athens, Florence, Mexico DF, Ibadan, Lima, Madrid, Barcelona, Bilbao, Port of Spain, Montevideo; *Associated Companies:* University Press Ltd, Ibadan; Libris (Thailand) Co. Ltd, Bangkok.

*Active publishing areas* anthropology, archaeology, architecture, art, belleslettres, bibles, bibliography, biography and memoirs, children's books (fiction, non-fiction, picture), commerce, current affairs, dictionaries, drama, economics, educational (infants, primary, secondary, technical, university), English language teaching, essays, general history, hymn and service books, journals, law, maps and atlases, medical, music, oriental, philosophy, poetry, political economy, prayer books, reference, science, sociology, theology and religion, educational software. Academic books published under. the imprint **Clarendon Press.** Trade paperbacks published under the imprint of **Oxford Paperbacks.**

**\*Paladin Books**—imprint of **William Collins Sons & Co. Ltd.** Paperback literary fiction; non-fiction.

**Pan Books Ltd** (1944), Cavaye Place, London SW10 9PG     *tel* 01-373 6070     *telex* 917466     *fax* 01-370 0746. *Distribution centre* Hamilton Close, Houndmills Industrial Estate, Basingstoke, Hants     *tel* (0256) 464481     *fax* (0256) 460675.

*Titles in print* 2019     *No. of titles published in 1988* 340

*Chairman* Nicholas Byam Shaw; *managing director* Alan Gordon Walker; *directors* David Bleasdale, Ian Chapman, Brian Davies, Mark Houlton.

*Active publishing areas* paperback originals/reprints of notable fiction/non-fiction, including novels, detective fiction, travel, adventure, war books, biography, memoirs, current affairs, humour, reference, crafts, practical handbooks. **Piccolo**—children's non-fiction; **Piper**—children's fiction/picture books; **Picador**—outstanding international fiction/non-fiction.

Education: study aids for school and college students including *Brodie's Notes on English Literature*; books for adult education, particularly in languages, business, management and professional education.

**\*Pandora Press** (imprint of **Unwin Hyman Ltd**), 15-17 Broadwick Street, London W1V 1FP     *tel* 01-439 3126     *telex* 23732 Unhy G     *fax* 01-734 3884. *Publisher:* Philippa Brewster.

Feminist press publishing. General fiction, crime fiction, biography, arts, media, health, current affairs, travel, humour, reference.

**\*Panther Books**—imprint of **William Collins Sons & Co. Ltd.** Mass market, paperback fiction and non-fiction.

**Papermac**—imprint of **Macmillan London Ltd.**

**\*Partridge Press** (1987), 61-63 Uxbridge Road, London W5 5SA     *tel* 01-579 2652     *telegraphic address* Transcable     *telex* 267974 Trnspb G     *fax* 01-579 5479. *Director:* Mark Barty-King. *Manager:* Debbie Beckermann. A division of **Transworld Publishers Ltd.** Sport and leisure.

**\*The Paternoster Press, Ltd.,** Paternoster House, 3 Mount Radford Crescent, Exeter, Devon EX2 4JW     *tel* (0392) 50631     *fax* (0392) 413317.

Biblical studies, Christian theology, philosophy, ethics, history, mission.

**\*Stanley Paul & Co., Ltd.** (1908), Brookmount House, 62-65 Chandos Place, Covent Garden, London WC2N 4NW     *tel* 01-240 3411     *telex* 261212 Lit Ldn G. *Directors:* A. J. V. Cheetham (Chairman), R. B. Bloomfield, P. C. K. Roche, J. M. Mottram. Imprint of **Century Hutchinson Ltd.**

Sports, games, hobbies and handicrafts, sporting biographies.

**\*Pavilion Books** (1980), 196 Shaftesbury Avenue, London WC2H 8JL    *tel* 01-836 1306    *telex* 268639 Eperon G    *fax* 01-240 7684. *Joint Chairmen:* Tim Rice, Michael Parkinson. *Directors:* Colin Webb, Pamela Webb, John Midgley, Pam Taylor, Elizabeth Harrison-Hall.
Cookery, travel, humour, cinema, theatre, music, sport, children's.

**\*Pelham Books, Ltd.** (1959) 27 Wrights Lane, London W8 5TZ    *tel* 01-937 7255    *telex* 917181/2 Emjaybuks    *fax* 01-937 8704.

*Titles in print* 450    *No. of titles published in 1988* 50

*Chairman* Alan Brooke; *directors* Roger Houghton (publisher), Peter Tummons.

*Active publishing areas* Pears Cyclopaedia, Junior Pears Encyclopaedia. Autobiographies of men and women in sport, sports handbooks, hobbies, crafts and pastimes, practical handbooks on dogs and others pets, country pursuits.

**\*Penguin Books Ltd.**, Bath Road, Harmondsworth, Middlesex UB7 0DA    *tel* 01-759 1984 and 5722    *telex* 933349    *telegraphic address* Penguinook, West Drayton    *London office* 27 Wrights Lane, London W8 5TZ    *tel* 01-938 2200    *telex* 917181/2    *fax* 01-937 8704.

*International group turnover* £232m

*Founder* Sir Allen Lane; *chief executive* Peter Mayer; *managing director* Trevor Glover; *directors* Elizabeth Attenborough, John Broom, Peter Carson, Stephen Hall, Brenda Johnson, Tony Lacey, John Peck, John Rolfe, John Webster, Patrick Wright, Jonathan Yglesias.

*Active publishing areas* for more than fifty years, the publishers of one of the largest paperback lists in the English language. The Penguin list embraces, both as originals and as reprints, fiction and non-fiction, poetry and drama, classics, works of reference, and many areas of more specialised interest.

*See also* Arkana, Fantail, Hamish Hamilton, Michael Joseph, Allen Lane, The Penguin Press, Puffin, Viking, Viking Kestrel, Frederick Warne.

**Pergamon Press plc** (1948), Headington Hill Hall, Oxford OX3 0BW    *tel* (0865) 64881    *telegraphic address* Pergapress, Oxford    *telex* 83177    *fax* (0865) 60285. *Directors:* Robert Maxwell, M.C. (Chairman), K. Maxwell (Deputy Chairman), G. F. Richards (Managing), A. J. Steel (Deputy Managing), R. N. Miranda (Deputy Managing, USA), B. R. Barrett and J. Gilgunn-Jones (Editorial), M. A. Sar (Marketing), H. A. Stephens (Company Secretary). *Overseas:* New York, Beijing, Frankfurt, São Paulo, Sydney, Tokyo, Toronto. *UK Subsidiary Companies:* Brassey's Defence Publishers Ltd., Pergamon Financial Data Services, Pergamon Infotech, The Aberdeen University Press Ltd.
Economics, educational (secondary, technical, university), medical research, science, technology, engineering, sociology, energy, environment, chess, general, electronic databases.

**\*Peterloo Poets** (1976), 2 Kelly Gardens, Calstock, Cornwall PL18 9SA    *tel* (0822) 833473. *Managing Director:* Harry Chambers. *Trustees:* Richard H. Francis, Linda Squire, David Selzer.
Poetry.

**\*Phaidon Press, Ltd.**, Musterlin House, Jordan Hill Road, Oxford OX2 8DP    *tel* (0865) 310655    *telex* 83308 Phaidon G    *fax* (0865) 310662    *tele-*

*graphic address* Phaidon Oxford *Distribution centre* Unit 2B, Ridgeway Trading Estate, Iver, Bucks.   *tel* (0753) 654747   *telex* 846440. Member of the Musterlin Group plc.

*Titles in print* 250     *No. of titles published in 1989* 40     *Turnover* £4.0m

*Chairman* George Riches; *managing director* Geoff Cowen; *directors* Derek Phillips (group financial), Roger Sears (editorial), Alan Peebles (production), Simon Haviland, Nicholas Hardyman, Chris Coleman (marketing); *managers* David Hamill (distribution), Mark Eastment (rights), Sally Dunsmore (publicity), Barbara Mercer (designer).

*Active publishing areas* fine arts, the history of art and civilization, decorative and performing arts, archaeology, history, music, photography, art instruction, reference, theatre.

**George Philip Ltd** (1834), 59 Grosvenor Street, London W1X 9DA   *tel* 01-493 5841   *telex* 27278   *fax* 01-491 3803.

*Titles in print* 1500     *No. of titles published in 1988* 120     *Turnover 1988* £9.4m

*Chairman* N. Thompson; *managing director* M. A. Bovill; *directors* J. A. Bennett, R. J. Bonnett, J. Gaisford, A. G. Poynter, W. J. Croser, A. J. Simpson, D. Rivers, B. M. Willett.

*Active publishing areas* maps, atlases, globes, travel, general trade books, educational books.

*Imprint* Osprey Publishing Ltd.

**Phillimore & Co., Ltd.** (incorporating **Darwen Finlayson Ltd.**), Shopwyke Hall, Chichester, West Sussex PO20 6BQ   *tel* (0243) 787636. *Hon. Pres.:* Lord Darwen. *Directors:* Philip Harris, J.P. (Chairman and Managing), Noel Osborne, M.A. (CANTAB.) (Editorial), Ian Macfarlane, F.C.A., Hilary Clifford Brown.
Local and family history; architectural history, archaeology, genealogy and heraldry; also Darwen County History Series. *The Local Historian* (Q.) Journal of the British Association for Local History.

**Piatkus Books** (1979), 5 Windmill Street, London W1P 1HF   *tel* 01-631 0710   *telex* 266082 Piatks G   *fax* 01-436 7137. *Distributor* AA Distribution Services Ltd, Dunhams Lane, Letchworth, Herts. SG6 1LF   *tel* (0462) 686241   *telex* 825751   AA Dist   *fax* (0462) 480295.

*Titles in print* 500     *No. of titles published in 1989* 100

*Managing director* Judy Piatkus; *directors* Philip Cotterell (marketing), Gill Cormode (editorial); *managers* Jane Sommerlad (publicity), Arlette Appleby (sales), Simon Colverson (production), David Harris (financial).

*Active publishing areas* fiction, leisure, women's interest, fashion, beauty, parenting, health, new age, arts, business, biography, gift books, stationery books.

**Picador**—see **Pan Books Ltd.**

**Piccadilly Press** (1983), 5 Canfield Place, London NW6 3BT   *tel* 01-625 9582   *telex* 295441   *fax* 01-328 8256. *Directors:* Brenda Gardner (Chairman and Managing), Philip Durrance (Secretary).
Children's hardback books.

**Piccolo**—see **Pan Books Ltd.**

**\*Picture Corgi** paperbacks—imprint of **Transworld Publishers Ltd.** Children's picture books.

**\*Pinter Publishers Ltd.** (1973) 25 Floral Street, London WC2E 9DS   *tel* 01-240 9233   *telex* 912881 Cwuktx G Attn PIN   *fax* 01-379 5553 *Distribution* Marston Book Services, P.O. Box 87, Oxford OX4 1LB   *tel* (0865) 791155   *telex* 837022   *fax* (0865) 791347.

*Titles in print* 520      *No. of titles published in 1988* 100

*Chairman* Ann Weyman; *managing director* Frances Pinter; *directors* Pamela Fulton (marketing), Iain Stevenson (editorial), Robert Macleod, Christopher Conolly-Smith, Mark Hawksworth; *commissioning editor* Vanessa Couchman; *marketing manager* Madeleine Parkyn.

*Active publishing areas* academic and professional publishers specialising in social sciences including international relations, politics, economics, new technology, linguistics, and humanities. **Belhaven Press** focuses on environmental topics such as geography, earth sciences and life sciences. Division: **Leicester University Press**, *q.v.*

**Piper**—see **Pan Books Ltd.**

**Pitkin Pictorials, Ltd.** (1941), North Way, Andover, Hants SP10 5BE   *tel* (0264) 334303   *telex* 47214   *fax* (0264) 334110. *Director:* Ian Corsie. Imprint of the **Octopus Publishing Group plc.**
Colour guidebooks to cathedrals, palaces and major tourist attractions.

**\*Pitman Publishing** (1845), 128 Long Acre, London WC2E 9AN   *tel* 01-379 7383   *telegraphic address* Ipandsons, London, WC2   *telex* 261367 Pitman G   *fax* 01-240 5771 Pitman Ldn. *Managing Director:* Peter Warwick.
Secretarial studies, business education, management, professional studies, information technology. M & E Handbooks; titles previously published by **Macdonald & Evans**.

**Plexus Publishing Ltd** (1973), 26 Dafforne Road, London SW17 8TZ   *tel* 01-672 6067   *telex* 947157 Plexus G   *fax* 01-672 1631. *Directors:* Terence Porter (Managing), Sandra Wake (Editorial). Also **Eel Pie Publishing**.
Film, music, biography, popular culture, fashion.

**Pluto Publishing Ltd** (1968), 345a Archway Road, London N6 5AA   *tel* 01-348 2724   *telex* 262433   *fax* 01-348 9133. *Directors:* Roger van Zwanenberg (Managing), Anne Beech (Editorial).
Social and political science including economics, history; cultural, international, women's studies.

**Poetry Wales Press** (1981), Andmar House, Trewsfield Industrial Estate, Tondu Road, Bridgend, Mid Glamorgan CF31 4LJ   *tel* (0656) 767834. *Director:* Mick Felton.
Poetry, prose, literary criticism, biography—mostly with relevance to Wales.

**Polity Press** (1983), Dales Brewery, Gwydir Street, Cambridge CB1 2LJ   *tel* (0223) 324315   *fax* (0223) 461385. *Directors:* Anthony Giddens, David Held, John Thompson.
Social and political theory, politics, sociology, history, economics, psychology, media and cultural studies, philosophy, theology, literary theory, feminism, human geography, anthropology.

**\*Polygon,** 22 George Square, Edinburgh EH8 9LF   *tel* 031-667 1011 ext. 2412   *fax* 031-667 7938.
New international fiction, including translations, oral history, general, Scottish, social and political (Determination series).

**\*Poplar Press Ltd**—imprint of **David & Charles Publishers plc.** Writing books.

**\*Popular Dogs Publishing Co., Ltd.**, Brookmount House, 62-65 Chandos Place, Covent Garden, London WC2N 4NW   *tel* 01-240 3411   *telex* 261212 Lit Ldn G. *Directors:* R. B. Bloomfield, P. C. K. Roche, J. M. Mottram. Imprint of **Century Hutchinson Ltd.**
Practical books on breeding, care, training, and general management of dogs.

**Price Stern Sloan Ltd** (1986), John Clare House, The Avenue, Cliftonville, Northampton NN1 5BT   *tel* (0604) 230344   *telex* 312686 Pss UK G   *fax* (0604) 230342. *Directors:* Paul Honeywell (Chairman), Tony Jones (Managing), Mike Haines (Development), Martyn Smith (Finance).
Children's early learning.

**Prism Press Book Publishers Ltd** (1974), 2 South Street, Bridport, Dorset DT6 3NQ   *tel* (0308) 27022   *telex* 265871 Monref G (ref: 84:MNU 247)   *fax* (0308) 27376. *Directors:* Julian King, Colin Spooner.
Non-fiction, including health, food, building, new age, feminism, politics, ecology.

**\*P.S.I. Policy Studies Institute,** 100 Park Village East, London NW1 3SR   *tel* 01-387 2171   *fax* 01-383 0914. *Director:* W. W. Daniel. *Head of External Relations:* Nicholas Evans. *Secretary:* Eileen M. Reid.
Economic, industrial and social policy, political institutions, social sciences.

**\*Puffin,** children's paperback imprint of **Penguin Books,** 27 Wrights Lane, London W8 5TZ   *tel* 01-938 2200. *Publishing Director:* Elizabeth Attenborough.
Children's paperback books—mainly reprints. Fiction, poetry, picture books, limited non-fiction.

**Purnell Books,** 66-73 Shoe Lane, Holborn, London EC4P 4AB   *tel* 01-377 4600   *telex* 885233 Macdon G   *fax* 01-583 4407/8. A division of **Macdonald & Co. (Publishers) Ltd.**

**Putnam & Co Ltd.** (1916), 24 Bride Lane, Fleet Street, London EC4Y 8DR   *tel* 01-583 2412   *telex* 8814206 Popper G   *fax* 01-936 2153. *Directors:* W. R. Blackmore (Managing), D. C. Greening.
**Putnam Aeronautical Books:** technical and reference.

**Quartet Books, Ltd.** (1972), 27-29 Goodge Street, London W1P 1FD   *tel* 01-636 3992   *telex* 919034 Namara G   *fax* 01-439 6489. *Directors:* N. I. Attallah (Chairman), S. Pickles, Z. Hourani. Member of the **Namara Group.**
General fiction and non-fiction, sociology, politics, topical issues, jazz, biography, crime, original paperbacks.

**Queen Anne Press,** 66-73 Shoe Lane, Holborn, London EC4P 4AB   *tel* 01-377 4600   *telex* 885233 Macdon G   *fax* 01-583 4407/8. Division of **Macdonald & Co. (Publishers) Ltd.**
Sports reference and celebrity books; heritage, travel, biography; tv tie-ins.

**Quiller Press Ltd.,** 46 Lillie Road, London SW6 1TN   *tel* 01-499 6529   *telex* 21120 Monref G   *fax* 01-381 8941. *Directors:* J. J. Greenwood, A. E. Carlile.
Publishers of sponsored books.
Guide books, history, industry, humour, architecture, cookery, aviation, nature.

**\*Radius**—imprint of **Century Hutchinson Publishing Ltd.** Politics and economics.

**\*Random Century,** 30-32 Bedford Square, London WC1B 3SG   *tel* 01-255 2393   *telex* 299080 Random G   *fax* 01-255 1620. *Chairman/Chief Executive:* A. J. V. Cheetham. See **Jonathan Cape Ltd, Century Hutchinson Ltd, Chatto & Windus Ltd.**

**Rapp & Whiting, Ltd.** All books published by Rapp & Whiting have been taken over by **André Deutsch, Ltd.**

**\*The Reader's Digest Association, Ltd.**, 25 Berkeley Square, London W1X 6AB  *tel* 01-629 8144  *telex* 264631  *telegraphic address* Readigest, London, W1. *Directors:* S. N. McRae (Managing), B. C. Gray, A. T. Lynam-Smith, R. G. Twisk, H. van Wyk, R. S. Hosie, M. L. Stockton, F. K. Ross, K. A. Gordon.
Monthly magazine, condensed and series books; also DIY, car maintenance, gardening, medical, handicrafts, law, touring guides, encyclopaedias, dictionaries, nature, folklore, atlases, cookery.

**Reed Information Services Ltd.** (1983). Incorporating **Kelly's Directories, Thomas Skinner Directories, Kompass Publishers, Dial Industry Publications, British Media Publications, British Leisure Publications,** Windsor Court, East Grinstead House, East Grinstead, West Sussex RH19 1XA  *tel* (0342) 26972  *telegraphic address* Infoservices, East Grinstead  *telex* Infser G 95127. *Directors:* A. H. Emery, R. J. E. Dangerfield (Chief Executive), D. W. Lee, J. R. Clayton, P. A. Oram, K. Burton, W. J. Irlam, M. S. Morris.
Reference books and directories.

**Reinhardt Books Ltd,** including **The Nonesuch Press Ltd,** 27 Wrights Lane, London W8 5TZ  *tel* 01-938 2200. *Directors:* Max Reinhardt (Chairman), Joan Reinhardt, John R. Hews, F.C.A. *Assistant Publisher:* Elizabeth Bowes Lyon. *Consultants:* John Ryder, Judy Taylor.
Biography, fiction, essays, belles-lettres, children's books.

**Religious and Moral Education Press,** Hennock Road, Exeter, Devon EX2 8RP  *tel* (0392) 74121  *telex* 42749 Wheatn G  *fax* (0392) 217170. An imprint of **Wheaton Publishers Ltd,** a member of the **Maxwell Pergamon Publishing Corporation plc.** *Managing Director:* Simon Goodenough.
Religious, moral, personal and social education.

**Renwick of Otley,** 45 Boroughgate, Otley, West Yorkshire LS21 1AG  *tel* (0943) 465555.

**\*Rider & Co.** (1892), Brookmount House, 62-65 Chandos Place, Covent Garden, London WC2N 4NW  *tel* 01-240 3411  *telex* 261212 Lit Ldn G. *Editorial Director:* Erica Smith. Imprint of **Century Hutchinson Ltd.**
Oriental religion and philosophy, mysticism and meditation.

**Rivelin Grapheme Press** (1984), The Annexe, Kennet House, 19 High Street, Hungerford, Berkshire RG17 0NL  *tel* (0488) 84645  *fax* (0488) 83018. *Director:* Snowdon Barnett.
Poetry.

**Robinson Publishing** (1983), 11 Shepherd House, Shepherd Street, London W1Y 7LD  *tel* 01-493 1064  *telex* 28905 Mon. ref G ref 778  *fax* 01-409 7226. *Partners:* Nicholas Robinson, Tim Brentnall.
General fiction and non-fiction, including paperback fiction omnibuses, fantasy and science fiction, crime, film, cookery and health.

**\*Robson Books** (1973), Bolsover House, 5-6 Clipstone Street, London W1P 7EB  *tel* 01-323 1223 and 637 5937  *fax* 01-636 0798  *telegraphic address* Robsobook, London, W1. *Managing Director:* Jeremy Robson.
General, biography, music, humour.

**\*George Ronald** (1939), 46 High Street, Kidlington, Oxford OX5 2DN  *tel* (0865) 841515  *telex* 837646 Talism  *telegraphic address* Talisman, Oxford  *fax* (0865) 841230. *Managers:* W. Momen, E. Leith.
Religion, specialising in the Baha'i Faith.

**\*Routledge.** A division of **Routledge, Chapman & Hall Ltd.,** 11 New Fetter Lane, London EC4P 4EE   *tel* 01-583 9855   *telex* 263398 Abpldn G   *cables* Elegiacs, London EC4 *Distribution Centre* ABP, North Way, Andover, Hampshire SP10 5BE *tel* (0264) 332424 *telex* 47214 *fax* (0264) 64418 *cables* APT Andover.

*Titles in print* 6000    *No. of titles published in 1988* 630    *Turnover* £10.5m

*Managing director* David Croom; *publishers* Peter Sowden (business), Gill Davies (social and behavioural science), Janice Price (humanities), Wendy Morris (reference); *marketing director* Malcolm Campbell.

*Active publishing areas* archaeology, anthropology, art, business and management, criminology, dictionaries, economics, education, geography, history, literary criticism, philosophy, political economy, psychiatry, psychology, reference, social administration, sociology, women's studies.

**\*Routledge & Kegan Paul**—incorporated in **Routledge.**

**Royal National Institute for the Blind** (1868), Production and Distribution Centre, Bakewell Road, Orton Southgate, Peterborough, Cambs. PE2 0XU   *tel* (0733) 370777   *fax* (0733) 371555. *Customer Services Manager:* Margaret Wilson.
Magazines and books for the blind, in Braille and Moon embossed types. Also tape-recorded books (*Talking Books*). For complete list of magazines see **Classified Index.**

**\*Sage Publications Ltd.** (1971), 28 Banner Street, London EC1Y 8QE   *tel* 01-253 1516   *telex* 296207 Sage G   *fax* 01-253 5206. *Directors:* David Hill (Managing), Lynn Adams, Ian Eastment, Stephen Barr, Mike Birch, George D. McCune (USA), Sara Miller McCune (USA).
Sociology, psychology, political and social sciences.

**The Saint Andrew Press,** 121 George Street, Edinburgh EH2 4YN   *tel* 031-225 5722   *telegraphic address* Free, Edinburgh, EH2 4YN   *telex* 727935 Chscot G. Section of **Church of Scotland Department of Communication.**
Theology and religion, church history.

**St. George's Press** (1969), 37 Manchester Street, London W1M 5PE   *tel* 01-486 5481. *Directors:* C. M. Ardito (Chairman), R. A. Duparc, The Hon. Julian Fane, J. M. Hatwell.
General (fiction and non-fiction), belles-lettres, educational (English as a foreign language).

**Salamander Books Ltd.** (1973), 52 Bedford Row, London WC1R 4LR   *tel* 01-242 6693   *telex* 261113 Salama G   *fax* 01-404 4926   *telegraphic address* Salamander London WC1. *Directors:* Jef Proost (Chairman), Malcolm H. Little (Managing), Ray Bonds, Philip de Ste. Croix, Keith Allen-Jones, David Spence, Philip Hughes.
Military subjects, natural history, music, gardening, hobbies, cookery, crafts, pets.

**Salvationist Publishing and Supplies, Ltd.,** 117-121 Judd Street, London WC1H 9NN   *tel* 01-387 1656.
Devotional books, theology, biography, world-wide Christian and social service, children's books, music.

**\*W. B. Saunders Co., Ltd.,** 24-28 Oval Road, London NW1 7DX   *tel* 01-267 4466   *telex* 25775 Acpres G. *Managing Director:* Joan M. Fujimoto.
Medical and scientific.

**K. G. Saur Ltd.**—see **Bowker-Saur Ltd.**

\*Sceptre—imprint of **Hodder & Stoughton Ltd.** Fiction and non-fiction paperbacks.

\*Schofield & Sims, Ltd. (1901), Dogley Mill, Fenay Bridge, Huddersfield HD8 0NQ  *tel* (0484) 607080  *telex* 51458 Comhud G for Schosims  *telegraphic address* Schosims, Huddersfield  *fax* (0484) 606815. *Directors:* John S. Nesbitt (Chairman), J. Stephen Platts (Managing), J. Brierley (Sales).
Educational (infants, primary, secondary, technical, music for schools), children's books.

\*Scholastic Publications Ltd. (1964), Marlborough House, Holly Walk, Leamington Spa, Warwickshire CV32 4LS  *tel* (0926) 813910  *telex* 312138 Spls G  *fax* (0926) 883331. *London Office* (**Hippo Books**): 10 Earlham Street, London WC2H 9RX  *tel* 01-240 5753  *telex* 264604 Sbslon G  *fax* 01-240 6927. *Directors:* J. E. Cox (Managing), M. R. Robinson Jr. (USA), R. M. Spaulding (USA), D. J. Walsh (USA).
Children's paperbacks, children's book clubs, books for teachers, primary classroom resources, magazines for primary school teachers.

**Scientific Publishing Co., Ltd.**, 40 Dalton Street, Manchester M4 4JP  *tel* 061-205 1514.
Engineering textbooks.

\*SCM Press Ltd. (1929) 26-30 Tottenham Road, London N1 4BZ  *tel* 01-249 7262  *telex* 295068 Theolo G  *fax* 01-249 3776.

*Titles in print* 450      *No. of titles published in 1988* 45      *Turnover* £1m

*Managing director and editor* John Bowden; *directors* Mark Hammer (production), Margaret Lydamore (associate editor and company secretary), Linda Foster (bookroom).

*Active publishing areas* theological books with special emphasis on biblical, philosophical and modern theology; books on religious education, sociology of religion and religious aspects of current issues.

**Scolar Press**—imprint of **Gower Publishing Group Ltd.** Arts and humanities.

**Scottish Academic Press Ltd.** (1969), 33 Montgomery Street, Edinburgh EH7 5JX  *tel* 031-556 2796. *Directors:* Douglas Grant, D. P. Dorward, A. A. Rodwell, R. B. R. Walker, H. Whittaker.
All types of academic books and books of Scottish interest.

**The Scout Association,** Baden-Powell House, Queen's Gate, London SW7 5JS  *tel* 01-584 7030  *fax* 01-581 9953  *telegraphic address* Scouting. *General Editor:* David Easton.
Technical books dealing with all subjects relevant to Scouting and monthly journal *Scouting*.

\*Scripture Union Publishing (1867), Scripture Union House, 130 City Road, London EC1V 2NJ  *tel* 01-782 0013  *fax* 01-782 0014. Christian Publishers and Booksellers.
Music, bible reading aids, Sunday school materials and Christian books especially for children and young people.

**B. A. Seaby** (1926), 8 Cavendish Square, London W1M 0AJ  *tel* 01-631 3707  *fax* 01-436 5189. *Directors:* E. R. Cox, D. Kidd, G. Manton, B. Reeds.
Numismatics, archaeology, history, travel, antiquities.

**Search Press Ltd.** (1962), Wellwood, North Farm Road, Tunbridge Wells, Kent TN2 3DR  *tel* (0892) 510850  *telex* 957258 Search G  *fax* (0892) 515903.

*Directors:* Charlotte de la Bedoyère, John M. Todd, The Hon. G. E. Noel, Ruth B. Saunders.
Philosophy, social sciences, literature, history, theology, exegesis, spirituality, educational, arts, crafts, leisure, cookery.

\***Martin Secker & Warburg Ltd** (Founded 1910; reconstructed and enlarged 1936), Michelin House, 81 Fulham Road, London SW3 6RB  *tel* 01-581 9393  *telex* 920191  *fax* 01-589 8419. *Distribution centre* Sanders Lodge Estate, Rushden, Northants. NN109RZ  *tel* (0933) 58521. Member of **Octopus Publishing Group plc.**
*No. of titles published in 1988* 45

*Chairman* Paul Hamlyn; *directors* Dan Franklin (publishing), Peter Kilborn (production), Martin Cowell (sales), Serena Davies (publicity), Peter Dyer (art), Robin Robertson (editorial), Clive Charles (company secretary).

*Active publishing areas* art, belles-lettres, biography and memoirs, cinema, fiction, history, poetry, jazz, crime, politics, theatre, travel.

**Serpent's Tail** (1986), Unit 4 Blackstock Mews, Blackstock Road, London N4 2DR  *tel* 01-354 1949  *fax* 01-354 5372. *Director:* Peter Ayrton.
Modern fiction in paperback: literary and experimental work, first novels and work in translation.

**Settle Press** (1983), Wigmore House Publishing Ltd, 10 Boyne Terrace Mews, London W11 3LR  *tel* 01-243 0695. *Directors:* D. Settle (Managing), M. Carter (Editorial).
Travel and guidebooks, general, fiction.

**Severn House Publishers** (1974), 35 Manor Road, Wallington, Surrey SM6 0BW  *tel* 01-773 4161  *fax* 01-773 4143. *Chairman:* Edwin Buckhalter.
Biography, music, history, natural history, fiction, romances, thrillers, detective, adventure, war, western, science fiction, film and TV tie-ins.

**Shakespeare Head Press** (1904), Basil Blackwell Ltd., 108 Cowley Road, Oxford OX4 1JF.
Finely printed books; scholarly works.

**Sheed & Ward Ltd.** (1926), 2 Creechurch Lane, London EC3A 5AQ  *tel* 01-283 6330. *Directors:* M. T. Redfern, K. G. Darke. Publishers of books, mostly by Catholics.
History, philosophy, theology, catechetics, scripture and religion.

\***Sheldon Press,** Holy Trinity Church, Marylebone Road, London NW1 4DU  *tel* 01-387 5282  *telegraphic address* Futurity, London  *fax* 01-388 2352. *Editorial Director:* Judith Longman. *Senior Editor:* Joanna Moriarty.
Popular medicine, health, self-help, psychology, religion, practical management.

\***Shepheard-Walwyn (Publishers), Ltd.** (1971), Suite 34, 26 Charing Cross Road, London WC2H 0DH  *tel* 01-240 5992  *fax* 01-379 5770. *Directors:* B. K. Shaw, A. R. A. Werner.
History, political economy, philosophy, religion; books in calligraphy; Scottish interest.

**John Sherratt & Son, Ltd.,** Hotspur House, 2 Gloucester Street, Manchester M1 5QR  *tel* 061-236 9963.
Educational (primary, secondary, technical, university), medical, practical handbooks, collector's books.

**Shire Publications Ltd.** (1966), Cromwell House, Church Street, Princes Risborough, Aylesbury, Bucks. HP17 9AJ  *tel* (08444) 4301. *Directors:* J. P. Rotheroe, J. W. Rotheroe.

*Discovering* paperbacks, Shire Albums, Shire Archaeology, Shire Natural History, Shire Ethnography, Shire Egyptology, Shire Garden History.

**Sidgwick & Jackson Ltd.** (1908), 1 Tavistock Chambers, Bloomsbury Way, London WC1A 2SG   *tel* 01-242 6081   *telex* 8952953   *fax* 01-831 0874. *Directors:* Earl of Stockton (Chairman), William Armstrong (Managing), R. Smith, J. Arora, S. B. Hill, Robert Gwyn Palmer, Richard Hartgill, Morven Knowles, Martin Neild.
Archaeology, biography, cinema, current affairs, fiction, future history, gardening, history, military history, music (pop and classical), political economy, show business, sociology, sport, travel, wine, cookery, crafts.

*****Simon & Schuster Ltd.** (1986), West Garden Place, Kendal Street, London W2 2AQ   *tel* 01-724 7577   *telex* 21702   *fax* 01-402 0639.   *Directors:* Brian Perman (managing), Nicholas Brealey (non-fiction), Maureen Waller (fiction), Lionel Foot, Lesley Toll, Tony Short, Ailsa Macalister (publicity). Fiction, non-fiction and children's imprints, Blue Murder (crime), Sportspages (sport), Positive Paperbacks (practical and self-help), Sprint (children's fiction).

**Thomas Skinner Directories**—imprint of **Reed Information Services Ltd.** International banking, finance, legal and building directories.

**Colin Smythe Ltd.** (1966), P.O. Box 6, Gerrards Cross, Bucks. SL9 8XA   *tel* (0753) 886000   *fax* (0753) 886469   *telegraphic address* Smythe books, Gerrardscross. *Directors:* Colin Smythe (Managing), Peter Bander van Duren, A. Norman Jeffares, Ann Saddlemyer, Leslie Hayward.
Biography, current affairs, histories, parapsychology, literary criticism, flyfishing, folk-lore, science and fantasy fiction, Irish interest and Anglo-Irish literature. Also **Dolmen Press** books.

*****Society for Promoting Christian Knowledge** (1698), Holy Trinity Church, Marylebone Road, London NW1 4DU   *tel* 01-387 5282   *telegraphic address* Futurity, London   *fax* 01-388 2352. *General Secretary:* P. N. G. Gilbert. *Editorial Director:* Judith Longman. *Editors:* Rachel Boulding, Philip Law.
Theology and religion. See also **Sheldon Press.**

**Soncino Press, Ltd.** (1929), 20 Cambridge Terrace, Gateshead, Tyne & Wear NE8 1RP   *tel* 091-490 1692.
Translations with commentaries of Hebrew classics. Theology and religion.

**Southside (Publishers), Ltd.** (1968)—subsidiary of **Canongate Publishing Ltd.**

*****Souvenir Press, Ltd.**, 43 Great Russell Street, London WC1B 3PA   *tel* 01-580 9307-8 and 637 5711   *telex* 24710 Souvnr G   *fax* 01-580 5064   *telegraphic address* Publisher, London.

*Titles in print* 600     *No. of titles published in 1988* 56

*Managing directors* Ernest Hecht, B.SC. (ECON.), B. COM; *director* A. Hecht; *executive directors* Rodney King, Jane Greenhalgh, Jeanne Manchee.

*Active publishing areas* archaeology, biography and memoirs, children's books (non-fiction, rewards), educational (secondary, technical), fiction, general, humour, practical handbooks, psychiatry, psychology, sociology, sports, games and hobbies, travel, supernatural, parapsychology, illustrated books.

*****SPCK**—see **Society for Promoting Christian Knowledge.**

**Neville Spearman Ltd.**—imprint of **The C. W. Daniel Company Ltd.** Mysticism.

**Spellmount Ltd., Publishers** (1983), 12 Dene Way, Speldhurst, Tunbridge Wells, Kent TN3 0NX   *tel* (089-286) 2860. *Directors:* Ian Morley-Clarke, Kathleen Morley-Clarke.
Biography, music, jazz, military, aviation and naval history, cricket, London historical guides. Associate company: **The Nutshell Publishing Co. Ltd.**

*****Sphere Books Ltd** (1966), Headway House, 66-73 Shoe Lane, London EC4P 4AB   *tel* 01-377 4600   *telex* 885233 Macdon G   *fax* 01-583 4407/8. *Distribution centre* Purnell, Paulton, Bristol BS18 5LQ   *tel* (0761) 413301   *telex* 44713   *fax* (0761) 419308. Part of the **Macdonald Group.**

*Titles in print* 1500   *No. of titles published in 1988* 250   *Turnover 1988* £11.7m

*Directors:* Nicholas Webb (managing), Barbara Boote (publishing), John O'Connor (sales and marketing), Julian Evans (Abacus), Peter Cotton (art).

*Active publishing areas* paperbacks: original fiction and non-fiction, reprints; **Abacus** and **Cardinal** trade paperbacks and reference.

*****Spindlewood** (1980), 70 Lynhurst Avenue, Barnstaple, Devon EX31 2HY   *tel* (0271) 71612. *Directors:* Michael Holloway, Anne Holloway.
Children's picture books; adult and children's fiction. History, travel and education titles.

*****E. & F. N. Spon Ltd.** (1834), 11 New Fetter Lane, London EC4P 4EE   *tel* 01-583 9855   *telex* 263398. *Directors:* P. Gardner (Managing), P. Read (Publishing), G. McDonald (Book Production), A. J. Davis (Finance), J. Lavender (Marketing). Division of **Chapman & Hall.**
Architecture, building, surveying, engineering, applied science, energy studies, leisure studies, construction, planning.

**Sportsprint**—imprint of **John Donald Publishers Ltd.** Sports.

**Spring Books**—imprint of **The Hamlyn Publishing Group Ltd.** Non-fiction.

**Springwood Books Ltd.,** Springwood House, The Avenue, Ascot, Berks. SL5 7LY   *tel* (0990) 24053   *telex* 8813271 Gecoms G. *Director:* Christopher Foster (Managing).
Astrology, childrens, fiction, biography, sport, history, literature, politics, humour, economics.

**Stacey International** (1974), 128 Kensington Church Street, London W8 4BH   *tel* 01-221 7166   *telex* 298768 Stacey G   *fax* 01-792 9288. *Directors:* Tom Stacey, C. S. Stacey, Geoffrey Milne (Managing).
Illustrated non-fiction, encyclopaedic books on regions and countries, Islamic and Arab subjects, World Affairs, art.

**Stainer & Bell, Ltd.** (1906), P.O. Box 110, 82 High Road, London N2 9PW   *tel* 01-444 9135. *Directors:* Allen Percival, C.B.E. (Chairman), Bernard Braley, A.C.I.S. (Deputy Chairman), Keith Wakefield (Joint Managing), Carol Wakefield (Joint Managing/Secretary), Joan Braley, John Hosier, C.B.E., Scott Stroman. Books on music, religious communication.

*****Stanford Maritime**—imprint of **A. & C. Black (Publishers) Ltd.**

**Star Books**—imprint of **W. H. Allen & Co. plc.** Paperbacks.

**Harold Starke Ltd.,** Pegasus House, 116-120 Golden Lane, London EC1Y 0TL   *tel* 01-253 2145   *telex* 975573 Burke G. *Directors:* Harold K. Starke (Chairman), Naomi Galinski (Managing).
Biography and memoirs, medical and reference.

*****Patrick Stephens Ltd.** (1967), Denington Estate, Wellingborough, Northants. NN8 2QD   *tel* (0933) 440033   *telex* 311072 Thopub G and 312511 Tpg

Bks *fax* (0933) 440512. *Directors:* David Young (Managing), Darryl Reach, Peter Winslow, F.C.A. (Secretary).

Aviation, biography, collecting, the countryside, fitness and sport, walking and mountaineering, maritime, military and wargaming, model making, motor cycling, motoring and motor racing, railways and railway modelling.

**The Sterling Publishing Group plc** (1978), P.O. Box 839, 86-88 Edgware Road, London W2 2YW *tel* 01-258 0066. *Chairman:* R. M. Cohen. *Managing Director:* R. M. Summers. *Directors:* D. M. Coughlan, R. G. B. Heller, V. L. Lewis, M. D. Preston, A. D. L. Robinson.

Reference, management and technology directories, leisure, commemorative publishing.

**Stevens and Sons Ltd** (founded 1799; incorporated 1889), South Quay Plaza, 184 Marsh Wall, London E14 9FT *tel* 01-538 8686 *telex* 929089 Itpinf G *fax* 01-538 8625. *Directors:* C. D. O. Evans (Chairman and Managing), J. Jenkins, H. Jones, A. Kinahan, R. McKay, B. Grandage, C. Tullo, D. Tebbutt, R. Greener, G. Francis, Jane Cramp. Subsidiary of International Thomson Professional Information/Thomson Information Services.

Law.

**Stillit Books, Ltd.**, 72 New Bond Street, London W1Y 0QY *tel* 01-493 1177. *telex* 23475. *Director:* Gerald B. Stillit.

Stillitron audio-visual, direct method, programmed, instantaneously electronically corrected, language systems. French, German, Spanish, Italian, Arabic and English as a foreign language.

**Studio Publications (Ipswich) Ltd.** (1975). A subsidiary of **Ladybird Books Ltd.** The Drift, Nacton Road, Ipswich, Suffolk IP3 9QR *tel* (0473) 270880 *telex* 98551 Studio G *fax* (0473) 270113. *Managing Director:* B. J. Henderson.

Children's novelty and early-learning titles, including activities, cookery, fairy stories. Imprints include: **Playskool** and **Stick-a-tale**.

**\*Studio Vista**—imprint of **Cassell plc.** Art, antiques and collecting, architecture and design, fine art and art history, illustrated and fine editions, photography.

**Sunflower Books,** 12 Kendrick Mews, London SW7 3HG *tel* 01-589 1862 *telex* 269388 Lonhan G *fax* 01-225 1033. *Directors:* P. A. Underwood (USA), J. G. Underwood, S. J. Seccombe.

Travel guide books.

**Sussex University Press** (1971), Sussex House, Falmer, Brighton, East Sussex BN1 9QZ *tel* (0273) 606755. Some publications distributed by **Scottish Academic Press Ltd.**, *q.v.*

All types of academic books.

**Alan Sutton Publishing, Ltd.** (1978), 30 Brunswick Road, Gloucester GL1 1JJ *tel* (0452) 419575 *fax* (0452) 302791. *Directors:* Alan Sutton, Nicholas Mills, Peter Clifford, Richard Bryant, Christopher Sackett, Dave Prigent, Kaye Montgomery.

Literature, history and archaeology, biography, letters and diaries, railways, travel and topography; illustrated general books; academic titles particularly in history and archaeology; paperback series include pocket classics and history.

**Swedenborg Society,** 20-21 Bloomsbury Way, London WC1A 2TH *tel* 01-405 7986.

Theology and religion.

**\*Sweet & Maxwell Ltd** (founded 1799; incorporated 1889), South Quay Plaza, 183 Marsh Wall, London E14 9FT *tel* 01-538 8686 *telex* 929089 Itpinf

G　*fax* 01-538 8625. *Directors:* C. D. O. Evans (Chairman and Managing) J. Jenkins, A. Kinahan, B. Grandage, C. Tullo, D. Tebbutt. Subsidiary of International Thomson Professional Information/Thomson Information Services.
Law.

**I. B. Tauris & Co. Ltd** (1983), 110 Gloucester Avenue, London NW1 8JA　*tel* 01-483 2681　*telex* 261507/3166 Tauris　*fax* 01-483 4541. *Directors:* I. Bagherzade, M. Cass, G. W. Green.
Modern history, politics, international relations, economics, current affairs.

**\*Tavistock Publications Ltd.**—incorporated in **Routledge.**

**\*Taylor & Francis, Ltd.**, 4 John Street, London WC1N 2ET　*tel* 01-405 2237-9. *President:* Professor Sir Nevill Mott, M.S., D.S.C., F.INST.P., F.R.S. *Directors:* Professor B. R. Coles, B.SC., D.PHIL., F.INST.P. (Chairman), Professor K. W. Keohane, C.B.E., B.SC., PH.D., F.INST.P. (Vice-Chairman), A. R. Selvey, F.C.C.A., F.B.I.M. (Managing), M. I. Dawes, E. Ferguson, M.A., S. M. A. Banister, M.A., Professor H. Baum, K. R. Courtney.
Educational (university), science: physics, and mathematics, chemistry, electronics, natural history, pharmacology and drug metabolism, medical science, astronomy, technology, history of science, ergonomics, production engineering, Falmer Press Ltd.

**Technical Press Ltd**—associate company of **Gower Publishing Group Ltd.** Technical books.

**Telegraph Books** (1920), Daily Telegraph, Peterborough Court at South Quay, 181 Marsh Wall, London E14 9SR　*tel* 01-538 5000 ext. 6829　*fax* 01-515 1665. *Publishing Director:* Marilyn Warnick.
Business, personal finance, crosswords, sport, travel and guides, maps and charts, cookery and wine, painting and drawing, general.

**Thomas Telford Ltd** (1972), Thomas Telford House, 1 Heron Quay,London E14 9XF　*tel* 01-987 6999　*telex* 298105 Civils G　*fax* 01-538 5746. *Directors:* A. G. Dawson (Managing), A. Levett, Lord Howie of Troon.
Professional and technical books, journals and magazines on civil engineering and associated areas.

**Temple Press.**—imprint of **The Hamlyn Publishing Group Ltd.** Atlases, maps and militaria.

**Teredo Books,** P.O. Box 430, Brighton, East Sussex BN1 6GT　*tel* (0273) 505432. *Managing Director:* Alex A. Hurst.
Maritime publications and marine art.

**\*Thames and Hudson Ltd,** 30-34 Bloomsbury Street, London WC1B 3QP　*tel* 01-636 5488　*telegraphic address* Thameshuds, London WC1　*telex* 25992 Thbook G　*fax* 01-636 4799. *Distribution centre* Thames and Hudson (Distributors) Ltd, 44 Clockhouse Road, Farnborough, Hants GU14 7QZ　*tel* (0252) 541602　*telex* 858425　*fax* (0252) 377380.

*Titles in print* 1625　　　*No. of titles published in 1988* 195

*Chairman* E. U. Neurath; *managing director* T. M. Neurath; *directors* E. Bates (company secretary), J. R. Camplin (editorial), T. L. Evans (sales), C. A. Ferguson (production), W. Guttmann (production), A. T. Hill (finance), S. Huntley (sales), C. M. Kaine (design), I. H. B. Middleton (rights), N. Stangos (editorial).

*Active publishing areas* art, archaeology and anthropology, architecture, photography, travel, social, military and classical history, fashion, literature and criticism, practical guides, mythology and religion, philosophy, psychology and sociology, science and technical, stage and screen, music.

**Thames Publishing** (1970), 14 Barlby Road, London W10 6AR  *tel* 01-969 3579. *Publishing Manager:* John Bishop.
Books about music, particularly by British composers. Preliminary letter essential.

**Thomson-Leng Publications,** Dundee DD1 9QJ  *tel* 23131  *telegraphic address* Courier, Dundee  *telex* 76380. London: 185 Fleet Street, London EC4A 2HS  *tel* 01-242 5086  *telegraphic address* Courier, London, EC4.
Publishers of newspapers and periodicals.
Children's books (annuals), fiction.

*****Stanley Thornes (Publishers) Ltd** (and **Hulton**), Old Station Drive, Leckhampton, Cheltenham, Gloucestershire GL53 0DN  *tel* (0242) 584429  *telex* 43593 Sthorn G  *fax* (0242) 221914.

*Titles in print* 1200  *No. of titles published in 1988* 155  *Turnover 1988* £4.9m

*Managing director* R. M. Kendall; *directors* M. S. Rigby, M. M. Van de Weijer, A. S. Brode, J. N. Samsom, J. C. Richardson, N. Morley.

*Active publishing areas* educational—primary, Bookshelf reading programme, secondary, further education.

*****Thorsons Publishers Ltd.** (1930), Denington Estate, Wellingborough, Northants. NN8 2RQ  *tel* (0933) 440033  *telex* 311072 Thopub G and 312511 Tpg Bks (ed)  *fax* (0933) 440512. *Directors:* D. J. Young (Managing), D. C. J. Palmer, P. A. Winslow, E. M. Campbell.
General life-style publishing, complementary medicine, health and nutrition; business, management and positive thinking; relationships and sex; pets, animal rights, organic gardening; crafts, vegetarian and special diets cookery. **Grapevine** imprint: practical books for women.

**Threshold Books Ltd** (1981), 661 Fulham Road, London SW6 5PZ  *tel* 01-731 4241  *telex* 896979 Tacs G  *fax* 01-371 5807. *Directors:* B. Cooper, D. Blunt.
Acquired by **The Kenilworth Press Ltd.**
Equestrian, natural history.

*****Times Books Ltd.** (1977), 16 Golden Square, London W1R 4BN  *tel* 01-437 9602  *telex* 897284 Arpub G  *fax* 01-434 2080. *Director:* Barry Winkleman (Managing).
Atlases, reference.

*****Alec Tiranti Ltd.**—taken over by **Academy Editions,** *q.v.*

**Tolley Publishing Co. Ltd** (1918), Tolley House, 2 Addiscombe Road, Croydon, Surrey CR9 5AF  *tel* 01-686 9141. *Directors:* B. G. K. Downing (Chairman), H. L. King (Managing), A. J. Fisher, N. H. Parmee, R. E. Webb, K. D. Ladbrook, K. R. Tingley.
Taxation, accountancy, company law and secretarial practice, employment law, social security and other law.

*****Transworld Publishers Ltd.,** 61-63 Uxbridge Road, London W5 5SA  *tel* 01-579 2652  *telex* 267974 Trnspb G  *fax* 01-579 5479.
Corgi, Bantam, Bantam Press, Young Corgi, Picture Corgi, Black Swan, Partridge Press, Doubleday, Freeway, Bantam Little Rooster, Yearling.

*Trentham Books Ltd** (1968), 151 Etruria Road, Stoke-on-Trent, Staffs. ST1 5NS   *tel* (0782) 274227   *telex* G367257 IC Light   *fax* (0782) 411115. *Directors:* Professor S. J. Eggleston (Managing), Gillian Klein, Barbara Wiggins. *Editorial office:* 28 Hillside Gardens, London N6 5ST   *tel* 01-348 2174.
Education, social policy, sociology of Europe.

**Triton Publishing Company Ltd.** (1964), 1A Montagu Mews North, London W1H 1AJ   *tel* 01-706 0486. *Directors:* D. G. Trustcott, F.C.A., Carolyn Whitaker.
Fiction and general non-fiction.

**Troubadour**—imprint of **Futura.** Historical romance paperbacks.

**Two-Can Publishing** (1987), 27 Cowper Street, London EC2A 4AP   *tel* 01-251 4232   *telex* 261234 Tlsyst G   *fax* 01-251 1610. *Directors:* Andrew Jarvis (Chairman), Ian Grant (Managing), Sara Lynn (Creative).
Children's non-fiction, activity and story books.

*Tycooly Publishing**—imprint of **Cassell plc.** Natural resources, agriculture and environment, scientific policy for economy of tropical and developing world.

**Unicorn Books,** 16 Laxton Gardens, Paddock Wood, Kent TN12 6BB   *tel* (0892 83) 3648. *Directors:* R. Green, M. D. Green.
Militaria, music, transport and collecting books.

**University of Wales Press** (1922), 6 Gwennyth Street, Cathays, Cardiff CF2 4YD   *tel* (0222) 231919   *fax* (0222) 396040.
Academic and educational (Welsh and English). Publishers of *Bulletin of the Board of Celtic Studies, Welsh History Review, Studia Celtica, Llen Cymru, Y Gwyddonydd, Efrydiau Athronyddol.*

*University Tutorial Press, Ltd.**—see **Unwin Hyman Ltd.**

*Unwin Hyman Ltd** (1986), 15-17 Broadwick Street, London W1V 1FP   *tel* 01-439 3126   *telex* 23732   *fax* 01-734 3884. *Distribution centre* DMS Ltd, Sheldon Way, New Hythe Lane, Larkfield, Nr Maidstone, Kent ME30 6SE   *tel* (0622) 882000   *telex* 965514   *fax* (0622) 718036.

*Titles in print* 3000    *No. of titles published in 1988* 500    *Turnover 1988* £14.7m

*Chairman and chief executive* Robin Hyman; *deputy chairman* Rayner Unwin; *directors* Christopher Blake, Nigel Britten, Mary Butler, Jim Dicks, Patric Duffy, Roger Jones, Christopher Sporborg, David Stark, Mark Streatfeild, John Taylor, Patrick Gallagher (Australia).
*Trade Division:* including **Unwin Paperbacks:** biography, travel, current affairs, Eastern religion (**Mandala**), crafts, design, health and childcare, sport, gardening, natural history and countryside, fantasy fiction, publishers of Pepys's Diary and J.R.R. Tolkien. **Pandora Press:** feminist publishing. *Education Division:* primary and secondary educational including mathematics, science, geography and humanities; former **University Tutorial Press** titles. *Academic Division:* tertiary, earth and life sciences, economics and business studies, social and political sciences, humanities.

**Usborne Publishing** (1973) 20 Garrick Street, London WC2E 9BJ   *tel* 01-379 3535   *telex* 8953598 Uspub G   *fax* 01-836 0705   *cables* Uspub London WC2

*Titles in print* 520    *No. of titles published in 1988* 40

*Directors* T. P. Usborne, Jenny Tyler, Robert Jones, David Lowe, Keith Ball, C. Rawson, D. Harte, L. Hunt.

*Active publishing areas* children's books, reference, practical, craft, natural history, computers.

**Vallentine, Mitchell & Co. Ltd.** (1950), Gainsborough House, 11 Gainsborough Road, London E11 1RS *tel* 01-530 4226 *telegraphic address* Valmico, London *telex* 897719 *fax* 01-530 7795. *Directors:* F. Cass (Managing), M. P. Zaidner.
Jewish studies.

**\*Van Nostrand Reinhold (INT.) Co. Ltd.**, 11 New Fetter Lane, London EC4P 4EE *tel* 01-583 9855 *telex* 263398. *Directors:* P. A. Gardner (Managing), A. J. Davis (Finance), D. Recaldin (Publishing), J. Lavender (Marketing), G. McDonald (Book Production). Division of **Chapman & Hall.**
Academic, aeronautics, architecture, electrical and electronics, engineering, mathematics, professional, reference, pure and applied science, technology, computers, management, accountancy, finance, food technology.

**The Vegetarian Society (UK), Ltd.**, Parkdale, Dunham Road, Altrincham, Cheshire WA14 4QG *tel* 061-928 0793.
Vegetarianism, recipes, wholefood nutrition and cookery; travel guide and handbook; bi-monthly magazine.

**Verso Ltd.** (1970), 6 Meard Street, London W1V 3HR *tel* 01-437 3546 and 434 1704 *fax* 01-734 0059. *Directors:* Colin Robinson (Managing), Robin Blackburn (Chairman), Tariq Ali, Ellen Wood.
Politics, biography, sociology, economics, history, philosophy, cultural studies.

**\*Viking,** hardcover imprint of **Penguin Books,** 27 Wrights Lane, London W8 5TZ *tel* 01-938 2200.

*Turnover* £6m

*Publishing director* Tony Lacey.

*Active publishing areas* fiction, general non-fiction, illustrated books; history, literature, art, architecture, biography and current affairs.

**\*Viking Kestrel,** children's hardcover imprint of **Penguin Books,** 27 Wrights Lane, London W8 5TZ *tel* 01-938 2200. *Publishing Director:* Elizabeth Attenborough.
Fiction, poetry, picture books, limited non-fiction.

**Virago Press** (1974), 20-23 Mandela Street, Camden Town, London NW1 0HQ *tel* 01-383 5150 *telex* 927560 *telegraphic address* Caterwaul London NW1 *fax* 01-383 4892.

*Titles in print* 600 *No. of titles published in 1988* 102 *Turnover* £2.1m

*Chairwoman* Carmen Callil; *managing directors* Ursula Owen and Harriet Spicer; *directors* Lennie Goodings, Alexandra Pringle, Ruth Petrie, Gil McNeil, Lynn Knight, Miles Emley.

*Active publishing areas* books for the general and educational market which highlight all aspects of women's lives. Fiction and non-fiction, educational and reference.

**Virgin Books**—imprint of **W. H. Allen & Co. plc.** Youth-oriented popular non-fiction.

**Virtue & Co., Ltd.** (1819), 25 Breakfield, Coulsdon, Surrey CR3 2UE *tel* 01-668 4632 *telex* 261507 ref 3393 *fax* 01-668 4102. *Director:* Michael Virtue.
Books for the catering trade and the home.

**Vision Press Ltd.** (1946), 28 Phillimore Walk, Kensington, London W8 7SA *tel* 01-938 2929 *fax* 01-938 2929. *Directors:* Alan Moore, B.A. (Managing), Amber G. Moore.

Art, film, history, literary criticism, music, theatre. **Artemis Press** imprint: education.

**Walker Books Ltd.** (1979), 87 Vauxhall Walk, London SE11 5HJ  *tel* 01-793 0909  *telex* 8955572  *fax* 01-587 1123. *Directors:* Sebastian Walker, Kate Mortimer.

Children's—mainly picture books; junior and teenage fiction.

**Warburg Institute,** University of London, Woburn Square, London WC1H 0AB  *tel* 01-580 9663.

Cultural and intellectual history, with special reference to the history of the classical tradition.

**Ward Lock Ltd**—see **Cassell plc.**

*****Ward Lock Educational Co. Ltd** (1952), T R House, 1 Christopher Road, East Grinstead, West Sussex RH19 3BT  *tel* (0342) 313844  *telex* 94011210 Blap G  *fax* (0342) 410471. *Directors:* Au Bak Ling (Chairman Hong Kong), Martin Marix Evans/Vincent Winter, Au King Kwok (Hong Kong), Au Wai Kwok (Hong Kong).

Secondary and primary pupil materials, Kent Mathematics Project, reading workshops, teachers' books, music books, history, religious education, environmental studies.

*****Frederick Warne (Publishers) & Co.** (1865), 27 Wrights Lane, London W8 5TZ  *tel* 01-938 2200  *telegraphic address* Warne, London, W8; and New York. Imprint of the **Penguin Group.**

*Titles in print* 250  *No. of titles published in 1988* 40  *Turnover 1988* £10.4m

*Directors:* Tony Lacey, John Rolfe, Stephen Hall, Sally Floyer.

*Active publishing areas* Beatrix Potter, *Huxley Pig, Bunnykins* and other classic children's books, Observer's Pocket Series, walking guides.

**Warwickshire Books**—imprint of **Wheaton Publishers Ltd.**

*****Franklin Watts** (1969, London; 1942, New York), 96 Leonard Street, London EC2A 4RH  *tel* 01-739 2929  *telex* 262655 Groluk G  *fax* 01-739 2318. *Directors:* David Kewley (Managing/Sales), Chester Fisher (Publishing), Marlene Johnson (Finance/Operations), Rita Ireland (Production). Division of **The Watts Group.**

Children's illustrated non-fiction, reference, education.

*****The Watts Group,** 96 Leonard Street, London EC2A 4RH  *tel* 01-739 2929  *telex* 262655 Groluk G  *fax* 01-739 2318. Division of **The House of Grolier Ltd.** *Directors:* David Kewley (Managing/Sales), Judith Elliot (Publisher: Orchard), Chester Fisher (Publisher: Franklin Watts), Marlene Johnson (Finance/Operations), Rita Ireland (Production).

Children's picture books, fiction, poetry, novelty books, non-fiction, reference, education. Imprints: Campbell Books, Orchard Books, Franklin Watts.

*****Wayland (Publishers) Ltd** (1969), 61-61A Western Road, Hove, East Sussex BN3 1JD  *tel* (0273) 722561  *telex* 878170 Wayland G  *fax* (0273) 29314.

*Titles in print* over 1200  *No. of titles published in 1988* 30 new series

*Chairman* A. S. Brode; *managing director* J. W. Lewis; *directors* P. Humphrey (editorial), P. Hyem (sales/distribution), K. Lilley (production); *manager* Leslie Mascall (publicity).

*Active publishing areas* children's information books for ages 5–18. **Firefly Books** (1989) elementary non-fiction imprint for ages 3–8.

*****Waymark**—see **AA Publishing.**

**Webb & Bower (Publishers) Ltd.** (1978), 5 Cathedral Close, Exeter, Devon EX1 1EZ *tel* (0392) 435362 and 210445 *cable* Webbower Exeter *telex* 42544 Webbow *fax* (0392) 211652. *Directors:* Richard Webb, Delian Bower.
Specialises in publishing illustrated non-fiction books for the UK, USA and international co-edition markets. Arts, crafts, biography, illustrated classics, topography, travel, nostalgia, gardening, food, wine, reference, general.

**George Weidenfeld & Nicolson Ltd.** (1949) 91 Clapham High Street, London SW4 7TA *tel* 01-622 9933 *telex* 918066 Wpwnab G *fax* 01-627 3361 *telegraphic address* Nicobar London SW4 *Distribution centre* AA Distribution Services Ltd, Dunhams Lane, Letchworth, Herts. SG6 1LF *tel* (0462) 686241 *telex* 8954130 *fax* (0462) 480295.

*Titles in print* 988 *No. of titles published in 1988* 223 *Turnover* £10m

*Chairman* Lord Weidenfeld; *managing directors* Alan Miles, Richard Hussey; *directors* Michael Dover, Christopher Falkus, David Roberts, Malcolm Gerratt, Fiona Kennedy, Nick Williams (editorial), Bud Maclennan (rights), Rose Scott (publicity), David Ross (sales), Diane Rowley (personnel).

*Active publishing areas* architecture, art, biography and memoirs, business, current affairs, economics, fiction, general, history, politics, sport, humour, cookery, crime, crafts and hobbies, gardening, science, sociology, travel.

**Wheaton Publishers Ltd,** Hennock Road, Marsh Barton, Exeter, Devon EX2 8RP *tel* (0392) 74121 *telex* 42749 Wheaton G *fax* (0392) 217170. *Managing Director:* Simon Goodenough. *Publishing Manager:* Simon Butler. Member of **Maxwell-Pergamon Publishing Corporation plc.**
Non-fiction: local history, natural history, topography, conservation, archaeology, guide books, facsimile editions. Fiction: TSB Peninsula Prizewinning annual novel.

**\*Wheatsheaf Books Ltd.**—see **Harvester Wheatsheaf.**

**Wheldon & Wesley Ltd.** Lytton Lodge, Codicote, Hitchin, Herts. SG4 8TE *tel* Stevenage (0438) 820370 *telex* 825562 Chacom G Wheld and 825353 Chacom G Wheld *fax* (0582) 419422 *Dialcom:* 72: Mag95466.
Natural history booksellers and publishers. Agency of the British Museum (Natural History) and Hunt Botanical Library.

**\*J. Whitaker & Sons, Ltd.,** 12 Dyott Street, London WC1A 1DF *tel* 01-836 8911 *fax* 01-836 2909. *Directors:* Peter Allsop, Louis Baum, Robin Baum, Richard Hunt, Alan Mollison, T. E. Sweetman, David Whitaker (Chairman), Sally Whitaker (Managing).
Reference including *Whitaker's Almanack* (1869). *The Bookseller* (1858), *British Books in Print* (1874), *Whitaker's Cumulative Book List* (1924), and other book trade directories.

**Whittet Books Ltd.** (1976), 18 Anley Road, London W14 0BY *tel* 01-603 1139 *telex* 826542 Teltex G (Whit). *Directors:* Annabel Whittet, John Whittet, Marion Kovach.
Architecture, gardening, topography, natural history, transport.

**Wildwood House Ltd.**—associate company of **Gower Publishing Group Ltd.** Business and general.

**\*John Wiley & Sons Ltd.** (incorporating **Interscience Publishers**) Baffins Lane, Chichester, West Sussex PO19 1UD *tel* (0243) 779777 *telex* 86290 Wibook G *fax* (0243) 775878 *BTG* 83 JWP001 *telegraphic address and cables* Wilebook, Chichester. Subsidiary of **John Wiley & Sons Inc.,** New York.

*Titles in print* 2000-2500 *No. of titles published in 1988* 270 *Turnover* £21m

*Chairman* W. B. Wiley (U.S.A.); *managing director* M. B. Foyle; *directors* A. H. Neilly, Jr. (U.S.A.), T. L. Davies, P. W. Ferris, J. H. Wilde, M. Bide, J. Jarvis, The Earl of March, P. Marriage, E. van Tongeren, C. R. Ellis.

*Active publishing areas* scientific, engineering, business, social science, mathematics, computing, medical.

**Wiley-Heyden Ltd**—associate company of **John Wiley & Sons Ltd.**

*****Philip Wilson Publishers Ltd.** (1975), 26 Litchfield Street, London WC2H 9NJ *tel* 01-379 7886 *telex* 22158 *fax* 01-836 7049. *Directors:* Philip Wilson, Juliana Powney, Anne Jackson, Adrian Burton, Mary Osborne.
Art.

*****Wisley Handbooks**—imprint of **Cassell plc.** Gardening.

*****H. F. & G. Witherby Ltd.**, 14 Henrietta Street, London WC2E 8QJ *tel* 01-836 2006. *Directors:* Livia Gollancz (Chairman), David Burnett (Managing), Stephen Bray; *Consultant:* Antony Witherby. Subsidiary of **Victor Gollancz Ltd**.
Natural history, fishing, ornithology, dogs, travel, cookery, wine, adventure.

**The Woburn Press** (1968), Gainsborough House, 11 Gainsborough Road, London E11 1RS *tel* 01-530 4226 *telegraphic address* Simfay, London *telex* 897719 Wmp G *fax* 01-530 7795. *Directors:* Frank Cass (Managing), A. E. Cass, M. P. Zaidner.
Non-fiction, Woburn Educational Series.

*****Wolfe Publishing Ltd.**, Brook House, 2-16 Torrington Place, London WC1E 7LT *tel* 01-636 4622 *telegraphic address* Wolfebooks London *telex* 8814230 *fax* 01-637 3021. *Chairman:* John F. Dill (USA), *Managing Director:* Michael Manson, *Directors:* Pat Daly, Daniel J. Doody (USA), Peter Heilbrunn, Colin MacPherson, Derrick Holman.
Colour atlases, full-colour photographic reference titles in diagnostic medicine, surgery, dentistry, veterinary medicine, pure and applied sciences.

**Oswald Wolff Books,** 8 Circus Lodge, Circus Road, London NW8 9JL *tel* 01-286 5654. *Director:* Mrs Ilse Wolff. An imprint of **Berg Publishers Ltd.**
German and European studies: literature and the arts, history, biography, current affairs.

**The Women's Press** (1978), 34 Great Sutton Street, London EC1V 0DX *tel* 01-251 3007 *telex* 919034 Namara G. *Managing Director:* Ros de Lanerolle.
Books by women in the areas of fiction, autobiography, history, art, health, politics.

**Woodhead-Faulkner (Publishers), Ltd.** (1972), Fitzwilliam House, 32 Trumpington Street, Cambridge CB2 1QY *tel* (0223) 66733 *telex* 818454 Wfpubl G. *Directors:* H. Hirschberg (Chairman), P. Williams, S. G. York, O. Davies. Subsidiary of **Simon & Schuster International Group.**
Finance and investment, management, technical, social and welfare topics.

**World International Publishing Ltd.,** Egmont House, P.O. Box 111, Great Ducie Street, Manchester M60 3BL *tel* 061-834 3110 *telex* 668609 World G *fax* 061-834 0059 *telegraphic address* World, Manchester. *Directors:* John McDonagh (Managing), Michael Herridge.
Children's paperbacks, early learning, activity, gift and information books, and annuals.

**John Wright**—imprint of **Butterworth Scientific Ltd.**

**Xanadu Publications Ltd** (1984), 19 Cornwall Road, London N4 4PH  *tel* 01-272 4895  *fax* 01-263 7708. *Director:* Richard Glyn Jones. *Distributors*: Gollancz Services Ltd.
True crime, fantasy, mystery and science fiction, humour, travel and cookery.

*****Yale University Press London** (1961), 23 Pond Street, London NW3 2PN  *tel* 01-431 4422  *telegraphic address* Yalepress, London  *telex* 896075  Yupldn G  *fax* 01-431 3755.

*Titles in print* 1500    *No. of titles published in 1988* 150    *Turnover 1988* £1.1m

*Active publishing areas* art, architecture, history, economics, political science, literary criticism, Asian and African studies, religion, philosophy, psychology, history of science.

*****Yearling** paperbacks—imprint of **Transworld Publishers Ltd.** Fiction for ages 8-11.

*****Young Corgi** paperbacks—imprint of **Transworld Publishers Ltd.** Fiction for ages 5-9.

**Young Library Ltd.** (1982), 45 Norfolk Square, Brighton, East Sussex BN1 2PE  *tel* (0273) 770610  *fax* (0273) 822274. *Directors:* Roger Cleeve (Managing), Robert Hartnoll.
General non-fiction for children's libraries—geography, history, natural history, social studies, science and technology.

*****Zed Books Ltd.** (1976), 57 Caledonian Road, London N1 9BU  *tel* 01-837 4014  *fax* 01-833 3960. *Directors:* Paul Westlake, Anna Gourlay, Anne Rodford, Robert Molteno, Mike Pallis, Diane Blackbourn, Ralph Smith.
Third World issues, international politics, current affairs, ecology, women's studies, Africa, Middle East, cultural studies.

**Zwan Publishing Ltd**—incorporated into **Pluto Publishing Ltd.**

*****A. Zwemmer Ltd.** (1951), 26 Litchfield Street, London WC2H 9NJ  *tel* 01-379 7886  *telex* 22158  *fax* 01-836 7049.
Architecture.


# AUSTRALIA

*Members of Australian Book Publishers' Association

**Access Press** (1979), 35 Stuart Street, Perth, W.A. 6000  *postal address* P.O. Box 132, Northbridge, W.A.  *tel* 09-328 9188  *fax* 09-328 4605. *Directors*: John Harper-Nelson (Chairman), Helen Weller (Managing). Australiana, fiction, poetry, children's, history, general. Privately financed books published and distributed.

*****Allen & Unwin Australia Pty Ltd.**, P.O. Box 764, 8 Napier Street, North Sydney, NSW 2059  *tel* 02-922 6399  *telex* 24 331  *fax* 02-922 4317. General trade, including fiction and children's books, academic, especially social science and history.

*****Angus & Robertson Publishers** (1886), 4 Eden Park, 31 Waterloo Road, North Ryde, NSW  *tel* 888-4111  *postal address* P.O. Box 290 North Ryde, NSW 2113  *telex* AA26452. *U.K.:* 16 Golden Square, London, W1R 4BN  *tel* 01-434 3767. *Chief Executive:* Terry Kitson. *Publisher:* Lisa Highton. General fiction and non-fiction, Australiana, poetry, pictorial, popular medicine, self-discovery, children's fiction and activity books, humour.

\***Edward Arnold (Australia) Pty. Ltd.** (1975), 80 Waverley Road, Caulfield East, Victoria 3145   *tel* 572-2211   *postal address* P.O. Box 234 Caulfield East, Victoria 3145   *telex* AA35974   *fax* (03) 572 2095   *cables* Edarnold. *Directors:* Michael Duffett (Managing), Graham Foxcroft, Richard Morris (UK). Educational, secondary, academic, professional, technical.

\***Australasian Publishing Co., Pty. Ltd.**—now known as **Random House Australia Pty. Ltd.**

\***The Australian Council for Educational Research, Ltd.,** P.O. Box 210, Hawthorn, Victoria, 3122   *tel* 03-819 1400   *fax* 03-819 5502. Range of books and kits: for teachers, psychologists, counsellors, students of education, researchers and parents.

**Blackwell Scientific Publications (Australia) Pty. Ltd.,** 107 Barry Street, Carlton, Victoria, 3053   *tel* 347 0300   *telegraphic address* Blackwell, Melbourne   *telex* 107 16421 via Keylink   *fax* 03-347 5001.

**Brooks Waterloo Publishers,** 36 Albert Road, South Melbourne, Victoria, 3205   *tel* 03-699 5000   *fax* 03-690 5099. Education, primary and secondary; management, financial, general.

\***Butterworths Pty. Limited,** 271-273 Lane Cove Road, North Ryde, N.S.W. 2113   *tel* 02-887-3444   *telex* AA122033   *fax* 02-887 4555.

\***Cambridge University Press Australian Branch,** 10 Stamford Road, Oakleigh, Melbourne 3166   *tel* 568 0322 and 35 Sophia Street, Surry Hills, Sydney 2010   *tel* 211 0604. *Director:* Kim W. Harris.

\***William Collins Pty Ltd.,** 55 Clarence Street, Sydney, N.S.W. 2000   *tel* 229-2800   *fax* 02-290 3763. *Directors:* T. J. Kitson, S. Macdonald, A. H. Stirton, G. R. Beachley, P. B.Montgomery, R. W. Fisher. General literature, fiction, children's books, Bibles. Head Office: 8 Grafton Street, London W1X 3LA.

\***The Craftsman's Press Pty. Ltd** (1981), 1st Floor, 108 Pacific Highway, P.O. Box 480, Roseville N.S.W. 2069   *tel* 02-464 469   *fax* 02-464 190. *Directors:* Geoffrey M. King (Chairman), Nevill S. Drury (Managing), Patrick Corrigan. Australian fine arts.

**Samuel French Ltd.,** represented by Dominie Pty. Ltd., Drama Department, 8 Cross Street, Brookvale, N.S.W. 2100   *tel* 9050201. Publishers of plays and agents for the collection of royalties for Samuel French Ltd., incorporating Evans Plays and Samuel French Inc., The Society of Authors, A.C.T.A.C., and Bakers Plays of Boston.

\***Golden Press Pty. Ltd.,** 46 Egerton Street, Silverwater, N.S.W. 2141   *tel* 02-648 5488   *fax* 02-648 5697. General children's books, and educational.

\***Heinemann Publishers Australia Pty. Ltd.**—see **Octopus Publishing Group Australia.**

\***Hill of Content Publishing Co. Pty., Ltd.** (1965), 86 Bourke Street, Melbourne, 3000   *tel*   654   3144   *telegraphic   address*   Colbook,   Melbourne   *telex* AA37396   *fax* 03-662 2527. *Directors:* M. Slamen, M. G. Zifcak, Michelle Anderson. Australiana, health, history, educational, general.

\***Hodder and Stoughton (Australia) Pty. Ltd.,** 10-16 South Street, (P.O. Box 386), Rydalmere, N.S.W. 2116   *tel* 02-638 5299   *telex* 24858   *fax* 02-684 4942. *Directors:* Michael Duffett (Managing), Philip Attenborough, John Clarke,

Graham Foxcroft, Bert Hingley, Richard Morris, David Wilson. Fiction, general, educational, children's, religious, hardback and paperback.

**Horwitz Grahame Pty. Ltd.,** including **Horwitz Publications, Martin Educational** and **Carroll's,** 506 Miller Street, Cammeray, 2062 *tel* 929-6144 *telex* 127833 *fax* (02) 957 1814. *Directors:* S. D. L. Horwitz (Chairman), P. D. L. Horwitz (Chief Executive), L. J. Moore, R. B. Fuller, Magazine and book publishers: non fiction, educational (primary, secondary and tertiary), reference books, technical, cookery, humour.

**\*Jacaranda Wiley Ltd.,** 33 Park Road, Milton, Queensland 4064 *tel* (07) 369 9755 *telex* AA 41845 *fax* 07-369 9139; 90 Ormond Road, Elwood, Victoria 3184 *tel* 03-531 8677; 140A Victoria Road, Gladesville, N.S.W., 2111 *tel* 02-816-2758. Also New Zealand, Hong Kong, *q.v. Managing Director:* K. J. Collins; *General Managers:* Q. Smith, G. Browne, P. Donoughue, B. Brennan. Educational, technical, atlases, software.

**\*Kangaroo Press Pty Ltd** (1980), 3 Whitehall Road, Kenthurst, New South Wales 2156 *tel* 02-654 1502 *telex* AA 176432 Duroff *fax* 02-654 1338. *Directors:* David Rosenberg, Priscilla Rosenberg. Gardening, craft, Australian history and natural history, collecting, fitness.

**Lansdowne Editions,** Division of **Weldons Young Productions Pty Ltd.,** 372 Eastern Valley Way, Willoughby, N.S.W. 2068 *tel* 02-406 9281 *telex* AA121546. *Chief Executive:* Grant Young. Limited editions—art, natural history, literature and Australiana.

**Lansdowne Press,** Division of **Weldons Young Productions Pty Ltd,** 372 Eastern Valley Way (P.O. Box 228), Willoughby N.S.W. 2068 *tel* 02-406 6288 *fax* 02-406 6919 *telex* AA121546. *Publishing Manager:* Anne Wilson. Practical books on Australian lifestyle, craft, children's art, Australiana.

**\*The Law Book Company Ltd.,** 44-50 Waterloo Road, North Ryde, N.S.W. 2113 *tel* 887 0177 *telex* 27995 *fax* 02-888 9706.

**\*Longman Cheshire Pty. Ltd.,** Longman Cheshire House, Kings Gardens, 95 Coventry Street, South Melbourne, Victoria, 3205 *tel* 03-697 0666 *telex* AA33501 *fax* 03-699 2041. *Managing Director:* N. J. Ryan. Educational publishers.

**\*Lothian Publishing Co. Pty. Ltd.,** 11 Munro Street, Port Melbourne, Victoria 3207 *tel* 03-645 1544 *fax* 03-646 4882. *Directors:* P. Lothian (Chairman & Managing), K. A. Lothian, E. McDonald, G. Matthews. Juveniles, health, gardening, general literature.

**\*The Macmillan Company of Australia Pty. Ltd.,** 107 Moray Street, South Melbourne, 3205 *tel* 699 8922 *telegraphic address* Scriniaire, Melbourne *telex* AA34454 *fax* 690 6938; 6-8 Clarke Street, Crows Nest, 2065, N.S.W *tel* 438-2988 *fax* 438 1984. *Managing Director:* J. Rolfe. All types of books.

**\*Melbourne University Press,** 268 Drummond Street, Carlton, Victoria, 3053 *tel* 347 3455 *fax* 344 6214 *postal address* P.O. Box 278, Carlton South, Victoria, 3053. Prepared to consider works of academic, scholastic or cultural interest, educational textbooks and books of reference. Representatives: North America, International Scholarly Book Services Inc *tel* 503-287 3093; Tokyo, Hong Kong and Singapore, United Publishers Services Ltd. *Chairman:* Professor J. R. V. Prescott. *Director:* B. D. Wilder.

**\*Thomas Nelson Australia,** 480 La Trobe Street, Melbourne, Victoria 3000 *tel* (03) 329 5199 *telex* AA33088 *fax* (03) 329 1204.

**\*Octopus Publishing Group Australia**—including **William Heinemann Australia**, **Heinemann Educational Australia**, and **Paul Hamlyn Publishing Division**. 85 Abinger Street, Richmond, Victoria, 3121 *tel* (03) 429 3622 *cables* Hebooks, Melbourne *telex* 35347 *fax* 429 5891. *Managing Director:* Sandy Grant. Educational and general fiction and non-fiction.

**\*Oxford University Press, Australia,** *Managing Director:* Sandra McComb. 253 Normanby Road, South Melbourne, Victoria 3205. *Postal address:* G.P.O. Box 2784Y, Melbourne, Victoria 3001 *cables* Oxonian, Melbourne *tel* 03-646 4200 *telex* AA 35330 ref. Oxonian *fax* 03-646 3251. Australian history, biography, literary criticism, general, including children's books, but excluding fiction. School books in all subjects.

**Pacific Publications (Aust.) Pty. Ltd.,** 4th Floor, 46 Kippax Street, Surry Hills, N.S.W. 2010 *telex* AA20124 *fax* 2883322. *Postal address:* G.P.O. Box 4245, Sydney, N.S.W., 2001. General and reference for Pacific Islands market and agricultural/technical.

**\*Penguin Books Australia Ltd.** (1946), (P.O. Box 257), 487 Maroondah Highway, Ringwood, Victoria 3134 *tel* 03-871 2400 *telegraphic address* Penguinook, Melbourne *fax* 03-870 9618. *Directors:* P. J. Field (Managing), R. E. Ford, T. D. Glover (Chairman), P. M. Mayer, T. J. Rix, N. J. Ryan, R. P. Sessions (Publishing), J. C. Strike, J. W. Webster. Fiction, general non-fiction, current affairs, sociology, economics, environmental, travel guides, anthropology, politics, children's.

**\*Pitman Publishing Pty. Ltd.**—an imprint of **Longman Cheshire Pty. Ltd.**

**\*Random House Australia Pty. Ltd,** Corner Bridge Road and Jersey Street, Hornsby, N.S.W. 2077 *tel* 476-2000 *telex* AA123274 *fax* 476-5871. *Directors:* G. A. Rutherford, J. D. Cody, J. E. Bullivant, R. Kirkpatrick, H. S. H. Master. General, fiction, juvenile, education, art and technical.

**Reed Books Pty. Ltd.,** 2 Aquatic Drive, Frenchs Forest, N.S.W. 2086 *tel* (02) 451 8122 *fax* (02) 452 2066. *Directors:* D. A. MacLellan, W. A. Templeman (Publishing), J. B. Broadley. General.

**Rigby Heinemann,** Division of **Octopus Publishing Group Australia**, 372 Eastern Valley Way, (P.O. Box 228) Willoughby, N.S.W. 2068 *tel* 02-406 9222 *telex* AA121546 *fax* 02-406 6919. *Publisher:* Nola Mallon. General (with emphasis on Australian), reference, technical, fiction, paperbacks and children's fiction.

**Shakespeare Head Press,** 5-01 Henry Lawson Business Centre, Birkenhead Point, Drummoyne, N.S.W. 2047 *tel* 819-9111. Educational. A Division of **Golden Press Pty. Ltd.**

**Sun Books Pty. Ltd.** (1965), 107 Moray Street, South Melbourne, Victoria 3205 *tel* 699 8922 *telegraphic address* Sunbooks. *Directors:* K. B. Stonier, J. Rolfe, N. G. Byam Shaw. Paperbacks—fiction, non-fiction, educational, especially Australian titles. Subsidiary of **The Macmillan Company of Australia Pty. Ltd.**

**\*University of Queensland Press** (1948), P.O. Box 42, St. Lucia, Queensland 4067 *tel* 377 2127 *telex* Univqld AA40315 Press *fax* (07) 870 8719. *General Manager:* L. C. Muller. Scholarly works, tertiary texts, Australian fiction, young adult fiction, poetry, history, and general interest.

**\*Viking O'Neil** (1987), 56 Claremont Street, South Yarra, Victoria 3141 *tel* 03-241-9901 *telex* AA36472 *fax* 03-241 0913. *Associate Director:* Lloyd J. O'Neil. *Publisher:* Peter Hyde. *Managing Editor:* Helen Duffy. Imprint of

**Penguin Books Australia Ltd.** Pictorial and general works relating to Australia, cartographic publications, craft, health.

*****Wild & Woolley** (1974), P.O. Box 41, Glebe, New South Wales 2037   *tel* 692-0166   *fax* 660-0627. *Director:* Pat Woolley. Fiction, literary criticism, political cartoons, drug information, politics. Australian authors only.

# CANADA

The following is a selected list; it includes only a few of the very many smaller firms, and of the specialist publishers. The introductory note on submitting manuscripts (at the start of the **Books** section) applies also to Canadian publishers.

*Members of the Canadian Book Publishers' Council
†Members of the Association of Canadian Publishers

**The Book Society of Canada, Limited—see Irwin Publishing.**

*****Butterworths,** 75 Clegg Road, Markham, Ontario, L3R 9Y6   *tel* 416-479 2665   *fax* 416-479 2826.

*****Canada Publishing Corporation** (1844), 164 Commander Boulevard, Agincourt, Ontario, M1S 3C7   *tel* 416-293-8141   *fax* 416-293 9009   *telegraphic address* Gagepub, Toronto. Publishers of elementary, secondary, post-secondary, university textbooks, medical and general reading publications, business education and vocational materials for high school and college. Professional and reference material, technical video production, electronic courseware, print music.
*Agents for:* Financial Post, Fraser Institute, Harrap's Ltd (Trade), Andrews, McMeel & Parker, Forkner Publishing Corp., Wm. Morrow, Scott Foresman Inc., Urban & Schwarzenberg, Wilshire Book, Bordas (Paris), Special Learning Corp, C.B.I., Hearst Books, Ivory Tower, Quill, Green Willow, Chivers Large Print Books, Van Nostrand Reinhold, Thieme Inc., Columbia Pictures Publications.

**Canadian Stage and Arts Publications Ltd.,** George Hencz, 263 Adelaide Street West, 5th Floor, Toronto, Ontario M5H 1Y2   *tel* 416-971-9516. Primarily interested in children's books of an educational nature, art books. Also publishes *Performing Arts in Canada*, a quarterly covering all aspects of the arts (Editor: Patricia Michael).

**The Carswell Company Ltd**, 2330 Midland Avenue, Agincourt, Ontario M1S 1P7   *tel* 416-291-8421   *telex* 065-25289   *fax* 416-291-3426. *President:* Alan Turnbull. Law, professional and reference.

*****Collier Macmillan Canada, Inc.** (1958), 1200 Eglinton Avenue East, Suite 200, Don Mills, Ontario M3C 3N1   *tel* 416-449-6030   *fax* 416-449-0068. *Director:* Ray Lee (President). *Australia:* Collier Macmillan Australia, 107 Moray Street, South Melbourne, Victoria 3205; *New Zealand:* Associated Book Publishers (N.Z.) Ltd., 61 Beach Road, Auckland; *USA:* Collier Macmillan International, 866 Third Avenue, New York, N.Y. 10022-6299; *South Africa:* Southern Book Publishers (Pty) Ltd., PO Box 548, Bergvlei 2012. Academic, technical, medical, educational, children's and adult, trade, computer books and software.

**Wm. Collins Sons & Co. (Canada) Ltd—see Harper & Collins Books of Canada Ltd.**

*****Copp Clark Pitman,** 2775 Matheson Boulevard East, Mississauga, Ontario L4W 4P7   *tel* 416-238-6074   *telex* 06-960413   *fax* 416-238-6075. *President:* Stephen

J. Mills. *Publication Director:* Marion Elliott. Educational textbooks for elementary, secondary and college, technical and business education. Preliminary letter required before submitting manuscript.

**Dominie Press Limited,** 1361 Huntingwood Drive, Unit H7, Agincourt, Ontario M1S 3J1 *tel* 416-291-5857.

**\*Doubleday Canada Ltd.** (1937), 105 Bond Street, Toronto, Ontario, M5B 1Y3 *tel* 416-977-7891 *fax* 416-977-0215. *President:* Peter Maik; *Vice-Presidents:* G. Cholack, J. Neale. *Secretary and Treasurer:* D. Z. McBride. General trade fiction and non-fiction, Dell mass market; Book Clubs.

**†Douglas & McIntyre Ltd.** (1964), 1615 Venables Street, Vancouver, B.C., V5L 2H1 *tel* 604-254-7191; 416-537-2501 *fax* 604-254-9099; 416-537-4647. General list including Canadian biography, art and architecture, natural history, history, North American anthropology/ethnology, Canadian fiction. Children's division (Groundwood Books) specializes in fiction and illustrated flats. Educational division in elementary social studies, health and reading. Agents for Thames and Hudson and Walker Books.

**†ECW Press** (1979), 307 Coxwell Avenue, Toronto, Ontario M4L 3B5 *tel* 416-694-3348. *President:* Jack David. *Secretary-Treasurer:* Robert Lecker. Literary criticism, indexes, bibliographies.

**†Fitzhenry & Whiteside Limited** (1966), 195 Allstate Parkway, Markham, Ontario L3R 4T8 *tel* 416-477-0030. *Directors:* R. I. Fitzhenry, Sharon Fitzhenry, Robert W. Read, Thomas Richardson. Trade, educational, college books.

**\*Gage Publishing Ltd**—see **Canada Publishing Corporation.**

**\*General Publishing Co., Limited,** 30 Lesmill Road, Don Mills, Ontario M3B 2T6 *tel* 416-445-3333 *telex* 06-986664 *fax* 416-445-5967. Fiction, non-fiction; mass market paperbacks.

**\*Harlequin Enterprises Ltd.** (1949), 225 Duncan Mill Road, Don Mills, Ontario, M3B 3K9 *tel* 416-445-5860 *telex* 06-966697. *Chairman:* W. L. Heisey; *President and C.E.O.:* David A. Galloway. Romance, action adventure.

**Harper & Collins Books of Canada Ltd/Harper & Collins Publishers Ltd,** 100 Lesmill Road, Don Mills, Ontario M3B 2T5 *tel* 416-445-8221 *telex* 06-966673 *fax* 416-445-9498. Publishers of general literature, trade and reference, Bibles, religious, mass market paperbacks, audio cassettes, compact discs, children's books. Publishers in Canada for Wm. Collins Sons & Co. Ltd, Totem Books, Pan Books Ltd, André Deutsch, Harvill Press Ltd, Adlard Coles Ltd, Colour Library International, Fontana, Farrar, Straus & Giroux, Mysterious Press, Armada Books, Carnival, Collins Willow, Dinosaur, Flamingo, Fount, Grafton, Hill & Wang, Incentive Publications, Lions, Noonday Press, Paladin, Picador Books, Piccolo Books, Picture Lions, Piper, Robinson, Young Lions, Ballinger Pub., Barnes & Noble, Basic Books, T. Y. Crowell, Caedmon, Carousel, Colophon, Icon Editions, J. B. Lippincott Jr, Perennial Library, Torch, Trophy.

**\*Holt, Rinehart & Winston of Canada, Ltd.,** 55 Horner Avenue, Toronto, Ontario, M8Z 4X6 *tel* 416-255-4491 *fax* 416-255-4046.

**House of Anansi Press Ltd.**(1967), 35 Britain Street, Toronto, M5A 1R7 *tel* 416-363-5444. *Directors:* Ann Wall (President), Harald Bohne, James Polk, Norma Goodger. Distributed by **Kershaw Publishing Co. Ltd.,** 7 Bury Place, London WC1A 2LA *tel* 01-430 2460. Poetry, fiction, non-fiction. Only Canadian writers.

†**Hurtig Publishers** (1967), 10560 105 Street, Edmonton, Alberta T5H 2W7 *tel* 403-426-2359 *fax* 403-429-5996. *President:* M. G. Hurtig. Reference, humour, biography, political science, Canadiana, energy, environment, The Canadian Encyclopedia.

\***Irwin Publishing,** division of **General Publishing Co. Ltd.,** 30 Lesmill Road, Don Mills, Ontario M3B 2T6 *tel* 416-445-3333 *telex* 06-988864. *President:* Brian O'Donnell. *Chairman:* Jack Stoddart. Educational books at the elementary, high school and college levels.
*Represent in Canada:* B. T. Batsford, Unwin Hyman (Educational), Heinemann Educational, Heinemann Medical, John Murray, McDougal Littell & Co.

**Kids Can Press Ltd,** 585 1/2 Bloor Street West, Toronto, Ontario M6G 1K5 *tel* 416-534-6389 *fax* 416-534-6152. *Publisher:* Valerie Hussey. Juvenile and young adult books. **Window Editions:** parenting books.

\*†**McClelland & Stewart Inc.** (1906), 481 University Avenue, Suite 900, Toronto, M5G 2E9 *tel* 416-598-1114 *fax* 416-598-7764. *Chairman/President and C.E.O.:* Avie Bennett. General and educational.

†**McGill-Queen's University Press** (1969), 855 Sherbrooke Street West, Montreal, Quebec H3A 2T7 *tel* 514-398-3750 *telex* 05-268510 *fax* 514-398-3594 and Watson Hall, Queen's University, Kingston, Ontario K7L 3N6 *tel* 613-545 2155 *fax* 613-545-6300. Academic.

\***McGraw-Hill Ryerson Ltd.,** 330 Progress Avenue, Scarborough, Ontario, M1P 2Z5 *tel* 416-293-1911 *fax* 416-293-0827. Educational and trade books.

\***Macmillan of Canada** (1905), a Division of **Canada Publishing Corporation,** 29 Birch Avenue, Toronto, Ontario M4V 1E2 *tel* 416-963-8830 *telex* 062 18018 *fax* 416-923-4821. Trade book publishers.

\***Nelson Canada** (1914), 1120 Birchmount Road, Scarborough, Ontario M1K 5G4 *tel* 416-752-9100 *telex* 06-963813 *fax* 752-9646. *Directors:* Alan G. Cobham (President), Brian D. Heer, Douglas R. Fletcher, Martin Keast, Peter McBride, Ben Wentzell. Elementary, high school, college textbooks; measurement and guidance, children's library.

†**Oberon Press,** 401A–350 Sparks Street, Ottawa, Ontario, K1R 7S8 *tel* 613-238-3275. General.

\***Oxford University Press, Canada,** 70 Wynford Drive, Don Mills, Ontario, M3C 1J9 *tel* 416-441-2941 *cables* Frowde, Toronto *telex* OUP-Tor-06-966518 *fax* 416-444-0427. *Manager:* M. Morrow. General, educational, juvenile and academic.

\***PaperJacks Ltd.,** *Editorial:* 330 Steelcase Road East, Markham, Ontario L3R 2M1 *tel* 416-475-1261 *fax* 416-475-7139.

\***Prentice-Hall Canada, Inc.,** (1960), 1870 Birchmount Road, Scarborough, Ontario M1P 2J7 *tel* 293-3621 *telex* 065-25184. *Directors:* R. M. Inkpen, E. E. Campbell, R. E. Snyder, Brian Kirwin, Susanne Foran. Educational (elementary, secondary, post-secondary), general history, natural history, politics, sports.

\***Stoddart Publishing Co. Ltd,** 34 Lesmill Road, Don Mills, Ontario M3B 2T6 *tel* 416-445-3333 *telex* 06-986664 *fax* 416-445-5967. Fiction and non-fiction.

**Tundra Books Inc.,** 1434 St Catherine Street West, Suite 308, Montreal, Quebec H3G 1R4 *tel* 514-932-5434 *cables* Tunbooks *fax* 514-861-6426. *President:* May Cutler. General trade and juvenile books; art books.

†**University of Toronto Press,** 10 St Mary Street, Suite 700, Toronto M4Y 2W8　*tel* 416-978-2231 (Editorial); 416-978-2239 (Administration).

# INDIA

*Members of the Federation of Indian Publishers

*Ajanta Books International** (1975), 1-UB Jawahar Nagar, Bungalow Road, Delhi 110 007　*tel* 2926182. *Proprietor:* S. Balwant. Social sciences and humanities, specialising in: politics, sociology, management, history, literature (Indian, and Western), education, linguistics, philosophy, archaeology, library science, fiction.

**Allied Publishers Limited,** 15 J. N. Heredia Marg, Ballard Estate, Bombay 400 038　*tel* 267926　*telex* 011-75909. *Managing Director:* S. M. Sachdev. Publishers of school and college textbooks; economics, education, psychology, sociology, and general books on current affairs and Oriental art. Exclusive agents in India for: A. & C. Black (Publishers) Ltd., W. and R. Chambers Ltd, Gerald Duckworth & Co. Ltd., Elsevier Applied Science Publishers Ltd, Graham & Trotman Ltd, MTP Press Ltd.

**Asia Publishing House,** imprint of **Jaisingh & Mehta Publishers Pvt. Ltd.,** Bhogilal Hargobindas Building, 18/20 K. Dubash Marg, Bombay, 400 023　*tel* 225353, 225425　*telex* 1171665 Quip In;　*fax* 225685. Indra Palace, Connaught Circus, New Delhi, 110 001. *New York Representative:* Apt Books Inc., 141 East 44th Street, New York, N.Y. 10017. Literature, general, including art, biography, economics, politics, world affairs, education, history, library, science, philosophy and psychology, science and technology, publish Air India's inflight magazine.

**Atma Ram & Sons** (1909), Post Box 1429, Kashmere Gate, Delhi, 110 006　*tel* 2518159, 2523082　*cables* Books Delhi. *Managing Proprietor:* Ish Kumar Puri; *Senior Director:* Sushil Puri. *Branch:* 17 Ashok Marg, Lucknow. Art, literature, reference, biography, fiction, economics, politics, education, history, philosophy, psychology, science, technology. Books published in English and Hindi languages. Translations and reprints of foreign books undertaken. Booksellers and importers of foreign books on a large scale.

**B.I. Publications Pvt. Ltd.,** 54 Janpath, New Delhi, 110001　*tel* 3325313　*telex* 031 63352 BI IN. *Chairman:* R. D. Bhagat. Scientific, technical, medical, business and industrial management, educational, children's, reference and general.

*S. Chand & Co. Ltd.** (1917), Ram Nagar, New Delhi 110 055　*tel* 772080　*telex* 031-2185　*telegraphic address* Eschand, New Delhi. *Directors:* S. L. Gupta, Rajendra Kumar Gupta, Ravindra Kumar Gupta. Science, technology, medicine, educational books, children's books.

*Children's Book Trust** (1957), Nehru House, 4 Bahadur Shah Zafar Marg, New Delhi 110002　*tel* 3316970　*telegraphic address* Childtrust, New Delhi. *Executive Trustee:* K. Shankar Pillai. Children's books.

**English Book Depot** (1923), 15 Rajpur Road, Dehra Dun (U.P.), 248 001　*tel* 23792, 23187. *Directors:* Dev Dutt and Sandeep Dutt. Military science, agriculture, forestry, geology and petroleum.

**\*Heritage Publishers** (1973), 4348 Madan Mohan Street, 4c Ansari Road, Daryaganj, New Delhi 110 002. *Proprietor:* B. R. Chawla. Social science, Indology, humanities.

**\*Hind Pocket Books Pvt. Ltd.,** G. T. Road, Shahdara, Delhi, 110032 *tel* 3320014, 2282046 *telegraphic address* Pocketbook Delhi. Paperbacks in Indian languages and English. *Managing Director:* D. N. Malhotra.

**Indian Press (Publications) Private, Limited,** 36 Pannalal Road, Allahabad (U.P.) *tel* 53190 *telegraphic address* Publikason. Branches and agencies in all principal towns of India. Publishers of *Saraswati Hindi Monthly Magazine*, and school, college, university and general books in Hindi, Bengali, English; Gurumukhi, Urdu, Marathi, Nepali languages. *Managing Director:* D. P. Ghosh.

**\*Jaico Publishing House** (1946/7), 121-125 Mahatma Gandhi Road, Bombay, 400 023 *tel* 276702, 276802 *telex* 11-3369 Jai In *telegraphic address* Jaicobooks Bombay *fax* 4939662. *Managing Director:* Ashwin J. Shah. History, politics, sociology, management, economics, psychology, philosophy, religion, law, crime.

**Kothari Publications,** Jute House, 12 India Exchange Place, Calcutta, 700001 *tel* 20-9563, 20-6572, 45-0009. *Cable:* Zeitgeist. *Proprietor:* Ing. H. Kothari of Sujangarh, Rajasthan. Technical, general and reference books. *Who's Who* series in India. Agents for many foreign publishers.

**The Little Flower Co.** (1929), Bhurangam Buildings, P.B. 1028, 43 Ranganathan Street, Thyagarayanagar, Madras 600 017 *tel* 441538 *telegraphic address* Lifco, Madras. Lifco books. General, fiction, technical, dictionaries, astrology, medicine, legal, commercial, educational and religious.

**Macmillan India Ltd.,** 2/10 Ansari Road, Darya Ganj, New Delhi 110 002. *Branches:* Bombay: Mercantile House, Magazine Street, Raey Road (East), Bombay, 400010; Bangalore: 12-A Mahatma Gandhi Road, Bangalore 560001; Madras: 40 Peters Road, Royapettah, Madras 600 014. Associate Company of Macmillan Publishers Ltd., London. Publishers of educational, scientific, humanities, literature, technical, medical, and general books. Agents in India, Burma, Ceylon, Nepal and Bangladesh for: Gill & Macmillan Ltd., Dublin, The Hamlyn Publishing Group Ltd.

**National Book Trust, India** (1957), A-5 Green Park, New Delhi 110 016 *tel* 664667, 664020, 664540 *telex* 031-73034 Nbt In.

**\*Orient Longman Ltd,** 3-6-272 Himayat Nagar, Hyderabad 500 029 *tel* 240 305/306, 240 294/297/391 *telex* 425 6803 Olex IN; and regional offices at Kamani Marg, Ballard Estate, Bombay 400 038; 17 Chittaranjan Avenue, Calcutta 700 072; 160 Anna Salai, Madras 600 002; 1/24 Asaf Ali Road, New Delhi 110 002; 80/1 Mahatma Gandhi Road, Bangalore 560 001; Birla Mandir Road, Patna 800 004; S C Goswami Road, Pan Bazar, Guwahati 781 001; Patiala House 16-A, Ashok Marg, Lucknow 226 001. Fiction and non-fiction, biography, history, philosophy, reference, children's literature, paperbacks, medicine, psychology, engineering, general and social science, technology, university, secondary and primary textbooks, educational materials. Associated with Longman Group Ltd, Sangam Books Ltd, The Universities Press (India) Pvt. Ltd, The Sangam Books (India) Pvt. Ltd. Agents and distributors in India for Longman Group Ltd, Penguin Books Ltd, Ladybird Books Ltd, Cambridge University Press, George Philip, UNESCO, Paris.

**\*Oxford University Press (Indian Branch).** *General Manager:* S. K. Mookerjee. *Head Office:* Post Box 43, YMCA Library Building, Jai Singh Road, New

Delhi 110001; *Branch Office:* Post Box 7035, 2/11 Ansari Road, Daryaganj, New Delhi 110002; Post Box 31, Oxford House, Apollo Bunder, Bombay 400039; G.P.O. Box 530, Faraday House, P17 Mission Row Extension, Calcutta 700013; Post Box 1079, Oxford House, Anna Salai, Madras 600006 *cables* Oxorient, Delhi, Oxonian, Delhi, Oxonian, Bombay, Oxonian, Calcutta, Oxonian, Madras *tel Head Office:* New Delhi 350490, 351312, 352769; *Branch Office:* New Delhi 27-3841-2, 27-7812, Bombay 202-1029, 202-1198, 202-1396; Calcutta 26-3533, 26-3534, 23-4832; Madras 47-2267, 47-2268, 47-2299 *telex Head Office:* 61108 Oxon; *Branch office:* Calcutta 4090 Oxon, Bombay 6737 Oxon, Madras 6504 Oxon. Publishers in all subjects. Agents in India, Burma, Sri Lanka and Nepal for Faber & Faber Ltd., and Ginn & Co. Ltd. (selected titles). It distributes books for the following university presses: Harvard, Princeton and Stanford.

**Penguin Books India Ltd** (1985), B4/246 Safdarjung Enclave, New Delhi 110029 *tel* 673538 *telex* 62062 Pengin. *Directors:* Patrick Wright (Chairman), Peter Mayer, Aveek Sarkar (Managing), Peter Carson, John Webster, Ganesh Nag, Arup Sarkar, M. J. Akbar, V. S. T. Shankardass, Rani Shankardass. *Publisher:* David Davidar. Fiction, non-fiction, history, biography, autobiography, belles-lettres, humour, sports, classics, poetry.

**Prentice-Hall of India Pvt Ltd,** M-97 Connaught Circus, New Delhi 110011 *tel* 352590/351779 *cables* Prenhall New Delhi *telex* 3161808 Ph In. *Chairman/ Managing Director:* Asoke K. Ghosh. Textbooks. *Associate Companies:* Prentice-Hall, UK, Prentice-Hall, Inc., USA.

**\*Rajpal & Sons,** Kashmere Gate, Delhi, 110006 *tel* 2523904 and 2519104 *telegraphic address* Rajpalsons, Delhi. Literary criticism, social and general, humanities, textbooks, juvenile literature, Hindi and English. *Managing Partner:* Vishwanath.

**Rupa & Co.,** P.O. Box 12333, 15 Bankim Chatterjee Street, Calcutta, 700073 *tel* 32-1291, 31-6597, 32-6335 *telegraphic address* Rupanco, Calcutta-73. Art, education, history, literature, fiction, philosophy, religion, sport pastimes. Representatives for Collins, Eyre & Spottiswoode, Foulsham, Wm. Heinemann, Merlin Press, Pan, Search Press, Sidgwick & Jackson, Souvenir Press, Spokesman, Frederick Warne.

**Sage Publications India Pvt Ltd,** 2nd Floor, 32 M-Block Market, Greater Kailash-I, New Delhi 110048 *tel* 6419884 *cables* Sagepub New Delhi 110048. *Managing Director:* Tejeshwar Singh. Social sciences. *Associate Companies:* Sage Publications Ltd, UK, Sage Publications, Inc., USA.

**Shiksha Bharati** (1955), Madarsa Road, Kashmere Gate, Delhi 110006 *tel* 2519104. Textbooks, popular science and children's books in Hindi and English; also juvenile literature. *Managing Partner:* Veena Malhotra.

**\*Sterling Publishers Pvt. Ltd.,** (1964) L-10 Green Park Extension, New Delhi, 110016 *tel* 669560. *Directors:* O. P. Ghai (Chairman), S. K. Ghai (Managing), Mrs. Vimla Ghai. Agriculture, biography, computer science, cookery, economics and commerce, education, history and Indology, language and literature, law, library science, management, medicine, military, philosophy and religion, politics, psychology and sociology.

**\*Tata McGraw-Hill Publishing Co. Ltd.** (1970), 4/12 Asaf Ali Road, New Delhi 110 002 *tel* 278251-2-3 *telex* 31-61979 Tmhd In *telegraphic address* Corinthian, New Delhi. *Directors:* J. J. Bhabha (Chairman), S. A. Sabavala, Dr. Francis A. Menezes, Dr. Malcolm S. Adiseshiah, J. C. Dastur, N. R. Subramanian, R. Radhakrishnan, Joseph L. Dionne, J. G. Wrede, Frederick G.

Perkins. Engineering, sciences, management, humanities, social sciences, computer science, electronics.

**\*D. B. Taraporevala Sons & Co., Private, Ltd.** (Original firm established 1864), 210 Dr. Dadabhai Naoroji Road, Bombay 400 001  *tel* 204-1433. *Directors:* Mrs. Manekbai J. Taraporevala and Miss Sooni J. Taraporevala. *Chief Executive:* Prof. Russi J. Tapaporevala. Books on India and on Indian interest, fine arts, handicrafts, pictorial albums, business, economics, education, electronics, psychology, cookery, domestic economy, pets, hobbies, reference, languages, religion, philosophy, mysticism, occult sciences, law, history, culture, mythology, sociology, health, medical, sex, science, technology, self-improvement, self-instruction, sports, Indian classics.

**Thacker & Co., Ltd.**, P.O. Box 190, 18-20 Kaikushru Dubash Marg (Rampart Row), Bombay 400 023  *tel* 242667, 242683, 242745  *telegraphic address* Booknotes, Bombay. *Chairman:* K. M. Diwanji. *Chief Executive:* Dhanraj K. Bhagat. *Managing Director:* J. M. Chudasama. Banking, gardening, cooking. Distributors for Ladybird Books, RotoVision, Walter Foster, Pan, Fontana, Hamlyn.

**The Theosophical Publishing House,** Adyar, Madras, 600020  *tel* 412904  *telegraphic address* Theotheca, Madras 600020. Theosophical, mystical and occult literature. Publishers of *The Theosophist,* official organ of the President, Theosophical Society. *Editor:* Mrs. Radha Burnier, International President of The Theosophical Society. *Manager:* R. Gopalaratnam.

**\*Vikas Publishing House Pvt Ltd.**, (1969), 5 Ansari Road, New Delhi 110 002  *tel* 273601, 279743, 866536  *telex* 592-252 Viph/In  *telegraphic address* Vikasbooks, New Delhi. *Managing Director:* Narendra Kumar. Science and technology, humanities and social sciences.

**\*Vision Books Pvt. Ltd.**, (1975). Head Office: Madarsa Road, Kashmere Gate, Delhi 110 006  *tel* 2517001, 2514274, 2512267; Editorial Office: 36-c Connaught Place, New Delhi 110 001  *tel* 332-8898, 332-9357  *telegraphic address* Visionbook New Delhi. *Directors:* Sudhir Malhotra (Managing), Kapil Malhotra, Vishwanath. Fiction (including Indo-Anglian and translation from Indian languages and other languages), Indian culture, politics, biography, travel, poetry, drama management, military, religion, anthropology, mountaineering, education, international relations. *Imprints:* Vision Books, Orient Paperbacks, Anand Paperbacks, Naya Sahitya.

**\*Wiley Eastern Ltd.** (1966), 4835/24 Ansari Road, Daryaganj, New Delhi, 110 002  *tel* 276802, 261487, 267996  *telegraphic address* Wileyeast  *telex* 031-66507 Welin. *Branches:* Bangalore, Bombay, Calcutta, Hyderabad, Madras. *Directors:* W. Bradford Wiley, A. H. Neilly, Jr., A. Machwe, E. B. Desai, A. R. Kundaji. Biology, physics, chemistry, mathematics, engineering sciences, humanities and social sciences.

## THE REPUBLIC OF IRELAND AND NORTHERN IRELAND

\*Members of the Irish Publishers' Association

**Academy Press Ltd.** (1976), 17 Brighton Square, Rathgar, Dublin 6  *tel* 01-962946. *Director:* Sean Browne.
Irish history, Anglo-Irish literature, literary criticism, art and art history.

**\*Appletree Press Ltd.** (1974), 7 James Street South, Belfast BT2 8DL  *tel* (0232) 243074  *telex* 9312100435 Monref G ref. ATP001  *fax* 246756; and Suite 521, Irish Life Centre, Talbot Street, Dublin  *tel* 746611. *Director:* John Murphy.

Academic, biography, cookery, educational, guide books, history, literary criticism, music, photographic, social studies, sport, travel.

**\*Attic Press** (1984), 44 East Essex Street, Dublin 2 *tel* 716367 *fax* 797224. *Manager:* Roisin Conroy. *Sales & Accounts:* Emer Dolphin. *Desk Editor:* Thérèse Caherty. *Editorial Consultant:* Ailbhe Smyth.
Feminist, women's studies, social comment, fiction, history.

**\*Blackstaff Press Ltd.** (1971), 3 Galway Park, Dundonald BT16 0AN *tel* (02318) 7161 *fax* (02318) 89552. *Chairman:* Michael Burns. *Managing Director:* Anne Tannahill.
Fiction, poetry, biography, history, art, academic, natural history, sport, politics, music, education, fine limited editions.

**The Blackwater Press**—imprint of **Folens & Co. Ltd.,** *q.v.*
General non-fiction, Irish interest.

**\*Boethius Press Ltd.** (1973), Clarabricken, Co. Kilkenny *tel* (56) 59746 *fax* (56) 59746. *Directors:* L. J. Hewitt, J. M. Hewitt, Mrs. J. M. Hewitt.
Topography of Great Britain and Ireland, natural history (particularly gardens), archaeology and history.

**\*Brandon Book Publishers Ltd** (1982), Cooleen, Dingle, Co. Kerry *tel* 066-51463. *Directors:* Steve MacDonogh, Bernard Goggin.
Biography, literature, politics, ficton, travel (Ireland), history, folklore.

**\*Brophy Educational Books Ltd** (1977), 108 Sundrive Road, Dublin 12 *tel* 01-973061 and 971617. *Directors:* Kevin T. Brophy (Managing), Mary Brophy.
School texts.

**\*Brophy International Publishing Ltd,** 108 Sundrive Road, Dublin 12 *tel* 01-973061 and 971617. *Directors:* K. T. Brophy, M. Brophy.
General non-fiction, religion, sport, entertainment, drama. Imprints: **Brophy Books, Canavaun Books**.

**Catholic Communications Institute of Ireland, Inc.**—see **Veritas Publications.**

**Dolmen Press Ltd.** Stock acquired by **Colin Smythe Ltd**—see UK list.

**The Educational Company of Ireland,** P.O.Box 43a, Ballymount Road, Walkinstown, Dublin 12 *tel* Dublin 500611 *fax* (01) 500993. *Executive Directors:* F. J. Maguire (Chief Executive), S. O'Neill, Ursula Ní Dhálaigh, P. McGann, R. McLoughlin. A trading unit of Smurfit Ireland Ltd.
Educational MSS. on all subjects in English or Gaelic.

**C. J. Fallon** (1927), Lucan Road, Palmerstown, Dublin 20 *tel* 265777 *fax* 268225. *Directors:* H. J. McNicholas (Managing), P. Tolan (Secretary), N. White (Editorial).
Educational text books.

**Folens & Co., Ltd.,** Airton Road, Tallaght, Co. Dublin *tel* 515311 *fax* 515306.
Educational (primary, secondary, comprehensive, technical, in English and Irish), educational children's magazines.

**\*Four Courts Press** (1969), Kill Lane, Blackrock, Co. Dublin *tel* 01-892922 *fax* 01-893072. *Directors:* Michael Adams, Gerard O'Flaherty.
Theology.

**Gallery Press** (1970), Loughcrew, Oldcastle, Co. Meath *tel* 049-41779. *Director:* Peter Fallon. *Allied Company:* Deerfield Publications Inc., Massachusetts.
Poetry, drama, occasionally fiction. Also, hand-printed limited editions poetry.

**\*Gill & Macmillan Ltd.** (1968), Goldenbridge, Inchicore, Dublin 8 *tel* 531005 *telex* 92197 Gilm EI *fax* 541688.

Biography or memoirs, educational (primary, secondary, university), history, philosophy, sociology, theology and religion, literature.

**The Goldsmith Press** (1972), Newbridge, Co. Kildare *tel* (045) 33613. *Directors:* D. Egan, V. Abbott, Peter Kavanagh. *Secretary:* Peter Mulreid.
Literature, art, Irish interest, poetry. *ERA* Review (occasional), *Goldsmith Poetry Calendar* (annually).

*****Institute of Public Administration** (1957), 59 Lansdowne Road, Dublin 4 *tel* 686233; Publications: 697011 *telegraphic address* Admin, Dublin. *Deputy Assistant Director and Head of Publishing:* James D. O'Donnell. *Assistant Manager:* Iain MacAulay.
Government, economic, law, social policy and administrative history.

*****Irish Academic Press** (1974), Kill Lane, Blackrock, Co. Dublin *tel* 01-892922 *fax* 01-893072. Publishes under the imprints **Irish University Press, Irish Academic Press** and **Ecclesia Press**. *Directors:* Michael Adams, Frank Cass, Gilbert Raff, Michael Philip Zaidner.
Scholarly books especially in history and law.

**Longman, Browne & Nolan**—now incorporated in **Educational Company of Ireland,** *q.v.*

*****The Mercier Press** (1945), P.O. Box 5, 4 Bridge Street, Cork *tel* Cork 504022 *telex* 75463 *fax* Cork 504216. *Directors:* Capt. J. M. Feehan, J. C. O'Connor, P. W. McGrath, D. J. Keily, C. U. O. Marcaigh, M. Feehan, L. McNamara, J. F. Spillane, A. C. Devitt.
Irish literature, folklore, history, politics, humour, ballads, education, theology, law.

**O'Brien Educational** (1976), 20 Victoria Road, Rathgar, Dublin 6 *tel* 979598 and 740354 *fax* 979274. *Directors:* Michael O'Brien, Bride Rosney.
Humanities, science, environmental studies, history, geography, English, Irish, art, commerce, music, careers, media studies.

**The O'Brien Press Ltd.** (1974), 20 Victoria Road, Rathgar, Dublin 6 *tel* 979598 *fax* 979274. *Directors:* Michael O'Brien, Valerie O'Brien.
Folklore, nature, fiction, architecture, topography, history, general, illustrated books, sport, anthropology, children, biography, tapes for children series include *Lucky Tree Books*, *Junior Biography Library*, *Urban Heritage*.

*****Poolbeg Press Ltd** (1976), Knocksedan House, Forrest Great, Swords, Co. Dublin *tel* 401133/401675 *telex* 32895 *fax* 403753. *Directors:* Philip Mac-Dermott, Breda Purdue (Marketing). *Editor:* Jo O Donoghue.
Fiction, public interest, women's interest, history, politics, current affairs, Children's Poolbeg and Young Poolbeg (teens).

*****Raven Arts Press** (1979), P.O. Box 1430, Finglas, Dublin 11. *Publisher:* Dermot Bolger.
Modern Irish poetry and literature.

**The Runa Press** (1942), 2 Belgrave Terrace, Monkstown, Dublin *tel* 801869 and 697180.
Belles-lettres, educational (university), essays, poetry, science, philosophy, psychoanalysis.

**School and College Publishing Ltd.** (1968), Taney Road, Dundrum, Dublin 14 *tel* 988554, 988398, 988075. *Directors:* Patrick M. O'Brien, Gilbert Brosnan, Mark Kavanagh, Michael Kelly.
Educational books for primary and secondary schools.

**\*Stationery Office** (1922), Bishop Street, Dublin 8 *tel* 781666 *telegraphic address* Enactments Dublin.
Parliamentary publications.

**\*Town House and Country House** (1981), 41 Marlborough Road, Donnybrook, Dublin 4 *tel* Dublin 686700 *fax* Dublin 687808. *Directors:* Treasa Coady, Éamon de Buitléar.
Environmental and natural history, general, children's.

**Turoe Press Ltd.** (1977), 69 Jones Road, Dublin 3 *tel* 01-786913. *Directors:* Michael Fenton, Margaret MacCurtain, Terry Prone, Michael Roberts, Catherine Rose.
Sociology, social issues, social history, reference, practical.

**\*Veritas Publications,** a division of the **Catholic Communications Institute of Ireland, Inc.,** Veritas House, Lower Abbey Street, Dublin 1 *tel* 788177 *fax* 744913. *UK:* Veritas Book & Video Distribution Ltd, Lower Avenue, Leamington Spa, Warwickshire CV31 3NP *tel* (0926) 451 730 *fax* (0926) 451 733.
Religion, including social and educational works, and material relating to the media of communication.

**Ward River Press**—imprint of **Poolbeg Press Ltd.** Irish non-fiction, art books, art prints, mass-market fiction.

**Wolfhound Press** (1974), 68 Mountjoy Square, Dublin 1 *tel* 740354. *Publisher:* Seamus Cashman. *Publishing Manager:* Siobhan Campbell.
Literary studies and criticism, fiction, art, biography, history, children's, law.


# NEW ZEALAND

\*Membership of the New Zealand Book Publishers' Association

**\*Auckland University Press** (1966), University of Auckland, Private Bag, Auckland *tel* (09) 737 654 *fax* (09) 33429. *Chairman of University Press Committee:* P. B. Durey. *Managing Editor:* Elizabeth Caffin. Represented by Oxford University Press. New Zealand studies—especially history and literature. Works of scholarship in general.

**\*Bush Press Communications Ltd.** (1979), P.O. Box 33-029, Takapuna, Auckland 9. *Governing Director and Publisher:* Gordon Ell. All New Zealand books: outdoor, wildlife, architecture, crafts, Maori, popular history; children's books.

**\*Butterworths of New Zealand, Ltd.,** 205-207 Victoria Street, Wellington *tel* (64-4) 851-479 *fax* (64-4) 851-598.

**\*The Caxton Press,** 113 Victoria Street, Christchurch, P.O. Box 25-088 *fax* (03) 657840. *Directors:* B. C. Bascand, E. B. Bascand. Fine printers and publishers since 1935 of New Zealand books of many kinds, including verse, fiction, biography, history, natural history, travel, gardening, children's books. Publish literary quarterly *Landfall (q.v.).*

**\*Century Hutchinson New Zealand Ltd.,** (1977), P.O. Box 40-086, 187 Archers Road, Glenfield, Auckland 10 *tel* 444-7197 *telex* 60824 *fax* 444-7524. *Directors:* J. Mottram (Chairman), L. Earney (Managing), J. Marks, M. L. Burnett, A. J. V. Cheetham, D. Ling. Fiction, junior books, educational and university, sports and pastimes, religion, non-fiction.

**\*William Collins Publishers Ltd.,** P.O. Box 1, Auckland *tel* 09-444-3740 *cables* Folio Auckland *fax* 09-444 1086. (Parent Company **William Collins PLC,** 8

Grafton Street, London W1X 3LA. *Director:* Robert W. Fisher (Managing). Publishers of general literature, fiction, non-fiction, Bibles, children's books, reference books, paperbacks.

*Heinemann Education—see **Octopus Publishing Group (NZ) Ltd.**

*Heinemann Publishers (NZ) Ltd—see **Octopus Publishing Group (NZ) Ltd.**

*Hodder & Stoughton Ltd.**, P.O. Box 3858, Auckland 1. *Showroom:* 46 View Road, Glenfield, Auckland 10 *tel* 444-3640 *telegraphic address* Expositor, Auckland *telex* NZ21422 *fax* 444-3646.

*Jacaranda Wiley Ltd,** 236 Dominion Road, 1st Floor, Mt Eden, Auckland 3 *tel* 687-070 *fax* 606-843 *postal address* C.P.O. Box 2259, Auckland 1. *Head Office:* Milton, Queensland 4064, Australia, *q.v.*

*Longman Paul Limited,** Private Bag, Takapuna, Auckland 9 *tel* 444-4968 *fax* 444-1470. Publishers of New Zealand educational books.

*John McIndoe Ltd.** (1968), 51 Crawford Street, P.O. Box 694, Dunedin *tel* 770-355 *fax* 771-982. *Directors:* I. Frame, E. P. Rogers. All categories.

*Mallinson Rendel Publishers Ltd.**, (1980), 5A Grass Street, P.O. Box 9409, Wellington *tel* 857-340. *Directors:* Ann Mallinson, David Rendel. Childrens, general New Zealand books, aviation.

*Nelson Price Milburn Ltd.**, 1 Te Puni Street, Petone *tel* 687179 *fax* 04-682-115 *postal address* P.O. Box 33005, Petone. *Managing Director:* Gil McGahey, *Chairman:* B. J. Rivers. Children's fiction, primary school texts, especially school readers and social studies, secondary and tertiary educational, general adult non-fiction.

*New Zealand Council for Educational Research** (1933), Box 3237, Education House, 178-182 Willis Street, Wellington 1 *tel* 847 939 *telegraphic address* Edsearch. Education, including educational administration and planning, vocational education and adult learning, special education, families, women and parents, rural education, early childhood education, higher education, Maori schooling, educational achievement tests, etc.

*Octopus Publishing Group (NZ) Ltd,** incorporating **Heinemann Reed, Paul Hamlyn** and **Heinemann Education**. Private Bag, Birkenhead, Auckland 10 *tel* (09) 480-6039 *fax* (09) 419-1212. *Agencies:* George Philip, Heinemann Professional & Technical Books, John Murray, Conran Octopus, Mitchell Beazley, Sterling Publishing, Octopus Publishing Group Australia Pty Ltd, Greenhouse Publications Pty Ltd, Ventura Publishing Ltd, BBC Enterprises Ltd, Pan Britannica, Heinemann Young Books, Secker & Warburg, Kingswood, Cedar, Methuen Drama, Leo Cooper, Eyre & Spottiswoode, Brimax, Daily Express, Brown Wells & Jacobs, Salamander, Budget Books Pty Ltd, Octopus Publishing Group, Associated Book Publishers, Ginn & Company, Grandreams, Heinemann Education Books, Rigby Heinemann (Australia), Ragged Bears, Heinemann Education Books Inc. (USA). *Chairman:* Nicolas Thompson. *Managing Director:* Alan Smith. *Director:* Kath Downie (Trade). *Financial Controller:* A. Stratton. New Zealand literature, specialist and technical titles, secondary and tertiary textbooks.

*Oxford University Press,** 1A Matai Road, Greenland, Auckland 5. *Postal address:* P.O. Box 11-149 Ellerslie, Auckland 5 *tel* 523-3134, 523-3702 *fax* 546-723 *cables* Oxonian, Auckland. *N. Z. Manager:* Jeff Olson. *Managing Editor:* Anne French.

**Pacific Publishers,** P.O. Box 5844, Auckland *tel* 775-196 *telex* NZ 60405. New Zealand and international books of all descriptions, general and educational.

**Pitman Publishing New Zealand Ltd.**, P.O.Box 38 688, 28 Fitzherbert Street, Petone, Wellington   *tel* 683-623. *Chairman:* Neil Ryan; *Managing Director:* Gil McGahey. Technical, educational, general, commercial, legal, art and crafts.

**\*Reed Methuen Publishers Ltd**—see **Octopus Publishing Group (NZ) Ltd.**

**\*Ray Richards Publisher** (1977), 3-49 Aberdeen Road, Castor Bay, Auckland *postal address* P.O. Box 31240 Milford, Auckland   *tel* 410 5681   *fax* 457-414. *Partners:* Ray Richards, Barbara Richards, Nicki Richards. Publishers for organisations; especially history, science, bibliography, military, equestrian, agriculture.

**Sweet & Maxwell (N.Z.) Ltd.**—see **Octopus Publishing Group (NZ) Ltd.**

**Alister Taylor Publishers** (1971), The Strand, Russell, Bay of Islands   *tel* Russell (0885) 37618. *Managing Directors:* Alister Taylor, Deborah Coddington. Publishers of New Zealand books; general, fine edition art books and catalogues raisonné, contemporary NZ and Australian art, information resource books, NZ social and political history.

**\*Victoria University Press** (1974), Victoria University of Wellington, Private Bag, Wellington   *tel* 721-000   *fax* 711-700. *Chairman of the Publications Committee:* Professor G. R. Hawke. *Editor:* Fergus Barrowman. Academic, scholarly books on New Zealand history, sociology, political history, architecture, economics, law, zoology, biology; also fiction, plays.

**Viking Sevenseas Ltd.**, 23b Ihakara Street, Paraparaumu   *tel* 058-71990   *telegraphic address* Vikseven. *Managing Director:* M. B. Riley. Factual books on New Zealand only.

# Other Commonwealth Publishers

## GHANA

**Emmanuel Publishing Services,** P.O. Box 5282, Accra. *Director:* E. K. Nsiah. Representing Oxford University Press, Faber & Faber Ltd., George Philip Ltd., University Press Ltd., Ibadan, Nigeria.

**Moxon Paperbacks** (1967), P.O. Box M 160, Accra   *tel* 665397   *telegraphic address* Moxon, Accra. *Partners:* James Moxon, Oliver Carruthers, Mark Gilbey. Crime, current affairs, biography, travel, fiction.

**Sedco Publishing Ltd.,** Sedco House, Tabon Street, North Ridge, Accra   *tel* 221332   *telex* 2456 Sedco GH   *cables* Sedco, Accra. *postal address* P.O. Box 2051, Accra.

## HONG KONG

**Jacaranda Wiley Ltd.,** 19D 257 Gloucester Road, Causeway Bay, Hong Kong *tel* 5-8331046. *Head Office:* Milton, Queensland 4064, Australia, *q.v.*

**Longman Group (Far East) Ltd.,** G.P.O. Box 223, Hong Kong *tel* 5-8118168   *fax* 5-657440.

**Macmillan Publishers (China) Limited,** Warwick House, East Wing, 19th Floor, Taikoo Trading Estate, 28 Tong Chong Street, Quarry Bay, Hong Kong   *tel* 5-8118781   *telex* 85969 Penhk Hx   *fax* 5-8110743. *Directors:* Nicholas Byam

Shaw (Chairman), Ken Derrick, Yiu Hei Kan, Rupert Li, Michael Hamilton, Brian Stonier. Educational and general books.

**Oxford University Press,** 18/F Warwick House, Taikoo Trading Estate, 28 Tong Chong Street, Quarry Bay, Hong Kong   *tel* 5-610221-4, 5-651351-8   *cables* Oxonian, Hong Kong   *telex* HX65522   *fax* 5-658491.

## KENYA

**Longman Kenya Ltd.,** P.O. Box 18033, Nairobi   *tel* 541345-7   *telex* 24101.

**Oxford University Press (East & Central Africa),** Abdulla Ismaily (Regional Manager), P.O.B. 72532, 1st Floor, Science House, Monrovia Street, Nairobi, Kenya   *cables* Oxonian Nairobi   *tel* Nairobi 336377.

## MALAYSIA

**Longman Malaysia Sdn. Berhad,** 2nd Floor, 3 Jalan Kilang A, off Jalan Penchala, 46050 Petaling Jaya, Selangor   *tel* 03-7920466   *telex* LMSB MA37600   *telegraphic address* Freegrove, Kuala Lumpur.

**Oxford University Press (East Asia),** R. E. Brammah (Regional Manager), Regional Office, 7 Jalan Semangat, P.O. Box 523, Jalan Sultan, 46760 Petaling Jaya, Selangor, Malaysia   *tel* 7551744, 7551841, 7551958   *telex* MA37283   *fax* 03-7568119.

## NIGERIA

**African Universities Press,** Pilgrim Books Ltd., PMB 5617 Ibadan. *Head Office:* Plot 1, Block P., New Oluyole Industrial Estate, Phase 2, Ibadan-Lagos Expressway, Ibadan   *tel* 022-317218   *cables* Pilgrim Ibadan   *telex* 20311-Box 078. *Directors:* Emmanuel A. Jaja, J. E. Leigh, Nicholas Perren. Educational, Africana.

**Evans Brothers (Nigeria Publishers), Ltd.,** Jericho Road, P.M.B. 5164, Ibadan   *tel* 417570, 417601, 417626   *telex* 31104 Edbook NG.

**Longman Nigeria, Ltd.,** Private Mail Bag, 21036, Ikeja   *tel* Lagos 964370, 901150-9   *telex* 26639.

**Macmillan Nigeria Publishers, Ltd.,** Oluyole Industrial Estate, Scheme 2, Lagos-Ibadan Expressway, Near Methodist High School, P.O. Box 1463, Ibadan, Oyo State   *tel* 316894, 316896-7. *Warehouse and Accounts:* Ilupeju Industrial Estate, Mushin, P.O. Box 264, Yaba, Lagos   *tel* 961188. *Directors:* Olu Anulopo, I. Ademokun, J. O. Dada, N. G. Byam Shaw, Geoff Denner, Prof. Babs Fafunwa, C. R. Harrison, Dr. Tai Solarin, A. Hikima, J. O. Ojelere.

**University Press Limited** (in association with **Oxford University Press**), *Managing Director:* M. O. Akinleye, Three Crowns Building, Jericho, Ibadan. *postal address* Private Mail Bag 5095, Ibadan   *tel* Ibadan 0-22 411356, 412386, 412313 and 413117   *telegraphic address* and *Cable:* Oxonian Ibadan.

## SINGAPORE

**Butterworth & Co. (Asia) Pte. Ltd.,** 30 Robinson Road, Unit 12-01, Tuan Sing Towers, Singapore 0104   *tel* 2241622   *telex* RS 42890 Bgasia   *fax* 2252939.

**Federal Publications (S) Pte Ltd.** (1957), Times Centre, 1 New Industrial Road, Singapore 1953   *tel* 2848844   *cables* Fedpubs, Singapore   *telex* RS 25713 Times S   *fax* 2889254. *General Manager:* Y. H. Mew. Educational, children's books and general reference books.

**Heinemann Publishers Asia (Pte) Ltd.** (1963), 37 Jalan Pemimpin, Apartment 07-04, Block B, Union Industrial Building, Singapore 2057 *tel* 2583255 *telex* RS 24299 Hebooks *fax* 2588279.

**Oxford University Press Pte. Ltd.**, Unit 221, Ubi Avenue 4, Singapore 1440 *tel* 7431066 *telex* RS 37960 Oxpres *cables* Oxonian, Singapore.

## TANZANIA

**Oxford University Press (East & Central Africa)**, P.O.B. 5299, Maktaba Road, Dar es Salaam *tel* Dar es Salaam 29209 *cables* Oxonian, Dar es Salaam.

## UGANDA

**Longman Uganda Ltd.**, P.O. Box 3409, Kampala *tel* Kampala 42940.

## ZIMBABWE

**William Collins International Ltd.**, P.O. Box 2800, Harare *tel* 721413.

**Longman Zimbabwe (Pvt.) Ltd.**, P.O. Box ST 125, Southerton, Harare *tel* Harare 62711 and 65945 *telegraphic address* Longman, Harare.

**Oxford University Press,** The College Press (Pvt) Ltd, P.O. Box 3041, Harare *tel* 66335. *Contact:* Sue McMillan.


## SOUTH AFRICA

*Members of South African Publishers' Association.

**Books of Africa (Pty) Ltd.**, 39 Atlantic Road, Muizenberg 7951, P.O. Box 10, Muizenberg 7950 *tel* (021) 888-316. *Directors:* T. V. Bulpin, M. Bulpin. Books on any subject about Africa.

*****Butterworth Publishers (Pty) Ltd.**, 8 Walter Place, Waterval Park, Mayville, Durban 4091 *tel* 294247 *telegraphic address* and *cables* Butterlaw, Durban *telex* 620730SA. *postal address* P.O. Box 792, Durban 4000.

**Collins Publishers (SA) (Pty) Ltd.**, 10-14 Watkins Street, Denver Ext. 4, Johannesburg. (P.O. Box 61342, Marshalltown, 2107) *tel* 622-2900 *fax* 6223553 *cables* Fontana, Johannesburg *telex* 4-23702SA. General publications, fiction, reference books, bibles, juveniles, school textbooks and paperbacks.

**Delta Books (Pty) Ltd.** (1980), P.O. Box 41021, Craighall, 2024. 111 Central Street, Houghton, Johannesburg 2196 *tel* 728-7121 *fax* 728-6311. *Directors:* Adriaan Donker, Karin Donker. Natural history, gardening, cookery, sport, health, practical and pictorial books.

*****Ad Donker (Pty) Ltd.** (1973), P.O. Box 41021, Craighall, 2024. 111 Central Street, Houghton, Johannesburg 2196 *tel* 728-7121 *fax* 728-6311. *Directors:* Adriaan Donker, Karin Donker, Michael Chapman, Greta Joffe. Africana, literature, history, academic, biography, socio-political.

*****Juta & Company Ltd.** (1853), P.O. Box 1010, Johannesburg, 2000 *tel* 23-5521 *telex* 4-82436(JHB) *fax* 613-5433(JHB) and P.O. Box 30, Cape Town, 8000. *tel* 71-1181 *telex* 5-23072 (Cape Town). Educational and legal publishers. General and educational booksellers and importers.

**Longman Penguin Southern Africa (Pty) Ltd.**—see **Maskew Miller Longman (Pty) Ltd.**

**\*Lovedale Press,** Private Bag X 1346, Alice, Ciskei 5700   *tel* 0404-31135-6-7. Educational, religious and general book publications for African market.

**Macdonald Purnell (Pty) Ltd.,** Head Office: 10 Burke Street, Randburg. *postal address* P.O. Box 1401, Randburg 2125 *telex* 4-24985 SA *fax* 011-7874420 *telegraphic address* Purprint. *Chairman:* K. Maxwell. *Managing Director:* Peter Matthews. Publishers of books of South African interest and stockists of general and juvenile books for the MPCC Group, Aiden Ellis, Arnold Wheaton, Brassey's, Macdonald & Co., Macdonald South Africa, Optima, Orbis, Pergamon Press, Religious & Moral Education Press, Queen Anne Press, Time Life, Futura Paperbacks, Tiger Books, Berlitz Travel Guides.

**\*Maskew Miller Longman (Pty) Ltd.,** Howard Drive, Pinelands 7405   *tel* 53-7750   *telex* 526053   *fax* (021) 534049. *postal address* P.O. Box 396, Cape Town, 8000. Educational and general publishers and booksellers; school stationery requirements.

**\*Oxford University Press (Southern African Branch),** James Clarke, *General Manager.* 5th Floor, Harrington House, 37 Barrack Street, Cape Town, 8001. *postal address* Box 1141, Cape Town, 8000. 306 Hyde Park Corner, Jan Smuts Avenue, Craighall 2196. *postal address* P.O. Box 41390, Craighall 2024. 12th Floor, Maritime House, C/o Salmon Grove & Esplanade, Durban 4001. *postal address* P.O. Box 37166, Overport 4067   *cables* Oxonian Cape Town; Oxonian Johannesburg; Oxonian Durban   *tel* Cape Town 021-45 7266; Johannesburg 011-7883617; Durban 031-304-7202   *telex* Capetown 9550022   *fax* Cape Town 021-457265.

**David Philip Publisher (Pty) Ltd.** (1971), P.O. Box 23408, Claremont, 7735, Cape Province   *tel* 21-64-4136   *telegraphic address* Philipub, Capetown   *telex* 527566 Ctcoc Philipub   *fax* 21-64-3358. *Directors:* David Philip, Marie Philip. Academic, history, social sciences, politics, theology, biography, belles-lettres, reference books, fiction, learners' texts, children's books.

**Pitman Publishing Co. S.A. (Pty) Ltd.** (1974), P.O. Box 396, Cape Town, 8000   *tel* 53-7750   fax (021) 53-4049. Division of **Maskew Miller Longman (Pty) Ltd.**

**Ravan Press (Pty) Ltd** (1972), 3rd Floor, Standard House, 40 De Korte Street, Braamfontein, Johannesburg   *postal address* P.O. Box 31134, Braamfontein 2017   *tel* 403-3925/6/7/8/9   *fax* 339-2439. *Manager:* Glenn Moss. African studies: history, politics, theology, social studies. Fiction, literature, children's, educational.

**The Science Press (Pty) Ltd.** (1981), P.O. Box 41021, Craighall 2024. 111 Central Street, Houghton, Johannesburg 2196   *tel* 728 7121   *fax* 728-6311. *Directors:* Adriaan Donker, Karin Donker. Medical, scientific and university textbooks.

**\*Shuter and Shooter (Pty) Ltd** (1925), 230 Church Street, and 199 Pietermaritz Street, Pietermaritzburg 3201, Natal   *tel* (0331) 946830/948881   *telegraphic address* Shushoo   *telex* 6-43771SA   *fax* (0331) 943096. *Directors:* M. N. Prozesky (Managing), J. S. Craib, C. L. S. Nyembezi, E. O. Oellermann, C. A. Roy, D. F. Ryder, W. N. Vorster, G. F. Walker, R. J. Watkinson.

**\*Southern Book Publishers (Pty) Ltd,** Southern Book House, 54 Andries Street, Wynberg, Johannesburg (PO Box 548, Bergvlei 2012)   *tel* 786-0001   *telex* 4-24235 SA   *fax* 011 787 7137. Publishers of academic, educational and general books as well as those of South African interest.

**Struik Winchester Publishers,** PO Box 3755, Cape Town, 8000. A division of Struikhof Publishers (Pty) Ltd. *tel* (021) 418 1410 *fax* (021) 216744 *telex* 5-26713SA. *Executive Director:* Pieter Struik. Natural history, cultural history, Africana.

**Struikhof Publishers,** P.O. Box 3755, Cape Town 8000. An operating division of The Struik Group (Pty) Ltd. *tel* (021) 216740 *telex* 5-26713 SA *fax* (021) 216744. *Executive Director:* Pieter Struik. General non-fiction.

\*J. L. Van Schaik (1914), P.O. Box 724, Pretoria, 0001 *tel* 012-21-2441 *telex* 3-22340 SA. Publishers of books in English, Afrikaans and African languages. Specialists in Afrikaans books.

**Witwatersrand University Press,** Wits 2050 *tel* 716 2029 *telex* 4-27125 SA *fax* 403-1926.

# UNITED STATES OF AMERICA

The following is a selected list; it includes only a few of the very many smaller firms, and of the specialist publishers. The introductory note on submitting manuscripts (at the start of the **Books** section) applies also to US publishers.

\*Members of the Association of American Publishers Inc.

**Abingdon Press,** Editorial and Business Offices: 201 Eighth Avenue S., P.O. Box 801, Nashville, Tennessee 37202 *tel* 615-749 6403 *fax* 615-749 6512. Editorial offices for academic and reference books: 2495 Lawrenceville Highway, Decatur, GA 30033 *tel* 404-636-6001 *fax* 404-636-5894. *General Manager:* Neil M. Alexander. Trade, professional, academic and reference— primarily directed to the religious market.

**Academy Chicago Publishers** (1975), 213 West Institute Place, Chicago, Illinois 60610 *tel* 312-644-1723 *fax* 312-751-7306. *Directors:* Anita Miller, Jordan Miller. Fiction, mystery, biography, travel, books of interest to women; quality reprints.

**And/Or Press Inc.** (1974), P.O. Box 2246, Berkeley, California 94701 *tel* 415-548-2124. Health and nutrition, life styles. No unsolicited work.

**Andrews & McMeel,** 4900 Main Street, Kansas City, Missouri 64112 *tel* 816-932-6700 *telex* 437007 *fax* 816-932-6706. *Vice-President* and *Editorial Director:* Donna Martin. General trade publishing, with emphasis on humour and consumer reference.

\*Arbor House/William Morrow, 105 Madison Avenue, New York, N.Y. 10016 *tel* 212-889 3050. *Publisher and Editor-in-Chief:* Alan D. Williams. Fiction, history and biography.

**Arcade Publishing,** 141 Fifth Avenue, New York, N.Y. 10010 *tel* 212-475-2633. *President and Editor-in-Chief:* Richard Seaver. General, including adult hard cover and paperbacks, children's and young adult books.

**Ashley Books Inc.** (1971), 4600 W. Commercial Blvd, Tamarac, FL 33319 *tel* 305-739-2221 *fax* 305-485-2287. *Directors:* Simeon Paget (Managing), Billie Young (President). Consumer, fiction, cookery, medical and health; books on making money and/or investments.

\*Atheneum Publishers (1960), a division of **Macmillan Publishing Co.**, 866 Third Avenue, New York, N.Y. 10022 *tel* 212-702-2000 *telex* 22595 Macm UR *fax* 212-319-1216. General, fiction, poetry, juveniles.

**\*Atlantic Monthly Press,** 19 Union Square West, New York, N.Y. 10003 *tel* 212-645-4462 *telex* 147105. *Editorial Director:* Gary Fisketjon. *Executive Editor and Vice-President:* Ann Godoff. (Books distributed by Little Brown & Co.) MSS. of permanent interest, fiction, biography, autobiography, history, current affairs, social science, belles-lettres, natural history, travel adventure.

**\*Avon Books** (1941), The Hearst Corporation, 105 Madison Avenue, New York, N.Y. 10016 *tel* 212-481-5600 *telegraphic address* Avon Books. *President and Publisher:* Carolyn Reidy. All subjects, fiction and non-fiction.

**Walter H. Baker Company** (1845), 100 Chauncy Street, Boston, Mass. 02111. *President:* M. Abbott Van Nostrand. *Editor:* John B. Welch. Plays and books on the theatre. Also agents for plays. *London agents:* Samuel French, Ltd., 52 Fitzroy Street, London, W1P 6JR.

**\*Bantam Doubleday Dell Publishing Group Inc,** 666 Fifth Avenue, New York, N.Y., 10103 *tel* 212-765-6500 *telex* 237992 and 277248 *fax* 212-765-3869 *cables* Bantambook New York. *Chairman of the Board of Directors:* Olaf Paeschke, *President and Chief Executive Officer:* Alberto Vitale, *Treasurer:* John Choi. *President and Publisher, International:* Alun Davies. Fiction, classics, biography, health, business, general non-fiction, social sciences, religion, sports, science, audio tapes, computer books.

**A. S. Barnes & Co.,** 3870 Murphy Canyon Road, Suite 203, San Diego, California 92123 *tel* 619-560-5163 *fax* 619-560-0045. An imprint of **Oak Tree Publications Inc.** General publishers.

**Beacon Press,** 25 Beacon Street, Boston, Mass., 02108 *tel* 617-742 2110. General non-fiction in fields of religion, ethics, philosophy, current affairs, history, literary criticism, psychology, sociology, anthropology and women's studies.

**Beech Tree Books,** a division of **William Morrow & Co., Inc.,** 105 Madison Avenue, New York, N.Y. 10016 *tel* 212-889-3050. *Publisher:* James D. Landis. General literature fiction and non fiction.

**\*R. R. Bowker Co.,** 245 West 17th Street, New York, N.Y. 10011 *tel* 212-645 9700. Outside North America: **R. R. Bowker** (a subsidiary of **Butterworths & Co. Ltd.**), Borough Green, Sevenoaks, Kent TN15 8PJ, England. Bibliographies and reference tools for the book trade and literary and library worlds, available in hardcopy, on microfiche, on-line and CD-ROM. Reference and 'how-to' books for graphic arts, music, art, corporate communications, computer industry, cable industry, and information industry.

**George Braziller Inc.** (1954), 60 Madison Avenue, Suite 1001, New York, N.Y. 10010 *tel* 212-889-0909 *telex* 422144 *fax* 212-689-5405. *President:* George Braziller. *Fine Arts Editor:* Adrienne Baxter. Philosophy, science, art, architecture, history, biography, fiction, environment, ecology, poetry.

**\*Cambridge University Press (American branch),** 40 West 20th Street, New York, N.Y. 10011 *tel* 212-924-3900 *fax* 212-691 3239.

**Carroll & Graf Publishers, Inc.** (1983), 260 Fifth Avenue, New York, N.Y. 10001 *tel* 212-889-8772. *President:* Herman Graf. *Publisher:* Kent Carroll. *Subrights:* James Mason. Mystery and science fiction, history, biography, literature, business, psychology.

**\*Collier Macmillan International,** 866 Third Avenue, New York, N.Y., 10022-6299 *tel* 212-702 2000. *Cable Address:* Pachamac, N.Y. *London:* Macmillan Distribution Ltd., Houndmills, Basingstoke, Hants. RG21 2XS *tel* (0256) 29242. Publishers of encyclopaedias, text and reference books, paperbacks, general trade and juvenile books.

**\*Columbia University Press,** 562 West 113th Street, New York, N.Y. 10025 *tel* 212-316-7100 *fax* 212-316-7169. *England:* 10 Watlington Road, Cowley, Oxford OX4 5NF *fax* (0865) 748401. Scholarly work in all fields and serious non-fiction of more general interest.

**Concordia Publishing House** (1869), 3558 S. Jefferson Avenue, St. Louis, Mo. 63118 *tel* 314-664-7000. Religious books, Lutheran perspective. Few freelance manuscripts accepted. Query first.

**Contemporary Books Inc.** 180 North Michigan Avenue, Chicago, Illinois, 60601 *tel* 312-782-9181 *fax* 312-782-3987. *President:* Harvey Plotnick. *Vice President and Executive Editorial Director:* Nancy Coffey. Non-fiction.

**\*The Continuum Publishing Corp.** (1980), 370 Lexington Avenue, New York, N.Y., 10017 *tel* 212-532-3650 *telex* 4974569 Conti *fax* 212-532-4922. *Chairman and Chief Executive Officer:* Werner Mark Linz. General non-fiction, education, literature, psychology, politics, sociology, literary criticism.

**\*Cornell University Press** (including **Comstock Publishing Associates**) (1869), 124 Roberts Place, Ithaca, New York 14850 *tel* 607-257-7000. Scholarly books. *Agents Overseas:* Trevor Brown Associates, Suite 7B, 26 Charing Cross Road, London WC2H 0LN.

**\*Crown Publishers, Inc.,** 225 Park Avenue South, New York, N.Y., 10003 *tel* 254-1600. *Executive:* Betty A. Prashker. General fiction, non-fiction, illustrated books.

**Devin-Adair Publishers, Inc.,** (1911), 6 North Water Street, Greenwich, Connecticut, 06830 *tel* 203-531-7755. Conservative politics, health and ecology, Irish topics, gardening and travel topics, homeopathy and holistic health books.

**\*Doubleday,** a division of **Bantam Doubleday Dell Publishing Group Inc.,** 666 Fifth Avenue, New York, 10103 *tel* 212-765-6500. *London:* 100 Wigmore Street, W1H 9DR *tel* 01-935 1269. Trade, general fiction and non-fiction. Anchor Press. Books For Young Readers. Foundation. Religious.

**Dryden Press**—see **Harcourt Brace Jovanovich Inc.**

**\*E. P. Dutton,** division of Penguin Books USA Inc., 2 Park Avenue, New York, N.Y. 10016 *tel* 212-725-1818 *fax* 212-532 6568. General publishers. General non-fiction, including biographies, adventure, history, travel; fiction, mysteries, juveniles, quality paperbacks.

**Facts on File Inc.** (1940), 460 Park Avenue South, New York, N.Y. 10016 *tel* 212-683-2244 *telex* 238552 *cables* Factsfile New York, *U.K. Office:* Collins Street, Oxford OX4 1XJ *tel* (0865) 728399. *President:* Howard Epstein, *Executive Vice President and Publisher:* Edward W. Knappman. *UK and European Manager:* Alan Goodworth. Information books and services for colleges, libraries, schools and general public.

**Farrar, Straus & Giroux, Inc.,** 19 Union Square West, New York City, N.Y., 10003 *tel* 212-741-6900 *telegraphic address* Farrarcomp, New York *telex* 667428 *fax* 212-633-9385. General publishers.

**Samuel French Inc.,** 45 West 25th Street, New York, N.Y. 10010 *tel* 212-206-8990 *fax* 212-206-1429. Play publishers and author's representatives (dramatic).

**David R. Godine, Publisher Inc.** (1970), Horticultural Hall, 300 Massachusetts Avenue, Boston, Massachusetts 02115 *tel* 617-536-0761. *President:* David R. Godine. Fiction, photography, history, natural history, art, biography, children's.

**\*Stephen Greene Press** (1957), 15 Muzzey Street, Lexington, Mass. 02173  *tel* 617-861-0170. *Editorial Director:* Thomas Begner. Americana, conservation and nature, country living, cook books, sports (skiing, snowshoeing, kayaking, riding, orienteering), crafts, general adult non-fiction, etc.

**Greenwillow Books,** a division of **William Morrow & Co., Inc.,** 105 Madison Avenue, New York, N.Y. 10016  *tel* 212-889-3050. *Senior Vice-President/Editor-in-Chief:* Susan Hirschman. Children's books.

**\*Grosset & Dunlap, Inc.,** 200 Madison Avenue, New York, N.Y., 10016  *tel* 212-951-8400. Adult non-fiction, juveniles, popular reference books, children's picture books, series books, activity books, and religious books.

**Grove/Weidenfeld & Nicolson** (1986), 841 Broadway, New York, N.Y. 10003  *tel* 212-614-7860  *telex* 6711993  *fax* 212-614-7915. *Chairman:* Lord Weidenfeld. *Publisher:* Aaron Asher. Non-fiction: history, biography, current events; fiction: popular and literary.

**Harcourt Brace Jovanovich Inc.,** 1250 Sixth Avenue, San Diego, California 92101  *tel* 619-231-6616. General publishers. Fiction, history, biography, etc.; college and school textbooks of all kinds; children's; technical; reference; religious; dictionaries. Imprints: **Holt Rinehart and Winston, Dryden Press, Saunders College.**

**\*Harper & Row, Publishers** (1817), 10 East 53rd Street, New York, N.Y., 10022  *tel* 212-207-7000  *cables* Harpsam, N.Y.  *telex* 12-5741(dom.), 62-501(intl). *President and Chief Executive Officer:* George Craig. Religious books division: Icehouse One, Suite 401, 151 Union Street, San Francisco, CA 94111  *tel* 415-477-4400  *fax* 415-421-5865. *London:* 34-42 Cleveland Street, London, W1P 5FB. Fiction, history, biography, poetry, science, travel, juvenile, educational, business, technical, medical and religious.

**Hastings House, Publishers New York, Ltd.,** 222 West 26th Street, New York, N.Y. 10001. *President:* Eric Kampmann. *Managing Director:* Peter Skutches. General, travel, graphic arts, sports, cookery and wines, children's books, communication arts (television, film, radio).

**\*D. C. Heath and Co.** International division of **Raytheon Co.,** 125 Spring Street, Lexington, Mass., 02173  *tel* 617-860-1340  *fax* 617-860-1508. Elementary, secondary, college textbooks.

**Hill & Wang** (1956), division of **Farrar, Straus & Giroux Inc.,** 19 Union Square West, New York, N.Y. 10003  *tel* 212-741-6900  *telex* 667428  *fax* 212-633-9385. *Editor-in-Chief:* Arthur W. Wang. *Publisher:* Steve Wasserman. General non-fiction, drama, history.

**\*Holiday House** (1935), 18 East 53rd Street, New York, N.Y., 10022  *tel* 212-688-0085. *Directors:* John Briggs (President), Margery Cuyler, Kate Briggs, David R. Rogers. General children's books.

**Holt, Rinehart and Winston** —see **Harcourt Brace Jovanovich Inc.**

**\*Houghton Mifflin Company** (1832), One Beacon Street, Boston, MA 02108  *tel* 617-725-5000  *telex* 4430255 Hmhq UI  *fax* 617-573-4916 (Trade), 617-227-5409 (School and College). Fiction, biography, history, works of general interest of all kinds, both adult and juvenile, also school and college textbooks in all departments, and standardised tests. Best length: 75,000-180,000 words; juveniles, any reasonable length.

**Keats Publishing Inc.** (1971), 27 Pine Street, P.O. Box 876, New Canaan, Connecticut 06840  *tel* (203) 966-8721. *Directors:* Nathan Keats (President), An Keats (Editor-in-Chief). Natural health and medical books.

**\*Alfred A. Knopf Inc.** (1915), a division of **Random House, Inc.**, 201 East 50th Street, New York, N.Y., 10022 *tel* 212-751 2600 *telegraphic address* Knopf, New York. General literature, fiction, belles-lettres, sociology, politics, history, nature, science, etc.

**David S. Lake Publishers,** 500 Harbor Boulevard, Belmont, California 94002 *tel* 415-592-7810. Elementary/High school special education materials. Textbooks, reading materials, teacher-aids, high school education materials, management and training materials.

**\*J. B. Lippincott Co.** (1792), East Washington Square, Philadelphia, Pa., 19105 *tel* 215-238-4200 *cables* Lippcot, Phila. Medical and nursing books and journals. A division of **Harper & Row Publishers Inc.**

**\*Little, Brown and Company,** 34 Beacon Street, Boston, Mass., 02108 *tel* 617-227-0730 *cables* Brownlit, Boston. General literature, especially fiction, nonfiction, biography, history, trade paperbacks, books for boys and girls, college, law, medical books. Art and photography books under the **Bulfinch Press/New York Graphic Society Books** imprint.

**Lothrop, Lee & Shepard Books** (1859), a division of **William Morrow & Co., Inc.**, 105 Madison Avenue, New York, N.Y. 10016 *tel* 212-889-3050 *fax* 212-689-2863. *Vice-President/Editor-in-Chief:* Dorothy Briley. Children's books only.

**Lyons & Burford,** 31 West 21st Street, New York, N.Y. 10010 *tel* 212-620-9580. Outdoor sport, natural history, general sports, art.

**\*McGraw-Hill Book Co.,** 1221 Avenue of the Americas, New York, N.Y. 10020 *tel* 212-512-2000. Professional and reference: engineering, scientific, business, architecture, encyclopaedias. College textbooks. High school and vocational textbooks: business, secretarial, career. Trade books. Microcomputer software; training courses for industry. See also McGraw-Hill Book Company (UK) Ltd., McGraw-Hill House, Maidenhead, England, and McGraw-Hill Ryerson Ltd. of Canada.

**David McKay Co., Inc.,** 201 East 50th Street, New York, N.Y. 10022 *tel* 212-751-2600 *telegraphic address* Davmacay. *President:* James Louttit. Non-fiction. Distributed by Fodor's Travel Guides.

**\*Macmillan Publishing Company** (A division of **Macmillan Inc**), (1896), 866 Third Avenue, New York, N.Y., 10022 *tel* 212-702-2000 *telegraphic address* Pachamac, N.Y. *President and Publisher:* Barry Lippman. General books.

**\*Julian Messner** (a division of **Simon & Schuster**), Prentice Hall Building, Englewood Cliffs, N.J. 07632 *tel* 201-592-2966. General non-fiction for ages through high school.

**Morehouse Publishing Co.,** 78 Danbury Road, Wilton, Conn. 06897 *tel* 203-762-0721 *fax* 203-762-0727. *Chairman:* Stanley Kleiman. *President & Publisher:* E. Allen Kelley. Religious books, religious education, texts, seminary texts, children's books.

**Morrow Jr. Books,** a division of **William Morrow & Co., Inc.,** 105 Madison Avenue, New York, N.Y. 10016 *tel* 212-889-3050 *fax* 212-689-9139. *Vice-President/Editor-in-Chief:* David Reuther. Children's books only.

**\*William Morrow & Co., Inc.,** 105 Madison Avenue, New York, N.Y., 10016 *tel* 212-889-3050. Allen Marchioni (Chairman and C.E.O.), Sherry Arden (President and Publisher, Adult Trade), James D. Landis (Senior V.P., Publisher, Beech Tree Books), Susan Hirschman (Senior V.P. Editor-in-Chief Greenwillow Books), Dorothy Briley (V.P. Editor-in-Chief Lothrop, Lee & Shepard),

David Reuther (V.P., Editor-in-Chief Morrow Jr. Books). General literature, fiction and juveniles. Interested in works dealing with American and non-fiction foreign life and history. Royalty.

**Thomas Nelson, Inc.** (1978), Nelson Place at Elm Hill Pike, P.O. Box 141000, Nashville, Tennessee 37214-1000   *tel* 615-889-9000. Publishers of bibles, religious, non-fiction and fiction general trade.

**W. W. Norton & Company, Inc.**, 500 Fifth Avenue, New York, N.Y. 10110   *tel* 212-354-5500   *fax* 212-869-0856. General fiction and non-fiction, music, boating, psychiatry, economics, family therapy, social work, reprints, college texts, science.

**Ottenheimer Publishers Inc.** (1890), 300 Reisterstown Road, Baltimore, Maryland 21208   *tel* 301-484-2100   *telex* 198110   *fax* 301-486-8301. *Directors:* Allan T. Hirsh, Jr., Allan T. Hirsh, III. Juvenile and adult non-fiction, reference.

**\*The Overlook Press,** 12 West 21st Street, New York, N.Y. 10010   *tel* 212-675 0585   *telex* 233776   *telegraphic address* Vikpress   *fax* 212-243-7676. Fiction, non-fiction, poetry, how-to manuals.

**\*Oxford University Press, Inc.,** 200 Madison Avenue, New York, N.Y. 10016   *tel* 212-679-7300   *cables* Frowde, New York. Scholarly, professional, reference, all non-fiction, bibles, college textbooks, religion, medicals, music.

**\*Pantheon Books,** a division of **Random House, Inc.,** 201 East 50th Street, New York, N.Y. 10022   *tel* 212-572-2404. Fiction, mysteries, belles-lettres, translations, philosophy, history and art, sociology, psychology, juvenile.

**Pergamon-Brassey's International Defense Publishers Inc.** (1984), (member of the **Pergamon Group**), 8000 Westpark Drive, Fourth Floor, McLean, Virginia 22102   *tel* 703-442 0900   *telex* 90-1811. *Senior Executive:* Franklin D. Margiotta, PH.D. All aspects of contemporary defence policy and national security.

**\*Praeger Publishers** (a division of **Greenwood Press Inc.**), One Madison Avenue, New York, N.Y. 10010   *tel* (212) 685-5300. Non-fiction on international relations, social sciences, economics, reference, contemporary issues, urban affairs, psychology, education.

**\*Prentice-Hall, Inc.** (1913), (a subsidiary of **Simon & Schuster**), Englewood Cliffs, New Jersey, 07632. Text, technical and general non-fiction, business selling and management books, juveniles; biographies and autobiographies. Freelance artists' and designers' work used.

**\*The Putnam Berkley Group Inc.,** 200 Madison Avenue, New York, N.Y. 10016   *tel* 212-576-8900. Publications of books in all divisions of literature. History, economics, political science, natural science, and standard literature. Also an important group of fiction. Children's books.

**Quill Paperbacks,** a division of **William Morrow & Co., Inc.,** 105 Madison Avenue, New York, N.Y., 10016   *tel* 212-889-3050. *Managing Editor:* Andrew Ambraziejus. General literature fiction and non-fiction.

**\*Rand McNally,** P.O. Box 7600, Chicago, Illinois 60680   *tel* 312-673-9100. Maps, guides, atlases, educational publications and globes; banking, financial, and business reference publications. *Chairman:* Andrew McNally III. *President:* Andrew McNally IV.

**\*Random House, Inc.,** 201 East 50th Street, New York, N.Y., 10022   *tel* 212-751-2600. General publishers.

**\*Rawson Associates,** a division of **Macmillan Publishing Co.,** 866 Third Avenue, New York, N.Y. 10022  *tel* 212-702-3436  *fax* 212-319-1216. *President:* Kennett L. Rawson. *Executive Vice-President:* Eleanor S. Rawson. Adult nonfiction and fiction.

**Fleming H. Revell Co.,** 184 Central Avenue, Old Tappan, New Jersey 07675  *tel* 201-768-8060  *fax* 201-768-2749. Religious books.

**Ronin Publishing Inc.,** Box 1035, Berkeley, California 94701  *tel* 415-540 6278. Management, humour. Preliminary letter essential; no unsolicited manuscripts or art work.

**Routledge, Chapman & Hall, Inc.,** 29 West 35th Street, New York, N.Y. 10001  *tel* 212-244 3336  *telegraphic address* Algernon New York  *telex* 6801368  *fax* 212-563-2269. *Directors:* John von Knorring, Edward R. Sands, William P. Germano (Editorial). Literary criticism, history, philosophy, psychology and psychiatry, politics, women's studies, life sciences, ecology, mathematics and statistics.

**\*St Martin's Press, Inc.,** 175 Fifth Avenue, New York, N.Y., 10010  *tel* 212-674-5151  *fax* 212-420-9314  *telegraphic address* Saintmart, New York. Trade, reference, college.

**Saunders College**—see **Harcourt Brace Jovanovich Inc.**

**\*Schocken Books Inc.,** (1945), 201 East 50th Street, New York, N.Y., 10022  *tel* 212-572-2517. Education, Judaica and holocaust studies, women studies, social sciences, literature, literary criticism. Imprint of **Random House.**

**\*Scribner Book Companies, Inc.** (1846) (A division of **Macmillan Inc.**), 866 Third Avenue, New York, N.Y. 10022  *tel* 212-702 2000. General publishers of standard books in education, biography, history, science, fiction, belles-lettres, juveniles.

**\*Simon & Schuster,** 1230 Avenue of the Americas, New York, N.Y. 10020  *tel* 212-698-7000. *Chairman:* Richard Snyder. *President, Trade Division:* Charles Hayward. *Editor-in-Chief, Trade Division:* Michael V. Korda. General nonfiction, fiction, biography, detective, humour, occasional novelty books. Manuscripts not addressed to an editor by name will be returned unread.

**\*Stanford University Press,** Stanford, California 94305  *tel* 415-723-9434. Scholarly non-fiction.

**Strawberry Hill Press** (1973), 2594 15th Avenue, San Francisco, California 94127  *tel* 415-664-8112. *President:* Jean-Louis Brindamour, PH.D, *Executive Vice-President and Art Director:* Ku Fu-Sheng, *Treasurer:* Edward E. Serres. Health, self-help, cookbooks, philosophy, religion, history, drama, science and technology, biography, mystery, Third World. No unsolicited MSS, preliminary letter and return postage essential.

**\*Taplinger Publishing Co., Inc.** (1955), 238 West 72nd Street, New York, N.Y. 10023  *tel* 212-877-1040  *telegraphic address* Taplinpub. Calligraphy, literature (including translated works into English), music, art and art criticism, nonfiction.

**\*Taylor & Francis, New York,** 3 East 44 Street, New York, N.Y. 10017  *tel* 212-867-1490  *fax* 212-867-1076. A member of the **Taylor & Francis Group.** Strategy and foreign affairs, oceanography and marine sciences, biological and biomedical sciences, scientific journals.

**Theatre Arts Books,** 29 West 35th Street, New York, N.Y. 10001  *tel* 212-244 3336. A division of **Routledge, Chapman & Hall Inc.** *President:* John von

Knorring. *Editorial Director:* William Germano. Successor to the book publishing department of Theatre Arts (1921-1948). Theatre, dance and allied books—costume, materials, tailoring, etc., a few plays.

**Charles E. Tuttle Co., Inc.** (1949), 28 South Main Street (P.O. Box 410), Rutland, Vermont 05701-0410 *tel* 802-773-8930 and 802-773-8229 *cables* Tuttbooks *fax* 802-773-6993. *President:* Donald E. Berg; and Suido I-chome, 2-6 Bunkyo-ku, Tokyo 112, Japan *tel* 811-7106-9 *cables* Tuttbooks, Tokyo *telex* 0272-3170 Tutbks J *fax* 811-6953. *President:* Nicholas J. Ingleton. Oriental art, culture, history, manners and customs, Americana.

**\*University of California Press,** 2120 Berkeley Way, Berkeley, California 94720. Publishes scholarly-books, books of general interest, series of scholarly monographs, and scholarly journals. *U.K.:* University Presses of California, Columbia, and Princeton, Avonlea, 10 Watlington Road, Cowley, Oxford OX4 5NF *tel* (0865) 748405 *fax* (0865) 748401.

**\*University of Chicago Press,** 5801 South Ellis Avenue, Chicago, Ill. 60637 *tel* 312-702-7700 *fax* 312-702-9756. Scholarly books and monographs, religious, medical and scientific books, general trade books, Chicago visual library micropublications, and 45 scholarly journals.

**\*University of Illinois Press** (1918), 54 East Gregory Drive, Champaign, Illinois 61820 *tel* 217-333-0950. *Director:* Richard L. Wentworth. American studies (history, music, literature), poetry, working-class and ethnic studies, anthropology, communications, special education and childhood development.

**\*Van Nostrand Reinhold** (1848), 115 Fifth Avenue, New York, N.Y. 10003 *tel* 212-254 3232 *cables* Readbooks Newyork *telex* 272562 Vnrc UR *fax* 212-254-9499, 212-475-2548. *President & C.E.O.:* Chester C. Lucido, Jr. Reference, encyclopedias, handbooks: architecture, business, design, energy, medicine, science and technology.

**\*Viking Penguin Inc.** (1925), 40 West 23 Street, New York, N.Y., 10010 *tel* 337-5200. *President:* Marvin Brown. *Editor-in-Chief, Adult Books:* Christine Pevitt. *Consulting Editor:* Malcolm Cowley. *Editors:* Amanda Vaill, Kathryn Court, Pam Dorman, Mindy Werner, Dawn Seferian, Tracy Brown, Barbara Williams, Charles Verrill, Daniel Frank, Nan Graham, Gerald Howard. *Editorial Director, Children's Books:* Regina Hayes. General books, fiction, nonfiction, biography, sociology, poetry, art, travel, children's books.

**Walker & Co.** (1960), 720 Fifth Avenue, New York, N.Y. 10019 *tel* 212-265-3632 *fax* 212-307-1704. Samuel S. Walker Jr. (President). General publishers, biography, history, religion, philosophy, natural history, and adventure, world affairs, criticism, mystery/suspense, thrillers, romances, westerns, juveniles, early childhood education, parenting.

**\*Warner Books Inc.** (1973), 666 Fifth Avenue, New York, N.Y. 10103 *tel* 212-484-2900 *telegraphic address* Warcom *fax* 212-484-2713. *President:* Laurence J. Kirshbaum. Fiction and non-fiction, hardcovers, trade paperbacks, mass market paperbacks, juveniles.

**\*Franklin Watts Inc.,** a subsidiary of **Grolier Inc.,** 387 Park Avenue South, New York, N.Y., 10016 *tel* 212-686-7070 *telex* 236537 *fax* 212-213-6435. Adult trade.

**\*Westminster/John Knox Press,** 100 Witherspoon Street, Louisville, Kentucky 40202-1396 *tel* 502-569-5000 *fax* 502-569-5018. Religious, academic, reference, general.

**Writer's Digest Books,** 1507 Dana Avenue, Cincinnati, Ohio 45207 *tel* 513-531-2222 *fax* 513-531-4744. Market Directories, books for writers, photographers, songwriters, plus selected how-to trade titles. **North Light** imprint: Art instruction and graphic arts books.

\***Yale University Press,** 302 Temple Street, New Haven, Connecticut, 06520 *tel* 203-432-0960 *telex* 963531 *fax* 203-432-0948. *postal address* 92A Yale Station, New Haven, Connecticut, 06520. *Director:* John G. Ryden. *London:* 23 Pond Street, Hampstead, London NW3 2PN *tel* 01-431 4422 *fax* 01-431 3755. Scholarly books.

# Who owns whom—a guide to current ownership in the UK book trade—June 1989

**W. H. Allen**
Allison & Busby, Crescent Books, Mercury, Planet, Star, Virgin Books

**Bertelsmann**
Doubleday, Transworld (incl. Bantam, Black Swan, Corgi, Partridge Press)

**B. T. Batsford**
Dryad Press, B. A. Seaby

**A. & C. Black**
Alphabooks, Art Guides, Ernest Benn, EP Publishing, Nautical Books, Stanford Maritime

**Blackie**
Abelard-Schuman, International Textbook Co.

**Butterworth** (part of Reed)
Bowker-Saur, Focal Press, D. W. Thorpe (Aust.), John Wright, Brewer's Publishing

**Cassell**
Arms & Armour Press, Blandford, Geoffrey Chapman, Javelin, Mansell, Mowbray, New Orchard Editions, Robert Royce, Studio Vista, Tycooly Publishing, Ward Lock

**Century Hutchinson** *see* Random Century

**James Clarke**
Patrick Hardy Books, Lutterworth Press

**Collins** (part of News International)
Adlard Coles, Armada, Collins Harvill, Collins Willow, Dinosaur, Dragon, Fontana, Fount, Grafton, Mayflower, Paladin, Panther, Thorsons (incl. Aquarian Press, William Kimber, Patrick Stephens)

**Conway Maritime**
Putnam

**David & Charles**
Poplar Press

**André Deutsch**
Rapp & Whiting

**Egmont**
World International

**Gollancz**
H. F. & G. Witherby

**Gower Publishing**
Scolar Press, Technical Press, Wildwood House

**Grisewood & Dempsey**
Brookfield Publishing (USA), Kingfisher, Parliamentary Research Services

**Harrap**
   Columbus

**J. H. Haynes**
   G. T. Foulis, Oxford Illustrated Press, Oxford Publishing Co.

**Hobsons Publishing**
   Johanson

**Hodder & Stoughton**
   Edward Arnold, Coronet, Diadem Books, Charles Griffin, Lloyd Luke (USA),
   Knight, New English Library, Sceptre

**Longman** (part of Pearson)
   Addison Wesley (USA), Churchill Livingstone, Ladybird, Longman Carter-
   mill, Macdonald & Evans, Oliver & Boyd, Pitman

**Macmillan**
   Pan, Papermac, Picador, St Martin's Press (USA), Sidgwick & Jackson

**Maxwell Communications**
   E. J. Arnold, Architectural Press, Brassey's Defence Publishers, Devon Books,
   Futura, Macmillan (USA), Macdonald, Optima, Pergamon Press, Queen Anne
   Press, Sphere, Wheaton

**Musterlin**
   Agon (Netherlands), Canongate, Equinox, Lennard Books, Phaidon Christies,
   Phaidon Press

**News Internatioanl**
   John Bartholomew, Collins, Geographia, Robert Nicholson, Times Books

**Octopus** (part of Reed)
   Brimax, Collingridge, Leo Cooper, Country Life, Dean's, Eyre & Spotts-
   iwoode, Ginn, Hamlyn, H. E. B., Heinemann, Methuen, Miller's Publications,
   Mitchell Beazley, Newnes, George Philip (incl. Osprey), Pitkin Pictorial, Rigby
   (Aust.), Secker & Warburg

**Pearson**
   Longman (q.v.), Penguin (q.v.)

**Penguin** (part of Pearson)
   Elm Tree, Stephen Greene Press (USA), Hamish Hamilton, Michael Joseph,
   New American Library (USA), Pelham, Pelican, Puffin, Rainbird, Viking,
   Viking Kestrel, Frederick Warne

**Presses de la Cité**
   Grisewood & Dempsey

**Random Century**
   Bodley Head, Jonathan Cape, Century Hutchinson (Arrow, Barrie & Jenkins,
   Benham Press, Business Books, Century, Cresset Press, Ebury Press, Hutchin-
   son, Muller, Blond & White, Popular Dogs, Radius, Rider & Co., Stanley
   Paul), Chatto & Windus, Hogarth Press

**Really Useful Group**
   Aurum

**Reed International**
   Butterworth (q.v.), Octopus (q.v.)

**Scholastic**
Hippo

**Simon & Schuster**
Philip Allan, Harvester Press, Prentice-Hall (USA), Wheatsheaf Books, Woodhead-Faulkner (incl. Martin Books)

**Sterling Publishing Group**
Debrett

**Thomson**
Chapman & Hall, Gee & Co., Jane's Information Group, Thomas Nelson, Routledge, E. & F. Spon, Sweet & Maxwell, Van Nostrand Reinhold

**Unwin Hyman**
Pandora Press, University Tutorial Press

**Weidenfeld & Nicolson**
Arthur Barker, J. M. Dent

**Wolters Kluwer**
Mary Glasgow, Hulton, Stanley Thornes, Wayland

# Top Hundred Chart of
# 1988 Paperback Fastsellers

## ALEX HAMILTON

The tables of paperback fastsellers on the succeeding pages form part of the tenth annual survey I have compiled for the *Guardian*. At this point it seems interesting to look back over the whole decade, as well as the year under review, and see what movements there may have been.

The immediate perception is that in a decade where so much has changed, even in publishing, the most conservative element seems to be where the big money is spent. I sometimes have the sensation of being like the follower of a professional tennis or golf circus, in which the same small number of stars are repeatedly encountering one another to play off for the big rewards. While every annual list throws up a selection of unknowns who overcome the calculations of the seeding committee, it is quite rare for a name to appear in the top 20 which has not been there before. If any one publishing house could corner the production of, say, Wilbur Smith, Jeffrey Archer, Catherine Cookson, Dick Francis, Len Deighton, John Le Carré, Jackie Collins and James Herbert, there would not be any commercial need for it to publish anyone else. That is a list biased towards authors with British passports—the most successful Americans have been Stephen King, Stephen King's pseudonyms, Sidney Sheldon, Danielle Steel and Virginia Andrews. Apart from the magic mixture that got them on the list in the first place, their other shared quality is their regularity: as reliable as certain birds migrating in the spring, familiar birdcalls are heard in the land, and a faithful readership duly appreciates their arrival.

Throughout the 1980s the fastseller lists have been dominated, in a ratio of four to one, by fiction. (And some of the successful categories of non-fiction, like diet books and astrology and certain examples of autobiography, seem to be as near to fiction as makes no difference.) Although Audrey Eyton's diet book, *The F-Plan*, went from its original 1,400,000 sale in the year of its publication to exceed 2 million, becoming thereby the fifth highest-selling paperback in the UK of the decade, above it are four fiction titles, with Sue Townsend just pipping Jeffrey Archer for the top spot, and incidentally figuring also in third place to his fourth.

For the first eight years of the period the number by women was 25 of the hundred, with only small fractional fluctuations. During the last two years that pattern has broken up—in the accompanying chart there are 44. The number of American imports has declined from 49 to 33.

The importance of a steady production is underlined by a few cumulative sales figures. Pan have 27 Dick Francis titles in print: none has gone any higher than this year's contribution, but the aggregate is now over 11 million, and the backlist this year yielded over half a million. There is the same behaviour on the Jackie Collins' titles: 11 have collected an extra score of 670,000, and her best property, *Hollywood Wives*, added 86,000 to reach 1,478,000, to make an overall Collins sale of 7,250,000.

Grafton recently reissued 29 Deighton titles. Since he joined them he has notched up 6.9 million, Barbara Taylor Bradford 6 million and Robert Ludlum 9.4 million. Jeffrey Archer's seven have all done over a million, for a Coronet total of over 12 million. Wilbur Smith, not for the first time at the head of the chart, has a hardcore buying public of 837,851—at any rate this is the lowest figure for any of his 19 Pan titles. Of these 14 have passed the million, for a grand total of 19,915,000. Corgi have sold 7 million Frederick Forsyths, and over 20 million Catherine Cooksons, and point with satisfaction at the recent development of Jilly Cooper, now on an aggregate of 2,700,000, as a Cookson for the 90s.

Anybody looking closely at the following chart, and thinking of making extrapolations or drawing social inferences, might take note of its design limitations. It is restricted to paperbacks published for the first time within the calendar year, which have achieved by the end of it a sale, nett of returns, in six figures. This last prescription has turned out to be convenient, because throughout the 1980s the number of paperbacks which have sold over 100,000 copies in that period has always been between 102 and 118 (this year it is 115).

The charts are no index of publishing efficiency. To save a lot of work with abacuses, the first ten here sold 6,456,304 copies for a return of £24,279,079, rather more than a quarter the results for the entire 100, which sold 24,401,361 copies for a gross of £90,370,561. Export was down, perhaps reflecting the strength of the pound against the dollar in that period, and the average retail cost per unit has risen in the last three years from £3.07 to £3.76.

| No | Title | Genre | Author | Imprint |
|----|-------|-------|--------|---------|
| 1 | Rage | Thriller | Wilbur Smith (Br) | Pan |
| 2 | The Parson's Daughter | Saga | Catherine Cookson (Br) | Corgi |
| 3 | Windmill Of The Gods | Fiction | Sidney Sheldon (Br) | Fontana |
| 4 | Savages | Adventure | Shirley Conran (Br) | Pan |
| 5 | Garden Of Shadows | Saga | Virginia Andrews (Br) | Fontana |
| 6 | Firefly Summer | Fiction | Maeve Binchy (US) | Coronet |
| 7 | Hot Money | Thriller | Dick Francis (Br) | Pan |
| 8 | Dirk Gently's... Agency | Humour | Douglas Adams (US) | Pan |
| 9 | Destiny | Saga | Sally Beauman (Ire) | Corgi |
| 10 | Sepulchre | Horror | James Herbert (Br) | NEL |
| 11 | Misery | Horror | Stephen King (Br) | NEL |
| 12 | Bill Bailey's Lot | Saga | Catherine Cookson (Br) | Corgi |
| 13 | Winter | Fiction | Len Deighton (Br) | Grafton |
| 14 | Pearls | Fiction | Celia Brayfield (US) | Penguin |
| 15 | Hip & Thigh Diet | Health | Rosemary Conley (Br) | Arrow |
| 16 | Ladies Of Missolonghi | Fiction | Colleen McCullough (Br) | Arrow |
| 17 | Fine Things | Fiction | Danielle Steel (Br) | Sphere |
| 18 | Neighbours: Behind... | Misc. | James Oram (Br) | A & R |
| 19 | Red Storm Rising | Fiction | Tom Clancy (Aus) | Fontana |
| 20 | The Eyes Of The Dragon | Horror | Stephen King (US) | Futura |
| 21 | The Weeping & Laughter | Fiction | Noel Barber (Aus) | Coronet |
| 22 | Winter Hawk | Fiction | Craig Thomas (US) | Fontana |
| 23 | Kaleidoscope | Fiction | Danielle Steel (US) | Sphere |
| 24 | Weaveworld | Fiction | Clive Barker (Br) | Fontana |
| 25 | Superhoroscopes '89 | Astrology | Anon (US) | Arrow |
| 26 | Presumed Innocent | Fiction | Scott Turow (US) | Penguin |
| 27 | Patriot Games | Fiction | Tom Clancy (Br) | Fontana |
| 28 | Glittering Images | Fiction | Susan Howatch (Br) | Fontana |
| 29 | At Close Quarters | Fiction | Gerald Seymour (US) | Fontana |
| 30 | Horoscopes 1989 | Astrology | Anon (US) | Grafton |
| 31 | Wolf Winter | Thriller | Clare Francis (Br) | Pan |
| 32 | The Janus Man | Thriller | Colin Forbes (Br) | Pan |
| 33 | Sarum | Fiction | Edward Rutherford (US) | Arrow |
| 34 | Shan | Fiction | Eric Van Lustbader (Br) | Grafton |
| 35 | Janet | Humour | Smith & Jones (Br) | Fontana |
| 36 | The Fatal Shore | History | Robert Hughes (Br) | Pan |
| 37 | Wildacre | Fiction | Philippa Gregory (US) | Penguin |
| 38 | The Golden Girls | Saga | Elvi Rhodes (Br) | Corgi |
| 39 | Yes Mama | Fiction | Helen Forrester (Aus) | Fontana |
| 40 | Jig | Thriller | Campbell Armstrong (Br) | Coronet |
| 41 | Washington Wives | Fiction | Maureen Dean (Br) | Grafton |
| 42 | Unforgettable Fire: U2 | Music | Eamon Dunphy (Br) | Penguin |
| 43 | Power Play | Romance | Penny Jordan (Br) | Worldwide |
| 44 | The Legacy | Saga | Linda la Plante (US) | Pan |
| 45 | Communion | Misc | Whitley Strieber (Br) | Arrow |
| 46 | Talking To Strange Men | Crime | Ruth Rendell (Br) | Arrow |
| 47 | The Dandelion Seed | Fiction | Lena Kennedy (US) | Futura |
| 48 | Heaven & Hell | Fiction | John Jakes (Br) | Fontana |
| 49 | Voyage | Fiction | Elizabeth Walker (Br) | Headline |
| 50 | The Mother's Daughter | Fiction | Marilyn French (US) | Pan |

| Price | Month | Home | Export | Gross | Product | No |
|---|---|---|---|---|---|---|
| 3.99 | May | 480,173 | 494,623 | 974,796 | £3,889,436 | 1 |
| 3.95 | March | 621,511 | 192,638 | 814,149 | £3,215,888 | 2 |
| 3.50 | Feb | 339,691 | 311,829 | 651,520 | £2,280,320 | 3 |
| 3.99 | July | 418,850 | 209,600 | 628,450 | £2,507,515 | 4 |
| 3.50 | May | 380,083 | 240,827 | 620,910 | £2,173,185 | 5 |
| 4.50 | Oct | 391,205 | 178,472 | 569,677 | £2,563,546 | 6 |
| 3.50 | Dec | 355,110 | 211,934 | 567,044 | £1,984,654 | 7 |
| 2.99 | June | 352,674 | 202,903 | 555,577 | £1,661,175 | 8 |
| 3.95 | April | 387,577 | 154,035 | 541,612 | £2,139,367 | 9 |
| 3.50 | June | 383,665 | 148,904 | 532,569 | £1,863,991 | 10 |
| 3.50 | Nov | 331,488 | 171,364 | 502,852 | £1,759,982 | 11 |
| 2.99 | Oct | 413,951 | 71,676 | 485,627 | £1,452,024 | 12 |
| 3.99 | Nov | 263,176 | 220,275 | 483,451 | £1,928,969 | 13 |
| 3.95 | Nov | 288,891 | 151,070 | 439,961 | £1,737,845 | 14 |
| 2.50 | Jan | 360,878 | 70,241 | 431,119 | £1,077,797 | 15 |
| 2.50 | March | 179,091 | 250,783 | 429,874 | £1,074,685 | 16 |
| 3.50 | July | 338,613 | 43,439 | 382,052 | £1,337,182 | 17 |
| 3.95 | Aug | 320,000 | 47,500 | 367,500 | £1,451,625 | 18 |
| 3.95 | Jan | 201,354 | 158,015 | 359,369 | £1,419,507 | 19 |
| 3.50 | Jan | 225,256 | 112,369 | 337,625 | £1,181,687 | 20 |
| 3.99 | Dec | 191,527 | 125,833 | 317,360 | £1,266,266 | 21 |
| 3.95 | April | 191,207 | 123,389 | 314,596 | £1,242,654 | 22 |
| 3.99 | Dec | 233,914 | 74,442 | 308,356 | £1,230,340 | 23 |
| 3.95 | Aug | 218,115 | 86,203 | 304,318 | £1,202,056 | 24 |
| 2.99 | June | 181,100 | 120,909 | 302,009 | £903,006 | 25 |
| 3.99 | Oct | 199,514 | 99,670 | 299,184 | £1,193,744 | 26 |
| 3.95 | Nov | 165,517 | 132,994 | 298,511 | £1,179,118 | 27 |
| 3.95 | June | 179,331 | 112,720 | 292,051 | £1,153,601 | 28 |
| 3.50 | Oct | 179,771 | 103,698 | 283,469 | £992,141 | 29 |
| 1.99 | Aug | 71,856 | 198,288 | 270,144 | £537,586 | 30 |
| 3.99 | Nov | 150,865 | 106,060 | 256,925 | £1,025,130 | 31 |
| 2.95 | Jan | 149,514 | 97,665 | 247,179 | £729,178 | 32 |
| 3.50 | June | 174,692 | 68,837 | 243,529 | £852,351 | 33 |
| 3.95 | May | 117,707 | 123,649 | 241,356 | £953,356 | 34 |
| 4.50 | Oct | 223,643 | 3,431 | 227,074 | £1,021,833 | 35 |
| 4.99 | April | 81,227 | 140,742 | 221,969 | £1,107,625 | 36 |
| 3.95 | March | 151,932 | 56,560 | 208,492 | £823,543 | 37 |
| 3.95 | Feb | 186,251 | 18,922 | 205,173 | £810,433 | 38 |
| 3.50 | Nov | 175,504 | 28,569 | 204,073 | £714,255 | 39 |
| 3.95 | Aug | 139,691 | 61,389 | 201,080 | £794,266 | 40 |
| 3.50 | July | 117,719 | 83,165 | 200,884 | £703,094 | 41 |
| 3.99 | Nov | 125,392 | 74,649 | 200,041 | £798,163 | 42 |
| 3.50 | Sep | 183,932 | 6,604 | 190,536 | £666,876 | 43 |
| 3.99 | Oct | 92,244 | 97,252 | 189,496 | £756,089 | 44 |
| 3.50 | Feb | 80,457 | 105,925 | 186,382 | £652,337 | 45 |
| 2.99 | Sep | 107,843 | 70,898 | 178,741 | £534,435 | 46 |
| 3.50 | Aug | 171,718 | 6,113 | 177,831 | £622,408 | 47 |
| 4.95 | Dec | 80,544 | 97,246 | 177,790 | £880,060 | 48 |
| 3.50 | Jul | 116,332 | 60,752 | 177,084 | £619,794 | 49 |
| 4.99 | Nov | 96,299 | 74,730 | 171,029 | £853,434 | 50 |

| No | Title | Genre | Author | Imprint |
|----|-------|-------|--------|---------|
| 51 | Sisters | Fiction | **Pat Booth** (US) | Arrow |
| 52 | Hermit Of Eyton Forest | Crime | **Ellis Peters** (US) | Futura |
| 53 | Daughter Of The Empire | Fantasy | **Feist & Wurts** (Br) | Grafton |
| 54 | The Radiant Way | Fiction | **Margaret Drabble** (Br) | Penguin |
| 55 | Silk Vendetta | Romance | **Victoria Holt** (US) | Fontana |
| 56 | Moon Tiger | Fiction | **Penelope Lively** (Br) | Penguin |
| 57 | Green Consumer Guide | Reference | **Various** (Br) | Gollancz |
| 58 | The Dark Tower | Fantasy | **Stephen King** (Br) | Sphere |
| 59 | Dingbats | Misc | **Paul Sellers** (US) | Corgi |
| 60 | Outbreak | Horror | **Robin Cook** (Br) | Pan |
| 61 | Mort | Fantasy | **Terry Pratchett** (US) | Corgi |
| 62 | Humour | Humour | **Jolliffe & Mayle** (Br) | Pan |
| 63 | Seventh Sanctuary | Thriller | **Daniel Easterman** (Br) | Grafton |
| 64 | Watchers | Fiction | **Dean R Koontz** (Br) | Headline |
| 65 | Under Eye Of Clock | Autobiog | **Christopher Nolan** (US) | Pan |
| 66 | Secret For Nightingale | Romance | **Victoria Holt** (Ire) | Fontana |
| 67 | First Lady | Fiction | **Erin Pizzey** (Br) | Fontana |
| 68 | Dreams Are Not Enough | Fiction | **Jacqueline Briskin** (Br) | Corgi |
| 69 | Peace On Earth | Thriller | **Gordon Stevens** (US) | Coronet |
| 70 | The Looney | Fiction | **Spike Milligan** (Br) | Penguin |
| 71 | The Stricken Land | Saga | **E V Thompson** (Br) | Pan |
| 72 | The Past Is Myself | Autobiog | **Christabel Bielenberg** (Br) | Corgi |
| 73 | Are You Lonesome… | Misc | **Barbin & Matera** (Br) | Arrow |
| 74 | Something To Fall… | Humour | **Maureen Lipman** (US) | Futura |
| 75 | Cold New Dawn | Fiction | **Ian St James** (Br) | Fontana |
| 76 | Bros Fact File | Pop | **Bros** (Br) | Fantail |
| 77 | First Born | Fiction | **Doris Mortman** (Br) | Coronet |
| 78 | The Rotation Diet | Health | **Martin Katahn** (US) | Corgi |
| 79 | Shadows On The Snow | Fiction | **Madge Swindells** (US) | Futura |
| 80 | Fatherhood | Autobiog | **Bill Cosby** (SA) | Bantam |
| 81 | Honour This Day | Adventure | **Alexander Kent** (US) | Pan |
| 82 | Fiddler's Ferry | Saga | **Iris Gower** (Br) | Corgi |
| 83 | Prince Of Tides | Fiction | **Pat Conroy** (Br) | Bantam |
| 84 | Daughter Of Northern… | Fiction | **Pamela Haines** (Br) | Fontana |
| 85 | Day Of Creation | Fiction | **J G Ballard** (Br) | Grafton |
| 86 | Not That Sort Of Girl | Fiction | **Mary Wesley** (Br) | Black S |
| 87 | Bastard's…Worst | Humour | **Adrian Edmondson** (Br) | Virgin |
| 88 | Dangerous In Love | Fiction | **Leslie Thomas** (Br) | Penguin |
| 89 | Going Solo | Autobiog | **Roald Dahl** (Br) | Penguin |
| 90 | Over The Edge | Thriller | **Jonathan Kellerman** (US) | Futura |
| 91 | Erin's Child | Romance | **Sheelagh Kelley** (Br) | Arrow |
| 92 | Floyd On Britain… | Cookery | **Keith Floyd** (Br) | BBC Books |
| 93 | League Of Night & Fog | Thriller | **David Morrell** (US) | NEL |
| 94 | Pussy Pie Hits Town | Humour | **Jolliffe & Graham** (Br) | Pan |
| 95 | A Fatal Inversion | Crime | **Barbara Vine** (Br) | Penguin |
| 96 | The Hearts…Of Men | Fiction | **Fay Weldon** (Br) | Fontana |
| 97 | Riches | Fiction | **Una-Mary Parker** (Br) | Headline |
| 98 | All My Worldly Goods | Romance | **Anne Weale** (Br) | Arrow |
| 99 | Stalker | Autobiog | **John Stalker** (Br) | Penguin |
| 100 | Summer Visitors | Saga | **Susan Sallis** (Br) | Corgi |

| Price | Month | Home | Export | Gross | Product | No |
|-------|-------|------|--------|-------|---------|-----|
| 3.50 | April | 64,350 | 101,597 | 165,947 | **£580,814** | 51 |
| 2.99 | July | 149,271 | 16,027 | 165,298 | **£494,241** | 52 |
| 3.99 | Oct | 110,344 | 54,909 | 165,253 | **£659,359** | 53 |
| 3.95 | Oct | 123,759 | 38,483 | 162,242 | **£640,855** | 54 |
| 3.95 | Sep | 91,618 | 68,965 | 160,583 | **£634,302** | 55 |
| 3.99 | Oct | 126,860 | 28,617 | 155,477 | **£620,353** | 56 |
| 4.99 | April | 153,921 | 689 | 154,610 | **£771,503** | 57 |
| 6.99 | Sep | 102,299 | 52,178 | 154,477 | **£1,079,794** | 58 |
| 1.99 | Oct | 152,667 | 223 | 152,890 | **£304,251** | 59 |
| 2.99 | April | 68,733 | 83,484 | 152,217 | **£455,128** | 60 |
| 2.99 | Nov | 127,400 | 24,533 | 151,933 | **£454,279** | 61 |
| 3.99 | Oct | 136,399 | 15,416 | 151,815 | **£605,741** | 62 |
| 3.95 | July | 59,353 | 91,138 | 150,491 | **£594,439** | 63 |
| 3.50 | May | 87,970 | 61,323 | 149,293 | **£522,525** | 64 |
| 2.99 | Oct | 95,816 | 50,755 | 146,571 | **£438,247** | 65 |
| 3.50 | March | 78,699 | 66,905 | 145,604 | **£509,614** | 66 |
| 3.95 | July | 72,218 | 71,798 | 144,016 | **£568,863** | 67 |
| 3.95 | May | 74,055 | 69,431 | 143,486 | **£566,769** | 68 |
| 3.50 | March | 51,220 | 89,158 | 140,378 | **£491,323** | 69 |
| 2.99 | Oct | 125,812 | 12,667 | 138,479 | **£414,052** | 70 |
| 2.99 | Feb | 97,132 | 35,901 | 133,033 | **£397,768** | 71 |
| 3.95 | Nov | 130,443 | 1,936 | 132,379 | **£522,897** | 72 |
| 3.50 | Oct | 45,662 | 85,653 | 131,315 | **£459,602** | 73 |
| 3.50 | Oct | 127,186 | 530 | 127,716 | **£447,006** | 74 |
| 3.95 | July | 66,921 | 60,058 | 126,979 | **£501,567** | 75 |
| 3.99 | Oct | 120,250 | 6,723 | 126,973 | **£506,622** | 76 |
| 3.99 | Nov | 83,952 | 41,742 | 125,694 | **£501,519** | 77 |
| 3.50 | Jan | 94,188 | 31,159 | 125,347 | **£438,714** | 78 |
| 3.50 | March | 99,856 | 25,175 | 125,031 | **£437,608** | 79 |
| 2.50 | March | 72,335 | 50,706 | 123,041 | **£307,602** | 80 |
| 3.50 | July | 85,673 | 35,359 | 121,032 | **£423,612** | 81 |
| 3.50 | June | 110,992 | 9,424 | 120,416 | **£421,456** | 82 |
| 3.95 | April | 70,308 | 49,542 | 119,850 | **£473,407** | 83 |
| 3.95 | Aug | 84,277 | 35,026 | 119,303 | **£471,246** | 84 |
| 2.99 | Sep | 77,153 | 41,747 | 118,900 | **£355,511** | 85 |
| 3.95 | July | 110,558 | 8,150 | 118,708 | **£468,896** | 86 |
| 3.99 | Oct | 103,580 | 14,347 | 117,927 | **£470,528** | 87 |
| 2.99 | Nov | 100,332 | 15,874 | 116,206 | **£347,455** | 88 |
| 3.99 | Nov | 99,311 | 16,097 | 115,408 | **£460,477** | 89 |
| 3.50 | May | 71,207 | 43,800 | 115,007 | **£402,524** | 90 |
| 3.99 | May | 91,282 | 23,188 | 114,470 | **£456,735** | 91 |
| 7.95 | Sep | 110,185 | 3,000 | 113,185 | **£899,820** | 92 |
| 3.99 | Oct | 59,994 | 52,971 | 112,965 | **£450,730** | 93 |
| 3.99 | Nov | 99,287 | 12,861 | 112,148 | **£447,470** | 94 |
| 3.50 | Dec | 75,603 | 36,372 | 111,975 | **£391,912** | 95 |
| 3.95 | Sep | 64,969 | 46,863 | 111,832 | **£441,736** | 96 |
| 3.50 | June | 56,423 | 55,336 | 111,759 | **£391,156** | 97 |
| 3.99 | Sep | 58,115 | 52,730 | 110,845 | **£442,271** | 98 |
| 3.50 | Oct | 98,748 | 11,149 | 109,897 | **£384,639** | 99 |
| 2.95 | May | 98,512 | 10,652 | 109,164 | **£322,033** | 100 |

# Book Packagers

Many modern illustrated books are created by book packagers, whose special skills are in the areas of book design and graphic content. Children's interests and informational how-to are the usual subject areas; such books match up the expertise of specialist writers, artists and photographers, usually freelances, with the craftsmanship of in-house desk editors and art editors.

Packaged books are often expensive to produce, beyond the cost parameters set by traditional publishers for their own markets; the packager recoups the expense by pre-selling titles to publishers in various countries. Thus packaged books are usually international in content and approach, avoiding local interests such as cricket or Cornish cream teas.

The working style in most packagers' offices is more akin to magazine publishing than to traditional book publishing, with creative groups concentrating on the complexities of integrating words and pictures for individual titles rather than merely manuscript editing for a broad publishing list.

The many opportunities for freelance writers, specialist contributors and consultants, photographers and illustrators will usually be short-term and high pressure; packagers rarely spend more than a year on any title. As packaged books are frequently the work of more than one "author" and because of the complications of the overseas rights deals that will be made and the formulae for packager's earnings, which are obviously only a proportion of a book's retail price, flat fees are often suggested rather than royalty agreements. Where royalties are appropriate, they will be based on the packager's receipts, but the expectation is that there will be more foreign language editions than a traditional publisher can achieve.

The Book Packagers Association (secretary: Rosemary Pettit, 147-149 Gloucester Terrace, London W2 6DX) is the forum for the exchange of creative and commercial experience in this branch of the publishing industry. The BPA has devised standard contracts to cover members' relationships with contributors and customers.

*Members of the Book Packagers Association.

**Adkinson Parrish Ltd.** Associate company of **Macdonald & Co. (Publishers) Ltd.**, *q.v.*

**Aladdin Books Ltd.** (1980), 70 Old Compton Street, London W1V 5PA *tel* 01-734 5186 *telex* 21115 Aladin *fax* 01-437 8415. *Directors:* Charles Nicholas, Lynn Lockett. Full design and book packaging facility.

*****Albion Press Ltd.** (1984), P.O. Box 52, Princes Risborough, Aylesbury, Bucks. HP17 9PR *tel* (084 44) 4018 *fax* (084 44) 3358. *Directors:* Emma Bradford, Neil Philip. Quality integrated illustrated titles specialising in literature, social history, fine and graphic arts, cookery, children's books. Supply finished books. Publishers' commissions undertaken.

**Alphabet & Image Ltd** (1972), Alpha House, South Street, Sherborne, Dorset DT9 3LU *tel* (0935) 814944 *fax* (0935) 816717. *Directors:* Anthony Birks-Hay, Leslie Birks-Hay. Complete editorial, picture research, photographic, design and production service for illustrated books on ceramics, beekeeping, horticulture, architecture, history, etc.

*****Amanuensis Books Ltd.** (1986), 12 Station Road, Didcot, Oxfordshire OX11 7LL *tel* (0235) 811066 *telex* 94016837 Aman G *fax* (0235) 510134. *Direc-*

*tors:* Loraine Fergusson, Kit Maunsell, Kim Richardson. High quality, illustrated non-fiction for the international co-edition market; all general subjects, specialising in medical handbooks for the layman. Opportunities for freelances.

**Antler Books Ltd.** (1980), P.O. Box 420, Warminster, Wilts. BA12 9XB *tel* (0985) 40189. *Directors:* John Stidolph, Dr. Susan Abbott. Packaging—production and printing of books and magazines. Picture research, editorial, design services. Supplies film to publishers. Part of **Berkswell Publishing Co. Ltd.**

**\*Beanstalk Books Ltd.** (1983), The Gardens House, Hever Castle Gardens, Nr. Edenbridge, Kent TN8 7ND *tel* (0892) 870912 *telex* 957320 Telexus G *fax* (0732) 863550. *Directors:* Shona McKellar, Penny Kitchenham. Specialists in highly illustrated books for adults and children and novelties; editorial, design and production service.

**\*Belitha Press Ltd.** (1980), 31 Newington Green, London N16 9PU *tel* 01-241 5566 *telex* 8950511 Oneone G ref. 32159001. *Directors:* Martin Pick, Richard Hayes, Rachel Pick (non-executive), Peter West, Peter Osborn, A.C.A. *Associate:* Marilyn Malin. Conception, editing, design and production of finished books, offering authors and illustrators close involvement at each stage. Specialises in high quality international co-editions for children and general books especially on Asia, preferably with potential for television tie-ins. Associated film production Company, Inner Eye Ltd.

**Bison Books Ltd.** (1974), Kimbolton House, 117a Fulham Road, London SW3 6RL *tel* 01-823 9222 *telex* 888014 Bison G *fax* 01-244 7139. *Director:* S. L. Mayer. Non-fiction illustrated titles principally history, military history, weaponry, natural history, transport, travel, sport, art.

**\*BLA Publishing Ltd.** (1981), T.R. House, Christopher Road, East Grinstead, West Sussex RH19 3BT *tel* (0342) 313844 *telex* 94011210 BLAP G *fax* (0342) 410471. *Directors:* Au Bak Ling (Chairman Hong Kong), Martin F. Marix Evans (Editorial), John Turner, Vincent Winter, Au King Kwok (Hong Kong), Au Chun Kwok (Hong Kong), Au Kam Wing (Hong Kong), Au Wai Kwok (Hong Kong). High quality illustrated reference books, particularly science dictionaries and encylopaedia, for the international market.

**David Booth (Publishing) Ltd** (1980), 1-6 Grand Parade, Brighton, East Sussex BN2 2QB *tel* (0273) 609999 *telex* 878942 Dbcroc *fax* (0273) 675095. *Directors:* David Booth (Chairman), Sonia Birch (Managing), Karen Jankel, Michael Bond. International co-edition children's book packager, specialising in novelty-activity. World-wide licence holder of *Paddington Bear* activity books. Board books, picture books, fiction and non-fiction.

**\*Breslich & Foss** (1978), Golden House, 28-31 Great Pulteney Street, London W1R 3DD *tel* 01-734 0706 *telex* 264188 Bresl *fax* 01-494 0854. *Directors:* Paula G. Breslich, K. B. Dunning. Books produced from MS to bound copy stage from in-house ideas. Specialising in the arts, sport, health, crafts, gardening, children's.

**\*Brown Wells and Jacobs Ltd.** (1981), 2 Vermont Road, London SE19 3SR *tel* 01-653 7670 *telex* 21685 Fotogr G *fax* 01-771 1765. *Director:* Graham Brown. Design, editorial, illustration and production of high quality illustrated children's and adult books; especially pop-up/novelty books. Opportunities for freelances.

**\*John Calmann and King Ltd.** (1976), 71 Great Russell Street, London WC1B 3BN *tel* 01-831 6351 *telex* 298246 Owls G *fax* 01-831 8356. *Directors:*

Marianne J. Calmann, Elisabeth Ingles, Laurence King, Paula Iley, Judy Rasmussen. Illustrated books on design, art, history, nature, architecture for international co-editions.

**Cameron Books** (1976), 2A Roman Way, London N7 8XG *tel* 01-609 4019 *telex* 291829 Tlx G *telegraphic address* Cameron London N7. *Directors:* Ian A. Cameron, Jill Hollis. Illustrated non-fiction including architecture, design, fine arts, the decorative arts and crafts, antiques, collecting, natural history, social history, films, food, and other non-fiction. **Edition** (1975). Design, editing, typesetting, production work from concept to finished book for other publishers.

***Philip Clark Ltd** (1981), 53 Calton Avenue, Dulwich Village, London SE21 7DF *tel* 01-693 5605 *telex* 8813433 Marine G *fax* 01-737 7881. *Director:* Philip Clark. Illustrated non-fiction for the international market, including books on wine, travel, natural history, windsurfing and other sports, children's reference and sponsored titles.

**Diagram Visual Information Ltd** (1967), 195 Kentish Town Road, London NW5 8SY *tel* 01-482 3633 *fax* 01-482 4932. *Director:* Bruce Robertson. Research, writing, design and illustration of reference books, supplied as film or manufactured copies. Opportunities for freelances.

***Eddison Sadd Editions Ltd.** (1982), St. Chad's Court, 146B Kings Cross Road, London WC1X 9DH *tel* 01-837 1968 *telex* 929879 ESE G *fax* 01-837 2025. *Directors:* Nicholas J. Eddison, Ian N. Jackson, Ros D. S. Edwards. Illustrated non-fiction books for the international co-edition market.

**Elvendon Press** (1978), The Old Surgery, High Street, Goring-on-Thames, Reading, Berks. RG8 9AW *tel* (0491) 873003 *fax* (0491) 874233. *Directors:* Ray Hurst, Bernice Hurst. Complete packaging service. Popular consumer titles, particularly food-related; magazines, directories and all types of publications for publishers, commercial companies and institutions.

**Equinox (Oxford) Ltd.** (1981), Musterlin House, Jordan Hill Road, Oxford OX2 8DP *tel* (0865) 310665 *telex* 83308 *fax* (0865) 310662. *Directors:* G. J. Riches (Chairman), B. T. Lenthall (Managing), D. M. Halford, J. G. Bateman, L. R. Clarke, D. M. Phillips, C. Sparling. Illustrated reference titles for the international market.

**Sadie Fields Productions Ltd.** (1983), 8 Pembridge Studios, 27A Pembridge Villas, London W11 3EP *tel* 01-221 3355 *telex* 262284 ref. 1255 *fax* 01-229 9651. *Directors:* Sheri Safran, David Fielder. Creates and produces international co-productions of pop-up, novelty and picture and board books for children.

**Graham-Cameron Publishing** (1984), 10 Church Street, Willingham, Cambridge CB4 5HT *tel* (0954) 60444 *fax* (0954) 61353. *Directors:* Mike Graham-Cameron, Helen Graham-Cameron. Books for commercial and industrial companies and institutions; children's books. No unsolicited manuscripts.

**Grisewood & Dempsey Ltd.** (1973), Elsley House, 24-30 Great Titchfield Street, London W1P 7AD *tel* 01-631 0878 *telex* 27725 *fax* 01-323 4694. *Directors:* D. Grisewood, J. M. Bourgois, Librairie Nathan S.A., J. Grisewood, J. M. Olliver, J. C. Richards. *Secretary:* M. Barrett. Packaging. General non-fiction; children's information books.

**Grub Street** (1981), Golden House, 28-31 Great Pulteney Street, London W1R 3DD *tel* 01-437 6114 and 6121 *telex* 931770 Wibu G *fax* 01-494 0887. *Director:* John B. Davies. Adult non-fiction; military, history, cookery, home and leisure, gifts and humour. Opportunities for freelances.

**Hambleside Creative Group** (1976), incorporating **Hambleside Publishers**, 13 Southgate Street, Winchester, Hampshire SO23 9DZ *tel* (0962) 840088 *telex* 477357 Hamble G *fax* (0962) 840144. *Directors:* D. R. Yellop, R. A. Jeffery, R. C. Yale, D. K. Sleap. Graphic art design, editorial and copy preparation, magazine publication, promotional literature, sport.

**Hamilton House Publishing** (1975), 17 Staveley Way, Brixworth Industrial Park, Northampton NN6 9EL *tel* (0604) 881889 *fax* (0604) 880735. *Directors:* Tony Attwood, Philippa Attwood. Mostly secondary school text books; tv and radio tie-ins and business books.

\*****Johnson Editions** (1980), 15 Grafton Square, London SW4 0DQ *tel* 01-622 1720 *fax* 01-720 9114. *Managing Director:* Lorraine Johnson. Practical and art-related books on gardening, cookery, interior design, fashion, architecture.

**Lexus Ltd.** (1980), 181 Pitt Street, Glasgow G2 4DR *tel* 041-221 5266. *Director:* P. M. Terrell. Reference book publishing (especially bilingual dictionaries) as contractor, packager, consultant. Translation.

**Frances Lincoln Ltd.** (1981) Apollo Works, 5 Charlton Kings Road, London NW5 2SB *tel* 01-482-3302 *telex* 21376 *fax* 01-485 0490. *Directors:* Frances Lincoln (Managing), J. S. Nicoll. Illustrated books suitable for international coeditions, art, archaeology, architecture, design, gardening, natural history, childcare, cookery, health, DIY, decorating, photography, computers, children's books.

\*****Market House Books Ltd.** (1981), 2 Market House, Market Square, Aylesbury, Bucks HP20 1TN *tel* (0296) 84911 *fax* (0296) 437073. *Directors:* Dr. Alan Isaacs, Dr. John Daintith, P. C. Sapsed. Compilation of dictionaries and reference books.

\*****Marshall Editions Ltd.** (1977), 170 Piccadilly, London W1V 9DD *tel* 01-629 0079 *telegraphic address* Marsheds, London W1 *telex* 22847 Marsh G *fax* 01-834 0785. *Directors:* Bruce Marshall, John Bigg, Barbara Anderson, Barry Baker. Highly illustrated non-fiction, for the co-edition market, including aviation, business and industry, photography and video, cookery, wines and spirits, crafts and hobbies, DIY, fashion and costume, beauty, gardening, health, military and war, natural history, nautical, science and technical.

**New Leaf Books Ltd.** (1973), BCM, New Leaf, London WC1N 3XX *tel* 01-435 3056 *telex* 261507 ref. 3228. *Directors:* Michael Wright, Susan Wright. Complete creation of illustrated book projects (mainly how-to) from concept to finished product with or without production services. Unsolicited MSS not accepted.

**Oyster Books** (1985), Sparrow Hill Way, Upper Weare, Nr. Axbridge, Somerset BS26 2LA *tel* (0934) 732251 *telex* 445673 Oyster G *fax* (0934) 732514. *Directors:* Jenny Wood, Tim Wood. Development of projects from conception through to CRC, film or finished books, including editorial, design and production service. Specialising in children's books, fiction, non-fiction and educational.

\*****Parke Sutton Limited** (1982), 8 Thorpe Road, Norwich NR1 1RY *tel* (0603) 667021 *fax* (0603) 760521. *Directors:* Ian S. McIntyre (Managing), Cris de Boos (Financial), Geoff Staff (Studio), Simon Scott (Publishing). Packagers of non-fiction books. Also publish newspapers, magazines and reference books for specific organisations. Opportunities for freelances.

\*****Phoebe Phillips Editions** (1977), 6 Berners Mews, London W1P 3DG *tel* 01-637 7933 and 1673 *fax* 01-436 4819 *telex* 912881 Telex G (AHN PPE). *Directors:*

Phoebe Phillips, (US), Tessa Clark. Packagers of international co-editions in all general subjects.

*Playne Books (1987), New Inn Lane, Avening, Tetbury, Glos. GL8 8NB  *tel* 045-383 5155  *fax* (045-383) 5590. *Director:* David Playne. Book packaging and production service. All stages of production undertaken from initial concept (editorial, design and manufacture) to delivery of completed books.

*Mathew Price Ltd (1983), Old Rectory House, Marston Magna, Yeovil, Somerset BA22 8DT  *tel* (0935) 851158  *telex* 46720 Mprice G  *fax* (0935) 851285. *Chairman:* Mathew Price. Illustrated fiction and non-fiction children's books for all ages for the international market.

*Quarto Publishing plc (1976), Quintet Publishing Ltd. (1984), QDOS Design Ltd. (1985), The Old Brewery, 6 Blundell Street, London N7 9BH  *tel* 01-700 6700  *telex* 298844 Quarto G  *telegraphic address* Quartopub  *fax* 01-700 4191. *Directors:* L. F. Orbach, R. J. Morley, M. J. Mousley, J. M. A. Manstead. International co-editions.

Roxby Press Ltd. (1974), 126 Victoria Rise, London SW4 0NW  *tel* 01-720 8872  *telex* 291829 Tlx G  *fax* 01-622 9528. *Directors:* Hugh Elwes (Managing), Lady Francis Seymour (Editorial), Anne Hunt (Foreign Rights Editor). International book packagers.

Sackville Design Group Ltd (1973), Hales Barns, New Street, Stradbroke, Nr. Eye, Suffolk IP21 5JG  *tel* (037 984) 8213  *telex* 97177 Sack G  *fax* (037 984) 797. *Directors:* Al Rockall, Heather Thomas. Highly visual colour illustrated books in field of home and leisure. Includes selling ideas of straight commissions from publishers.

*Savitri Books Ltd. (1983), Southbank House, Suite 106, Black Prince Road, London SE1 7SJ  *tel* 01-587 1590  *telex* 295555  *fax* 01-735 1555. *Director:* Mrinalini S. Srivastava. Packaging, design, production.

Sceptre Books (1982), Time and Life Building, New Bond Street, London W1Y 0AA  *tel* 01-499 4080  *telex* 22557. *Managing Director:* David Owen. Conceive, design, edit and produce finished books; work with publishers on joint ventures.

*Sheldrake Press Ltd (1979), 188 Cavendish Road, London SW12 0DA  *tel* 01-675 1767  *fax* 01-675 7736. *Director:* Simon Rigge. Original illustrated non-fiction; travel, home improvement, cookery, history of technology, music; children's stationery.

Sports Editions Limited (1987), 3 Greenlea Park, Prince George's Road, London SW19 2JD  *tel* 01-640 1116  *telex* 8955022 Asport G  *fax* 01-648 5240. *Directors:* Richard Dewing, Steve Powell. Packagers of sports and leisure books, offering full service of design, production and print.

*Swallow Books (1982), 260 Pentonville Road, London N1 9JY  *tel* 01-278 1483  *fax* 01-278 7277. *Directors:* S. M. Adamson, Michael Edwards, Richard Hayes, Erik Pordes. Illustrated non-fiction: reference, cookery, gardening, lifestyle, craft, art and design, natural history, travel.

*Templar Publishing Co., Pippbrook Mill, London Road, Dorking, Surrey RH4 1JE  *tel* (0306) 76361. *Directors:* Richard Carlisle (Chairman), Richard Whinfrey (Managing), Del Tucker (Publishing), Amanda Wood (Editorial), Co Van Woerkom (Production). Children's picture and illustrated information books; also adult illustrated non-fiction. Most titles aimed at international co-edition market. Established links with major co-publishers in UK, USA, Australia and throughout Europe.

**\*Thames Head,** a Division of **BLA Publishing Ltd,** T.R. House, Christopher Road, East Grinstead, West Sussex RH19 3BT   *tel* (0342) 313844   *telex* 94011210 Blap G   *fax* (0342) 410471. *Sales:* John Turner. Illustrated international co-editions, general non-fiction, militaria, history, travel guides and practical crafts.

**\*Toucan Books Limited** (1985), Albion Courtyard, Greenhills Rents, London EC1M 6BN   *tel* 01-251 3921   *fax* 01-251 1692. *Directors:* Robert Sackville West, Adam Nicolson, John Meek. International co-editions; editorial, design and production services.

**Ventura Publishing Ltd.** 11-13 Young Street, London W8 5EH   *tel* 01-221 6395   *telex* 8953658 Venpub G   *fax* 01-938 3575. *Directors:* R. D. Ellis (Managing), D. Hall. Specialise in production of high quality children's novelty books including the *Spot* books by Eric Hill. Illustrated adult leisure and general interest non-fiction for the international co-edition market.

**\*Victoria House Publishing Ltd.** (1980), Victoria House, 4 North Parade, Bath BA1 1LF   *tel* (0225) 463401   *telex* 449218 Josmor G   *fax* (0225) 460942. *Directors:* David Bailey, William Derraugh, Joanna Verney, Michael J. Morris, William Gaspero. International children's co-editions.

**\*Wordwright** (1987), 2-6 Ellington Place, Ellington Road, London N10 3DG   *tel* 01-992 4477 (general), 01-444 0505 (editorial)   *fax* 01-883 6571. *Directors:* Charles Perkins, Veronica Davis. Full packaging service—research, editorial, design and production. Also assesses and prepares MSS for the US market. Opportunities for freelances.

# *Doing It Yourself*
## Self-publishing in the Nineties
### PETER FINCH

### Why bother?

You've tried all the usual channels and been turned down; your work is uncommercial, specialised, technical; you are concerned with art while everyone else is obsessed with cash; you need a book out quickly; you want to take up small publishing as a hobby; you've heard that publishers make a lot of money out of their authors and you'd like a slice—all reason enough. But be sure you understand what you are doing before you begin.

*But isn't this cheating? It can't be real publishing—where is the critical judgement? Publishing is a respectable activity carried out by firms of specialists. Writers of any ability never get involved.*

But they do. Start self-publishing and you'll be in good historical company: Horace Walpole, Balzac, Walt Whitman, Virginia Woolf, Gertrude Stein, John Galsworthy, Rudyard Kipling, Beatrix Potter, Lord Byron, Thomas Paine, Mark Twain, Upton Sinclair, W. H. Davies, Zane Grey, Ezra Pound, D. H. Lawrence, William Carlos Williams, Alexander Pope, Robbie Burns, James Joyce, Anais Nin and Lawrence Stern. All these at some time in their careers dabbled in doing it themselves. William Blake did nothing else. He even made his own ink, handprinted his pages and got Mrs Blake to sew on the covers.

### But today it's different

Not necessarily. This is not vanity publishing we're talking about although if all you want to do is produce a pamphlet of poems to give away to friends then self-publishing will be the cheapest way. Doing it yourself today can be a valid form of business enterprise. Look at the huge success last year of the late Aeron Clement with his story of badgers, *The Cold Moons*: 8000 self-produced hardbacks sold in 3 months and then brought out as a best-selling paperback by Penguin. Clement self-published with the help of his local publican from Llandeilo in West Wales—hardly a base from which to take the book world by storm but this is just what he did.

### Can anyone do it?

Certainly. If you are a writer then a fair number of the required qualities will already be in hand. If, in addition, you can put up a shelf then the manufacture of the book to go on it will not be beyond you. The more able and practical you are then the cheaper the process will be. The utterly inept will need to pay others to help them, but it will still be self-publishing in the end.

### Where do I start?

With research. Read up on the subject. Make sure you know what the parts of a book are. Terms like *verso*, *recto*, *prelims*, *dummy*, *typeface* and *point size* all have to lose their mystery. You will not need to become an expert but you will need a certain familiarity. Don't rush. Learn.

*What about ISBN numbers?*

International Standard Book Numbers—a standard bibliographic code, individual to each book published, are used by booksellers and librarians alike. They are issued free of charge by the Standard Book Numbering Agency, 12 Dyott Street, London WC1A 1DF. Write giving the basic details of your proposed book and, if appropriate, you will receive an ISBN by return.

*Next?*

Put your book together—be it the typed pages of your novel, your selected poems or your nature notes and drawings—and see how large a volume it will make. Follow the details on preparation of typescript given elsewhere in this yearbook. No real idea of what your book should look like? Anything will not do. Go to your local bookshop and hunt out a few contemporary examples of volumes produced in a style you would like to emulate. Ask the manager for advice. Take your typescript and your examples round to a number of local printers (find these through *Yellow Pages*) and ask for a quote. This costs nothing and will give you an idea of what the enterprise is likely to involve.

*How much?*

It depends. How long is a piece of string? You will not get a pamphlet of poems out for less than a few hundred pounds while a hardbacked work of prose will come in well above £2000. Unit cost is important. The larger the number of copies you have printed the less each will cost. Print too many and the total bill will be enormous. Books are not cheap, certainly not in the quantities an individual can handle.

*Can I make it cost less?*

Yes. Do some of the work yourself. If it's poems and you are prepared to manage with text set on a typewriter then that can make a considerable saving. Could you accept home production and run the pages off on a borrowed duplicator? Or staple together sheets produced on an office photocopier? Text prepared on a word processor with a daisy-wheel printer can be very presentable. Home binding, if your abilities lie in that direction, can save a fair bit. What it all comes down to is the standard of production you want and indeed at whom your book is aimed. Books for the commercial market place need to look like their fellows, specialist publications can afford to be more eccentric.

*Who decides how it looks?*

You do. No one should ever ask a printer simply to produce a book. You should plan the design of your publication with as much care as you would a house extension. Books which sell are those which stand out in the bookshop. Spend as much time and money as you can on the cover. It is the part of the book your buyer will see first. Look at the volumes in bookshop displays especially those in the window. Imitate British paperback design, it's the best in the world.

*How many copies should I produce?*

Small press poetry pamphlets sell about 300 copies, new novels sometimes manage 2000, literary paperbacks 10,000, mass-market blockbusters over a million. But that is generally where there is a sales team and whole distribution organisation behind the book. You are an individual. You must do all yourself. Do not on the one hand end up with a prohibitively high unit cost by ordering too few copies. One hundred of anything is usually a waste of time. On the other hand can you really sell 3000? Will shops buy in dozens? They will probably only want twos and threes. Take care. Research your market first.

*How do I sell it?*

With all your might. This is perhaps the hardest part of publishing. It is certainly as time consuming as both the writing of the work and the printing of it put together. To succeed here you need a certain flair and you should definitely not be of a retiring nature. If you intend selling through the trade (and even if you don't you are bound to come into contact with bookshop orders at some stage) your costing must be correct and *worked out in advance*. Shops will want at least 33% of the selling price as discount. You'll need about the same again to cover your distribution, promotion and other overheads leaving the final third to cover production costs and any profit you may wish to make. Take your unit production cost and multiply by at least 4. Commerical publishers often multiply by as much as 9.

Do not expect the trade to pay your carriage costs. Your terms should be 33% post free on everything bar single copy orders. Penalise these by reducing your discount to 25%. Some shops will suggest that you sell copies to them on *sale or return*. This means that they only pay you for what they sell and then only after they've sold it. This is a common practice with certain categories of publications and often the only way to get independent books into certain shops; but from the self-publisher's point of view it should be avoided if at all possible. Cash in hand is best but expect to have your invoices paid by cheque at a later date. Buy a duplicate pad in order to keep track of what's going on. Phone the shops you have decided should take your book or turn up in person and ask to see the buyer. Letters and sample copies sent by post will get ignored. Get a freelance distributor to handle all of this for you if you can. Check the trade section of Cassell's *Directory of Publishing* or advertise for one in *The Bookseller*. They will want another 12% or so commission on top of the shops' discount—but expect to have to go it alone.

*What about promotion?*

A vital aspect often overlooked by beginners. Send out as many review copies as you can, all accompanied by slips quoting selling price and name and address of the publisher. Never admit to being that person yourself. Invent a name, it will give your operation a professional feel. Ring up newspapers and local radio stations ostensibly to check that your copy has arrived but really to see if they are prepared to give your book space. Try to think of an angle for them, anything around which they can write a story. Buying advertising space rarely pays for itself but good local promotion with 100% effort will generate dividends.

*And what if it goes wrong?*

Put all the unsolds under the bed or give them away. It has happened to lots of us. Even the big companies who are experienced at these things have their regular flops. It was an adventure and you did get your book published. On the other hand you may be so successful that you'll be at the London Book Fair selling the film rights and wondering if you've reprinted enough. Whichever way it goes— good luck.

*Where to learn more:*

Peter Finch, *How To Publish Yourself*, Allison and Busby, 1988.
Harry Mulholland, *Guide to Self Publishing*, Mulholland Wirral, 1984.
Ian Templeton, *Publish it Yourself and Make it Pay*, Pikers Pad, 1985.
Roy Lewis and John B. Easson, *Publishing and Printing at Home*, David and Charles, 1984.

# Vanity Publishing

A reputable publisher very rarely asks an author to pay for the production of his work, or to contribute to its cost, or to undertake to purchase copies. The only exception is in the case of a book of an extremely specialised nature, with a very limited market or perhaps the first book of poems by a new writer of some talent. In such instances, especially if the book is a good one making a contribution to its subject, an established and reliable publisher will be prepared to accept a subvention from the author to make publication possible, and such financial grants often come from scientific or other academic foundations or funds. This is a very different procedure from that of the *vanity publisher* who claims to perform, for a fee to be paid by the author, all the many functions involved in publishing a book.

In his efforts to secure business the vanity publisher will usually give exaggerated praise to an author's work and arouse equally unrealistic hopes of its commercial success. The distressing reports we have received from embittered victims of vanity publishers underline the importance of reading extremely carefully the contracts offered by such publishers. Often these will provide for the printing of, say, two thousand copies of the book, usually at a quite exorbitant cost to the author, but will leave the 'publisher' under no obligation to bind more than a very limited number. Frequently, too, the author will be expected to pay the cost of any effective advertising, while the 'publisher' makes little or no effort to promote the distribution and sale of his book. Again, the names and imprints of vanity publishers are well known to literary editors, and their productions therefore are rarely, if ever, reviewed or even noticed in any important periodical. Similarly, such books are hardly ever stocked by the booksellers.

*We repeat, therefore: except in rare instances, never pay for publication, whether for a book, an article, a lyric, or a piece of music.* If a work is worth publishing, sooner or later a publisher will be prepared to publish it at his own expense. But if a writer cannot resist the temptation of seeing his work in print, in book form, he should consider the possibility of self-publishing. If, after all, he decides to approach a vanity publisher, even though he has to pay a substantial sum, he should first discover just how much or how little the publisher will provide and will do in return for the payment he demands.

See also the **Agents** section for literary agents.

# Poetry

## Poetry Publishing Today

PETER FORBES
*Editor, Poetry Review*

and

JONATHAN BARKER
*Literature Officer, The British Council*

Poets have many advantages over other would-be writers when it comes to getting into print. Aspiring novelists may have several MSS in the drawer and absolutely nothing in the way of publication to justify calling themselves a writer, but poets can enter the fray relatively painlessly, a poem at a time, and success, grand or modest, is possible for many hundreds of them. What's more, there is an established system for attaining a reputation as a poet, although many who enter the lists are unaware of it. Even readers of this *Yearbook* sometimes seem to throw all caution and wise counsel to the winds, when submitting work, as if the advice given here applied to everyone except themselves. The first rule is that there are no shortcuts, and yes, *this does apply to you.*

So, what is this system? The first thing to bear in mind are those hundreds of poets already mentioned enjoying modest success. This means poems in the recognised poetry magazines, followed by volume publication by a major poetry publisher. But, unless you are already involved in the poetry world, you're unlikely to be able to name more than a handful of living poets, especially younger ones. And for every poet achieving that coveted first volume there are dozens with plausible track records knocking on the door. In other words, the fame and fortune accruing to poets, in an increasingly publicity-conscious age, is strictly limited. Many begin sending out their work with totally unreal expectations. Only the likes of Tony Harrison, Seamus Heaney and Ted Hughes achieve anything like the glamour associated with writers of fiction and biography. On the other hand, only those who are not in the end cut out to be poets will fail to understand the true rewards of writing and publishing poetry—most poetic reputations are extremely hard won and deserved.

So where do you start? Most budding poets are afflicted by excessive self-consciousness and anxiety concerning questions of protocol, copyright and the like. This article will answer those questions; but the first rule is to realise that submitting poetry is a very down-to-earth business—there is no magic formula, and personal revelations will not help the cause of your work. The first question to ask, before the envelope is sealed, is should I really be sending my work out

248

at all? If, in answer to the question, how many current poetry books have you read in recent years? the answer is, none, almost certainly the postage would be better saved and spent on those unread volumes. Anybody writing poetry needs to have read some representative poetry of the time, and very many really gifted poets begin by imitating some master. The place to start is in the anthologies. Some worth looking at are: Blake Morrison and Andrew Motion's *Penguin Book of Contemporary British Poetry* (Penguin, 1982), Edward Lucie Smith's *British Poetry Since 1945*, 2nd revised edition (Penguin, 1985), David Constantine's *Poetry Book Society Anthology 1988–1989* (Hutchinson, 1988) and Christopher Reid's *Poetry Book Society Anthology 1989–1990* (Hutchinson, 1989). The poetry magazines listed below will give a good flavour of contemporary verse, together with reviews of the new collections. Like any other subject, the more you know, the easier it is to learn more.

So, you have read a good deal of contemporary verse—what next? Ideally you should do two things. You should subscribe and submit to a few magazines that publish the kind of poetry you feel sympathetic to, and you should join a poetry group or workshop.

## MAGAZINES

There are two main kinds of magazine outlet for poetry: general literary magazines which print some poems, and specialist poetry magazines: the little magazines. The first category is of little interest to the beginner, normally printing work by experienced poets, even if not yet published in book form. The little magazines are the place to start. But which one? There are literally hundreds of little poetry magazines—almost all are run as part-time activities by one or two dedicated people. A few have Arts Council Grants, a track record, and a reasonable expectation of survival long enough to print your poem when accepted. As you might expect, these are rather freer with rejection slips than with acceptances. Emerging poets usually get to know the little magazine scene well. There are always newish magazines coming along which have a livelier profile and a greater openness to new contributors; established magazines sometimes gain a new editor with a vigorous policy. It helps to know all this, but only experience will teach it. A common error among beginner poets is to assume that it must be easy to publish in the less-well-known magazines. It is always difficult to gain acceptance anywhere, and that first acceptance is a significant step. To impress just one person, who's read your work cold amongst the work of dozens of other people's, is a real feat.

Most poetry magazines have circulations of less than a thousand, but the big little magazines—*London Magazine*, *PN Review*, *Poetry Review*, *Stand*—have considerably more—up to 4500 (*London Magazine*, *PN Review* and *Stand* also feature other kinds of writing but their reputation as poetry magazines is high). Newish poetry magazines of considerable liveliness and promise include *Acumen*, *Prospice*, *The Rialto* and *Verse*. Certain magazines have a particular character: *Ambit* has always featured a blend of sci-fi, street-cred and quality illustrations; *Agenda* is—among other things—one of the few outlets for translations from pre-twentieth-century poetry; *Poetry World* is devoted to contemporary translation; and so on. A few magazines have traditionally been popular with new poets: *Outposts*, run for over 40 years until his death by Howard Sergeant, and now edited by Roland John; *Orbis*; *Poetry Wales* (for which you don't have to be Welsh but it helps). Although *Poetry Review*, as the Poetry Society's magazine, is the highest circulation strictly poetry magazine and one of the most prestigious, it is extremely hospitable to new writers.

Payment in the little magazines is unlikely to be more than £15 and could be no more than a free copy of the magazine. The other magazines which publish some poetry can be more rewarding; it must be said, however, that all is not well with this sector. Once upon a time magazines like *Encounter*, *The Listener*, *New Statesman*, *The Times Literary Supplement* were *the* places in which to make a poetic reputation, but although they all still publish poems there has been a decline. *New Statesman & Society* and *The Listener* publish far fewer poems than before, which means that poetry readers no longer expect to find poems there. Other than *The Observer*, which does occasionally print new work, the quality newspapers normally only print poems from books under review. Another literary magazine outlet, *The Literary Review*, now publishes little serious poetry. *The Spectator* nowadays prints more poems than it did and *Encounter* remains a good outlet, but overall it is not an encouraging picture.

It must be stressed that anyone seriously hoping to appear in the poetry magazines should, in principle, subscribe to at least two or three. The magazines are the lifeblood of poetry and all have great difficulty in making ends meet. Their habitual postbags contain dozens of submissions for every single new subscription, and editors learn to love the small envelope and fear the large one: the smallest envelopes almost always contain subscriptions or at least enquiries, and 'the larger the envelope the worse the submission' is a kind of Murphy's Law of poetry editing—which brings us to the mechanics of submission.

## *How to submit poems to magazines*

1. Your poems must be typed, preferably on A4 and only one poem to the page. Your name and address should appear on each poem.
2. Send no more than six poems at a time. Never send a book-length collection unless a large batch is requested by the editor.
3. Always send an adequate stamped addressed envelope. Adequate means two things: it should be neither too small nor too large an envelope and the postage should be correct. If only six poems are sent the postage will be the standard rate. Too large or small envelopes make life miserable for the editor. Handling the sheer bulk of mail is always a problem. *Poetry Review* receives about 5000 submissions, or more than 30,000 poems a year. Trying to stuff too many poems into tiny envelopes is not conducive to a judicial editorial frame of mind. On the other hand, it is wrong to put A4 typescript into a large envelope with card stiffening and DO NOT BEND written on it, or to insert poems into bulky ring binders or plastic wallets. Typescript is not precious artwork—it can and will be bent. So, *fold* your poems once and put them in an envelope abut 10″ × 7″, with a similar self-addressed and stamped envelope folded inside. Submissions from outside the UK or submissions to foreign magazines must include return postage—either adequate postage stamps of the relevant country or International Reply Coupons, obtainable from post offices. It is helpful when sending poems abroad to specify that the poems needn't be returned—postage can then be kept to the minimum necessary for a letter in reply. Editors are not obliged to return work without return postage and most simply cannot afford to. So sending a submission without an sae is a complete waste of time.
4. Do not write to editors asking for free sample copies. Buy one. Send a cheque. If you don't know the price, send the magazine a note, including sae, asking for details.
5. Given the size of the postbag and the fact that most poetry magazines are quarterly or less frequent, don't expect (though you may sometimes get) a quick response. And don't pester the editor—who has a magazine to produce—by phoning. If after two months you haven't heard, it's a good idea to send a

reminder. Unfortunately, decisions sometimes take even longer than this. If you feel you must try your poems elsewhere, simply write to the editor withdrawing the poems. They are then free and he has no rights over them, whether he replies or not.

6. Always keep copies of your poems. Editors generally accept no responsibility for unsolicited material. It is your responsibility to make sure your work is not lost.

7. Don't use special pleading in your covering letter. If you have published before, in any reputable outlet, it is worth telling the editor, otherwise the covering letter is a mere formality, offering the poems for publication. If and when an editor accepts work he will usually then want to know a bit about you—not before.

8. Don't ask the editor for advice, however politely. If he or she is seriously interested advice may well be tendered freely, but the editor is not there as a counsellor but to produce the best magazine possible. The Poetry Society (21 Earls Court Square, London SW5 9DE) runs a Criticial Service specifically to provide what the editor cannot. It costs money of course, as it should, since providing a critique is a time-consuming business.

*Markets—poetry magazines*

Full details of those magazines marked with an asterisk can be found in earlier sections of the *Yearbook*. The Poetry Library publishes a regularly updated list of poetry magazines—write, sending a large sae, to The Poetry Library, South Bank Centre, Royal Festival Hall, London SE1 8XX. A fuller list of poetry magazines appears in *Small Presses and Little Magazines of the UK and Ireland*, 7th edition, £1.80 inc. p&p from Oriel Bookshop, The Friary, Cardiff CF1 4AA.

| | |
|---|---|
| *Acumen | Oxford Poetry |
| *Agenda | Pennine Platform |
| *Ambit | *Poetry Durham |
| Aquarius | *Poetry Ireland Review (Ire) |
| *Argo | *PN Review |
| Bête Noire | *Poetry Nottingham |
| *Chapman | *Poetry Review |
| Creative Language | *Poetry Wales |
| *Cyphers (Ire) | *Prospice |
| The Echo Room | *The Rialto |
| *Envoi | *The Salmon (Ire) |
| *Honest Ulsterman (Ire) | Sheaf |
| *Iron | *Slow Dancer |
| Joe Soap's Canoe | Smoke |
| *Krino (Ire) | Spokes |
| Label | *Stand Magazine |
| Lines Review | Staple |
| *Margin | *Stride |
| New Departures | Temenos |
| *Ninth Decade | Tracks (Ire) |
| *Numbers | *Verse |
| Ore | Westwords |
| *Orbis | Weyfarers |
| *Other Poetry | The Wide Skirt |
| *Outposts | Writing Women |

*Markets—literary magazines, weeklies and others which publish poetry*

| | |
|---|---|
| Artrage | London Review of Books |
| Country Life | New Statesman & Society |
| The Countryman | The New Welsh Review |
| Critical Quarterly | The Observer |
| Encounter | Planet |
| The Green Book | The Spectator |
| Kunapipi | The Times Literary Supplement |
| The Listener | WASAFIRI: Caribbean, African |
| The Literary Review | Asian and associated literatures |

## BOOK PUBLICATION

Submitting a collection of poems to a book publisher should not be considered lightly. If at least half of the poems have been published in magazines listed in this *Yearbook* and/or you've won a few prizes, you should definitely consider it. A collection is usually 40–50 poems (the standard length of a poetry collection is 64 pages). In submitting a collection, you must keep a copy of the MS, send return postage, and be prepared to wait—six months is not unusual.

### Major trade publishers

These are the household names everyone dreams of being published by. In recent years, though, many have removed themselves from the poetry market completely, leaving a few who maintain active lists and who do occasionally take on new poets. These are Faber & Faber, Chatto & Windus, Oxford University Press (hereafter OUP), Century Hutchinson, Secker & Warburg, Penguin/Viking. A few other publishers have the occasional star poet: Deutsch with Geoffrey Hill, Macmillan with Charles Causley and R. S. Thomas, Collins Harvill with Roy Fuller, and there is usually a recognised publisher dipping a toe in the market. Paladin have recently produced several books of avant garde poetry, and look as if they mean business. But most of these are unlikely to take on a new poet—and of the big six, Penguin specialise in selected poems by poets like U. A. Fanthorpe, James Fenton, Tony Harrison, Geoffrey Hill and Jeremy Reed, who have already made considerable reputations with other publishers. So, only Faber, Secker, OUP, Chatto and Century Hutchinson are seriously in the market for new poets. It is sobering to see how few new poets they have taken on in recent years. Faber's last young signing was Oliver Reynolds back in 1985; in the same period Chatto have taken on Selima Hill, Fred D'Aguiar, Alan Jenkins, Mick Imlah and Lachlan Mackinnon. OUP have Carole Satyamurti and Michael Donaghy (both prizewinners in the National Poetry Competition), and Secker, who are building a new list, have Adam Thorpe (another National Poetry Competition prizewinner), James Lasdun and Simon Lapington, all with recent first collections. It is also worth remembering that most of the poets signed to major publishers have already published books by other publishers. Poets are poached and some are dropped. The newcomer is thus in competition with established names.

In recent years, there has been an increasing tendency for the major publishers to favour poets who have won one of the major competitions, especially The Poetry Society's National Poetry Competition or the biennial Arvon Foundation International Competition. Faber have a series called *Poetry Introduction* in which about six poets are given anthology space and the Faber imprint as a way of floating them in the big pool. One or two usually eventually achieve full Faber publication. This practice has now been taken up by Chatto and, amongst the specialist presses, by Peterloo, and is a welcome innovation. Another important source of early recognition for poets are the annual Eric Gregory Awards run by the Society of Authors (see **Literary prizes and awards**). These are cash awards, made to promising poets under 30 years of age, on the basis of merit and circumstances. An anthology of the winners is usually produced, about every two years, but the Award is prestigious enough to carry weight without such publication.

## Specialist poetry presses

There have always been small poetry presses, but as the trade publishers were drawing in their poetic horns in the 1970s, some of the subsidised small presses began to take on a new dimension. A few of these now constitute the main outlet for poetry book publication, and match the majors in attractive production, prestige, and often in marketing flair. Bloodaxe Books, in particular, based in Newcastle, has become legendary for a very full and imaginative publishing programme, including many new poets. In 1989 first full volumes were scheduled by Marion Lomax, Maura Dooley, Pauline Stainer, George Charlton, Deborah Randall and Jo Shapcott.

The big league comprises Bloodaxe, Carcanet, Peterloo, Anvil, Seren (imprint of Poetry Wales Press), and the rapidly growing Enitharmon and Littlewood. All of these are more prolific than the majors. In 1989 Peterloo published its 100th volume, and has a reputation for publishing late-starters, although it is equally hospitable to the young poet. Peterloo poets have sometimes gone on to other major publishers—Peter Scupham to OUP, Philip Gross to Faber, Sylvia Kantaris to Secker, then Bloodaxe, and this one press has had a considerable impact on poetry in the last ten years. Anvil and Carcanet are both committed to poetry in translation but have published a substantial number of poets for the first time, some to considerable acclaim, such as Carol Ann Duffy and Dick Davis (Anvil) and Alison Brackenbury, Sujata Bhatt and Vikram Seth (Carcanet). Enitharmon is an old name under new ownership in the last two years. Based in Hampshire it has a southern England flavour but is in no way a regional press. Rivelin Grapheme, in Hungerford, is a mainstream regionally located press. Littlewood is decidedly northern in character but definitely of national standing.

Some of these publishers are represented by the Password Distribution Service, whose catalogue (free on receipt of an A4 sae from Password Books, 23 New Mount Street, Manchester M4 4DE) is a good introduction to the range of work currently being produced.

In Scotland, Canongate, Mainstream and Polygon maintain small poetry lists, southern Ireland has Dedalus, Gallery and Raven Arts, and northern Ireland, Blackstaff.

All of the presses mentioned so far are mainstream publishers. There are presses dedicated to more specialised tendencies—what used to be called the 'underground'. Pig Press in Durham and Allardyce Barnett in Sussex are devoted to modernist and avant garde poetry. In addition, there are numerous small presses working in this area which belong to the Association of Little Presses: they produce a catalogue, including names and addresses of publishers (available at £2.00 plus p&p from the Association of Little Presses, 89a Petherton Road, London N5 2QT). More information on small presses is available in *Small Presses and Little Magazines of the UK and Ireland* (address given earlier) and the *Small Press Yearbook 1989* (available at £5.99 plus p&p from Small Press Group of Britain, BM BOZO, London WC1N 3XX).

Black British poets increasingly appear in the mainstream lists but presses devoted to their work include Dangaroo, Lokamaya, Bogle L'Overture and Race Today. Several bookshops in London and elsewhere specialise in Black writing, including poetry, and a visit to one is well worthwhile. The Poetry Library produces a list of bookshops specialising in Black writing in London.

Of the feminist presses, Virago has the largest poetry list, although it is a very small part of their output. Women's Press and Onlywomen Press publish some poetry, as do the Gay Men's Press.

## VANITY PUBLISHING

Attention is drawn to the separate article on vanity publishing. There are many publishers who will offer to publish your poetry for a fee. This is not a last resort but no resort at all. If a reputable publisher will not accept your work, or if you are not content with magazine publication, there are two real options: one is to abandon ambitions of volume publication; the other is self-publication. The latter is expensive and usually fruitless (magazines almost never review such books), but at least does not carry the stigma that attaches to vanity publication.

## COPYRIGHT

The copyright act defines a poem, be it four or 400 lines long, as a complete work. It is therefore not permitted to photocopy poems published in books and periodicals without permission until 50 years after the death of the author when the work comes out of copyright.

In Britain all works are protected by copyright as soon as written. The person who creates a work is the prime owner of 'intellectual property'. There is no actual need to put the copyright symbol © on each poem you send out to a magazine, although, for practical reasons, it is advisable to put your name and address on each poem you send to a magazine editor for consideration. Each and every poem you write is automatically protected by copyright and you as the author have the right to be identified as the author, and to choose where it should be published *if* an editor wants to publish it. You can retain the serial rights of a poem published in a magazine and submit it elsewhere if you choose so long as you include a note of where it has appeared previously. But, that said, you will find that magazine editors will not generally be interested in publishing work which has already appeared in other magazines, and you must never submit work to more than one outlet at a time.

## GROUPS AND WORKSHOPS

Poetry workshops are inevitably less formal than printed outlets: they are as varied as the people who run them. Some have quasi-official status, being run by writers in residence attached to Regional Arts Associations, colleges, libraries, or local authority evening classes or arts departments. Others are loose groupings of individuals who meet in their own homes. Some have impressive records of success in terms of members getting into print.

A good workshop will provide what the hard-pressed editor cannot: detailed comment on work-in-progress with the aim of better realising the writer's intentions. Of course, in such a situation personalities intrude and not all advice may be well meant, but a real workshop, and there are many, will sharpen up a developing poet's style quicker than anything else. A workshop also comprises an invaluable swap shop of knowledge about the magazines. It is common for a rash of poems from one workshop to appear in a magazine after an initial success by a member. And if members sometimes attend the best workshop of all, those of the Arvon Foundation (see later), a link is made to the big 'real' world of poetry.

Local poetry workshops vary in standard, but you should certainly try to make contact if there is one near to you. Unfortunately there is no complete register, and provision varies widely. The places to look are: your local Regional Arts

Association (see **Societies** for addresses) (but they may well not know of all in your area), local arts centre and library; sometimes the local press will carry an article about a new workshop starting up. A list for London is produced by the Poetry Library—write, sending a large sae,to the address given earlier. If there is a magazine based in your region, you could, as a last resort, write to the editor, but as with all such requests, you must send an sae. If you're keen and there is one, you'll find it.

## COMPETITIONS

As already mentioned, publishers are increasingly impressed by competition success. Entering competitions and submitting to magazines are complementary activities. Both have strengths and weaknesses. To win a major competition clearly makes a bigger splash than publication in the most prestigious magazine, but one of the smaller prizes is probably worth less than a good magazine appearance. There are dozens of competitions, but two dominate the field: The Poetry Society's annual National Poetry Competition and the biennial Arvon Foundation International Poetry Competition; plus The Observer National Children's Poetry Competition.

1. The National Poetry Competition.
This annual competition, founded by The Poetry Society in 1978, is for previously unpublished poems written in English. Entries are accepted from the United Kingdom, the Channel Islands and Ireland. First prize is usually £2000 and there are other cash prizes. An annual anthology is produced of the winners. Full details on entry fee, etc. from The National Poetry Competition, The Poetry Society, 21 Earls Court Square, London SW5 9DE.

2. The Arvon Foundation International Poetry Competition.
This competition, founded in 1980, is awarded biennially for previously unpublished poems written in English. Entries are accepted from Great Britain and abroad. The next competition is scheduled for 1991. First prize is £5000 plus other cash prizes. An anthology is produced of the winners. Full details on entry fee, etc. from Arvon Foundation Poetry Competition, Kilnhurst, Kilnhurst Road, Todmorden, Lancashire OL14 6AX.

3. The Observer National Children's Poetry Competition.
This is Britain's biggest annual competition for poetry by young people, with prizes for both individuals and for school entries. Winners appear in *The Observer Magazine* and in a separate anthology. Full details from National Children's Poetry Competition, The Observer Magazine, Chelsea Bridge House, Queenstown Road, London SW8 4NN.

There's a clutch of substantial competitions: the TLS/Cheltenham Festival competition, the Peterloo, Leek, Bridport, Rhyme International: each year brings a new crop. Competitions always charge an entry fee and should always offer prizes to the winners.

For a regularly updated list of the main poetry competitions, send an A4 sae to the Poetry Library, South Bank Centre, Royal Festival Hall, London SE1 8XX.

## AWARDS AND PRIZES

See **Literary prizes and awards** section, or there is a complete list in the *Guide to literary prizes, grants and awards in Britain and Ireland* compiled by Book Trust and the Society of Authors, 5th edition 1988, £3.25 inc. p&p. Consult this in central reference libraries or order from Book Trust, 45 East Hill, Wandsworth, London SW18 2QZ.

LITERARY FESTIVALS

Your local Regional Arts Association (see **Societies** for addresses) will be able to let you know if there is an annual literature festival in your area. If there is one it may well include events connected with poetry. These festivals are a good way of getting to hear other writers read from and talk about their work. They often have bookshops with a selection of curent literary publications, too.

# Organisations and Educational Information

## ARVON FOUNDATION

Everyone who has been involved in writing for any length of time should eventually seriously consider attending one of the Arvon Foundation's creative writing courses. These are residential, last for five days, and the course fee includes all accommodation, food and tuition. The tutors are themselves writers, and students benefit both from their guidance, and—just as important—from discussion with other students. There are two separate centres running five day residential courses, from whom annual details of courses are available:

The Arvon Foundation at Totleigh Barton, Sheepwash, Beaworthy, Devon EX21 5NS

The Arvon Foundation at Lumb Bank, Hebden Bridge, West Yorkshire HX7 6DF.

The Arvon Foundation also organise a major international poetry competition every two years (*see* Competitions).

## EDUCATION

*Children's poetry*

1. Some courses organised by the Arvon Foundation are intended for younger writers (*see* Arvon Foundation).
2. Each year *The Observer* newspaper organises the National Children's Poetry Competition. The Schools' Poetry Association, under the directorship of David Orme, each year organises the Young Poet of the Year Award (see **Literary prizes and awards** section).

*Poetry in the classroom*

1. **Poems on the Underground** produce poems by known poets for display on the London Underground. These make excellent and relatively inexpensive display material in classrooms. Distribution is now handled by The Poetry Society. For more information write enclosing an sae to: Education Department, The Poetry Society, 21 Earls Court Square, London SW5 9DE.
2. The **Poetry Library** at the South Bank Centre in London now houses the Signal Collection—the most comprehensive and accessible collection of modern poetry for children. For more information on this and other South Bank Centre services for children and teachers, including events in the Centre's main programme, write to The Librarian, Poetry Library, South Bank Centre, Royal Festival Hall, London SE1 8XX.
3. The **Poetry Society** at the National Poetry Centre offers a range of activities and services for children and teachers, including *Stanza*, a termtime newsletter for teacher members of the Society. They also administer the W. H. Smith Poets

in Schools Scheme. Write for full information to the Education Department, at address given above.

4. The **Schools' Poetry Association** produces poetry posters for use in the classroom and *Schools' Poetry Review*, recently renamed *Creative Language*, a magazine aimed at helping teachers of English in schools liven up the teaching of contemporary poetry. Write for information with sae to The Schools' Poetry Association, 27 Pennington Close, Colden Common, near Winchester, Hants SO21 1UR.

5. Jill Bennett and Aidan Chambers' *Poetry for Children: A Signal Book Guide* (£2.75 + p&p from Thimble Press, Lockwood, Station Road, South Woodchester, Glos. GL5 5EQ) is an important guide to current poetry publications for children.

## POETRY BOOK SOCIETY

The Poetry Book Society is a book club, founded in 1953, devoted to contemporary poetry. Like all book clubs it offers books to members at discount prices, and other inducements to membership. Each year members receive four quarterly books of new poetry chosen by independent selectors appointed by the Board of Management. With the book comes the free quarterly *Bulletin* containing information on the books recommended each quarter and, at Christmas, a free annual anthology of new poems. A membership form with further information is available from the Membership Department, Poetry Book Society Ltd, 21 Earls Court Square, London SW5 9DE.

## POETRY LIBRARY AND OTHER LIBRARIES

1. The **Poetry Library** was set up by the Arts Council in 1954 and is the central national bibliographical information resource in the subject area of modern English language poetry. Membership is free. Books are available for reference and loan, and may be borrowed via your local library through the LASER national interlibrary loan network. The collection includes all the current poetry magazines and over 35,000 items dating from 1912 to the present, including books, pamphlets, poster poems, poemcards, pictures of poets, press cuttings, audio and video cassettes. The library has a current awareness information role on poetry events and publications, and disseminates information in the form of regularly updated lists of poetry magazines, competitions, groups and workshops in and around London, bookshops selling poetry, etc. available free on receipt of an A4 sae. The Poetry Library is now part of the South Bank Literature Centre in London and is open seven days a week. Write for information to The Librarian, Poetry Library, South Bank Centre, Royal Festival Hall, London SE1 8XX (*see also* South Bank Centre).

2. The **Scottish Poetry Library** organises poetry readings and houses a collection of twentieth-century poetry written in Scotland in English, Scots and Gaelic, as well as older Scottish poetry and a selection of poetry from other countries. Books are available by post in Scotland and a newsletter is issued to members. Details are available from The Librarian, Scottish Poetry Library, Tweedale Court, 14 High Street, Edinburgh EH1 1TE.

3. The **Northern Arts Poetry Library** is a collection of over 6000 books published in Britain since 1968 and loans books free by post to members resident in the North-East and Cumbria. Write for information on membership to The Librarian, Northern Arts Poetry Library, County Library, The Willows, Morpeth, Northumberland NE61 1TA.

4. **Poetry Ireland** run the Austin Clarke Library, a collection of 6000 volumes of modern poetry. Poetry Ireland also organise readings, and provide both a

newsletter and a book club offering four of the best new poetry books published in Ireland each year. For more information on membership contact: Poetry Ireland, The Austin Clarke Library, 44 Upper Mount Street Dublin 2, Republic of Ireland.

5. All these specialist libraries are centres for information. Your local branch library can also be an invaluable information resource. It will normally have details of poetry groups and workshops in your area, may have details of national poetry competitions and, through its shelves, you will be able to discover some of the poetry publishers of today. If your local library does not have work by an author you want, ask to borrow something from the Poetry Library at the South Bank Centre through the national interlibrary loan network, for a small fee, by filling in a book requisition form with bibliographical details of the title you want to read.

## THE POETRY SOCIETY AT THE NATIONAL POETRY CENTRE

The Poetry Society is situated at the National Poetry Centre in London, and organises a wide range of services for the entire poetry community, including an effective Education Service, administering the National Poetry Competition and awards such as the European Poetry Translation Prize and the Alice Hunt Bartlett Prize, helping organise poetry readings nationally, running a Critical Service which provides professional advice for a fee for poets, publishing an invaluable list of practical books for poets, and a bookshop which can supply new books through the post. Membership brings all this, plus a subscription to *Poetry Review* and reduced price admittance to all events at the Society's headquarters. For most of the year poetry readings are organised at the Society on Tuesday and Thursday evenings. For more information contact the Membership Department, The Poetry Society, 21 Earls Court Square, London SW5 9DE.

## REGIONAL ARTS ASSOCIATIONS

A list of the Literature Officers of each of the Regional Arts Associations is available from the Research and Information Unit of the Arts Council, 105 Piccadilly, London W1V 0AU on receipt of an A4 sae. You can contact the Regional Arts Association in your area (see **Societies** for addresses) and discover if there are writers' groups and workshops or a literary festival nearby, or perhaps a local writer in residence who may be able to offer advice on your work.

## SOUTH BANK CENTRE

A new home for literary events in London has been created within the South Bank Centre with the Arts Council Poetry Library as its base. The South Bank Centre Literature programme aims to reflect the diversity of writing within the British Isles and beyond. Most literature events take place in The Voice Box situated next to the Poetry Library, others in the Purcell Room and Queen Elizabeth Hall. The continuing New Voices series presents the work of emerging poets, novelists and short story writers, and the literature programme includes one-off readings, thematic series, literature/dance events and writers' workshops, and a writer in residence. For more information and to be placed on the mailing list contact the Literature Officer, South Bank Centre, Royal Festival Hall, London SE1 8XX (*see also* Poetry Library).

## FURTHER READING TO BUY OR CONSULT

Michael Baldwin, *The way to write poetry*, Hamish Hamilton
Sandy Brownjohn, *Does it have to rhyme: teaching children to write poetry*, Hodder

Rosalind Fergusson (ed.), *The Penguin rhyming dictionary*, Penguin
Peter Finch, *How to publish your poetry*, Allison & Busby
G. S. Fraser, *Metre, rhyme and free verse*, Methuen
John Medlin, *Poetry live: British and Irish poetry 1987*, Poetry Society/Book Trust (available from Book Trust)
Philip Davies Roberts, *How poetry works: the elements of English poetry*, Penguin
James Vinson and D. L. Kirkpatrick (eds), *Contemporary poets*, 4th edition, 1985, St James Press, £37.50. (The standard reference book listing living English-language poets.)

See also the **Agents** section for literary agents; the **Illustration and design** section for verses in greetings cards; the **Societies and prizes** section.

# Scripts for theatre, radio, tv and film

## Marketing a play

JULIA JONES
*Society of Authors*

As soon as a play is written, it is protected under the copyright laws of this country. No formalities are necessary here to secure copyright protection but it is a good plan to deposit a copy with the bank and take a dated receipt for it, so as to be able to prove the date of its completion, if this should be necessary at some time either, for example, to enforce a claim for infringement of copyright or to rebut such a claim. The copyright belongs to the author unless and until he parts with it and this he should never do, since the copyright is in effect the sum total of all his rights in his work. He should, so far as possible deal separately with the component rights which go to make up the copyright and grant limited licences for the principal rights with, where customary or necessary, limited interests in the ancillary rights. A West End production agreement (see below) illustrates this principle.

The author can try to market the play himself, but once a play is accepted, it is wise to have professional assistance. There is no standard author's contract in this country; all points are, therefore, open for negotiation and the contractual complications are best handled by a reputable literary agent.

Although most ambitious young playwrights visualise a West End opening for their plays, the first step, except for the established dramatist, is usually to try to place the play with a repertory company known to be interested in presenting new plays. It is wise to write to the company first, giving salient details, such as type of play, size of cast, number of sets, etc., and ask if the management would be willing to read it. This saves the frustration and expense of copies of the play being kept for long periods by managements who have no interest in it. (Do not send your only copy of the play away—this seems obvious, but many authors have suffered the torment of having to rewrite from memory when the only copy has been lost.) It is also possible to get a first production by entering the play for the various competitions which appear from time to time, but in this case great care should be taken to study the rules and ensure that the organisers of the competition do not acquire unreasonably wide rights and interests in the entries.

Many repertory companies will give a new play a try-out production in the hope that it will be seen by London managements and transfer to the West End. For the run at the repertory company's own theatre the company will receive a licence for a given period from a fixed date and pay the author a royalty of between 6 per cent and 10 per cent calculated on the gross box office receipts. In return for the risk involved in presenting a new play, the repertory company will expect a share in the author's earnings from subsequent professional stage productions of the play during a limited period (usually two years). Sometimes on transfer the West End management will agree to take over responsibility for part or all of this payment.

The contract, for repertory or West End production, or for the use of any other rights in the play, should specify precisely the rights to which it refers, the territory covered, the period of time covered, the payments involved and make it clear that all other rights remain the property of the author.

For a first-class production in the West End of London, usually preceded by a short provincial tour, the author's contract will include clauses dealing with the following main heads of agreement. The substance, as well as the phrasing of these clauses will vary considerably, but those given below probably represent the average, as do the figures in brackets, which must not be assumed to be standard:

### 1. U.K. option

In consideration of a specified minimum sum (between £500 and £1000) as a non-returnable advance against royalties, the Manager shall have the exclusive option for a specified period (usually six months) to produce the play in a first-class theatre in the West End of London (preceded possibly by a tour of specified number of weeks) with an extension for a further period upon payment of a further similar sum.

### 2. U.K. licence

When the Manager exercises his option he shall have the U.K. licence for a specified period (three or five years) from the date of the first performance under the licence such licence to terminate before the expiry of the specified period if
(a) the play is not produced before a specified date;
(b) (i) less than a specified number (between 50 and 75) of consecutive professional performances are given and paid for in any year; or
(ii) the Manager has not paid at the beginning of any year a non-returnable advance against royalties. This variant on clause (b) (i) prevents the rights being tied up for a year while waiting to check if the qualifying performances have been given and is thus desirable from the author's point of view.

### 3. U.S. option

If the Manager gives a specified number (usually 24) of consecutive performances in the West End he shall have an option exercisable within a specified period of the first West End performance (six weeks) to produce the play on Broadway on payment of a specified non-returnable advance on royalties (between £500 and £1000).

### 4. U.S. licence

When the Manager exercises his option the Broadway licence shall be for a specified period (3 years) on terms not less favourable than those specified in the Minimum Basic Agreement of the Dramatists' Guild of America.

### 5. Other rights

Provided the play has run for the qualifying period (usually 24 performances) the Manager acquires interests in some of the other rights as follows:
(i) *Repertory*. The author should reserve these rights paying the Manager a share (one-third) of his royalties for a specified period (two years after the end of the West End run or the expiry of the West End licence whichever is the shorter.) The author agrees not to release these rights until after the end of the West End

run without the Manager's consent, this consent not to be unreasonably withheld. It is recommended that a play should be released to theatres on the A list immediately after the end of the West End run, and to theatres on the B list within three months from the end of the West End run, if an option for a tour has not been taken up by then, otherwise at the end of the tour. The Theatres on these lists are those recommended by the Theatres' National Committee for immediate and early release of plays to repertory.

(ii) *Amateur.* The author should reserve these rights and pay the Manager no share in his royalties, but should undertake not to release these rights for an agreed period, to allow the repertory theatres to have maximum clear run.

(iii) *Radio, Television, and Video.* The author should reserve these rights but it may well be in his interest not to release them until some time after the end of the West End run. During the run of the play in the West End, however, the Manager may arrange for an extract from the play to be broadcast or televised for publicity purposes, the author's fee for such broadcast or television performances being paid to him in full without any part of it going to the Manager.

(iv) *Film.* If the Manager has produced the play for the qualifying period it is expected that the author will pay him a percentage (often 20 per cent) of the author's net receipts from the disposal of the film rights, if these rights are disposed of within a specified period (one year) from the last West End performance. If the Manager has also produced the play on Broadway for the qualifying period the author is expected to allow him a further percentage (20 per cent) of the author's net receipts from the disposal of the film rights if the rights are disposed of within a specified time (one year) of the last Broadway performance. This is a field where the established dramatist can, not unnaturally, strike a much better bargain than the beginner. In no case, however, should the total percentage payable to the Manager exceed 40 per cent.

(v) *Foreign Language.* These rights should be reserved to the author, the Manager receiving no share of the proceeds.

(vi) *Cassette.* These rights should be specifically reserved to the author.

Other clauses which should appear include:

*(a) A royalty clause* setting out the royalties which the author shall receive from West End and touring performances of the play—usually a scale rising from 5 per cent through 7½ per cent to 10 per cent. If the author is registered for VAT, provision for VAT should be included here.

*(b) Cast approval, etc.* The author should be consulted about the casting and the director of the play, and in some cases may be able to insist on approval of the casting of a particular part.

*(c) Rehearsals, scripts, etc.* The author should be entitled to attend all rehearsals of the play and no alteration in the title or script should be made without the author's consent. All approved alterations in or suggestions for the script should become the author's property. In this clause also should appear details about supply of tickets for the author for opening performances and any arrangements for tickets throughout the West End run.

*(d) Credits.* Details of billing of the author's name on posters, programmes and advertising matter should be included.

*(e) Lord Chamberlain's Licence.* The Theatres Act 1968 abolishes the power of the Lord Chamberlain to censor stage plays and play licences are no longer required. However, it is obligatory for managers to deposit a copy of the script on which the public performance of any new play is based with the Keeper of Manuscripts, British Library, London, WC1, within one month of the performance.

*(f)* The author will normally warrant that the play contains nothing that is obscene or defamatory or that infringes copyright.

There must also be:

*(g)* An accounting clause giving details of payment and requiring a certified statement of box office receipts.

*(h)* A clause giving the conditions under which the agreement may be assigned or sub-leased.

*(i)* A termination clause, stating the conditions under which the agreement shall terminate.

ARRANGEMENTS FOR OTHER RIGHTS AFTER THE FIRST-CLASS RUN OF THE PLAY

### Repertory

The author or his representative will license repertory performances for a fixed royalty on the gross box office receipts—usually 10 per cent for a new play immediately after its West End run, dropping perhaps to 7½ per cent in later years.

### Amateur

The author or his representative will license amateur performances of the play for a flat fee (normally between £15 and £25).

### Publication

A firm specialising in acting editions of plays may offer to publish the play in which case it will expect to license amateur performances and collect the fees on a commission basis (20 per cent to 50 per cent). The publication contract will also usually provide for the author to receive a royalty of 10 per cent of the published price of every copy sold.

### Radio and television

Careful negotiation is required and care should be taken that repeat fees for repeat performances are included in the contract in addition to the initial fee for the first broadcast.

### Film rights

Professional advice is absolutely necessary when dealing with a film contract as there are many complications. The rights may be sold outright or licensed for a number of years—usually not less than 7 or 10 or more than 15. The film company normally acquires the right of distribution throughout the world in all languages and expects a completely free hand in making the adaptation of the play into a film.

### Foreign rights

It is usual to grant exclusive foreign language rights for the professional stage to an agent or translator who will arrange for a translation to be prepared and produced—it is wise to ask for evidence of the quality of the translator's work unless the translator is very well known. The financial arrangement is usually an advance against royalties for a given period to enable a translation to be prepared and then a licence to exploit the translation for a further period after production (usually five years).

# Markets for Stage Plays

It is not easy for a new or comparatively unknown writer to find a management willing to present his play. The Royal Court Theatre and some other similarly enterprising organisations present a number of plays by new authors. The new and inexperienced writer may find it easier to persuade amateur drama groups or provincial repertory theatres to present his work. A further possible market may be found in the smaller fringe theatre companies.

*The Stage* reports productions of most new plays first produced by repertory theatres and a study of this journal may reveal other potential new markets for plays.

The Arts Council of Great Britain publishes a brochure, *Theatre Writing Schemes*, which gives details of various forms of assistance available to playwrights and to theatres wishing to commission new plays. The help given by the Arts Council includes Bursaries (including the John Whiting Award), help to writers who are being commissioned or encouraged by a theatre company, and Supplements to authors' royalties. There is a number of Resident Dramatists' Attachment Awards available and some support is available towards the costs of writers' workshops. Copies of the brochure and further information may be obtained from The Drama Director, The Arts Council of Great Britain, 105 Piccadilly, London W1V 0AU.

It is probable that competitions for full-length and one-act plays and other special opportunities for new plays will be announced after the *Yearbook* has gone to press, and writers with plays on the stocks would do well to watch carefully for announcements in the Press. *The Observer*, *The Author*, *Drama*, *Amateur Stage*, and *The Stage*, are the journals in which announcements are most likely to appear.

Sketches for revues and broadcasting and plays for youth organisations are in demand. Sketches are usually bought outright, but in any case authors should make quite certain of what rights they will be disposing before accepting any offer.

In every case it is advisable to send a preliminary letter before submitting a manuscript. Suggestions for the preparation of manuscripts will be found in the article **Typescripts**.

Writers of plays are also referred to **Marketing a Play** and to the sections on **Radio** and **Television**, media which provide a very big market for the writers of plays.

In the following lists an asterisk denotes that Theatre Club membership is required.

## LONDON

**\*Bush Theatre,** Shepherd's Bush Green, London W12 8QD   *tel* 01-602 3703 (Administration); 01-743 3388 (Box Office).

**Michael Codron Ltd.,** Aldwych Theatre Offices, Aldwych, London WC2B 4DF   *tel* 01-240 8291   *fax* 01-240 8467.

**Compass Theatre Ltd.,** 13 Shorts Gardens, London WC2H 9AT   *tel* 01-379 7501.

**Ray Cooney Presentations Ltd.,** 1-3 Spring Gardens, Trafalgar Square, London SW1A 2BD    *tel* 01-839 5098-9.

**English Stage Company Ltd.,** Royal Court Theatre, Sloane Square, London SW1W 8AS    *tel* 01-730 5174.

**Façade,** 11 Lower John Street, London W1R 3PE    *tel* 01-494 0738. Develops, promotes and produces new musicals.

**Clare Fox and Brian Kirk Ltd,** Suite 17 1st Floor, 26 Charing Cross Road, London WC2H 0DG    *tel* 01-379 4985 and 4676    *fax* 01-379 5898.

**John Gale,** Strand Theatre, Aldwych, London WC2B 5LD    *tel* 01-240 1656.

**Greenwich Theatre Ltd.,** Greenwich Theatre, Crooms Hill, London SE10 8ES    *tel* 01-858 4447.

**Half Moon Theatre,** 213 Mile End Road, London E1 4AA    *tel* 01-791 1141.

**Hampstead Theatre,** Swiss Cottage Centre, London NW3 3EX    *tel* 01-722 9224.

**Independent Theatrical Productions Ltd,** Monro House, 40-42 King Street, Covent Garden, London WC2E 8JS    *tel* 01-240 9891    *fax* 01-379 5748.

**Bill Kenwright Ltd,** 59 Shaftesbury Avenue, London W1V 7AA    *tel* 01-439 4466    *fax* 01-437 8370.

*****King's Head Theatre,** 115 Upper Street, London N1 1QN    *tel* 01-226 1916.

**Knightsbridge Theatrical Productions Ltd.,** c/o 2nd Floor, Winchmore House, 12-15 Fetter Lane, London EC4A 1JJ    *tel* 01-583 8687    *fax* 01-583 0046.

**Libby Productions Ltd.,** Toby Rowland, Prince of Wales Theatre, Coventry Street, London W1V 8AS    *tel* 01-930 4031.

**Lyric Theatre Hammersmith,** King Street, London W6 0QL    *tel* 01-741 0824    *fax* 01-741 7694.

**National Theatre,** South Bank, London SE1 9PX    *tel* 01-928 2033    *telex* 297306 Nattre G    *fax* 01-620 1197.

*****Orange Tree Theatre,** 45 Kew Road, Richmond, Surrey TW9 2NQ    *tel* 01-940 0141.

**Polka Children's Theatre,** 240 The Broadway, London SW19 1SB    *tel* 01-542 4258.

**Questors Theatre,** Mattock Lane, Ealing, London W5 5BQ    *tel* 01-567 0011.

**Royal Shakespeare Company,** Barbican Theatre, Barbican, London EC2Y 8BQ    *tel* 01-628 3351    *fax* 01-374 0818.

**Peter Saunders Ltd.,** Vaudeville Theatre Offices, 10 Maiden Lane, London WC2E 7NA    *tel* 01-240 3177    *fax* 01-497 9505.

*****Soho Poly Theatre,** 16 Riding House Street, London W1P 7PD    *tel* 01-580 6982.

**Tabard Theatre,** 2 Bath Road, Turnham Green, Chiswick, London W4 1LW    *tel* 01-995 6035/01-747 8256.

**H. M. Tennent Ltd.,** Globe Theatre, Shaftesbury Avenue, London W1V 7HD    *tel* 01-437 3647    *fax* 01-439 1357.

**Theatre Royal, Stratford East,** Gerry Raffles Square, Stratford, London E15 1BN    *tel* 01-534 7374.

**The Tricycle Theatre Company,** Tricycle Theatre, 269 Kilburn High Road, London NW6 7JR    *tel* 01-372 6611.

**Triumph Theatre Productions Ltd.,** Suite 4, Waldorf Chambers, 11 Aldwych, London WC2B 4DA   *tel* 01-836 0186   *telex* 263480 Taprod G   *fax* 01-240 7511.

**Unicorn Theatre for Children,** Arts Theatre, 6-7 Gt. Newport Street, London WC2H 7JB   *tel* 01-379 3280. (Plays for children up to age of 12 only.)

\*Warehouse Theatre, 62 Dingwall Road, Croydon CR0 2NF   *tel* 01-681 1257.

**Michael White,** 13 Duke Street, St. James's, London SW1Y 6DB   *tel* 01-839 3971   *fax* 01-839 3836.

**The Young Vic,** 66 The Cut, London SE1 8LZ   *tel* 01-633 0133.

PROVINCIAL

**Abbey Theatre,** Lower Abbey Street, Dublin 1   *tel* 748741   *fax* 729177. The Abbey Theatre mainly produces plays written by Irish authors or on Irish subjects. Foreign plays are however regularly produced.

**Belgrade Theatre,** Belgrade Square, Coventry CV1 1GS   *tel* (0203) 256431.

**Birmingham Repertory Theatre, Ltd.,** Broad Street, Birmingham B1 2EP   *tel* 021-236 6771   *fax* 021-236 7883.

**Bristol Old Vic Company,** Theatre Royal, King Street, Bristol BS1 4ED   *tel* (0272) 277466.

**Chester Gateway Theatre Trust, Ltd.,** Gateway Theatre, Hamilton Place, Chester CH1 2BH   *tel* (0244) 44238.

**Chichester Festival Theatre Productions Company Ltd.,** Chichester Festival Theatre, Oaklands Park, Chichester, West Sussex PO19 4AP   *tel* (0243) 784437.

**Churchill Theatre Trust Ltd.,** High Street, Bromley, Kent BR1 1HA   *tel* 01-464 7131.

**Colchester Mercury Theatre Ltd.,** Balkerne Gate, Colchester, Essex CO1 1PT   *tel* (0206) 577006.

**The Coliseum Theatre,** Fairbottom Street, Oldham OL1 3SW   *tel* 061-624 1731.

**Contact Theatre Company,** Oxford Road, Manchester M15 6JA   *tel* 061-274 3434.

**Crucible Theatre Trust Ltd.,** The Crucible Theatre, Norfolk Street, Sheffield S1 1DA   *tel* (0742) 760621   *fax* (0742) 701532.

**Derby Playhouse, Ltd.,** Theatre Walk, Eagle Centre, Derby DE1 2NF   *tel* (0332) 363271.

**Druid Theatre Company,** Druid Lane Theatre, Chapel Lane, Galway, Eire   *tel* (091) 68617 and 68660.

**The Duke's Playhouse,** Moor Lane, Lancaster LA1 1QE   *tel* (0524) 67461.

**Dundee Repertory Theatre,** Tay Square, Dundee DD1 1PB   *tel* (0382) 27684.

**Everyman Theatre,** Regent Street, Cheltenham, Glos. GL50 1HQ   *tel* (0242) 512515   *fax* (0242) 224305.

**Farnham Repertory Company, Ltd.,** The Redgrave Theatre, Brightwells, Farnham, Surrey GU9 7SB   *tel* (0252) 727000   *fax* (0252) 712350.

**Grand Theatre,** Singleton Street, Swansea SA1 3QJ   *tel* (0792) 475242.

**Harrogate Theatre,** Oxford Street, Harrogate, North Yorkshire HG1 1QF   *tel* (0423) 502710.

**The Hornchurch Theatre Trust, Ltd,** The Queen's Theatre, Billet Lane, Hornchurch, Essex RM11 1QT   *tel* Hornchurch 56118   *fax* Hornchurch 52348.

**Horseshoe Theatre Co.,** The Shrubbery, Cliddesden Road, Basingstoke, Hants RG21 3ER   *tel* (0256) 55844.

**Leicester Haymarket Theatre,** Belgrave Gate, Leicester LE1 3YQ   *tel* (0533) 530021   *telex* 341019 Lehay G.

**Liverpool Repertory Theatre, Ltd.,** Liverpool Playhouse, Williamson Square, Liverpool L1 1EL   *tel* 051-709 8478.

**Lyceum Theatre,** Heath Street, Crewe, Cheshire CW1 2DA   *tel* (0270) 588105   *fax* (0270) 582145.

**Merseyside Everyman Theatre Company Ltd.,** 5-9 Hope Street, Liverpool L1 9BH   *tel* 051-708 0338.

**New Victoria Theatre,** Etruria Road, Newcastle under Lyme ST5 0JG   *tel* (0782) 717954. New purpose built theatre in the round, presenting new plays, major classics, adaptations, documentaries.

**Northampton Repertory Players, Ltd.,** Royal Theatre and Opera House, Guild-hall Road, Northampton NN1 1EA   *tel* (0604) 38343.

**Northcott Theatre,** Stocker Road, Exeter, Devon EX4 4QB   *tel* (0392) 56182.

**Nottingham Playhouse,** Nottingham Theatre Trust Ltd., Wellington Circus, Nottingham NG1 5AF   *tel* (0602) 474361.

**Nuffield Theatre,** University Road, Southampton SO9 5NH   *tel* (0703) 671871.

**Octagon Theatre,** Howell Croft South, Bolton BL1 1SB   *tel* (0204) 29407.

**Oxford Stage Company Ltd.,** 12 Beaumont Street, Oxford OX1 2LW   *tel* (0865) 723238.

**Palace Theatre,** Clarendon Road, Watford, Herts. WD1 1JZ   *tel* (0923) 35455.

**Palace Theatre Trust Ltd.,** London Road, Westcliff-on-Sea, Essex SS0 9LA   *tel* (0702) 347816.

**Peacock Theatre,** The Abbey Theatre, Lower Abbey Street, Dublin 1   *tel* 748741   *fax* 729177. The experimental theatre associated with the Abbey Theatre and presents mostly new writing as well as exploring the entire canon of world drama.

**Perth Theatre Ltd.,** 185 High Street, Perth PH1 5UW   *tel* (0738) 38123.

**Plymouth Theatre Royal,** Theatre Royal, Royal Parade, Plymouth, Devon PL1 2TR   *tel* (0752) 668282   *telex* 45115 Troyal G   *fax* (0752) 671179.

**Royal Exchange Theatre Company Ltd.,** The Royal Exchange, St. Ann's Square, Manchester M2 7DH   *tel* 061-833 9333   *fax* 061-832 0881.

**Royal Lyceum Theatre Company Ltd.,** Royal Lyceum Theatre, Grindlay Street, Edinburgh EH3 9AX   *tel* 031-229 7404.

**St. Andrews Byre Theatre,** Abbey Street, St. Andrews KY16 9LA   *tel* (0334) 76288.

**Salisbury Playhouse,** Malthouse Lane, Salisbury, Wiltshire SP2 7RA   *tel* (0722) 20117.

**Scarborough Theatre Trust Ltd.,** Stephen Joseph Theatre in the Round, Valley Bridge, Scarborough, North Yorkshire YO11 2PL   *tel* (0723) 370540.

**Swan Theatre,** The Moors, Worcester WR1 3EF　*tel* (0905) 726969　*fax* (0905) 723738.

**Thorndike Theatre,** Church Street, Leatherhead, Surrey KT22 8DF　*tel* (0372) 376211.

**Towngate Theatre,** Pagel Mead, Basildon, Essex SS14 1DW　*tel* (0268) 53134.

**Traverse Theatre,** 112 West Bow, Grassmarket, Edinburgh EH1 2HH　*tel* 031-226 2633.

**Tyne Theatre Company,** 67A Westgate Road, Newcastle upon Tyne NE1 4AG　*tel* (091) 232 3366　*fax* (091) 261 9699.

**Watermill Theatre Ltd.,** Bagnor, Newbury, Berkshire RG16 8AE　*tel* (0635) 45834.

**The West Yorkshire Playhouse,** Quarry Hill Mount, Leeds LS9 8AW　*tel* (0532) 442141　*fax* (0532) 448252. Twin auditoria complex—with a policy of encouraging new writing; community theatre; Young People's Theatre programme.

**Windsor Theatre Company (Capoco Ltd.),** Theatre Royal, Windsor, Berks. SL4 1PS　*tel* (0753) 863444.

**The Wolsey Theatre,** Civic Drive, Ipswich, Suffolk IP1 2AS　*tel* (0473) 218911.

**York Citizens' Theatre Trust, Ltd.,** Theatre Royal, St. Leonard's Place, York YO1 2HD　*tel* (0904) 658162　*fax* (0904) 611534.

**Yvonne Arnaud Theatre Management Ltd.,** Yvonne Arnaud Theatre, Millbrook, Guildford, Surrey GU1 3UX　*tel* (0483) 64571　*fax* (0483) 64071.

## TOURING COMPANIES

**Avon Touring Theatre Co.,** The Albany Centre, Shaftesbury Avenue, Montpelier, Bristol BS6 5LL　*tel* (0272) 555436. Has a policy of employing writers for new work.

**Black Theatre Co-Operative Ltd,** 8 Bradbury Street, London N16 8JN　*tel* 01-249 9150.

**Compass Theatre Company,** The Leadmill, 6-7 Leadmill Road, Sheffield S1 4SF　*tel* (0742) 755328.

**Gay Sweatshop Theatre Co.,** P.O. Box 820, London NW1 8LW　*tel* 01-722 1491.

**Hull Truck Theatre Co. Ltd.,** Spring Street Theatre, Spring Street, Hull HU2 8RW　*tel* (0482) 224800　*fax* (0482) 228546.

**Joint Stock Theatre Group,** 123 Tottenham Court Road, London W1P 9HN　*tel* 01-388 9719. Plays created from workshops.

**Live Theatre,** 8 Trinity Chare, Quayside, Newcastle upon Tyne NE1 3DF　*tel* (091) 261 2694.

**The London Bubble (Bubble Theatre Company),** 3/5 Elephant Lane, London SE16 4JD　*tel* 01-237 4434.

**M6 Theatre Company,** Theatre Workshop, Heybrook School, Park Road, Rochdale, Lancashire OL12 9BJ　*tel* (0706) 355898.

**Major Road Theatre Company,** 29 Queens Road, Bradford, West Yorkshire BD8 7BS　*tel* (0274) 480251.

**Manx National Theatre Company,** 4 Athol Terrace, Castletown, Isle of Man   *tel* (0624) 823182   *fax* (0624) 824339. Primarily interested in comedy. Send MSS to Vanessa Stead, Literary Manager, enclosing International Reply Coupons.

**Monstrous Regiment,** 123 Tottenham Court Road, London W1P 9HN   *tel* 01-387 4790.

**New Prometheus Touring Co.,** Box Prom, c/o Housman's Bookshop, 5 Caledonian Road, London N1 9DX   *tel* 01-836 7071.

**Northumberland Theatre Company,** The Playhouse, Bondgate Without, Alnwick, Northumberland NE66 1PQ   *tel* (0665) 602586.

**Orchard Theatre Company,** 108 Newport Road, Barnstaple, N. Devon EX32 9BA   *tel* (0271) 71475.

**Paines Plough,** The Writers Company, 121-122 Tottenham Court Road, London W1P 9HN   *tel* 01-380 1188.

**Perspectives Theatre Co-operative Ltd.,** c/o Mansfield Community Arts Centre, Leeming Street, Mansfield, Notts. NG18 1NG   *tel* (0623) 35225. Has a policy of employing writers for new work.

**Quicksilver Theatre for Children** (formerly Theatre of Thelema), 4 Enfield Road, London N1 5AZ   *tel* 01-241 2942.

**Red Ladder Theatre Co.,** Cobden Avenue, Lower Wortley, Leeds LS12 5PB   *tel* (0532) 792228.

**Solent People's Theatre,** The Heathfield Centre, Valentine Avenue, Sholing, Southampton SO2 8EQ   *tel* (0703) 443943.

**Theatre Centre,** Hanover School, Noel Road, Islington, London N1 8BD   *tel* 01-354 0110.

**Women's Theatre Group,** 5 Leonard Street, London EC2A 4AQ   *tel* 01-251 0202. Women writers only.

## PUBLISHERS SPECIALISING IN THE PUBLICATION OF PLAYS

(For other particulars regarding Publishers, see under **Book Publishers**.)

**Atheneum Publishers,** 866 Third Avenue, New York, N.Y. 10022.

**Walter H. Baker Company,** 100 Chauncy Street, Boston, Mass. 02111.

**Faber & Faber Ltd.,** 3 Queen Square, London WC1N 3AU.

**Samuel French Ltd.,** 52 Fitzroy Street, London W1P 6JR.

**Samuel French Inc.,** 45 West 25th Street, New York, N.Y. 10010.

**Kenyon-Deane Ltd.,** 311 Worcester Road, Malvern, Worcestershire WR14 1AN.

**Macmillan Education Ltd.,** Houndmills, Basingstoke, Hants RG21 2XS.

**Methuen London,** Michelin House, 81 Fulham Road, London SW3 6RB.

**J. Garnet Miller Ltd.,** 311 Worcester Road, Malvern, Worcestershire WR14 1AN.

**New Playwrights' Network,** 35 Sandringham Road, Macclesfield, Cheshire SK10 1QB   *tel* (0625) 25312.

(For a list of periodicals dealing with the Theatre see the **Classified Index**.)

## *Writing for Broadcasting in the Nineties*

JOCELYN HAY
*Chairman, Voice of the Listener*

By the summer of 1990 new legislation on broadcasting is likely to be in place which will have far-reaching implications for viewers, listeners and writers. The broadcasting climate will be harsher and more competitive; finance harder to find. Programmes involving the written word therefore, especially on radio, could be threatened, because speech is generally more expensive to broadcast than music.

The most worrying aspect of the changes for writers concerns the future of the BBC. BBC Radio provides the world's largest market for plays and the Government's desire to change the basis of BBC funding from the licence fee to subscription TV begs the question of how BBC Radio will be financed without the licence. BBC income, already squeezed by indexation of the licence fee, may be further reduced after 1991 if the Government carries out its threat to reduce the index below the rate of inflation. An even larger question mark hangs over the BBC after 1996 when its charter runs out.

The threat of so much uncertainty makes the television market difficult for writers. The high cost of television drama is leading to a search for more co-funding and for overseas sales but also to less risk taking and more international themes, even by the BBC. On the commercial side the threat to profits and future stability makes companies reluctant to consider long-term projects, particularly those like documentaries, educational, religious or children's programmes, appealing to minority audiences.

But the outlook is not all gloom. The radio drama budget is secure until mid-1990 and the BBC is looking for new material for Radio 3 and for an innovative late evening slot on Radio 4. The BBC/Radio Times Competitions for comedy scripts and young playwrights will also continue at least for the next two years.

The market for drama and the spoken word on Independent Radio has been minimal but the relaxation of the rules on sponsorship may encourage a few stations to experiment. LBC's sponsored five minute dramatisations of classics have been popular and, like the 'plays with a message' produced by Radio Clyde with sponsorship from the Health Education Council, could provide a model. Cable and satellite operators, who are unlikely to have money for many commissions because of their high start-up costs, may also consider sponsored material and the key to that door lies with the increasing number of independent producers.

The market for speech on non-broadcast cassettes is another growth area. It consists mainly of dramatised readings and short stories but an expanding range of specialist audio magazines and video 'how to do it programmes' is being produced for in-car and home use. One airline has commissioned two series of commercially sponsored half hour dramas for its in-flight entertainment—but it was the writer's idea and he found the sponsor and buyer.

The message for writers in the 1990s, therefore, must be to keep abreast of the changes and to make their needs known both to the broadcasters and to the Government who are forcing the pace. They must also be quick and flexible enough to seize new opportunities from the new outlets that undoubtedly will arise, albeit often in different form.

# British Broadcasting Corporation

For fuller information see *Writing for the BBC*—a guide for writers on possible markets for their work within the BBC. The 8th edition is available from DMS Ltd., 3 Sheldon Way, Larkfield, Maidstone, Kent ME20 6SE (£3·95 + £1·50 p.&p.).

## TELEVISION

### Drama

Original plays dealing with contemporary problems are most wanted. Plays needing only a few sets and characters start at an advantage. Specially-shot film sequences should only be written into a script if essential for the story. No standardised layout is expected in unsolicited scripts. Dialogue should be set out in a way that makes it clearly distinguishable from 'stage directions' and sound/visual effects. Further details about length and type of plays currently required are available from Script Unit.

*All scripts* should be clearly typed and sent to Head of Script Unit, BBC Television Centre, London, W12 7RJ, from whom a leaflet, *BBC Television Script Requirements* is available. *Please enclose an sae.*

## RADIO

### Short stories

Short stories specially written for broadcasting will be considered. A short story written for a fifteen-minute broadcasting space should be between 2300 and 2500 words in length.

### Drama Department

The Department broadcasts several hundred new plays and adaptations every year, in addition to series and serials, dramatic features and readings. There is therefore a very large market regularly available to the freelance writer. A free leaflet, *Notes on Radio Drama*, giving basic guidance on the technique of radio writing and also on the market is available from the Script Editor (Radio Drama), BBC, Broadcasting House, Portland Place, London W1A 1AA to whom all submissions should be addressed.

### Music

The music policy of the BBC, dedicated to the encouragement of the best music old and new, continues to enlarge its range. Audition sessions for professional soloists and ensembles are held every week, except in July and August, with an outside professional assessor on the listening panel.

A Music Panel of distinguished musicians meets regularly to advise on the suitability for performance of the large number of MSS. constantly submitted. The BBC also commissions from British composers works of various kinds. These have included opera and works for special occasions. Incidental music is also commissioned for features and drama. In the case of music commissioned by the BBC the original score is now returned to the composer at his request and not as in the past automatically retained by the BBC.

*Light Entertainment*
Careful consideration is given to new ideas for Light Entertainment programmes by the Script Editor and senior members of the Light Entertainment Department. The chief requirement is originality; the vast majority of scripts sent in are merely variations of existing programmes. A particular need exists for topical sketches and 'one-liners' for programmes such as *Week Ending*. In general it is inadvisable to write scripts for a particular star artist unless the writer has a really intimate knowledge of the artist's work; and even then the material for 'solo' performances (as distinct from scripts for comedy series) is almost invariably provided by the artists themselves. No real decision can be reached on a new proposition until the completed script is seen: but the Script Editor is prepared to look at detailed synopses and specimen dialogue and offer opinions if requested. Fees are a matter for negotiation with the Corporation's Copyright Department. Typewritten scripts should be addressed to the Script Editor (Light Entertainment), BBC Broadcasting House, London, W1A 1AA.

## BROADCASTING RIGHTS AND TERMS

Contributors are advised to check latest details of fees with the BBC

*Specially written material for television*
For the period to 30th November 1989 the rates for one performance of a 60-minute original television play are a minimum of £3145 for a play written by a beginner and a 'going rate' of £4950 for an established writer, or *pro rata* for shorter or longer timings. Half the fee is paid on a work being commissioned and half on its acceptance as being suitable for television. If the work is submitted it is paid for on acceptance. Fees for a 50-minute episode in a series during the same period are a minimum of £2590 for a beginner and a 'going rate' of £3745 for an established writer. Fees for a 50-minute dramatisation are a minimum of £1815 for a beginner and a £2665 'going rate' for an established writer. All fees are subject to negotiation above the minima.

*Specially written material for radio*
Fees are assessed on the basis of the type of material, its length, the author's status and experience in writing for radio. For the period to 31st March 1990 fees for one performance of specially written radio dramas in English (other than educational programmes) are £17.23 a minute for beginners and a 'going rate' of £26.20 a minute for established writers. Fees for submitted material are paid on acceptance, and for commissioned material half on commissioning and half on acceptance as being suitable for broadcasting.

*Short stories specially written for radio*
Fees range from £93.00 for 15 minutes.

*Stage plays for television*
Fees for stage plays are negotiable.

*Published material for radio* (for the period to 30th June 1990)
Domestic service: Dramatic works: £8.55 per minute; Prose works: £8.55 per minute; Prose works required for dramatisation: £6.67 per minute; Poems: £8.55 per half minute.
External Services: English language services: Dramatic works: £4.10 per minute for up to five broadcasts; Prose works: £4.10 per minute for up to five broadcasts; Prose works required for dramatisation: £3.10 per minute for up to five broad-

casts; Poems: £4.10 per *half* minute for up to five broadcasts. For Foreign language services one fifth of the rate for English language services.

*Published prose and poems for television*

Prose works, £13.35 per minute; poems £15.50 per half minute.

*Repeats in BBC programmes*

Further proportionate fees are payable for repeats.

*Use abroad of recordings of BBC programmes*

If the BBC sends abroad recordings of its programmes for use by overseas broadcasting organisations on their own networks or stations, further payments accrue to the author, usually in the form of additional percentages of the basic fee paid for the initial performance. This can apply to both sound and television programmes.

*Value Added Tax*

A self-billing system for V.A.T. was introduced in January 1978 for programmes made in London. This now covers radio, external services and television.

### TALKS FOR TELEVISION

Contributors to talks will be offered the standard Television talks contract which provides the BBC certain rights to broadcast the material in a complete, abridged and/or translated manner, and which provides for the payment of further fees for additional usage of the material whether by television, domestic radio and external broadcasting. The contract also covers the assignment of material and limited publication rights. Alternatively a contract taking all standard rights may be negotiated. Fees are arranged by the contract authorities in London and the Regions.

### TALKS FOR RADIO

Contributors to talks for domestic Radio and External Broadcasting may be offered either the standard talks contract which takes rights and provides for residual payments as does the Television standard contract above or be offered an ARR (All Rights) Contract which takes all broadcasting and non-paying audience rights where the contribution is of a short, ephemeral nature, not exceeding an air-time of five minutes and which has set fees or disturbance money payable, or an ARC contract where no payment is made which provides an acknowledgement that a contribution may be used by the BBC.

## ADDRESSES

Letters addressed to speakers c/o the BBC will be forwarded, but may be opened before being forwarded. Letters marked "Personal" are forwarded unopened.

### LONDON

**Head Office:** Broadcasting House, London W1A 1AA *tel* 01-580 4468 *telex* 265781 *telegraphic address & cables* Broadcasts, London.

**Television:** Television Centre, Wood Lane, London W12 7RJ *tel* 01-743 8000 *telex* 265781 *telegraphic address* Telecasts, London.

**Publications:** 35 Marylebone High Street, London W1M 4AA *tel* 01-580 5577 *telegraphic address* Broadcasts, London.

**External Broadcasting:** P.O. Box 76, Bush House, Strand, London WC2B 4PH   *tel* 01-240 3456   *telex* 265781   *telegraphic address & cables* Broadbrit, London.

## BBC NATIONAL REGIONS

**Northern Ireland:** Broadcasting House, Ormeau Avenue, Belfast BT2 8HQ   *tel* (0232) 244400.

**Scotland:** Broadcasting House, Queen Margaret Drive, Glasgow G12 8DG   *tel* 041-330 2345.
*Edinburgh Office:* Broadcasting House, Queen Street, Edinburgh EH2 1JF   *tel* 031-243 1200.
*Aberdeen Representative:* Broadcasting House, Beechgrove Terrace, Aberdeen AB9 2ZT   *tel* (0224) 635233.

**Wales:** Broadcasting House, Llantrisant Road, Llandaff, Cardiff CF5 2YQ   *tel* (0222) 564888.
*Bangor Office:* Broadcasting House, Meirion Road, Bangor, Gwynedd LL57 2BY   *tel* (0248) 362214.
*Swansea Office:* 32 Alexandra Road, Swansea SA1 5DZ   *tel* (0792) 54986.

## BBC ENGLISH REGIONAL BROADCASTING

**Midlands Region:** Broadcasting Centre, Pebble Mill, Birmingham B5 7QQ   *tel* 021-472 5353.

**North-East Region:** Broadcasting Centre, Woodhouse Lane, Leeds LS2 9PX   *tel* (0532) 441188.
Broadcasting House, 54 New Bridge Street, Newcastle-upon-Tyne NE1 8AA   *tel* (0632) 20961.

**North-West Region:** New Broadcasting House, P.O. Box 27, Oxford Road, Manchester M60 1SJ   *tel* 061-236 8444.

**South and East Region:** Elstree Centre, Clarendon Road, Borehamwood, Herts. WD6 1JF   *tel* 01-953 6100.

**South and West Region:** Broadcasting House, Whiteladies Road, Bristol BS8 2LR   *tel* (0272) 732211.

## OTHER REGIONAL ADDRESSES

**Norwich:** St. Catherine's Close, All Saints Green, Norwich NR1 3ND   *tel* (0603) 619331.

**Southampton:** South Western House, Canute Road, Southampton SO9 1PF   *tel* (0703) 226201.

**Plymouth:** Broadcasting House, Seymour Road, Mannamead, Plymouth PL3 5BD   *tel* (0752) 229201.

## OVERSEAS OFFICES

**U.S.A.:** 630 Fifth Avenue, New York, N.Y. 10111, U.S.A   *tel* 212-581-7100   *cables* Broadcasts, New York City   *telex* 620150.

**Canada:** Suite 1220, Manulife Centre, 55 Bloor Street West, Toronto, Ontario   *tel* 925-3891   *cables* Loncalling, Toronto   *telex* 06-23577.

**Cairo Bureau:** Flat 42, 23 Kasr El Nil Street, P.O. Box 2040, Cairo, Egypt   *tel* Cairo 745898 and 748040   *telex* 94169 Mytim Un.

**South East Asia Bureau:** P.O. Box 434, Maxwell Road Post Office, Singapore 9008 *telex* RS 35414.

**South American Office:** Casilla de Correo, 1566 Buenos Aires, Argentina *tel* 3926439 *telex* Florida 734.

**Australia and New Zealand:** Westfield Towers, 100 William Street, Sydney, N.S.W. 2011, Australia *tel* Sydney 3586411 *cables* Loncalling, Sydney *telex* 20705.

**India:** 1 Nizamuddin East, New Delhi 110013 *tel* 616108 *telex* 31 2927 Bbc in *cables* Loncalling, Newdelhi.

**France:** 155 rue du Faubourg Saint-Honoré, BP 487 08, 75366 Paris, Cedex 08 *tel* 561-9700 *cables* Broadbrit, Paris *telex* 650341.

**Germany:** BBC Buero, 1 Berlin 12, Savignyplatz 6, W. Germany *tel* West Berlin 316773, 316263 *telex* Berlin 184469.

**Belgium:** P.O. Box 50, International Press Centre, 1041 Brussels *tel* Brussels 736-8015 *telex* 25912.

## BBC LOCAL RADIO STATIONS

Local Radio also affords opportunities for writers to submit short stories and plays. A number of stations hold play-writing or short story competitions where the winners have their work broadcast. Others consider original work from local writers. Material should be submitted to the Programme Organiser.

**Bedfordshire,** BBC Radio Bedfordshire, Hastings Street, Luton, Bedfordshire LU1 5BA *tel* (0582) 459111.

**Birmingham,** BBC Radio WM (West Midlands), Pebble Mill Road, Birmingham B5 7SD *tel* 021-472 5141 *telex* 339210.

**Bristol,** BBC Radio Bristol, 3 Tyndalls Park Road, Bristol BS8 1PP *tel* (0272) 741111 *telex* 449170.

**Cambridgeshire,** BBC Radio Cambridgeshire, Broadcasting House, 104 Hills Road, Cambridge CB2 1LD *tel* (0223) 315970 *telex* 817776.

**Cleveland,** BBC Radio Cleveland, P.O. Box 1548, Broadcasting House, Newport Road, Middlesbrough, Cleveland TS1 5DG *tel* (0642) 225211 *telex* 58203.

**Cornwall,** BBC Radio Cornwall, Phoenix Wharf, Truro, Cornwall TR1 1UA *tel* (0872) 75421 *telex* 45728.

**Coventry,** BBC CWR, 25 Warwick Road, Coventry CV1 2WR *tel* (0203) 559911.

**Cumbria,** BBC Radio Cumbria, Hilltop Heights, London Road, Carlisle CA1 2NA *tel* (0228) 31661 *telex* 64165.

**Derby,** BBC Radio Derby, 56 St. Helen's Street, Derby DE1 3HY *tel* (0332) 361111 *telex* 37257.

**Devon,** BBC Radio Devon, P.O. Box 100, St. David's Hill, Exeter, Devon EX4 4DB *tel* (0392) 215651 *telex* 42440.

**Essex,** BBC Essex, 198 New London Road, Chelmsford, Essex CM2 9AB *tel* (0245) 262393.

**Furness,** BBC Radio Furness, Broadcasting House, Hartington Street, Barrow-in-Furness, Cumbria *tel* (0229) 36767.

**Gloucestershire,** BBC Radio Gloucestershire, London Road, Gloucester GL1 1SW *tel* (0452) 308585.

**Guernsey,** BBC Radio Guernsey, Commerce House, Les Banques, St. Peter Port, Guernsey *tel* (0481) 28977 *telex* 4191456.

**Hereford and Worcester,** BBC Hereford and Worcester, Hylton Road, Worcester WR2 5WW *tel* (0905) 748485.

**Humberside,** BBC Radio Humberside, 63 Jameson Street, Hull HU1 3NU *tel* (0482) 23232 *telex* 527031.

**Jersey,** BBC Radio Jersey, Broadcasting House, Rouge Bouillon, St. Helier, Jersey *tel* (0534) 70000 *telex* 4192381.

**Kent,** BBC Radio Kent, Sun Pier, Chatham, Kent ME4 4EZ *tel* (0634) 46284 *telex* 965011.

**Lancashire,** BBC Radio Lancashire, King Street, Blackburn, Lancashire BB2 2EA *tel* (0254) 62411 *telex* 63491.

**Leeds,** BBC Radio Leeds, Broadcasting House, Woodhouse Lane, Leeds LS2 9PN *tel* (0532) 442131 *telex* 557230.

**Leicester,** BBC Radio Leicester, Epic House, Charles Street, Leicester LE1 3SH *tel* (0533) 27113 *telex* 34401.

**Lincolnshire,** BBC Radio Lincolnshire, Radio Buildings, Newport, Lincoln LN1 3DF *tel* (0522) 40011 *telex* 56186.

**London,** BBC Radio London, 35A Marylebone High Street, London W1A 4LG *tel* 01-486 7611 *telex* 267223.

**Manchester,** BBC Radio Manchester, P.O. Box 90, New Broadcasting House, Oxford Road, Manchester M60 1SJ *tel* 061-228 3434 *telex* 668708.

**Merseyside,** BBC Radio Merseyside, 55 Paradise Street, Liverpool L1 3BP *tel* 051-708 5500 *telex* 629364.

**Newcastle,** BBC Radio Newcastle, Broadcasting Centre, Barrack Road, Newcastle-upon-Tyne NE99 1RN *tel* 091-232 4141 *telex* 537007.

**Norfolk,** BBC Radio Norfolk, Norfolk Tower, Surrey Street, Norwich, Norfolk NR1 3PA *tel* (0603) 617411 *telex* 975515.

**Northampton,** BBC Radio Northampton, P.O. Box 1107, Abingdon Street, Northampton NN1 2BE *tel* (0604) 20621 *telex* 311812.

**Nottingham,** BBC Radio Nottingham, York House, Mansfield Road, Nottingham NG1 3JB *tel* (0602) 415161 *telex* 37464.

**Oxford,** BBC Radio Oxford, 242-254 Banbury Road, Oxford OX2 7DW *tel* (0865) 53411 *telex* 83571.

**Sheffield,** BBC Radio Sheffield, Ashdell Grove, 60 Westbourne Road, Sheffield S10 2QU *tel* (0742) 686185 *telex* 54400.

**Shropshire,** BBC Radio Shropshire, 2-4 Boscobel Drive, Shrewsbury, Shropshire SY1 3TT *tel* (0743) 248484.

**Solent,** BBC Radio Solent, South Western House, Canute Road, Southampton SO9 4PJ *tel* (0703) 631311 *telex* 47420.

**Stoke-on-Trent,** BBC Radio Stoke-on-Trent, Conway House, Cheapside, Hanley, Stoke-on-Trent, Staffordshire ST1 1JJ *tel* (0782) 208080 *telex* 36104.

**Sussex,** BBC Radio Sussex, Marlborough Place, Brighton BN1 1TU *tel* (0273) 680231 *telex* 87313.

**Swindon,** BBC Wiltshire Sound, Broadcasting House, Prospect Place, Swindon SN1 3RW *tel* (0793) 513626.

**York,** BBC Radio York, 20 Bootham Row, York YO3 7BR    *tel* (0904) 641351    *telex* 57444.

# Independent Broadcasting

**Independent Broadcasting Authority,** 70 Brompton Road, London, SW3 1EY    *tel* 01-584 7011    *fax* 01-589 5533. The Authority does not produce programmes, and material intended for broadcasting on the Authority's service should be addressed to the programme contractors, who are responsible for supplying programmes for transmission.

**Channel Four Television Company Ltd.,** 60 Charlotte Street, London W1P 2AX    *tel* 01-631 4444    *fax* 01-637 4872. Commissions programmes (does not make them) for broadcast during the whole week throughout the United Kingdom.

## TELEVISION

*Material required* by the programme contractors as listed below depends upon the contract held by the Company, i.e. London mid-week programmes will obviously differ from those for the Midlands. In all cases scripts are preferred to synopses. Programmes should be planned with natural breaks for the insertion of advertisements. These companies also provide some programmes for Channel 4.

**Anglia Television Ltd.,** Anglia House, Norwich NR1 3JG    *tel* (0603) 615151    *fax* (0603) 631032. 48 Leicester Square, London WC2H 7FB    *tel* 01-321 0101    *fax* 01-930 8499. Provides programmes for the East of England during the whole week and drama and natural history programmes. Drama submissions only through an accredited agency or similar source.

**Border Television plc,** The Television Centre, Carlisle CA1 3NT    *tel* (0228) 25101. Provides programmes for The Borders and the Isle of Man, during the whole week. Occasionally scripts are commissioned from outside sources. Suggestions should be sent to the Controller of Programmes in Carlisle.

**Central Independent Television plc,** Central House, Broad Street, Birmingham B1 2JP    *tel* 021-643 9898. East Midlands Television Centre, Nottingham NG7 2NA    *tel* (0602) 863322. Provides programmes to the ITV Network and the East and West Midlands seven days a week. Central's requirements are constantly changing, and interested professional writers are asked to contact the Script Unit in Nottingham for information. Writers are advised to send photocopies rather than original unsolicited manuscripts.

**Channel Television,** The Television Centre, St. Helier, Jersey, C.I.    *tel* (0534) 68999    *telex* 4192265 (CTV JYG)    *fax* (0534) 59446. Provides programmes for the Channel Islands during the whole week relating mainly to Channel Islands news and current affairs.

**Grampian Television plc,** Queens Cross, Aberdeen AB9 2XJ    *tel* (0224) 646464    *telex* 73151. Albany House, 68 Albany Road, West Ferry, Dundee DD5 1NW    *tel* (0382) 739363. 23-25 Huntly Street, Inverness IV3 5PR    *tel* (0463) 242624. 29 Glasshouse Street, London W1R 5RG    *tel* 01-439 3141. Provides programmes for North Scotland during the whole week.

**Granada Television Limited,** Granada Television Centre, Manchester M60 9EA    *tel* 061-832 7211 and 36 Golden Square, London W1R 4AH    *tel* 01-734

8080. Provides programmes for North-West England throughout the week. Granada has for some time largely pursued a policy of initiating its own dramatic material or adaptations of established works like *The Jewel in the Crown*, Brideshead Revisited, *Lost Empires*, *The Adventures of Sherlock Holmes*. It is, therefore, advisable for writers to make their approach through agents who would have some knowledge of Granada's current requirements.

**HTV Ltd.,** HTV Wales, The Television Centre, Culverhouse Cross, Cardiff CF5 6XJ   *tel* (0222) 590590. HTV West, The Television Centre, Bristol BS4 3HG   *tel* (0272) 778366. 99 Baker Street, London W1M 2AJ   *tel* 01-486 4311. The Television Centre, Pontcanna, Cardiff CF1 9XL   *tel* (0222) 590590. The Civic Centre, Mold, Clwyd CH7 1YA   *tel* (0352) 55331. Provides programmes for Wales and West of England during the whole week. Produces programmes for home and international sales.

**LWT,** South Bank Television Centre, London SE1 9LT   *tel* 01-620 1620. Provides programmes for Greater London and much of the Home Counties area from Friday 5.15 p.m. to Monday 6.00 a.m.

**Scottish Television plc,** Cowcaddens, Glasgow G2 3PR   *tel* 041-332 9999. Provides programmes for Central Scotland during the whole week, *Material:* Scripts for contemporary series and ideas and formats for programmes with a Scottish or international flavour. Approach in the first instance to the Controller of Drama, Robert Love.

**TVS Entertainment plc,** Television Centre, Southampton SO9 5HZ   *tel* (0703) 634211   *telex* 477217   *fax* (0703) 834380. Television Centre, Vinters Park, Maidstone ME14 5NZ   *tel* (0622) 691111 and 60-61 Buckingham Gate, London SW1E 6AJ   *tel* 01-828 9898. Provides programmes for the South and South East of England during the whole week.

**Thames Television plc,** 306 Euston Road, London NW1 3BB   *tel* 01-387 9494; 149 Tottenham Court Road, London W1P 9LL   *tel* 01-387 9494. Provides programmes for the London area from Monday to Friday 5.15 p.m.
Currently not accepting unsolicited programme material. Enquiries only, in writing to: Central Registry, Thames Television plc, Teddington Studios, Teddington, Middlesex TW11 9NT.

**TSW-Television South West Ltd.,** Derry's Cross, Plymouth PL1 2SP   *tel* (0752) 663322   *telex* 45566   *fax* (0752) 671970. Provides programmes for South-West England during the whole week.

**Tyne Tees Television Ltd,** The Television Centre, City Road, Newcastle upon Tyne NE1 2AL   *tel* (091) 261 0181   *telex* 53279   *fax* (091) 222 0013. 15 Bloomsbury Square, London WC1A 2LJ   *tel* 01-405 8474   *telex* 266316   *fax* 01-242 2441. Ground Floor, United House, Piccadilly, York YO1 1PQ   *tel* (0904) 610666   *fax* (0904) 610236. Corporation House, Corporation Road, Middlesbrough TS1 2RX   *tel* (0642) 219181   *fax* (0642) 249961. Serving the North of England seven days a week, 24 hours a day.

**Ulster Television, plc,** Havelock House, Ormeau Road, Belfast BT7 1EB   *tel* (0232) 328122   *fax* (0232) 246695. 6 York Street, London, W1H 1FA   *tel* 01-486 5211. Provides programmes for Northern Ireland during the whole week. Company staff provide majority of scripts, but occasionally they are commissioned from other sources.

**Yorkshire Television, Ltd.,** The Television Centre, Leeds LS3 1JS   *tel* (0532) 438283   *telex* 557232. Television House, 32 Bedford Row, London WC1R 4HE   *tel* 01-242 1666   *telex* 295386. Yorkshire Television is a Network

Company which produces many programmes for the ITV Network and the Yorkshire area throughout the week.

**Independent Television News, Ltd.,** ITN House, 48 Wells Street, London W1P 4DE   *tel* 01-637 2424. Provides the national and international news programmes for all ITV areas.

**TV-am plc,** Breakfast Television Centre, Hawley Crescent, London NW1 8EF   *tel* 01-267 4300. A national service of Independent breakfast television seven days a week.

## INDEPENDENT LOCAL RADIO

**ILR Aberdeen:** NorthSound Radio, 45 Kings Gate, Aberdeen AB2 6BL   *tel* (0224) 632234.

**ILR Ayr:** West Sound, Radio House, 54 Holmston Road, Ayr KA7 3BD   *tel* (0292) 283662.

**ILR Belfast:** Downtown Radio, P.O. Box 96, Kiltonga Industrial Estate, Newtownards, Northern Ireland BT23 4ES   *tel* (0247) 815555.

**ILR Birmingham:** BRMB Radio, P.O. Box 555, Radio House, Aston Road North, Aston, Birmingham B6 4BX   *tel* 021-359 4481-9.

**ILR Borders:** Radio Borders Ltd, c/o Radio Forth, Forth House, Forth Street, Edinburgh EH1 3LF   *tel* 031-556 9255.

**ILR Bournemouth:** Two Counties Radio, 5-7 Southcote Road, Bournemouth BH1 3LR   *tel* (0202) 294881.

**ILR Bradford:** Pennine FM, P.O. Box 235, Pennine House, Forster Square, Bradford BD1 5NP   *tel* (0274) 731521.

**ILR Brighton:** Southern Sound, Radio House, Franklin Road, Portslade, East Sussex BN4 2SS   *tel* (0273) 422288.

**ILR Bristol:** GWR, P.O. Box 2000, Bristol BS99 7SN   *tel* (0272) 279900.

**ILR Bury St. Edmunds:** Saxon Radio, Long Brackland, Bury St. Edmunds, Suffolk IP33 1JY   *tel* (0284) 701511.

**ILR Cambridge & Newmarket:** CN.FM, c/o Hereward Radio, P.O. Box 225, Queensgate Centre, Peterborough PE1 1XJ   *tel* (0733) 46225.

**ILR Cardiff:** Red Dragon Radio, Radio House, West Canal Wharf, Cardiff CF1 5JX   *tel* (0222) 384041.

**ILR Coventry:** Mercia Sound, Hertford Place, Coventry CV1 3TT   *tel* (0203) 28451.

**ILR Doncaster:** FM Hallam, P.O. Box 194, Hartshead, Sheffield S1 1GP   *tel* (0742) 71188.

**ILR Dundee/Perth:** Radio Tay, P.O. Box 123, Dundee DD1 9UF   *tel* (0382) 29551.

**ILR East Kent:** Invicta Radio, 15 Station Road East, Canterbury CT1 2RB   *tel* (0227) 67661.

**ILR Eastbourne/Hastings:** Southern Sound, P.O. Box 2000, Brighton BN41 2SS   *tel* (0273) 430111.

**ILR Edinburgh:** Radio Forth, Forth House, Forth Street, Edinburgh EH1 3LF   *tel* 031-556 9255.

**ILR Exeter/Torbay:** DevonAir Radio, The Studio Centre, 35-37 St. David's Hill, Exeter EX4 4DA    *tel* (0392) 30703.

**ILR Glasgow:** Radio Clyde, Clydebank Business Park, Clydebank, Glasgow G81 2RX    *tel* 041-941 1111.

**ILR Gloucester & Cheltenham:** Severn Sound, P.O. Box 388, Old Talbot House, 67 Southgate Street, Gloucester GL1 1TX    *tel* (0452) 423791.

**ILR Great Yarmouth & Norwich:** Radio Broadland, St. George's Plain, Colegate, Norwich NR3 1DD    *tel* (0603) 630621.

**ILR Guildford:** County Sound, The Friary, Guildford, Surrey GU1 4YX    *tel* (0483) 505566.

**ILR Hereford/Worcester:** Radio Wyvern, 5-6 Barbourne Terrace, Worcester WR1 3JM    *tel* (0905) 612212.

**ILR Humberside:** Viking FM, Commercial Road, Hull HU1 2SA    *tel* (0482) 25141.

**ILR Inverness,** Moray Firth Radio, P.O. Box 271, Inverness IV3 6SF    *tel* (0463) 224433.

**ILR Ipswich:** Radio Orwell, Electric House, Lloyds Avenue, Ipswich IP1 3HZ    *tel* (0473) 216971.

**ILR Leeds:** Radio Aire, P.O. Box 362, Leeds LS3 1LR    *tel* (0532) 452299.

**ILR Leicester:** Leicester Sound, Granville House, Granville Road, Leicester LE1 7RW    *tel* (0533) 551616.

**ILR Liverpool:** Radio City, P.O. Box 194, 8-10 Stanley Street, Liverpool L69 1LD    *tel* 051-227 5100.

**ILR London (General and Entertainment Service):** Capital Radio, Euston Tower, London NW1 3DR    *tel* 01-388 1288.

**ILR London (News & Information Service):** London Broadcasting Company (LBC), Gough Square, London EC4P 4LP    *tel* 01-353 1010.

**ILR Luton/Bedford:** Chiltern Radio, Chiltern Road, Dunstable, Bedfordshire LU6 1HQ    *tel* (0582) 666001.

**ILR Maidstone & Medway:** Invicta Radio, 37 Earl Street, Maidstone ME14 1PS    *tel* (0622) 679061.

**ILR Manchester:** Piccadilly Radio, 127-131 The Piazza, Piccadilly Plaza, Manchester M1 4AW    *tel* 061-236 9913.

**ILR Milton Keynes:** MKFM, Home Farm, Old Stratford, Milton Keynes MK19 6AX    *tel* (0582) 666001.

**ILR Newport (Gwent):** Red Dragon Radio, Radio House, West Canal Wharf, Cardiff CF1 5JX    *tel* (0222) 384041.

**ILR Northampton:** Hereward Road, P.O. Box 1557, 73 Abington Street, Northampton NN1 2HW    *tel* (0604) 29811.

**ILR Nottingham:** Radio Trent, 29-31 Castle Gate, Nottingham NG1 7AP    *tel* (0602) 581731.

**ILR Oxford/Banbury:** Fox FM, The Blackwell Group, Beaver House, Hythe Bridge Street, Oxford OX1 2ET    *tel* (0865) 792111.

**ILR Peterborough:** Hereward Radio, P.O. Box 225, Queensgate Centre, Peterborough, Cambs. PE1 1JX    *tel* (0733) 46225.

**ILR Plymouth:** Plymouth Sound, Earl's Acre, Alma Road, Plymouth PL3 4HX   *tel* (0752) 27272.

**ILR Portsmouth:** Ocean Sound, Whittle Avenue, Segensworth West, Fareham, Hants PO15 5PA   *tel* (0489) 589911.

**ILR Preston & Blackpool:** Red Rose Radio, P.O. Box 301, St. Paul's Square, Preston, Lancashire PR1 1YE   *tel* (0772) 556301.

**ILR Reading:** Radio 210 Thames Valley, P.O. Box 210, Reading RG3 5RZ *tel* (0734) 413131.

**ILR Reigate & Crawley:** Radio Mercury, Broadfield House, Brighton Road, Crawley RH11 9TT   *tel* (0293) 519161.

**ILR Sheffield & Rotherham:** FM Hallam, P.O. Box 194, Hartshead, Sheffield S1 1GP   *tel* (0742) 71188.

**ILR Southend/Chelmsford:** Essex Radio, Radio House, Clifftown Road, Southend-on-Sea, Essex SS1 1SX   *tel* (0702) 333711.

**ILR Stoke-on-Trent:** Signal Radio, Studio 257, 67-73 Stoke Road, Stoke-on-Trent, Staffordshire ST4 2SR   *tel* (0782) 417111.

**ILR Swansea:** Swansea Sound, Victoria Road, Gowerton, Swansea SA4 3AB   *tel* (0792) 893751.

**ILR Swindon/West Wiltshire:** GWR, P.O. Box 2000, Swindon, Wiltshire SN4 7EX   *tel* (0793) 853222.

**ILR Teesside:** TFM Radio, 74 Dovecot Street, Stockton-on-Tees, Cleveland TS18 1HB   *tel* (0642) 615111.

**ILR Tyne & Wear:** Metro FM, Long Rigg, Swalwell, Newcastle upon Tyne NE99 1BB   *tel* 091-488 3131.

**ILR Wolverhampton & Black Country:** Beacon Radio, P.O. Box 303, 267 Tettenhall Road, Wolverhampton WV6 0DQ   *tel* (0902) 757211.

**ILR Wrexham & Deeside:** Marcher Sound/Sain-Y-Gororau, The Studios, Mold Road, Gwersyllt, Wrexham, Clwyd LL11 4AF   *tel* (0978) 752202.

**Independent Radio News (IRN).** A subsidiary of LBC which acts as a news agency for all other ILR Companies by providing spoken and other live material and a teleprinter service. Address as LBC above.

# Overseas Radio and Television Companies

## AUSTRALIA

**Australian Broadcasting Corporation,** Box 9994, GPO, Sydney, NSW 2001. Manager for Europe: Australian Broadcasting Corporation, 54 Portland Place, London, W1N 4DY. The Australian Broadcasting Corporation is a statutory authority established by Act of Parliament and responsible to Parliament. It provides television and radio programmes in the national broadcasting service and operates Radio Australia. It operates six symphony orchestras and stages concerts throughout Australia.

ABC television restricts its production resources to work closely related to the Australian environment. For this reason scripts submitted from outside Australia in the field of television drama and short stories have little chance of success. ABC radio also looks principally to Australian writers for the basis of its drama output. However, ABC radio is interested in reading or auditioning new creative material of a high quality from overseas sources and this may be submitted in script or taped form. No journalistic material is required. Talks on international affairs are commissioned.

**Federation of Australian Commercial Television Stations,** 44 Avenue Road, Mosman, NSW 2088  *tel* 960 2622  *telex* 121542  *fax* 02-969 3520. There are at present 50 commercial television stations in Australia; all are members of FACTS.

The following six stations accept freelance material:

**ATN Channel 7,** Australian Television Network, Amalgamated Television Services Pty. Ltd., Television Centre, Epping, NSW 2121  *tel* 877 7777  *telegraphic address* Telecentre, Sydney  *telex* AA 20250  *fax* 877 7886. Willing to consider original television material of all types, especially 60 minute drama series/serials, 30 minute situation-comedy series and children's drama series/serials that have received a 'C' classification. Material should have an *Australian* background and deal with *Australian* characters. For series submit sample script with some future story-lines.

**BTQ Channel 7,** Brisbane TV Limited, Sir Samuel Griffith Drive, Mt. Coot-Tha, GPO Box 604, Brisbane 4001  *tel* (07)369 7777  *fax* 07-858 2970  *telegraphic address* Beeteeque. Writers should be Australian-based. Children's Educational-type series, children's entertainment programmes and local drama (Queensland writers only).

**HSV Channel 7,** HSV Channel 7 Pty. Ltd., 119 Wells Street, South Melbourne, Victoria 3205  *tel* 03-697-7777. For requirements see ATN Channel 7.

**National Nine Network** (TCN 9 Sydney; GTV 9 Melbourne; QTQ, 9 Brisbane; NWS 9 Adelaide; STW 9 Perth), c/o TCN Channel 9, 24 Artarmon Road, Willoughby 2068  *tel* 02-430 0444  *telex* A20514. *Director of Programmes* (drama and light enterainment): Ronald Haynes. *Drama Consultant:* Lynn Bayonas, Lynn Bayonas Productions, 3 Barncleuth Square, Kings Cross 2011. Interested in receiving material from freelance writers strictly on the basis of payment for material or ideas used. No necessity for writers to be Australian-based, but membership of the Australian Writers' Guild is helpful.

**NSW Channel 9,** Southern Television Corporation Pty. Ltd., 202 Tynte Street, PO Box 9, North Adelaide, South Australia 5006  *tel* 267 0111  *telegraphic address* Newsnine, Adelaide  *telex* 82238  *fax* (08) 267-3996.

**STW Channel 9,** Swan Television & Radio Broadcasters Limited, PO Box 99, Tuart Hill, Western Australia 6060  *tel* 349 9999  *telegraphic address* Swantel, Perth  *telex* AA92142  *fax* (09) 349-2110. Writers should be Australian-based.

## CANADA

**Canadian Broadcasting Corporation,** PO Box 500, Station 'A', Toronto, M5W 1E6 Ontario  *tel* 416-925-3311.

**Canadian Radio-television and Telecommunications Commission,** Ottawa, Ontario, K1A 0N2 *General information:*  *tel* (819) 997-0313. *Visual Ear*. 819-994-0423. The federal authority which regulates telecommunications and the broadcasting system in Canada.

## INDIA

**All India Radio,** Akashvani Bhavan, Parliament Street, New Delhi, 110 001 (*telex* AVDG 031-6585) is a part of the Ministry of Information and Broadcasting of the Government of India which operates the broadcasting network in the country. There are 97 stations covering almost the entire area of the country and catering to the various social, cultural and linguistic needs of the people. Programmes consist of news, music, talks, plays, discussions, documentary features and special audience programmes for women, children, industrial workers and rural audiences.

*External Services Division* of All India Radio broadcasts programmes in 23 languages. The object of these programmes is to entertain Indians abroad and keep them in touch with the events and developments in India.

*The Commercial Service* is broadcast over 29 AIR stations.

*The National Channel* commenced in May 1988.

**Television:** Director General, Doordarshan India (Television), Mandi House, Corpenicus Marg, New Delhi 110 001 *tel* 382094 *telex* 3166143. Covers most of India, providing a wide variety of programmes, both educational and for entertainment. Some commercial advertising.

## IRELAND

**Radio Telefis Eireann,** Donnybrook, Dublin 4 *tel* (01) 693111 *telex* 93700 *fax* 838140. The Irish national broadcasting service operating radio and television.

**Television:** script requirements: original television plays, length 52 minutes, preferably set in Ireland or of strong Irish interest. Plays should be sent to the Head of Drama. Guidelines on writing plays for television are available from the Head of Television Drama. Before submitting material to Current Affairs, Drama, Features, or Young People's programmes, authors are advised to write to the department in question.

**Radio:** talks and short stories (length 14 minutes) in Irish or English suitable for broadcasting: features, dramatic or narrative and plays are welcomed and paid for according to merit. Plays should run 30, 60 or 90 minutes. Guidelines on writing for radio are available from the R.T.E. Radio Drama Department, Radio Centre, Donnybrook, Dublin 4.

Recent broadcasting lesiglation allowed for the setting up of the **Irish Radio and Television Commission:** Marine House, Clanwilliam Court, Dublin 2 *tel* (01) 760966.

Independent, commercial, national and community radio services are due to be in operation in 1990, as well as an independent national television service.

## NEW ZEALAND

**Radio New Zealand Ltd,** Chief Executive, Beverley Wakem, PO Box 2092, Wellington, C1 *tel* 741-555 *fax* 741 440 *telex* NZ31031. A 24 hour state-owned radio enterprise controlling a NZ-wide group of commercial community stations and two public service non-commercial networks, and also a limited shortwave service directed primarily to the Southwest Pacific Islands and Southeastern Australia.

**Television New Zealand Ltd,** PO Box 3819, Auckland *tel* (09) 366 0831 *telex* NZ 63047 Tvnzho *fax* (09) 389 347. *Chairman:* Brian Corban; *Director General:* Julian Mountner. **Auckland Television Centre** *tel* (09) 792 880.

TVNZ is a state-owned enterprise with stations in all four main centres. It owns and operates Television One, Network Two and three subsidiary companies, South Pacific Pictures Ltd, Avalon Ltd and Broadcasting Communications Ltd.

**TVNZ Avalon Ltd,** PO Box 30 945, Lower Hutt, Wellington    *tel* (04) 666 969    *fax* (04) 678 959. *Managing Director:* Reg Russ.

**TVNZ Christchurch,** PO Box 1945, Christchurch    *tel* (03) 799 600    *fax* (03) 657 882.

**TVNZ Dunedin & TVNZ Natural History Unit,** PO Box 474, Dunedin    *tel* (024) 741 414    *fax* (024) 741 302.

**South Pacific Pictures Ltd,** PO Box 35 656, Browns Bay, Auckland 10    *tel* (09) 479 3000    *fax* (09) 479 3007. *Managing Director:* John McRae.

**Broadcasting Communications Ltd,** PO Box 2396, Wellington    *tel* (04) 741 2000    *fax* (04) 734 956. *Managing Director:* Arthur Stacey.

## SOUTH AFRICA

**South African Broadcasting Corporation,** Private Bag XI, Auckland Park 2006    *tel* 714-9111    *fax* 714-3106. Operates five national networks: Radio South Africa, Radio Suid-Afrika, Radio 5, Radio Orion, and Radio Allegro, and seven regional services, Radio Highveld, Radio Port Natal, Radio Good Hope, Radio Lotus, Radio Jacaranda, Radio Algoa, Radio Oranje. The nine radio services in Nguni and Sotho languages broadcast in Zulu, Xhosa, Southern Sotho, Northern Sotho, Tswana, Venda, Tsonga, Swazi and Ndebele. The External Service known as Radio RSA, *The Voice of South Africa*, transmits programmes to all corners of the world.

*Plays.* Most types are produced—classical and modern dramas, comedies and thrillers, original radio plays and adaptations of stories, etc. Contributions are welcomed in all sections. The most convenient lengths are 30, 60 and 90 minutes. The Afrikaans network also accepts high quality material for translation. Programmes are typical of modern commercial radio, and serials of 15-minute episodes are widely used. Series of self-contained episodes of 15, 30 or 60 minutes are also acceptable. Variety programmes of 30 minutes' duration are always in demand.

*Feature Programmes.* Material of topical, scientific and historical interest of 30 to 60 minutes' duration is welcomed.

*Talks.* Most are commissioned locally, but outstanding material of particular interest may be submitted. Most suitable length is 5, 10 and 15 minutes.

*Short Stories.* There are occasional openings for short stories of 1500-1800 words.

*Light Entertainment.* Variety material, light entertainment scripts, and light plays with music may be submitted. The SABC particularly needs first-class variety material.

*Youth and Children's Programmes.* Plays, talks, stories and serials may be submitted. Lengths: plays, up to 15 minutes, and 30 minutes for youth; stories, from 5 to 10 minutes.

It should be stressed that all outside contributors should take into consideration the fact that Radio South Africa caters for a South African public.

*Television.* There are four television services in seven languages.

# Markets for Screenplays

### JEAN McCONNELL

There have been setbacks for the British film industry recently. Nevertheless, a market still exists—particularly material being made for television or for videograms, with which many film companies are now very actively engaged.

The recommended approach is through a recognised literary agent, but most film companies have a story department to whom material can be sent for consideration. But it is a good idea to check with the company first to make sure it is worth your while.

It is a fact that many of the feature films these days are based on already best-selling books, but there are some companies, particularly those with a television outlet, which will sometimes accept unsolicited material if it seems to be exceptionally original. It is obviously sensible to try to sell your work to a company which is currently in active production, such as those listed below. *But again remember the best way to achieve success is through the knowledge and efforts of a literary agent.*

When a writer submits material direct to a company, some of the larger ones, usually those American based, may request that a Release Form be signed before they are prepared to read it. This document is ostensibly designed to absolve the company from any charge of plagiarism if they should be working on a similar idea; also to limit their liability in the event of any legal action. The writer must make up his own mind whether he wishes to sign this but, in principle, it is not highly recommended.

## Markets for Screenplays and Television Programmes

**Amalgamated Portman Productions,** Television Centre, Mobbs Lane, Epping, NSW 2121, Australia   *tel* 877 7777   *fax* 877 7886. Joint venture between Portman Productions London and the Australian Televison Network, producing for the Australian and International markets. Will consider original material for telefeatures, mini series and series, with an Australian background and featuring Australian characters.

**Buena Vista Productions Ltd,** 31-32 Soho Square, London W1V 6AP *tel* 01-734 8111   *telex* 21532 (will only consider material submitted through an agent). Television programmes.

**Children's Film and Television Foundation Ltd.,** Goldcrest Elstree Studios, Borehamwood, Herts. WD6 1JG   *tel* 01-953 0844   *fax* 01-207 0860.

**The Walt Disney Company Ltd.,** 31-32 Soho Square, London W1V 6AP   *tel* 01-734 8111   *telex* 21532   *fax* 01-439 8741 (will only consider material submitted through an agent). Films.

**Mark Forstater Productions Ltd,** 8a Trebeck Street, London W1Y 7RL   *tel* 01-408 0733   *telex* 8954665 Vbstlx G ref MFP   *fax* 01-499 8772. Films.

**Goldcrest Films and Television Ltd.,** (1981), 36-44 Brewer Street, London W1R 3HP   *tel* 01-437 8696. Queries to Scripts and Projects Department.

**Hammer Film Productions, Ltd.,** Goldcrest Elstree Studios, Borehamwood, Herts. WD6 1JG   *tel* 01-953 1600.

**HandMade Films** (1978), 26 Cadogan Square, London SW1X 0JP   *tel* 01-581 1265 (will only consider material submitted through an agent).

**ITC Entertainment Group Ltd,** 24 Nutford Place, London W1A 6AE   *tel* 01-262 3262   *fax* 01-724 0160. *Production Director:* Debra Allanson.

**Michael Klinger: Communications & Entertainment,** 19 Watford Road, Radlett, Herts. WD7 8LF   *tel* (0923 85) 3255   *fax* (0923 85) 5757. Films.

**London Film Productions Ltd.,** 44A Floral Street, London WC2E 9DA   *tel* 01-379 3366   *telex* 896805   *fax* 01-240 7065. *Head of Production and Development* and *Managing Director:* Rosie Bunting.

**Merchant Ivory Productions Ltd.** (1962). Hanover House, 14 Hanover Square, London W1R 0BE   *tel* 01-437 1200 and 439 4335   *telex* 94013757 Mipl G   *fax* 01-734 1570.

**Paramount Pictures (UK), Ltd.,** UIP House, 45 Beadon Road, London W6 0EG   *tel* 01-741 9041. Material only accepted through agents.

**Pergamon Educational Productions,** Hennock Road, Exeter EX2 8RP   *tel* (0392) 74121   *telex* 42749 Wheatn G   *fax* (0392) 217170. Member of the Maxwell Pergamon Publishing Corporation plc. *Publishing Manager:* Barry Sutcliffe. Educational programme-making for television, video, cable and satellite.

**Twentieth Century-Fox Productions Ltd.,** Twentieth Century House, 31/32 Soho Square, London W1V 6AP   *tel* 01-437 7766 (will only consider material submitted through an agent).

**Tyburn Productions Ltd.,** Pinewood Studios, Iver Heath, Bucks. SL0 0NH   *tel* (0753) 651700   *telex* 847505   *fax* (0753) 656844. Submissions to Gillian Garrow, Director of Research and Development.

**Warner Bros. Productions Ltd.,** 135 Wardour Street, London W1V 4AP   *tel* 01-437 5600 (will only consider material submitted through an agent).

**Welbeck Film Distributors Ltd.,** 52 Queen Anne Street, London W1M 9LA   *tel* 01-935 1186.

**Zenith Productions Ltd,** 15 St. George Street, London W1R 9DE   *tel* 01-499 8006   *cables* Zenithfilms London W1   *telex* 23348 Zenith   *fax* 01-895 9572. *Head of Development:* Archie Tait. No unsolicited scripts.

# Literary Agents Specialising in Plays, Films, Television and Radio

Full particulars about Agents and Notes to which special attention is called will be found in the section entitled **Agents.**

*US Literary Agents

A & B Personal Management Ltd.
Yvonne Baker Associates
*Georges Borchardt, Inc.
*Brandt & Brandt Literary Agents Inc.
Rosemary Bromley Literary Agency
*James Brown Associates Inc.
Serafina Clarke
Jonathan Clowes
Elspeth Cochrane Agency
Rosica Colin Ltd.
Jane Conway-Gordon
Cruickshank Cazenove Ltd.
Curtis Brown
*Liz Darhansoff Literary Agency
Reg Davis-Poynter
Felix De Wolfe
Susan Dunnett Management
*Ann Elmo Agency
Fact & Fiction Agency Ltd.
Film Rights, Ltd.
Laurence Fitch Ltd.
Jill Foster Ltd.
John French Artists Agency Ltd.
Eric Glass
David Grossman Literary Agency
Xandra Hardie Literary Agency
Hatton & Baker Ltd.
Duncan Heath Associates
David Higham Associates, Ltd.
Valerie Hoskins
Teresa Howard Associates
Michael Imison Playwrights Ltd.
International Scripts
John Johnson (Authors Agent) Ltd.
Juvenila
Frances Kelly Agency
Dieter Klein Associates
Peter Knight Agency
Lemon Unna & Durbridge Ltd.
*Ellen Levine Literary Agency Inc.
Babara Levy Literary Agency

Christopher Little Literary Agent.
London Independent Books, Ltd.
L. R. Associates
Andrew Mann Ltd.
Blanche Marvin
MBA Literary Agents
*Peter Miller Agency Inc.
Richard Milne
William Morris Agency (UK) Ltd.
*Harold Ober Associates Inc.
*Fifi Oscard Associates, Inc.
Mark Paterson & Associates
Penman Literary Agency
The Peters Fraser & Dunlop Group Ltd.
PVA Management Ltd.
Radala & Associates
Douglas Rae
Margaret Ramsay Ltd.
*Rodell, Marie-Frances Collin Literary Agency
Rostrum Literary Agency Ltd.
Tessa Sayle Agency
*Susan Schulman
*Scott Meredith Literary Agency Inc.
James Sharkey Associates Ltd.
The Sharland Organisation Ltd.
Anthony Sheil Associates, Ltd.
*Shukat Co. Ltd.
*Singer Media Corporation
Micheline Steinberg Playwrights' Agent
*Sterling Lord Literistic Inc.
*Roslyn Targ
Jon Thurley
Harvey Unna and Stephen Durbridge, Ltd.
Lorna Vestey
*Austin Wahl Agency Inc.
*Wallace Literary Agency Inc.
Warner Chappell Plays Ltd.
A. P. Watt Ltd.
*Rhoda Weyr Agency
*Williams Wesley Winant

# Illustration and design

## Opportunities for Freelance Artists

### CAMILLA BRYDEN-BROWN

FINE ART

Opportunities for freelance artists are more numerous than is generally supposed. For fine art such as painting, it is best to contact galleries, of which there are many in this country, particularly in London. It is worth remembering, though, that they have the choice of a large market and specialise in a fairly limited field. If you want to exhibit at these galleries, perhaps to have a one-man show, it is advisable to find out about the type of exhibitions they hold. This you can do by visiting each gallery yourself and assessing the current work. It is best to visit likely galleries frequently in order to get to know their work and how they function. *The Arts Review Yearbook* (£11.95, plus £2.00 postage and packing), published by Arts Review, 69 Faroe Road, London W14 0EL *tel* 01-603 7530 and 8533, contains a guide to London and Regional Galleries—including a description of the type of work in which they specialise and also a list of Art Organisations. If you decide to approach a gallery, it is usual to write to the director with a short description, and photographs of some of your work, with a stamped addressed envelope for their return. The photographs should be clear, but not necessarily up to reproduction quality. It is possible to take the photographs yourself, but most towns have commercial photographers who work freelance for industry. Ask for an estimate first. Some of the greetings-card manufacturers already listed in this book are interested in paintings for reproduction. It would be wiser to write to them, if possible enclosing good colour transparencies of your work, before becoming involved in the expense of packing and sending paintings by post or carrier. Other useful reference books for the artist are the *London Art and Artists Guide*, 5th edition (£6.95) and *The Artists Directory*, 3rd edition (£8.95); both published by Art Guide Publications, 35 Bedford Row, London WC1R 4JH *tel* 01-242 0946.

One of the best methods of displaying and selling paintings is at the annual Summer Exhibition at the Royal Academy in London. Anyone can submit work, which is put to the Selection Committee and the Hanging Committee. Sending in days are in April and these dates must be strictly adhered to. A handling fee allows artists to enter up to three pieces of work at currently £8.00 per entry. Should any subsequently be hung and sold the Royal Academy charges commission at 25% plus VAT. Full details will be found in the leaflet of regulations entitled *Notice to Artists* which is obtainable from early February each year by sending an sae to The Registry, 'Summer Exhibition', The Royal Academy of

Arts, Piccadilly, London W1V 0DS (*tel* 01-439 7438). This leaflet refers to the exhibition of the coming summer of that year. If requests for it are sent at other times of the year the Royal Academy can only send the leaflet from the previous February. Other exhibitions are listed in *Arts Review* (£1.95 fortnightly), which has a comprehensive exhibition guide for the whole of Great Britain, and the *Artist's and Illustrator's Magazine* (£1.50 monthly).

ILLUSTRATION AND DESIGN

For a career in the field of illustration and design it is advisable to have a training in illustration, and also in typography if possible. Although the latter is not absolutely essential, it is helpful to the artist and to the publisher. Now that desk top publishing and illustration software programs are available on personal computers the possibility of producing work with integrated type and drawing is fact. These programs and the printers and scanners are being improved at such speed that in the near future it will be practicable for an illustrator to present some work ready for press. Artists who launch into freelance work often do so gradually from the security of full-time employment, probably in the same field. It is useful to have the experience of working with a publisher or in an advertising agency or a studio first, as this gives the artist valuable background knowledge of suppliers and sources of work. Training in illustration can be obtained through a recognised course at art school, or through employment in a studio. Either method is an advantage, for even the most brilliantly gifted illustrator should know how to think in terms of printed work and to realise how work will reduce and reproduce.

Once an artist feels competent to accept commissions it is important to be available and reliable. Both these attributes are essential, and busy clients will not be bothered with artists who say vaguely that they had to go away or that the children were ill. Freelance work is a business, and will stand or fall by the competence or otherwise of the staff—you.

THE FOLIO

Artists who have already been in full-time employment in an advertising agency or publishing house will know of clients who are prepared to give them commissions, and if one commission is a success it will very often lead to another. For all artists, but particularly those with no connections, it is essential to make up a professional folio of work, spending some time and money on it, and showing as versatile a range of work as possible. For instance, it should include work in line, pencil, ink, line and tone, two or more colour line and full colour, and be on a variety of subjects. There are excellent folders, plastic envelopes or elaborate specimen books or cases containing plastic folders, for sale at most shops which stock equipment for designers. An overall colour scheme for your presentation helps to make your work look well-organised and professional. Designs or samples should be neatly trimmed and mounted on coloured cover paper (try black if in doubt) of a size to fit the folder or envelope. Paste the specimens of work on the cover paper, but do not use petroleum-based rubber solution if the sample of work is to be enclosed in a plastic envelope.

Gradually you will collect together printed specimens as the commissions increase, and your folio of work should be brought up to date all the time. Always get as many samples as you can beg, although if it is a book you may receive only one copy. In this case, see if you can get some extra dust-jackets so that should the first one become worn you can replace it; if necessary buy more copies of the book if that should also become worn. The publisher may well give you a discount on books on which you have worked. Any book specimens should be kept separately in plastic bags, but it would be expedient to ask for spare block pulls of your illustrations early on in the proceedings, and they should be mounted up in your specimen book. Try to keep your specimens immaculate.

When the specimen folder is complete it is time to type letters to the production manager of as many publishing houses as practicable, asking for an interview in order to show your work, whether for illustrations or for book-jackets, or both. It would be wise to design an attractive personal stationery range which can be an excellent advertisement of your work. There are print shops that will produce your design very well and advise you if you are not skilled in typography or finished artwork. Usually they print by lithography quickly and at a reasonable price. A letterheading, preferably A4 because this is the most popular size and therefore is easily filed, can also be used as a compliment slip, invoice and estimate if necessary. A business card can be very useful. Space these letters out, or you may find yourself with too many appointments in one week. The production managers will usually grant you interviews (be on time), since they are interested in seeing new work, and they will probably be helpful about prices too, if you have no experience in this field. Book-publishing houses as a rule are not able to pay as highly as advertising agencies or popular magazines but they are usually fair. Do not overlook educational departments of publishing houses for there is considerable scope for illustrating modern school books. You may have to accept low fees to begin with until you know your market and your worth, but you will be gaining valuable knowledge and experience. Newspapers are another source of work, also magazines.

At each interview it would be a good idea to ask if there is anyone else in the firm who would be interested in seeing your work, such as the advertising manager or in some firms the editors, who occasionally commission artists. Do not expect to be seen by other people in the firm at the same time as your first interview, but be prepared to come back another time. It would be better not to leave your samples to be seen by other people, particularly if you have only one folio. You will be needing your folio for other interviews, and there is a very real danger that it will go astray, or that specimens will be damaged beyond use, with no redress. If your work is liked and your first commission is satisfactory, you will often find that you will be recommended to other people in similar fields.

You would be very wise to make a contract with the publisher when commissioned. Some of the well-known illustrators have fought hard and long for fair conditions. The Society of Illustrators have produced a Standard Form of Contract. It is important for illustrators to realise that the artwork remains the property of the artist, and so does the copyright, and this includes commissioned work. You should make clear from the outset that the work belongs to you and that definitely you want it returned. Publishers have a sad history of losing artwork.

Advertising agencies frequently use the services of artists' agents, who can be good or bad, but if you are accepted on the books of a good one life will be much easier for you. Agents generally work very hard on behalf of both clients and artists: they take the brief, negotiate the price and commission you to do the work, usually taking 25 to 30 per cent of the fee. Although this percentage may seem high, you should remember that they do a lot of work on your behalf and invariably manage to get a more professional fee for you than you can obtain for yourself, even after the percentage has been deducted.

FEES

There is no definite rule in assessing fees. A simple method of calculation is to decide upon a weekly salary and the number of hours of work for a normal week. This salary is then divided by the number of hours, which gives a basic hourly rate. Rent, rates, heating, telephone and other general studio costs should be considered, materials bought especially for a commission have to be added to the invoice concerned. As a rough guide one third of a fee will be payable to the Inland Revenue. Time spent at meetings with clients and the travelling time and cost involved should be added to the time sheet.

This solution may appear to be simple but it will be seen that the hourly rate is high. Many clients offer low fees and it is sometimes necessary to choose between accepting work at little or no return when the result is a good specimen of work, or to do without work. One of the greatest problems to the freelance artist is the artist in full-time employment who is prepared to accept commissions out of hours for a lower fee. With no studio overheads and a regular salary the market is spoilt for the serious professional.

ADVERTISING AGENCIES

Advertising agencies employ art buyers who are very skilled and capable people and should be approached by a letter similar to that previously described, giving details of the type of work at which you are best. Here again, once you have obtained the interview and shown your work, you might ask if there is anyone else who would be interested, not necessarily at that moment.

STUDIOS

Studios exist in most cities, and the type of their work varies; some specialise in purely commercial work in finished lettering and finished artwork, and they employ highly skilled and extremely able artists. Often their work involves the use of airbrushes and photographic skills, but they do sometimes employ free-lance artists for specific commissions, and may well like to have photocopies of your work on file in case they need drawings or diagrams for catalogues or similar uses. Technical drawing is called technical drawing with good reason and requires specific training. If you feel your work would be of interest to a studio, write to the studio manager and ask for an interview. Should they ask for photographs of your work, a commercial photographic studio will prepare these for you. If you wish to have photographs made, the photographic studio will help you with the details and give you prices before they take on the work. Photocopies may be acceptable, especially now that colour copying is available. The studio might offer to photocopy work which they might like to keep for future reference.

GRAPHIC DESIGNERS

A graphic designer, who may be running a one-man studio of his own and doing freelance design and typography (designing for printing), may also use illustrators from time to time. They will not be able to use your work all the time, even if they like it, as not all their commissions require drawings. The more versatile you are the more opportunities are available to you, and artists skilled only in very specialised fields, such as lettering and illumination, usually know where to offer their work.

IMPORTANCE OF RELIABILITY

Remember also that once you have started to get commissions, you must be accurate and reliable, as well as available. If you are given a date for the work, it must be presented on time, even if this means sitting up half the night before. Do not, for example, fall back on the excuse of mild illness or you will lose sympathy and understanding should you have the misfortune to be more seriously ill. Once you have received the commission you are part of a team, even though you may not know the other members of it. There are often unforeseen events which hold up production anyway, and it is as well to see that you do not come to be considered one. It is wise to take trouble over the presentation, and you have only yourself to blame if you have not protected your finished work adequately. It is distressing to have one's precious work destroyed or damaged, the more so if it means doing it all again.

You will discover that once you have started freelance work your commissions will build up gradually, although most artists have some periods when there is little work available. Use these 'rests' advantageously to prepare more specimen drawings and to experiment with new techniques and equipment, and to make sure your folio is ready to show again. At such times you should be looking for new outlets, visiting more agencies and publishers, or checking with the ones you have visited in the past.

Above all decide whether or not you really want to do this work: are you sure it is not just a pleasant day-dream with the appeal of being called an artist. It is hard work, but if you have ability and are consistent, reliable, enthusiastic and optimistic, even at those times when there is a lull, then you will be happy and successful.

# Markets for Artists

## ART AGENTS AND COMMERCIAL ART STUDIOS

In their own interests Artists are advised to make preliminary enquiries before submitting work, and to ascertain terms of work. Commission varies but averages 25-30 per cent. **The Association of Illustrators** (full details under **Societies**) provides a valuable service for illustrators, agents and clients.

**A.L.I. Press Agency, Ltd.,** Boulevard Anspach 111-115, B9—1000 Brussels, Belgium *tel* 02 512.73.94. *Director:* G. Lans. Cartoons, comics, strips, puzzles, entertainment features, illustrations for covers, posters in syndication. All feature material for newspapers and magazines. The biggest choice in picture stories for children and adults. Market for transparencies.

**Allied Artists Ltd,** 24 York Street, London W1H 1FE *tel* 01-487 2750 *fax* 01-487 2753. *Director:* G. R. Mills. Specialising in realistic figure illustration particularly for magazines, bookjackets, video and advertising, and also other illustration styles for promotions and publishing. Extensive stocks of second rights illustrations for syndication.

**Associated Freelance Artists Limited,** 19 Russell Street, London WC2B 5HP *tel* 01-836 2507-8. *Directors:* Eva Morris, Doug FitzMaurice. Freelance illustrators mainly in children's and educational fields; strip illustration; book design; character merchandising; greeting cards.

**Beint & Beint** (1976), 3 Leigh Street, London WC1H 9EW *tel* 01-383 4363 *fax* 01-387 7206. *Proprietor:* Michele Beint. Illustrations in a variety of styles for advertising, design groups and some publishing.

**David Lewis Illustration Agency** (1974), Worlds End Studios, 134 Lots Road, London SW10 0RJ *tel* 01-351 4333 *telex* 893851 Wrenst G *fax* 01-351 5044. *Contacts:* David Lewis and Matthew Doyle. All types of illustration for a variety of applications. Sae with samples essential. *Average rate of commission:* 25%-30%.

**Ian Fleming Associates Ltd** (1970), 1 Wedgwood Mews, 12-13 Greek Street, London W1V 5LW *tel* 01-734 8701 *fax* 01-439 3400. *Managing Director:* Ian Fleming. Illustration and lettering for advertising and publishing. *Rate of commission* 33⅓%.

**The Garden Studio** (1929), 5 Broad Court, Covent Garden, London WC2B 5QH *tel* 01-836 3653 *fax* 01-240 2704. *Managing Agents:* John Havergal, Harry Lyon-Smith. All illustration markets covered. *Commission* 25-33%.

**Simon Girling & Associates** (1985), The Old Station, Station Road, Hadleigh, Suffolk IP7 5JE *tel* (0473) 824083 *fax* (0473) 827846. *Partners:* Simon Girling, Juliette Clarke. Illustrations for book publishing (childrens and adult), encyclopaedias, magazines, dust jackets, greeting cards. *Commission:* 25%.

**Graham-Cameron Illustration** (1988), 10 Church Street, Willingham, Cambridge CB4 5HT *tel* (0954) 60444 *fax* (0954) 61353. *Partners:* Mike Graham-Cameron, Helen Graham-Cameron. All forms of illustration for book publishers, advertising agencies, magazines and journals. Specialises in children's and educational markets.

**John Hodgson Agency** (1965), 1 Charlotte Street, London W1P 1DH   *tel* 01-580 3773   *fax* 01-636 1657. Illustrations for advertising, publishing, design. *Rate of commission:* 25%.

**Image by Design** (1987), 46 Castle Street, Frome, Somerset BA11 3BW   *tel* (0373) 61323. *Partners:* John R. Brown, Burniece M. Williamson. Artwork for prints, greeting cards, calendars, posters, stationery, book publishing, jigsaw puzzles, tableware, ceramics. *Commission:* negotiable.

**Libba Jones Associates** (1983), Hopton Manor, Hopton, Nr Wirksworth, Derbyshire DE4 4DF   *tel* (062 985) 353   *fax* (062 985) 577. High quality artwork and design for china, greetings cards and gift wrap, jigsaw puzzles, calendars, prints, posters, stationery, book illustration, fabric design. Submission of samples required for consideration.

**Juvenilia.** *Proprietor:* Mrs. Rosemary Bromley, Avington, Winchester, Hants SO21 1DB   *tel* (096278) 656. Professional artwork for the children's market considered. Picture books—particularly author illustrated. No games or play books. Preliminary letter with sae. Terms 20%. Return postage for artwork and acknowledgement imperative.

**Linden Artists Ltd** (1962) 86 Petty France, London SW1H 9EA   *tel* 01-222 3050 and 4065   *fax* 01-233 0175. Illustrations for advertising, publishing, packaging. *Rate of commission:* from 25%.

**London Art Services Ltd.,** 175 Bermondsey Street, London SE1 3UW   *tel* 01-403 4181. Artists, designers, illustrators and photographers. Art studio offering service in illustration, lettering, general art work, photography.

**John Martin Artists, Ltd.,** 5 Wardour Street, London W1V 3HE   *tel* 01-734 9000   *fax* 01-734 9770. *Directors:* W. Bowen-Davies, C. M. Bowen-Davies, B. L. Bowen-Davies. *Production Manager:* W. Bowen-Davies. Illustrations for children (educational and fictional), dust jackets, paperbacks, magazines, encyclopaedias, advertising.

**Meiklejohn Illustration** (1971), 28 Shelton Street, Covent Garden, London WC2H 9JN   *tel* 01-240 2077   *fax* 01-836 0199. All types of illustration.

**N. E. Middleton Ltd,** 44 Great Russell Street, London WC1B 3PA   *tel* 01-580 1999   *fax* 01-436 8760. General.

**Miss Carter Publications** (1972), 25 Silverwell Street, Bolton BL1 1PP   *tel* (0204) 386608. *Partners:* Keith and Patricia Lee. Fine art print publishers and artists agents.

**Maggie Mundy Illustrators' Agency,** The Studio, 206 Hammersmith Road, London W6   *tel* 01-741 5862 and 748 9458   *fax* 01-748 5532. Represents 30 artists for all aspects of illustration in publishing and advertising.

**Oxford Illustrators Ltd** (1968), Aristotle Lane, Oxford OX2 6TR   *tel* (0865) 512331   *fax* (0865) 512408. Studio of 35 full-time illustrators working for publishers, business and industry—science, technical, airbrush, graphic, medical, biological, botanical, figure, cartoon, maps, diagrams, graphs. Macintosh generated artwork with Linotronic 300 output.

**Rogers & Co., Artists' Agents**—now **Temple Rogers Artists' Agency.**

**Russell & Russell Associates** (1987), 26 Stockport Village, Hooper Street, Stockport, Cheshire SK1 1AY   *tel* 061-474 7131. *Partners:* George Russell, Janice Russell. All artwork considered for greeting cards, calendars, prints, posters, decorative stationery, advertising. *Rates:* 30%.

**Specs Art Agency** (1982), 1 Clarence Road, Cheltenham, Glos., GL52 2AY    *tel* (0242) 515951    *fax* (0242) 518862. *Director:* Roland Berry. High quality illustration work for advertisers, publishers and all other forms of visual communication.

**Temple Rogers Artists' Agency**, Room 29, Russell Chambers, The Piazza, Covent Garden, London WC2E 8AA    *tel* 01-379 0441. Illustrations for children's educational books, picture strips and magazine illustrations. Specialising in realistic figure drawing. *Commission:* by arrangement.

**Michael Woodward Licensing** (1980), Parlington Hall, Parlington, Aberford, West Yorkshire LS25 3EG    *tel* (0532) 813913    *fax* (0532) 813911. *Proprietor:* Michael R. Woodward. International art agency and art library with offices in New York and Antwerp. Specialists in greeting cards, posters, prints, calendars. Character merchandising division. Terms on application. Freelance artists please send samples.

**Young Artists** (1970), 144 Royal College Street, London NW1 0TA    *tel* 01-267 9661    *fax* 01-284 0486. Book covers, editorial, advertising. *Average rate of commission:* 30%.


## DRAWINGS, DESIGNS AND VERSES FOR CARDS, ETC.

In their own interest artists are advised to write giving details of the work which they have to offer, and asking for requirements before submitting the work.
    *Member of the Greeting Card and Calendar Association.

**Arnold Barton Cards Ltd.**—see **Hambledon Studios.**

**Athena International,** P.O. Box 918, Harlow, Essex CM20 2DU    *tel* (0279) 641125. *Art Directors:* P. Rodriguez, T. Jones, T. Taffs. Designs for greetings cards, gift tags, gift wrap, and general stationery. Paintings and illustrations of a professional standard for reproduction as prints and posters. S.A.E. essential for return of work.

*****Carlton Cards Ltd.,** Mill Street East, Dewsbury, West Yorkshire WF12 9AW    *tel* 465200.

**C.C.A. Stationery Ltd.,** Eastway, Fulwood, Preston PR2 4WS    *tel* (0772) 794508. Publishers of personalised wedding stationery and Christmas cards. Pleased to consider any original artwork but verses not required.

**Dryad,** P.O. Box 38, Northgates, Leicester LE1 9BU    *tel* (0533) 510405    *telex* 341766 Dryad G    *fax* (0533) 515015. Dryad *500 Series,* full colour craft booklets, workcards and patterns.

*****Simon Elvin Ltd** (1978), Wooburn Industrial Park, Wooburn Green, Bucks. HP10 0PE    *tel* (06285) 26711. *Directors:* S.P. Elvin, J.E. Elvin. Drawings.

**Fine Art Graphics Ltd.** (Incorporating **Raphael Tuck & Sons Ltd.**), Dawson Lane, Dudley Hill, Bradford BD4 6HW    *tel* (0274) 689514    *telex* 517669    *fax* (0274) 651218. *Managing Director:* D. B. Roxburgh; *Studio Manager:* N. Rae. Fine art, greeting card and calendar publishers.

*****Giesen & Wolff** (1908), Kaygee House, Dallington, Northampton NN5 7QW    *tel* (0604) 55411    *telex* 311009 Kaygee G    *fax* (0604) 759157. *Director:* Gordon Wood. Illustrations: floral studies, child and baby figures. Will consider verses.

**Hambledon Studios Ltd,** Hambledon House, Marlborough Road, Accrington, Lancashire BB5 6BX    *tel* (0254) 872266    *telex* 635169 Cardac G    *fax* (0254)

872079. *Brands:* Arnold Barton, Donny Mac, Reflections, New Image. *Art Managers:* D. Jaundrell, J. Ashton, D. Fuller. Designs suitable for reproduction as greetings cards.

*Hayes Greeting Card Publishers Ltd.** (1984), Thames View, Newtown Road, Henley-on-Thames, Oxon RG9 1HQ   *tel* (0491) 410454. *Directors:* M.S. Belsten, R.H. Parker. Artwork: floral, cute, traditional.

*Jarrold & Sons Ltd** (1770), Colour Publications, Barrack Street, Norwich NR3 1TR   *tel* (0603) 660211   *telex* 97497   *telegraphic address* Jarrold, Norwich   *fax* (0603) 662748. *Directors:* P.J. Jarrold, R.E. Jarrold, A.C. Jarrold, P. Sharman, D. Clark, R. Bussey, G. Bloxsom, P. Merttens. Drawings, transparencies (35mm or larger). Postcards, calendars, pictorial books on natural history, topography, hobbies, architecture. No verses.

**Kardonia Ltd.,** Farrier Street, Worcester WR1 3BH   *tel* (0905) 611294.

**Leeds Postcards** (1979), P.O. Box 84, Leeds LS1 1HU   *tel* (0532) 468649. Workers co-operative. Publishers and producers of campaign postcards for the labour, environmental, women's and international justice movements.

*Henry Ling & Son (London) Ltd.,** Chiddingstone Causeway, Nr. Tonbridge, Kent TN11 8JP   *tel* (0892) 870333   *telex* 8813271 Gecoms G ref H087   *fax* (0892) 870466. Artwork for greeting cards; no verses.

**The Medici Society, Ltd.,** 34-42 Pentonville Road, London N1 9HG   *tel* 01-837 7099. Requirements: paintings suitable for reproduction as large prints or greeting cards. Preliminary letter requested.

**Miss Carter Publications** (1972), 25 Silverwell Street, Bolton BL1 1PP   *tel* (0204) 386608. Oil and watercolour paintings to professional standards.

**Montague Ward**, Lime Trees, Cousley Wood, Wadhurst, East Sussex TN5 6EY   *tel* (089288) 3673. *Proprietor:* Kate Wilson. Artwork or transparencies (preferably 5″ × 4″) for greeting cards, prints, calendars, jigsaws, tableware, ceramics, book illustration. Preliminary letter with small selection of work and return postage requested.

*Panache Studio Ltd** (1985), Station Road, Henley on Thames, Oxon RG9 1LQ   *tel* (0491) 578383   *telex* 847279 HMK HO G   *fax* (0491) 578817. Drawings, humorous verses.

*Photo Production Ltd,** Featherby Road, Gillingham, Kent ME8 6PJ   *tel* (0634) 33241. Artwork for greeting card design; will consider verses.

*Rainbow Cards Ltd** (1977), Post Office Buildings, Station Road, Albrighton, Wolverhampton WV7 3QH   *tel* (090 722) 4347. *Directors:* M. Whitehouse, R. Fellows, J.F. Whitehouse, I. Mackintosh. Drawings for greeting cards; will consider verses.

**Felix Rosenstiel's Widow & Son, Ltd.,** Fine Art Publishers, 33-35 Markham Street, London SW3 3NR   *tel* 01-352 3551. Invite offers of originals of a professional standard for reproduction as picture prints for the picture framing trade. Oil paintings and strong water-colours. Any type of subject considered. Also subjects for decorative stationery trade.

*Royle Publications, Ltd.,** Royle House, Wenlock Road, London N1 7ST   *tel* 01-253 7654. Greeting cards, calendars, fine art reproductions and social stationery. Only accept work in colour.

*Rust Craft Greeting Cards (U.K.) Ltd.**—see **Carlton Cards Ltd.**

**\*Scandecor Ltd** (1967), 3 Armadale Road, Feltham, Middlesex TW14 0LU   *tel* 01-890 8174   *telex* 934367   *fax* 01-844 0926. *Directors:* G. Huldtgren, A. Inghammar. Drawings all sizes.

**\*W. N. Sharpe Ltd.** Bingley Road, Bradford BD9 6SD   *tel* (0274) 542244   *telex* 51408   *fax* (0274) 496099. Greetings cards, gift wrap. Artwork in colour, verses considered.

**Solomon & Whitehead (Guild Prints) Ltd.**, Lynn Lane, Shenstone, Staffs. WS14 0DX   *tel* (0543) 480696   *telex* 334727 Solo G   *fax* (0543) 481619. Fine Art prints framed and unframed.

**Noel Tatt Ltd.** (1954), Coombe Valley Road, Dover CT17 0EU   *tel* (0304) 211644   *fax* (0304) 240470. *Directors:* Noel Tatt, Vencke Tatt, Derek Bates, Anthony Sharpe, Paul Tatt, Robert Dixon. Greetings cards, prints, postcards.

**Thomas Leach Limited,** 54 Ock Street, Abingdon-on-Thames, Oxfordshire OX14 5DE   *tel* (0235) 20444   *fax* (0235) 554270. (Address to David J. Leach.) Sketches of religious subjects suitable for reproduction as Christmas or Easter Cards.

**\*United Greeting Card Co. (UK) Ltd.** (1969), River Park, Billet Lane, Berkhamsted, Herts. HP4 1EL   *tel* (0442) 871381. *Directors:* R. H. Seddon, M. Howard. Ideas and artwork for humorous greeting cards.

**\*Valentines of Dundee, Ltd.**, P.O. Box 74, Kinnoull Road, Dundee DD1 9NQ   *tel* (0382) 814711. Everyday greeting cards, Christmas cards, gift wraps, social stationery, St. Valentine's Day, Easter, Mother's Day, Father's Day, calendars. Address to *The Director of Product Management.*

**Webb Ivory Ltd.**, Queen Street, Burton-on-Trent, Staffs. DE14 3LP   *tel* (0283) 66311. Greeting card designs, particularly Christmas, suitable for charities and up-market ranges.

---

See also the **Articles, reports and short stories** and the **Books** sections for lists of magazines, book publishers and packagers; the **Agents** section for literary agents (particularly for children's book illustration).

It is recommended that artists read the article on copyright in the **Law and regulations** section; the **Publishing practice** section for information about formal agreements.

# Photography

## The Freelance Photographer and the Agent

### BRUCE COLEMAN

Photographic agencies and libraries have a dual role in the service they provide. They meet the needs and demands of Picture Editors, Picture Researchers and Art Buyers and, at the same time, provide a service to the freelance photographer. The enterprising photographer, wishing to penetrate the publishing market, would do well to consider employing the services of an agent whose knowledge of current trends and client contact will gear the photographer's output to the requirements of the markets. The complexities of reproduction rights are best left to an agent—that's if the photographer wishes to protect the copyright of his work!

Selecting the right agent very much depends on the type of work the photographer is producing and he should, therefore, take a look at several agencies before choosing the one he thinks will be of advantage to him. Some agents, for example, work in the syndication area, selling news and topical pictures to the world's press; others are in the stock business maintaining a library of photographers' work orientated to the editorial market. Agents normally do not sell pictures outright but lease them for a specific use and fee from which they deduct a commission. A good photograph in the hands of a good agent can be published several times over and bring in royalties for many years.

Before submitting your work to an agent, a preliminary letter is recommended enquiring whether he is accepting new photographers and asking for details of his specific needs.

The agent will wish to see an initial presentation of at least two hundred photographs and the photographer should indicate the number of photographs he plans to submit in the course of a year. Agents are keen to encourage the active photographer who can supply a regular stream of good quality work. Serious attention should be given to the caption of every picture as this can often mean the difference between a sale or a rejection. A caption should be brief and legible and an example of a good nature caption would be:

> Spotted Hyena (C. crocuta)
> Serengeti
> Aggressive behaviour

or, a geographical caption:

> Canada: Northwest Territories
> Eskimo fur trappers and dogsled

Some time spent on the presentation of your work, editing for composition, content, sharpness and, in the case of transparencies, colour saturation, will create a favourable impression. When submitting original colour transparencies, to ensure they are protected from damage and also to facilitate easy examination, place them in clear plastic sleeves, never between glass. Do not submit transparencies which you may require for personal use as it is quite impossible for an agent to recall pictures at short notice from his client.

One final point, never supply similar photographs to more than one agent as the problems created by almost identical pictures appearing, say, on a calendar or a greeting card can be embarrassing and costly to rectify. Indeed, for this reason, many agents insist on an exclusive arrangement between themselves and their photographers.

## How to run your own Picture Library

### JOHN FELTWELL

Photographers seeking to have someone else place their work should consider the possibilities of engaging a photographic agency (*see* Bruce Coleman's piece above). Photographers wishing to market their work themselves, either as specialist libraries listed below, or those wishing to establish a library, might find useful the following guidelines and tips.

It is important to draw up terms of business to cover items such as search fee, holding fee, and particularly loss or damage to transparencies (£50 to £500 per transparency. See 'Booking in of Projects' in *Picture Research* article.) A month is reasonable time for transparencies to be reviewed, thereafter a weekly holding fee per transparency is recommended, unless stated otherwise. Search fees (up to £30) may or may not be waived if transparencies are accepted. Reproduction rights should be calculated according to copyright limitations, whether non-exclusive UK only, English speaking countries, world rights, etc., as well as size (small 'editorial' size to front cover). Sliding scales are required. Agree fees, including future fees, before publication.

Beware of and budget for use of transparencies by editors for preparation of 'dummies'; pictures used may not be accounted for in-house by the resident picture researcher if acquired by editors, sub-editors, etc. Forbid any slide projection of transparencies. Be wary of the use of transparencies from which artists can derive ideas, unless arranged. Beware of supplying private individuals (or freelances) who are naive to procedures. Some libraries ask for an official letter of request from the publisher.

The photographer's transparencies are treasured possessions. Unfortunately *some* publishers and magazines do not see it like that and treat them as dispensable and with some irreverence. You can be sure that picture researchers who are members of SPREd (full details at end of *Picture Research* article) know all about looking after transparencies and they are safe in their hands. Reminders and disputes are regrettably part of the game.

Make sure that dispatched transparencies (all sleeved) are well packed by whatever means (messenger, recorded, registered post) and are properly insured—and that the recipient knows when his or her liability starts and finishes. This includes transit to printers away from publishers' premises. Once accepted, transparencies may lie up for several months waiting to be used, this can run on to a year, unless strictly controlled. Arrange for payment six months after acceptance or on publication, whichever happens first, otherwise it might be on publication, some time off. Specify that transparencies are returned from printers in a clean condition without any printers' solvents, but with original mounts.

The *British Association of Picture Libraries and Agencies* (BAPLA) (13, Woodberry Crescent, London N10 1PJ, 01-883 2531) mostly represents commercial and institutional libraries. Smaller libraries, who are perhaps more vulnerable to disputes, can only be assisted (the right is reserved) by BAPLA after first year membership (full £230).

# List of Agencies and Picture Libraries

*Member of The British Association of Picture Libraries and Agencies

**\*A-Z Botanical Collection Ltd,** Bedwell Lodge, Cucumber Lane, Essendon,Hatfield, Herts. AL9 6JB  *tel* (0707) 49091  *fax* (0707) 46613. Colour transparencies of plant life world-wide, 5 × 4, 6 × 6, 35mm.

**Aardvark Productions** (incorporating the library of **Michael Leach** A.R.P.S.), Brookside, Kinnerley, Oswestry, Shropshire SY10 8DB  *tel* (069 185) 639. General wildlife subjects, particularly mammals and special emphasis on urban wildlife.

**Academic File News Photos** (1985), Centre for Near East, Asia and Africa Research (NEAR), 172 Castelnau, London SW13 9DH  *tel* 01-741 5878  *telex* 940 12777 Near G  *fax* 01-741 5671. *Director:* Sajid Rizvi. Daily news coverage in UK and general library of people and places, with special reference to the Middle East, North Africa and Asia. New photographers welcomed to cover UK and abroad.

**\*Ace Photo Agency** (1980), 22 Maddox Street, London W1R 9PG  *tel* 01-629 0303  *fax* 01-495 6100. General library: people, industry, travel, commerce, skies, sport, music and natural history. World wide syndication. *Terms:* 50%. S.A.E. for enquiries.

**\*Action Plus** (1986), 54-58 Tanner Street, London SE1 3LL  *tel* 01-403 1558  *telex* 8951182 Gecoms G  *fax* 01-403 1526. All sport, action, leisure pictures. *Terms:* 50%.

**Aerofilms Limited** (1919), Gate Studios, Station Road, Boreham Wood, Herts. WD6 1EJ  *tel* 01-207 0666  *fax* 01-207 5433. Comprehensive library of vertical and oblique aerial photographs of U.K., large areas with complete cover.

**Air Photo Supply** (1963), 42 Sunningvale Avenue, Biggin Hill, Kent TN16 3BX  *tel* (0959) 74872. Aircraft and associated subjects, South-East England, colour and monochrome. No other photographers' material required.

**Al Ahram** (1983), Dyffryn, Bolahaul Road, Cwmffrwd, Carmarthen, Dyfed SA31 2LP  *tel* (0267) 233625. Natural history, landscape, travel (especially Egypt), children, outdoor activities, sports. Formats 35mm, 6 × 7cm, 5 × 4in. Other photographers' work not accepted.

**Bryan and Cherry Alexander Photography** (1973), Higher Cottage, Manston, Sturminster Newton, Dorset DT10 1EZ  *tel* (0258) 73006. Arctic regions with emphasis on Eskimos and Lapps.

**\*All-Sport Photographic Ltd.** (1972), All-Sport House, Greenlea Park, Prince George's Road, Colliers Wood, London SW19 2JD  *tel* 01-685 1010  *fax* 01-648 5240. International sport and leisure.

**Rev. J. Catling Allen,** St Giles House, Little Torrington, Devon EX38 8PS   *tel* (0805) 22497. Library of colour transparencies (35 mm.) and black and white photographs of Bible Lands, including archaeological sites and the religions of Islam and Judaism. Medieval abbeys and priories, cathedrals and churches in Britain. Also historic, rural and scenic Britain. (Not an agent or buyer.)

**American History Picture Library,** 3 Barton Buildings, Bath BA1 2JR   *tel* (0225) 334213. Photographs, engravings, colour transparencies covering the exploration, social, political and military history of North America from 15th to 20th century. Conquistadores, Civil War, Gangsters, Moon landings, etc. Prints and photos purchased.

**\*Ancient Art & Architecture Photo Library,** 6 Kenton Road, Harrow-on-the-Hill, Middlesex HA1 2BL   *tel* 01-422 1214   *fax* 01-422 1214. Specialising in the civilisations of the Middle East, Mediterranean countries, Europe, Asia, Americas, from ancient times to recent past, their arts, architecture, landscapes, beliefs, peoples past and present.

**Andes Press Agency** (1983), 26 Padbury Court, London E2 7EH   *tel* 01-739 3159. *Director:* Carlos Reyes. Social, political and economic aspects of Latin America, Africa, Asia, Europe and Britain. Specialising in contemporary world religions.

**\*Heather Angel,** Highways, 6 Vicarage Hill, Farnham, Surrey GU9 8HJ   *tel* (0252) 716700   *fax* (0252) 727464. Colour transparencies (35 mm. and 2¼ in. square) and monochrome prints with world-wide coverage of natural history and biological subjects including landscapes, gardens, close-ups, and underwater images; also China. Detailed catalogues on request.

**\*Animal Photography** (1955), 4 Marylebone Mews, New Cavendish Street, London W1M 7LF   *tel* 01-935 0503. Horses, dogs, cats, East Africa, Galapagos.

**Aqua Pics,** 73 Rosehill Drive, Bransgore, Christchurch, Dorset BH23 8NR   *tel* (0425) 73430. Fishing: trout, coarse, sea, big game, tropical reef; whaling, travel, flora, fauna, scrimshaw, yachting, windsurfing.

**\*Aquila Photographics,** Haydon House, Alcester Road, Studley, Warwickshire B80 7AN   *tel* (052 785) 2357. Specialists in ornithological subjects, but covering all aspects of natural history in both colour and black and white.

**Arctic Camera,** Derek Fordham (1978), 66 Ashburnham Grove, Greenwich, London SE10 8UJ   *tel* 01-692 7651. Colour transparencies of all aspects of Arctic life and environment.

**\*Ardea London Ltd.,** 35 Brodrick Road, London SW17 7DX   *tel* 01-672 2067 and 8787   *fax* 01-672 8787. Su Gooders. Specialist world-wide natural history photographic library of animals, birds, plants, fish, insects, reptiles.

**\*Aspect Picture Library Ltd** (1971), 40 Rostrevor Road, London SW6 5AD   *tel* 01-736 1998 and 731 7362   *telex* 934999 Txlink G, quoting MBX 219994671   *fax* 01-731 7362. General library including wildlife, tribes, cities, industry, science, space.

**The Associated Press Ltd.,** News Photo Department, The Associated Press House, 12 Norwich Street, London EC4A 1BP   *tel* 01-353 1515, 01-353 0356 (Picture Desk direct no.)   *fax* 01-583 0218. News and feature pictures.

**\*Aviation Photographs International** (1970), 15 Downs View Road, Swindon, Wilts. SN3 1NS   *tel* (0793) 497179. All types of aviation. Assignments undertaken.

**Aviation Picture Library** (Austin J. Brown,) (1970), 1a Chandos Road, Redland, Bristol BS6 6PG *tel* (0272) 731406 *telex* 449610 Taymax *pager* Call 01-840 7000. Request Pager No. 0388296 and give your contact telephone number. Worldwide aviation photographic library, dynamic views of aircraft. Travel library including Europe and Caribbean. Material taken since 1960. Commissions undertaken.

**B. & B. Photographs** (1974), Dodds, Clifford Chambers, Stratford upon Avon, Warwickshire CV37 8HX *tel* (0789) 204636. 35 mm. colour library of horticulture (especially pests and diseases) and biogeography (worldwide), natural history (especially Britain) and biological education.

**Alan Band Associates (Bandphotos),** 25 Longdown Road, Farnham, Surrey GU10 3JL *tel* (0252) 713022 *telex* 858623 Telbur G. International news and feature picture service for British and overseas publishers.

*****Barnaby's Picture Library,** 19 Rathbone Street, London W1P 1AF *tel* 01-636 6128-9 *fax* 01-637 4317. Requires photographs for advertising and editorial publication. Photographs not purchased, sender retains copyright.

*****BBC Hulton Picture Library—see Hulton Picture Company.**

**Dr Alan Beaumont,** 52 Squires Walk, Lowestoft, Suffolk NR32 4LA *tel* (0502) 560126. World-wide collection of monochrome prints and colour transparencies (35 mm. and 6 x 7 cm.) of natural history, countryside, windmills and aircraft. Subject lists available. No other photographers required.

**Bee Photographs—see Heritage & Natural History Photography.**

**Stephen Benson Slide Bureau,** 45 Sugden Road, London SW11 5EB *tel* 01-223 8635. World: agriculture, archaeology, architecture, commerce, everyday life, culture, environment, geography, science, tourism. Speciality: South America, the Caribbean, Australasia and Nepal. Assignments undertaken.

**BIPS-Bernsen's International Press Service, Ltd.,** 9 Paradise Close, Eastbourne, East Sussex BN20 8BT *tel* (0323) 28760. (For full details see under **Syndicates, News and Press Agencies.**)

*****John Blake Picture Library** (1975), 26 Malvern Drive, Thornbury, Bristol, Avon BS12 2HY *tel* (0454) 418321 and 413240. England, Scotland and Wales; landscapes, architecture, churches, gardens, countryside, towns and villages. General topography of Europe, the Americas and Middle and Far East. Horse Trials covered including Badminton and Gatcombe Park. *Terms:* 50%.

**Blitz News & Photo Agency** (1988), Blitz Photographic Studios, 41a London Road, Bognor Regis, West Sussex PO21 1PQ *tel* (0243) 830407. Comprehensive library of colour transparencies and monochrome prints (35 mm., medium and large formats). Action and sports photography (especially yachting and motorsport, including Le Mans 24hr race), travel, natural history, landscapes and aerial, reportage, personalities, news, advertising shots, general. Commissions undertaken and photographers accepted. *Terms:* 50%. Catalogue on request.

**Bodleian Library,** Oxford, OX1 3BG *tel* (0865) 277000/277214 *fax* (0865) 277182. Photographic library of 30,000 35 mm. (5″ x 4″ to order) colour transparencies, of subjects mostly from medieval manuscripts with iconographical index to illuminations.

*****Janet and Colin Bord,** Melysfan, Llangwm, Corwen, Clwyd LL21 0RD *tel* (049 082) 472. Library of black and white photographs and colour transparencies, specialising in the prehistoric and Roman sites of Britain, but also covering rural and scenic Britain in general, e.g. landscapes, wild flowers, villages, churches. Also strange phenomena. Do not act as agents for other photographers.

**Boxing Picture Library,** 3 Barton Buildings, Bath BA1 2JR *tel* (0225) 334213. Prints, engravings and photos of famous boxers, boxing personalities and famous fights from 18th century to recent years.

**\*Bridgeman Art Library,** 19 Chepstow Road, London W2 5BP *tel* 01-727 4065, 229 7420 *fax* 01-792 8509. Documentary and fine art collection; specialists in top quality colour transparencies relating to the arts: European and Oriental paintings and prints, Christmas material, antiques, arms and armour, history, natural history, maps, manuscripts, sculpture, topography, transport and many other subjects. Catalogue available.

**\*Britain on View Photographic Library,** official photographic library for British Tourist Authority and English Tourist Board. Thames Tower, Black's Road, London W6 9EL *tel* 01-846 9000 *fax* 01-563 0302. General UK travel including many special subjects. Colour, black and white. Mon. to Fri. 11 am–1 pm, 2–4 pm.

**Hamish Brown,** 21 Carlin Craig, Kinghorn, Fife KY3 9RX *tel* (0592) 890422. Photographs and 35 mm. transparencies of Scottish sites and topographical, Morocco, mountain ranges of Europe, Africa, India and South America.

**\*Camera Press Ltd** (1947), Russell Court, Coram Street, London WC1H 0NB *tel* 01-837 4488/9393/1300/0606 *cable address* Camrapres London *telex* 21654 Camrap G *fax* 01-278 5126. B&w prints and colour transparencies covering British Royalty, portraits of world statesmen, politicians, entertainers, sportspersons, etc., documentary, animals, fashion, human interest. *Terms:* 50%.

**\*Camerapix** – see **C.P.L. (Camerapix Picture Library).**

**\*J. Allan Cash Photolibrary (J. Allan Cash Ltd.),** 74 South Ealing Road, London W5 4QB *tel* 01-840 4141. Worldwide photographic library; travel, landscape, natural history, sport, industry, agriculture. Details available for photographers interested in contributing.

**Celtic Picture Library** (1985), 4 Rhodfa Gwilym, St. Asaph, Clwyd LL17 0UU *tel* (074574) 395. All subjects relating to Wales: ancient monuments, crafts and customs, conservation, farming, industry, landscapes, tourism, environment, wildlife.

**\*The Central Press Photos Ltd**—see **Hulton Picture Company.**

**\*Cephas Picture Library,** 20 Trafalgar Drive, Walton on Thames, Surrey KT12 1NZ *tel* (0932) 241903 *fax* (0932) 68481. People, places, agriculture, industry, religion, architecture, travel, food and wine, crafts; wine industry and vineyards. *Terms:* 50%

**Christmas Archives** (1978), Wassail House, 64 Severn Road, Cardiff CF1 9EA *tel* (0222) 41120. (For full details see under **Editorial, Literary and Production Services.**)

**\*City Syndication Ltd.**—see **Monitor Syndication.**

**Bruce Coleman Inc.,** 381 Fifth Avenue, New York, N.Y., 10016-3314, USA *tel* 212-683-5227 *telex* 429093 Bcinc *fax* 212-689-6140. *President:* Norman Owen Tomalin. Specialising exclusively in colour transparencies. All formats from 35 mm. acceptable. All subjects required.

**\*Bruce Coleman Ltd.,** 17 Windsor Street, Uxbridge, Middlesex UB8 1AB *tel* (0895) 57094 *telex* 932439 *fax* (0895) 72357. Colour transparencies on natural history, ecology, environment, geographical, archaeological, anthropology, agriculture, science, scenics and travel.

**Colorific Photo Library,** Garden Offices, Gilray House, Gloucester Terrace, London W2 3DF  *tel* 01-723 5031  *fax* 01-262 6870. Handling photographs of top international photographers, most subjects currently on file, upwards of 150,000 images. Represent *Life* Picture Service and *Sports Illustrated.* New York agencies: Black Star, Contact Press Images Inc., Wheeler Pictures, Picture Group, Visages, Los Angeles; Cosmos, Paris; Focus, Germany; Camara Tres, Brazil.

**\*C.P.L. (Camerapix Picture Library),** 8 Ruston Mews, London W11 1RB  *tel* 01-221-0077  *telex* 263996; and P.O. Box 45048 Nairobi, Kenya  *tel* 23511, 334398  *telex* 22576. Africa, Middle East, Asia; portraits, agriculture, industry, tribal cultures, landscapes. Wildlife including rare species. Islamic portfolio; Mecca, Medina, Muslim pilgrimage. Further material available from collection held in Nairobi.

**Crafts Council Picture Library** (1973), 12 Waterloo Place, London SW1Y 4AU  *tel* 01-930 4811  *fax* 01-930 4810. The Library contains a card index register of all crafts people known to the Crafts Council; an extensive slide library, available on loan, covering ceramics, lettering, bookbinding, textiles, silver/metal, jewellery, wood/furniture and toys/baskets; an information desk for general queries.

**\*Lupe Cunha** (1987), 6 Raynton Road, Enfield, Middlesex EN3 6BP  *tel* (0992) 760072  *fax* 01-363 7127 (bureau). Specialist library on all aspects of childhood from pregnancy to school age, including large section devoted to health and child development. Commissioned photography undertaken. Also represents collection on Brazil for Brazil Photo Agency. *Terms:* 50%.

**John H. Cutten Associates,** 76 Northways, London NW3 5DL  *tel* 01-586 7812. Library includes portraits of notable personalities from the 19th century to present day. Transparencies of philosophers, psychologists, scientists. Also historical and unusual.

**The Dance Library** (1983), P.O. Box 6, Moreton-in-Marsh, Glos. GL56 0RQ  *tel* (0608) 74414. Contemporary and historical dance: classical ballet, jazz, tap, disco, popping, ice dancing, musicals, variety, folk, tribal rites and rituals.

**Das Photo** (1975), Cherry Trees, 1 Chatton Row, Bisley, Surrey GU24 9AP  *tel* Brookwood (04867) 3395 and Chalet le Pin, Domaine de Bellevue 181, 5482 Septon, Belgium  *tel* (086) 32 24 26. Arab countries, Americas, Europe, Amazon, folklore, world festivals, archaeology, people, Biblical, markets, sailing, motor bikes.

**Dennis Davis Photography** (1984), The Flat, Himbleton Manor, Droitwich, Worcs. WR9 7LE  *tel* (090) 569 506. Rare breeds of domestic livestock, agricultural landscapes, country life, architecture—interiors and exteriors, landscape and coastal.

**\*James Davis Travel Photography,** 30 Hengistbury Road, New Milton, Hants BH25 7LU  *tel* (0425) 610328  *fax* (0425) 638402. *Proprietor:* James Davis. Stock transparency library specialising in world-wide travel photographs. Supply tour operators, publishers, advertising agents, etc. Terms 50% to photographers.

**\*Peter Dazeley;** Extensive Golf Library from 1970. The Studios, 5 Heathmans Road, Parsons Green, London SW6 4TJ  *tel* 01-736 3171  *fax* 01-736 3356.

Players, tournaments, courses world-wide and various related material. Colour, black and white.

**Derbyshire Scene** (1989), 66 Norfolk Street, Glossop, Derbyshire SK13 9RA *tel* (045 74) 62997. The Derbyshire County and all its aspects: people, places, life and natural history. *Terms:* 50%.

**George A. Dey** (1986), 'Drumcairn', Aberdeen Road, Laurencekirk, Kincardineshire, Scotland AB3 1AJ *tel* (05617) 8845. Scottish Highland landscapes, Highland Games, forestry, castles of N.E. Scotland, veteran cars, North Holland.

\*Douglas Dickins Photo Library (1946), 2 Wessex Gardens, Golders Green, London NW11 9RT *tel* 01-455 6221. World-wide collection of colour transparencies (mostly 6 × 6 cm., some 35 mm.) and b&w prints (10 × 8 in. originals), specialising in Asia, particularly India and Indonesia; also, USA, Canada, France, Austria and Switzerland.

**Gordon Dickson** (1975) Flagstones, 72 Catisfield Lane, Fareham, Hants. P015 5NS *tel* (0329) 42131. Colour transparencies of fungi, in natural habitat; also butterflies, moths, beetles. No other photographers required.

\*C. M. Dixon, The Orchard, Marley Lane, Kingston, Canterbury, Kent CT4 6JH *tel* (0227) 830075. Europe and Ethiopia, Iceland, Sri Lanka, Tunisia, Turkey, USSR. Main subjects include agriculture, archaeology, architecture, clouds, geography, geology, horses, industry, meteorology, mosaics, mountains, occupations, people.

**Ecoscene** (1987), Sally Morgan, 4 Heatherview Cottages, Shortfield, Frensham, Surrey GU10 3BH *tel* (025125) 4395. Man's effect on the environment, particularly industry, pollution; also ecology, habitats, conservation and urban wildlife. *Terms:* 55% to photographer.

**Edifice** (1987), 14 Doughty Street, London WC1N 2PL *tel* 01-405 9395 *fax* 01-267 3632. Architecture (especially detail), landscape, gardening. No other photographers' material required.

**T. Malcolm English,** B.A., L.R.P.S., M.R.AE.S., 3 The Bakery, Silver Street, Stevington, Beds. MK43 7QN *tel* (02302) 4150. Aviation photographic library specialising in military, historic and air weapons.

\*Greg Evans Photo Library (1979), 91 Charlotte Street, London W1P 1LB *tel* 01-636 8238 *fax* 01-436 2318. World-wide travel and winter skiing; UK travel, people, industrial, commercial, social, animals, food and sports. Commissions undertaken. *Terms:* 50%. No search/service fee.

\*Mary Evans Picture Library, 59 Tranquil Vale, Blackheath, London SE3 0BS *tel* 01-318 0034 *fax* 01-852 7211. Over two million historical illustrations from antiquity to the recent past. Also runs of British and foreign illustrated periodicals. Special collections: Sigmund Freud Copyrights, Society for Psychical Research, Fawcett Library (women's rights), Bruce Castle Museum, Ernst Dryden Collection and London University Harry Price Collection.

\*Eyeline Photos (1979), 259 London Road, Cheltenham GL52 6YG *tel* (0242) 513567 *telex* 43432 DSA G ref Eyeline *fax* (0242) 573498. Watersports, particularly sailing and powerboating, world-wide; equestrian events. *Terms:* 50%.

\*Feature-Pix Colour Library (World Pictures), 21 Great Chapel Street, London W1V 3AQ *tel* 01-437 2121 *fax* 01-439 1307. *Directors:* Gerry Brenes, Joan

Brenes, David Brenes. Colour transparencies (2¼ in. sq. or larger), on travel and allied subjects. Undertake photography on assignment for tour operators, National Tourist Offices. *Terms:* 50% to photographer.

**Vivien Fifield** (1981), 10 Claremont Road, Teddington, Middx TW11 8DG *tel* 01-943 3516. Engravings, drawings and black-and-white photographs covering the history of science, medicine and technology up to the late 1930s.

**Focus Picture Library,** 75A Selby Road, Garforth, Leeds LS25 1LR *tel* (0532) 863016. Transparencies, 35 mm. & 6 x 9 cm. Landscapes, rivers, buildings, British Isles, especially Yorkshire and Northern Counties. Also popular European regions, especially Greece. Assignments undertaken. No new photographers required.

**Ron and Christine Foord,** 155b City Way, Rochester, Kent ME1 2BE *tel* (0634) 847348. Colour picture library of 1000 species of wild flowers, British insects, garden flowers, pests and diseases, indoor plants, cacti, countryside views.

**Fortean Picture Library,** Melysfan, Llangwm, Corwen, Clwyd LL21 0RD *tel* (049 082) 472. Library of colour and black and white pictures covering all strange phenomena: UFOs, Loch Ness Monster, ghosts, Bigfoot, witchcraft, etc.

**Fotomas Index,** 74 Newman Street, London W1P 3LA *tel* 01-636 4148. Specialises in supplying pre-20th century (mostly pre-Victorian) illustrative material to publishing and academic worlds, and for television and advertising. Complete production back-up for interior decor, exhibitions and locations. Photography for publishers.

**Fotosports International** (1969), The Barn, Swanbourne, Bucks. MK17 0SL *tel* (029672) 773; 227 27th Manhattan Beach, California 90266, USA *tel* 213-545 9368/213-823-0074; 21 Sylvana Way, Willeton, WA 6155, Australia *tel* 09-457-9078. Sports events and players, domestic, European, international. American football, athletics, baseball, cricket, golf, motor sport, tennis, soccer.

*****Fox Photos**—see **Hulton Picture Company.**

*****Frank Lane Picture Agency Ltd.,** Pages Green House, Wetheringsett, Stowmarket, Suffolk IP14 5QA *tel* (0728) 860789 *fax* (0728) 860222. Natural history and meteorology.

**Frost Historical Newspaper Collection,** 8 Monks Avenue, New Barnet, Herts. EN5 1DB *tel* 01-440 3159. (For full details see **Historical Newspaper Loan Service** under **Editorial, Literary and Production Services.**)

**Brian Gadsby** (Visual Life), Middle Barmston Farm, District 15, Washington, Tyne & Wear NE38 8LE *tel* (091) 416 5454 and 2859179. Colour (2¼ in. sq., 6 × 4.5 cm. and 35 mm.) and black and white prints. Wide range of subjects but emphasis on travel, children, natural history.

**Colin Garratt**—see **Steam Locomotives of the World Photo Library.**

*****Geoscience Features,** 6 Orchard Drive, Wye, Nr. Ashford, Kent TN25 5AU *tel* Wye (0233) 812707. *Director:* Dr. Basil Booth. Colour library (35 mm to 5 in-4 in). Natural history, ecology, geology, geography, macro/micro, natural phenomena. Americas, Africa, Australasia, Europe, Indian Sub-Continent, S.E. Asia. Incorporates K.S.F. colour library.

**Geoslides,** 4 Christian Fields, London SW16 3JZ *tel* 01-764 6292. *Library Director:* John Douglas. Geographical and general interest of subjects from Africa, Asia, Antarctic, Arctic and sub-Arctic areas. Australian cover through

Associate Picture Library: Blackwoods S.A. Interested only in large recent collections of relevant colour transparencies, regionally based. *Terms:* 50% on UK sales. Photographs for all types of publications, television, advertising.

**Mark Gerson Photography,** 3 Regal Lane, Regents Park Road, London NW1 7TH *tel* 01-286 5894 and 01-267 9246. Portrait photographs of personalities, mainly literary, in colour and black and white from 1950 to the present. No other photographers' material required.

**Globe Photos Inc.,** 275 7th Avenue, New York, N.Y. 10001, USA *tel* 212-689 1340 *telex* 427578 Glbphto. Picture stories for magazines or stock photos. Colour transparencies only. Send International Reply Coupons for return of material.

**John Glover** (1979), 2 Struan Cottages, Church Fields, Witley, Godalming, Surrey GU8 5PP *tel* (042 879) 3322. Gardening, U.K. landscapes, native flora. Commissions undertaken.

**\*Fay Godwin's Photo Files** (1979), 36 Camden Square, London NW1 9XA *tel* 01-267 1034 *telex* 295931 Unicom G *fax* 01-267 6026. Colour and black and white photographs covering portraits of writers, landscapes of the British Isles, North Sea oil, Yorkshire mills, welfare services, education.

**Martin and Dorothy Grace** (1984), 40 Clipstone Avenue, Mapperley, Nottingham NG3 5JZ *tel* (0602) 208248. General British natural history, specialising in native trees, shrubs, flowers, habitats and ecology.

**Tim Graham** (1970), 31 Ferncroft Avenue, London NW3 7PG *tel* 01-435 7693 *fax* 01-431 4312. British Royal Family in this country and on tours; background pictures on royal homes, staff, hobbies, sports, cars etc. English and foreign country scenes.

**Greater London Photograph Library,** 40 Northampton Road, London EC1R 0HB *tel* 01-633 6759. Over 350,000 photographs of London and the London area from *c.* 1860 to 1986. Especially strong on local authority projects—schools, housing, open spaces, etc.

**Greek Island Photos** (1985), Willowbridge Publishers, Bridge House, Southwick Village, Nr Fareham, Hants PO17 6DZ *tel* (0705) 375570. Country and urban facets of most Greek islands. Commissions undertaken.

**Robert Haas Photo Library** (1978), 11 Cormont Road, Camberwell, London SE5 9RA *tel* 01-326 1510. Holland, Greek Islands, Morocco, Scottish oil industry, Nottinghill Carnival, skies. *Specialities:* people; New York City, Lloyd's of London, Channel Tunnel.

**\*Robert Harding Picture Library,** 17A Newman Street, London W1P 3HD *tel* 01-637 8969 *cables* Rohard W1. Photographic library. Require photographs for editorial publications which must be of outstanding quality. Telephone or write for details.

**Harper Horticultural Slide Library,** 219 Robanna Shores, Seaford, Virginia 23696, USA *tel* 804-898 6453. 100,000 35 mm. slides of plants and gardens.

**Heritage & Natural History Photography,** Dr. John B. Free, 37 Plainwood Close, Summersdale, Chichester, West Sussex PO19 4YB *tel* (0243) 533822. Natural history, agriculture, archaeology. Colour transparencies on: bees and bee keeping, insects and small invertebrates, tropical crops and flowers, people, occupations and religious life in Arabia, Bangladesh, India, Iran, Japan, Mexico, Nepal, Thailand, Mediterranean countries.

**Historical Picture Service,** 3 Barton Buildings, Bath BA1 2JR *tel* (0225) 334213. Engravings, prints and photographs on all aspects of history from ancient times to 1920. Special collection Old London: buildings, inns, theatres, many of which no longer exist.

**Pat Hodgson Library,** Jasmine Cottage, Spring Grove Road, Richmond, Surrey TW10 6EH *tel* 01-940 5986. Small social history collection of 19th century engravings. Special picture research in 19th century periodicals, prints, etc. also undertaken. Modern black-and-white photographs: topographical and archaeological.

*****Holt Studios Photographic Library (Agricultural)** (1981), The Courtyard, 24 High Street, Hungerford, Berks. RG17 0NF *tel* (0488) 83523 *telex* 848507 ref. Holt *fax* (0488) 83511. Worldwide agriculture: crop production and protection, including healthy crops and relevant weeds, pests, diseases and deficiencies. Farming, people, machines, landscapes and environmental factors. Livestock. Assignments undertaken.

**Horizon International Creative Images** (1978), 7 Bury Place, London WC1A 2LA *tel* 01-831 1109 *fax* 01-831 9005. Transparencies: travel, people, sport, special effects, abstracts and illustrations.

**Eric Hosking,** O.B.E., HON. F.R.P.S., F.I.I.P., and **David Hosking,** A.R.P.S., 20 Crouch Hall Road, London N8 8HX *tel* 01-340 7703 *fax* (0728) 860222. Natural history subjects, especially birds covering whole world. Also Dr D.P. Wilson's unique collection of marine photographs.

*****Hulton Picture Company,** Unique House, 21-31 Woodfield Road, London W9 2BA *tel* 01-266 2662 *fax* 01-289 6392. More than 20 million pictures on all subjects from pre-history to the 1980s. Based on *Picture Post* and now including the **Keystone Collection.** Agents in the UK for The Bettmann Archive.

*****The Hutchison Library** (1976), 118b Holland Park Avenue, London W11 4UA *tel* 01-229 2743 *fax* 01-792 0259. General colour library; worldwide subjects: agriculture, environments, festivals, human relationships, industry, landscape, peoples, religion, towns, travel.

*****The Illustrated London News Picture Library,** 20 Upper Ground, London SE1 9PF *tel* 01-928 6969. Engravings, photographs, illustrations in black-and-white and colour from 1842 to present day, especially 19th and 20th century social history, wars, portraits, royalty. Travel archive including The Thomas Cook collection.

**Images Photo Agency** (1982), 4th Floor, Min Yip Building, 67 Jervois Street, Hong Kong *tel* 5-442255 *fax* 5-459263. *Directors:* Chris Smith, Neil Farrin. General photographic library; also pictures of old Hong Kong. *Terms:* 50%.

**International Press Agency (Pty) Ltd** (1934), P.O. Box 67, Howard Place 7450, South Africa *tel* 021-531926 *telex* 5-26837SA *fax* 021-538789. Press photos for South African market.

**JS Library International** (1979) 101A Brondesbury Park, London NW2 5JL *tel* 01-451 2668 *fax* 01-459 0223. The Royal Family, world-wide travel pictures, particularly the African continent, stage and screen celebrities, authors, world-wide general material. New material on any subject, in any quantity, always urgently required. Assignments undertaken.

*****Keystone Collection**—see **Hulton Picture Company.**

**Lakeland Life Picture Library** (1979), Langsett, Lyndene Drive, Grange-over-Sands, Cumbria LA11 6QP *tel* (05395) 33565. English Lake District: industries, crafts, sports, shows, customs, architecture, people. Not an agency.

**\*Landscape Only** (1986), 60 Poland Street, Soho, London W1V 3DF   *tel* 01-437 2655, 01-734 7344. Outdoor subjects: villages, countryside, places, landscape, countries, travel, towns, cities. *Terms:* 50%.

**Lears Magical Lanterns** (1976), 'Bodlandeb', Morfa Nefyn, Pwllheli, Gwyedd LL53 6AG   *tel* (0758) 720510. Lantern slides on all subjects of Victorian and Edwardian times.

**Lensmen Ltd., Press P.R. Photo Agency,** Lensmen House, Essex Street, East, Dublin 2   *tel* Dublin 773447.

**\*The MacQuitty International Collection,** 7 Elm Lodge, River Gardens, Stevenage Road, London SW6 6NZ   *tel* 01-385 6031. 300,000 photographs covering aspects of life in 70 countries: archaeology, art, buildings, flora and fauna, gardens, museums, people and occupations, scenery, religions, methods of transport, surgery, acupuncture, funeral customs, fishing, farming, dancing, music, crafts, sports, weddings, carnivals, food, drink, jewellery and oriental subjects. Period: 1920 to present day.

**Madeleine** (1983), 15 Wallace Avenue, Worthing, West Sussex BN11 5RA   *tel* (0903) 503551. Cinema—British and American motion-picture and screen personalities from 1930 to the present.

**Mander & Mitchenson Theatre Collection** (a Registered Charity), The Mansion, Beckenham Place Park, Beckenham, Kent BR3 2BP   *tel* 01-658 7725. Prints, drawings, photographs, programmes, etc., theatre, opera, ballet, music hall, and other allied subjects including composers, playwrights, etc. All periods. Available for books, magazines, T.V.

**Mansell Collection, Ltd.,** 42 Linden Gardens, London W2 4ER   *tel* 01-229 5475.

**John Massey Stewart,** 20 Hillway, Highgate, London N6 6QA   *tel* 01-341 3544. Large collection Russia/USSR: topography, people, culture, etc., plus Russian and Soviet history, 2000 pre-revolutionary PCs, etc. Also Britain, Europe, Asia (including Mongolia and South Korea), Alaska, USA, etc.

**\*S. & O. Mathews,** Stitches Farm House, Eridge, East Sussex TN3 9JB   *tel* Rotherfield (089285) 2848. British life and landscape, topography, gardens and flora.

**Chris Mattison,** 138 Dalewood Road, Beauchief, Sheffield S8 0EF   *tel* (0742) 364433. Colour library specialising in reptiles and amphibians; other natural history subjects; habitats and landscapes in S.E. Asia, South America, U.S.A., Mexico, Mediterranean. Captions or detailed copy supplied if required. No other photographers' material required.

**Robin May Collection,** 23 Malcolm Road, London SW19 4AS   *tel* 01-946 8965. Library specialises in Western Americana and the theatrical arts.

**Merseyside Photo Library** (1989), 62a-64a Pensby Road, Heswall, Wirral, Merseyside L60 7RE   *tel* 051-342 8850   *fax* 051-342 7241 (operated by Ron Jones Associates). Library specialising in images of Liverpool and Merseyside; now being expanded to include NW England, other destinations and general stock photos. Catalogue list available. Travel photography commissions undertaken.

**M.G.W. Picture Library,** Military and General Warfare, 3 Pyrford Drive, Eaton, Norwich, Norfolk NR4 6HB   *tel* (0603) 502554. Colour and black/white pictures covering the world's armies, navies, airforces, elite and special forces, police and para military. War, terrorism, riot, rescue and relief aid. Assignments undertaken, all formats acceptable. *Terms:* 50/50.

**Military History Picture Library,** 3 Barton Buildings, Bath BA1 2JR  *tel* (0225) 334213. Prints, engravings, photographs, colour transparencies covering all aspects of warfare and uniforms from ancient times to present.

**Model Picture Library and Kappa** (1975), 7 Bury Place, London WC1A 2LA  *tel* 01-831 1109  *fax* 01-831 9005. Transparencies: people, human interest, girl pictures.

\*Monitor Syndication** (1960), 17 Old Street, London EC1V 9HL  *tel* 01-253 7071  *telex* 24718. *General Manager:* David Willis. Specialists in portrait photographs of leading national and international personalities from politics, trade unions, entertainment, sport, and royalty. Incorporates the **City Syndication** library.

**Mountain Visions** (1984), Graham and Roslyn Elson, 25 The Mallards, Langstone, Havant, Hampshire PO9 1SS  *tel* (0705) 478441. Colour transparencies of mountaineering, skiing, and associated travel, in Europe, N. Africa, Himalayas, Arctic, Far East and Australia.

\*David Muscroft Snooker Photography** and **David Muscroft Picture Library** (1977) 16 Broadfield Road, Heeley, Sheffield S8 0XJ  *tel* (0742) 589299  *fax* (0742) 550113. Snooker; most other sports, Northern England news, personalities, features, events. Falkland Islands from 1880.

**The Mustograph Agency,** 19 Rathbone Street, London W1P 1AF  *tel* 01-636 6128-9  *fax* 01-637 4317. Britain only. General subjects of countryside life, work, history and scenery.

**National Motor Museum, Beaulieu,** Photographic Library, Beaulieu, Hants SO4 7ZN  *tel* (0590) 612345  *fax* (0590) 612624. All aspects of motoring, cars, commercial vehicles, motor cycles, traction engines, etc. Illustrations of period scenes and motor sport. Also large library of 5 in. x 4 in. and smaller colour transparencies of veteran, vintage and modern cars, commercial vehicles and motor cycles.

**Natural History Photographic Agency**—see **NHPA.**

**Natural Image,** Dr Bob Gibbons (1982), 49 Bickerley Road, Ringwood, Hants BH24 1EG  *tel* (0425) 478742. Colour library covering natural history, gardening, countryside and travel. Special emphasis on conservation. Commissions undertaken. *Terms:* 60% to photographer.

**News Blitz International,** 5 Via Cimabue, 00196 Rome, Italy  *tel* 36 00 620, 36 19 014, 36 01 489  *telex* 623676 Blitz I  *fax* 361 90 14 (see **Syndicates, News and Press Agencies**).

\*NHPA,** Little Tye, 57 High Street, Ardingly, West Sussex RH17 6TB  *tel* (0444) 892514  *fax* (0444) 892168. Represents 50 of the world's leading natural history photographers covering a wide range of fauna and flora. Specialisations include high-speed photography, a large Kalahari Bushmen collection, and the wildlife of North America and southern Africa. UK agents for Australasian Nature Transparencies.

**Northpix** (1976), 75A Bold Street, Liverpool L1 4EZ  *tel* 051-708 6044. News, sport, features; wire facilities.

**Frank Nowikowski** (1985), Avd Callao 545, Piso 4º, 1022 Buenos Aires, Argentina. *UK contact:* 3 Bush Drive, Rugeley, Staffs. WS15 2AO  *tel* (0889) 58 4885. 4 × 5in Scottish landscapes; East Africa (Kenya, Tanzania, Zimbabwe, Ethiopia): social, wildlife, landscape; South America (Argentina, Uruguay, Peru); Italy; children, education.

**Orion Press,** 55 1-Chome, Kanda Jimbocho, Chiyoda-ku, Tokyo, 101, Japan *tel* (03) 295-1400 *fax* (03) 295-0227 *telex* J2 4447 Orionprs.

**Christine Osborne Pictures** including **Middle East Pictures & Publicity** (1975), 53a Crimsworth Road, London SW8 4RJ *tel* 01-720 6951. Muslim countries. Asia, Indo-Pak subcontinent, Pacific. Socio-economic, land use, travel, food; over 60 countries.

***Oxford Scientific Films Ltd., Photo Library,** Long Hanborough, Oxford OX7 2LD *tel* (0993) 881881 *telex* 83147 Viaor OSF *fax* (0993) 882808. Comprehensive colour transparencies of wildlife and scenics worldwide. Illustrated articles on natural history topics. Agents for *Animals Animals* and *Earth Scenes*, New York. Representatives in New York, Tokyo, Milan, Barcelona, Frankfurt, Copenhagen, Paris.

***Panos Pictures** (1986), 8 Alfred Place, London WC1E 7EB *tel* 01-631 1590 *telex* 9419293 Panos G *fax* 01-436 8293. All aspects of Third World rural and urban life; deforestation, desertification, pollution, agriculture, health, etc. *Terms:* 50% to photographer.

**Rosemary Pardoe,** Flat One, 36 Hamilton Street, Hoole, Chester CH2 3JQ. Heraldic subjects, especially royal arms in churches, hatchments; also inn signs (heraldic and general). Not an agency.

**Ann & Bury Peerless,** 22 King's Avenue, Minnis Bay, Birchington-on-Sea, Kent CT7 9QL *tel* Thanet (0843) 41428. Art, architecture, geography, history, social and cultural aspects in India, Pakistan, Bangladesh, Sri Lanka, Thailand, Malaysia and parts of the Middle East, Egypt and Africa. Specialist material on world religions: Hinduism, Buddhism, Jainism, Sikhism.

***Photo Flora** (1982), 46 Jacoby Place, Priory Road, Birmingham B5 7UN *tel* 021-471 3300. British wild plants; Mediterranean botany and travel; Egypt, ancient and present day; North India.

***Photo Library International,** P.O. Box 75, Leeds LS7 3NZ *tel* (0532) 623005 *telex* 55293 Chacom G/PLI *fax* (0532) 625366. Colour transparencies 35 mm. to 10 x 8. Most subjects. New material always welcome.

***The Photo Source—see The Telegraph Colour Library.**

***The Photographers' Library** (1978), 81A Endell Street, Covent Garden, London WC2H 9AG *tel* 01-836 5591. Requires material on worldwide travel, industry, agriculture, commerce, sport, people, leisure, girls, scenic. Colour only. Terms: 50%.

***Photo Resources,** The Orchard, Marley Lane, Kingston, Canterbury, Kent CT4 6JH *tel* (0227) 830075. Ancient civilisations, art, archaeology, world religions, myth, and museum objects covering the period from 30,000 B.C. to A.D. 1900.

**Pictor Di Federico Pagni,** Via Adige 11, 20135 Milan, Italy *tel* (02) 551 80300 *fax* (02) 5464295. General photo libraries: Milan, London, Paris Munich.

**Pictor International, Ltd.,** Twyman House, 31-39 Camden Road, London NW1 9LR *tel* 01-482 0478 *telex* 21497 *fax* 01-267 1396. International photographic library—all subjects, especially industry technology, people. *Rates:* 50%.

**Pictor International,** 12 rue Rougemont, 75009 Paris, France *tel* 42 46 12 05 *telex* 281 361 F *fax* 47 70 06 25. General photo libraries: Paris, London, Milan, Munich, New York, Sydney, Tokyo. Genuine international sales network.

**Pictorial Press, Ltd.** 13 Berners Street, London W1P 3DE    *tel* 01-255 1468    *telex* 264876. *Directors:* A. F. Gale, K. V. Gale, S. M. Gale. Handles features, personalities especially royalty and pop music, nudes, historical cars and transport, teenage life, military, especially Second World War; also landscapes, families, people at work. SAE essential.

*****Picturepoint, Ltd.**, Hurst House, 157-169 Walton Road, East Molesey, Surrey KT8 0DX    *tel* 01-941 4520    *fax* 01-979 6671. Have ready world-wide markets for high quality colour transparencies. Any subject other than *news*. Minimum of 250 pictures in first submission. Send by Registered Mail enclosing stamps or I.R.C. for returns. *Terms:* 5 year contract, 50% commission.

**Sylvia Pitcher** (1968), 75 Bristol Road, Forest Gate, London E7 8HG    *tel* 01-552 8308 and 2nd Floor, 28 Hatton Wall, London EC1N 8JH    *tel* 01-430 0318. Specialist in rural south east USA, including musicians, blues, jazz, old time country.

**Pixfeatures** (Mr. P.G. Wickman), 5 Latimer Road, Barnet, Herts    *tel* 01-449 9946. Picture-features, preferably topical. Especially for sale to British, German, South African, Spanish and American magazines. 35% of all sales, unless otherwise arranged.

*****Planet Earth Pictures: Seaphot Ltd** (1969) 4 Harcourt Street, London W1H 1DS    *tel* 01-262 4427    *fax* 01-706 4042. Marine, surface and underwater; natural history and environments on land and underwater; people, places; space.

*****Popperfoto (Paul Popper Ltd)**, 24 Bride Lane, London EC4Y 8DR    *tel* 01-353 9665-6    *telex* 8814206    *fax* 01-936 2153. Offer and require documentary and feature photos (black and white and colour) from all countries of the world. Collection includes Exclusive News Agency, Odhams Periodicals Photo Library, Conway Picture Library, Reuters, United Press International (UPI) Library, and Planet.

**Power Pix International Picture Library** – see **S.&I. Williams Power Pix International Picture Library.**

*****Premaphotos Wildlife,** 2 Willoughby Close, King's Coughton, Alcester, War. B49 5QJ    *tel* (0789) 762938. Library of 35 mm. transparencies of own work only by K.G. Preston-Mafham and Dr. R.A. Preston-Mafham. Wide range of natural history subjects from around the world. All work done in the field.

**Press Association Photos** (the news picture service of The Press Association), 85 Fleet Street, London EC4P 4BE    *tel* 01-353 7440    *telex* 922330    *fax* 01-353 5191.

**Punch Cartoon Library** (1841), *Punch*, 245 Blackfriars Road, London SE1 9UY    *tel* 01-921 5900    *fax* 01-353 7796. Comprehensive collection of cartoons and illustrations, indexed under subject categories: humour, historical events, politics, fashion, sport, etc.

*****Retna Pictures Ltd** (1984), 1 Fitzroy Mews, Cleveland Street, London W1P 5DQ    *tel* 01-388 3444    *fax* 01-383 7151. Library of colour transparencies and b&w prints of rock and pop performers, show business personalities, celebrities, actors and actresses, travel and general stock library.

**Rich Research** (1978), 1 Bradby House, Carlton Hill, St. John's Wood, London NW8 9XE    *tel* 01-624 7755. *Director:* Diane Rich. Professional picture research and fee negotiation. Visuals found for books, films, television, advertising agencies and exhibitions. Fast access to world-wide sources.

*Ann Ronan Picture Library, Wheel Cottage, Bishops Hull, Taunton, Somerset TA1 5EP *tel* (0823) 252737 *fax* (0823) 336785. Woodcuts, engravings, etc., of history of science and technology from c.1500–c.1900.

The Royal Photographic Society (1853), The R.P.S. National Centre of Photography, The Octagon, Milsom Street, Bath BA1 1DN *tel* (0225) 462841. Exhibitions; library of books, photographs and photographic equipment.

Royal Society for Asian Affairs, 2 Belgrave Square, London SW1X 8PJ *tel* 01-235 5122. Archive library of original 19th and 20th century black-and-white photographs, glass slides, etc., of Asia. Publishes *Asian Affairs* 3 times p.a.

*Science Photo Library (1979), 112 Westbourne Grove, London W2 5RU *tel* 01-727 4712 *fax* 01-727 6041. Scientific photography of all kinds—medicine, technology, space, nature.

SCR Photo Library (1943), Society for Cultural Relations with the USSR, 320 Brixton Road, London SW9 6AB *tel* 01-274 2282. Russian and Soviet life and history. Comprehensive coverage of cultural subjects: art, theatre, folk art, costume, music. Also posters and theatre props, artistic reference and advice. Research by appointment only.

*Sealand Aerial Photography (1976), Goodwood Airfield, Goodwood, Chichester, West Sussex PO18 0PH *tel* (0243) 781025 *fax* (0243) 531422. Aerial photo coverage of any subject that can be photographed from the air in the U.K. Most stock on 2¼" format colour negative/transparency. Subjects constantly updated from new flying.

*Sefton Photo Library, 30-30A Mason Street, Manchester, M4 5EY *tel* 061-832 7670, 061-834 9423. *Director:* S. Samuels. General library covering Britain, the world, sport, leisure, etc. Submissions considered from other photographers. Assignments undertaken.

S & G Press Agency, Ltd., 68 Exmouth Market, London EC1R 4RA *tel* 01-278 1223. Send photographs, but negatives preferred. Press photographs and vast photo library.

Mick Sharp (1981), Eithinog, Waun, Penisarwaun, Caernarfon, Gwynedd LL55 3PW *tel* Llanberis 872425. Archaeology, ancient monuments, historic buildings, churches and general landscape of the British Isles and Brittany. Archaeological sites, courtyard houses in Iraq; pueblos, cliff dwellings, kivas, mission churches and petroglyphs of New Mexico.

*Brian and Sal Shuel (1975), 13 Woodberry Crescent, London N10 1PJ *tel* 01-883 2531 *fax* 01-883 9215. Traditional British customs, bridges, London.

*Skyscan Balloon Photography (1984), Stanway Grounds, Stanway, Cheltenham, Glos. GL54 5DR *tel* (0242 621) 357 *fax* (0242 621) 471. Aerial views of British landscapes, cities, heritage sites, taken from remotely controlled cameras suspended beneath a tethered balloon.

The Slide File (1978) 79 Merrion Square South, Dublin 2 *tel* 686086 *fax* 608332. Specialise in Eire and Northern Ireland: landscapes, Irish natural history, agriculture and industry, Irish people and their traditions, Celtic archaeological heritage.

Patrick Smith Associates (1964), Gloucester House, High Street, Borth, Dyfed SY24 5NZ *tel* (0970) 871296. South London 1950-77, mid-Wales, aviation. The Patrick Smith Collection, comprising of the London photographs, now in The Museum of London.

**Society for Anglo-Chinese Understanding** (1965), 152 Camden High Street, London NW1 0NE    *tel* 01-485 8241. Colour transparencies and b&w prints of China.

**Society for Cultural Relations with the USSR**—see **SCR Photo Library**.

**Source Photographic Archives** (1974), 66 Claremont Road, Sandymount, Dublin 4    *tel* 607090. *Director:* Thomas Kennedy. Mostly recent photographs by living photographers on many different subjects.

**Southern Media Services,** division of **Maximedia Pty. Ltd,** P.O. Box 140, Springwood, New South Wales 2777, Australia    *tel* (047) 514967    *telex* AA 10720589    *fax* (047) 515545. *Directors:* Nic van Oudtshoorn, Daphne van Oudtshoorn. Stock colour library, also illustrated features.

*****Spectrum Colour Library,** 146 Oxford Street, London W1N 9DL    *tel* 01-637 3682. Require high quality colour transparencies for all markets. Need all subjects except topical or "hot news" pictures—list of requirements available on receipt of stamped, addressed envelope.

*****Sporting Pictures (UK) Ltd.,** 7A Lambs Conduit Passage, Holborn, London WC1R 4RG    *tel* 01-405 4500    *fax* 01-831 7991. *Director:* Crispin J. Thruston. *Librarians:* Mark Whitmore, Duncan Bond. Specialising in sports, sporting events, sportsmen.

*****Steam Locomotives of the World Photo Library** (1969), The Square, Newton Harcourt, Leics. LE8 0FQ    *tel* (053759) 2068. Thousands of professional railway photographs from Colin Garratt's world-wide collection. Steam trains of all shapes and sizes, in every climate and mood. Colour transparencies, black and white. New colour brochure available on request.

**Peter Stiles Picture Library,** 50 Chippers Road, Worthing, Sussex BN13 1DG    *tel* (0903) 61978. Specialising in horticulture, plus natural history, pictorial views. Sequences and illustrated features. Own pictures only. Commissions undertaken.

*****Tony Stone Worldwide,** 28 Finchley Road, St. John's Wood, London NW8 6ES    *tel* 01-586 7671    *fax* 01-722 9305. International colour transparency library. Subjects required: travel, people, natural history, commerce, industry, technology, historic transport, etc. *Terms* 50-50.

*****Survival Anglia Photo Library** (1960), Brook House, 113 Park Lane, London W1Y 4DX    *tel* 01-321 0101    *telex* 299689 Salldn    *fax* 01-493 2598. Outstanding natural history collection, by some of world's top wildlife photographers, the result of 30 years of the award-winning ITV programme 'Survival'. *Terms:* 50%.

**Sutcliffe Gallery,** 1 Flowergate, Whitby, Yorkshire YO21 3BA    *tel* (0947) 602239. Collection of 19th-century photography all by Frank M. Sutcliffe, HON. F.R.P.S. (1853-1941). Especially inshore fishing boats and fishing community, also farming interests. Period covered 1872 to 1910.

*****Syndication International Ltd.,** 4-12 Dorrington Street, London EC1N 7TB    *tel* 01-404 0004    *telex* 267503    *fax* 01-430 2437. Supplier of publishing material and international rights for news pictures and text. Comprehensive photo library specialising in pop, royalty, personalities. Agents for Mirror Group Newspapers.

*****The Telegraph Colour Library** (now representing **The Photo Source**), Unit C1, Enterprise Business Estate, Mastmaker Road, London E14 9TE    *tel* 01-987 1212    *fax* 01-538 3309. Over 300,000 transparencies covering a wide range of subjects: technology, industry, health, countries, people, transport, sport and landscapes; comprehensive space exploration collection.

**Theatre Museum,** 1E Tavistock Street, Covent Garden, London WC2E 7PA *tel* 01-836 7891 ext. 129 *fax* 01-836 5148. The Theatre Museum is not a picture library, but has extensive collections of prints, drawings, playbills, programmes, press cuttings, photographs, theatre documents including the Enthoven Collection, the Guy Little Photographic Collection, the London Archives of the Dance, the Dame Marie Rambert-Ashley Dukes Ballet Collection, the M.W. Stone Toy Theatre Collection, the Gerald Morice Puppetry Collection, the British Puppet Theatre Guild's Collection of Puppets, the Harry R. Beard Theatre Collection, the Antony Hippisley Coxe Circus Collection, the British Council's and the Arts Council of Great Britain's collections of theatre designs and the collections of the British Theatre Museum Association and the Friends of the Museum of Performing Arts. Much of the material in the collections is being reorganised into a new archive housed in Olympia and is temporarily unavailable, but full details may be obtained from the above address.

**\*Three Lions**—see **Hulton Picture Company.**

**\*Topham Picture Library** (1928), P.O. Box 33, Edenbridge, Kent TN8 5PB *tel* Cowden (034 286) 313 *telex* 95351 *fax* (034 286) 244. Historic Library: personalities, warfare, royalty, topography, France, natural history. World news file from original sources: UPI, INP, Press Association, Central News, Planet News, Alfieri, Pictorial Press, etc.

**Transworld Feature Syndicate (UK) Ltd.,** Scope Features, 26 St Cross Street, London EC1N 8HH *tel* 01-405 2997.

**Travel Photo International,** 8 Delph Common Road, Aughton, Ormskirk, Lancashire L39 5DW *tel* (0695) 423720. Touristic interest including scenery, towns, monuments, historic buildings, archaeological sites, local people. Specialising in travel brochures and books. *Terms:* 50%.

**Travel Trade Photography,** Colour Library, 22 Princedale Road, London W11 4NJ *tel* 01-727 5471. *Principal:* Teddy Schwarz. Landscapes, townscapes, ancient monuments and buildings of historical interest in England and foreign countries, peoples, and their customs. Return postage essential. *Terms:* 50%.

**\*Tropix Photographic Library** (1973), 156 Meols Parade, Meols, Wirral, Merseyside L47 6AN *tel* 051-632 1698. All human and environmental aspects of tropics, sub-tropics and non-tropical developing countries. **Merseyslides** (subsidiary division): North of England photos. Welcome new collections for both areas. Preliminary enquiry essential. *Terms:* 50%.

**Ulster Photographic Agency** (1985), 22 Casaeldona Park, Belfast BT6 9RB *tel* (0232) 795738. Motoring and motorsport. *Terms:* 50%.

**\*Universal Pictorial Press & Agency, Ltd.** (1929), New Bridge Street House, 30-34 New Bridge Street, London EC4V 6BN *tel* 01-248 6730 *telex* 8952718 Unipix G *fax* 01-489 8982. Suppliers of a daily press and library service to the national and provincial press, periodicals and television companies throughout the British Isles and overseas. Notable political, company, academic, legal, diplomatic, church, military, pop, arts, entertaining and sports personalities and well-known views and buildings.

**Van Hallan, Bill Bates,** 16 Blenheim Road, Basing, Basingstoke, Hampshire RG24 0HP *tel* (0256) 465217.

**John Vickers Theatre Collection,** 27 Shorrolds Road, London SW6 7TR  *tel* 01-385 5774. Archives of British theatre and portraits of actors, writers and musicians by John Vickers from 1938-1974.

**Vidocq Photo Library** (1983), 9 Vicarage Street, Frome, Somerset BA11 1TX  *tel* (0373) 64548. Worldwide travel pictures, natural history, architecture, outdoor activities, sports, landscapes, aircraft, animals. No fee for inclusion in our Register of Photographers; photographs not retained, only details of available stock. *Terms:* 60% to photographer.

*****Viewfinder Colour Photo Library** (1984), The Production House, 147A St Michaels Hill, Bristol BS2 8DB  *tel* (0272) 731729 and 237268. Colour library covering industry, agriculture, transport, people, worldwide travel; detailed sections on South West England and Wales. *Terms:* 50% to photographer.

**Vision International** (1979), 79 Great Titchfield Street, London W1P 7FN  *tel* 01-636 9516  *telex* 23539  *telegraphic address* Visint London. Travel, fine art, gardens and plants, wildlife, natural history, architecture, landscapes, medicine, pregnancy, birth, child development, abstracts.

**Wales Scene,** Melysfan, Llangwm, Corwen, Clwyd LL21 0RD  *tel* (049 082) 472. Library of black and white photographs and colour transparencies on the landscape of Wales: scenery, towns and villages, churches, antiquities, rural life. Do not act as agents for other photographers.

**Simon Warner,** Whitestone Farm, Stanbury, Keighley, West Yorkshire BD22 0JW  *tel* Haworth (0535) 44644. Landscape/countryside pictures, featuring especially Yorkshire. Commissions accepted. No other photographers.

**Waterways Photo Library** (1976), 39 Manor Court Road, London W7 3EJ  *tel* 01-840 1659. *Contact:* Derek Pratt. British inland waterways; canals, and rivers; bridges, aqueducts, locks and all waterside architectural features; waterway holidays, boats, fishing; town and countryside scenes.

**Weimar Archive** (1983), 8-9 The Incline, Coalport, Telford, Shropshire TF8 7HR  *tel* (0952) 680050. Modern Germany, specialising in Weimar Republic, rise of Hitler and German arts and culture in 19th and 20th centuries.

**Welfare History Picture Library** (1975), Heatherbank Museum of Social Work, 163 Mugdock Road,Milngavie, Glasgow G62 8ND  *tel* 041-956 2687. Social history and social work, especially child welfare, workhouses, prisons, hospitals, slum clearance, women's movement, social reformers and their work. Catalogue on request.

*****Werner Forman Archive** (1975), 36 Camden Square, London NW1 9XA  *tel* 01-267 1034  *telex* 295931 Unicom G  *fax* 01-267 6026. Art, architecture, archaeology, history and peoples of ancient, oriental and primitive cultures.

**Western Americana Picture Library,** 3 Barton Buildings, Bath BA1 2JR  *tel* (0225) 334213. Prints, engravings, photographs and colour transparencies on the American West, cowboys, gunfighters, Indians, including pictures by Frederic Remington and Charles Russell, etc. Interested in buying pictures on American West.

**Roy J. Westlake,** A.R.P.S. Photo Library, 31 Redwood Drive, Plympton, Plymouth PL7 3FS  *tel* (0752) 336444. Britain, especially the West Country. Landscape subjects suitable for book illustrations, calendars, greeting cards, travel brochures, etc. Also camping, caravanning and inland waterways subjects in Britain, including rivers and canals. Other photographers work not accepted.

**\*Eric Whitehead Picture Agency and Library** (1984), P.O. Box 33, Kendal, Cumbria LA9 4SU    *tel* (0539) 33166 and (0860) 534767 (24 hours). Covers assignments for news contacts and publishers and operates a picture library specialising on news, sport (mainly snooker), landscapes, mountaineering, northern subjects and general interest. Assignments undertaken for public relations clients and the media.

**Derek G. Widdicombe,** Worldwide Photographic Library, Oldfield, High Street, Clayton West, Huddersfield HD8 9NS    *tel* (0484) 862638. Landscapes, seascapes, architecture, human interest of Britain and abroad, moods and seasons, buildings and natural features. Holds copyright of Noel Habgood, F.R.P.S. Collection.

**Wilderness Images** (1977), 70 Foster Road, Kempston, Bedford MK42 8BU    *tel* (0234) 854848. The Canadian Rockies, British Columbia, Alberta.

**\*Wilderness Photographic Library,** *Director:* John Noble, F.R.G.S. 2 Kent View, Kendal, Cumbria LA9 4HE    *tel* (0539) 28334. Mountain and wilderness regions, travel and adventure, and associated aspects; also Antarctic exploration and wildlife.

**Wildlife Matters Photographic Library** (1980), Dr John Feltwell, Marlham, Henley Down, Battle, East Sussex TN33 9BN    *tel* (0424 83) 566. 2¼in sq and 35mm colour transparencies: ecology, conservation and environment; habitats and pollution; general natural history, especially entomology; Mediterranean wildlife; rain forests; oblique aerial pics of countryside, especially Channel Tunnel. **Plants 2000**—special collection of over 2000 garden plants world-wide: trees, grasses, herbs; 100 garden portfolios in Europe and USA; garden design. Commissions accepted.

**\*S. & I. Williams, Power Pix International Picture Library** (1968), Castle Lodge, Wenvoe, Cardiff CF5 6AD    *tel* (0222) 595163    *telex* 995411    *fax* (0222) 593905. Worldwide travel, people and views, girl and "mood-pix", sub-aqua, aircraft, flora, fauna, agriculture, children. Agents worldwide.

**Timothy Woodcock** (1983), 82 Sirdar Road, Wood Green, London N22 6RD    *tel* 01-889 7459. British architecture, landscape, seascape and heritage; children, parenthood and education; gardens and gardening. *Terms:* 50%.

**\*Woodmansterne Publications Ltd.,** Watford Business Park, Watford, Herts. WD1 8RD    *tel* (0923) 228236    *fax* (0923) 245788. Britain, Europe, Holy Land; architecture, cathedral and stately home interiors; general art subjects; museum collections; natural history, butterflies, geography, volcanoes, transport, space; opera and ballet; major state occasions; British heritage.

**Murray Wren Picture Library,** 3 Hallgate, London SE3 9SG    *tel* 01-852 7556. Outdoor nudes; nudist holiday resorts and activities in Europe and elsewhere; historic and erotic art of the nude through the ages.

# Markets for Photographers

Photographers are advised to study carefully the detailed requirements of journals at the beginning of the *Yearbook*. Book publishers, especially those issuing technical books and school books, will be glad to know the range of subjects covered by a photographer.

## GREETINGS, VIEWCARD, CALENDAR AND COLOUR SLIDES

A preliminary letter to ascertain requirements is advisable.
So far as colour is concerned, and most of the firms mentioned below are concerned with colour, usually colour transparencies are required. Very few firms will consider 35mm. frames; 5 in. x 4 in. is preferred, and 3¼ x 2¼ is acceptable. 2¼ in. square is the minimum size acceptable to film libraries and agencies. Only top quality transparencies should be submitted; inferior work is never accepted. *Postage for return of photographs should be enclosed.*

\*Member of the Greeting Card and Calendar Association

**Arnold Barton Cards Ltd.—See Hambledon Studios.**

**Athena International,** P.O. Box 918, Harlow, Essex CM20 2DU   *tel* (0279) 641125. *Art Directors:* P. Rodriguez, T. Jones, T. Taffs. Professional quality transparencies for posters, prints and postcards, preferably not 35 mm. S.A.E. essential for return of work.

**C.C.A. Stationery Ltd.,** Eastway, Fulwood, Preston PR2 4WS   *tel* (0772) 794508. Personalised wedding stationery, Christmas cards.

**E.T.W. Dennis & Sons, Ltd.,** Printing House Square, Melrose Street, Scarborough, Yorkshire YO12 7SJ   *tel* (0723) 500555   *fax* (0723) 500545. Interested in first class transparencies for reproduction as local view postcards and calendars. 3¼ x 2¼ in. or 35 mm. transparencies ideal for postcard reproduction.

**\*J. Arthur Dixon, DRG (UK) Ltd.,** Forest Side, Newport, Isle of Wight PO30 5QW   *tel* Isle of Wight (0983) 523381   *telex* 86188   *fax* (0983) 529719. Greeting cards, postcards, gift wrap and booklets.

**\*Giesen & Wolff** (1908), Kaygee House, Dallington, Northampton NN5 7QW   *tel* (0604) 55411   *telex* 311009 Kaygee G   *fax* (0604) 759157. *Director:* Gordon Wood. Transparencies, 2¼ in. sq. minimum, views, floral. Will consider verses.

**Hambledon Studios Ltd.,** Hambledon House, Marlborough Road, Accrington, Lancashire BB5 6BX   *tel* (0254) 872266   *telex* 635169 Cardac G   *fax* (0254) 872079. *Brands:* Arnold Barton, Donny Mac, Reflections, New Image. *Art Managers:* D. Jaundrell, J. Ashton, D. Fuller. Photographs for reproduction as greeting cards.

**\*Hayes Greeting Card Publishers Ltd.** (1984), Thames View, Newtown Road, Henley-on-Thames, Oxon RG9 1HQ   *tel* (0491) 410454. *Directors:* M. S. Belsten, R. H. Parker. Transparencies 35mm upward.

**Kardonia, Ltd.,** Farrier Street, Worcester WR1 3BH   *tel* (0905) 611294.

**Leeds Postcards** (1979), P.O. Box 84, Leeds LS1 1HU   *tel* (0532) 468649. Workers co-operative. Publishers and producers of campaign postcards for the labour, environmental, women's and international justice movements.

**\*Henry Ling & Son (London) Ltd.,** Chiddingstone Causeway, Nr. Tonbridge, Kent TN11 8JP  *tel* (0892) 870333  *telex* 8813271 Gecoms G ref HO87  *fax* (0892) 870466. Transparencies of art work for greeting cards.

**Lowe Aston Calendars, Ltd.,** Saltash, Cornwall PL12 4HL  *tel* (0752) 842233. Calendar printers.

**The Medici Society, Ltd.,** 34-42 Pentonville Road, London N1 9HG  *tel* 01-837 7099. Photographs suitable for reproduction as greeting cards. Preliminary letter requested.

**\*Panache Studio Ltd** (1985), Station Road, Henley on Thames, Oxon RG9 1LQ  *tel* (0491) 578383  *telex* 847279 HMK HO G  *fax* (0491) 578817. Photographs of finished artwork, transparencies, humorous verses.

**\*Photo Production Ltd.,** Featherby Road, Gillingham, Kent ME8 6PJ  *tel* (0634) 33241. Transparencies; will consider verses.

**\*Royle Publications, Ltd.,** Royle House, Wenlock Road, London N1 7ST  *tel* 01-253 7654. Colour transparencies required for two calendars, *Moods of Nature* and *Gardens of Britain*. Natural landscape photography taken in Britain and abroad or pictures of ornate flower gardens in Britain.

**\*J. Salmon Ltd.,** 100 London Road, Sevenoaks, Kent TN13 1BB  *tel* Sevenoaks 452381. Picture postcards, calendars and greeting cards.

**\*Scandecor Ltd.** (1967), 3 Armadale Road, Feltham, Middlesex TW14 0LU  *tel* 01-890 8174  *telex* 934367  *fax* 01-844 0926. *Directors:* G. Huldtgren, A. Inghammar. Transparencies all sizes.

**Noel Tatt Ltd** (1954), Coombe Valley Road, Dover CT17 0EU  *tel* (0304) 211644  *fax* (0304) 240470. *Directors:* Noel Tatt, Vencke Tatt, Derek Bates, Anthony Sharpe, Paul Tatt, Robert Dixon. Greeting cards, prints and postcards.

**Vision International** (1979), 79 Great Titchfield Street, London W1P 7FN  *tel* 01-636 9516  *telex* 23539.

---

See also the **Articles, reports and short stories** and the **Books** sections for lists of magazines and publishers.

# Picture research

## Picture Research

### JUDITH HARRIES

Picture research is the term given to the selection, procurement and collection of illustrations suitable for reproduction. In recent years this trade has developed and diversified enormously, so that it is no longer largely confined to supplying the requirements of book and magazine publishers. Picture researchers are widely used by packaging companies, advertising agencies and film, television and video companies. However an account of the methods applying to publishing research will provide the fullest general guide to the craft. Publishers either employ a researcher full-time, or submit their requests to freelance researchers, and some commercial picture libraries offer their own research facilities.

A picture researcher is responsible, to a large extent, for the publisher's end product. The publisher's needs may be highly specialised, but there is nearly always a choice of pictures. The researcher makes this initial choice, whether it be between different views of a subject or between pictures of a different quality. For example, when asked for a picture of the Eiffel Tower the researcher would be quite correct in either presenting a worm's eye view, an aerial view, or both. In this case quality would really mean different techniques, i.e., a picture illustrating the architectural structure of the tower or a picture indicating the splendid view it gives of Paris. The only indication an editor may give in his request may be whether he requires a portrait or a landscape shaped picture. The researcher is also responsible for copyright permission, correct acknowledgement and providing the editor with all the information about the photograph as a basis for caption copy. A picture researcher fully employed by a group of publishers, or one publisher, is expected to attend to everything. This includes the payment of all reproduction fees (new editions to be remembered) and the safe return of any material from the printer to the source. If not directly involved in these final stages the freelance researcher can at least check their completion. Costs must be kept down at all times (in the case of a freelance researcher this will ensure that she never lacks work).

Publishers who employ a permanent researcher will always be appreciative of any material which does not have to be returned, being formed into a picture library of their own, or a reference "bank".

Picture research can cover a tremendous variety of topics but there is a fundamental core to the actual research. For me, the process from beginning to end, forms the following pattern.

Each separate request is booked in, just as a production department books in a manuscript. The title, author, date of publication, number of copies going into print, the sales market, and the budget allocation for pictures are noted. General information is wanted by anyone who may supply a picture; certain facts may influence their decision. For example, publication date may be far ahead, and the picture wanted elsewhere (you then offer to have a copy made at your expense); or sometimes in the case of a syndication department, or a foreign source, the number of copies going into print affects the permission fee. Remember to set some of your budget aside for extras, which will probably include any photocopying you want done, and print fees. (Some agencies keep their stock in negative form only.)

Colour transparencies are very valuable and require special attention. They are usually signed for and the indemnity for loss or damage varies enormously. It may be £50 or £500 for each transparency. The loan period is usually one month and if a transparency is not returned on the requested date the borrower is asked to pay a holding fee. This fee, for each transparency for every week it is held, varies with each library or agency.

The *British Association of Picture Libraries (BAPLA)* was founded in 1975. A great majority of commercial picture libraries and several institutional libraries are members of the Association. Their aim is to promote fair and honest trading within the profession and between members and their clients. *Address:* 13 Woodberry Crescent, London N10 1PJ.

TYPE OF RESEARCH

The line of research depends entirely on the type of picture one is looking for. It is not logical to go to a photograph library dealing in news pictures for an engraving, nor is it ideal to go to the same library for a photograph of a bar of chocolate when you can approach the maker of that particular bar and be given a picture with no reproduction fee. So, content and design dictate the direction on one's research. Many professional authors (scientists, doctors, engineers, architects, etc.) submit illustrations with their manuscripts, or their needs are highly specialised, and the research clear-cut. The author may have an idea of the illustrations he wants, but not every picture asked for will be available, and the researcher involved should have access to the manuscript so that substitutes can be found. *Most important*, at this stage, is the checking of any information necessary to obtain the picture required. "Wants" may be expressed loosely, e.g. "Royalty visiting the Empire and Colonies in 1907." In this case one would need to know which of the royal family was referred to and which country, before approaching a source. It is much more efficient to do the fact finding before contacting any would-be source, as it just slows up the process having your list queried by an agency, or a picture library.

Reference libraries are of great service to a picture researcher for information. When there is no obvious source for a particular picture one can work backwards from printed material. This applies when a "want" is expressed in general terms, e.g. "a twentieth-century woodcut". One can go straight to books on the subject, select a number of artists and examples of their work from which a choice can be made. The source is then traceable from the library book. Useful libraries in London are:

British Library Reading Room
London Library
United States Reference Library,
  US Embassy

Victoria and Albert Museum
  Library
Westminster Central
  Reference Library

CONTACTING SOURCES

It is a good idea to visit, at some time, picture agencies and libraries with whom you will be constantly dealing. It is necessary to be familiar with their stock, and *their* system. It is particularly helpful if you can single out one member of their staff, and deal with that person whenever possible. Personal relations may be vital when you need a certain picture in a hurry, but cannot leave your office. Many projects can be dealt with, as time goes on and you accumulate more information, over the telephone or by sending out want lists. A want list should be specific to each source, as it is a waste of time and effort to have a number of agencies and libraries duplicating the request. An agency's time is just as valuable as the researcher's, and where a wide choice is involved a visit can eliminate a research fee, but please telephone first. Many agencies operate an appointment system and they do so because they can deal more efficiently with the client's request.

*Most important*, at this stage, is to see that every picture is clearly marked with the agency's name. It is also a good idea to count the number of pictures, and write the figures down, even if the agency sends its own list. This will eliminate any disagreement about the number of pictures supplied. This is to be followed up by noting down the number of pictures you return (and the date) either as unsuitable for selection, or when a definite choice has been made.

COVER PICTURE AND CAPTIONS COPY

A researcher is not responsible for deciding on cover material but is often asked to provide suitable material for selection by the editor and the art department. If a picture reproduced inside a book is repeated on the cover the researcher may quite reasonably ask for a reduction on the cover rate remembering that a cover rate is usually double that of an "inside" reproduction fee. At this point you make certain that all pictures have their correct captions, and that all relevant information has been passed on to the publisher or editor. It is a good idea to discuss any print fees or reproduction rates at the beginning of the assignment with each individual source. These rates can vary enormously.

LAST STAGES

A researcher employed by a publisher would now write to each source, confirming what pictures were being used. An acknowledgement list to be included in the book would also be prepared at this point.

A freelance researcher should retain a copy of the list of pictures supplied to the publisher. (This list will be of sources, and costing.) Reproduction fees are usually paid on publication day, although it is a good policy to pay freelance photographers on completion of their work. (Their work can be irregular, and this arrangement is advantageous to both.) After publication, the final task is to ensure the safe return of any material from the printer (and this includes the cover picture) back to you. A permanently employed researcher is usually responsible for the safe return of any material back to its source. If a picture is damaged, or lost, you must see that it is paid for. In the case of photographs worked on by the art department you are responsible for paying for a replacement print. A freelance researcher does not usually have these responsibilities.

Professional picture researchers jot down every useful source, and a card index system is a time-saving one. Useful addresses, ranging from collections and agencies to freelance photographers, and private individuals are filed in categories, e.g. Scientific, Geographical, Political, Transport, etc. Against each source one can note useful details such as: research fee (if required), willingness to send material through the post, how prompt their service is, and if one must make an appointment in advance of a visit. The card index provides quick reference, but a comprehensive file is necessary. This can be made by dividing a looseleaf file into three sections:

In the *first* section file any literature from public collections, museums, government offices, and other official bodies, such as permission conditions, reproduction details, and application forms;

in the *second* section, keep a complete record of the detailed fees of all sources;

the *last* section will be a comprehensive version of your quick-reference card index file, i.e. a complete subject list from each source (where available). It will include any up-to-date information on new subjects they cover. These lengthy subject lists cannot be accommodated on a simple card index.

SOURCES

These are endless and international. The obvious ones being: public collections, publishers, photographers, agencies, and commercial picture libraries. One is guided to these and others through books such as those listed below (and of course the pages immediately preceding this article!) The first two books listed below are invaluable to all users of photographs and vital to every picture researcher's reference shelf.

*The Picture Researcher's Handbook: An International Guide to Picture Sources— and How to Use Them* (Hilary and Mary Evans), 4th edition, Van Nostrand Reinhold. Now considerably enlarged, with over 1000 entries. Obtainable direct from their trade counter distribution centre (*tel* (0264) 332424 *fax* (0264) 64418). Full price £24.95; discount available on request. Also available by post from Mary Evans Picture Library, 59 Tranquil Vale, London SE3 0BS (*tel* 01-318 0034 *fax* 01-852 7211).

*Directory of British Photographic Collections*, published by William Heinemann on behalf of The Royal Photographic Society. The Directory, as its title implies (and for the first time), comprehensively lists all the photographic collections in the British Isles. It gives a detailed description of each collection, including subject matter and all other relevant details specific to each collection; location; number of photographs; type and size; owner/custodian; historical data; photographer; further sources of information; accessibility; details of inspection, loan, sale and reproduction.

*World of Learning*, Europa Publications, London (annually). Lists museums, learned societies, universities, galleries, etc.

*International Directory of Arts*, Verlag Muller KG, of Frankfurt. A comprehensive 2-volume directory of museums, galleries, universities, academies, collections, associations, dealers, publishers, collectors, etc., throughout the world. Technical data appears in English, French, German, Italian and Spanish.

*The State Association of the Press Photographic Agencies and Archives in Western Germany*. Bundesverband der Pressebild—Agenturen Bilderdierste und Bildarchive e.V. 8000 München 22-Maximilianstr. 17.

*Official Museum Directory of America and Canada* (Latest edition 1970) Ed. U.S. association of museums. Crowell-Collier Education Corporation.

*Guide to the Special Collections of Prints and Photographs in the Library of Congress*, Paul Vanderbilt. Government Printing Office, Washington.
*The Libraries Yearbook 1985–87.* Obtainable from James Clarke & Co. Ltd, P.O. Box 60, Cambridge CB1 2NT (*tel* (0223) 350865   *fax* (0223) 66951). Full price £30.00; discount available on request.
*Picture Source Book for Social History*, Allen & Unwin, London 1961. A 6-volume work with a wealth of pictures, indicating their sources.
*Sources of Illustration 1500-1900*, Adams & Dart, London 1971.


EXHIBITIONS

These are now becoming an excellent opportunity of seeing a wide variety of photography, both foreign and British, and include the work of many young photographers. Exhibitions are held in a number of places and, more and more, the daily newspapers are drawing attention to them, as well as reviewing the exhibitions. The weekly *British Journal of Photography* also lists current exhibitions. The Photographers' Gallery, besides giving us an opportunity to see some marvellous photography, has a very good bookstand where one may look at (and buy!) books on early and contemporary photography. There is also a study centre. A number of exhibitions of photography are sponsored by the Arts Council of Great Britain. Both the Photographers' Gallery and the Arts Council have advance mailing lists, and some specialist galleries in London are listed below.
**Camera Work,** 121 Roman Road, London, E2.
**Half Moon Gallery,** 27 Alie Street, London, E1.
**Photographers' Gallery,** 5 & 8 Great Newport Street, London, WC2.
**Serpentine Gallery,** Kensington Gardens, London, W2.
**Victoria and Albert Museum,** South Kensington, London, SW7.
**Whitechapel Art Gallery,** High Street, London, E1.

The galleries listed below are located outside London and exclusively show photography, both Victorian and Contemporary. The Gallery of Photography in Southampton is particularly good about forwarding details of their exhibitions and lectures. It is always a good idea to be on as many mailing lists as possible.
**Gallery of Photography,** The University, Southampton.
**John Hayward Gallery,** Southampton.
**Impressions Gallery of Photography,** 17 Colliergate, York, YO1 2BN.
**National Museum of Photography and Film,** Bradford.
**Open Eye Gallery,** Whitechapel, Liverpool.
**The Photogallery,** The Forresters Arms, Shepherd Street, St. Leonards-on-Sea, East Sussex.
**The Photographers' Corridor,** University College, Cardiff.
**The Photographic Gallery,** 41 Charles Street, Cardiff.
**Royal Photographic Society,** National Centre of Photography, The Octagon, Milson Street, Bath, BA1 1DN.
**Side Photographic Gallery,** 9 Side, Newcastle-upon-Tyne.
**Sutcliffe Gallery,** 1 Flowergate, Whitby.

# Picture Research Course

The Book House Training Centre offers training in picture research. It is a two-day course, which is also offered as an evening class, designed for those working in book publishing. The objective of the course is to give a professional approach to the search for and use of suitable sources; to make picture researchers aware of all the implications of their task: suitability for reproduction, legal and financial aspects, efficient administration.

Details of the course, with the outline of the programme, may be obtained from Book House Training Centre, 45 East Hill, Wandsworth, London, SW18 2QZ   *tel* 01-874 2718/4608.

The London School of Publishing now offers a course in picture research twice a year—Spring and Autumn. Each course lasts eight weeks and there is one lecture a week. Further details may be obtained from Mark Featherstone-Witty, 47 Red Lion Street, London, WC1R 4PF   *tel* 01-405 9801.

*The Art of Picture Research* by Hilary Evans (David & Charles) is a useful introduction to picture research as a profession. It covers everything from qualifications needed to do picture research to everyday aspects of the job and also covers career opportunities. Available from the Mary Evans Picture Library, 59 Tranquil Vale, London SE3 0BS (*tel* 01-318 0034   *fax* 01-852 7211), £13.50, including postage and packing.

# S.P.R.Ed. (Society of Picture Researchers and Editors)

S.P.R.Ed. was formed in 1977 as a professional body with a Code of Practice for picture researchers and editors. It is a meeting-place for people to discuss ideas, share problems and exchange information. It aims to provide a number of services and has established a Freelance Register for those members available for free-lance work and provides a Freelance Engagement Form for freelance researchers wishing to use a standard contract.

S.P.R.Ed. holds regular monthly meetings and publishes a quarterly news magazine which can be purchased on a yearly subscription by non-members. Advertising space can also be bought in this publication. S.P.R.Ed. also arranges meetings for its members at the Photographers' Gallery, 5 & 8 Great Newport Street, London WC2 to see the work of photographers, photographic libraries and other illustrative collections.

Those interested in further details should write to The Secretary, BM Box 259, London WC1N 3XX   *tel* 01-404 5011.

See also the **Books** section for lists of publishers; the **Photography** section.

# Music

## Music Publishers

### UNITED KINGDOM

Copyright in musical compositions comprises (*a*) the right of publication in print and sale of printed copies; (*b*) the right of public performance, and (*c*) the right to use the work for the purpose of making gramophone records, sound films or other similar contrivances. The musical composer should bear that in mind when entering into an agreement for the publication of his work.

Rutland Boughton's warning to amateurs given many years ago, still stands. He said that amateurs, "like the more hardened professional composers, find pleasure in seeing their musical thoughts in print. Because of that human weakness they become the prey of tenth-rate publishers, who offer to issue their music for them (however poor and ineffective it may be) *if they will pay for the privilege. If a piece of music is worth publishing a publisher will be willing to pay for it in cash or royalty.*" Music publishers requiring work for issue on cash or royalty terms no more advertise in the public press for music and lyrics than a first-class publisher of books advertises for MSS. on that basis.

The publishers in the following list are all members of the Performing Right Society except those marked †. The list does not include all publisher-members of the Performing Right Society.

**Lyrics without a musical setting are not accepted unless stated by individual firms**

**Arcadia Music Publishing Co., Ltd.,** P.O. Box 1, Rickmansworth, Herts. WD3 3AZ  *tel* 01-584 6671. Light orchestral.

**Banks Music Publications (Ramsay Silver),** The Old Forge, Sand Hutton, York YO4 1LB  *tel* (0904) 86472. Publishers of choral and instrumental music.

**Bardic Edition** (1987), 6 Fairfax Crescent, Aylesbury, Bucks. HP20 2ES  *tel* (0296) 28609. Piano, vocal, chamber, choral, educational, orchestral and music for all instruments.

**Belwin-Mills Music Ltd**—now distributed by **International Music Publications.**

**A. & C. Black (Publishers) Ltd.** (1978), 35 Bedford Row, London WC1R 4JH  *tel* 01-242 0946  *telegraphic address* Biblos, London, WC1  *telex* 32524 Acblac *fax* 01-831 8478. Song books and instrumental books for children.

**Boosey & Hawkes Music Publishers, Ltd.,** 295 Regent Street, London W1R 8JH  *tel* 01-580 2060  *telex* 8954613 Boosey G  *fax* 01-436 5675. General and educational.

**Bosworth & Co., Ltd.** (1889), 14-18 Heddon Street, London W1R 8DP   *tel* 01-734 4961, 0475   *fax* 01-734 5285. Orchestral, chamber, instrumental, operetta, church, educational, piano, violin and part-songs.

**Bourne Music Ltd.**, 34-36 Maddox Street, London W1R 9PD   *tel* 01-493 6412, 6583. Popular and educational music.

**Cambridge University Press** (1534). The Edinburgh Building, Shaftesbury Road, Cambridge CB2 2RU   *tel* (0223) 312393   *telegraphic address* Unipress, Cambridge   *telex* 817256 Cupcam   *fax* (0223) 315052. *Chief Executive and Secretary of the Press Syndicate:* Geoffrey A. Cass, M.A. *Deputy Chief Executive:* Philip E.V. Allin, M.A. *Managing Director* (Publishing Division): Anthony K. Wilson, M.A. *Press Editorial Director:* Jeremy Mynott, PH.D. *Press Marketing Director:* David A. Knight, M.A. Books on music and history of music; music books for schools.

**Campbell Connelly Group of Companies**, 8-9 Frith Street, London W1V 5TZ   *tel* 01-434 0066   *telex* 21892   *fax* 01-439 2848. General and popular.

**Chester Music—J. & W. Chester/Edition Wilhelm Hansen London Ltd.** (1860), 8-9 Frith Street, London W1V 5TZ   *tel* 01-434 0066   *telex* 21892   *fax* 01-439 2848. Concert and educational works.

**Cramer Music** (1824), 23 Garrick Street, London WC2E 9AX   *tel* 01-240 1612. General and educational.

**De Wolfe, Ltd.**, 80-88 Wardour Street, London W1V 3LF   *tel* 01-439 8481-6   *telex* 265014 Topcd-G   *fax* 01-437 2744. Symphonic recorded orchestral (English and foreign). Comprehensive library of recorded music on disc and tape. Extensive effects library. Original film scores. Recording studio.

**Dix Ltd.** (1922)—see **EMI Music Publishing Ltd.**

†**East-West Publications (UK) Ltd.** (1977), Newton Works, 27-29 Macklin Street, London WC2B 5LX   *tel* 01-831 6767. *Chairman:* L. W. Carp. *Editor:* B. Thompson. Piano, guitar, recorder and vocal music.

**Emerson Edition Ltd.** (1972), Windmill Farm, Ampleforth, North Yorkshire YO6 4HF   *tel* (04393) 324. *Managing Director:* June Emerson. Specialist publisher of music for wind instruments only.

**EMI Music Publishing Ltd,** 127 Charing Cross Road, London WC2H 0EA   *tel* 01-434 2131   *telemessages/cables* Emimus   *telex* 269189   *fax* 01-434 3531. Comprising Dix Ltd, B. Feldman & Co. Ltd, Francis, Day & Hunter Ltd, KPM Music Group, The Peter Maurice Music Co. Ltd, Keith Prowse Music Publishing Co. Ltd, Reynolds Music, Robbins Music Corp. Ltd, Screen Gems-EMI Music Ltd.

**Faber Music, Ltd.** (*1966), 3 Queen Square, London WC1N 3AU (Subsidiary of Faber & Faber, Ltd. (1929)   *tel* 01-278 7436   *telex* 299633 Faber G   *fax* 01-278 3817   *telegraphic address* Fabbaf, London, WC1. *Directors:* Donald Mitchell (President), Robin Boyle (Chairman & Chief Executive), Martin Kingsbury (Vice-Chairman & Director of Publishing), Sally Cavender, Piers Hembry, Thomas H. Pasteur, Wendy Thompson. A general list of the highest quality, comprising both old and new music, and music books.

**Fairfield Music Co., Ltd.,** Borough Green, Sevenoaks, Kent TN15 8DT   *tel* (0732) 883261   *telex* 95583   *fax* (0732) 882978. London Showroom: 8 Lower James Street, London, W1   *tel* 01-734 8080. Contemporary orchestral, instrumental, chamber and film music.

**B. Feldman & Co. Ltd.**—see **EMI Music Publishing Ltd.**

**Fentone Music Ltd.,** Fleming Road, Earlstrees, Corby, Northants. NN17 2SN *tel* (0536) 60981 *telex* 312305 Hondel G *fax* (0536) 401075 *cables* Fentone, Corby. Agents for Fenette Music, Earlham Press, Mimram Music, all of Corby, VEB Breitkopf & Härtel, Friedrich Hofmeister, Deutscher Verlag für Musik, Pro Musica Verlag, all of Leipzig, F.E.C. Leuckart of Munich, Edizioni Bèrben, Ancona, Italy, F & R. Walsh Publications, London, Hänssler Verlag, Stuttgart, Notaset, Wiesbaden.

**First Time Music (Publishing) UK Ltd.** (1986), 12 Trewartha Road, Praa Sands, Penzance, Cornwall TR20 9ST *tel* (0736) 762826. *Managing Director:* Roderick G. Jones. Popular, country, folk, gospel music. Music for choirs.

**Forsyth Bros., Ltd.** (1857), 126 Deansgate, Manchester M3 2GR *tel* 061-834 3281 *fax* 061-834 0630. Educational piano and instrumental music. Modern Teaching material. U.K.Distributors of *Music Minus One* and *Pocket Songs*.

**Francis, Day & Hunter Ltd.**—see **EMI Music Publishing Ltd.**

**Glocken Verlag, Ltd.** (1946), 12-14 Mortimer Street, London W1N 7RD *tel* 01-580 2827 *cables* Operetta, London W1 *telex* 888735 Jowein G *fax* 01-436 9616. *Directors:* R. M. Toeman, R. G. Holt. Musical works by Franz Lehar.

†**Gresham Books,** The Gresham Press, P.O. Box 61, Henley-on-Thames, Oxfordshire RG9 3LQ *tel* (073 522) 3789. *Chief Executive:* Mrs. M. V. Green. Hymn books for churches and schools.

**Gwynn, Cwmni Cyhoeddi (Cyf.),** Y Gerlan, Heol Y Dŵr, Penygroes, Gwynedd LL54 6LR *tel* Penygroes (0286) 881797. Publishers of Welsh Educational and International Choral Music. Official music publishers to the Welsh Folk Song Society, The Welsh Folk Dance Society, The Court of the National Eisteddfod.

**Hughes & Son, Publishers** (1820), Clôs Sophia, Cardiff CF1 9XY *tel* (0222) 343421 *telex* 94017032 Sian G *fax* (0222) 341643. Welsh music, Welsh language, television related material, educational publications.

†**International Music Publications,** Woodford Trading Estate, Southend Road, Woodford Green, Essex IG8 8HN *tel* 01-551 6131 *fax* 01-551 3919. Standard and popular, educational, instrumental tutors, band and choral music. Sole representatives of **Columbia Pictures Publications.**

**Janus Music** (1978), Flat 11, 100 Friars Avenue, Roehampton, London SW15 3DU *tel* 01-785 7094. *Proprietor:* C. J. Gordon. Recorder music, educational woodwind music, contemporary wind music, contemporary piano music.

**Alfred A. Kalmus Ltd.,** 2-3 Fareham Street, Dean Street, London W1V 4DU *tel* 01-437 5203-4 *fax* 01-437 6115. *Trade:* 38 Eldon Way, Paddock Wood, Tonbridge, Kent TN12 6BE *tel* 089-283 3422 *telex* 95374. Sole representatives of Universal Edition A.G., Vienna, Universal Edition (London) Ltd, Universal Edition, A.G. Zurich, Universal Edition S.P.A., Milan; Theodore Presser Co, Lea Pocket Scores, Hargail Music Inc., International Music Co, Boelke-Bomart Inc., European American Music Corp, Bourne Music, Belmont Music, Kelton Publications, Trio Associates, all U.S.A.; Doblinger Edition, Vienna, Polish Editions, Cracow (complete Chopin-Paderewski), Supraphon, Prague, Harmonia Uitgave, Hilversum, Artia, Prague, Panton, Prague, Berandol, Canada, Billaudot, France, Boccaccini and Spada, Italy, Aldo Bruzzichelli, Italy, Breitkopf & Härtel, Wiesbaden, West Germany, Musikwissenschaftlicher Verlag, Austria, Musica Rara, France, Fraser-Enoch, Kent, Musical New Services, Wiltshire; Olivan Press, London; Broekmans & Van Poppel, Amsterdam, Loux Music Publishing, USA, Zen-On, Japan; Power

Music, West Yorkshire, Virgo Music, West Midlands. Serious music of all types.

**KPM Music Group**—see **EMI Music Publishing Ltd.**

**Alfred Lengnick & Co., Ltd.** (1892), Purley Oaks Studios, 421A Brighton Road, South Croydon CR2 6YR   *tel* 01-660 7646. Music publishers and importers. Publishers of Brahms' and Dvorak's works. Specialise in educational music, leading publishers of English contemporary music. Always ready to consider MSS. of any type. Agents for CeBeDeM (Brussels); Iceland Music Information Centre (Iceland).

**Leonard, Gould & Bolttler,** 60-62 Clerkenwell Road, London EC1M 5PY   *tel* 01-253 6346. General and educational.

**MCA Music Ltd.,** 139 Piccadilly, London W1V 9FH   *tel* 01-629 7211   *telex* 22219 MCA GRP   *fax* 01-499 9419.

**The Peter Maurice Music Co. Ltd.**—see **EMI Music Publishing Ltd.**

**Music Sales Ltd,** 8-9 Frith Street, London W1V 5TZ   *tel* 01-434 0066   *telex* 21892   *fax* 01-439 2848. General and popular.

**Novello & Co., Ltd.** (1811), Borough Green, Sevenoaks, Kent TN15 8DT   *tel* (0732) 883261   *telex* 95583   *fax* (0732) 882978. London Showroom: 8 Lower James Street, London W1   *tel* 01-734 8080. Classical and modern orchestral, instrumental, vocal and choral music, church music, school and educational music books.

†**Novello Hire Library,** incorporating **Goodwin & Tabb,** Borough Green, Sevenoaks, Kent TN15 8DT   *tel* (0732) 883261   *telex* 95583   *fax* (0732) 882978. Vocal, choral and orchestral hire libraries.

**Octava Music Co., Ltd.** (1938), 12-14 Mortimer Street, London W1N 7RD   *tel* 01-580 2827   *cables* Operetta, London W1   *telex* 888735 Jowein G   *fax* 01-436 9616.

**Oxford University Press** (Oxford University Press established 1478. Music Dept. constituted 1923). Music Department. Walton Street, Oxford OX2 6DP   *tel* (0865) 56767   *telex* 837330   *fax* (0865) 56646. Orchestral, instrumental, operatic, choral, vocal works, church and organ music by early and modern composers, educational music, courses, and books on music.

**Paterson's Publications Ltd.,** 8-10 Lower James Street, London W1R 3PL   *tel* 01-287 5060   *fax* 01-287 0816. Pianoforte, vocal, choral, orchestral, instrumental, educational and bagpipe music; also musical greetings cards.

**Peters Edition, Ltd.** (1938), 10-12 Baches Street, London N1 6DN   *tel* 01-253 1638. Copyright/Hire:   *tel* 01-251 5094; Promotion/Editorial:   *tel* 01-251 6732   *fax* 01-490 4921. Peters Edition, Hinrichsen Edition, Collection Litolff. Classical and modern (piano, organ, other instrumental, vocal, choir and brass band) music.

**The Polyphone Music Co., Ltd.,** P.O. Box 1, Rickmansworth, Herts. WD3 3AZ   *tel* 01-584 6671. Light orchestral.

**Keith Prowse Music Publishing Co. Ltd.**—see **EMI Music Publishing Ltd.**

†**Reynolds Music**—see **EMI Music Publishing Ltd.**

**G. Ricordi & Co. (London), Ltd.** (1808), The Bury, Church Street, Chesham, Bucks. HP5 1JG   *tel* (0494) 783311   *fax* (0494) 784427   *telegraphic address* Ricordi, Chesham. Publishers of Italian opera, music for piano, classical and contemporary, operatic arias, songs, choral large scale works and part songs for all voices, orchestral works, classical and contemporary, instrumental, string, woodwind, brass tutors, exercises, etc., guitar music of all types.

**Roberton Publications,** The Windmill, Wendover, Aylesbury, Bucks. HP22 6JJ *tel* (0296) 623107. *Partners:* Kenneth Roberton, Margaret Roberton. Choral and educational; also piano, chamber, orchestral, and music for all instruments. Represent Albert House Press, London, Bardic Editions, Aylesbury, Fulcrum Music Publications Cheltenham, Hardie Press, Edinburgh; Leslie Music Supply, Oakville, Ontario; Music 70, Fort Lauderdale, Florida, Paraclete Press, Orleans, Massachusetts; Paul Price Publications, New Jersey, Scottish Music Publishing, Glasgow.

**Schott & Co., Ltd.** (1835), 48 Great Marlborough Street, London W1V 2BN *tel* 01-437 1246 *telex* 298738 G *fax* 01-437 0263. Music of a serious and educational nature.

**Sea Dream Music** (1976), 236 Sebert Road, Forest Gate, London E7 0NP *tel* 01-534 8500. *Senior Partner:* S.A. Law. Christian based rock, blues and folk.

**Shapiro Bernstein & Co. Ltd,** 8-9 Frith Street, London W1V 5TZ *tel* 01-434 0066 *telex* 21892 *fax* 01-439 2848. General and popular.

**Sheet Music Publishing** (1978) 133-137 Kilburn Lane, London W10 4AN *tel* 01-497 2444. *Contact:* V. Faraguer. Library music, pop, jazz, country, classical, disco, Latin American, children's series, tutors for schools.

**R. Smith & Co., Ltd.** (1857), P.O. Box 210, Watford, Herts. WD2 4YG *Delivery:* Unit 2, Paramount Industrial Estate, Sandown Road, Watford, Herts, WD2 4YG *tel* (0923) 34146.

†**Sphemusations,** Gramercy House, 12 Northfield Road, Onehouse, Stowmarket, Suffolk IP14 3HF *tel* (0449-61) 3388. Serious music, brass band, choral, instrumental and educational. Records of modern works. Tapes.

**Stainer & Bell, Ltd.,** P.O. Box 110, 82 High Road, East Finchley, London N2 9PW *tel* 01-444 9135. Book and music publishers including the imprints of **Augener, Belton Books, Galliard, Stainer & Bell, A. Weekes, Joseph Williams.**

**Swan & Co. (Music Publishers), Ltd.,** P.O. Box 1, Rickmansworth, Herts. WD3 3AZ *tel* 01-584 6671. Light orchestral.

**Sylvester Music Co., Ltd.,** 80-82 Wardour Street, London W1V 3LF *tel* 01-437 4933-4 *telex* 265014 Topcd-G *fax* 01-437 2744. Popular and orchestral music. Comprehensive library of recorder music on disc and tape. Extensive effects library. Specially composed scores. Transfers to tape and film.

**Thames Publishing** (1970), 14 Barlby Road, London W10 6AR *tel* 01-969 3579. Serious music of all types, particularly vocal, choral and instrumental. Manuscripts welcome *but should always be preceded by a letter.*

**United Music Publishers, Ltd.** (1932), 42 Rivington Street, London EC2A 3BN *tel* 01-729 4700 *fax* 01-739 6549. Agents for the principal French music publishing houses and specialise in the sale of French, Spanish and other foreign music. Also contemporary English works.

**Universal Edition (London), Ltd.,** 2-3 Fareham Street, Dean Street, London W1V 4DU *tel* 01-437 5203 and 6880. Serious music of all types.

**Warner Chappell Music Ltd.,** 129 Park Street, London W1Y 3FA *tel* 01-629 7600. Brussels, Hamburg, Johannesburg, Los Angeles, Madrid, Milan, Bussum, Nashville, New York, Paris, Stockholm, Sydney, Tokyo, Toronto, Zurich.

**Warren & Phillips** (1906), 126 Deansgate, Manchester M3 2GR *tel* 061-834 3281 *fax* 061-834 0630. Educational piano and instrumental music. Modern teaching material.

**Josef Weinberger Ltd.** (1885), 12-14 Mortimer Street, London W1N 7RD *tel* 01-580 2827 (4 lines) *cables* Operetta, London, W1 *telex* 888735 Jowein G *fax* 01-436 9616. *Directors:* R. G. Holt, R. M. Toeman. *Executive Directors:* G. Barker, K. Dixon, G. Kingsley, J. Schofield. Theatrical and music publishers.

**Workers' Music Association** (1936), 29B Norbury Court Road, London SW16 4HU *tel* 01-679 4365. General music organisation with emphasis on the social aspects of music. Publications, music courses.

# Overseas

## IRELAND

**Boethius Press Ltd** (1973), Clarabricken, Kilkenny *tel* and *fax* (056) 59746. *Directors:* L. J. Hewitt, J. M. Hewitt, Mrs. J. M. Hewitt. Early music in facsimile and edition, opera, history of musical education.

## UNITED STATES OF AMERICA

**Associated Music Publishers, Inc.,** 225 Park Avenue South, New York, N.Y. 10003 *tel* 212-254-2100 *telex* 428351 *fax* 212-254-2013.

**Belwin-Mills Publishing Corporation,** 15800 N.W. 48th Avenue, Miami, Florida 33014.

**Birch Tree Group Ltd.** (1876), 180 Alexander Street, Princeton, New Jersey 08540 *tel* 609-683-0090. *President:* David K. Sengstack. *Division:* Center for Music and Young Children.

**Boosey & Hawkes, Inc.,** 24 West 57th Street, New York, N.Y. 10019 *tel* 212-757-3332 *fax* 212-262-2012. Symphonic, opera, ballet, concert, and educational music.

**Bourne Co.,** 5 West 37th Street, New York, N.Y. 10018 *tel* 212-391-4300 *fax* 212-391-4306. Publishers of popular, standard, choral, educational wind band, instrumental, production and film music.

**John Church Company,** c/o Theodore Presser Co., Bryn Mawr, Pennsylvania 19010 *tel* 215-525-3636 *fax* 215-527 7841. Established 1854. Considers suitable MSS. from composers. Does not use or buy songs or lyrics unless with a musical setting. Publication at the firm's expense only.

**Roger Dean Publishing,** 501 East Third Street, Dayton, Ohio 45401-0802 *tel* 513-228-6118. Division of **The Lorenz Corporation**. Manuscripts for schools and colleges.

**Oliver Ditson Company,** c/o Theodore Presser Co., Bryn Mawr, Pennsylvania 19010 *tel* 215-525-3636 *fax* 215-527-7841. Established 1793. Considers suitable MSS. from composers. Does not use or buy songs or lyrics unless with a musical setting. Publication at the firm's expense only.

**Elkan-Vogel, Inc.,** c/o Theodore Presser Co., Bryn Mawr, Pennsylvania 19010 *tel* 215-525-3636 *fax* 215-527-7841. Considers suitable MSS. from composers. Does not use or buy songs or lyrics unless with a musical setting. Publication at the firm's expense only.

**H. W. Gray Publications,** 15800 N.W. 48th Avenue, Miami, Florida 33014. Division of **Columbia Pictures Publications.** Choral music of all types and arrangements. Organ music, sacred songs.

**Heritage Music Press,** 501 East Third Street, Dayton, Ohio 45401-0802   *tel* 513-228-6118. Division of **The Lorenz Corporation.** Manuscripts for elementary, junior-high and high schools (secondary schools).

**Hinrichsen Edition,** C.F. Peters Corporation, 373 Park Avenue South, New York, N.Y. 10016   *tel* 212-686-4147. Classical and contemporary music.

**International Music Company,** 5 West 37th Street, New York, N.Y. 10018   *tel* 212-391-4200   *fax* 212-391-4306. Publishers of music for instrumental solo, duet, trio, quartet, quintet, large ensembles, voice; study scores, opera scores; concerto and aria orchestral parts on hire.

**Laurel Press,** 40 Music Square East, Nashville, Tennessee 37203   *tel* 615-244 5588. Division of **Lorenz Creative Services.** Gospel music.

**Lorenz Publishing Co.,** 501 East Third Street, Dayton, Ohio 45401-0802   *tel* 513-228-6118. Considers for purchase anthems and church organ voluntaries. Division of **The Lorenz Corporation.**

**Mercury Music Corporation,** c/o Theodore Presser Co., Bryn Mawr, Pennsylvania 19010   *tel* 215-525-3636   *fax* 215-527-7841. Considers suitable MSS. from composers. Does not use or buy songs or lyrics unless with a musical setting. Publication at the firm's expense only.

**Merion Music, Inc.,** c/o Theodore Presser Co., Bryn Mawr, Pennsylvania 19010   *tel* 215-525-3636   *fax* 215-527-7841. Established 1953. Considers suitable MSS. from composers. Does not use or buy songs or lyrics unless with a musical setting. Publication at the firm's expense only.

**Mills Music Inc.,** 15800 N.W. 48th Avenue, Miami, Florida 33014. Division of **Columbia Pictures Publications.**

**C. F. Peters Corporation,** 373 Park Avenue South, New York, N.Y. 10016   *tel* 212-686-4147. (Edition Peters, Hinrichsen Edition, and other European music publications, in U.S.A.).

**Theodore Presser Co.,** Bryn Mawr, Pennsylvania 19010   *tel* 215-525-3636   *fax* 215-527-7841. Established 1883. Considers suitable MSS. from composers. Does not use or buy songs or lyrics unless with a musical setting. Publication at the firm's expense only.

**The Sacred Music Press,** 501 East Third Street, Dayton, Ohio 45401-0802   *tel* 513-228-6118. *Editor:* Dale Wood. Division of **The Lorenz Corporation.**

**G. Schirmer Inc.,** 225 Park Avenue South, New York, N.Y. 10003   *tel* 212-254-2100   *telex* 428351   *fax* 212-254-2013.

**Sonshine Productions,** 40 Music Square East, Nashville, Tennessee 37203   *tel* 615-244 5588. Division of **Lorenz Creative Services.** Contemporary sacred music.

**Triune Music Inc,** 40 Music Square East, Nashville, Tennessee 37203   *tel* 615-244 5588. Division of **Lorenz Creative Services.** Sacred music.

**Warner/Chappell Music Inc.,** 9000 Sunset Boulevard, Penthouse, Los Angeles, California 90069   *tel* 213-273-3323   *cables* Wang, Los Angeles. Includes, among others, the following companies: WB Music Corp., Warner-Tamerlane

Publishing Corp., Harms Inc., M. Witmark, Remick, Advanced, New World Music Corp., Pepamar Music Corp., Schubert Music Publishing Corp., Weill-Brecht-Harms Company Inc., Viva Music Inc., Zapata Music Inc., Curtom Publishing Co. Inc., Rodart Music Corp., Jalynne Corp, Twentieth Century Fox Music Corp., House of Gold Music, Foster Frees Music Inc., Pendulum Music, Chappell Music, Unichappell, Rightsongs, Ricks Music.

Qui reason manque religious?

Pablica Corp. Harmon, Phi Weekends R. ... ... ... W. ... W. of
Alman Corp. T ... ... Mon ... ... ... ... subscriber closer unbishing C origing
Boy will ... ... ... alpan ... ... M ... ... L. ... Rumish ... sille ... ... ... ... ...
is Cor ... ... Cor ... per King, Green Johnson Cook, Twenmir resolum
is Ma ... ... Harmon. ... ... ... ... Fei ... Pi ... ... ... sic ... ... ... I ... hum
church ... ... right ... ... ... ... ... the ... all Publications ... ... Monat
ppi

# Agents

## Literary Agents

The Association of Authors' Agents (see **Societies**) is the trade association of British agents. Members meet regularly and commit themselves to observe a code of practice in the conduct of their business. They are designated with an asterisk in the following list. All agents listed below were circulated with a questionnaire with a view to providing pertinent information and are asked to keep this information up to date.

It should be noted that most agents do not charge a fee for marketing or placing manuscripts. Some firms charge a reading fee which is refunded on acceptance of the material. Most agents in this list will suggest revision of worth-while manuscripts where necessary, suggesting in the first instance that revision should be done by the author. In certain cases, an agency is prepared to recommend a qualified person not connected with their agency to undertake revision. In a few cases where agencies themselves are prepared to undertake revision, this fact is clearly stated. In their own interests writers are strongly recommended to think twice before agreeing to pay for revision. Some agents are prepared to give an author a report and advice on a MS and they make an appropriate charge for this. Any reference to 'Short MSS' is almost invariably to short stories and not to journalistic articles.

Literary agents exist to sell saleable material. It must be remembered that, while they are looking for new writers and are often prepared to take immense pains with a writer whose work, in their opinion, shows potential quality or distinctive promise, agents do not exist to teach people how to write. Short manuscripts, unless they are of an exceptional nature, are unlikely to be profitable or even to pay an agent for the work involved. Writers must not expect agents, publishers or editors to comment at length on unsuitable work submitted to them, although often they are asked to do so. Every writer must expect disappointments, especially at the outset of his career, but if he has something to say and knows how to say it, then eventually (if he is patient) he will learn how to satisfy an editor's requirements, or alternatively he will learn that he should give up attempting to write and turn to some other form of activity. He must not expect other people to tell him his mistakes, although not infrequently a new writer is helped in this way by an agent, editor or publisher who has detected a spark of promise in a manuscript submitted to him.

If a writer of some proven ability is contemplating using an agent, he is advised in his own interests *to write a preliminary letter* to ascertain whether the agent will consider him as a potential client. He should also enquire the agent's terms if they are not given in the entry in the following pages. Reputable agents do not accept work unless they consider it to be of a marketable standard and an author submitting work to an agent for the first time *should therefore enclose return postage*. Most agents prefer a synopsis and specimen chapters to be sent in the first instance. This enables the agent to react faster. It is not advisable for a writer to send work to more than one agent at the same time. This is not only a waste of time, but could cause complications.

This list of literary agents does not purport to be exhaustive. If any who are not included would like to receive a copy of the questionnaire and to be considered for inclusion, application should be made to the publishers.

## UNITED KINGDOM

*Membership of The Association of Authors' Agents.

**A & B Personal Management Ltd.** (1982), 5th Floor, Plaza Suite, 114 Jermyn Street, London SW1Y 6HJ   *tel* 01-839 4433   *telex* 21901 Jwppl G   *telegraphic address* Abpersman London SW1. *Directors:* R. W. Ellis, P. R. Ellis. Full-length MSS. (home 12½%, overseas 15%). Theatre, films, television, radio (12½%). Synopsis required initially from writers submitting work for first time. No reading fee for synopsis, plays or screen plays, but fee charged for full-length MSS. Return postage required.

*__Aitken & Stone Ltd,__ incorporating **Hughes Massie Ltd.,** 29 Fernshaw Road, London SW10 0TG   *tel* 01-351 7561   *telex* 298391   *fax* 01-376 3594. *Directors:* Gillon Aitken, Brian Stone, Sally Riley, Andrew Wylie (U.S.A.). Full-length MSS (home 10%, U.S.A. 15%, translations 20%). U.S.A. associates: Wylie, Aitken & Stone Inc., Suite 2106, 250 West 57th Street, New York, NY 10107   *tel* (212) 246 0069. Preliminary letter and return postage essential.

*__Jacintha Alexander Associates__ (1981), 47 Emperor's Gate, London SW7 4HJ   *tel* 01-373 9258. *Proprietor:* Jacintha Alexander; *Associate:* Julian Alexander. Full length MSS. Films, television, radio (home 15%, abroad 20%). Will suggest revision. Works in conjunction with agents in New York and Europe. No reading fee, but preliminary letter with sae essential.

**Darley Anderson,** Estelle House, 11 Eustace Road, London SW6 1JB   *tel* 01-385 6652   *fax* 01-386 5571. Specialises in all types of women's fiction, family saga, historical, romance, crime, thrillers, horror, westerns; non-fiction: show business, health, self-help, environment, practical books for women, devotional, popular religion, parapsychology and supernatural. Full-length and short MSS (home 15%, overseas 15-20%), performance rights (15-20%). Offers world-wide representation; can arrange PR and author publicity through associated PR company; editorial guidance on selected MSS. Preliminary letter and return postage essential.

**Yvonne Baker Associates** (1987), 8 Temple Fortune Lane, London NW11 7UD   *tel* 01-455 8687. An agent for theatre and television writers primarily. Full length and short MSS (no books or short stories). Theatre, radio (10%), television, films (12½%). No reading fee, but sae essential.

*__Blake Friedmann Literary, TV & Film Agency Ltd.__ (1977), 37-41 Gower Street, London WC1E 6HH   *tel* 01-631 4331   *telex* 9312102498 Bf G   *fax* 01-323 1274. *Directors:* Carole Blake, Julian Friedmann, Barbara Jones, Conrad Williams. Full-length MSS. Fiction: thrillers, contemporary and historical women's novels; non-fiction: investigative books, biography, travel; no poetry or plays, (home 15%, overseas 20%). Specialise in film, television and video rights;

place journalism and short stories. Represented in France, Germany, Greece, Holland, Israel, Italy, Scandinavia, Turkey, Canada, South America, Latin America, Japan; and in USA by Writers House Inc. Preliminary letter, synopsis and first two chapters preferred. No reading fee.

**David Bolt Associates,** 12 Heath Drive, Send, Surrey GU23 7EP   *tel* Woking (04862) 21118.
Specialises in biography, fiction, theology. Full-length MSS. (home 10%, overseas 19%; all other rights including film, video and television 10%). No unsolicited short stories or play scripts. Will sometimes suggest revision. Works in association with overseas agencies worldwide. Preliminary letter preferred.

**Rosemary Bromley Literary Agency,** Avington, Winchester, Hants SO21 1DB   *tel* (096278) 656.
Specialise in biography, travel, leisure. Full-length fiction and non-fiction (home 10%, overseas from 15%.) No poetry. No reading fee. Preliminary letter with return postage essential. For children's books see **Juvenilia.**

**Felicity Bryan** (1988), 2A North Parade, Banbury Road, Oxford OX2 6PE   *tel* (0865) 513816   *telex* 83147 Viaor G (ref: Bryan)   *fax* (0865) 310055.
Fiction and general non-fiction (home 10%, overseas 20%); will suggest revision where appropriate. Performance rights handled by Curtis Brown; translation rights handled by Andrew Nurnberg Associates; works in conjunction with US agents. Preliminary letter essential; no reading fee.

**Diane Burston** (1984), 46 Cromwell Avenue, Highgate, London N6 5HL   *tel* 01-340 6130.
General fiction and non-fiction. Full-length MSS and short stories (home 10%, overseas 20%, USA 15%). No reading fee, but preliminary enquiry and sae essential.

**\*Campbell Thomson & McLaughlin, Ltd.,** 31 Newington Green, London N16 9PU   *tel* 01-249 2971   *telegraphic address* Peterlaine, London, N16   *fax* 01-923 1375. *Directors:* John McLaughlin, John Parker, Timothy Webb, Charlotte Bruton, Hal Cheetham.
Full-length book MSS. (home 10%, overseas up to 20% including commission to foreign agent). No poetry, plays or television scripts or short stories. U.S.A. agents represented: Raines & Raines, 71 Park Avenue, New York, N.Y., 10016; The Fox Chase Agency, Inc., The Public Ledger Building, Independence Square, Philadelphia, Pa 19106. Representatives in most European countries. No reading fee, but return postage required. Subsidiary company: **Peter Janson-Smith Ltd.**

**\*Carnell Literary Agency** (1951), Danes Croft, Goose Lane, Little Hallingbury, Herts. CM22 7RG   *tel* (0279) 723626. *Proprietor:* Pamela Buckmaster.
All MSS. except poetry. Specialises in science/fantasy fiction. Works in conjunction with many foreign agents. Home 10%, overseas 10% or 19% through sub-agent. No reading fee, but sae for acknowledgement. Outline plus first two chapters initially—return postage essential.

**Christy & Moore Ltd**—see **Anthony Sheil Associates Ltd.**

**\*Serafina Clarke** (1980), 98 Tunis Road, London W12 7EY   *tel* 01-749 6979.
Full-length MSS. (home 10%, overseas 15-20%). Theatre, films, television, radio (10-15%). Works in conjunction with agents overseas. No reading fee, but preliminary letter and return postage essential.

**\*Jonathan Clowes Ltd.** (1960), 22 Prince Albert Road, London NW1 7ST   *tel* 01-722 7674   *telex* 23973 Clowes G   *fax* 01-722 7677. *Directors:* Jonathan Clowes, Ann Evans, Donald Carroll, Enyd Williams.

Full-length MSS. (home and Europe 10%,USA 15%). Theatre, films, television and sound broadcasting. Works in association with agents in most foreign countries. No reading fee but preliminary letter essential.

**Elspeth Cochrane Agency** (1967), 11-13 Orlando Road, London SW4 0LE   *tel* 01-622 0314. *Director:* Miss Elspeth Cochrane.
Full-length MSS. (home and overseas 10%). Theatre, films, television, sound broadcasting (10%). No reading fee.

**Dianne Coles Literary Agency** (1980), The Old Forge House, Sulgrave, Banbury, Oxon OX17 2RP   *tel* (0295) 76692/50731   *fax* (0295) 271454.
Full-length MSS: leisure, craft, women's, biography, general non-fiction, literary fiction, limited children's (home 10%, others 20%). USA office. Preliminary letter, synopsis and sae essential; also names of agents and publishers previously contacted.

**Rosica Colin Limited** (1949), 1 Clareville Grove Mews, London, SW7 5AH   *tel* 01-370 1080   *telegraphic address* Colrep, London, SW7   *fax* 01-244 6441.
*Directors:* Sylvie Marston, Joanna Marston.
All full-length MSS. (home 10%, overseas 20%). Theatre, films, television and sound broadcasting (10%). Works in U.S.A., European countries and overseas. No reading fee.

**\*Jane Conway-Gordon** (1982), 1 Old Compton Street, London W1V 5PH   *tel* 01-494 0148.
Full length MSS., theatre, films, television, radio (home 10%, overseas 20%). Represented in all foreign countries. No reading fee but preliminary letter and return postage essential.

**\*Rupert Crew Limited** (1927), King's Mews, London WC1N 2JA   *tel* 01-242 8586   *fax* 01-831 7914   *telegraphic address* Authorship, Holb., London.
*Directors:* F. R. Crew, K. A. Crew, D. Montgomery, S. Russell.
International business management, available to a limited clientele, for authors seeking world representation: the agency specialises in promoting major book projects—non-fiction, general and women's fiction—especially those having serialisation potential. Preliminary letter. Commission 10%-20% by arrangement. No reading fees. Also acts independently as publishers' consultants.

**Cruickshank Cazenove Ltd** (1983), 97 Old South Lambeth Road, London SW8 1XU   *tel* 01-735 2933   *fax* 01-820 1081. *Director:* Harriet Cruickshank.
Fiction and non-fiction, film, television,theatre and radio scripts (home 10%, overseas varies). Works with agents abroad. No reading fee but preliminary letter essential with s.a.e. Also agent for directors and designers.

**Curtis Brown & John Farquharson,** 162-168 Regent Street, London W1R 5TB   *tel* 01-872 0331   *telex* 920379   *fax* 01-872 0332   *cables* Browncurt, London W1. *Chairman:* Robert Loder. *Directors:* Peter Murphy, Michael Shaw, Diana Baring, Andrew Best, Tim Curnow (Australia), Charles Elton, Sue Freathy, Anne McDermid, Anthea Morton-Saner, Leah Schmidt, Diana Mackay, Elizabeth Stevens. Part owner of Curtis Brown Ltd, New York, 10 Astor Place, New York, N.Y. 10003   *tel* 212-473-5400, and of Curtis Brown Canada Ltd.,   *tel* 516-537-7924   *fax* 516-537-7365. Sole owner of Curtis Brown (Australia) Pty. Ltd., 27 Union Street or P.O. Box 19, Paddington, Sydney, N.S.W. 2021, Australia   *tel* (612) 331 5301.
Agents for the negotiation in all markets of novels, general non-fiction, children's books and associated rights (home 10%, USA 15%, Canada and foreign 20%). Preliminary letter essential; no reading fee. MSS. for films, theatre, television and radio. Also agents for directors and designers.

**Reg Davis-Poynter,** 118 St. Pancras, Chichester, West Sussex PO19 4LH  *tel* (0243) 779047 and 11 Bolt Court, Fleet Street, London EC4A 3DQ  *tel* 01-353 9365.
Specialising in contemporary history, politics, sociology, popular science, modern music, jazz. Full-length MSS. (home 15%, overseas 20%). Theatre, films, television, radio (10%). Works with agents in Germany, Scandinavia, Japan, Italy, France, USA. No reading fee but preliminary letter and return postage essential. Also acts as publishing consultant.

**Felix De Wolfe** (1946), Manfield House, 376 Strand, London WC2R 0LR  *tel* 01-379 5767  *telex* 931770 A/B W1BU G.
Theatre, films, television, sound broadcasting, fiction. Works in conjunction with many foreign agencies.

**Dorian Literary Agency** (1986), 35 Longcroft Avenue, Brixham, Devon TQ5 0DS  *tel* (08045) 59390. *Proprietor:* Dorothy Lumley.
Full-length MSS preferred, fiction and non-fiction (home 10%, overseas 15%, translations 20-25%), performance rights (10%); will suggest revision where appropriate. Both newcomers and established writers welcome. Works in conjunction with agencies in most countries; negotiates direct with USA. No reading fee.

**John Dorman** (1983), 20 Mill Street, Shipston-on-Stour, Warwickshire CV36 4AW  *tel* (0608) 63435  *carphone* (0836) 275935  *telex* 418253 Protlx G.
Non-fiction only, specializing in sport, leisure, health and fitness. Full-length and short MSS. (home 10%, overseas 15%). No reading fee, but preliminary letter essential.

**Susan Dunnett Management** (1987), 16 John Campbell Road, London N16 8JZ  *tel* 01-241 6560.
Drama, drama comedy, light entertainment (10%); will suggest revision where appropriate. Works in conjunction with foreign agencies. No reading fee.

**Fact & Fiction Agency Ltd,** 16 Greenway Close, London NW9 5AZ  *tel* 01-205 5716. *Directors:* Roy Lomax, Vera Lomax.
Television, radio (home 10%, overseas 15%). By introduction only.

\***John Farquharson Ltd.** (1919), 162-168 Regent Street, London W1R 5TB  *tel* 01-872 0331  *telex* 920379  *fax* 01-872 0332. *Directors:* Vivienne Schuster (Managing), Michael Shaw, Jane Gelfman (USA), Deborah Schneider.
Full-length MSS. (home 10%, overseas 20% including commission to foreign agents). U.S.A. Branch: John Farquharson Ltd., 250 West 57th Street, New York, N.Y. 10107.

**Film Link Literary Agency** (1979), 31 Oakdene Drive, Tolworth, Surrey KT5 9NH  *tel* 01-330 3182. *Director:* Yvonne Heather.
Specialising in fiction for women's market and unusual non-fiction. Full-length MSS. (home 10%, overseas 15-20%). No short stories or poetry. Will suggest revision where appropriate. Works in conjunction with overseas agents. Preliminary letter, synopsis and sae essential.

**Film Rights Ltd** (1932), 483 Southland House, Black Prince Road, Albert Embankment, London SE1 7SJ  *tel* 01-735 8171. *Directors:* D. M. Sims, Maurice Lambert, Laurence Fitch.
Theatre, films, television and sound broadcasting (10%). Represented in U.S.A. and abroad.

**Laurence Fitch Ltd** (1952) (incorporating The London Play Company) (1922), 483 Southland House, Black Prince Road, Albert Embankment, London SE1 7SJ  *tel* 01-735 8171. *Directors:* F. H. L. Fitch, Joan Potts, W. Corlett.

Theatre, films, television and sound broadcasting. Also works with several agencies in New York and in Europe.

**Jill Foster Ltd.** (1976), 19A Queen's Gate Terrace, London SW7 5PR    *tel* 01-581 0084/5    *fax* 01-581 0080.
Theatre, films, television, sound broadcasting (10%). Particularly interested in film and television comedy and drama. No novels or short stories. No reading fee. Preliminary letter essential.

**\*Fraser & Dunlop Ltd**—see **The Peters Fraser & Dunlop Group Ltd.**

**\*Fraser & Dunlop Scripts Ltd**—see **The Peters Fraser & Dunlop Group Ltd.**

**John French Artists Agency Ltd,** 26-28 Binney Street, London W1Y 1YN    *tel* 01-629 4159. *Directors:* John French, Janet Welch.
All MSS, home and overseas (10%). Theatre, films, television, radio (10%). Reading service available, details on application. s.a.e. must be enclosed with all MSS.

**Jüri Gabriel,** 35 Camberwell Grove, London SE5 8JA    *tel* 01-703 6186.
Literary fiction; quality non-fiction (current specialisations: medical, military, academic). Full-length MSS (home 10%, overseas 20%), performance rights (10%); will suggest revision where appropriate. No short stories, articles, verse or books for small children. No reading fee; return postage essential.

**Eric Glass Ltd.** (1932), 28 Berkeley Square, London W1X 6HD    *tel* 01-629 7162    *telegraphic address* Blancheric, London, W1    *telex* 296759 Kallin G; ref. 101    *fax* 01-499 6780. *Directors:* Eric Glass, Janet Crowley.
Full-length MSS only. Theatre, films, television, and sound broadcasting. Will occasionally recommend someone for revision of promising material if the author is unable to undertake it. No reading fee. Sole representatives of the French Society of Authors (Societé des Auteurs et Compositeurs Dramatiques).

**\*Christine Green (Author's Agent) Ltd.** (1984), 2 Barbon Close, London WC1N 3JX    *tel* 01-831 4956    *fax* 01-831 4840.
Fiction and general non-fiction. Full-length and short MSS. (home 10%, overseas 20%). Works in conjunction with agencies in Europe and Scandinavia. No reading fee, but preliminary letter and return postage essential.

**\*Elaine Greene Ltd.** (1962), 31 Newington Green, London N16 9PU    *tel* 01-249 2971    *cable address* Peterlaine, London, N16    *fax* 01-923 1375. *Directors:* Elaine Greene (U.S.A.), Carol Heaton, Ilsa Yardley, Timothy Webb.
Full-length MSS, fiction and non-fiction; books, television, radio, film (home 10%, overseas 15-20%, translation 20%). Works in conjunction with agencies in most countries. No reading fee. No unsolicited MSS accepted without an introductory letter from the author describing the work and enclosing return postage.

**\*The Jane Gregory Agency** (1982), Riverside Studios, Crisp Road, Hammersmith, London W6 9RL    *tel* 01-741 3646    *telex* 268141 Metmak G    *fax* 01-846 9039.
Full-length MSS (home 10%, USA 20%, translation 20%); no short stories, poetry, plays, film scripts, academic or children's books. UK representative for Simon & Schuster Inc., New York. Preliminary letter and synopsis preferred, plus return postage. No reading fee.

**Gregory & Radice Authors' Agents** (1986), Riverside Studios, Crisp Road, Hammersmith, London W6 9RL    *tel* 01-741 3646    *telex* 268141 Metmak G    *fax* 01-846 9039. *Partners:* Jane Gregory, Dr Lisanne Radice.

Specialists in thrillers, crime and suspense novels. Full-length MSS (home 10%, USA 20%, translation 20%). Preliminary letter and synopsis preferred, plus return postage. No reading fee.

**\*David Grossman Literary Agency Ltd.** (1976), 110-114 Clerkenwell Road, London EC1M 5SA   *tel* 01-251 5046-7   *telex* 263404 Bk Biz G.
Full-length and short MSS. (home 10-15%, overseas 15-20% including foreign agent's commission). Performance rights (15%). Works in conjunction with agents in New York, Europe, Japan. No reading fee, but preliminary letter required.

**The June Hall Literary Agency Ltd** (member of The Peters Fraser & Dunlop Group Ltd), 5th Floor, The Chambers, Chelsea Harbour, Lots Road, London SW10 0SF   *tel* 01-352 4233   *fax* 01-352 7356. *Directors:* Kenneth Ewing (Joint Chairman), Michael Sissons (Joint Chairman and Managing Director), Shân Morley Jones (Deputy Managing Director), Lucinda Culpin, Tim Corrie, Caroline Dawnay. *Consultant:* June Hall.
Specialists in the negotiation of all rights in general fiction and non-fiction (home/overseas 10-20%). No unsolicited manuscripts accepted without an introductory letter from the author describing the work, and return postage. No reading fee.

**\*Xandra Hardie Literary Agency** (1986), 9 Elsworthy Terrace, London NW3 3DR   *tel* 01-722 0178   *fax* 01-586 6230.
Full-length MSS (home 15%, USA 20%, elsewhere 20%). Television, radio (10%). No reading fee, but preliminary letter essential. Foreign rights: **Marsh & Sheil Ltd.**

**Hatton & Baker Ltd.** (1980), 18 Jermyn Street, London SW1Y 6HN   *tel* 01-439 2971   *telex* 263026 Hatbak   *fax* 01-439 7633. *Directors:* Richard Hatton, Terence Baker, Michelle Kass.
Films, television, radio (10%). No reading fee.

**Headline Enterprises Ltd.** (1971), 19a Queen's Gate Terrace, London SW7 5PR   *tel* 01-584 8568   *fax* 01-581 0080. *Directors:* Malcolm Hamer, Jill Foster.
Specialise in sport and guide books. Full-length non-fiction MSS. (home up to 15%, overseas up to 20%). No reading fee.

**\*A. M. Heath & Co. Ltd.** (1919), 79 St. Martins Lane, London WC2N 4AA   *tel* 01-836 4271   *telegraphic address* Script, London, WC2   *cables* Script, London   *telex* 27370   *fax* 01-497 2561. *Directors:* Mark Hamilton, Michael Thomas, William Hamilton, Sara Fisher.
Full-length MSS. (home 10%, U.S.A. 15%, translation 20%). Theatre, films, television and sound broadcasting (15%). Agents in U.S.A. and all European countries and Japan. No reading fee.

**Duncan Heath Associates Ltd,** Paramount House 162–170 Wardour Street, London W1V 3AT   *tel* 01-439 1471   *telex* 263361 ParaUK   *fax* 01-439 7274. *Directors:* Duncan Heath, Susan Rodgers, Jonathan Altaras, Michael Foster, Ian Amos.
Specialising in scripts for film, theatre, radio, tv (home 10%, overseas 10%). Works in conjunction with International Creative Management Inc., Los Angeles and New York. No reading fee.

**\*David Higham Associates Ltd.** (1935), 5-8 Lower John Street, Golden Square, London W1R 4HA   *tel* 01-437 7888   *telex* 28910   *fax* 01-437 1072. *Directors:* Bruce Hunter, Jacqueline Korn, Anthony Crouch, John Rush, Elizabeth Cree, Anthony Goff, Ania Corless.

Agents for the negotiation of all rights in fiction, general non-fiction, plays, film and television scripts (home 10%, USA 15%, translation 19%). U.S.A. Associate Agency: Harold Ober Associates Inc. Represented in all foreign markets. Preliminary letter and return postage essential. No reading fee.

**Vanessa Holt Associates, Ltd** (1989), 59 Crescent Road, Leigh-on-Sea, Essex SS9 2PF  *tel* (0702) 73787  *fax* (0702) 471890. Also based in London.
General adult fiction and non-fiction (home 10%, overseas 20%). Works in conjunction with many foreign agencies. No reading fee.

**Valerie Hoskins** (1983), Eagle House, 109 Jermyn Street, London SW1Y 6HB  *tel* 01-839 2121  *fax* 01-321 0860. *Proprietor:* Valerie Hoskins in association with Jeremy Conway Ltd.
Theatre, films, television and radio *only.* (10% home and maximum 20% overseas.) No reading fee, but s.a.e. appreciated. Works in conjunction with overseas agents. Preliminary letter essential.

**Teresa Howard Associates** (1984), 298 South Lambeth Road, London SW8 1UJ  *tel* 01-720 6858.
Theatre, films, television, radio (home 10%, overseas 12½%). Not taking on new clients.

*****Tanja Howarth** (1970), 19 New Row, London WC2N 4LA  *tel* 01-240 5553  *telex* 27370  *fax* 01-379 0969. *Partners:* Tanja Howarth, Charlotte Oldfield.
Full-length MSS, fiction and non-fiction (home 10%, USA 15%, translation 20%). No reading fee.

**Hughes Massie Ltd**—see **Aitken & Stone Ltd.**

**Michael Imison Playwrights Ltd** (formerly Dr Jan Van Loewen Ltd), 28 Almeida Street, London N1 1TD  *tel* 01-354 3174. *Directors:* Michael Imison, M.A., Alan Brodie, B.A., LL.B., Tamsyn Imison, B.SC.
Specialise in stage plays, also cover radio, TV, film (home 10%, overseas 15%), preliminary letter essential, no fiction or general MSS. New York Office: Michael Imison Playwrights Ltd., Box 1006, Ansonia Station. New York, N.Y. 10023  *tel* 212-874-2671. Australian Office: Michael Imison Playwrights Ltd., 1/7 Cliff Street, Milson's Point, Sydney, N.S.W. 2061  *tel* 929-7363. Represented in all major countries. No reading fee, but send sae.

**International Literary Agency** (1965), The Chambers, Chelsea Harbour, Lots Road, London SW10 0XF  *tel* 01-351 4763  *telegraphic address* Interlitag London *fax* 01-351 4809. Anthony Guest Gornall. *Associate:* Nicki Kennedy.
Concerned only with translation rights exclusively for The Peters Fraser & Dunlop Group Ltd, including The June Hall Literary Agency, London, Harold Matson Company Inc., New York, Sterling Lord Literistic, Inc., New York.

**International Copyright Bureau Ltd.** (1905), Suite 8, 26 Charing Cross Road, London WC2H 0DG  *tel* 01-836 5912  *fax* 01-379 7731  *telegraphic address* Volscius London WC2. *Directors:* Joy Westendarp, J. C. H. Hadfield (Secretary).
Theatre, films, television, radio (home 10%, overseas 19%). Works in conjunction with agents in New York and most foreign countries. Preliminary letter essential.

**International Scripts** (1979), 1 Norland Square, Holland Park, London W11 4PX  *tel* 01-229 0736. *Directors:* H. P. Tanner, J. Lawson. *Agent:* Liz Moseley.
Specialising in full-length contemporary and women's fiction, general non-fiction (10% home, 20% overseas). First works 15%. Films, television, radio,

theatre (10-20%). No poetry. Works with overseas agents world-wide. Return postage and preliminary synopsis/sample preferred.

**Mary Irvine** (1974), 11 Upland Park Road, Oxford OX2 7RU *tel* (0865) 513570. Specialising in women's fiction and family sagas. Full-length and short MSS (home 10%, USA 15%, translations 20%). Works with agents in USA, Europe, Japan. No reading fee. No unsolicited MSS. Preliminary letter and return postage required.

*****John Johnson (Authors' Agent) Ltd.** (1956), Clerkenwell House, 45-47 Clerkenwell Green, London EC1R 0HT *tel* 01-251 0125 *fax* 01-251 2172. Full-length and short MSS. (home 10%, overseas 10%, if foreign agent is concerned maximum of 20%), theatre, television, sound broadcasting (10%). Works in conjunction with agents in US and many European countries. No reading fee, but preliminary letter and sae essential.

*****Jane Judd Literary Agency** (1986), 6 Thornhill Grove, London N1 1JG *tel* 01-607 0273 *telex* 444 322. Full-length MSS only (home 10%, overseas 20%). Works with agents in U.S.A. and most foreign countries. No reading fee, but preliminary letter and sae essential.

**Juvenilia** (1973), Avington, Winchester, Hants. SO21 1DB *tel* (096278) 656. *Proprietor:* Mrs. Rosemary Bromley. Full-length MSS. for the children's market, fiction and non-fiction (home 10%, overseas from 15%). No verse. Short stories only if specifically for picture books, radio or TV. Theatre, films, television, radio (10%). No unsolicited MSS.; preliminary letter with sae and full details essential. No reading fee. Postage for acknowledgement and return of material imperative.

**J. W. Productions Literary Associates** (1986), 14 Nottingham Mansions, Nottingham Street, London W1M 3FJ *tel* 01-487 2834. *Director:* Jennifer Watts. Mainly interested in full-length MSS suitable for dramatisation after publication (home/overseas 20%), performance rights (15-20%); will suggest revision where appropriate. Works in conjunction with Marjorie O. Windsor, Suite 505, 717 Eglinton Ave West, Toronto, Ontario M5N 1C9, Canada. Do not send scripts without writing first. No reading fee.

*****Frances Kelly Agency** (1978), 111 Clifton Road, Kingston-upon-Thames, Surrey KT2 6PL *tel* 01-549 7830. Full-length and short MSS. (home 10%, overseas 20%). Television, radio (10%). Non-fiction: general and academic, reference and professional books; all subjects. *U.S. Associate:* The Balkin Agency, 850 West 176 Street, New York, N.Y. 10033. No reading fee, but no unsolicited MSS; return postage and preliminary letter requested.

**Dieter Klein Associates** (1980), 1 Newburgh Street, London W1V 1LH *tel* 01-734 0880 *telex* 22861 Metmark G *fax* 01-439 1580. Represents, in all markets, leading full-length contemporary fiction (except science fiction) and non-fiction writers from the UK and US—biography, architectural history, history, cookery and music (home 15%, overseas 20%, translations 20%). No children's books, poetry or drama. Works with agents in most European countries, Japan, USA. UK representatives for Carl Hanser Verlag of Munich and Fromm International Publishing Corporation of New York. No reading fee, but preliminary letter essential with sae.

**Peter Knight Agency** (1985), 20 Crescent Grove, London SW4 7AH *tel* 01-622 1467. *Director:* Peter Knight. *Associates:* Ann King-Hall, Caroline Figini, Peter Mackay Miller.

Full-length MSS. (home 10%, overseas 20%); but no short stories, or poetry. Theatre, films, television, radio (15%). Works in conjunction with agents worldwide. Reading fee.

**Lemon Unna & Durbridge Ltd,** 24 Pottery Lane, Holland Park, London W11 4LZ    *tel* 01-229 9216/7, 01-727 1346    *telex* 27618 Author G    *fax* 01-727 9037. *Directors:* Stephen Durbridge, Sheila Lemon, Girsha Reid, Wendy Gresser, Nigel Britten.
Specialises in theatre, film, television and radio. Novels represented only for existing clients. Commission 10% unless sub-agents employed overseas; works in conjunction with agents in USA and all foreign countries. No reading fee, but return postage and preliminary letter essential.

**\*Barbara Levy Literary Agency** (1986), 21 Kelly Street, London NW1 8PG    *tel* 01-485 6037    *fax* 01-284 0292. *Director:* Barbara Levy. *Associate:* John Selby.
Full-length MSS. only; also films, television and radio (home 10%, overseas by arrangement). No reading fee, but preliminary letter and return postage essential.

**Christopher Little Literary Agent** (1976), 49 Queen Victoria Street, London EC4N 4SA    *tel* 01-236 5881    *telex* 883968 Heads G    *fax* 01-236 7625.
Specialising in non-fiction, full-length fiction; thrillers, crime, historical, romance. Full-length MSS. (home 20%, overseas 20%). Films, television (20%). Reading fee £35 + VAT.

**London Independent Books, Ltd.** (1971), 1A Montagu Mews North, London W1H 1AJ    *tel* 01-706 0486. *Directors:* Carolyn Whitaker, Patrick Whitaker.
Specialises in travel, fantasy fiction, cinema, jazz, show business. Full-length MSS. (home 15%, overseas 20%). Films, television and sound broadcasting (15%). Will suggest revision of promising MSS. No reading fee.

**Andrew Lownie** (1988), 122 Bedford Court Mansions, Bedford Square, London WC1B 3AH    *tel* 01-636 4917    *fax* 01-436 1324.
Some fiction, but mainly non-fiction, in particular intelligence (home 10%, overseas 20%). No reading fee, but return postage requested.

**L.R. Associates** (1987), 10 Mandeville Road, Aylesbury, Bucks. HP21 8AA    *tel* (0296) 437674. *Partners:* John Goodchild, Ruth Goodchild.
Specialises in children's and adult fiction, military history. Full-length and short MSS. (home 15%, overseas 25%). Films (10%), theatre, television, radio (25%). No unsolicited MSS. Reading fee £10.

**MacLean Dubois (Writers & Agents)** (1978), 10 Rutland Square, Edinburgh EH1 2AS    *tel* 031-229-6185    *fax* 031-228 1319. *Associates:* Charles MacLean, R. A. A. McCall-Smith, P. A. Maguire, Piers Schreiber, Richenda Miers, S. W. Otterburn. Patrick Deedes-Vincke, 38 bis Rue de Rivoli, 75004 Paris    *tel* 40 27 06 98.
Full-length MSS. general fiction and non-fiction, children's, biography, history, photography. Specialises in literary fiction, Scottish history and topography, food and wine, historical fiction. *Terms:* 10% home, 19% U.S., translation varies. Editing, copywriting and book packaging services also available.

**\*Andrew Mann Ltd.** (1974), 1 Old Compton Street, London W1V 5PH    *tel* 01-734 4751    *cables* Manscript, London W1. *Directors:* Anne Dewe, Tina Betts. *Consultant:* Andrew Mann.
Full-length MSS (home 10%, USA. 15% Europe 19%). Theatre. films, television, radio (10%). Associated with agents in Europe and USA. No reading fee, but no unsolicited manuscripts.

**Manuscript ReSearch** (1988), 5 St. Pauls Mews, Shepton Mallet, Somerset BA4 5BN *tel* (0749) 5435. *Proprietor:* T. G. Jenkins.
Specialising in crime/thrillers, historical romance, biographies. Full-length MSS (home 10%, overseas 20%), performance rights (15%); short MSS only from established clients. Will suggest and undertake revision where appropriate (from £50 per script; retyping service extra). No reading fee, but sae for script return essential.

**Marsh & Sheil Ltd.** (1985), 43 Doughty Street, London WC1N 2LF *tel* 01-405 7473 *telex* 94013093 Mars G *fax* 01-831 2127. Anthony Sheil, Paul Marsh, Susanna Nicklin.
Translation rights only.

**M. C. Martinez Literary Agency** (1988), 60 Oakwood Avenue, Southgate, London N14 6QL *tel* 01-886 5829 *fax* 01-247 7854. *Proprietor:* Mary Caroline Martinez.
Fiction, children's books, arts and crafts, DIY, cookery, travel (home 10%, overseas 20%), performance rights (10%); will suggest revision where appropriate. Works in conjunction with foreign agencies. Preliminary letter and sae required; no reading fee.

**Blanche Marvin,** 21A St. John's Wood High Street, London NW8 7NG *tel* 01-722 2313.
Full-length MSS. (home 12½% + 12½% overseas). Theatre, films, television, sound broadcasting. No reading fee but postage extra. Return postage essential.

***MBA Literary Agents Ltd.** (1971), 45 Fitzroy Street, London W1P 5HR *tel* 01-387 2076 and 4785. *Directors:* Diana Tyler, John Richard Parker, Meg Davis.
Full-length MSS. (home 10%, overseas 20%). Theatre, television, radio (10%), films—negotiable. No reading fee. Works in conjunction with agents in most countries.

**Richard Milne Limited** (1956), 28 Makepeace Avenue, Highgate, London N6 6EJ *tel* 01-340 7007. *Directors:* R. M. Sharples, K. N. Sharples.
Specialising in scripts for films, television, sound broadcasting (10%). Unable to represent any additional authors at present.

***William Morris Agency (U.K.) Ltd** (1965), 31-32 Soho Square, London W1V 5DG *tel* 01-434 2191 *telex* 27928 Wmaldn G *fax* 01-437 0238 *telegraphic address* Willmorris London. *Managing Director:* Steve Kenis. *Literary Department:* Lavinia Trevor.
Full-length MSS. fiction and non-fiction (home 10%, overseas 20%). Also theatre, film, television, radio (10%). *U.S. Office:* William Morris Inc., New York. No reading fee. Preliminary letter essential.

**Negotiate Ltd** (1986), 22 Braid Avenue, Edinburgh EH10 6EE *tel* 031-452 8408 *telex* 72165 *fax* 031-452 8388. *Directors:* Gavin Kennedy, John Benson, Trevor Webster.
Specialise in the negotiation of the author's contract and all rights.

***Maggie Noach Literary Agency** (1982), 21 Redan Street, London W14 0AB *tel* 01-602 2451.
General fiction and non-fiction; non-illustrated children's books. Full-length MSS (home 10%, overseas 20%). Works with agents in USA and most foreign countries. No reading fee, but preliminary letter essential.

***Andrew Nurnberg Associates Ltd.,** Clerkenwell House, 45-47 Clerkenwell Green, London EC1R 0HT *tel* 01-251 0321 *cables* Nurnbooks, London *telex* 23353 *fax* 01-251 0584.

Specialising in the sale of translation rights of English and American authors into European languages.

**\*Deborah Owen Ltd.** (1971), 78 Narrow Street, Limehouse, London E14 8BP   *tel* 01-987 5119/01-987 5441   *fax* 01-538 4004. Deborah Owen, Judith Dooling. Full-length MSS. (home 10%, overseas 15%). All types of literary material except plays, scripts, children's books or poetry. No unsolicited MSS. without preliminary letter and sae.

**\*Mark Paterson & Associates** (1955), 10 Brook Street, Wivenhoe, Colchester, Essex CO7 9DS   *tel* (0206 22) 5433-4   *fax* (0206) 222990   *telex* 988805 Patem G.
Full-length MSS including clinical psychology and psychiatry (20% including subagent's commission). No short stories or articles. Preliminary letter required.

**John Pawsey** (1981), Hollybrae, Hill Brow Road, Liss, Hants. GU33 7PS   *tel* (0730) 893065.
Full-length popular fiction and non-fiction MSS., television and radio (home 10%, overseas 19%). No unsolicited material, poetry, short stories or original film and stage scripts. Preliminary letter and return postage with all correspondence essential. Works in association with agencies in the U.S.A. and Europe. Will suggest revision if MS. sufficiently promising. No reading fee.

**Penman Literary Agency** (1950), 175 Pall Mall, Leigh-on-Sea, Essex SS9 1RE   *tel* Southend (0702) 74438. *Director:* Leonard G. Stubbs, F.R.S.A.
Full-length novel MSS. (home 10%, overseas 15%). Also theatre, films, television, sound broadcasting (10%). Revision undertaken by agency at author's request; fees depending upon amount of revision required. No reading fee.

**\*A. D. Peters & Co. Ltd**—see **The Peters Fraser & Dunlop Group Ltd.**

**\*The Peters Fraser & Dunlop Group Ltd,** 5th Floor, The Chambers, Chelsea Harbour, Lots Road, London SW10 0XF   *tel* 01-376 7676   *telex* 28965 Script G   *fax* 01-352 7356. *Directors:* Kenneth Ewing (Joint Chairman), Michael Sissons (Joint Chairman and Managing Director), Anthony Jones, Pat Kavanagh, Tim Corrie, Maureen Vincent. *Incorporating* A. D. Peters & Co. Ltd, Watergate Film Services Ltd, Fraser & Dunlop Scripts Ltd, Fraser & Dunlop Ltd, The June Hall Literary Agency Ltd. *Associated Agencies:* Intercontinental Literary Agency, Sterling Lord Literistic (New York).
Specialists in the negotiation of all rights in general fiction and non-fiction, film and television scripts, plays, and certain specialist and academic works (home/overseas 10-20%). No unsolicited manuscripts accepted without an introductory letter from the author describing the work, and return postage. No reading fee.

**Laurence Pollinger Limited,** 18 Maddox Street, London W1R 0EU   *tel* 01-629 9761   *telegraphic address* Laupoll, London, W1   *fax* 01-629 9765. *Directors:* Gerald J. Pollinger, Margaret Pepper. *Secretary:* Denzil De Silva.
Authors' agents for all material with the exception of original film stories, poetry and free-lance journalistic articles. Dramatic associate, Micheline Steinberg. Terms are a commission of 15% of the amounts obtained, except on translation sales, where the total commission of 20% may include the commission to the associate in the territory concerned. No reading fee. An editorial contribution may be requested.

**\*Murray Pollinger** (1969), 4 Garrick Street, London WC2E 9BH   *tel* 01-836 6781   *telegraphic address* and *cables* Chopper, London, WC2.

Agents for the negotiation in all markets of novels for both adults and children (home 10%, overseas 20%). Preliminary letter and synopsis required; also names of agents and publishers previously contacted. No reading fee.

**\*Shelley Power Literary Agency Ltd.** (1976), P.O. Box 149a, Surbiton, Surrey KT6 5JH   *tel* 01-398 7723   *fax* 01-398 8723.
General fiction and non-fiction. Full-length MSS (home 10%, U.S.A 15%, translations 19%). No children's books, poetry or plays. Works in conjunction with agents abroad. No reading fee, but preliminary letter essential.

**PVA Management Ltd,** Alpha Tower, Paradise Circus, Birmingham B1 1TT   *tel* 021-643 4011   *fax* 021-633 3947. *Managing Director:* Paul Vaughan.
Full-length and short MSS. (home and overseas 15%). Theatre, films, television, radio (15%).

**Radala & Associates** (1970), 17 Avenue Mansions, Finchley Road, London NW3 7AX   *tel* 01-794 4495   *telex* 295441   *fax* 01-209 1231. *Directors:* Richard Gollner, István Siklôs. *Associate:* Neil Hornick.
Full-length MSS. (10% U.K., 15% overseas). Fiction and non-fiction. Books, films, television, sound broadcasting. Electronic publishing division, including video, audio tape, computer program packages for multimedia publishing production companies.

**Douglas Rae (Management) Ltd.** (1975), 28 Charing Cross Road, London WC2H 0DB   *tel* 01-836 3903-4.
Full-length MSS. (home 10%, overseas 15%). Theatre, films, television (10%).

**Margaret Ramsay Ltd.** (1953), 14A Goodwin's Court, St. Martin's Lane, London WC2N 4LL   *tel* 01-836 7403, 01-240 0691 and 01-836 6807   *fax* 01-836 6807. *Directors:* M. Ramsay, Tom Erhardt.
MSS. Theatre, films, television, sound broadcasting only (commission 10%). Works in conjunction with agents in U.S.A. and in all foreign countries. Preliminary letter essential. No reading fee.

**Jim Reynolds Associates** (1988), Westbury Mill, Westbury, Nr Brackley, Northants. NN13 5JS   *tel* (0280) 701582   *fax* (0280) 703640 (ref: Jim Reynolds). *Directors:* Jim Reynolds, Ann Reynolds.
Full-length MSS—quality fiction, biography, social, political and military history, current affairs, investigative journalism, cricket (home 10%, overseas 19%); will suggest revision where appropriate. Works in conjunction with foreign agencies. No reading fee.

**Patricia Robertson** (1985), Flat 1, 87 Caledonian Road, London N1   *tel* 01-278 9982   *fax* 01-837 3486.
General fiction and non-fiction. Full-length MSS (home 10%, U.S.A. 15%, translation 20%). No playscripts or poetry. Works in conjunction with agents overseas. No reading fee. Preliminary letter please.

**\*Rogers, Coleridge & White Ltd.** (1967), 20 Powis Mews, London W11 1JN   *tel* 01-221 3717   *telex* 25930 Debrog G   *fax* 01-229 9084   *telegraphic address* Debrogers, London, W11. *Directors:* Deborah Rogers, Gill Coleridge, Patricia White (U.S.A.). *Consultant:* Ann Warnford-Davis.
Full-length book MSS. including children's books (home 10%, U.S.A. 15%, translations 20%). *U.S.A. Associate:* International Creative Management, 40 West 57th Street, New York, N.Y. 10019. No unsolicited MSS considered without a preliminary letter describing work and giving publishing history. No reading fee but return postage with MSS essential.

**Rostrum Literary Agency Ltd** (1986), Suite 477, Royal Exchange, Manchester M2 7DD *tel* 061-456 8035 *fax* 061-483 4747. *Directors:* Eric Falk, Marj Falk.
Fiction and non-fiction; biography, autobiography; theatre, television, books on cookery, gardening, entertainment; (home 10%, overseas 19%.) Preliminary letter and return postage essential. No reading fee.

**Herta Ryder** (1984), c/o Toby Eady Associates Ltd., 7 Gledhow Gardens, London SW5 0BL *tel* 01-370 6292 and 948 1010.
Specialises in novels for older children, adult fiction and non-fiction. Full-length MSS. (home 10%, USA 15%, overseas 20%). Represented by agents in all major foreign countries. No reading fee. Preliminary letter welcomed.

*****Tessa Sayle Agency,** 11 Jubilee Place, London SW3 3TE *tel* 01-823 3883 (5 lines) *telegraphic address* Bookishly, London SW3 *fax* 01-823 3363. *Publishing:* Tessa Sayle; *Film, TV and Theatre:* Penny Tackaberry.
Full-length MSS. (home 10%, overseas 20%). Plays, films, television, sound broadcasting (10%). U.S.A. Associates: Liz Darhansoff Literary Agency, 1220 Park Avenue, New York, N.Y. 10028. Represented in all foreign countries. No reading fee.

**James Sharkey Associates Ltd** (1983), 3rd Floor Suite, 15 Golden Square, London W1R 3AG *tel* 01-434 3801-6 *telex* 295251 Jsalon G *fax* 01-494 1547. *Literary Executive:* Sebastian Born.
Full-length MSS (home 10%, overseas 20%). Theatre, films, television, radio (10%). Works with various agencies in USA. No reading fee.

**The Sharland Organisation Ltd** (1988), 9 Marlborough Crescent, Bedford Park, London W4 1HE *tel* 01-742 1919 *fax* 01-995 7688. *Directors:* Mike Sharland, E. Glyn Hughes, Alice Sharland.
Mainly performance rights, theatre, films, television, sound broadcasting, books—full-length MSS (home 10%, overseas 19%); will suggest revision where appropriate. Also assist TV and film directors to find suitable material. Work in conjunction with overseas agents. Sae required; no reading fee.

*****Anthony Sheil Associates Ltd.** (1962), incorporating Christy & Moore Ltd. (1912) and Richard Scott Simon Ltd. (1971), 43 Doughty Street, London WC1N 2LF *tel* 01-405 9351 *telegraphic address* Novelist, London *telex* 94013094 Cweasy G ref. 19008175 (Easylink) *fax* 01-831 2127. *Directors:* Anthony Sheil, Giles Gordon, Paul Marsh, Janet Fillingham, Mic Cheetham.
Full-length MSS (home 10%, U.S.A. 20%, translations 20%). Theatre, films, television, sound broadcasting (10%). Translations: see **Marsh & Sheil Ltd.** Preliminary letter and return postage essential.

*****Caroline Sheldon Literary Agency** (1985), 71 Hillgate Place, London W8 7SS *tel* 01-727 9102.
Full-length MSS (home 10%, overseas 20%). General adult fiction, women's fiction, and children's books, longer than 10,000 words. No reading fee. Synopsis and first three chapters with return postage required initially.

**Dasha Shenkman Associates** (1987), 56 Queen's Gate Terrace, London SW7 5PJ *tel* 01-581 4935 *fax* 01-581 0705.
Full-length MSS, non-fiction and fiction, but no short stories, poetry, plays or film/TV scripts (home 15%, overseas 20%), performance rights (15%). Represented in all foreign markets. No reading fee, but preliminary letter required.

**Sheri Safran Literary Agency Ltd.** (1979), 8 Pembridge Studios, 27A Pembridge Villas, London W11 3EP *tel* 01-221 3355 *telex* 262284 ref. 1255 *fax* 01-229 9651.

Non-fiction titles for, by and about women; and children's books. Preliminary letter with outline or partial MSS together with return postage and self addressed envelope essential. *Terms:* home 15% overseas 20%. See also: **Sadie Fields Productions Ltd. (Book Packagers).** No reading fee.

**Jeffrey Simmons,** 10 Lowndes Square, London SW1X 9HA *tel* 01-235 8852 *fax* 01-245 9777.
Specialise in adult fiction, biography, autobiography, show business, law, crime. Full-length MSS. (home from 10%, overseas from 15%). Will suggest revision. No reading fee, but preliminary letter essential.

**\*Richard Scott Simon Ltd**—see **Anthony Sheil Associates Ltd.**

**Carol Smith** (1976), 25 Hornton Court, Kensington High Street, London W8 7RT *tel* 01-937 4874 *fax* 01-938 5323.
Full-length and short MSS. (home 10%, U.S.A. 15%, translation 20%). Will suggest revision of promising MSS. Works in conjunction with many foreign agencies. No reading fee, but preliminary letter essential. Please enclose return postage.

**Solo Literary Agency Ltd.** (1978), 49-53 Kensington High Street, London W8 5ED *tel* 01-376 2166 *telex* 925235 Solo G *fax* 01-938 3165. *Directors:* Don Short (Managing), Wendy Short (Secretary).
Specialising in celebrity and autobiographical books. Fiction from established authors only (home 15%, overseas 20%).

**Spokesmen**—see **Curtis Brown.**

**Elaine Steel** (1986), 25-27 Oxford Street, London W1R 1RF *tel* 01-437 1090 *telex* 8954713 Alfa G *fax* 01-434 1726.
Full-length and short MSS. (home 10%, overseas 20%). Theatre, films, television, sound broadcasting (10%). Will suggest revision. *U.S. Associates:* Geoffrey Sandford, Susan Bergholz. No reading fee.

**\*Abner Stein,** 10 Roland Gardens, London SW7 3PH *tel* 01-373 0456 and 370 7859 *fax* 01-370 6316.
Full-length and short MSS (home 10%, overseas 19%). No reading fee.

**Micheline Steinberg Playwrights' Agent** (1987), 110 Frognal, London NW3 6XU *tel* 01-794 0414 *fax* 01-435 3783.
Full-length MSS—theatre, films, television, radio (home 10%, overseas 15%). Dramatic Associate for Laurence Pollinger Ltd; works in conjunction with agents in USA and other countries. No reading fee, but preliminary letter essential and return postage with MSS.

**Peter Tauber Press Agency** (1950), 94 East End Road, London N3 2SX *tel* 01-346 4165 *telegraphic address* Tauberpres, London N3. *Directors:* Peter Tauber, Martha Tauber, Robert Tauber.
Full length MSS only (20% worldwide). No scripts, poetry or children's. No unsolicited MSS, preliminary letter, synopsis and sae essential. Published authors only.

**Jon Thurley,** M.A. (1976), 213 Linen Hall, 156-170 Regent Street, London W1R 5TA *tel* 01-437 9545-6.
Literary and dramatic work for all media. Commission: home 10%, overseas 20%. American and European representation arranged geared to specific projects. No reading fee.

**Jane Turnbull** (1986), 13 Wendell Road, London W12 9RS *tel* 01-743 9580 *fax* 01-749 6079.

Fiction and non-fiction (home 10%, North America 15%, translations 20%), performance rights (15%); will suggest revision where appropriate. No children's books. Works in conjunction with Aitken & Stone for sale/translation rights; negotiates direct with USA and Canada. Preliminary letter essential; no reading fee.

**\*Harvey Unna & Stephen Durbridge (1975) Ltd,** 24-32 Pottery Lane, Holland Park, London W11 4LZ   *tel* 01-727 1346   *cables* Undur, London, W11   *fax* 01-727 9037. *Directors:* Stephen Durbridge, Girsha Reid. *Consultant:* Harvey Unna.
See Lemon Unna & Durbridge Ltd.

**Dr Jan Van Loewen Ltd.—see Michael Imison Playwrights Ltd.**

**\*Vardey & Brunton Associates** (1985), Studio 8, 125 Moore Park Road, London SW6 4PS   *tel* 01–384 1248   *telex* 923753 (ref: 355)   *fax* 01-384 1246. *Directors:* Lucinda Vardey, Carolyn Brunton.
Full-length MSS—all general fiction and non-fiction (home 10%, overseas 20%), films, television and radio (20%); will suggest revision where appropriate. No children's books, science fiction or academic. Works in conjunction with overseas agents. No reading fee.

**Lorna Vestey** (1971), 33 Dryburgh Road, London SW15.
Full-length MSS. (home 10%, U.S.A. 15%, other overseas 20%). Films, television, sound broadcasting (10%). No unsolicited MSS.

**\*Ed Victor Ltd.** (1976), 162 Wardour Street, London W1V 3AT   *tel* 01-734 4795   *telex* 263361   *fax* 01-494 3400   *telegraphic address* Victorious, London W1. *Directors:* Ed Victor, Carol Ryan, Caroline Daubeny, Leon Morgan.
Full-length MSS but no short stories, film/TV scripts, poetry or plays. (home 15%, U.S.A. 15%, translation 20%). Theatre, film, television, sound broadcasting rights (15%). Represented in all foreign markets. No unsolicited manuscripts.

**S. Walker Literary Agency** (1939), 96 Church Lane, Goldington, Bedford MK41 0AS   *tel* Bedford 216229. *Partners:* Alan Oldfield, Cora-Louise Oldfield. *Consultant:* E. K. Walker.
Full-length novels only (home 10%, overseas 20% including 10% to overseas agent). Do not handle short topical articles or poetry. Works in conjunction with agencies in most European countries, and also negotiates directly with foreign publishers. No reading fee but preliminary letter and return postage essential.

**Warner Chappell Plays Ltd** (formerly **English Theatre Guild, Ltd.**) (1938), part of **Warner Chappell Music Ltd.,** 129 Park Street, London W1Y 3FA   *tel* 01-629 7600   *telex* 268403   *fax* 01-499 9718.
Specialises in stage plays. Works in conjunction with overseas agents. Preliminary letter essential.

**Watergate Film Services Ltd—see The Peters Fraser & Dunlop Group Ltd.**

**\*Watson, Little Ltd,** Suite 8, 26 Charing Cross Road, London WC2H 0DG   *tel* 01-836 5880 and 379 3077   *fax* 01-379 7731. *Directors:* Sheila Watson, Amanda Little.
Full-length MSS (home 10%, overseas 19%; all other rights including film, software, video and television 10%). No short stories or play scripts. Will sometimes suggest revision. Works in association with US agency and many foreign agencies. Preliminary letter please.

**\*A. P. Watt Ltd.** (1875), 20 John Street, London WC1N 2DL  *tel* 01-405 6774  *telegraphic address* Longevity, London  *telex* 297903 Apwatt G  *fax* 01-831 2154. *Directors:* Hilary Rubinstein, Caradoc King, Linda Shaughnessy, Rod Hall, Imogen Parker.
Full-length MSS; dramatic works for all media (home 10%, U.S. and foreign 20% including commission to U.S. or foreign agent). No poetry. Works in conjunction with agents in U.S.A. and most European countries and Japan. No reading fee. Preliminary letter please.

**\*Dinah Wiener Ltd.** (1985), 27 Arlington Road, London NW1 7ER  *tel* 01-388 2577  *telex* 264550 Dinah G  *telegraphic address* Dinalit London NW1.
Full-length MSS only, fiction and general non-fiction; no plays, scripts, poetry, short stories or children's books. Commission 15% home, 20% overseas, 15% film and television in association. U.S. office: Suite 21a, 7-13 Washington Square North, New York, N.Y. 10003. No reading fee, but preliminary letter and return postage essential.

## UNITED STATES OF AMERICA

\*Membership of the Society of Authors' Representatives

It has long been customary among literary agencies that the agent retains a 10% or 15% commission on domestic sales and up to 20% on foreign sales, subject to various exceptions and special policies established by each agent individually. Some agencies charge a reading fee for unsolicited MSS and for the work of beginners and new writers, such fees sometimes being refunded on the acceptance of the material. Members of the Society of Authors' Representatives do not charge a reading fee.
In all cases, and in their own interests, writers are advised to send a preliminary letter with a self-addressed, stamped envelope (or an International Reply Coupon if writing from outside the USA) and to ascertain terms before submitting MSS.

**American Play Company Inc.,** 19 West 44th Street, Suite 1206, New York, N.Y. 10036  *tel* 212-921-0545. *President:* Sheldon Abend.

**\*Julian Bach Literary Agency Inc.,** 747 Third Avenue, New York, N.Y. 10017  *tel* 212-753-2605  *telex* 668359  *cables* Turtles, New York  *fax* 212-688-8297.

**The Balkin Agency Inc.,** 850 West 176th Street, New York, N.Y. 10033  *tel* 212-781-4198. *Director:* Richard Balkin.
Full-length MSS. only (home 15%, overseas 20%). Adult non-fiction only. Query first. May suggest revision. Agents in all major countries. *British representative:* Radala & Associates. No reading fee.

**Virginia Barber Literary Agency, Inc.** (1974), 353 West 21st Street, New York, N.Y. 10011  *tel* 212-255-6515  *telex* 212-493-3790  *fax* 212-691-9418. *Directors:* Virginia Barber, Mary Evans.
General fiction and non-fiction (home 10-15%, overseas 20% for new authors), performance rights (10-15% for new authors); will suggest revision. Has co-agents in all major countries; Abner Stein handles UK rights. No reading fee.

**Bill Berger Associates Inc.,** 444 East 58th Street, New York, N.Y. 10022  *tel* 212-486-9588. *President:* William P. Berger; *Vice-President* and *Treasurer:* Henriette E. Neatrour.
Full-length and short MSS. (home 10%, Great Britain 15%, translations 20%). No reading fee.

**\*Lois Berman,** The Little Theatre Building, 240 West 44th Street, New York, N.Y. 10036  *tel* 212-575-5114.
Dramatic writing only (and only by recommendation).

**Blassingame-Spectrum Corp.** (1978), 432 Park Avenue South, Suite 1205, New York, N.Y. 10016  *tel* 212-532-7377. *Director:* Eleanor Wood. *Foreign Rights:* Ralph M. Vicinanza.
No unsolicited MSS; preliminary letter with return postage essential. *Commission:* 10% domestic, 20% foreign.

**\*Georges Borchardt Inc.** (1967), 136 East 57th Street, New York, N.Y. 10022  *tel* 212-753-5785  *telegraphic address* Literary New York  *telex* 423421 Literary  *fax* 212-838-6518. *Directors:* Georges Borchardt, Anne Borchardt.
Full-length and short MSS. (home 10%, British 15%, translations 20%). Theatre, films, television, radio (10%). Agents in most foreign countries. No unsolicited MSS. No reading fee.

**\*Brandt & Brandt Literary Agents Inc.,** 1501 Broadway, New York, N.Y. 10036  *tel* 212-840-5760  *telegraphic address* Bromasite New York.
Full-length and short MSS. (home 10%, overseas 15-20%). Theatre, films, television and radio (10%). *British representative:* A. M. Heath & Co. Ltd. No reading fee.

**\*The Helen Brann Agency Inc.,** 94 Curtis Road, Bridgewater, CT 06752  *tel* 203-354-9580  *fax* 203-355-2572.

**\*James Brown Associates Inc.—see Curtis Brown Ltd.**

**\*Curtis Brown Ltd.,** 10 Astor Place, New York, N.Y. 10003  *tel* 212-473-5400  *fax* 212-529-6706. *Chairman:* Perry Knowlton, *President:* Peter Ginsberg.

**\*John Cushman Associates Inc.—see Curtis Brown Ltd.**

**Liz Darhansoff Literary Agency,** 1220 Park Avenue, New York, N.Y. 10128  *tel* 212-534-2479  *fax* 212-996-1601.
Full-length and short MSS (home 10%, overseas 20%). Theatre, films, television, radio (15%). Works with agents throughout Europe; Tessa Sayle Agency in U.K. No reading fee.

**\*Joan Daves Literary Agency** (1952), 21 West 26th Street, New York, N.Y. 10010  *tel* 212-685-9573  *telex* 620103 Writers-Joda  *fax* 212-685-1781  *cables* Jodabooks, New York.
Full-length MSS or a detailed outline of n-f projects (home 10%, overseas 20%). No reading fee. No unpublished writers.

**\*Anita Diamant,** 310 Madison Avenue, New York, N.Y. 10017  *tel* 212-687-1122.

**\*Candida Donadio & Associates, Inc.,** 231 West 22nd Street, New York, N.Y. 10011  *tel* 212-691-8077.
Literary book agents, fiction and non-fiction.

**Dorese Agency,** 1400 Ambassador Street, Los Angeles, California 90035  *tel* 213-556-0710. Alyss Barlow Dorese.

**\*Ann Elmo Agency,** 60 East 42nd Street, New York, N.Y. 10165  *tel* 212-661-2880. *Directors:* Ann Elmo, Lettie Lee.
Full-length fiction and non-fiction MSS. (home 15%, overseas 20%). Theatre, films, television (15%). Will suggest revision when MSS. is promising. Works with foreign agencies. No reading fee.

**Frieda Fishbein Ltd.,** 2556 Hubbard Street, Brooklyn, N.Y. 11235  *tel* 212-247-4398.

**\*The Fox Chase Agency Inc.,** The Public Ledger Building, Room 930, Independence Square, Philadelphia, Pa 19106 *tel* 215-625-2450.

**\*Robert A. Freedman Dramatic Agency, Inc.,** (formerly **Harold Freedman Brandt & Brandt Dramatic Dept., Inc.**), 1501 Broadway, Suite 2310, New York, N.Y. 10036 *tel* 212-840-5760.

**\*Samuel French Inc.,** 45 West 25th Street, New York, N.Y. 10010 *tel* 212-206-8990 *fax* 212-206-1429.

**Jay Garon-Brooke Associates Inc.,** 415 Central Park West, New York, N.Y. 10025 *tel* 212-866-3654. Writer must be referred by an editor or a client. Will not read unsolicited MSS. *London:* Abner Stein, *tel* 01-373 0456.

**Goodman Associates, Literary Agents** (1976), 500 West End Avenue, New York, N.Y. 10024 *tel* 212-873-4806 *fax* 212-580-3278. *Partners:* Arnold P. Goodman, Elise Simon Goodman.
Adult book length fiction and non-fiction (home 15%, overseas 20%). No reading fee.

**Sanford J. Greenburger Associates, Inc.,** 55 Fifth Avenue, New York, N.Y. 10003 *tel* 212-206-5600.

**\*Blanche C. Gregory Inc.,** Two Tudor City Place, New York, N.Y. 10017 *tel* 212-697 0828.

**\*John Hawkins & Associates, Inc.** (formerly **Paul R. Reynolds, Inc.**) (1893), 71 West 23rd Street, Suite 1600, New York, N.Y. 10010 *tel* 212-807-7040 *cable address:* Carbonato, New York *fax* 212-807-9555. *President:* John Hawkins, *Vice-President:* William Reiss, *Foreign Rights:* Elsie Stern, *Permissions:* Sharon Friedman.

**Frederick Hill Associates** (1979), 1842 Union Street, San Francisco, California 94123 *tel* 415-921-2910.
Full-length fiction and non-fiction (home 15%, overseas 20%). Will suggest revision. Works in conjunction with agents in Scandinavia, France, Germany, Holland, Japan, Spain. No reading fee.

**\*International Creative Management, Inc.,** 40 West 57th Street, New York, N.Y. 10019 *tel* 212-556-5600 *telex* 125422 or 661562 Icmnyk *fax* 212-556-5665.

**\*JCA Literary Agency Inc.,** Suite 4-A, 242 West 27th Street, New York, N.Y. 10001 *tel* 212-807-0888.

**Daniel P. King** (1974), 5125 North Cumberland Boulevard, Whitefish Bay, Wisconsin 53217 *tel* 414-964-2903 *telex* 724389 *fax* 414-964-6860.
Specialist in mystery and crime fiction and non-fiction.

**\*Lucy Kroll Agency,** 390 West End Avenue, New York, N.Y. 10024 *tel* 212-877-0627 *fax* 212-769-2832.

**\*The Lantz Office,** 888 Seventh Avenue, New York, N.Y. 10106 *tel* 212-586-0200 and 9255 Sunset Boulevard, Los Angeles, California 90069 *tel* 213-858-1144.

**Michael Larsen-Elizabeth Pomada Literary Agents** (1972), 1029 Jones Street, San Francisco, California 94109 *tel* 415-673 0939. *Partners:* Michael Larsen and Elizabeth Pomada.
Full-length MSS. (home 15%, overseas 20%). Works in conjunction with agents in Hollywood, Europe, Israel, Japan, South America. Preliminary letter, with sae, essential.

**\*Lescher & Lescher, Ltd.** (1966), 67 Irving Place, New York, N.Y. 10009 *tel* 212-529-1790 *telegraphic address* Micawber. *Directors:* Robert Lescher, Susan Lescher.
Full-length and short MSS. (home 10-15%, overseas 20%). No reading fee.

**\*Ellen Levine Literary Agency, Inc.** (1980), Suite 1205, 432 Park Avenue South, New York, N.Y. 10016 *tel* 212-899-0620.
Full-length MSS. (home 10%, overseas 20%). In conjunction with co-agents, theatre, films, television, (10%). Will suggest revision. Works in conjunction with agents in Europe, Japan, Israel, Argentina. *UK representative:* A. P. Watt. No reading fee; preliminary letter essential.

**\*Literistic, Ltd.**—see **Sterling Lord Literistic Inc.**

**\*Gerald McCauley Agency, Inc.,** P.O. Box AE, Katonah, N.Y. 10536 *tel* 914-232-5700.

**Kirby McCauley Ltd.,** 432 Park Avenue South, Suite 1509, New York, N.Y. 10016 *tel* 212-683-7561 *fax* 212-679-0508. *Directors:* Kirby McCauley, Kay McCauley. **The Pimlico Agency Inc.,** subsidiary of Kirby McCauley Ltd. Contact: Claudia Wernick.

**McIntosh, McKee & Dodds, Inc.,** 276 Fifth Avenue, New York, N.Y. 10001 *tel* 212-679-4490 *cables* Halmatson *fax* 212-545-1224.

**\*McIntosh & Otis Inc.** (1928), 310 Madison Avenue, New York, N.Y. 10017 *tel* 212-687 7400.

**\*Elisabeth Marton,** 96 Fifth Avenue, New York, N.Y. 10011 *tel* 212-225-1908 *fax* 212-675-6265. *Partners:* Elisabeth Marton, Tonda Marton.

**\*Harold Matson Company, Inc.** (1937), 276 Fifth Avenue, New York, N.Y. 10001 *tel* 212-679-4490 *cables* Halmatson *fax* 212-545-1224.
Full-length MSS. (home 10%, U.K. 19%, translation 19%). No unsolicited MSS. No reading fee.

**\*Helen Merrill Ltd,** 435 West 23rd Street, Suite 1A, New York, N.Y. 10011 *tel* 212-691-5326.

**Peter Miller Agency Inc.** (1976), P.O. Box 760, Old Chelsea Station, New York, N.Y. 10011 *tel* 212-929-1222 *fax* 212-206-0238. *President:* Peter Miller.
Full-length and short MSS (home 15%, overseas 25%). Films, television (10-20%). Works in conjunction with agents in Germany, Japan, Spain. Preliminary enquiry with synopsis and resumé essential.

**Robert P. Mills Ltd,** c/o Richard Curtis Associates, 164 East 64th Street, New York, N.Y. 10021 *tel* 212-371-9481 *fax* 212-750-9142.

**\*William Morris Agency Inc.,** 1350 Avenue of the Americas, New York, N.Y. 10019 *tel* 212-586-5100.

**New Wave**—see **Pegasus International Inc.**

**\*Harold Ober Associates Inc.,** 40 East 49th Street, New York, N.Y. 10017 *tel* 212-759-8600 *telegraphic address* Litober *telex* 236112 *fax* 212-759-9428. *Directors:* Dorothy Olding, Claire M. Smith, Phyllis Westberg.
Full-length MSS. (home 10%, British 15%, overseas 20%). Theatre, films, television, radio (10%). Will suggest revision. *London representative:* David Higham Associates. No reading fee.

**\*Fifi Oscard Associates Inc.,** 19 West 44th Street, New York, N.Y. 10036 *tel* 212-764-1100 *fax* 212-870 5019. *President:* Fifi Oscard. *Directors:* Kevin D. McShane, Ivy Fischer Stone.

Full-length MSS (home 15%, overseas 20%). Theatre, films, television, radio (10%). Will suggest revision. Works in conjunction with many foreign agencies. No reading fee, but no unsolicited submissions.

**Pegasus International Inc.,** literary and film agents. P.O. Box 5470, Winter Park, Fla 32793-5470  *tel* 407-831-1008. *Director:* Gene Lovitz, *Client Contact and Assistant Director:* Carole Morling.
Non-fiction, fiction, regency and historical romances, juveniles, horror or science fiction, TV/film scripts (home 10%, overseas 10% unless another agent used). Will suggest revision. Evaluation fee charged for unpublished authors. Personal telephone calls returned anywhere in the world.

**Perkins' Literary Agency,** P.O. Box 48, Childs, Maryland 21916  *tel* 301-398-2647.
Full-length MSS (home 15%, overseas 20%), film/television (20%); will suggest revision. Reading fee.

**Porter, Dierks & Lovitz**—see **Pegasus International Inc.**

*****Raines & Raines** (1961), 71 Park Avenue, New York, N.Y. 10016  *tel* 212-684-5160  *telegraphic address* Rainesbuck New York. *Directors:* Theron Raines, Joan Raines, Keith Korman.
Full-length MSS. (home 15%, overseas 20%). Works in conjunction with overseas agents. No unsolicited MSS.

*****Flora Roberts Inc.,** 157 West 57th Street, New York, N.Y. 10019  *tel* 355-4165.

*****Marie Rodell-Frances Collin Literary Agency** (1948), 110 West 40th Street, New York, N.Y. 10018  *tel* 212-840-8664  *cables* Rodellitag, New York. *Director:* Frances Collin.
Full-length MSS. (home 15%, overseas 25%). Theatre, films, television, radio (20%). Works in conjunction with agents throughout the world. No reading fee. Please enclose post paid envelope or International Reply Coupon.

*****Rosenstone/Wender,** 3 East 48th Street, 4th Floor, New York, N.Y. 10017  *tel* 212-832-8330.

*****Russell & Volkening Inc.,** 50 West 29th Street, New York, N.Y. 10001  *tel* 212-684-6050.

*****Schaffner Agency** (1948), 264 Fifth Avenue, New York, N.Y. 10001  *tel* 212-689-6888  *fax* 212-545-8324. *Directors:* Timothy Schaffner, Patrick Delahunt.
Full-length MSS. (home 10% and overseas 7½%). *British representative:* A. M. Heath & Co. Ltd. No reading fee.

*****Susan F. Schulman Literary & Dramatic Agents Inc.,** 454 West 44th Street, New York, N.Y. 10036  *tel* 212-713-1633  *fax* 212-315-4782.
Agents for negotiation in all markets (with coagents) of fiction, general non-fiction, children's books, academic and professional works, and associated subsidiary rights including plays, film and television. (home 15%, United Kingdom 7½%, overseas 20%). Return postage required.

**Scott Meredith Literary Agency Inc.** (1941), 845 Third Avenue, New York, N.Y. 10022  *tel* 212-245-5500  *cables* Scottmere  *telegraphic address* Esemela 224705  *fax* 212-755-2972. *President:* Scott Meredith, *Vice-Presidents:* Jack Scovil, Theodore Chichak, *Subsidiary Rights:* William T. Haas.
Full-length and short MSS. (home 10%, overseas 20%). Theatre, films, television, radio (10%). Will read unsolicited MSS., queries, outlines. Single fee charged for readings, criticism and assistance in revision. London: Mark Hamilton, A. M. Heath & Co. Ltd.

**Charlotte Sheedy Literary Agency, Inc.,** 41 King Street, New York, N.Y. 10014 *tel* 212-633-2288 *fax* 212-633-6261.

*****The Shukat Company Ltd.,** 340 West 55th Street, Suite 1-A, New York, N.Y. 10019 *tel* 1-212-582-7614 *telex* 6502224600 MC1 UW *fax* 212-315-3752. Scott Shukat.
Theatre, films, novels, television, radio (15%). No reading fee. No unsolicited material accepted.

**Singer Media Corporation,** 3164 West Tyler Avenue, Anaheim, California 92801 *tel* 714-527-5650 *telegraphic address* Singerbook *fax* 714-527-0268. *Directors:* Veena Uberoi (Executive Vice-President), Kurt Singer (President). Full-length MSS. including romance, westerns, biography (home 15%, overseas 20%); short MSS. (home 10%, overseas 15%). Films, television, radio (15%, overseas 20%). Represented in most countries abroad.

**The Spectrum Literary Agency,** 432 Park Avenue, South, Suite 1205, New York, N.Y. 10016 *tel* 212-532-7377.
No unsolicited MSS. Send query with sae.

*****Philip G. Spitzer Literary Agency,** 788 Ninth Avenue, New York, N.Y. 10019 *tel* 212-265-6003.

*****Sterling Lord Literistic, Inc.,** One Madison Avenue, New York, N.Y. 10010 *tel* 212-696-2800 *fax* 212-686-6976 *cables* Literistic New York. *Directors:* Peter Matson, Sterling Lord, Michael Sissons, Anthony Jones.
Full-length and short MSS (home 10%, overseas 19%). Theatre, films, television, radio (10%). Will suggest revision. Represented in Europe by Intercontinental Literary Agency. U.K. representative: The Peters Fraser & Dunlop Group Ltd. No reading fee.

**H. N. Swanson, Inc.** (1934), 8523 Sunset Boulevard, Los Angeles, California 90069 *tel* 213-652-5385 *telegraphic address* Swanie. *Directors:* H. N. Swanson, Ben Kamsler.
Full-length MSS. (home 10%, overseas 20%). Theatre, films, television, radio. No reading fee.

*****Roslyn Targ Literary Agency, Inc.,** 105 West 13th Street, New York, N.Y. 10011 *tel* 212-206 9390 *cables* Rosbooks, New York *telex* 62193 *fax* 212-989-6233.
Full-length MSS (home 10%, unpublished authors 15%, overseas 20%). Films, television, radio (10%). Will suggest revision to those authors taken on. Affiliates in most foreign countries. No reading fee; preliminary letter with s.a.e. essential.

**Ralph Vicinanza Ltd,** 432 Park Avenue South, Suite 1205, New York, N.Y. 10016 *tel* 212-725-5133 *telex* 4945337.
No unsolicited MSS. *Commission:* 10% domestic, 20% foreign.

**Austin Wahl Agency, Ltd.** (1935), Suite 342, Monadnock Building, 53 West Jackson Boulevard, Chicago, Illinois 60604 *tel* 312-922-3331. *President:* Thomas Wahl.
Full-length and short MSS. (home 15%, overseas 20%). Theatre, films, television (10%). No reading fee; professional writers only.

*****Wallace Literary Agency, Inc.** (1988), 177 East 70th Street, New York, N.Y. 10021 *tel* 212-570-9090 *fax* 212-772-8979. *Directors:* Lois Wallace, Thomas C. Wallace.
Full-length MSS. (home 10%, U.K. 20%, overseas 20%). Film, television, theatre for agency clients (10%). Will suggest revision. No unsolicited manuscripts.

**Watkins/Loomis Agency, Inc.,** 150 East 35th Street, New York, N.Y. 10016   *tel* 212-532-0080   *cables* Anwat, Newyork   *fax* 212-889-0506. *London:* Abner Stein (U.K.), Marsh & Sheil Ltd (foreign).

**Rhoda Weyr Agency** (1983), 216 Vance Street, Chapel Hill, NC 27514   *tel* 919-942 0770.
General non-fiction and fiction with particular interest in science, history, biography. Full-length MSS for fiction; proposal for n-f (home 10%, overseas 20%). Theatre, films, television, radio (10%). Co-agents in all foreign markets. Sase required.

**Williams Wesley Winant** (1976), 180 East 79th Street, New York, N.Y. 10021   *tel* 212-RE-4-0988. *Directors:* William A. Winant III, Jean Valentine Winant. Theatre (full length, short plays) (home 10%, overseas 15%). Will suggest revision. No reading fee.

**Writers House Inc.** (1974), 21 West 26th Street, New York, N.Y. 10010   *tel* 212-685 2400   *telex* 620103 Writers   *fax* 212-685-1781. *President:* Albert Zuckerman.
Full-length MSS (home 15%, overseas 20%). No reading fee.

*****Mary Yost Associates, Inc.** (1958), 59 East 54th Street, New York, N.Y. 10022   *tel* 212-980-4988   *telegraphic address* Mybooks.
Full-length and short MSS. (home and overseas 10%). Works with individual agents in all foreign countries. Will suggest revision. No reading fee.

## *Others*

Most of the agents whose names and addresses are given below work in association with an agent in London.
In all cases, and in their own interests, writers are advised to send a preliminary letter and to ascertain terms before submitting MSS. or books.

### ARGENTINA

**International Editors Co.,** Avenida Cabildo 1156, 1426 Buenos Aires   *tel* 786-0888   *telex* 24518 Blibro AR   *fax* 541-786-0888.

**Lawrence Smith,** B.A. (1938), Avenida de los Incas 3110, 1426 Buenos Aires   *tel* 552-5012   *cables* Litagent, Baires.

### AUSTRALIA

**Curtis Brown (Australia) Pty., Ltd.,** 27 Union Street, Paddington, N.S.W. 2021   *tel* (02) 361 5301/(02) 361 6161   *fax* 360 3935   *cables* Browncurt.

### BRAZIL

**Heloisa Martins-Costa,** Agencia Literaria Carmen Bacells, Rua João Lira 97-202, Leblon, 22430 Rio de Janeiro, RJ   *tel* 294-3248   *cables* Copyright Rio   *telex* (021) 33961 Alcp   *fax* 294-6884.

**Karin Schindler, Rights Representative** (formerly **Dr J. E. Bloch Literary Agency**), Caixa Postal 19051, 04599 São Paulo, S.P   *tel* 241-9177   *cables* Copyright Sãopaulo   *fax* 241-9077.

### CANADA

**Curtis Brown Canada Ltd.,**   *tel* 516-537-7924   *fax* 516-537-7365.

## CZECHOSLOVAKIA

**Dilia** Theatrical and Literary Agency, Vyšehradská 28, 128 24 Prague 2 *tel* 296651-5 *telex* 121367 dili c.

**Lita** Slovak Literary Agency, Zámočnicka 9, 815-30 Bratislava *tel* 334801, 334806, 334346 *telegraphic address* Lita Bratislava.

## FRANCE

**Bureau Littéraire International Marguerite Scialtiel,** Geneviève Ulmann, 14 rue Chanoinesse, 75004 Paris *tel* (1) 43 54 71 16.

**D.M. Agence Littéraire** (formerly **McKee & Mouche**), 12 rue du Regard, 75006 Paris *tel* 45 48 45 03 and 42 22 42 33.

**Patrick Deedes-Vincke,** 38 bis rue de Rivoli, 75004 Paris *tel* 40 27 06 98.

**Robert Fouques Duparc** (1986), 21 rue de Verneuil, 75007 Paris *tel* (1) 42 60 58 77 *telex* 264918 Trace F Ext. 683.

**Agence Hoffman,** 77 boulevard Saint-Michel, 75005 Paris *tel* 43265694 *cables* Aghoff *telex* 203605.

**La Nouvelle Agence,** Mary Kling, 7 rue Corneille, 75006 Paris *tel* 43-25-85-60 *fax* 43-25-47-98.

**Mme Michelle Lapautre,** 6 rue Jean Carriès, 75007 Paris *tel* 4734-82-41 *telex* 205 247 (France) *fax* 47-34-00-90.

**Mme. Greta Strassova,** 4 rue Git-Le-Coeur, 75006 Paris *tel* 46 33 34 57.

## GERMANY

**Brigitte Axster,** Am Fronhof 3, D-4005 Meerbusch 1, (bei Düsseldorf) *tel* 02105-10096.

**Geisenheyner & Crone,** Gymnasiumstrasse 31B, 7000 Stuttgart-1 *tel* 0711-293738 *telex* 722664 Wdpat *fax* 0711-2261748.

**Agence Hoffman,** Seestrasse 6, 8000 Munich 40 *tel* (089) 39 64 02 *telex* 521 5661 *fax* (089) 33 93 85.

**Andrew Hunter Lee** (1988). *Directors:* A. Lee, Eva Herz, Angélica Bohne. Neidenburger Str. 1, D-7500 Karlsruhe *tel* 0721-688403.
Full-length MSS, medicine, pharmacy, plants and general (home/overseas 10%): will suggest revision (10%). Works in conjunction with UK and German agencies. Reading fee for non-European languages only.

**Thomas Schlück,** Literary Agency, Hinter der Worth 12, 3008 Garbsen 9 *tel* 05131-93053 *telex* 923419 Litag d *fax* 05131-93045.

## HUNGARY

**Artisjus.** Agency for Literature, Theatre and Music of the Hungarian Bureau for the Protection of authors' rights, Vörösmarty tér 1, Budapest V. *Post address:* H-1364 Budapest PB 67 *tel* 184-704 *cables* Artisjus *telex* 226527 Arjus H.

## ITALY

**Agenzia Letteraria Internazionale SRL,** 41 via Manzoni, 20121 Milan *tel* 6572465, 6572594, 6572596 *telex* 323574 Linali I *fax* 02 659 71 71.

**ILA—International Literary Agency—U.S.A.** (1969). I-18010 Terzorio-IM *tel and fax* (39 184) 48-40-48. Also c/o Wreschner, 10 West 74th Street, New York, N.Y. 10023 *tel* 212-877-2605. Publishers' Agent, interested in bestsellers and mass market books. *Speciality:* Books on collecting and antiques.

**Living Literary Agency** (1976). *Director:* Elfriede Pexa. Via Fra Cristoforo 2, 20142 Milan *tel* (02) 8439413 *telex* 314880 Attn Living *fax* (02) 8436522. Full-length MSS, English-language fiction and general non-fiction (home 10%, overseas 20%); films/television (5%), radio (10%); will suggest revision. Reading fee.

**News Blitz International** (1949), Via Cimabue 5, 00196 Rome *tel* 36 01 489, 36 00 620, 36 19 014 *telex* 623676 Blitz I *fax* 06 361 90 14.

## JAPAN

**Orion Literary Agency,** 1-58 Kanda-Jimbocho, Chiyoda-ku, Tokyo, 101 *tel* 03-295-1405 *telegraphic address* Orionagy, Tokyo *telex* J24408 Orionagy *fax* 03-295-4366.

## NETHERLANDS

**International Drama Agency,** P.O. Box 30030, 1003 BA Amsterdam *tel* 020-36 77 54/020-34 08 74 *fax* 020-36 73 55. Francis Lonnee.

**Internationaal Literatuur Bureau B.V.,** Postbus 10014, 1201 DA, Hilversum *tel* 035-21 35 00 *telex* 73201 ILB *fax* 035-21 57 71. Menno Kohn.

**United Dutch Dramatists,** Hemmo B. Drexhage, de Perponcherstraat 116, 2518 TA The Hague *tel* 070-46 97 38.

## NEW ZEALAND

**Richards Literary Agency** (1976), 3-49 Aberdeen Road, Castor Bay, Auckland 9 *postal address* P.O. Box 31240, Milford, Auckland 9 *tel* 410-5681 *fax* (005 649) 410 5681. *Partners:* Ray Richards, Barbara Richards, Nicki Richards. Full-length MSS, fiction, non-fiction, juvenile, educational, academic books; films, television, radio (home 10%, overseas 10-20%). Preliminary letter, synopsis with sae required. No reading fee.

## NIGERIA

**Joe-Tolalu & Associates (Nigeria) Limited** (1983), 5A Oremeji Street, Off Medical Road, P.O. Box 7031, Ikeja-Lagos *tel* 01-932929, 01-931505. *Directors:* Joseph Omosade, Tosin Awolalu, Foluke Awolalu.
Full-length MSS, fiction and non-fiction, short MSS, picture books only (home 10-15%, overseas 15-20%), performance rights (10%), translations (15%); will suggest revision. Works in conjunction with overseas agents. Preliminary letter essential; no reading fee.

## PORTUGAL

**Ilidio da Fonseca Matos,** Rua de S. Bernardo, 68-3, 1200 Lisbon *tel* 66 97 80, 715 44 45 *cables* Ilphoto.

## SCANDINAVIA, including FINLAND

**Arlecchino Teaterförlag,** Gränsvägen 14, S-131 41 Nacka, Sweden *tel* 08-718 17 18.

**A/S Bookman,** Fiolstraede 12, DK-1171, Copenhagen K, Denmark *tel* 33 14 57 20 *fax* 33 12 00 07.

**Gösta Dahl & Son, AB,** Aladdinsvägan 14, S-161 38 Bromma, Sweden *tel* 08 25 62 35.

**Leonhardt Literary Agency aps,** Studiestraede 35, DK-1455 Copenhagen K, Denmark *tel* 01-132523 *cables* Leolitag *fax* 01-134992.

**Licht & Licht,** Maglemosevej 46, DK-2920 Charlottenlund, Denmark    *tel* 31 61 09 08    *cables* Literagent    *telex* 21131 licht dk    *fax* 31 61 11 25.

**Suzanne Palme Literary Agency,** Oscarsgt. 60, Oslo 2, Norway    *postal address* P.O. Box 7112, Homansbyen, 0307 Oslo 3, Norway    *tel* 44 81 74    *cables* Palmebook    *telex* 79786.

**Gustaf von Sydow** (1988), Lorensbergsvägen 76, S 136 69 Haninge, Sweden    *tel* 46-8-776 10 54. *Directors:* Gustav von Sydow, Elizabeth von Sydow. Handles television, film, celebrity and news features in Sweden, Norway, Denmark and Finland.

## SOUTH AFRICA

**Frances Bond Literary Agency** (1985), 32b Stanley Teale Road, Westville North 3630, Natal    *tel* 031-824532    *postal address* P.O. Box 223, Westville 3630.

**Elizabeth Crompton-Lomax Agency** (1985), 6 Eagle Hill, Yellowwood Park, Durban, Natal 4001    *tel* 031-421732.

**International Press Agency (Pty) Ltd.,** P.O. Box 67, Howard Place 7450    *tel* (021) 531926    *fax* (021) 538789. *Manager:* Terry Temple; *Editor:* Rose-Ann Myers. *London Office:* Ursula A. Barnett, 19 Avenue South, Surbiton, Surrey KT5 8PJ    *tel* 01-390 4414    *fax* 01-398 8723.

**Sandton Literary Agency** (1982), P.O. Box 785799, Sandton 2146    *tel* 011-4428624. *Directors:* J. Victoria Canning, M. Sutherland. Full-length MSS and screenplays. Works in conjunction with: (*UK*) Joan Beakbane, Jacob's Ladder, Low Habberley, Kidderminster, Worcs. DY11 5RF, (*USA*) H. N. Swanson, Inc., Los Angeles.

## SPAIN

**Miss Carmen Balcells,** Agencia Literaria Carmen Balcells, Diagonal 580, Barcelona 08021    *tel* 200-89-33, 200-85-65    *cables* Copyright, Barcelona    *telex* 50 459 Copy E and 50936 Kopi E    *fax* 200-70-41.

**International Editors Co., S.A.,** Rambla Cataluña 63, 3º-1ª, 08007 Barcelona    *tel* 215-88-12    *telex* 98478 Rght E.

**Julio F. Yañez,** Agencia Literaria, Via Augusta 139, 6º-2ª, 08021 Barcelona    *tel* 200 71 07    *telex* 97348 GNLT-E    *fax* 209 48 65.

## SWITZERLAND

**Paul & Peter Fritz AG Literary Agency** , Jupiterstrasse 1, 8032 Zürich    *postal address* Postfach, 8032 Zürich    *tel* (01) 53 41 40    *fax* (01) 53 20 35.

**Liepman AG.,** Maienburgweg 23, 8044 Zürich    *tel* (01) 261 76 60    *cables* Litagent    *telex* 817573 lita    *fax* (01) 47 01 24. Dr. Ruth Liepman, Eva Koralnik, Ruth Weibel.

**Mohrbooks Literary Agency,** Klosbachstrasse 110, CH-8032 Zürich    *tel* (01) 251 16 10    *telex* 56830    *fax* (01) 262 52 13. Rainer Heumann.

**Niedieck Linder AG,** Wehrenbachhalde 34, CH-8053 Zürich, Postbox 153    *tel* (01) 53 65 92    *telex* 817 585 120 Com ch. *E-Mail (Geomail):* Net 1: Nck.

---

See also **Scripts for theatre, radio, tv and film** section for agents specialising in these fields.

---

# Character Merchandisers

A number of agents specialise in the handling of rights connected with the promotion of characters from books, television programmes etc., or with the books and programmes themselves. This is a selective listing, both of agents and of properties handled.

**BBC Licensing, BBC Enterprises Ltd.**, Room C241, Woodlands, 80 Wood Lane, London W12 0TT     *tel* 01-576 2554     *telex* 934678     *fax* 01-743 0393. Representing BBC TV and Radio and a selection of copyright owners.
Properties include *The Archers, Antiques Roadshow, Mrs Beeton, Doctor Who, EastEnders, Every Second Counts, Going Live, Grange Hill, Howards' Way, Jimbo and the Jet Set, Magic Roundabout, P. C. Pinkerton, Postman Pat, A Question of Sport, Radio 1, 2, 3, and 4, Top of the Pops, Victorian Kitchen Garden*.

**Copyright Promotions Ltd.**, 88-94 Tottenham Court Road, London W1P 9HE     *tel* 01-580 7431     *telex* 28992 Cpl Ldn     *fax* 01-631 1147.
Properties include *The Mr. Men, Little Miss, Danger Mouse, Victoria Plum, Pink Panther, Tom and Jerry, Wind in the Willows, My Little Pony, Rainbow Brite, Roland Rat, Mask, Bertie Bassett, World Wildlife Fund, Adrienne Weiss, Action Force, Auntie Em, Ivy Cottage, Visionaries, Jammie Pies, Monopoly, Beano & The Dandy, Cats, Phantom of the Opera, Starlight Express*, etc.

**The Copyrights Company Ltd,** 22 Crawford Place, London W1H 1JE     *tel* 01-723 6034     *telex* 298830 Bearup     *fax* 01-723 0463.
Properties include *Beatrix Potter, Paddington Bear, Brambly Hedge, Spot*, and other book-related properties for merchandise licensing.

**JWE Special Projects Ltd.**, 16 Owen Mansions, Queens Club Gardens, London W14 9RS     *tel* 01-385 5072     *fax* 01-385 6274.

**Link Licensing Ltd** (1986), United Newspaper Building, 23-27 Tudor Street, London EC4Y 0HR     *tel* 01-353 7305/6     *telex* 417109 Linkho G     *fax* 01-583 3479. *Directors:* Claire L. Derry, David A. Hamilton.
Properties: *Barney, Count Duckula, Trap Door, What-a-Mess, Hippo & Duck*.

**Marvel Licensing,** Arundel House, 13-15 Arundel Street, London WC2R 3DX     *tel* 01-497 2121.
Properties include *The Marvel Super Heroes, The Real Ghostbusters, Sylvanian Families, Dino Riders, Rambo, Red Heat, Mountains of the Moon*.

**Noddy Subsidiary Rights Company Ltd.**, Macdonald & Co. (Publishers) Ltd., Headway House, 66-73 Shoe Lane, London EC4P 4AB     *tel* 01-377 4600     *telex* 885233 Macdon G     *fax* 01-583 4407/8. *Contacts:* John O'Connor, Sylvia Rosen.
Property: *Noddy*.

# PART TWO

# General Information

# Finance

## Income Tax for Writers and Artists

PETER VAINES, F.C.A., A.T.I.I.
*Chartered Accountant*
*Barrister at Law*

This article is intended to explain the impact of taxation on writers and others engaged in similar activities. Despite attempts by many Governments to simplify our taxation system, the subject has become increasingly complicated and the following is an attempt to give a broad outline of the position. At the time of writing the proposals in the Budget have been set out in detail in the Finance Bill which will emerge in due course as the Finance Act 1989. The changes proposed in the Finance Bill are reflected in this article.

## HOW INCOME IS TAXED

### (a) Generally

Authors are usually treated for tax purposes as carrying on a profession and are taxed in a similar fashion to other professional persons, i.e. as self-employed persons assessable under Schedule D. This article is directed to self-employed persons only, because if a writer is employed by another in whatever capacity he will be subject to the rules of Schedule E where different considerations apply—substantially to his disadvantage. Attempts are often made by employed persons to shake off the status of "employee" and to attain "freelance" status so as to qualify for the advantages of Schedule D, such attempts meeting with varying degrees of success. The problems involved in making this transition are considerable and space does not permit a detailed explanation to be made here—proper advice is necessary if the difficulties are to be avoided.

Particular attention has been paid by the Inland Revenue to Fleet Street journalists and to those engaged in the TV and film industry with a view to reclassifying them as employees so that PAYE is deducted from their earnings. This blanket treatment has been extended to other areas and although it is obviously open to challenge by individual taxpayers, it is always difficult to persuade the Inland Revenue to change their views.

There is no reason why an employed person cannot carry on a freelance business in his spare time. Indeed, aspiring authors, painters, musicians, etc., often derive so little income from their craft that the financial security of an employment, perhaps in a different sphere of activity, is necessary. The existence of the employment is irrelevant to the taxation of the freelance earnings although it is most important not to confuse the income or expenditure of the employment with the income or expenditure of the self employed activity. The Inland Revenue are aware of the advantages which can be derived by an individual having "freelance" income from an organisation of which he is also an employee, and where such circumstances are contrived, it is of course extremely difficult to convince an Inspector of Taxes that a genuine freelance activity is being carried on.

For those starting in business or commencing work on a freelance basis the Inland Revenue produce a very useful booklet entitled "Starting in Business (IR28)", which is available from any tax office.

## (b) Income

For income to be taxable it need not be substantial, nor even the author's only source of income; earnings from casual writing are also taxable but this can be an advantage, because occasional writers do not often make a profit from their writing. The expenses incurred in connection with writing may well exceed any income receivable and the resultant loss may then be used to reclaim tax paid on other income. There may be deducted from the income certain allowable expenses and capital allowances which are set out in more detail below. The possibility of a loss being used as a basis for a tax repayment is fully appreciated by the Inland Revenue who sometimes attempt to treat casual writing as a hobby so that any losses incurred cannot be used to reclaim tax; of course by the same token any income receivable would not be chargeable to tax. This treatment may sound attractive but it should be resisted vigorously because the Inland Revenue do not hesitate to change their mind when profits begin to arise. However, in the case of exceptional or non-recurring writing, such as the autobiography of a sports personality or the memoirs of a politician, it could be better to be treated as pursuing a hobby and not as a professional author. Sales of copyright are chargeable to capital gains tax only (and not income tax), unless the recipient is a professional author.

## (c) Royalties

However, where the recipient is a professional author, a series of cases has laid down a clear principle that sales of copyright are taxable as income and not as capital receipts. Similarly, lump sums on account of, or in advance of royalties are also taxable as income in the year of receipt, subject to a claim for spreading relief (see below).

Copyright royalties are generally paid without deduction of Income Tax. However, if royalties are paid to a person who normally lives abroad, tax will be deducted by the payer or his agent at the time the payment is made unless arrangements are made with the Inland Revenue for payments to be made gross.

## (d) Arts Council Grants

Persons in receipt of grants from the Arts Council or similar bodies have been concerned for some time whether or not such grants were liable to Income Tax. In 1979, the Arts Council and other interested bodies engaged in detailed discussions with the Inland Revenue which culminated in the issue of a Statement of Practice regarding the tax treatment of those awards. Grants and other receipts of a similar nature have now been divided into two categories---those which are to be treated by the Inland Revenue as chargeable to tax and those which are not. Category A awards are considered to be taxable and arise from the following:
(1) Direct or indirect musical, design or choreographic commissions and direct or indirect commission of sculpture and paintings for public sites.
(2) The Royalty Supplement Guarantee Scheme.

(3) The contract writers' scheme.
(4) Jazz bursaries.
(5) Translators' grants.
(6) Photographic awards and bursaries.
(7) Film and video awards and bursaries.
(8) Performance Art Awards.
(9) Art Publishing Grants.
(10) Grants to assist with a specific project or projects (such as the writing of a book) or to meet specific professional expenses such as a contribution towards copying expenses made to a composer or to an artist's studio expenses.

Awards made under category B are not chargeable to tax and are as follows:
(1) Bursaries to trainee directors.
(2) In-service bursaries for theatre directors.
(3) Bursaries for associate directors.
(4) Bursaries to people attending full time courses in arts administration (the practical training course).
(5) In-service bursaries to theatre designers and bursaries to trainees on the theatre designers' scheme.
(6) In-service bursaries for administrators.
(7) Bursaries for actors and actresses.
(8) Bursaries for technicians and stage managers.
(9) Bursaries made to students attending the City University Arts Administration courses.
(10) Awards, known as the Buying Time Awards, made not to assist with a specific project or professional expenses but to maintain the recipient to enable him to take time off to develop his personal talents. These at present include the awards and bursaries known as the Theatre Writing Bursaries, awards and bursaries to composers, awards and bursaries to painters, sculptures and print makers, literature awards and bursaries.

This Statement of Practice has no legal force and is used merely to ease the administration of the tax system. It is open to anyone in receipt of a grant or award to disregard the agreed statement and challenge the Inland Revenue view on the merits of their particular case. However, it must be recognised that the Inland Revenue do not issue such statements lightly and any challenge to their view would almost certainly involve a lengthy and expensive action through the Courts.

The tax position of persons in receipt of literary prizes is clearer following a decision by the Special Commissioners in connection with the Whitbread Literary Award. In that case it was held that the prize was not part of the author's professional income and accordingly not chargeable to tax. The decisions of the Special Commissioners are not reported unless an appeal is made to the High Court and the Inland Revenue have chosen not to appeal against this decision. Elsewhere in this *Yearbook* will be found details of the many literary awards which are given each year and this decision is of considerable significance to the winners of each of these prizes. It would be unwise to assume that all such awards will be free of tax as the precise facts which were present in the case of the Whitbread award may not be repeated in another case; however it is clear that an author winning a prize has some very powerful arguments in his favour, should the Inland Revenue seek to charge tax on the award.

## ALLOWABLE EXPENSES

To qualify as an allowable business expense, expenditure has to be laid out wholly and exclusively for business purposes. Strictly there must be no "duality of purpose", which means that expenditure cannot be apportioned to reflect the private and business usage, e.g. food, clothing, telephone, travelling expenses, etc. However, the Inland Revenue do not usually interpret this principle strictly and are prepared to allow all reasonable expenses (including apportioned sums) where the amounts can be commercially justified. It should be noted carefully that the expenditure does not have to be "necessary", it merely has to be incurred "wholly and exclusively" for business purposes; naturally, however, expenditure of an outrageous and wholly unnecessary character might well give rise to a presumption that it was not really for business purposes. As with all things, some expenses are unquestionably allowable and some expenses are equally unquestionably not allowable---it is the grey area in between which gives rise to all the difficulties and the outcome invariably depends on negotiation with the Inland Revenue.

Great care should be taken when claiming a deduction for items where there is a "duality of purpose" and negotiations should be conducted with more than usual care and courtesy---if provoked the Inspector of Taxes may well choose to allow nothing. An appeal is always possible although unlikely to succeed as a string of cases in the Courts has clearly demonstrated. An example is the case of *Caillebotte* v. *Quinn* where the taxpayer (who normally had lunch at home) sought to claim the excess cost of meals incurred because he was working a long way from his home. The taxpayer's arguments failed because he did not eat only in order to work, one of the reasons for him eating was in order to sustain his life; a duality of purpose therefore existed and no tax relief was due. Other cases have shown that expenditure on clothing can also be disallowed if it is the kind of clothing which is in everyday use, because clothing is worn not only to assist the pursuit of one's profession but also to accord with public decency. This duality of purpose may be sufficient to deny relief---even where the particular type of clothing is of a kind not otherwise worn by the taxpayer. In the recent case of *Mallalieu* v. *Drummond* a lady barrister failed to obtain a tax deduction for items of sombre clothing purchased specifically for wearing in Court. The House of Lords decided that a duality of purpose existed because clothing represented part of her needs as a human being.

Despite the above Inspectors of Taxes are not usually inflexible and the following expenses are among those generally allowed:

(a) Cost of all materials used up in the course of preparation of the work.

(b) Cost of typewriting and secretarial assistance, etc.; if this or other help is obtained from one's spouse then it is entirely proper for a deduction to be claimed for the amounts paid for the work. The amounts claimed must actually be paid to the spouse and should be at the market rate although some uplift can be made for unsocial hours, etc. Payments to a wife (or husband) are of course taxable in her (or his) hands and should therefore be most carefully considered. The wife's earnings may also be liable for National Insurance contributions and if care is not taken these contributions can more than outweigh the tax savings.

(c) All expenditure on normal business items such as postage, stationery, telephone, answering machine, agent's fees, accountancy charges, photography, subscriptions, periodicals, magazines, etc., may be claimed. The cost of daily papers should not be overlooked if these form part of research material. Visits to theatres, cinemas, etc., for research purposes may also be permissible (but not of course the cost relating to guests). Unfortunately expenditure on all types of business entertaining is specifically denied tax relief.

(d) If work is conducted at home, a deduction for "use of home" is usually allowed providing the amount claimed is reasonable. If the claim is based on an appropriate proportion of the total costs of rent and rates, light and heat, cleaning and maintenance, insurance, etc. then care should be taken to ensure that no single room is used *"exclusively"* for business purposes, because this may result in the Capital Gains Tax exemption on the house as the only or main residence being partially forfeited. However, it would be a strange household where one room was in fact used exclusively for business purposes and for no other purpose whatsoever (e.g. storing personal bank statements and other private papers); the usual formula is to claim a deduction on the basis that most or all of the rooms in the house are used at one time or another for business purposes, thereby avoiding any suggestion that any part was used exclusively for business purposes.

(e) The appropriate business proportion of motor running expenses may also be claimed although what is the appropriate proportion will naturally depend on the particular circumstances of each case; it should be mentioned that the well known scale benefits, whereby one is taxed accordingly to the size and cost of the car, do not apply to self-employed persons.

(f) It has been long established that the cost of travelling from home to work (whether employed or self-employed) is not an allowable expense. However, if home is one's place of work then no expenditure under this heading is likely to be incurred and difficulties are unlikely to arise.

(g) Travelling and hotel expenses incurred for business purposes will normally be allowed but if any part could be construed as disguised holiday or pleasure expenditure, considerable thought would need to be given to the commercial reasons for the journey in order to justify the claim. The principle of "duality of purpose" will always be a difficult hurdle in this connection---although not insurmountable.

(h) If a separate business bank account is maintained, any overdraft interest thereon will be an allowable expense. This is the *only* circumstance in which overdraft interest is allowed for tax purposes and care should be taken to avoid overdrafts in all other circumstances.

(i) Where capital allowances (see below) are claimed for a television, video, record or tape player, etc., used for business purposes an appropriate proportion of the costs of maintenance and repair of the equipment may also be claimed.

Clearly many other allowable items may be claimed in addition to those mentioned above. Wherever there is any reasonable business motive for some expenditure it should be claimed as a deduction although one should avoid an excess of imagination as this would naturally cause the Inspector of Taxes to doubt the genuineness of other expenses claimed.

The question is often raised whether the whole amount of an expense may be deducted or whether the VAT content must be excluded. Where VAT is reclaimed from the Customs and Excise (on the quarterly returns made by a registered person), the VAT element of the expense cannot be treated as an allowable deduction. Where the VAT is not reclaimed, the whole expense (inclusive of VAT) is allowable for Income Tax purposes.

## CAPITAL ALLOWANCES

### (a) Allowances

Where expenditure of a capital nature is incurred, it cannot be deducted from income as an expense—a separate and sometimes more valuable capital allowance being available instead. Capital allowances are given for many different types of expenditure, but authors and similar professional people are likely to claim only for "plant and machinery"; this is a very wide expression which may include motor cars, typewriters, computers and other business machines, televisions, record and cassette players used for business purposes, books—and even a horse!

Plant and machinery qualify for a 25% allowance in the year of purchase and 25% of the reducing balance in subsequent years.

The reason these allowances can be more valuable than allowable expenses is that they may be wholly or partly disclaimed in any year that full benefit cannot be obtained—ordinary business expenses cannot be similarly disclaimed. Where, for example, the income of an author does not exceed his personal allowances, he would not be liable to tax and a claim for capital allowances would be wasted. If the capital allowances were to be disclaimed their benefit would be carried forward for use in subsequent years.

Careful planning with claims for capital allowances is therefore essential if maximum benefit is to be obtained, especially where the spouse also has income chargeable to tax.

As an alternative to capital allowances claims can be made on the "renewals" basis whereby all renewals are treated as allowable deductions in the year; no allowance is obtained for the initial purchase, but the cost of replacement (excluding any improvement element) is allowed in full. This basis is no longer widely used, as it is considerably less advantageous than claiming capital allowances as described above.

Leasing is a popular method of acquiring fixed assets, and where cash is not available to enable an outright purchase to be made, assets may be leased over a period of time. Whilst leasing may have financial benefits in certain circumstances, in normal cases there is likely to be no *tax* advantage in leasing an asset where the alternative of outright purchase is available. Indeed, leasing can be a positive disadvantage in the case of motor cars with a new retail price of more than £8000. If such a car is leased, only a proportion of the leasing charges will be tax deductible.

### (b) Books

The question of whether the cost of books is eligible for tax relief has long been a source of difficulty. The annual cost of replacing books used for the purposes of one's professional activities (e.g. the annual cost of a new *Writers' and Artists' Yearbook*) has always been an allowable expense; the difficulty arose because the initial cost of reference books etc. (for example when commencing one's profession) was treated as capital expenditure and no allowances were due as the books were not considered to be "plant". However, the matter has now been clarified by the case of *Munby* v. *Furlong* in which the Court of Appeal decided that the initial cost of law books purchased by a barrister was expenditure on "plant" and eligible for capital allowances. This is clearly a most important decision, particularly relevant to any person who uses expensive books in the course of exercising his profession.

## PENSION CONTRIBUTIONS

### (a) Personal pensions

Where a self-employed person pays annual premiums under an approved personal pension policy, tax relief may now be obtained each year for the following amounts:

| Age at 6/4/89 | Maximum % |
|---|---|
| 35 and under | 17.5% (max) £10,500 |
| 36 – 45 | 20% (max) £12,000 |
| 46 – 50 | 25% (max) £15,000 |
| 51 – 55 | 30% (max) £18,000 |
| 56 and over | 35% (max) £21,000 |

These figures do not apply to existing retirement annuity policies; these remain subject to the old limits which are unchanged.

These arrangements can be extremely advantageous in providing for a pension as premiums are usually paid when the income is high (and the tax relief is also high) and the pension (taxed as earned income when received) usually arises when the income is low and little tax is payable. The reduction in the rates of income tax to a maximum of 40% this year makes this decision a little more difficult because the tax advantages could go into reverse. When the pension is paid it could, if rates rise again, be taxed at a higher rate than the rate of tax relief at the moment. One would be deferring income in order to pay more tax on it later. However, this involves a large element of guesswork, and many people will be content simply with the long-term pension benefits.

### (b) Class 4 National Insurance Contributions

Allied to pensions is the payment of Class 4 National Insurance contributions, although no pension or other benefit is obtained by the contributions; the Class 4 contributions are designed solely to extract additional amounts from self-employed persons and are payable in addition to the normal Class 2 (self-employed) contributions. The rates are changed each year and for 1989-90 self-employed persons will be obliged to contribute 6.3% of their profits between the range £5050–£16,900 per annum, a maximum liability of £746.55 for 1989-90. This amount is collected in conjunction with the Schedule D Income Tax liability and appears on the same assessment; the comments below regarding assessments, appeals and postponement apply equally to Class 4 contributions although interest does not ordinarily accrue on their late payment. Tax relief is available for one half of the Class 4 contributions.

## SPREADING RELIEF

### (a) Relief for copyright payments

Special provisions enable authors and similar persons who have been engaged on a literary, dramatic, musical or artistic work for a period of more than twelve months, to spread certain amounts received over two or three years depending on the time spent in preparing the work. If the author was engaged on the work for a period exceeding twelve months, the receipt may be spread backwards over two years; if the author was engaged on the work for more than 24 months, the receipt may be spread backwards over three years. (Analogous provisions apply to sums received for the sale of a painting, sculpture or other work of art.)

The relief applies to:

a. lump sums received on the assignment of copyright, in whole or in part;

b. sums received on the grant of any interest in the copyright by licence;

c. non-returnable advances on account of royalties;

d. any receipts of or on account of royalties or any periodical sums received within two years of first publication.

A claim for spreading relief has to be made within eight years from 5th April following the date of first publication.

### (b) Relief where copyright sold after ten years

Where copyright is assigned (or a licence in it is granted) more than ten years after the first publication of the work, then the amounts received can qualify for a different spreading relief. The assignment (or licence) must be for a period of more than two years and the receipt will be spread forward over the number of years for which the assignment (or licence) is granted—but with a maximum of six years. The relief is terminated by death, but there are provisions enabling the deceased author's personal representatives to re-spread the amounts if it is to the beneficiaries' advantage.

The above rules are arbitrary and cumbersome, only providing a limited measure of relief in special circumstances. The provisions can sometimes be helpful to repair matters when consideration of the tax position has been neglected, but invariably a better solution is found if the likely tax implications are considered fully in advance.

## COLLECTION OF TAX

### Assessments

In order to collect the tax which is due on the profits of authorship the Inland Revenue issue an assessment based on the income for the relevant period. Normally the income to be assessed will be that for the previous year (e.g. the 1989–90 assessment will be based on the accounts made up to some date in 1988–89—perhaps 31st December 1988 or 5th April 1989). However, there are complicated rules for determining the income to be assessed in the years immediately after commencement, and in the years immediately prior to the discontinuance of the profession, and if for any reason there is a change in the date to which accounts are made up. When an assessment is received it should be examined carefully.

(a) If it is correct, the tax should be paid on the dates specified. Usually the tax is payable in two equal instalments, on 1st January in the year of assessment and on the following 1st July. If payment is delayed then interest may arise—see below.

(b) If the assessment is incorrect (for example, if it is estimated), then prompt action is required. An appeal must be lodged within 30 days of the date of issue of the assessment specifying the grounds of the appeal. An appeal form usually accompanies the notice of assessment. (If for some reason an appeal cannot be lodged within the 30 days the Inland Revenue are often prepared to accept a late appeal, but this is at their discretion and acceptance cannot be guaranteed.) If there is any tax charged on an incorrect assessment it cannot simply be forgotten, because it will become payable despite any appeal, unless an application for "postponement" is also made. (This may be done by completing the bottom half of the appeal form.) Tax can be postponed only where there are grounds for believing that too much tax has been charged, and the Inspector of Taxes will agree to postpone tax only if these grounds are reasonable. The tax which is not postponed will usually be payable on the normal due dates. It is necessary to consider claims for postponement most carefully to ensure that approximately the correct amount of tax remains payable; otherwise an unfortunate (and expensive) charge to interest could arise. It is important to recognise that "postponement" does not mean elimination; it simply means that payment of tax may be deferred, and after six months interest will start to run on any tax which has been postponed but which is ultimately found to be payable. As agreement of the final liability may take a long time, a large amount of interest can arise unless a reasonably accurate amount has been paid on time.

### Interest

Interest is chargeable on overdue tax at a variable rate, currently approximately 13% per annum and does not rank for any tax relief, which makes the Inland Revenue a very expensive source of credit. Where the amount of interest is less than £30 in any year it is not usually collected but should the interest exceed £30 the full amount will be payable and it is extraordinarily difficult to persuade the

Inland Revenue to withdraw a charge to interest—even where the delay is their fault.

However, the Inland Revenue can also be obliged to pay interest at the same rate (known as repayment supplement) tax-free where repayments are delayed. The rules relating to repayment supplement are less beneficial and even more complicated than the rules for interest payable but they do exist and can be very welcome if a large repayment has been delayed for a long time.

*Example*

Author's accounts made up to 30th April 1988 showing profits of £10,000 giving rise to tax of (say) £1500.

Assessment issued in September 1989 for 1989–90 in an estimated figure of £15,000—tax charged £2500.

Appeal must be made within 30 days of issue.

Application for postponement must also be made within 30 days to postpone £1000 of the tax charged.

Tax therefore becomes payable thus:

| | | |
|---|---|---|
| 1st Jan. 1990 | | £750 |
| 1st July 1990 | | £750 |

(If no application for postponement were to be made £1250 would become payable on each of these dates. When the final liability is agreed the excess of £1000 would be refunded but that could take some time, and repayment supplement might not apply.)

Unfortunately life is never as simple as the above illustration would suggest, but it serves to demonstrate the principle.

## VALUE ADDED TAX

The activities of writers, painters, composers, etc., are all "taxable supplies" within the scope of VAT and chargeable at the standard rate. (Zero rating which applies to publishers, booksellers, etc., on the supply of books does not extend to the work performed by writers; the position is less clear with regard to authors writing for foreign persons. Changes were made in the VAT rules from 1st January 1978 with the effect that zero rating does not always apply. Proper advice should be sought if there is any doubt regarding the correct treatment.) Accordingly, authors are obliged to register for VAT if their income exceeds certain limits; the annual limit has recently been increased to £23,600 per annum with effect from 15th March 1989, but there is a quarterly limit of £8000, which if exceeded may render the author liable to registration.

Delay in registering can be a most serious matter because if registration is not effected at the proper time, the Customs and Excise can (and invariably do) claim VAT from all the income received since the date on which registration should have been made. As no VAT would have been included in the amounts received during this period the amount claimed by the Customs and Excise must inevitably come straight from the pocket of the author.

He may be entitled to seek reimbursement of the VAT from those whom he ought to have charged VAT but this is obviously a matter of some difficulty and may indeed damage his commercial relationships. Since 1985 the position has become considerably worse because a penalty now arises for late registration. The rules are extremely harsh and are imposed automatically even in cases of innocent error. It is therefore extremely important to monitor the income very carefully because if in any period of three months the income exceeds £8000, the Customs & Excise must be notified within 30 days of the end of the period. Failure to do so will give rise to an automatic penalty of 30% of the VAT which should have been paid; this will always be a substantial amount. It should be emphasized that this is a penalty for failing to submit a form and has nothing to do with any real or potential loss of tax. Furthermore, whether the failure was innocent or deliberate will not matter. Only the existence of a "reasonable excuse" will be a defence to the penalty. However, a reasonable excuse does not include ignorance, error, a lack of funds or reliance on any third party. It should be particularly noted that neither the Customs & Excise nor the VAT Appeal Tribunal have any power to reduce the amount of any penalty for failing to register for VAT. It has also been announced that further and equally harsh penalties are to be introduced concerning the late submission of returns and underdeclarations of VAT in addition to those which already exist.

However it is possible to regard VAT registration as a privilege and not a penalty, because only VAT registered persons can reclaim VAT paid on such expenditure as stationery, telephone, professional fees, etc., even typewriters and other plant and machinery (excluding cars). However, many find that the administrative inconvenience—the cost of maintaining the necessary records and completing the necessary forms—more than outweighs the benefits to be gained from registration and prefer to stay outside the scope of VAT for as long as possible.

## OVERSEAS MATTERS

The general observation may be made that self employed persons resident and domiciled in the United Kingdom are not well treated with regard to their overseas work, being taxable on their world wide income. It is important to emphasise that if fees are earned abroad, no tax saving can be achieved merely by keeping the money outside the country. Although exchange control regulations no longer exist to require repatriation of foreign earnings, such income remains taxable in the U.K. and must be disclosed to the Inland Revenue; the same applies to interest or other income arising on any investment of these earnings overseas. Accordingly whenever foreign earnings are likely to become substantial, prompt and effective action is required to limit the impact of U.K. and foreign taxation. In the case of non resident authors it is important that arrangements concerning writing for publication in the U.K., e.g. in newspapers, are undertaken with great care. A recent case concerning the wife of one of the great train robbers who provided detailed information for a series of articles in a Sunday newspaper is most instructive. Although she was acknowledged to be resident in Canada for all the relevant years, the income from the articles was treated as arising in this country and fully chargeable to U.K. tax.

The United Kingdom has double taxation agreements with many other countries and these agreements are designed to ensure that income arising in a foreign country is taxed either in that country or in the United Kingdom. Where a withholding tax is deducted from payments received from another country (or where tax is paid in full in the absence of a double taxation agreement), the amount of foreign tax paid can usually be set off against the related U.K. tax liability. Many successful authors can be found living in Eire because of the complete exemption from tax which attaches to works of cultural or artistic merit by persons who are resident there. However, such a step should only be contemplated having careful regard to all the other domestic and commercial considerations and specialist advice is essential if the exemption is to be obtained and kept; a careless breach of the conditions could cause the exemption to be withdrawn with catastrophic consequences.

## COMPANIES

When an author becomes successful the prospect of paying tax at the higher rate may drive him to take hasty action such as the formation of companies, etc., which may not always be to his advantage. Indeed some authors seeing the exodus into tax exile of their more successful colleagues even form companies in low tax areas in the naive expectation of saving large amounts of tax. The Inland Revenue are fully aware of the opportunities and have extensive powers to charge tax and combat avoidance. Accordingly such action is just as likely to *increase* tax liabilities and generate other costs and should never be contemplated without expert advice; some very expensive mistakes are often made in this area which are not always able to be remedied.

To conduct one's business through the medium of a company can be a most effective method of mitigating tax liabilities, and providing it is done at the right time and under the right circumstances very substantial advantages can be derived. However, if done without due care and attention the intended advantages will simply evaporate. At the very least it is essential to ensure that the company's business is genuine and conducted properly with regard to the realities of the situation. If the author continues his activities unchanged, simply paying all the receipts from his work into a company's bank account, he cannot expect to persuade the Inland Revenue that it is the company and not himself who is entitled to, and should be assessed to tax on, that income. It must be strongly emphasised that many pitfalls exist which can easily eliminate all the tax benefits expected to arise by the formation of the company. For example, company directors are employees of the company and will be liable to pay much higher National Insurance contributions; the company must also pay the employer's proportion of the contribution and a total liability of nearly 20% of gross salary may arise. This compares most unfavourably with the position of a self-employed person. Moreover on the commencement of the company's business the individual's profession will cease and the Inland Revenue have the power to re-open earlier years assessments and may be able to increase the liabilities for previous years; this is always a crucial factor in determining the best moment when the changeover to a company should take place.

No mention has been made above of personal reliefs and allowances (for example the single and married persons allowances, etc.); this is because these allowances and the rates of tax are subject to constant change and are always set out in detail in the explanatory notes which accompany the Tax Return. The annual Tax Return is an important document and should not be ignored because it is crucial to one's tax position. Indeed, it should be completed promptly with extreme care because the Inland Revenue treat failures to disclose income very harshly, invariably exacting interest and penalties— sometimes of substantial amounts. If filling in the Return is a source of difficulty or anxiety, comfort may be found in the Consumer Association's publication *Money Which?—Tax Saving Guide*; this is published in March of each year and includes much which is likely to be of interest and assistance.

# Social Security Contributions

J. PHILIP HARDMAN, f.c.a., f.t.i.i.
*Chartered Accountant*

## INTRODUCTION

In general, every individual who works in Great Britain either as an employee or as a self-employed person is liable to pay social security contributions. The law governing this subject is complicated and the following should only be regarded as a summary of the position.

All contributions are payable in respect of years ending on 5th April, the classes of contributions being as follows:

*Class 1* These are payable by employees (primary contributions) and their employers (secondary contributions) and are based on earnings.

*Class 2* These are flat rate contributions, payable weekly by the self employed.

*Class 3* These are weekly flat rate contributions, payable on a voluntary basis in order to provide, or make up entitlement to, certain social security benefits.

*Class 4* These are payable by the self employed in respect of their trading or professional income and are based on earnings.

## EMPLOYED OR SELF EMPLOYED?

The question as to whether a person is employed under a contract *of* service and is thereby an employee liable to Class 1 contributions, or performs services (either solely or in partnership) under a contract *for* service and is thereby self employed liable to Class 2 and Class 4 contributions, often has to be decided in practice. Probably the best guide can be found in the case of *Market Investigations Limited* v. *Minister of Social Security* (1969 2 WLR 1) when Cooke J. remarked as follows:

". . . the fundamental test to be applied is this: 'Is the person who has engaged himself to perform these services performing them as a person in business on his own account?' If the answer to that question is 'yes', then the contract is a contract for services. If the answer is 'no', then the contract is a contract of service. No exhaustive list has been compiled and perhaps no exhaustive list can be compiled of the considerations which are relevant in determining that question, nor can strict rules be laid down as to the relative weight which the various considerations should carry in particular cases. The most that can be said is that control will no doubt always have to be considered, although it can no longer be regarded as the sole determining factor; and that factors which may be of importance are such matters as
—whether the man performing the services provides his own equipment,
—whether he hires his own helpers,
—what degree of financial risk he takes,
—what degree of responsibility for investment and management he has, and
—whether and how far he has an opportunity of profiting from sound management in the performance of his task."

There have been three cases in recent years, all dealing with musicians, which provide further guidance on the question as to whether an individual is employed or self-employed.

*Midland Sinfonia Concert Society Ltd.* v. *Secretary of State for Social Services* (1981 ICR 454)

A musician, employed to play in an orchestra by separate invitation at irregular intervals and remunerated solely in respect of each occasion upon which he does play, is employed under a contract for services. He is therefore self-employed, not an employed earner, for the purposes of the Social Security Act 1975, and the orchestra which engages him is not liable to pay National Insurance contributions in respect of his earnings.

*Addison* v. *London Philharmonic Orchestra Limited* (1981 ICR 261)

This was an appeal to determine whether certain individuals were employees for the purposes of section 11(1) of the Employment Protection (Consolidation) Act 1978.

The Employment Appeal Tribunal upheld the decision of an industrial tribunal that an associate player and three additional or extra players of the London Philharmonic Orchestra were not employees under a contract of service, but were essentially freelance musicians carrying on their own business.

The facts found by the industrial tribunal showed that, when playing for the orchestra, each appellant remained essentially a freelance musician, pursuing his or her own profession as an instrumentalist, with an individual reputation, and carrying on his or her own business, and they contributed their own skills and interpretative powers to the orchestra's performances as independent contractors.

*Winfield* v. *London Philharmonic Orchestra Limited* (ICR 1979, page 726)

This case dealt with the question as to whether an individual was an employee within the meaning of section 30 of the Trade Union and Labour Relations Act 1974.

The following remarks by the appeal tribunal are of interest in relation to the status of musicians:

". . . making music is an art, and the co-operation required for a performance of Berlioz's *Requiem* is dissimilar to that required between the manufacturer of concrete and the truck driver who takes the concrete where it is needed. . . It took the view, as we think it was entitled on the material before it to do, that the company was simply machinery through which the members of the orchestra managed and controlled the orchestra's operation . . . In deciding whether you are in the presence of a contract of service or not, you look at the whole of the picture. This picture looks to us, as it looked to the industrial tribunal, like a co-operative of distinguished musicians running themselves with self and mutual discipline, and in no sense like a boss and his musician employees."

Other recent cases have concerned a professional dancer and holiday camp entertainers, and there are special arrangements as regards workers in the film industry. In two recent cases income from part-time lecturing was held to be from an employment.

Accordingly, if a person is regarded as an employee under the above rules, he will be liable to pay contributions even if his employment is casual, part time or temporary.

Furthermore, if a person is an employee and also carries on a trade or profession either solely or in partnership, there will be a liability to more than one class of contributions (subject to certain maxima—see below).

*Exceptions*

There are certain exceptions to the above rules, those most relevant as regards artists and writers being:

(a) The employment of a wife by her husband, or vice versa, is disregarded for social security purposes unless it is for the purposes of a trade or profession (for example, the employment of his wife by an author would not be disregarded and would result in a liability for contributions if her salary reached the minimum levels).

(b) The employment of certain relatives in a private dwelling house in which both employee and employer reside is disregarded for social security purposes provided the employment is not for the purposes of a trade or business carried on at those premises by the employer. This would cover the employment of a relative (as defined) as a housekeeper in a private residence.

(c) In general, lecturers, teachers and instructors engaged by an educational establishment to teach on at least four days in three consecutive months are regarded as employees, although this rule does not apply to fees received by persons giving public lectures.

## CLASS 1 CONTRIBUTIONS BY EMPLOYEES AND EMPLOYERS

As mentioned above, these are related to earnings, the amount payable depending upon whether the employer has applied for his employees to be "contracted-out" of the State earnings-related pension scheme; such application can be made where the employer's own pension scheme provides a requisite level of benefits for his employees and their dependents.

Up to 6th October 1985, when earnings reached the lower earnings limit primary and secondary Class 1 contributions were payable on earnings up to the upper earnings limit, although for contracted-out employments there were reduced rates of contributions in respect of earnings between the lower and upper limits.

From 6th October 1985 the upper earnings limit for secondary contributions, but not for primary contributions, was removed, and contribution rates on lower earnings reduced.

Contributions are normally collected via the PAYE tax deduction machinery.

### Employees liable to pay contributions

These are payable by any employee who is aged 16 years and over (even though he may still be at school) and who is paid an amount equal to, or exceeding, the lower earnings limit (see below).

Nationality is irrelevant for contribution purposes and, subject to special rules covering employees not normally resident in Great Britain, Northern Ireland or the Isle of Man, or resident in countries with which there are reciprocal social security agreements, contributions must be paid whether the employee concerned is a British subject or not provided he is gainfully employed in Great Britain.

### Employees exempt from liability to pay contributions

Persons over pensionable age (65 for men and 60 for women) are exempt from liability to pay primary contributions, even if they have not retired.

However, the fact that an employee may be exempt from liability does not relieve an employer from liability to pay secondary contributions in respect of that employee.

### Rate of employees' contributions

For earnings paid on or after 6th April 1989 employees are liable at rates of 5%, 7% or 9% on all their earnings (before PAYE and other deductions) up to and including the upper earnings limit depending upon the particular band into which their earnings fall (see below). It is emphasized that the rate of contributions attributable to the band into which a person's weekly, monthly, etc., earnings fall is applied to *all* those earnings (up to the upper limit) and not merely to the earnings falling into that band. The above three rates of primary contributions are reduced to 3%, 5% and 7% from 6th April 1988 in respect of earnings above the lower and up to and including the upper earnings limit for contracted-out employments.

For earnings paid after 5th October 1989, the rate of employees' contributions, where the earnings are not less than the lower earnings limit, is 2% of earnings to the lower earnings limit and 9% of earnings between the lower and upper earnings limits (7% for contracted-out employments).

Certain married women who made appropriate elections before 12th May 1977 may be entitled to pay a reduced rate of 3.85%. However, these ladies will have no entitlement to benefits in respect of these contributions.

*Employers' contributions*

All employers are liable to pay contributions on the gross earnings of employees. As mentioned above, an employer's liability is not reduced as a result of employees being exempted from, or being liable to pay only the (3.85%) reduced rate of, contributions.

For earnings paid on or after 6th October 1985 employers are liable at rates of 5%, 7%, 9% or 10.45% on earnings paid (without any upper earnings limit) depending upon the particular band into which the earnings fall (see below). The rate of contributions attributable to the band into which the earnings fall is applied to *all* those earnings and not merely to the earnings falling into that band. The above four rates of secondary contributions are reduced to 1.2%, 3.2%, 5.2% and 6.65% from 6th April 1988 in respect of earnings above the lower earnings limit and up to and including the upper earnings limit for contracted-out employments.

The employer is responsible for the payment of both employees' and employer's contributions, but is entitled to deduct the employees' contributions from the earnings on which they are calculated. Effectively, therefore, the employee suffers a deduction in respect of his social security contributions in arriving at his weekly or monthly wage or salary.

Special rules apply to company directors and persons employed through agencies.

*Rates of Class 1 contributions and earnings limits from 6th April 1989*

| Earnings per week | Rates payable on all Earnings | | | |
| | Contracted In | | Contracted Out | |
| | Employee | Employer | Employee | Employer |
| £ | % | % | % | % |
| Below 43.00 | - | - | - | - |
| 43.00 – 74.99 | 5.00 | 5.00 | *5.00/3.00 | *5.00/1.20 |
| 75.00 – 114.99 | 7.00 | 7.00 | *7.00/5.00 | *7.00/3.20 |
| 115.00 – 164.99 | 9.00 | 9.00 | *9.00/7.00 | *9.00/5.20 |
| 165.00 – 325.00 | 9.00 | 10.45 | *9.00/7.00 | *10.45/6.65 |
| Over £325.00 | 9.00 of £325 | 10.45 | *9.00/7.00 of £325 | †10.45/6.65 |

*The first figure is the rate to the lower earnings limit and the second is to the top of the earnings.

†10.45% to lower earnings limit and above upper earnings limit; 6.65% between these limits.

*Rates of Class 1 contributions and earnings limits from 6th October 1989*
The above rates remain the same, except that the rates of employees' contributions on earnings paid after 5th October 1989 are:

| Earnings per week £ | Contracted In | Contracted Out |
|---|---|---|
| Below 43.00 | nil | nil |
| 43.00–325.00 | 2% to lower earnings limit, 9% between lower and upper earnings limits | 2% to lower earnings limit, 7% between lower and upper earnings limits |

*Items included in, or excluded from, earnings*
Contributions are calculated on the basis of a person's gross earnings from his employment. This will normally be the figure shown on the tax deduction card, except where the employee pays superannuation contributions and from 6th April 1987 charitable gifts---these must be added back for the purposes of calculating Class 1 liability. Profit-related pay exempt from income tax is not exempt from social security contributions.

Earnings include salary, wages, overtime pay, commissions, bonuses, holiday pay, payments made while the employee is sick or absent from work, payments to cover travel between home and office, and payments under the statutory sick pay and maternity pay schemes.

However, certain payments, some of which may be regarded as taxable income for income tax purposes, are ignored for social security purposes. These include gratuities paid other than by the employer, redundancy payments and payments in lieu of notice, certain payments in kind, reimbursement of specific expenses incurred in the carrying out of the employment, benefits given for personal reasons (e.g. wedding and birthday presents), compensation for loss of office, and meal vouchers which can only be redeemed for food or drink.

DSS booklet NI 269 gives a list of items to include in or exclude from earnings for Class 1 contribution purposes.

*Maximum contributions*

There is a limit to the total liability for social security contributions payable by a person who is employed in more than one employment, or is also self employed or a partner.

Where only non contracted-out Class 1 contributions, or non contracted-out Class 1 and Class 2 contributions, are payable, the maximum contribution is limited to 53 primary Class 1 contributions at the maximum weekly non-contracted-out standard rate. For 1989/90 the maximum will thus be £1,550.25.

However, where contracted-out Class 1 contributions are payable, the maximum primary Class 1 contributions payable for 1989/90 where all employments are contracted-out are £1,251.33.

Where Class 4 contributions are payable in addition to Class 1 and/or Class 2 contributions, *the Class 4 contributions are restricted* so that they shall not exceed the excess of £971.80 (i.e. 53 Class 2 contributions plus maximum Class 4 contributions) over the aggregate of the Class 1 and Class 2 contributions.

*Miscellaneous rules*

There are detailed rules covering a person with two or more employments; where a person receives a bonus or commission in addition to a regular wage or salary; and where a person is in receipt of holiday pay.

# CLASS 2 CONTRIBUTIONS BY THE SELF EMPLOYED

*Rate*

Class 2 contributions are payable at the rate of £4.25 per week as from 6th April 1989.

*Exemptions from Class 2 liability*

These are as follows:

(1) A man over 65 or a woman over 60.
(2) A person who has not attained the age of 16.
(3) A married woman or, in certain cases, a widow could elect prior to 12th May 1977 not to pay Class 2 contributions.
(4) Persons with small earnings (see below).
(5) Persons not ordinarily self employed (see below).
(6) Persons in receipt of invalid care allowance.
(7) Persons in receipt of sickness or invalidity benefits or unemployability supplements, or maternity allowances, or incapable of work or in prison or legal custody.

*Small earnings*

Any person who can show that his net self employed earnings per his profit and loss account (as opposed to taxable profits):

(1) for the year of application are expected to be less than a specified limit (£2,350 in the 1989/90 tax year); or
(2) for the year preceding the application were less than the limit specified for that year (£2,250 for 1988/89) and there has been no material change of circumstances;

may apply for a certificate of exception from Class 2 contributions. Certificates of exception must be renewed each tax year. At the Secretary of State's discretion the certificate may commence up to 13 weeks before the date on which the application is made. Despite a certificate of exception being in force, a person who is self employed is still entitled to pay Class 2 contributions if he wishes, in order to maintain entitlement to social security benefits.

*Persons not ordinarily self employed*

Part-time self employed activities as a writer or artist are disregarded for contribution purposes if the person concerned is not ordinarily employed in such activities and has a full-time job as an employee. There is no definition of "ordinarily employed" for this purpose but the D.S.S. regard a person who has a regular job and whose earnings from spare-time occupation are not expected to be more than £800 per annum as falling within this category. Persons qualifying for this relief do not require certificates of exception. It should be noted that many activities covered by this relief would probably also be eligible for relief under the small earnings rule (see above).

*Method of payment*

Class 2 contributions may be paid by purchasing stamps to be fixed to contribution cards, or alternatively application may be made to pay contributions by direct debit through a bank account or the Post Office giro system.

*Overpaid contributions*

If, following the payment of Class 2 contributions, it is found that the earnings are below the exception limit (e.g. the relevant accounts are prepared late), the Class 2 contributions that have been overpaid cannot be reclaimed.

## CLASS 3 CONTRIBUTIONS

These are payable voluntarily, at the rate of £4.15 per week from 6th April 1989 by persons aged 16 or over with a view to enabling them to qualify for a limited range of benefits if their contribution record is not otherwise sufficient. In general, Class 3 contributions can be paid by employees, the self employed and the non employed.

Broadly speaking, no more than 52 Class 3 contributions are payable for any one tax year, and contributions are not payable after the end of the tax year in which the individual concerned reaches the age of 64 (59 for women).

Class 3 contributions may be paid by purchasing stamps to be fixed to contribution cards, or by direct debit through a bank account or the Post Office giro system.

## CLASS 4 CONTRIBUTIONS BY THE SELF EMPLOYED

*Rate*

In addition to Class 2 contributions, self employed persons are liable to pay Class 4 contributions. These are calculated at the rate of 6.30% on the amount of profits or gains chargeable to income tax under Schedule D Case I or II which exceed £5,050 per annum but which do not exceed £16,900 per annum for 1989/90. Thus the maximum Class 4 contribution is 6.30% of £11,850—i.e. £746.55 for 1989/90.

For the tax year 1989/90, Class 4 contributions are based on the income tax assessment for 1989/90 (for example, the profits of the year ending 31st December 1988) and so on for subsequent years.

The income tax assessment on which Class 4 contributions are calculated is after deducting capital allowances and losses, but before deducting personal tax allowances or retirement annuity premiums.

Class 4 contributions produce no additional benefits, but were introduced to ensure that self employed persons as a whole pay a fair share of the cost of pensions and other social security benefits without the self employed who make only small profits having to pay excessively high flat rate contributions.

For 1985/86 and subsequent years, one half of the Class 4 contributions (as finally settled) is deductible in computing total income. It should be noted that this deduction is given in arriving at total income for income tax purposes and not in arriving at the profits assessable under Schedule D. Where a wife's earnings election is in force or the couple have elected to be taxed separately, it appears that the deduction is given against her income and not that of her husband. Although the legislation states that a claim is necessary, in practice the deduction will be given automatically. This deduction is broadly equivalent to that available to employers for tax purposes in respect of their secondary contributions, and was introduced to rectify the previous anomaly in that employers, but not the self employed, were eligible for tax relief for the contributions they bore. Where deferment of Class 2 and 4 contributions has been obtained, it should be ensured that the eventually assessed Class 4 contributions, if any, are allowed for income tax purposes.

*Payment of contributions*

In general, contributions are calculated and collected by the Inland Revenue together with the income tax under Schedule D Case I or II, and accordingly the contributions are due and payable at the same time as the income tax liability on the relevant profits.

*Persons exempt from Class 4 contributions*

The following persons are exempt from Class 4 contributions:

(1) Men over 65 and women over 60 at the commencement of the year of assessment (i.e. on 6th April).

(2) An individual not resident in the United Kingdom for income tax purposes in the year of assessment.

(3) Persons whose earnings are not "immediately derived" from carrying on a trade, profession or vocation (for example, sleeping partners and, probably, limited partners).

(4) A child under 16 on 6th April of the year of assessment.

(5) Persons not ordinarily self employed (see above as for Class 2 contributions).

*Calculation of liability for married persons and partnerships*

The Class 4 liability of a husband and wife is calculated separately although the liability is that of the husband. If however a husband or wife has elected to be assessed separately for income tax purposes, or if they have jointly elected that the wife's earned income should be taxed as if she were a single person, the election will also apply for Class 4 purposes. This means that the Class 4 contributions of the wife will be assessed on, and collected from, her instead of her husband.

As regards partnerships, each partner's liability is calculated separately, and the Inland Revenue will normally collect each partner's Class 4 liability in the partnership name as is the case with the income tax liability of the partnership under Schedule D. If a partner also carries on another trade or profession, the profits of all such businesses are aggregated for the purposes of calculating his Class 4 liability; in these circumstances the Class 4 liability in respect of his share of partnership profits may be assessed separately and not in the partnership name.

When an assessment has become final and conclusive for the purposes of income tax, it is also final and conclusive for the purposes of calculating Class 4 liability.

## SOURCES OF FURTHER INFORMATION

Further information can be obtained from the many booklets published by the Department of Social Security, and from Accountants Digest No. 228 published by The Institute of Chartered Accountants in England and Wales. Individuals resident abroad should address their enquiries to the D.S.S. Overseas Branch, Newcastle-upon-Tyne, NE98 1YX.

# Social Security Benefits

K. D. BARTLETT, F.C.A.
*Chartered Accountant*

Social security benefits are quite difficult to understand. There are many leaflets produced by the Department of Health and Social Security and this article is written to try to simplify some of the more usual benefits that are available under the Social Security Acts. It deliberately does not cover every aspect of the legislation but the references given should enable the relevant information to be easily traced. These references are to the leaflets issued by the Department of Health and Social Security.

It is usual for only one periodical benefit to be payable at any one time. If the contribution conditions are satisfied for more than one benefit it is the larger benefit that is payable. Benefit rates shown below are those payable from week commencing 10th April 1989.

Employed persons (Category A contributors) are covered for all benefits. Certain married women and widows (Category B contributors) who elected to pay at the reduced rate receive only attendance allowance, guardian's allowance and industrial injuries benefits. Other benefits may be available dependent on their husbands' contributions.

Self-employed persons (Class 2 and Class 4 contributors) are covered for all benefits except earnings-related supplements, unemployment benefit, widow's and invalidity pensions and widowed mother's allowance.

The major changes, which take place from the week beginning 10th April 1989, are:

(1) An extra £70 million, on top of general increases, to help over three million children in the poorest families.

(2) To mark the 10th anniversary of Motability, the Government will contribute £5 million to a special trust fund to match a £5 million contribution from the private sector.

(3) Extra help with heating in very cold weather.

(4) Contributory and similar benefits to be increased by the retail price index of 5.9 per cent (more in some cases due to a minor error correction in the calculation of the RP1 in an earlier period).

(5) A once and for all adjustment to income support levels to help meet the minimum 20 per cent contribution which recipients will have to make to the community charge.

(6) No increase in child benefit but additional increases for the child allowances and premiums in income support, family credit and housing benefit.

## FAMILY BENEFITS

### Child Benefits (CH 1)

Child Benefit is payable for all children who are either under 16 or under 19 and receiving full-time education at a recognised educational establishment. The rate is £7.25 a week per child. It is payable to the person who is responsible for the child but excludes foster parents or people exempt from United Kingdom tax. A higher benefit (£5.20 a week more) is payable for the first or only child in a one parent family.

## Maternity Benefits

Help with maternity expenses is given to selected people from the Social Fund. To be eligible the claimant must be receiving Income Support or Family Credit. £85 is paid for each new or adopted baby reduced by the amount of any savings over £500 held by the claimant or his or her family.

## Maternity Pay

Statutory Maternity Pay (SMP) was introduced for female employees who leave employment because of pregnancy.

SMP is applicable to those who have worked for 26 weeks by the 15th week before the expected date of confinement. This 15th week is known as the qualifying week (Q.W.). The other qualifying conditions are that the woman must:
(1) be pregnant at the 11th week before the expected week of confinement, or already have been confined
(2) have stopped working for her employer wholly or partly because of pregnancy or confinement;
(3) have average earnings of not less than the lower earnings limit for the payment of National Insurance Contributions which is in force during her Q.W;
(4) provide her employer with evidence of her expected week of confinement;
(5) provide her employer with notice of her maternity absence.

## Rates of SMP

There is a higher and a lower rate. The higher rate of SMP is 90% of an employee's weekly earnings and is paid for the first 6 weeks for which there is entitlement to SMP. To be eligible for the higher rate, a woman must meet all the qualifying conditions and have been employed by the employer for a continuous period of at least two years if she worked for more than 16 hours a week. Her service must continue into the Q.W.

The lower rate of SMP is a set rate reviewed each year. The rate for the tax year beginning 6th April 1989 is £36.25 per week. It is paid for 18 weeks to those not entitled to the higher amount and for up to 12 weeks to those who receive the higher rate for the first 6 weeks.

SMP is taxable and also subject to National Insurance contributions. The gross amount of SMP and the employer's portion of National Insurance payable on the SMP can be recovered from the State by deducting the amounts from the amount normally due for PAYE and National Insurance deductions payable to the Collector of Taxes.

## Guardian's Allowance (NI 14)

This is paid at the rate of £8.95 a week to people who have taken orphans into their own family. Usually both of the child's parents must be dead and at least one of them must have satisfied a residence condition.

The allowance can only be paid to the person who is entitled to child benefit for the child (or to that person's spouse). It is not necessary to be the legal guardian. The claim should be made within three months of the date of entitlement.

# BENEFITS FOR HANDICAPPED OR DISABLED PEOPLE

## Mobility Allowance (NI 211)

This is a non-contributory benefit payable to persons aged between 5 and 65 who are unable to walk because of physical disablement. The allowance is £24.40 per week. It is not taxable.

*Attendance Allowance* (NI 205)

This is payable to persons aged 2 or over who are so severely disabled physically or mentally that they require frequent attention during the day or night or frequent attention for both day and night. A higher rate (£34.90 a week) is payable if attention is required day and night and a lower rate of £23.30 is payable if attention is required only in the day or in the night. The attendance allowance board decide whether, and for how long, a person is eligible for this allowance. Attendance allowance is not taxable.

## BENEFITS FOR THE ILL OR UNEMPLOYED

*Statutory Sick Pay* (NI 27, NI 16 and NI 244)

In the majority of cases the employer now has the responsibility of paying Sick Pay to its employees. The payment is dependent on satisfying various conditions in respect of periods of incapacity, periods of entitlement, qualifying days and rules on notification of absence. The rules are quite complicated and reference should be made to the relevant booklets for further clarification but the key points are:

(1) Payment is made by the employer.
(2) There is a possibility of two rates of payment dependent on the employee's gross average earnings.
(3) The employee must not be capable of work and must do no work on the day concerned.
(4) SSP is not usually payable for the first three working days.
(5) The maximum entitlement is 28 weeks in any period of incapacity.
(6) Notification must be made by the employer but this procedure must be within statutory guidelines.
(7) Payment can be withheld if notification of sickness is not given in due time.

The employer can recover the gross amount of SSP paid together with the 7% of all SSP payments made in respect of 1988/89, as compensation for their share of National Insurance Contributions paid on SSP.

*Invalidity Benefit* (NI 16A)

An invalidity pension is substituted for sickness benefit or SSP after this has been paid for 168 days of incapacity. To qualify one must be unable to work and have been entitled to sickness benefit for 168 days in a period of interruption of employment. This pension is currently £43.60 a week.

An invalidity allowance is payable with invalidity pension to those who are more than 5 years away from retirement age. The rates are as follows:

Standard rate of invalidity pension:

|  | £ |
|---|---|
| Single person | 43.60 |
| Spouse or adult dependant | 26.40 |

Invalidity allowance:

|  |  | £ |
|---|---|---|
| (i) | Higher rate | 9.20 |
| (ii) | Middle rate | 5.80 |
| (iii) | Lower rate | 2.90 |

For each dependent child £8.95 is payable.

*Severe Disablement Allowance* (NI 252)

This is a benefit for people under pensionable age who cannot work because of physical or mental ill health and do not have sufficient NI contributions to qualify for sickness or invalidity benefit. The basic allowance is £26.20 a week. There are increases of £15.65 a week for adult dependants and £8.95 for each dependent child.

*Invalid Care Allowance* (NI 212)

This is a taxable benefit paid to people of working age who cannot take a job because they have to stay at home to look after a severely disabled person.

*Unemployment Benefit* (NI 12)

Unemployment benefit is payable for a maximum period of one year in any period of interruption of employment. Once this year's unemployment pay is reached a claimant cannot qualify again until he has worked as an employee for at least 13 weeks and has worked in each of these weeks for 16 hours or more.

To be eligible the claimant must be unemployed but available for work but can be disqualified from receiving benefit for a period of up to 6 weeks if he lost his employment without just cause or failed to accept suitable employment offered.

Unemployment benefit is not payable for the first three days of a period of interruption of employment, in the same way as for sickness benefit.

Persons over 18 should register for work at their local Employment Office or Job Centre and should go to their local unemployment benefit office to claim benefit. Either a P45 or a note of their national insurance number should be produced. Persons under 18 should register for work at their local Youth Employment Office. Unemployment benefit is reduced, pound for pound, for those whose pensions exceed £35 a week.

The standard rate of unemployment benefit is £34.70 for a single person and £21.20 for a wife or other adult dependant.

## PENSIONS AND WIDOW'S BENEFITS (NP 23, NP 35, NP 31)

The State Pension is divided into two parts—the basic pension, presently £43.60 per week for a single person or £69.80 per week for a married couple, and the State Earnings Related Pension Scheme, which will after it matures on the present basis pay a pension of 25% of revalued earnings between the lower and upper earnings limits.

The cost of the State Earnings Related Pension Scheme (SERPS) has been a major political consideration for some time. In order to reduce the long term cost of the Scheme, benefits will be reduced for those retiring or widowed after the year 2000. The benefits will be reduced as follows:

(1) The pension will be based on lifetime average earnings rather than the best 20 years as at present.

(2) The pension will be calculated on the basis of 20% of earnings between the lower and upper earnings limit rather than 25%. This will be phased in over 10 years from the tax year 2000/2001.

(3) Presently all of a member's State Earnings Related Benefit is inherited by a surviving spouse. For deaths occurring after April 2000 this will be reduced to 50%.

Women paying standard rate contributions into the Scheme are eligible for the same amount of pension as men but five years earlier, from age 60. If a woman stays at home to bring up her children or to look after a person receiving attendance allowance she can have her basic pension rights protected without paying contributions.

The widow's pension and widowed mother's allowance also consists of a basic pension and an additional earnings related pension. The full amount of the additional pension applies only if the husband has contributed to the new Scheme for at least 20 years.

*Widow's Benefits*

From 11th April 1988 there are three main widow's benefits:
(1) Widow's payment, which has replaced the widow's allowance which has been abolished;
(2) Widowed mother's allowance;
(3) Widow's pension.

Widow's payment

This is a new allowance, curently a lump sum payment of £1,000 payable to widows who were bereaved on or after 11th April 1988. It is payable immediately on the death of the husband. Entitlement to this benefit is based on the late husband's contribution record but no payment will be made if the widow is living with another man as husband and wife at the date of death. The late husband must have actually paid contributions on earnings of at least 25 times the weekly or lower earnings limit for a given tax year in any tax year ending before his death (or ending before he reached pensionable age if he was over 65 when he died). The equivalent number of Class 2 or voluntary Class 3 contributions will be sufficient.

When claiming, the widow should complete the form on the back of the death certificate and send it to the local social security office. On receipt of this information the DHSS will send the claimant a more detailed form (BD8) which, once completed, has to go back to the social security office. It is important to claim the benefit within twelve months of the husband's death.

Widowed mother's allowance (NP 45)

If a widow is left with children to look after she is entitled to a widowed mother's allowance provided that her late husband had paid sufficient national insurance contributions. These contributions are:
(a) 25 Class 1, 2 or 3 contributions before age 65 and before 6th April 1975; or
(b) contributions in any one tax year after 6th April 1975 on earnings of at least 25 times the weekly lower earnings limit for that year.

It is important that the widow is looking after either her own child or her husband's child and that the child is under 16 or, if between the age of 16 and 19, is continuing in full-time education.

The allowance stops immediately if the widow remarries and will be suspended if she lives with a man as his wife. From 10th April 1989 the amounts payable are as follows:

|  | £ |
|---|---|
| Basic allowance | 43.60 |
| Increase for a child | 8.95 |

Where a husband's contributions only satisfied the first test above, the basic allowance may be payable at a reduced rate. This reduction does not alter the rate of an increase for a child.

Widow's pension (NP 45)

A widow who is over the age of 45 when her husband dies may be eligible for a widow's pension unless she is eligible for the widowed mother's allowance. In this situation the widow's pension becomes payable when the widowed mother's allowance ends, provided she is still under the age of 65. However, where a woman had been receiving widowed mother's allowance, she becomes entitled to a widow's pension if she is between the ages of 45 and 65 when the allowance ends, no matter what her age may have been when her husband died. Before 11th April 1988 a widow aged 40 or over could qualify for a widow's pension.

*Qualification conditions*
(a) The contributions conditions must be satisfied and these conditions are the same as those for the widowed mother's allowance above.
(b) The widow must not be receiving the widowed mother's allowance.
(c) When her husband died she was aged between 45 and 65 or she was entitled to widowed mother's allowance and is aged between 45 and 65 when her widowed mother's allowance finished.

*Cessation of Widow's Pension*
(a) Entitlement finishes if the widowed mother's allowance stops because she has remarried.
(b) Widow's pension must not be claimed when the payment of the widowed mother's allowance has been suspended because the widow is in pension or is living with a man as his wife.

From 10th April 1989 the amount payable is as follows:

|  | £ |
|---|---|
| Basic pension | 43.60 |
| Increase for each dependent child for whom child benefit is payable | 8.95 |

From 11th April 1988 both the basic and additional pension will be paid at a reduced rate if the widow was aged under 55:

(a) when her husband died, if she did not subsequently become entitled to widowed mother's allowance; or
(b) when her widowed mother's allowance ceased to be paid. The relevant rates from April 1989 are as follows:

| *Age related* | £ |
|---|---|
| Age 54 | 40.55 |
| 53 | 37.50 |
| 52 | 34.44 |
| 51 | 31.39 |
| 50 | 28.34 |
| 49 | 25.29 |
| 48 | 22.24 |
| 47 | 19.18 |
| 46 | 16.13 |
| 45 | 13.08 |

*Funeral Expenses*
The death grant was abolished from 6th April 1987. It has been replaced by a payment from the Social Fund where the claimant is in receipt of Supplementary Benefit, Family Income Supplement or Housing Benefit. The full cost of a reasonable funeral is paid, reduced by any savings over £500 held by the claimant or his family.

## FAMILY CREDIT

Family credit replaced family income supplement (FIS) with effect from 11th April 1988. Family credit is a tax-free benefit payable to families in Great Britain where:
(1) the claimant or partner is engaged in remunerative work for 24 hours or more per week; and

(2) there is at least one child under 16 in the family (or under 19 if in full-time education up to and including A level or OND standard) for whom the claimant and/or partner is responsible.

Entitlement to family credit is determined by comparing the family's normal income with a prescribed amount, known as the "applicable amount". The current applicable amount is £54.80. Eligible families fall into two income groups:
(i) those whose total income does not exceed the applicable amount. Such families will be entitled to the appropriate maximum amount of family credit payable; and
(ii) those whose total income does exceed the applicable amount but by an amount which still allows some entitlement. To determine eligibility, a prescribed percentage (currently 70%) of the excess income (over and above the applicable amount) is deducted from the appropriate maximum family credit. If there is an amount left (i.e. the figure is a plus sum of at least 50p) the family will be able to receive family credit equal to this amount, rounded to the nearest penny.

*Maximum family credit benefit rates (from 10th April 1989)*

| | |
|---|---|
| Adult | £33.60 |
| Child | |
| aged less than 11 years | £ 7.30 |
| aged 11 to 15 years | £12.90 |
| Young Person | |
| aged 16–17 years | £16.35 |
| aged 18 years | £23.30 |

An award is normally made for a period of 26 weeks. Changes of circumstances during this period will not usually affect the award.

*Capital and income*

Families where the claimant and partner together hold capital in excess of £6,000 will not be entitled to family credit.    The resources of a family taken into account as income for family credit are the aggregate of their normal net earnings and other income plus any tariff income. Certain payments are disregarded in the calculation of income.

## INCOME SUPPORT (SB1, SB20)

Income support has replaced supplementary benefit. It is usually only payable to eligible persons who are unemployed or people who work less than 24 hours a week. If a person or partner works for 24 hours or more on average per week in "remunerative" work, then no income support is payable.

Income support gives financial assistance towards regular weekly needs only. Claimants with exceptional needs will now have to apply for payments (in the form of a loan or grant) from the social fund.

The person's income must be insufficient to bring him up to the designated minimum level of income, known as the "applicable amount". The applicable amount is made up of a "basic" personal allowance plus "additional" premiums for those with additional needs, e.g. pensioners. People who are entitled to income support and who have no income at all will be entitled to the appropriate applicable amount in full. Those who have an income will receive income support equal to the difference between their income and the appropriate applicable amount.

As with supplementary benefit, there is a limit to the amount of capital a person can hold before income support is affected. Those who have capital above £6,000 are disqualified from receiving income support altogether.

As in the case of supplementary benefit, eligibility for income support is, in most instances, dependent on the claimant being "available for work". Where a person is disqualified from receiving unemployment benefit (or would be if it were otherwise payable), for such reasons as being dismissed from his or her former job because of misconduct, entitlement to income support will also be affected.

## GRANTS FROM LOCAL AUTHORITIES

### *Housing Benefit* (RR1)

Housing benefit is the scheme which helps people pay their rent and/or rates. Both the local council and the DHSS are involved in running the scheme, which affects about one in three households. Anyone can apply, including pensioners, the unemployed or those in work. Housing Benefit can be paid to Council housing associations or private tenants, or owner occupiers. It is possible to receive Housing Benefit either by a reduction in rent or rates or by receiving a rent allowance. One should apply to the DHSS first of all, which will ensure the earliest possible start to any benefit you might receive. The DHSS will then advise the Council to see if you are eligible for Supplementary Benefit, so that the Housing Department can arrange the Housing Benefit. Alternatively if the claimant is not eligible for Supplementary Benefit then he should complete a Standard Housing Benefit claim form and return it to the Housing Department.

The above does not set out to cover every aspect of the Social Security Acts Legislation.

Further information can be obtained from the local office of the Department of Health and Social Security or from Accountants Digest No. 225 published by the Institute of Chartered Accountants in England and Wales. Readers resident abroad who have queries should write to the Department's Overseas Branch, Newcastle upon Tyne, NE98 1YX.

# Law and regulations

## British Copyright Law

### AMANDA L. MICHAELS, M.A.

## INTRODUCTION

Copyright is a creature of statute. There have been a series of Copyright Acts over the years, gradually extending the scope of this area of the law so as to offer protection to the expanding types of media used by writers, artists and communicators of all types.

On 1st August 1989, the Copyright Act 1956, previously the major Act in this field, was replaced by the Copyright, Designs and Patents Act 1988 ("the Act"). The Act sets out to restate the law of copyright. Much of the law in it is a true restatement of the pre-existing law, especially in so far as it relates to the essentials of what may be a copyright work and how it may be protected. To this end, section 172 of the Act in particular provides that mere changes of expression from the old law shall not be taken as denoting a substantive change in the law, whilst prior decisions may be referred to as an aid to construction of the new Act.

However, there is a good deal in the new Act which is innovatory (see, for instance, the comments below on the new design right, and the repercussions upon infringement actions of section 51 in the section on infringement), as well as a number of provisions where one might well ask whether all that is intended is a change of expression from the old law, or whether a change of words implies a change of substance.

The general reader should therefore be aware that the old law, and old texts on the subject, may not apply to new copyright works. There are also complicated transitional provisions (in Schedule 1 to the Act) relating to pre-existing works and infringements, and reference may need to be made to these and to the old law for some years to come. Users of this handbook may particularly need to note that forms of publishing and licensing agreements suitable for use under the old law may need revision in the light of the new Act.

In an article of this length, it will not be possible to deal fully with all the changes in the law effected by the new Act, nor indeed with all the complexities of this technical area of the law. The purpose of the article is rather to set out the basic principles of copyright protection, and to indicate the areas which may be of particular interest to readers of this general handbook, whilst issuing a general warning that there are numerous matters which are not dealt with.

## WORKS CAPABLE OF COPYRIGHT PROTECTION

Copyright protection has always protected the *form* in which the artist/author has set out his inspiration, not the underlying idea. So, plots, artistic ideas, systems and themes cannot be protected by copyright. Whilst an idea remains no more than that, it can be protected only by the law relating to confidential information (see, e.g., the case of *Fraser* v. *Thames TV Ltd* [1984] QB 44: plot of a projected TV series). The law of copyright prevents the copying of the material form in which the idea has been presented, or of a substantial part thereof, measured in terms of quality, not quantity.

The Act therefore starts out, in section 1, by setting out a number of different categories of works which can be the subject of copyright protection. These are:
  (a) original literary, dramatic, musical or artistic works,
  (b) sound recordings, films, broadcasts, or cable programmes, and
  (c) typographical arrangements of published editions.

These works are further defined in sections 3 to 8. The definitions are not identical to those in the 1956 Act. A literary work, for instance, is defined as: "any work, other than a dramatic or musical work, which is written, spoken or sung, and accordingly includes: (a) a table or compilation, and (b) a computer program." A musical work means: "a work consisting of music, exclusive of any words or action intended to be sung, spoken or performed with the music." An artistic work means: "(a) a graphic work, photograph, sculpture or collage, irrespective of artistic quality, (b) a work of architecture being a building or model for a building, (c) a work of artistic craftsmanship."

The definitions of literary and musical works should not mislead one into thinking that, contrary to the basic rule that copyright protects the form and not the idea, works can be protected *before* being reduced into tangible form. Section 3 (2) specifically provides that no copyright shall subsist in a literary, musical or artistic work until it has been recorded in writing or otherwise.

On the other hand, all that is required to achieve copyright protection is to record the original work in any appropriate medium. Once that has been done (assuming that the qualifying features set out below are present) copyright will subsist in the work without any formality of registration or otherwise. As long as the work is produced in some tangible form there is, for instance, no need for it to be published in any way for the protection to attach to it. (Please note, however, that although this lack of formality applies here and in most European countries, the law of the USA does differ—see article: **U.S. Copyright**). The common idea that one must register a work at Stationers Hall, or send it to oneself or to, say, a bank, in a sealed envelope is misleading in so far as it implies that one will not have any copyright protection if one fails to do this. All that this precaution may do is provide some proof in an infringement action (whether as plaintiff or defendant) of the date of creation of one's work.

## ORIGINALITY

Section 1 provides that, in order to gain copyright protection, literary, dramatic, artistic and musical works must be original. Similarly, there are provisions which exclude from copyright protection sound recordings or films which are mere copies of pre-existing sound recordings and films, broadcasts which infringe rights in another broadcast or cable programmes which consist of immediate retransmissions of broadcasts.

The test of originality for other types of works may not be quite that expected by the layman. Over a number of years, the courts have held that a work need not be original in the sense of showing innovative or cultural merit, but that it needs only to have been the product of skill and labour on the part of the author, although merely making a "slavish copy" of a drawing does not count: see *Interlego AG* v. *Tyco Industries* [1988] 1 WLR 678. This can be seen from various sections in the Act, for instance in the definition of certain artistic works, and in the fact that it offers copyright protection to works such as compilations (like football pools coupons or directories) and tables (including mathematical tables).

On the other hand, "works" comprising the titles of books or periodicals, or advertising slogans, which may have required a good deal of original thought, generally are not accorded copyright protection, because they are too short to be deemed literary works.

See, too, the limited protection given to drawings of a functional or engineering type in the sections on infringement and design right below.

## QUALIFICATION

The Act is limited in its effects to the UK (and to colonies to which it may be extended by Order in Council). It is aimed primarily at protecting the works of British citizens, or works which were first published here. However, in line with the requirements of various international conventions to which the UK is a party, copyright protection in the UK is also accorded to the works of nationals of many foreign states which are also party to these conventions, as well as to works first published in those states.

The importance of these rules (which largely repeat similar provisions of the 1956 Act) mainly arises when one is trying to find out whether a pre-existing foreign work is protected by copyright here: for instance, if one wishes to make a film based upon a foreign novel. Within the confines of this article, all that can be said is that there have been numerous different Orders in Council regulating the position for most of the major countries of the world, including the other member states of the EEC and the USA, and further Orders continue to be made, but that in every case it will be wise to check the position.

## OWNERSHIP

The general rule is that a work will initially be owned by its author, the author being the creator of the work, or in the case of a film or sound recording, the person who makes the arrangements necessary for it to be made.

One essential exception to the general rule is that the copyright in a work of an employee produced in the course of his employment will belong to his employer, subject to any agreement to the contrary.

There can be joint authorship of a work where the work is produced by several people in such collaboration that the contribution of one is not distinct from the contribution of the other. Thus, where two people collaborate to write a song, one producing the lyrics and the other the music, there will be two separate works, owned by each of them separately. But where two people write a play, each rewriting what the other produces, there will be a joint work. The importance of knowing whether the work is joint or not arises firstly in working out the duration of the copyright (see below) and secondly from the fact that joint works can only be exploited with the agreement of all the joint authors (i.e., all of them have to join in any licence), although each of them can sue for infringement.

## DURATION OF COPYRIGHT

Copyright in a literary, dramatic, artistic or musical work expires fifty years after the end of the calendar year in which the author dies. If there were joint authors, the fifty-year period will run from the end of the year in which the last of them dies. However, there is an important exception to this general rule in the case of artistic works which have been industrially exploited, limiting the length of copyright protection to twenty-five years from the date of first marketing of articles made according to the design (see section 52).

If the author is unknown, the copyright will expire fifty years after the work is first made available to the public, by being performed, broadcast, exhibited, etc, depending upon the nature of the work (see section 12(2) of the Act).

If the work is "computer-generated", copyright will expire fifty years from the date when the work was made. Copyright in a typeface runs for only twenty-five years from when it was first published.

Sound recordings will lose their copyright fifty years from the end of the year in which they are made, unless they have been released during that period, when they will enjoy copyright protection for fifty years after release. Similarly, copyright in broadcasts will expire fifty years after the end of the year in which they are made and that in cable programmes, fifty years after they are included in a cable programme.

These provisions are not identical with those under earlier Acts. For instance, in the 1956 Act photographs were protected for only fifty years from publication, whereas now they are treated like all other artistic works. Where one is dealing with works made before the Act came into force, one will need to look firstly at the substantive provisions of the relevant old law, to see whether the work enjoyed copyright protection immediately before the Act came into force, and then at the transitional provisions to be found in Schedule 1 of the Act (and in some cases also the similar transitional provisions of the 1956 Act itself, found in Schedule 7 thereof). The need to check the duration of any protection will be particularly strong where an industrial design is concerned.

## DEALING WITH COPYRIGHT WORKS: ASSIGNMENT AND LICENSING

As will be seen below, ownership of the copyright in a work gives the exclusive right to deal with the work in a number of ways, and essentially stops all unauthorised exploitation of the work. Copyright works can be exploited by their owners in two ways. To put it at its most simple, the whole right in the work may be sold, with the owner retaining no interest therein (except, possibly, for payment); this is what is known as assignment. Alternatively, the owner may grant a licence to another to exploit the right, whilst retaining overall ownership. Agreements dealing with copyright should make it clear whether it is an assignment or a licence which is being granted, and should clearly define the scope of any assignment or licence. The question of the new moral rights (see below) will also have to be considered by parties negotiating an assignment or licence.

An assignment must be in writing, signed by or on behalf of the assignor, but no other formality is required. One can make an assignment of future copyright (under section 91). Where the author of a projected work agrees that he will assign the rights in the future work to another, the copyright vests in the assignee immediately upon the creation of the work without further formalities. This facility may be used where works are commissioned from the author, as the specific provisions as to ownership of commissioned works which existed in the 1956 Act are not reproduced as such in the new Act, save in respect of works protected by the new design right (see below). Writing will be required to bring the section into effect.

These rules do not, apparently, affect the pre-existing law on beneficial interests in copyright. Essentially, these rules were applied where someone had been commissioned to create a work for another, in circumstances in which copyright did not vest automatically in the latter, but the court found that it was the parties' mutual intention that the copyright should belong to the "commissioner". Their effect was that the court would hold that the "commissioner" was the equitable or beneficial owner of the copyright, and the author was obliged to assign the copyright to him.

Rights may be assigned by will, and where a bequest is given of an original document, etc., embodying an unpublished copyright work, the bequest will carry the copyright.

Licences do not need to take any form in particular, and may indeed be granted orally. However, an exclusive licence (i.e., one which excludes even the copyright owner himself from exploiting the work in the manner foreseen by the licence) must be in writing, if the licensee is to enjoy rights in respect of infringements concurrent with those of the copyright owner.

Both assignments and licences can, and most frequently do, split up the various rights contained within the copyright. So, for instance, a licence might be granted to one person to publish a novel in hardback and to another to publish in softback, to a third person might be granted the film, television and video rights, and to yet a fourth the right to translate the novel into other languages.

In practice, assignments may, and licences probably will, often confer rights according to territory, dividing the USA from the EEC or different EEC countries one from the other. Two comments must be made about this. Firstly, it must be appreciated that such an agreement would be dealing with a bundle of different national copyrights, as each country's law generally extends only to its own borders; it must be noted that each country's law on copyright protection, on licensing and on infringement may differ. Secondly, when purporting to divide rights between different territories of the EEC there is a danger that one will infringe the competition rules of the EEC (in the main Articles 30–36 and 85–86 of the Treaty of Rome), and professional advice should be taken to ensure that one is not in breach of these rules, which would render the parties liable to large fines, as well as making the agreement void in whole or in part.

Licences can also, of course, be of varying lengths. There is no need for a licence to be granted for the whole term of copyright; indeed this would be unusual, if not foolish. Well-drafted licences will provide for termination on breach, including the failure of the licensee to exploit the work properly, and on the bankruptcy or winding up of the licensee.

## INFRINGEMENT

Copyright is infringed by doing any of a number of specified acts in relation to the copyright work, without the authority of the owner. In all forms of infringement, it suffices if a substantial part of the original is used, and the question is one to be judged according to quality not quantity (see, e.g., *Ravenscroft* v. *Herbert* [1980] RPC 193).

The form of infringement common to all forms of copyright works is that of copying. This means reproducing the work in any material form.

In the case of a two-dimensional artistic work, reproduction can mean making a copy in three dimensions, and vice versa, although there is an important limitation on this general rule in section 51 of the Act, which provides that in the case of a "design document or model" (defined as a record of a design of any aspect of the shape or configuration, internal or external, of the whole or part of an article, other than surface decoration) for something which is not itself an artistic work according to the definition given above, it shall be no infringement to make an article to that design. This would appear to mean that whilst it would be an infringement to make an article from a design drawing for, say, a sculpture, it will not be an infringement to make a handbag from a copy of the design drawing therefor, or from a handbag which one has purchased. In order to protect such designs one will have to rely upon the new design right or upon a registered design (for both see below). However, under the transitional provisions, the right to rely upon copyright protection for any such designs made before commencement of the new Act will continue until 1st August 1999 (see Schedule 1, para. 19).

Copying of a film, broadcast or cable programme can include making a copy of the whole or a substantial part of any one image forming part thereof (see section 17(4)). Presumably this means that copying one frame of the film would be an infringement, as it was under the previous law (see *Spelling Goldberg Productions* v. *BPC* [1981] RPC 283).

Copying is generally proved by showing substantial similarities between the original and the alleged copy, plus an opportunity to copy. Surprisingly often, minor errors in the original are reproduced by an infringer.

Copying need not be direct, so that, for instance, where the copyright is in a fabric design, copying of the material, without ever having seen the original drawing, will still be an infringement.

Issuing copies of a work to the public when it has not previously been put into circulation in the UK is also an infringement of all types of work.

Other acts which may amount to an infringement depend upon the nature of the work. It will be an infringement of the copyright in a literary, dramatic or musical work to perform it in public, whether by live performance or by recordings, etc. Similarly, it is an infringement of the copyright in a sound recording, film, broadcast or cable programme to play or show it in public.

One rather different form of infringement is to make an adaptation of a literary, dramatic or musical work. An adaptation includes, in the case of a literary work, a translation, in the case of a non-dramatic work, making a dramatic work of it, and in the case of a dramatic work, making a non-dramatic work of it. An adaptation of a musical work is a transcription or arrangement of it.

There are also a number of "secondary" infringements. These consist not of making the infringing copies, but of dealing with them in some way. So, it is an infringement to import an infringing copy into the UK, and to possess in the course of business, or to sell, hire, offer for sale or hire, or distribute in the course of trade an infringing copy. However, none of these acts will be an infringement unless the alleged infringer knew or had reason to believe that the articles were infringing copies.

Other secondary infringements consist of permitting a place to be used for a public performance in which copyright is infringed and supplying apparatus to be used for infringing public performance, again, in each case, with safeguards for innocent acts.

## EXCEPTIONS TO INFRINGEMENT

The Act provides a large number of exceptions to the rules on infringement, many of which are innovatory. They are, indeed, far too numerous to be dealt with here in full. However, they include:
- fair dealing with literary, dramatic, musical or artistic works for the purpose of research or private study;
- fair dealing for the purpose of criticism or review;
- incidental inclusion of a work in an artistic work, sound recording, film, broadcast, or cable programme;
- various educational exceptions (see sections 32–36);
- various exceptions for libraries (see sections 37–44);
- various exceptions for public administration (see sections 45-50);

- dealing with a work where the author cannot be identified and the work seems likely to be out of copyright;
- public recitation, if accompanied by a sufficient acknowledgement;
- recording broadcasts or cable programmes at home for use at a more convenient time.

## REMEDIES FOR INFRINGEMENT

The copyright owner has all the remedies offered to other owners of property. Usually the owner will want one or both of two things: firstly, to stop the infringement continuing and, secondly, compensation.

In almost all cases, at trial an injunction will be sought, stopping the continuation of the infringement. Where an infringement is threatened, the courts will in appropriate cases make a "quia timet" injunction to prevent the infringement ever taking place. A very useful remedy offered by the courts is the "interlocutory injunction". This is a form of interim relief, applied for at short notice, with a view to stopping a damaging infringement at an early stage, without having to await the outcome of a full trial. Interlocutory injunctions are not always granted in copyright cases, but it is generally worth considering the matter when first an infringement comes to notice (delay in bringing the interlocutory application may be fatal to its success).

Otherwise, financial compensation may be sought in one of two forms. Firstly, damages may be granted for infringement. These will usually be calculated upon evidence of the loss caused to the plaintiff, frequently upon the basis of what would have been a proper licence fee had the defendant sought a licence for the acts complained of. Additional damages may be awarded in rare cases for flagrant infringements.

Under the old law, a plaintiff could also claim conversion damages, which were often assessed at a much higher level than infringement damages. However, these cannot be claimed under the Act.

Damages will not be awarded, in any event, for infringements where the infringer did not know, and had no reason to believe, that copyright subsisted in the work. This exception may of course be hard to rely upon where, although the infringer had no actual knowledge of the copyright, the work was of such a nature that he should have known that copyright would subsist in it.

An alternative to a claim for damages will be a claim for an account of profits; this is an equitable remedy, however, and is therefore discretionary.

A copyright owner may also apply for delivery up of the infringing copies (sections 99 and 113–15).

Finally, there are various criminal offences relating to the making, importation, possession, sale, hire, distribution, etc., of infringing copies (see sections 107–10).

## DESIGN RIGHT

Many industrial designs previously protected by copyright will now be effectively excluded from relying on copyright, by reason of the provisions of section 51 of the Act, described in INFRINGEMENT above. However, many such designs will instead be protected by the new "design right" created by sections 213–64 of the Act.

The protection of the new right will be given to original designs consisting of the shape or configuration (internal or external) of the whole or part of an article. A design is not to be considered original if it was commonplace in the design field in question at the time of its creation. Nor will designs be protected if they consist of a method or principle of construction, or are dictated by the shape, etc., of an article to which the new article is to be connected or of which it is to form part.

The new right will be granted only to designs made by qualifying persons (in this part of the Act meaning UK and EEC citizens or residents or others to whom the right may be extended) or commissioned by a qualifying person, or first marketed in the UK, another EEC state or any other country to which the provision may be extended by Order in Council.

The design right lasts only fifteen years from the end of the year in which it was first recorded or an article made to the design, or (if shorter) ten years from the end of the year in which articles made according to the design were first sold or hired out.

The designer will be the owner of the right, unless he made it in pursuance of a commission, in which case the commissioner will be the first owner of the right. The same rule applies as in copyright, that an employee's designs made in the course of his employment will belong to the employer.

The right given to the owner of a design right is the exclusive right to reproduce the design for commercial purposes. The rules as to assignments and licensing and as to infringement, both primary and secondary, are substantially similar to those described above in relation to copyright, as are the remedies available.

This new design right will co-exist with the scheme of registered designs of the *Registered Designs Act* 1949 (as amended by the Act), which provides a monopoly right renewable for up to twenty-five years in respect of designs which have been accepted on to a register. Registered designs must contain features which appeal to and are judged by the eye, unlike designs protected by the design right.

## MORAL RIGHTS

Another new departure in the Act is the provision of "moral rights", commonly known as the rights of "paternity" and "integrity".

The right of "paternity" is for the author of a copyright literary, dramatic, musical or artistic work, and the director of a copyright film, to be identified as the author/director in a number of different situations, largely whenever the work is published, performed or otherwise commercially exploited (section 77).

However, the right does not arise unless it has been "asserted" by the author or director, by appropriate words in an assignment, or otherwise by an instrument in writing (section 78), or in the case of an artistic work by ensuring that the artist's name appears on the frame, etc. Writers should therefore aim to ensure that all copies of their works carry clear assertions of their rights under this provision, so that all who read their works are bound thereby (see below).

There are exceptions to the right, especially where, in particular, the first ownership of the copyright vested in the author's or director's employer.

The right of "integrity" is not to have one's work subjected to "derogatory treatment". This is defined as meaning an addition to, deletion from, alteration to, or adaptation of a work (save for a translation of a literary or dramatic work or an arrangement of a musical work involving no more than a change of key or register) which amounts to distortion or mutilation of the work or is otherwise prejudicial to the honour or reputation of the author/director.

Again, infringement of the right takes place when the maltreated work is published commercially or performed or exhibited in public. There are various exceptions set out in section 81 of the Act, in particular where the publication is in a newspaper, etc., and the work was made for inclusion therein or made available therefor with the author's consent.

Where the copyright in the work vested first in the author's or director's employer, he has no right to "integrity" unless he was identified at the time of the relevant act or was previously identified on published copies of the work.

These rights subsist for as long as the copyright in the work subsists.

The third moral right conferred by the Act is not to have a literary, dramatic, musical or artistic work falsely attributed to one as author, or to have a film falsely attributed to one as director, again where the work in question is published, publicly performed, etc.

This right subsists until twenty years after a person's death.

None of these rights can be assigned during the person's lifetime, but all of them will either pass on the person's death as directed by his will or will fall into his residuary estate.

A fourth but rather different moral right is conferred by section 85. It gives a person who has commissioned the taking of photographs for private purposes a right to prevent copies of the work being issued to the public, etc.

The remedies for breach of these moral rights are those for breach of a statutory duty. Both damages and an injunction can be sought in appropriate cases, although section 103(2) specifically foresees the granting of an injunction qualified by a right to the defendant to do the acts complained of, albeit subject to a suitable disclaimer.

## NOTICE

*I, AMANDA LOUISE MICHAELS, hereby assert and give notice of my right under section 77 of the Copyright, Designs and Patents Act 1988 to be identified as the author of the foregoing article.*

*AMANDA MICHAELS*

## FURTHER READING

*The Copyright Acts*

Copyright, Designs and Patents Act 1988, HMSO, £12.50 net
Design Copyright Act 1968, HMSO, 45p net
Copyright Act 1956, HMSO, £7.50 net
    Amendments: 1971 3p net; 1982 40p net; 1983 80p net
Cable and Broadcasting Act 1984, HMSO, £5.55 net
Copyright (Computer and Software) Amendment Act 1985, HMSO, 40p net
Copyright Act 1911, HMSO, £3.80 net

*Other books*

Black, T. *Intellectual Property in Industry*, Butterworths, 1989.
Dworkin, G. and Taylor, R. *Blackstone's Guide to the Copyright, Designs and Patents Act 1988*, Blackstone Press, 1989.
Laddie, Prescott and Vitoria. *The Modern Law of Copyright*, Butterworths, 1980. o.p. 2nd ed. in preparation; expected early 1990.
Skone James, E. P., J. F. Mummery and J. Rayner James. *Copinger and Skone James on Copyright*, Sweet and Maxwell, 12th ed, 1980. £120.00. 13th ed. in preparation; expected early 1990.

# U.S. Copyright

GAVIN McFARLANE, LL.M., PH.D.
*Barrister*

## THE SYSTEM OF INTERNATIONAL COPYRIGHT

*The international copyright conventions*
There is no general principle of international copyright which provides a uniform code for the protection of right owners throughout the world. There are however two major international copyright conventions which lay down certain minimum standards for member states, in particular requiring members to accord to right owners of other members the same protection which is granted to their own nationals. One is the higher standard Berne Convention of 1886, the most recent revision of which was signed in Paris in 1971. The other is the Universal Copyright Convention signed in 1952 with lower minimum standards, and sponsored by Unesco. This also was most recently revised in Paris in 1971, jointly with the Berne Convention. To this latter Convention the United States has belonged since 1955. On 16 November 1988, the Government of the United States deposited its instrument of accession to the Paris Revision of the Berne Convention. The Convention entered into force as regards the United States on 1 March 1989.

*Summary of the Universal Copyright Convention*
(1) The fundamental intent is to accord reciprocally in each member state to nationals of all other member states the same protection as that member grants to its own nationals.
(2) The minimum term of protection is the life of the author and twenty-five years after his death (by contrast with the Berne Convention which demands a term of the life of the author and a post-mortem period of fifty years).
(3) Any national requirement as a condition of copyright of such formalities as deposit, registration, notice, payment, or manufacture or publication within that state shall be satisfied for all works first published outside its territory and of which the author is not one of its nationals if all copies bear the symbol © accompanied by the name of the copyright owner and the year of first publication.
(4) Publication for the purposes of the Universal Convention means the reproduction in tangible form and the general distribution to the public of copies of a work from which it can be read or otherwise visually perceived.
(5) The effect of American ratification of the Universal Copyright Convention on 16 September 1955 was to alter completely the nature of the protection granted by the United States to copyright works originating abroad. The previous policy of American domestic law had been extremely restrictive for foreign authors, particularly those writing in the English language. But in consequence of ratification American law was amended to exempt from many of these restrictions works published in other member states, or by nationals of other member states. Recent amendments have relaxed the position even further.

*Effect on British copyright owners*
The copyright statute of the United States having been brought into line with the requirements of the Universal Copyright Convention, compliance with the formalities required by American law is all that is needed to acquire protection

for the work of a British author first published outside the United States. Even these formality requirements have been largely removed now that the United States has joined the Berne Convention.

## SUMMARY OF UNITED STATES COPYRIGHT LAW

### Introduction of new law

After many years of debate, the new Copyright Statute of the United States was passed on 19 October 1976. The greater part of its relevant provisions came into force on 1 January 1978. It has extended the range of copyright protection, and further eased the requirements whereby British authors can obtain copyright protection in America. New Public Law 100–568 of 31 October 1988 has made further amendments to the Copyright Statute which were necessary to enable ratification of the Berne Convention to take place.

### Works protected in American law

Works of authorship include the following categories:
(1) literary works;
*Note:* Computer programs are classified as literary works for the purposes of United States copyright. In *Whelan Associates Inc.* v. *Jaslow Dental Laboratory Inc.* (1987) F.S.R.1, it was held that the copyright of a computer program could be infringed even in the absence of copying of the literal code if the structure was part of the expression of the idea behind a program rather than the idea itself.
(2) musical works, including any accompanying words;
(3) dramatic works, including any accompanying music;
(4) pantomimes and choreographic works;
(5) pictorial, graphic and sculptural works;
(6) motion pictures and other audiovisual works;
(7) sound recordings, but copyright in sound recordings is not to include a right of public performance.

### The rights of a copyright owner

(1) To reproduce the copyrighted work in copies or phonorecords;
(2) to prepare derivative works based upon the copyrighted work;
(3) to distribute copies or phonorecords of the copyrighted work to the public by sale or other transfer of ownership, or by rental, lease or lending;
(4) in the case of literary, musical, dramatic and choreographic works, pantomimes, and motion pictures and other audiovisual works, but NOT sound recordings, to perform the copyrighted work publicly;
(5) in the case of literary, musical, dramatic, and choreographic works, pantomimes, and pictorial, graphic, or sculptural works, including the individual images of a motion picture or other audiovisual work, to display the copyrighted work publicly.
(6) By the Record Rental Amendment Act 1984, s.109 of the Copyright Statute is amended. Now, unless authorised by the owners of copyright in the sound recording and the musical works thereon, the owner of a phonorecord may not, for direct or indirect commercial advantage, rent, lease or lend the phonorecord. A compulsory licence under s.115(c) includes the right of a maker of a phonorecord of non-dramatic musical work to distribute or authorise the distribution of the phonorecord by rental, lease, or lending, and an additional royalty is payable in respect of that.
(7) The Semiconductor Chip Protection Act 1984 adds to the Copyright Statute a new chapter on the protection of semiconductor chip products.

*Manufacturing requirements*

With effect from 1 July 1982, these ceased to have effect. Prior to 1 July 1982, the importation into or public distribution in the United States of a work consisting preponderantly of non-dramatic literary material that was in the English language and protected under American law was prohibited unless the portions consisting of such material had been manufactured in the United States or Canada. This provision did not apply where, on the date when importation was sought or public distribution in the United States was made, the author of any substantial part of such material was not a national of the United States or, if a national, had been domiciled outside the United States for a continuous period of at least one year immediately preceding that date.

Thus since 1 July 1982, there is no manufacturing requirement in respect of works of British authors. Certain interested groups in the United States still lobby for the restoration of the manufacturing clause in American law. Countries such as Britain will no doubt oppose this vigorously through diplomatic channels. With American ratification of the Berne Convention, the formalities previously required in relation to copyright notice, deposit and registration have been greatly modified.

*Formalities: notice, deposit and registration*

(1) Notice of copyright

Whenever a work protected by the American Copyright Statute is published in the United States or elsewhere by authority of the copyright owner, a notice of copyright shall be placed on all publicly distributed copies. This shall consist of (i) either the symbol © or the word "Copyright" or the abbreviation "Copr." plus (ii) the year of first publication of the work, plus (iii) the name of the copyright owner.

(2) Deposit

Unless exempted by the Register of Copyrights, the owner of copyright or the exclusive right of publication in a work published with notice of copyright in the United States shall within three months of such publication deposit in the Copyright Office for the use or disposition of the Library of Congress two complete copies of the best edition of the work (or two records, if the work is a sound recording). Penalties are provided for failure to comply with the requirement of deposit.

(3) Registration

While deposit is mandatory, registration for copyright in the United States is optional. However, any owner of copyright in a work first published outside the United States may register a work by making application to the Copyright Office with the appropriate fee, and by depositing one complete copy of the work. This requirement of deposit may be satisfied by using copies deposited for the Library of Congress. But it is vital to note that no action may be brought for infringement of copyright in the United States until registration of the claim to copyright has been made according to the statutory provisions.

(*Note:* These requirements have been made discretionary now that the United States has joined the Berne Convention.)

*Duration of copyright*

An important change in the new American law is that in general, copyright in a work created on or after 1 January 1978 endures for a term of the life of the author, and a period of fifty years after the author's death. This brings the United States into line with most other advanced countries, and with the further amendments made by Public Law 100–568 of 31 October 1988 has enabled her government to ratify the higher standard Berne Convention. Copyright in a work created before 1 January 1978, but not published or copyrighted before then, subsists from 1 January 1978, and lasts for the life of the author and a post-mortem period of fifty years.

Any copyright, the first term of which under the previous law was still subsisting on 1 January 1978, shall endure for twenty-eight years from the date when it was originally secured, and the copyright proprietor or his representative may apply for a further term of forty-seven years within one year prior to the expiry of the original term. In default of such application for renewal and extension, the copyright shall end at the expiration of twenty-eight years from the date copyright was originally secured.

The duration of any copyright, the renewal term of which was subsisting at any time between 31 December 1976 and 31 December 1977, or for which renewal registration was made between those dates, is extended to endure for a term of seventy-five years from the date copyright was originally secured.

*These alterations are of great importance for owners of existing American copyrights.*

All terms of copyright provided for by the sections referred to above run to the end of the calendar year in which they would otherwise expire.

## Public performance

Under the previous American law the provisions relating to performance in public were less generous to right owners than those existing in the copyright law of the United Kingdom. In particular, performance of a musical work was formerly only an infringement if it was "for profit". Moreover, the considerable American coin-operated record-playing machine industry (juke boxes) had obtained an exemption from being regarded as instruments of profit, and accordingly their owners did not have to pay royalties for the use of copyright musical works.

Now by the new law one of the exclusive rights of the copyright owner is, in the case of literary, musical, dramatic and choreographic works, pantomimes, and motion pictures and other audiovisual works, to perform the work publicly, without any requirement of such performance being "for profit". By Section 114 however, the exclusive rights of the owner of copyright in a sound recording are specifically stated not to include any right of public performance.

The position of coin-operated record players (juke boxes) is governed by the new Section 116A, inserted by Public Law 100–568 of 31 October 1988. It covers the position of negotiated licences. Limitations are placed on the exclusive right if licences are not negotiated.

These extensions of the scope of the right of public performance should augment the royalty income of authors, composers and publishers of musical works widely performed in the United States. All such right owners should ensure that their American interests are properly taken care of.

## Mechanical right–alteration of the rate of royalty

Where sound recordings of a non-dramatic musical work have been distributed to the public in the United States with the authority of the copyright owner, any other person may, by following the provisions of the law, obtain a compulsory licence to make and distribute sound recordings of the work. This right is known in the United Kingdom as "the mechanical right". Notice must be served on the copyright owner, who is entitled to a royalty in respect of each of his works recorded of either two and three fourths cents or one half of one cent per minute of playing time or fraction thereof, whichever amount is the larger. Failure to serve or file the required notice forecloses the possibility of a compulsory licence and, in the absence of a negotiated licence, renders the making and distribution of such records actionable as acts of infringement.

## Transfer of copyright

Under the previous American law copyright was regarded as indivisible, which meant that on the transfer of copyright, where it was intended that only film rights or some other such limited right be transferred, the entire copyright nevertheless had to be passed. This led to a cumbersome procedure whereby the author would assign the whole copyright to his publisher, who would return to the author by means of an exclusive licence those rights which it was not meant to transfer.

Now it is provided by Section 201(d) of the Copyright Statute that (1) the ownership of a copyright may be transferred in whole or in part by any means of conveyance or by operation of law, and may be bequeathed by will or pass as personal property by the applicable laws of intestate succession and (2) any of the exclusive rights comprised in a copyright (including any subdivision of any of the rights set out in *The rights of a copyright owner* above) may be transferred as provided in (1) above and owned separately. The owner of any particular exclusive right is entitled, to the extent of that right, to all the protection and remedies accorded to the copyright owner by that Statute. This removes the difficulties which existed under the previous law, and brings the position much closer to that existing in the copyright law of the United Kingdom.

## Copyright Royalty Tribunal

A feature of the new United States law is the establishment of a Copyright Royalty Tribunal, with the purpose of making adjustments of reasonable copyright royalty rates in respect of the exercise of certain rights, mainly affecting the musical interests. The Tribunal is to consist of five commissioners appointed by the President with the advice and consent of the Senate for a term of seven years each. This body will perform in the United States a function similar to the new Copyright Tribunal in the United Kingdom.

The new American law spells out the economic objectives which its Copyright Tribunal is to apply in calculating the relevant rates. These are:

(1) to maximise the availability of creative works to the public;
(2) to afford the copyright owner a fair return for his creative work and the copyright user a fair income under existing economic conditions;
(3) to reflect the relative roles of the copyright owner and the copyright user in the product made available to the public with respect to relative creative contribution, technological contribution, capital investment, cost, risk, and contribution to the opening of new markets for creative expression and media for their communication.
(4) to minimise any disruptive impact on the structure of the industries involved and on generally prevailing industry practices.

Every final determination of the Tribunal shall be published in the Federal Register. It shall state in detail the criteria that the Tribunal determined to be applicable to the particular proceeding, the various facts that it found relevant to its determination in that proceeding, and the specific reasons for its determination. Any final decision of the Tribunal in a proceeding may be appealed to the United States Court of Appeals by an aggrieved party, within thirty days after its publication in the Federal Register.

## Fair use

One of the most controversial factors which held up the introduction of the new American copyright law for at least a decade was the extent to which a balance should be struck between the desire of copyright owners to benefit from their works by extending copyright protection as far as possible, and the pressure from users of copyright to obtain access to copyright material as cheaply as possible— if not completely freely.

The new law provides by Section 107 that the fair use of a copyright work, including such use by reproduction in copies or on records, for purposes such as criticism, comment, news reporting, teaching (including multiple copies for classroom use), scholarship or research is not an infringement of copyright. In determining whether the use made of a work in any particular case is a fair use, the factors to be considered shall include:

(1) the purpose and character of the use, including whether such use is of a commercial nature or is for non-profit educational purposes;
(2) the nature of the copyrighted work;
(3) the amount and substantiality of the portion used in relation to the copyrighted work as a whole; and
(4) the effect of the use upon the potential market for or value of the copyrighted work.

It is not an infringement of copyright for a library or archive, or any of its employees acting within the scope of their employment, to reproduce or distribute no more than one copy of a work, if:

(1) the reproduction or distribution is made without any purpose of direct or indirect commercial advantage;
(2) the collections of the library or archive are either open to the public or available not only to researchers affiliated with the library or archive or with the institution of which it is a part, but also to other persons doing research in a specialised field, and
(3) the reproduction or distribution of the work includes a notice of copyright.

It is not generally an infringement of copyright if a performance or display of a work is given by instructors or pupils in the course of face to face teaching activities of a non-profit educational institution, in a classroom or similar place devoted to instruction.

Nor is it an infringement of copyright to give a performance of a non-dramatic literary or musical work or a dramatico-musical work of a religious nature in the course of services at a place of worship or other religious assembly.

It is also not an infringement of copyright to give a performance of a non-dramatic literary or musical work other than in a transmission to the public, without any purpose of direct or indirect commercial advantage and without payment of any fee for the performance to any of the performing artists, promoters or organisers if either (i) there is no direct or indirect admission charge or (ii) the proceeds, after deducting the reasonable costs of producing the performance, are used exclusively for educational, religious or charitable purposes and not for private financial gain. In this case the copyright owner has the right to serve notice of objection to the performance in a prescribed form.

Note the important decision of the Supreme Court in *Sony Corporation of America* v. *Universal City Studios*. (No. 81-1687, 52 USLW 4090.) This decided that the sale of video-recorders to the public does not amount to contributory infringement of the rights in films which are copied as a result of television broadcasts of them. (The practice known as time-switching.) Among other reasons for their decision advanced by the majority of the judges was their opinion that even unauthorised time-switching is legitimate fair use.

## REMEDIES FOR COPYRIGHT OWNERS

### Infringement of copyright

Copyright is infringed by anyone who violates any of the exclusive rights referred to in *The rights of a copyright owner* above, or who imports copies or records into the United States in violation of the law. The owner of copyright is entitled to institute an action for infringement so long as that infringement is committed while he or she is the owner of the right infringed. Previously, no action for infringement of copyright could be instituted until registration of the copyright claim had been made, but this requirement has been modified now that the United States has ratified the Berne Convention.

### Injunctions

Any court having civil jurisdiction under the copyright law may grant interim and final injunctions on such terms as it may deem reasonable to prevent or restrain infringement of copyright. Such injunction may be served anywhere in the United States on the person named. An injunction is operative throughout the whole of the United States, and can be enforced by proceedings in contempt or otherwise by any American court which has jurisdiction over the infringer.

### Impounding and disposition of infringing articles

At any time while a copyright action under American law is pending, the court may order the impounding on such terms as it considers reasonable of all copies or records claimed to have been made or used in violation of the copyright owner's exclusive rights; it may also order the impounding of all plates, moulds, matrices, masters, tapes, film negatives or other articles by means of which infringing copies or records may be reproduced. A court may order as part of a final judgement or decree the destruction or other disposition of all copies or records found to have been made or used in violation of the copyright owner's exclusive rights. It also has the power to order the destruction of all articles by means of which infringing copies or records were reproduced.

### Damages and profits

An infringer of copyright is generally liable either for the copyright owner's actual damage and any additional profits made by the infringer, or for statutory damages.

(1) The copyright owner is entitled to recover the actual damages suffered by him as a result of the infringement, and in addition any profits of the infringer which are attributed to the infringement and are not taken into account in computing the actual damages. In establishing the infringer's profits, the copyright owner is only required to present proof of the infringer's gross revenue, and it is for the infringer to prove his or her deductible expenses and the elements of profit attributable to factors other than the copyright work.

(2) Except where the copyright owner has persuaded the court that the infringement was committed wilfully, the copyright owner may elect, at any time before final judgement is given, to recover, instead of actual damages and profits, an award of statutory damages for all infringements involved in the action in respect of any one work, which may be between $250 and $10,000 according to what the court considers justified.

(3) However, where the copyright owner satisfies the court that the infringement was committed wilfully, the court has the discretion to increase the award of statutory damages to not more than $50,000. Where the infringer succeeds in proving that he was not aware that and had no reason to believe that his acts

constituted an infringement of copyright, the court has the discretion to reduce the award of statutory damages to not less than $100.

*Costs: time limits*

In any civil proceedings under American copyright law, the court has the discretion to allow the recovery of full costs by or against any party except the Government of the United States. It may also award a reasonable sum in respect of an attorney's fee.

No civil or criminal proceedings in respect of copyright law shall be permitted unless begun within three years after the claim or cause of action arose.

*Criminal proceedings in respect of copyright*

(1) Anyone who infringes a copyright wilfully and for purposes of commercial advantage and private financial gain shall be fined not more than $10,000 or imprisoned for not more than one year, or both. However, if the infringement relates to copyright in a sound recording or a film, the infringer is liable to a fine of not more than $25,000 or imprisonment for not more than one year or both on a first offence, which can be increased to a fine of up to $50,000 or imprisonment for not more than two years or both for a subsequent offence.

(2) Following a conviction for criminal infringement a court may in addition to these penalties order the forfeiture and destruction of all infringing copies and records, together with implements and equipment used in their manufacture.

(3) It is also an offence knowingly and with fraudulent intent to place on any article a notice of copyright or words of the same purport, or to import or distribute such copies. A fine is provided for this offence of not more than $2,500. The fraudulent removal of a copyright notice also attracts the same maximum fine, as does the false representation of a material particular on an application for copyright representation.

*Counterfeiting*

By the Piracy and Counterfeiting Amendment Act 1982, pirates and counterfeiters of sound recordings and of motion pictures now face maximum penalties of up to five years imprisonment or fines of up to $250,000.

*Colouring films*

The United States Copyright Office has decided that adding colour to a black and white film may qualify for copyright protection whenever it amounts to more than a trivial change. The decision of Congress in the United States courts on the point is still awaited.

## GENERAL OBSERVATIONS

The copyright law of the United States has been very greatly improved as a result of the new statute passed by Congress on 19 October 1976. (Title 17, United States Code.) Apart from lifting the general standards of protection for copyright owners to a much higher level than that which previously existed, it has on the whole shifted the balance of copyright protection in favour of the copyright owner and away from the copyright user in many of the areas where controversy existed. But most important for British and other non-American authors and publishers, it has gone a long way towards bringing American copyright law up to the same standards of international protection for non-national copyright proprietors which have long been offered by the United Kingdom and the other major countries, both in Europe and elsewhere in the English speaking world. The ratification by the United States of the Berne Convention with effect from 1 March 1989 is an action which finally puts American copyright law on par with the protection offered by other major countries.

# *Libel*

## JAMES EVANS and ANTONY WHITAKER

What follows is an outline of the main principles of the law of Libel, with special reference to points which appear most frequently to be misunderstood. But it is no more than that, and specific legal advice should be taken when practical problems arise. The law discussed is the law of England and Wales. Scotland has its own, albeit somewhat similar, rules.

## LIBEL: LIABILITY TO PAY DAMAGES

English law draws a distinction between defamation published in permanent form and that which is not. The former is libel, the latter slander. "Permanent form" includes writing, printing, drawings and photographs and radio and television broadcasts. It follows that it is the law of libel rather than slander which most concerns writers and artists professionally, and the slightly differing rules applicable to slander will not be mentioned in this article.

Publication of a libel can result in a civil action for damages, an injunction to prevent repetition and/or in certain cases a criminal prosecution against those responsible, who include the writer (or artist or photographer), the printers, the publishers, and the editor, if any, of the publication in which the libel appeared. Prosecutions are rare. Certain special rules apply to them and these will be explained below after a discussion of the question of civil liability, which in practice arises much more frequently.

Civil libel cases, for which legal aid is not available, are usually heard by a judge and jury, and it is the jury who decide the amount of any award. It is not necessary for the plaintiff to prove that he has actually suffered any loss, because the law presumes damage. While the main purpose of a libel claim is to compensate the plaintiff for the injury to his reputation, a jury may give additional sums either as "aggravated" damages, if it appears a defendant has behaved malevolently or spitefully, or as "exemplary", or "punitive", damages where a defendant hopes the economic advantages of publication will outweigh any sum awarded against him. Damages can also be "nominal" if the libel complained of is trivial. It is generally very difficult to forecast the amounts juries are likely to award, though recent awards against newspapers have disclosed a tendency towards considerable generosity.

In an action for damages for libel, it is for the plaintiff to establish that the matter he complains of (1) has been published by the defendant, (2) refers to himself, (3) is defamatory. If he does so, the plaintiff establishes a *prima facie* case. However, the defendant will escape liability if he can show he has a good defence. There are five defences to a libel action. They are Justification, Fair Comment, Privilege, S.4 of the Defamation Act, 1952, Apology, etc., under the Libel Acts, 1843 and 1845. A libel claim can also become barred under the Limitation Acts, as explained below. These matters must now be examined in detail.

## THE PLAINTIFF'S CASE

(1) "Published" in the legal sense means communicated to a person other than the plaintiff. Thus the legal sense is wider than the lay sense but includes it. It

follows that the content of a book is published in the legal sense when the manuscript is first sent to the publishing firm just as much as it is when the book is later placed on sale to the public. Both types of publication are sufficient for the purpose of establishing liability for libel, but the law differentiates between them, since the scope of publication can properly be taken into account by the jury in considering the actual amount of damages to award.

(2) The plaintiff must also establish that the matter complained of refers to himself. It is of course by no means necessary to mention a person's name before it is clear that he is referred to. Nicknames by which he is known or corruptions of his name are just two ways in which his identity can be indicated. There are more subtle methods. The sole question is whether the plaintiff is indicated to those who read the matter complained of. In some cases he will not be unless it is read in the light of facts known to the reader from other sources, but this is sufficient for the plaintiff's purpose. The test is purely objective and does not depend at all on whether the writer intended to refer to the plaintiff.

It is because it is impossible to establish reference to any individual that generalisations, broadly speaking, are not successfully actionable. To say boldly "All lawyers are crooks" does not give any single lawyer a cause of action, because the statement does not point a finger at any individual. However, if anyone is named in conjunction with a generalisation, then it may lose its general character and become particular from the context. Again if one says "One of the X Committee has been convicted of murder" and the X Committee consists of, say, four persons, it cannot be said that the statement is not actionable because no individual is indicated and it could be referring to any of the committee. This is precisely why it is actionable at the suit of each of them as suspicion has been cast on all.

(3) It is for the plaintiff to show that the matter complained of is defamatory. What is defamatory is decided by the jury except in the extreme cases where the judge rules that the words cannot bear a defamatory meaning. Various tests have been laid down for determining this. It is sufficient that any one test is satisfied. The basic tests are : (i) Does the matter complained of tend to lower the plaintiff in the estimation of society? (ii) Does it tend to bring him into hatred, ridicule, contempt, dislike or disesteem with society? (iii) Does it tend to make him shunned or avoided or cut off from society? The mere fact that what is published is inaccurate is not enough to involve liability; it is the adverse impact on the plaintiff's reputation that matters.

"Society" means right-thinking members of society generally. It is by reference to such people that the above tests must be applied. A libel action against a newspaper which had stated that the police had taken a statement from the plaintiff failed, notwithstanding that the plaintiff gave evidence that his apparent assistance to the police (which he denied) had brought him into grave disrepute with the underworld. It was not by their wrongheaded standards that the matter fell to be judged.

Further, it is not necessary to imply that the plaintiff is at fault in some way in order to defame him. To say of a woman that she has been raped or of someone that he is insane imputes to them no degree of blame, but nonetheless both statements are defamatory.

Sometimes a defamatory meaning is conveyed by words which on the face of them have no such meaning. "But Brutus is an honourable man" is an example. If a jury finds that words are meant ironically they will consider this ironical sense when determining whether the words are defamatory. In deciding therefore whether or not the words are defamatory, the jury seek to discover what, without straining the words or putting a perverse construction on them, they will be understood to mean. In some cases this may differ substantially from their literal meaning.

Matter may also be defamatory by innuendo. Strictly so called, an innuendo is a meaning that words acquire by virtue of facts known to the reader but not stated in the passage complained of. Words, quite innocent on the face of them, may acquire a defamatory meaning when read in the light of these facts. For example, where a newspaper published a photograph of a man and a woman, with the caption that they had just announced their engagement, it was held to be defamatory of the man's wife since those who knew that she had cohabited with him were led to the belief that she had done so only as his mistress. The newspaper was unaware that the man was already married, but some of its readers were not.

## DEFENCES TO A LIBEL ACTION

### Justification

English law does not protect the reputation that a person either does not or should not possess. Stating the truth therefore does not incur liability, and the plea of justification—namely, that what is complained of is true in substance and in fact—is a complete answer to an action for damages. However, this defence is by no means to be undertaken lightly. For instance, to prove one instance of using bad language will be insufficient to justify the allegation that a person is "foulmouthed". It would be necessary to prove several instances, and the defendant is obliged in most cases to particularise in his pleadings giving details, dates and places. However, if there are two or more distinct charges against the plaintiff the defence will not fail by reason only that the truth of every charge is not proved, if the words not proved to be true do not materially injure the plaintiff's reputation having regard to the truth of the remaining charges. It is for the defendant to prove that what he has published is true, not for the plaintiff to disprove it, though if he can do so, so much the better for him.

One point requires special mention. It is insufficient for the defendant to prove that he has accurately repeated what a third person has written or said or that such statements have gone uncontradicted when made on occasions in the past. If X writes "Y told me that Z is a liar", it is no defence to an action against X merely to prove that Y did say that. X has given currency to a defamatory statement concerning Z and has so made it his own. His only defence is to prove that Z is a liar by establishing a number of instances of Z's untruthfulness. Nor is it a defence to prove that the defendant genuinely believed what he published to be true. This might well be a complete answer in an action, other than a libel action, based on a false but non-defamatory statement. For such statements do not incur liability in the absence of fraud or malice, which, in this context, means a dishonest or otherwise improper motive. Bona fide belief, however, may be relevant to the assessment of damages, even in a libel action.

Special care should be taken in relation to references to a person's convictions, however accurately described. Since the Rehabilitation of Offenders Act, 1974, a person's convictions may become "spent" and thereafter it may involve liability to refer to them. Reference to the Act and orders thereunder must be made in order to determine the position in any particular case.

### Fair comment

It is a defence to prove that what is complained of is fair comment made in good faith and without malice on a matter of public interest.

"Fair" in this context means "honest". "Fair comment" means therefore the expression of the writer's genuinely held opinion. It does not necessarily mean opinion with which the jury agree. Comment may therefore be quite extreme and still be "fair" in the legal sense. However, if it is utterly perverse the jury may be led to think that no one could have genuinely held such views. In such a case the defence would fail, for the comment could not be honest. "Malice" here includes the popular sense of personal spite, but covers any dishonest or improper motive.

The defence only applies when what is complained of is comment as distinct from a statement of fact. The line between comment and fact is notoriously difficult to draw in some cases. Comment means a statement of opinion. The facts on which comment is made must be stated together with the comment or be sufficiently indicated with it. This is merely another way of saying that it must be clear that the defamatory statement is one of opinion and not of fact, for which the only defence would be the onerous one of justification. The exact extent to which the facts commented on must be stated or referred to is a difficult question, but some help may be derived in answering it by considering the purpose of the rule, which is to enable the reader to exercise his own judgement and to agree or disagree with the comment. It is quite plain that it is not necessary to state every single detail of the facts. In one case it was sufficient merely to mention the name of one of the Press lords in an article about a newspaper though not one owned by him. He was so well known that to mention his name indicated the substratum of fact commented upon, namely his control of his group of newspapers. No general rule can be laid down, save that, in general, the fuller the facts set out or referred to with the comment the better. These facts must always be true, except that in an action for libel partly in respect of allegations of fact and partly of expressions of opinion, a defence of fair comment will not fail by reason only that the truth of every allegation of fact is not proved, if the expression of opinion is fair comment, having regard to such of the facts alleged or referred to in the matter complained of as are proved.

The defence only applies where the matters commented on are of public interest, i.e. of legitimate concern to the public or a substantial section of it. Thus the conduct of national and local government, international affairs, the administration of justice, etc., are all matters of public interest, whereas other people's private affairs may very well not be, although they undoubtedly interest the public, or provoke curiosity.

In addition, matters of which criticism has been expressly or impliedly invited, such as publicly performed plays and published books, are a legitimate subject of comment. Criticism need not be confined merely to their artistic merit but equally may deal with the attitudes to life and the opinions therein expressed.

It is sometimes said that a man's moral character is never a proper subject of comment for the purpose of this defence. This is certainly true where it is a private individual who is concerned, and some authorities say it is the same in the case of a public figure even though his character may be relevant to his public life. Again, it may in some cases be exceeding the bounds of fair comment to impute a dishonourable motive to a person, as is frequently done by way of inference from facts. In general, the imputation is a dangerous and potentially expensive practice.

## Privilege

In the public interest, certain occasions are privileged so that to make defamatory statements upon them does not incur liability. The following are privileged in any event: (i) fair, accurate, and contemporaneous reports of public judicial proceedings in England published in a newspaper, (ii) Parliamentary papers published by the direction of either House, or full republications thereof. The following are privileged provided publication is made only for the reason that the privilege is given and not for some wrongful or indirect motive: (i) fair and accurate but non-contemporaneous reports of public judicial proceedings in England, whether in a newspaper or not, (ii) extracts of Parliamentary papers, (iii) fair and accurate reports of Parliamentary proceedings, (iv) a fair and accurate report in a newspaper of the proceedings at any public meeting held in the United Kingdom. The meeting must be bona fide and lawfully held for a lawful purpose and for the furtherance or discussion of any matter of public concern. Admission to the meeting may be general or restricted. In the case of public meetings, the defence is not available, if it is proved that the defendant has been requested by the plaintiff to publish in the newspaper in which the original publication was made a reasonable letter or statement by way of explanation or contradiction, and has refused or neglected to do so, or has done so in a manner not adequate or not reasonable having regard to all the circumstances. This list of privileged occasions is by no means exhaustive, but they are those most commonly utilised.

## S.4 of the Defamation Act, 1952

The defence provided by the above section is only available where the defamation is "innocent". As has been seen, liability for libel is in no way dependent on the existence of an intention to defame on the part of the defendant and the absence of such an intention does not mean that the defamation is "innocent".

Defamation is innocent if the publisher did not intend to publish the matter complained of about the plaintiff and did not know of circumstances by virtue of which it might be understood to refer to him, or, if the matter published was not defamatory on the face of it, if the publisher did not know of circumstances by virtue of which it might be understood to be defamatory. Further the publisher must have exercised all reasonable care in relation to the publication. If the publisher has published matter innocently, he should make an "offer of amends" to the party aggrieved. This consists of an offer to publish a correction and apology and as far as practicable to inform others to whom the alleged libel has been distributed that the matter is said to be defamatory. If the offer of amends is accepted, it is a bar to further proceedings against the person making the offer. If rejected, the making of the offer affords a defence provided the defendant can prove that he did publish innocently and made the offer as soon as practicable after learning that the matter published was or might be defamatory. The offer must not have been withdrawn and must have been expressed to be for the purposes of the defence under S.4 and have been accompanied by an affidavit. It is vital that the offer should be made swiftly, but it is inadvisable to make it without professional advice owing to its technicality.

An example of the first type of innocent publication is where a reference to a person by name has been understood to refer to another person of the same name and this could not reasonably have been foreseen.

An example of the other type of innocent publication is the case referred to earlier in this article of the man pictured with "his fiancée". The publishers did not know that he was already married and that accordingly the picture and caption could be understood to be defamatory of his wife.

In practice all the conditions for a successful defence under this section are infrequently fulfilled.

## Apology under the Libel Acts, 1843 and 1845

This defence is rarely utilised, since if any condition of it is not fulfilled, the plaintiff must succeed and the only question is the actual amount of damages. It only applies to actions in respect of libels in newspapers and periodicals. The defendant pleads that the libel was inserted without actual malice and without gross negligence and that before the action commenced or as soon afterwards as possible he inserted a full apology in the same newspaper, etc., or had offered to publish it in a newspaper, etc., of the plaintiff's choice, where the original newspaper is published at intervals greater than a week. Further a sum must be paid into court with this defence to compensate the plaintiff.

## Limitation

In general, unless an action is started within three years of publication, a libel claim becomes "statute-barred" through lapse of time. But successive and subsequent publications, such as the issue of later editions of the same book, or the sale of surplus copies of an old newspaper, can give rise to fresh claims.

## CRIMINAL LIABILITY IN LIBEL AND RELATED AREAS

Whereas the object of a civil action is to obtain compensation for the wrong done or to prevent repetition, the object of criminal proceedings is to punish the wrongdoer by fine or imprisonment or both. There are four main types of writing which may provoke a prosecution:

        (1) defamatory libel
        (2) obscene publications
        (3) sedition and incitement to racial hatred
        (4) blasphemous libel

(1) The publication of defamatory matter is in certain circumstances a crime as well as a civil wrong. But whereas the principal object of civil proceedings will normally be to obtain compensation, the principal object of a criminal prosecution will be to secure punishment of the accused, for example by way of a fine. Prosecutions are not frequent, but there have been signs of late of a revival of interest. There are important differences between the rules applicable to criminal libel and its civil counterpart. For example, a criminal libel may be "published" even though only communicated to the person defamed and may be found to have occurred even where the person defamed is dead, or where only a group of persons but no particular individual has been maligned. During election campaigns, it is an "illegal practice" to publish false statements about the personal character or conduct of a candidate irrespective of whether they are also defamatory.

(2) It is an offence to publish obscene matter. By the Obscene Publications Act, 1959, matter is obscene if its effect is such as to tend to deprave and corrupt persons who are likely, having regard to all relevant circumstances, to read, see or hear it. "To deprave and corrupt" is to be distinguished from "to shock and disgust". It is a defence to a prosecution to prove that publication of the matter in question is justified as being for the public good, on the ground that it is in the interests of science, literature, art or learning, or of other objects of general concern. Expert evidence may be given as to its literary, artistic, scientific or other merits. Playwrights, directors and producers should note that the Theatres Act, 1968, though designed to afford similar protection to stage productions, does not necessarily prevent prosecutions for indecency under other statutes.

(3) Writings which tend to destroy the peace of the Realm may be prosecuted as being seditious or as amounting to incitement to racial hatred. Seditious writings include those which advocate reform by unconstitutional or violent means or incite contempt or hatred for the Monarch or Parliament. These institutions may be criticised stringently, but not in a manner which is likely to lead to insurrection or civil commotion or indeed any physical force. Prosecutions are a rarity, but it should be remembered that writers of matter contemptuous of the House of

Commons, though not prosecuted for seditious libel are, from time to time, punished by that House for breach of its Privileges, although, if a full apology is made, it is often an end of the matter. The Public Order Act 1986 makes it an offence, irrespective of the author's or publisher's intention, to publish, or put on plays containing, threatening, abusive or insulting matter if hatred is likely to be stirred up against any racial group in Great Britain.

(4) Blasphemous libel consists in the vilification of the Christian religion or its ceremonies. The offence lies essentially in the impact of what is said concerning, for instance, God, Christ, the Bible, the Book of Common Prayer, etc.; it is irrelevant that the publisher does not intend to shock or arouse resentment. While temperate and sober writings on religious topics however anti-Christian in sentiment will not involve liability, if the discussion is "so scurrilous and offensive as to pass the limit of decent controversy and to outrage any Christian feeling", it will.

# The Florence Agreement and its Nairobi Protocol

This Agreement, on the Importation of Educational, Scientific and Cultural Materials, generally known as the Florence Agreement, was adopted by the Unesco General Conference in Florence in 1950 and came into force on 21 May 1952. It is concerned with the free flow of a wide variety of articles including books and the removal of tariff and trade obstacles. The principal undertaking of the contracting states is the exemption of books and other educational, scientific and cultural imports from customs duties, and the granting of licences and foreign exchange as far as possible for their importation. Books of every sort are included in the Agreement, not exempting those printed abroad from the work of an author in the importing country. Unbound sheets do not come under the Agreement.

The following is an up-to-date list of the States parties to the Agreement: Afghanistan, Austria, Barbados, Belgium, Bolivia, Burkina-Faso, Cameroon, Congo, Cuba, Cyprus, Democratic Kampuchea, Denmark, Egypt, El Salvador, Fiji, Finland, France, Gabon, Germany (Federal Republic of), Ghana, Greece, Guatemala, Haiti, Holy See, Hungary, Iran, Iraq, Ireland, Israel, Italy, Ivory Coast, Japan, Jordan, Kenya, Lao People's Democratic Republic, Liechtenstein, Luxembourg, Madagascar, Malawi, Malaysia, Malta, Mauritius, Monaco, Morocco, Netherlands, New Zealand, Nicaragua, Niger, Nigeria, Norway, Oman, Pakistan, Philippines, Poland, Portugal, Romania, Rwanda, San Marino, Sierra Leone, Singapore, Socialist People's Libyan Arab Jamahiriya, Solomon Islands, Spain, Sri Lanka, Sweden, Switzerland, Syrian Arab Republic, Tanzania (United Republic of), Thailand, Tonga, Trinidad and Tobago, Tunisia, Uganda, United Kingdom, United States of America, Viet-Nam (Socialist Republic of), Yugoslavia, Zaire, Zambia.

A Protocol to the Florence Agreement or Nairobi Protocol adopted by the Unesco General Conference in Nairobi in 1976 came into force on 2 January 1982. It is open only to states which are parties to the Agreement. The Protocol broadens the scope of the Agreement by extending the benefits it offers to additional objects and by granting further benefits to a number of materials. The following States adhere to the Protocol: Barbados, Belgium, Denmark, Egypt, Finland, France, Greece, Holy See, Iraq, Ireland, Italy, Luxembourg, Netherlands, Portugal, San Marino, United Kingdom, Yugoslavia.

# Mechanical-Copyright Protection Society Ltd.

The Society was formed in 1910 by a group of music publishers in anticipation of the introduction of new legislation which for the first time would provide for the protection of copyright material by mechanical reproduction.

This became effective on the introduction of the Copyright Act 1911 when only the music box, piano roll, cylinder and disc recordings were known.

Since those days the Society has grown with the technical advances into sound film, radio and television recordings, magnetic tape and videocassettes, and now grants licences in all matters affecting recording rights, both in the U.K. and throughout the world by virtue of its affiliation with other similar organisations and agencies.

Membership of the Society is open to all music copyright owners, composers, lyric writers and publishers. There is no entrance fee or subscription.

Enquiries for membership should be addressed to the Membership Department, Elgar House, 41 Streatham High Road, London, SW16 1ER *tel* 01-769 4400.

# The Performing Right Society, Ltd.

The Performing Right Society is an Association of Composers, Authors and Publishers of copyright musical works, established in 1914 to collect royalties for the public performance, broadcasting and diffusion by cable of such works and their use by diffusion services; also to restrain unauthorised use thereof.

Licences are granted which convey the necessary permission for the public performance of any of the works of its members and those of the affiliated national societies of more than 30 other countries. The combined membership thus represented by the Society is about 500,000. Over 200,000 places of entertainment are covered by the Society's licence in the British Isles alone.

The Society does not control the performance of non-musical works (plays, sketches, etc.), but its licence is required for the use of its international repertoire in variety, as overture, entr'acte or exit music, or for any other form of live or mechanical performances (excluding operas, operettas, musical plays, specially written music for plays, revues or pantomimes (apart from interpolations therein of independent items) and ballets).

The constitution of the Society is that of a Company limited by guarantee having no share capital. The General Council consists of twelve composers and authors and twelve music publishers elected by the members from among their own number. The Society is not a profit-making organisation, the whole of the royalties it collects being distributed amongst its members and the affiliated societies after deduction of administration expenses and contributions to the PRS Members' Fund, established for the benefit of necessitous members and their dependants.

There are two distributions of general performing fees each year, and two distributions of broadcasting fees. The Annual General Meeting is usually held in July.

Applicants for membership are required to pay an initial admission fee, but no further subscriptions or fees are charged. All composers of musical works and authors of lyrics or poems which have been set to music are eligible for membership, provided that they satisfy the current membership criteria.

The Society has available for free loan a new film entitled *PRS – The Movie*. For details of this and for further information contact the Public Relations Department at PRS, 29-33 Berners Street, London, W1P 4AA *tel* 01-580 5544.

## Public Lending Right

JOHN SUMSION
*Registrar of Public Lending Right*

### FOR WRITERS AND ILLUSTRATORS OF BOOKS

*Outline*

Under the PLR system, payment is made from public funds to authors (writers, translators and illustrators) whose books are lent out from public libraries. Payment is made once a year, in February, and the amount each author receives is proportionate to the number of times (established from a sample) that his books were lent out during the previous year (July to June).

*The legislation*

PLR was created, and its principles established, by the Public Lending Right Act 1979 (HMSO, 30p). The Act required the rules for the administration of PLR to be laid down by a scheme. That was done in the Public Lending Right Scheme 1982 (HMSO, £2.95), which includes details of transfer (assignment), transmission after death, renunciation, trusteeship, bankruptcy, etc. Amending orders made in 1983, 1984 and 1988 have been consolidated in December 1988 (S.I. 2070, £4.00).

*How the system works*

From the applications he receives, the Registrar of PLR compiles, to hold on his computer, a register of authors and books. A representative sample is recorded, consisting of all loans from thirty public libraries. This is then multiplied in proportion to total library lending to produce, for each book, an estimate of its total annual loans throughout the country. Each year the computer compares the register with the estimated loans to discover how many loans are credited to each registered book for the calculation of PLR payments. The computer does this using code numbers—in most cases the ISBN printed in the book.

Parliament allocates a sum each year (£3,500,000 in 1989/90) for PLR. This Fund pays the administrative costs of PLR and reimburses local authorities for recording loans in the sample libraries. The remaining money is then divided in order to work out how much can be paid for each estimated loan of a registered book.

*Limits on payments*

(1) *Bottom limit*. If all the registered interests in an author's books score so few loans that they would earn less than £1 in a year, no payment is due.
(2) *Top limit*. If the books of one registered author score so high that the author's PLR earnings for the year would exceed £6,000, then only £6,000 is paid. No author can earn more than £6,000 in PLR in any one year.

Money that is not paid out because of these limits belongs to the Fund and increases the amounts paid that year to other authors.

*The sample*

The sample represents only public libraries (no academic, private or commercial ones) and only loans made over the counter (not consultations of books on library premises). The reference sections of public libraries are not included in PLR. It follows that only those books which are loaned from public libraries can earn PLR and make an application worthwhile.

The sample consists of the entire loans records for a year in thirty public libraries representatively spread through England, Scotland, Wales and Northern Ireland. Sample loans are about 1.5% of the national total. In order to counteract sampling error, libraries in the sample change every two to three years. Loans are totalled every twelve months for the period 1 July to 30 June.

An author's entitlement to PLR depends, under the 1979 Act, on the loans scored by his books in the sample. This score is multiplied to produce regional and national estimated loans.

## ISBNs

PLR depends on the use of code numbers to identify books lent and to correlate loans with entries on the register so that payment can be made. Chiefly the system uses the International Standard Book Number—the ISBN—which consists of ten digits and is usually printed with the publishing information on the back of the title page; it may also be on the back or back flap of the jacket or cover. Examples are: 0 10 541079 9 and 185036110x.

Some books—particularly those published before 1970—lack an ISBN; if the book has no ISBN, the Registrar will allocate to it another code number so that it can still score loans and earn PLR. However, where there is an ISBN, an author who applies for registration is asked to give it on his application form. Different editions (for example, 1st, 2nd, hardcover, paperback, large print) of the same book have different ISBNs.

## Authorship

In the PLR system the author of a book is the writer, illustrator, translator, compiler, editor or reviser, provided that his name is on the book's title page. He is eligible for PLR as an author even if he does not own the copyright. PLR and copyright are different. Note also that:

(1) Illustrators include photographers, provided that the photographer is (in the words of section 48 of the Copyright Act 1956) 'the person who, at the time when the photograph is taken, is the owner of the material on which it is taken'.

(2) For the registration of an author who is less than 18 years old the application must be made by his parent or guardian. Upon reaching the age of 18, the author should apply for the PLR to be registered in his own name: until this is done the PLR belongs to the parent or guardian.

(3) A compiler or editor must also have written at least 10% of the book's contents or more than ten pages of text.

(4) A reviser may be regarded as an editor.

(5) A translator receives a fixed 30% share.

The sole writer of a book may not be its sole author because, for PLR, all the eligible contributors named on the title page are its co-authors.

## Co-authorship/illustrators

In the PLR system the authors of a book are those writers, translators, editors, compilers and illustrators whose names appear on the title page. Authors must apply for registration before their books can earn PLR. Books with *no more* than three named writers (excluding translators, editors and compilers) or illustrators can be registered for PLR.

## Applications from writers and/or illustrators

Writers and illustrators must apply for registration jointly. At least one of them must be eligible and they must jointly specify what share of PLR each will take. They must agree and sign the form even if one or two are ineligible or do not wish to register for PLR. If they are not all eligible, those who are will receive a share(s) specified in the joint application. PLR can be any whole percentage. Illustrators and joint writers may only register more than 50% if justified by their actual contribution to the book. Detailed advice is available from the PLR office, and a change to allow single applications for joint-author books may be introduced early in 1990.

*Applications from translators*

Translators may apply, without reference to other authors, for a 30% fixed share (to be divided equally between joint translators). Translators do not have to be named on the title page but must be credited in the book.

*Applications from editors and compilers*

An editor or compiler who has also made a significant written contribution to the book, and who is named on the title page, may apply, either with others or without reference to them, to register a 20% share provided he has written 10% of the book or more than ten pages of text: this should be substantiated by photocopies of the title and contents pages. The share of joint editors/compilers is 20% in total to be divided equally.

An application from an editor or compiler to register a greater percentage share must be accompanied by supporting documentary evidence of actual contribution. A special form is available from the PLR Office.

*Dead or missing co-authors*

Where it is impossible to include a co-author on the form because that person is dead or untraceable, then the surviving co-author or co-authors may submit an application without the dead or missing co-author, but must name the co-author and provide supporting evidence as to why that co-author has been omitted. The living co-author(s) will then be able to register a share in the book which will be 20% for the illustrator (or illustrators) and the residual percentage for writer (or writers).

If this percentage is to be divided between more than one writer or illustrator, then this will be in equal shares unless some other apportionment is requested and agreed by the Registrar.

Writers or illustrators may apply for a different percentage apportionment, and the Registrar will register different percentage shares if it is reasonable in relation to the authors' contribution to the particular book. Detailed advice and forms are available from the PLR Office.

The PLR Office keeps a file of missing authors (mostly illustrators) to help applicants locate co-authors. Help is also available from publishers, the writers' organisations, and the Association of Illustrators, 1 Colville Place, London W1.

*Life and death*

Authors can only be registered for PLR during their lifetime. However, for authors registered during their lifetime, books can later be registered if first published within one year before their death or ten years afterwards. New versions of titles registered by the author can be registered posthumously.

*Eligible authors*

If he is (in the senses described above) the author or a co-author of a book that is eligible (as described below), then he is eligible for PLR registration provided that he is resident in the United Kingdom or the Federal Republic of Germany. A resident in these countries (for PLR purposes) has his only home there or his principal home there. The United Kingdom does not include the Channel Islands or the Isle of Man.

*Eligible books*

In the PLR system each separate edition of a book is registered and treated as a separate book.

A book is eligible for PLR registration provided that:

(1) it has an eligible author (or co-author) named on its title page;

(2) it is printed and bound (paperbacks counting as bound);

(3) copies of it have been put on sale (i.e. it is not a free handout and it has already been published);

(4) it is not a newspaper, magazine, journal or periodical;

(5) it does not have more than three writers or illustrators named on the title page;

(6) the authorship is personal (i.e. not a company or association) and the book is not crown copyright;

(7) it is not wholly or mainly a musical score.

*Notification and payment*

Every registered author receives from the Registrar an annual statement of estimated loans for each book and the PLR due.

## SAMPLING ARRANGEMENTS

*Libraries*

The scheme specifies the eight regions within which either two or more service points have to be designated. With such a small sample, random selection would not necessarily produce a statistically more accurate result than consciously aiming for a reasonable spread—considering as many factors as possible likely to influence the result.

From July 1989 the service points, designated in close collaboration with the public libraries and local authorities involved, are at: Colchester, Haywards Heath, Littlehampton, Bury St Edmunds, Crowborough, Paignton, Shrewsbury, Melksham, Farnborough, Hull (Derringham Bank), Chorley, Fleetwood, Durham City, Sheffield (Broomhill), Dudley, Stockport, Pontefract, South Shields, Acton, Uxbridge, Redbridge (Gant's Hill), Sutton (Middleton Circle), Cardiff, Aberystwyth, Aberystwyth Mid-Area Mobile, Dundee, Blairgowrie, Glasgow (Dennistoun), Newry, Belfast (Lisburn Road).

Participating local authorities are reimbursed on an actual cost basis for additional expenditure incurred in providing loans data to the PLR Office. The extra PLR work mostly consists of modifications to computer programs to accumulate data already held in the local authority computer and to produce a monthly magnetic tape to be sent to the PLR Office at Stockton-on-Tees.

## SUMMARY OF THE SIXTH YEAR'S RESULTS

*Registration: authors*

When registration closed for the sixth year (30th June 1988) the number of books registered was about 140,570, for 16,037 authors. This included 493 West German authors.

*Library loans*

The ISBN was used for 88% of the books; the remaining 12% were identified by author and title referring to the PLR database.

The sample loans were 1.08% of total issues from UK public libraries—623 million per annum.

Because the sampling strength is different in each region, the calculation is done in two stages. For example the loans recorded in Wales are multiplied by 81 because issues in the two Welsh sampling points represent 1.2% of borrowings from all public libraries in Wales; but in London the multiplication factor is 90 since only 1.1% of issues from all London libraries have been sampled.

*Eligible loans*

Of these 623 million estimated loans, 238 million belong to books on the PLR register. The loans credited to registered books—38.2% of all library borrowings—qualify for payment. The remaining 61.8% of loans relate to books that are ineligible for various reasons, to books written by dead or foreign authors, and to books that have simply not been applied for.

*Money and payments*

Most of the setting up and computer system was paid for in previous financial years: £372,000 in 1981/1982, £350,000 in 1982/1983 and £107,000 in 1983/84.

Operating the Scheme this year cost £352,000 plus payments to local authorities of £39,000. The Rate per Loan for 1988/1989 was set at 1.45 pence and calculated to distribute all the £3,109,000 available. The total of PLR distribution and costs is therefore the full £3.5 million which the Government provided in 1988/1989.

Within this £3,109,000, some £344,000 would have gone to the most popular authors—but the maximum limit of £6,000 per author has in effect transferred this money to increase payments to other authors.

The numbers of authors in various payment categories are as follows:

|  |  | £ |
|---:|---|---|
| 67 | payments at | 6,000 maximum |
| 22 | payments at | 5,000–5,999 |
| 163 | payments between | 2,500–4,999 |
| 411 | payments between | 1,000–2,499 |
| 593 | payments between | 500–999 |
| 3,101 | payments between | 100–499 |
| 8,865 | payments between | 1–99 |
| 13,222 | TOTAL | |

There were also 2,815 registered authors whose books earned them *nil* payment.

## RECIPROCAL ARRANGEMENTS

In 1981--1982 reciprocal arrangements with West Germany were demanded by the writers—fearful that they might lose the West German PLR they had enjoyed since 1974. The West German Scheme, although loan based, is very different in most other respects. There is no question of harmonisation, but simple reciprocity was included in changes brought into effect in January 1985. Authors can apply for West German PLR through the Authors' Licensing and Collecting Society. (Comparison of PLR schemes internationally and consideration of prospects for reciprocity are covered in the Registrar's April 1988 Report to the Advisory Committee, *PLR in Practice*, John Sumsion, £9.90 incl. U.K. postage, from the PLR office.)

## ADVISORY COMMITTEE

The PLR Advisory Committee was reconstituted in 1988 under the chairmanship of Mr David Whitaker to advise both the Minister for the Arts and the Registrar on matters concerning PLR.

## CRITICAL FEATURES REVIEWED

On the question of practical feasibility, the central question has been how a writer can collect when the value of each transaction is so small that, with conventional methods, the cost of collecting the money would be far greater than its value. (There is an obvious parallel here with photocopying.)

We now have a basically satisfactory way of calculating PLR remuneration. The objections to PLR as being infeasible or impractical have been completely overcome through the use of the latest available library computing technology and an approach familiar to businessmen dealing with stock control problems.

An important result has been the provision of information on book loans and author payments so that future developments and improvements in PLR can be based on a factual review of public library lending. This is included in *PLR in Practice* (op. cit.) and also in *PLR Loans—A Statistical Exploration*, A. Hasted et al., £16.50 from the PLR office.

PLR application forms, information and publications can be obtained from The Registrar, PLR Office, Bayheath House, Prince Regent Street, Stockton-on-Tees, Cleveland TS18 1DF *tel* (0642) 604699. The Minister's Annual Report to Parliament and the statutory accounts may be obtained from this address or from H.M.S.O.

# The Authors' Licensing and Collecting Society Ltd

ALCS was set up in 1977 to collect and distribute money to writers for payments which authors and other copyright holders are unable to collect individually. For instance, under Federal German law Public Lending Right payments to foreign authors can only be paid through a collecting society. And in Britain there is no way in which an author could individually collect fees due to him for the copying of his work in schools except at a cost far in excess of the fees themselves.

ALCS is a non-profit-making company limited by guarantee (i.e. not having a share capital). It is run by members through a Council of Management on which the Society of Authors and the Writers' Guild of Great Britain are represented.

ALCS is affiliated to CISAC (International Confederation of Authors' and Composers' Societies) and through it maintains constant links with continental European and overseas collecting societies. It also has reciprocal or bilateral agreements with societies in many individual countries.

## ADMINISTRATION

The Council of Management has twelve members, all of whom are active writers. Four are elected by and from the Ordinary Members of ALCS, four are nominated by the Society of Authors and four by the Writers' Guild. They meet as often as business requires and are unpaid. The office is run by the Secretary General and a small staff.

## POWERS

On joining, members transfer to the Society the power to administer on their behalf specific rights which they are unable to exercise as individuals. Under the Society's constitution ALCS may administer (a) in the United Kingdom and the Republic of Ireland and (b) in other countries:
    the lending right (for foreign schemes);

the reprography right in published works;
the private and off-air-recording right;
the cable TV right

(where such a right can be exercised by an individual, the Society does not intervene).

An extra right to be exercised in the UK and Republic of Ireland can be added by a Special Resolution of a General Meeting (requiring a majority of votes). An extra overseas right can be added by the Council, provided it decides that the right can only be effectively administered by collective means. Members are entitled to opt out of any right that is added after they joined.

## AREAS OF CURRENT ACTIVITY

### Foreign PLR

Since 1980 ALCS has distributed to its members over £700,000 from the Federal German Republic collecting society, VG WORT. Further money is held in Germany on behalf of British writers who have not yet joined ALCS. Those eligible to receive German PLR through ALCS are:

living British authors resident anywhere;
heirs of British authors through successor membership;
foreign writers resident in Britain, writing in English;
British illustrators.

### Reprography

Set up in 1983 by the Publishers' Licensing Society and ALCS, the Copyright Licensing Agency (CLA) is now well-established and offers licences for reprography. ALCS is responsible for paying writers their share in any fees collected from such licences. See the following article.

### Cable and satellite broadcasting

ALCS has agreements with Belgium, Holland and several Scandinavian countries, through the relevant collecting societies, for distribution of monies received for the simultaneous cabling of BBC TV programmes.

It is also monitoring the situation with regard to satellite broadcasts and will act as and when necessary on behalf of British writers.

## GENERAL

ALCS serves on the British Copyright Council and the PLR Advisory Committee, now appointed by the Minister for the Arts. It keeps a watchful eye on all matters affecting authors as copyright holders. Its principal aims are twofold; to press for and make practical the establishment of collecting schemes by statute or voluntary agreement; and to make sure that the writers' share is a just one.

## TO JOIN

ALCS is financed at present by membership fees and a percentage handling charge for distribution. The current annual subscription is £5.75 (including VAT). To join the Society, write for an application form to: The Membership Secretary, 7 Ridgmount Street, London WC1E 7AE *tel* 01-580-2181.

Members of The Society of Authors and The Writers' Guild have free membership of ALCS.

# The Copyright Licensing Agency Ltd
## CLA

Sixteen years have passed since 1973, when interest groups in the UK started to prepare submissions to the government-appointed committee under the Hon. Mr Justice Whitford about ways of regulating copying from books, journals and periodicals. These interest groups, representing owners of copyright, were seeking both a mechanism of control and just recompense for authors and publishers while at the same time continuing to satisfy the reasonable demands of a modern information-driven society.

When it was eventually published in 1977, the Whitford Report on Copyright and Designs Law suggested, as the best likely solution to the problem, a collective administration system for copying rights organised by the rights owners themselves.

This recommendation spawned first the Wolfenden Committee that brought together representatives of authors' societies and publishers' associations, and then the de Freitas committee that hammered out and fashioned, with these two sometimes antagonistic groups, a mutually acceptable constitution for such a licensing body. The outcome was the formation of the Copyright Licensing Agency, CLA, in April 1982 and its incorporation in January 1983 as a non-profit making company limited by guarantee. The Agency, which is primarily concerned with licensing "heavy user" groups, issued its first licence in May 1984.

CLA is 'owned' by the Authors' Licensing & Collecting Society (ALCS) and the Publishers Licensing Society (PLS) in that they are its members. ALCS's members are the Society of Authors (SoA), the Writers' Guild of Great Britain (WGoGB) and the Association of Authors' Agents (AAA); and PLS's members are the Publishers Association (PA), the Periodical Publishers Association (PPA) and the Association of Learned and Professional Society Publishers (ALPSP). All are represented on CLA's board of twelve directors, six being ALCS nominations and six PLS nominations.

CLA has six main functions and these are:

> to obtain mandates from publishers and authors in association with ALCS and PLS;

> to license users for copying extracts from books, journals and periodicals;

> to collect fees from licensed users for such copying;

> to maintain a system of record-keeping sufficient to provide statistically acceptable information on which to calculate a fair apportionment of the distributable income;

> to pay ALCS and PLS their correct shares of the distributable income and provide sufficient data to enable these societies to pay individual authors and publishers;

> to institute such legal proceedings as may be necessary for the enforcement of the rights entrusted to the Agency.

CLA sees its principal licensing areas in the UK as being *education*, *government* and *industry*. Each of these broad categories has three or four sub-groups. In company with nearly all other RROs around the world, CLA started licensing in the general education sector. The first major development occurred in April

1986, when three-year voluntary licensing agreements with the country's local education authorities (LEAs) came into effect; in April 1989 these licenses were extended for a further three years; copying in all thirty thousand or so state colleges and schools is now covered by such licenses. The Agency also licenses the independent education sector through its licensing scheme for independent schools.

With the general education sector (5 to 16 years) covered, CLA next turned its attention to higher and further education (HE & FE) and during 1989, after several years of negotiating, finalised arrangements whereby universities, polytechnics, independent colleges and language schools, etc. all became licensed from 1 January 1990. Three-year licenses once again were the norm.

Having successfully negotiated the local education authority licences with a joint committee of representatives appointed by the Association of County Councils (ACC), the Association of Metropolitan Authorities (AMA) and the Convention of Scottish Local Authorities (CoSLA), CLA will try to license the non-LEA parts of local government in one fell swoop with a similar committee but expanded to include representatives of the Association of District Councils (ADC) and the Association of London Authorities (ALA).

It is the Agency's intention to deal with central government on a ministry by ministry basis, starting with the Department of Trade & Industry (DTI) as the sponsors of the Copyright, Designs and Patents Act 1988; the Department of Education and Science (DES), as educational institutions are already licensed; and the National Health Service, (NHS) which, with 1.25 million employees, is the largest employer in western Europe.

Public bodies, i.e. those organisations for which government ministers have some accountability (e.g. The British Council), may have to be dealt with in some non-collective manner.

Trade, industry, commerce and the professions present CLA with its greatest challenge because of their size and diversity. A first step has already been taken, however, with the setting up of a joint task force with the Confederation of British Industry (CBI). This CBI/CLA working party, chaired by an industrialist, will examine the best way or ways forward, concentrating initially on manufacturing industry, with particular emphasis on R&D-driven sectors such as pharmaceuticals, chemicals, engineering, electronics, aerospace and oil fuel.

Basically, CLA is a banking operation with legal overtones: it collects fees from licensed users in respect of acts of photocopying from books and serials and other copying such as microfiche printing and, after deducting its administration costs and any reserves or provisions the Board may decide, distributes the balance to ALCS and PLS for them to pay to authors and publishers.

CLA currently offers two basic services, that is, licences to copy, authorised by many individual owners of copyright, both of which offer the collective repertoire of copyright works mandated to CLA by those owners:

> a *collective user* arrangement such as that made with the associations representing local education authorities for state colleges and schools;

> a *transactional user* service for those institutions where a suitable representative organisation, such as an LEA, is unable or unwilling to provide the level of administrative support which a collective user scheme requires, e.g. implementation and supervision of a sampling system, single cheque payment, etc.

Both types of licence are valid for a specific period, usually two or three years. Under a collective user arrangement the level of copying for a group of institutions is mutually agreed and a global fee set; this fee total is then apportioned by the organising body amongst its constituents and paid by them to CLA on presentation of an invoice from CLA. With the transactional user scheme, fees are paid on a straight cost per copy-page basis; returns to CLA are made at regular, agreed intervals, and a self-billing system is used.

Importantly, from the user community's standpoint, CLA indemnifies all licensees against any inadvertent infringement of copyright.

Right from the outset, the authors' representatives insisted first that writers should benefit individually and directly from the copying of their works and that the money should not go to authors' societies for "social benefit" purposes, as is the case in some parts of the world. Secondly, they insisted that the individual authors' shares should be paid to them directly, and not through the accounting systems of their publishers.

In order to fulfil these requirements CLA had to devise a title-based distribution system and a form of record-keeping suitable for a stratified and statistically sound sample of the licensees. Some form of itemised record-keeping, therefore, is necessary on the part of both categories of licence holders. With *collective user* licensing, a rotating sample of about 5% of institutions in each broad category is required to maintain records of their copying, which are returned to CLA at agreed intervals, where they are checked and analysed. *Transactional user* licensees are required to keep records of all their copying.

Controlled record-keeping is crucial to CLA because the statistical information extracted from these records of copying is used as the basis for making payments to copyright owners whose works have been copied.

Once a licence has been issued, it has been relatively simple, so far, to collect fees. It is quite another matter, however, to edit, process, and analyse the returns of copying, and to calculate the correct amounts due to copyright owners.

In the distribution CLA made in the Autumn of 1987 which covered the period since the issue of the first licence in May 1984 to September 1986, the works of some 10,000 authors on 1,600 publishing imprints were copied.

On return to the Agency, the record-keeping forms, which are regarded and treated as strictly confidential documents, some of which are deemed to be personal data under the Data Protection Act 1984, are:

> checked by the licensing officer responsible to ensure that the conditions of the licence are being adhered to;

> scrutinised by the data preparation department to validate the information being submitted, e.g. missing ISBN/ISSNs etc. are searched for;

> keyed for computer analysis;

> subjected to a final edit for data quality.

The results are analysed and summaries produced showing pages copied, by ISBN/ISSN, by title, by author, and by publisher. Apportionments are then calculated, statements produced and cheques drawn.

The existence of the International Standard Book Number (ISBN) and the International Standard Serial Number (ISSN) systems is a great benefit to CLA and makes the Agency's task that much easier than it would otherwise be.

The CLA Board decided that the first distribution to members would be £1.4 million (US$2.3 million) and would be paid in two parts: the first tranche of just over £500,000 in October 1987, and the balance of around £900,000 in March/April 1988. Thereafter, payments to rights owners would be made every six months. At the time of writing CLA has distributed nearly £2.5 million to members.

The returns submitted by state colleges and schools on CLA's structured sample enabled or statisticians to confirm that copying in this sector is now in the order of 110 million pages per annum from copyright books and serials, which supports the estimates produced by earlier surveys on which the initial LEA global fee was based.

It must be emphasised that a CLA licence is not a carte blanche to copy without restrictions. The conditions are clearly set down and are required to be displayed alongside every copying machine within the control of the licensee. The wording of the notices may vary slightly depending on the category of the licensee, but the core message is always the same! CLA also produces various user guides for issue to employees, and there is a warning sticker that goes on top of machines to act as a reminder to copier users.

For CLA there is comfort in knowing that it is not alone in pioneering the collective administration of copying rights. Counterpart organisations to CLA now exist in sixteen other countries – Australia, Austria, Canada, Denmark, Finland, France, Iceland, the Netherlands, New Zealand, Norway, South Africa, Spain, Sweden, Switzerland, the United States and West Germany – nearly all of them in membership of IFRRO, the International Federation of Reproduction Rights Organisations. RROs are also presently being formed in Italy and Japan.

Finally, the broader the repertoire an RRO can offer its licensees the better, and it is a priority of CLA to secure reciprocal agreements with counterpart organisations overseas, particularly those in English-speaking countries where UK books, journals and periodicals are being widely and extensively copied, and, equally, where much publishing in the English language takes place.

Critics of collecting societies say that they spend pounds to distribute pennies. From the start, this is a potential criticism of which the CLA directors were acutely conscious. As far back as November 1982 the board designate set down in its minutes that on no account were CLA's administration costs to exceed 20% of the fee income. The Agency has done much better than that: CLA's overhead is working out at about 15% of the fee income, and it continually strives to reduce that level where possible. It is, however, in the business of handling large numbers of documents and processing a great deal of information, and to do so efficiently in this day and age a high degree of office automation is required and technological wizardry does not come cheap.

CLA's aim is to distribute as much as it can, as fast as it can, and as efficiently as it can. It believes that £2.5 million, distributed between October 1987 and April 1989, speaks louder than any words, and demonstrates better than anything else the Agency's resolve to achieve its objectives.

Further information from The Secretary, The Copyright Licensing Agency Ltd., 33–34 Alfred Place, London, WC1E 7DP. *tel* 01–436 5931.

# Chartered Society of Designers
# Code of Professional Conduct

This is an abbreviated version of the Code of Professional Conduct issued by the Chartered Society of Designers. A complete copy is available from 29 Bedford Square, London WC1B 3EG (35p to members; 65p to non-members). See also entry in **Societies.**

## INTRODUCTION

1. This Code issued by the Chartered Society of Designers establishes a workable pattern of professional conduct for the benefit of its members and of those who employ their services.
2. All members of the Society undertake as a condition of membership that they will abide by this Code.
3. The Council of the Society has empowered its Conduct Committee to question any member thought to be behaving in a manner contrary to this Code and may as a result of the Committee's report reprimand, suspend or expel that member.
4. When members are working or seeking work abroad they will observe the rules of professional conduct currently in use in that country.

## THE DESIGNER'S PROFESSIONAL RESPONSIBILITIES

5. Designers work primarily for the benefit of their clients or their employers. Like everyone engaged in professional activities, designers have responsibilities not only to their clients or employers but also to their fellow practitioners and to society at large. It follows therefore that designers who are members of the Society accept certain obligations specifically in regard to these responsibilities.

## THE DESIGNER'S RESPONSIBILITY TO HIS CLIENT OR EMPLOYER

6. Good professional relations between a designer and an employer or client depend on the designer's acceptance of the need to be professionally and technically competent and on his/her ability to provide honourable and efficient advice and performance.
7. They will also depend on the reliance which the employer or client can place on a designer's integrity in all confidential matters relating to his/her business.
8. No member may work simultaneously for more than one employer or client known to be in competition, without their knowledge and approval. Similarly no member, or his/her associates or staff, may divulge information confidential to their client or employer without their consent, subject to any requirement under law.
9. The Society believes that it is in the interest of the design profession and of industry that the employment of qualified designers should be increased. Members may therefore promote their own services and those of their profession in a manner appropriate to the various fields of practice in which they work. It is essential, however, that any claims made by them, or by those acting for them, are factually correct, honourable and clear as to their origin, and that the effect shall not be at variance with this Code nor cause harm to their fellow members.
10. It is normal for designers to be paid for their professional services, whether executive or advisory. The Society recommends methods of charging which it

considers appropriate for various types of work, but members will use their own judgement in agreeing fees with their clients.

11. The Society recommends conditions of engagement to enable proper working relationships to be established between members and their clients.

12. Whereas members will make for their clients the best possible trading arrangements with contractors, manufacturers and suppliers, their responsibilities to contractors or suppliers are as professionally important as are their responsibilities to their clients. They must therefore be prepared to act as impartial arbitrators, if need be, to ensure fair dealing on both sides.

13. Members may not divert to their own advantage any discounts, reductions or other financial benefits offered as inducement by contractors, manufacturers or suppliers. Similarly members must disclose to their clients any financial involvement which they may have with contractors or suppliers they may recommend.

14. On the other hand, if a member is also a manufacturer, retailer or agent in his/her own right, a member may accept those financial terms which are normally honourably offered within the trade, provided they accrue to his/her company or organisation and not to himself/herself privately.

15. Although the relationship between a staff designer and employer may well differ from that between consultant and client, the employed designer, who is a member of the Society, shall accept a responsibility to the employer on the same terms of professional integrity and confidentiality.

THE DESIGNER'S RESPONSIBILITY TO HIS FELLOW PRACTITIONERS

16. From time to time members may find themselves called upon to comment on other designers' work and in a consultative capacity may reasonably be expected to do so. Personal opinion must play a significant part in any criticism, but members should be aware of the fine dividing line between objective and destructive criticism. Personal denigration amongst members is regarded as intolerable and the Society will support any member who is shown to have been so affronted.

17. Similarly the Society regards copying or plagiarism with intent as wholly unprofessional.

18. No member shall knowingly seek to supplant another designer currently working on a project whether satisfactorily or not. There are occasions when more than one designer may be engaged on the same project. Where, however, a member suspects that his/her engagement may supplant rather than augment the service of another, he/she shall seek an assurance from the client that any previous association with another designer has been terminated.

19. Neither shall a member charge nor receive a fee, neither make nor receive a gift or other benefit, from a fellow member, in recognition of a recommendation to a post or an assignment.

20. Members should assure themselves that competitions they may be invited to assess or may wish to enter are in accordance with the Society's regulations for holding of design competitions.

# Publishing practice

## Agreements

### PUBLISHERS' AGREEMENTS

#### ROYALTY AGREEMENTS

The royalty agreement is now the most usual arrangement between author and publisher, and almost invariably the most satisfactory for the author. It provides for the payment to the author of a royalty of an agreed percentage on all copies of the book which are sold. The rate of royalty varies with circumstances: for hardback general books it is often ten per cent of the published price (or the equivalent percentage of the sum received by the publisher). Lower rates will be payable on copies sold at a high discount, for example in some export areas, to major wholesalers and to book clubs. There may be a provision for the rate to rise after the sale of a specified number of copies. Similarly, most authors can secure in their contracts provision for an advance from the publisher in anticipation and on account of the specified royalties, and the amount of this advance will depend largely upon the publisher's estimate of the book's prospect of sales.

Because many publishers' invoicing and stock control are now computerised there is a trend towards paying royalties on the price received—which can easily be read from a computer printout—rather than on the published price. Appropriate adjustments are of course made to the royalty figure, and the arrangement is of no intrinsic disadvantage to the author.

Most publishing houses nowadays have printed or word-processed agreement forms in which blanks are left for the insertion of the proposed royalty rates, the sum payable in advance, and so on. The terms are usually agreed between author and publisher before the form is completed, but the fact that a printed form or word-processed agreement has been signed by the publisher does not mean that an author, before signing it, cannot discuss any of its clauses with the publisher. The majority of publishers value the establishment of confidence and understanding between themselves and their authors and are willing to make reasonable amendments.

It is impossible to set out in detail here the numerous provisions of publishing agreements or to comment on the differing effects of these upon different sorts of book. Every sensible author will scrutinise any agreement carefully before signing it, will not hesitate to ask the publisher to explain any point in it which is not clear, and if in any doubt will seek professional advice from a reliable literary agent, or the Society of Authors, or one of the few firms of solicitors who specialise in authors' business.

The careful author will look for a comprehensive clause setting out the contingencies in which the contract is to terminate, what happens if the publisher goes out of business or is taken over, and whether the publisher can sell his rights in the book to a third party without consulting the author.

The agreement should specify the respective responsibilities of author and publisher in the provision of illustrations, indexes, etc. Unexpected fees for reproducing illustrations can swiftly eat up an advance.

The author will examine the clauses covering the handling of overseas sales, American rights and subsidiary rights (film, serial, broadcasting, etc.) which for some books may well bring in more than the book publication rights.

Consider carefully clauses giving the publisher an option to publish future works and clauses which may restrict a specialist author's future output by preventing him or her from writing other books on the same subject. The author should also be sure that he or she understands what the contract proposes in relation to cheap editions, 'remainders', sheet sales, reprints and new editions.

OUTRIGHT SALE

Outright sale of copyright for an agreed sum is rarely suggested by a publisher, and hardly ever to be recommended, though it may be justified in special cases, as when an author is commissioned to supply a small amount of text as a commentary for a book which consists primarily of illustrations. It is a survival from the days when copyright meant, for all practical purposes, merely the exclusive right of publication in book form. So long as it was possible to gauge approximately a book's potential sales and the profit to be anticipated, the value of a copyright could be fairly accurately estimated. But to-day, anything from a thousand to a million copies of a book may be sold, and when the various subsidiary rights—the film rights in particular—may prove either valueless or worth thousands of pounds, any arrangement for an outright sale of copyright must be a gamble in which the author is likely to be the loser.

PROFIT-SHARING AND COMMISSION AGREEMENTS

Under a profit-sharing agreement the publisher bears the cost of production, but the author makes no money until the book shows a profit, at which point the profit is divided in agreed proportions between author and publisher. In theory this sounds fair, but it is rarely satisfactory in practice. Such agreements can lend themselves readily to abuse, largely because of the difficulty of defining the term 'profit'.

Under a commission agreement the author bears the cost of production and pays the publisher a commission for marketing the book. If no publisher is prepared to publish a work on the normal royalty basis, the chances are that the author who decides to finance his or her own publication will lose most, if not all, of the money outlaid. In consequence commission agreements, save in exceptional circumstances, are to be discouraged. Many good publishers refuse to handle books on commission in any circumstances whatsoever; others confine their commission publishing to authoritative books of a highly specialised or scholarly nature. The specialist author who decides that commission publishing is justified by special circumstances should make sure that the firm which offers such an arrangement is reputable and able to market the book efficiently.

No firm of standing will publish fiction or poetry on commission, and publishers offering to do so should be given a wide berth. There are a few firms ready to exploit the vanity of a would-be author. Such firms ask the author for a large sum as 'a contribution towards the cost' of producing the book. Too often it more than covers the cost of bringing out a small and shoddy edition, which the 'publisher' makes no effort to distribute.

Publishing agreements are lucidly discussed at considerable length in Sir Stanley Unwin's *The Truth About Publishing* (8th edition 1976 Unwin Hyman Ltd.). *Publishing Agreements: A Book of Precedents* (3rd edition 1988, edited by Charles Clark, Unwin Hyman Ltd. £20.00) gives a detailed stock of precedents forming a base for the founding of agreements.

## NET BOOK AGREEMENT

The Net Book Agreement is an arrangement, approved by the Restrictive Practices Court as operating in the public interest, designed to improve the availability of a wide range of books to the public through a wide range of outlets. The Agreement, operated by the Publishers Association, enables (but does not require) any publishers who are signatories (whether or not in membership of the PA) to enforce a minimum retail price (the net price) for individual titles, then known as 'net books'. In this way, booksellers are encouraged to hold wide-ranging stocks, secure in the knowledge that the prices of their books, and the value of their stocks, will not be undermined by other retailers who do not provide similar levels of stock or customer-service, such as handling special orders. The Restrictive Practices Court held that, without such a system, the availability of books and the number of booksellers would be reduced, book prices would overall be higher, and fewer titles would be published, with particular loss to those of literary and scholastic value.

Under the arrangement, libraries open to the public, schools and school and church book agencies may be supplied by booksellers at permitted discounts on the net price. School books are normally sold non-net (not subject to the Agreement).

# Book Clubs

Book Clubs provide their members with selected books (offered either as a main choice or alternative choice) at book club prices, usually through the mail on a regular basis. In order to acquire selected books at special prices book club members are required to commit to the purchase of a number of selections over a given period.

Book Clubs can enjoy relatively secure sales and offer savings to their members by buying or printing considerable numbers of copies and offering them to members who have indicated their interest in the type of books offered. These sales can provide valuable revenues to the authors and the publishers of the selected books.

In the case of books otherwise sold as 'net books' through booksellers (see **Net Book Agreement**), the conduct of book clubs is regulated by Book Club Regulations administered by the Publishers Association. These regulations are designed to ensure fairness between book clubs and booksellers offering the same titles.

Sales to book clubs are usually made by the original publisher under the terms of the contract between publisher and author—usually providing a royalty on the number of copies sold.

**Academy Book Club,** Namara Group, 51 Beak Street, London W1R 3LF   *tel* 01-437 2131.

**Artists' Book Club Ltd.** (Monthly), P.O. Box 178, Oxford OX2 8RP   *tel* (0865) 310663   *telex* 83308   *fax* (0865) 310662. *Managing Director:* Jean-Claude Peissel. Member of Musterlin Group plc.

**Artists' Choice,** (Quarterly) Artists' Choice Ltd., P.O. Box 3, Huntingdon, Cambridgeshire PE18 0QX   *tel* Bythorn (080-14) 201.

**Book Club Associates,** 87 Newman Street, London W1P 4EN   *tel* 01-637 0341   *fax* 01-631 3262.

| *Monthly Book Clubs* | *Quarterly Book Clubs* |
| --- | --- |
| Ancient & Medieval History Book Club | Arts Guild |
| | Cricket Book Club |
| Childrens Book of the Month Club | Encounters |
| | Executive World |
| History Guild | Home Computer Club |
| The Literary Guild | On the Road |
| Military and Aviation Book Society | Railway Book Club |
| | Readers Choice |
| Mystery & Thriller Guild | |
| World Books | |

**Bookmarx Club,** (Quarterly), IS Books Ltd., 265 Seven Sisters Road, London N4 2DE   *tel* 01-802 6145.

**Books for Children,** (Monthly), Time-Life International Ltd, Park House, Dollar Street, Cirencester, Gloucestershire GL7 2AN   *tel* (0285) 67081.

**Bookworm Club, The,** Children's Club in Schools (6 p.a.), Heffers Booksellers, 20 Trinity Street, Cambridge CB2 3NG.

**Computer Users Book Club (Cub Club)** (Quarterly), Unit 7, Blaina Enterprise Centre, Rising Sun Industrial Estate, Blaina, Gwent NP3 3JW  *tel* (0495) 292169  *fax* (0495) 292404.

**The Folio Society,** 202 Great Suffolk Street, London SE1 1PR  *tel* 01-407 7411  *fax* 01-3786684. *Showroom:* The Folio Gallery, 5 Royal Arcade, 28 Old Bond Street, London W1X 3HB.

**The Leisure Circle,** (Quarterly), York House, Empire Way, Wembley, Middlesex HA9 0PF  *tel* 01-902 8888.

**Letterbox Library,** (Quarterly), Childrens Books Co-operative, 8 Bradbury Street, London N16 8JN  *tel* 01-254 1640.

**New Left Review Editions,** 6 Meard Street, London W1V 3HR  *tel* 01-734 8839.

**Odhams Leisure Group Ltd.,** (Subsidiary of K.L.P. Group Plc), Denington Road, Wellingborough, Northants NN8 2PY  *tel* (0933) 228848. Women's interest series: cookery, needlecraft, children's products.

**Poetry Book Society,** (Quarterly), 21 Earls Court Square, London SW5 9DE  *tel* 01-244 9792.

**Pooh Corner Book Club,** For all things Pooh, High Street, Hartfield, East Sussex TN7 4AE  *tel* (0892) 770453.

**Readers Union Ltd.,** P.O. Box 6, Brunel House, Newton Abbot, Devon TQ12 2DW  *tel* (0626) 332828  *telex* 42904 Books G  *fax* 0626-64463.

Anglers Book Society
Belief: The Religious Book Society
Birds and Natural History Book Society
Country Book Society
Craft Book Society
Craftsman Book Society
Design Book Club
Equestrian Book Society
Field Sports Book Society
Gardeners Book Society
Golf Book Club
Maritime Book Society
Music Book Society
Nationwide Book Service incorporating Phoenix Book Society
Needlecraft Book Society
Photographic Book Society
Ramblers and Climbers Book Society
Travel and Exploration Book Society
World of Nature Book Club

**Red House Children's Book Club,** (12 p.a.), Cotswold Business Park, Witney, Oxfordshire OX8 5YF  *tel* (0993) 771144.

**Scholastic Publications Ltd,** Marlborough House, Holly Walk, Leamington Spa, Warwickshire CV32 4LS  *tel* (0926 81) 3910  *telex* 312138 Spls G  *fax* (0926) 883331.

**Travel Book Club,** (Quarterly), 248–250 Lavender Hill, London SW11 1JW  *tel* 01-228 6730  *fax* 01 924 1139.

**Women's Press Bookclub, The,** (Quarterly), The Women's Press Ltd., 34 Great Sutton Street, London EC1V 0DX  *tel* 01-253 0009.

# International Standard Book Numbering (ISBN)

The Standard Book Numbering (SBN) system was introduced in this country in 1967. It became the International Standard Book Numbering (ISBN) system three years later.

The overall administration of the international system is done from Berlin, by the International ISBN-Agentur, Staatsbibliothek Preussicher Kulturbesitz, D-1000 Berlin 30, Postfach 1407, West Germany.

In this country the system is administered by the Standard Book Numbering Agency Ltd., 12 Dyott Street, London, WC1A 1DF. The Agency was set up before the scheme became international, which is why that word does not appear in its title.

Over the years a number of misconceptions have grown up about ISBNs, and this article endeavours to put right some of these.

The Standard Book Numbering Agency gets a large number of telephone calls, many of which follow a common pattern. For instance:

*Are they legal? Do we have to have them?*

There is no legal requirement for a book to carry an ISBN. But it is useful to educational authorities, certain library suppliers, public libraries and some computer using distributors, and is now essential to booksellers using the teleordering system. The introduction of Public Lending Right has also made ISBNs of importance to authors.

*I am about to publish a book. Must I deposit a copy with the ISBN Agency to obtain copyright?*

No. Copyright is obtained by the simple act of publication. However, by law, a copy of every new book must be deposited at the Copyright Receipt Office of the British Library, 2 Sheraton Street, London, W1V 4BH. The copyright office issues a receipt, and this has, in the past, proved useful when a dispute has arisen over the date of publication.

Titles deposited are catalogued by the British National Bibliography, which records ISBNs where available. Perhaps a confusion about copyright and ISBNs arises from this, but the ISBN, of itself, has nothing to do with copyright.

*What are the fees for ISBNs?*

No charge is made for the allocation of an ISBN. Various publishers who allocate their own usually ask the Agency to supply a computer print out of all the ISBNs available to the publisher, with check digits calculated. A small charge is made for this print out.

If the publisher does not allocate his own ISBNs, not only is there no charge, he may not even know about them. For a few years after the system was introduced, books catalogued by the BNB or Whitakers may have been assigned ISBNs by the Agency for listing purposes, without reference to the publisher. However, with the widespread use of numbers it is now customary to consult all publishers before any are assigned.

*Are you a Government Department?*

No. Our parent company pays taxes; we get no subsidy from anyone. In most other countries the costs *are* borne by the state, through the national library system which frequently administers the scheme overseas.

*Do I need an ISBN for a Church Magazine?*

No. But you may need an ISSN (International Standard Serial Number). These are obtainable from the U.K. National Serials Data Centre, the British Library, 2 Sheraton Street, London, W1V 4BH.

Incidentally, a yearbook can have both an ISBN and an ISSN.

*We would prefer to have our own identifier as we do not consider ourselves within the English speaking group.*

This comes from publishers with devolution in mind. Usually Welsh, less often Irish. The group system within the ISBN scheme is not quite so categoric as to be dictated by language considerations only. A group is defined as a "language, geographic or other convenient area". There is no strict logic applied, just pragmatism as to what is most *convenient* for trading purposes.

*I would prefer not to be involved with ISBNs, but there is this Public Lending Right, and the author says . . .*

Well, yes. ISBNs have now taken on a new significance; they help authors towards a little more money. The recording system for PLR dues is machine based, and uses ISBNs where available. It is more convenient for the libraries who provide the sample loan statistics if ISBNs are printed in books, but this is not a legal requirement and the system *can* work without ISBNs. However, it works better, and with lower overheads (and so more money available to be allocated to authors) if ISBNs *are* in books.

*I want my book to reach as wide a market as possible, so I must have an ISBN.*

The ISBN will not automatically sell a book. If the book, like that famous mousetrap, is a better one, the world will beat a path to its door. However, the ISBN will oil the wheels of distribution and it is therefore advisable to have one.

*Will you supply an ISBN for a carton of assorted painting books?*

No. In the words of the ISBN manual (available from the SBN agency at £3.50, cash with order), 'an ISBN identifies one title, or edition of a title, from one specific publisher, and is unique to that title or edition'. It is now additionally used to identify computer software and maps. It is not designed for a carton of assorted painting books.

*How does a publisher who knows nothing about the system and does not want regularly to allocate his own numbers get an ISBN?*

The Agency is willing to supply ISBNs for future books, to all the small publishers who have neither the continuity of staff nor the facilities for assigning their own. This offer extends not only to new books, but also to new editions and reprints. If they have not had ISBNs before, publishers should ask the SBN Agency for a standard application form. Written answers are required to six basic questions. Publishers already in the Agency records can obtain ISBNs on request, provided that they can quote firm details of title, edition and the kind of binding.

If, at any stage, a publisher who has not previously assigned his own ISBNs wishes to take over the allocation of his own numbers from the Agency he will be welcome to do so. But it is essential that due warning is given. Otherwise the publisher may assign one number to a given title, and the Agency may well assign a completely different number.

Reproduced by kind permission of the Standard Book Numbering Agency Ltd.

# Preparation of materials, resources

*Books, Research and Reference Sources for Writers*

MARGARET PAYNE, A.L.A.

Almost every writing project will involve the use of books or research at some stage. Some references are quickly found; others require accumulating numerous books or information files on a specific topic and visits to specialist libraries or other relevant places or people. Although research can be an interest or pleasure in itself, it can also be time-consuming, cutting into writing or earning time. Even checking a single fact can take hours or days if you ask the wrong question or check the wrong source first. No article or book can hope to solve all problems— sometimes there are no answers, or the lack of information is itself the answer— but a few guidelines as to routines and sources may save much time and money. The following is an introduction to printed sources. For a more detailed approach, including guides to original and unpublished material, it is recommended you consult Ann Hoffmann's *Research for Writers*, 3rd ed. Black, 1986, £6.95, a most useful book which covers methods, sources, specific organisations and specialist libraries.

Suggestions for a core collection of reference books to own are given below under the WRITER'S REFERENCE BOOKSHELF. The final choice of title often depends on personal preference and interests, space, the frequency with which it needs to be consulted, its cost and the proximity of your nearest public reference library. Anyone living in or near a large city has an advantage over the country dweller. Those living within easy reach of London have the best advantage of all: a choice of major reference libraries; a variety of specialist sources such as headquarters of various societies, companies and organisations; academic and other specialist libraries and the government and the copyright British Library. The latter is the ultimate rather than the first choice, however. Often a question can be answered much nearer home, but you may find the further back in time you go, or the more detailed your research, the further afield you need to travel.

## CHECKING A FACT

*What do you really want to know?*

Clarifying your question in advance can save much work for you or your researcher. If you want to check someone's date of birth and know the person is alive or very recently dead and in *Who's Who*, then ask for that book, or phrase your telephone request so that the librarian goes straight to that source. Do not start with general questions such as 'Where are the biographies?' In a branch library you may be shown sections of individual lives; on the telephone you are adding to British Telecom's profits and your telephone bill, as well as wasting time. If the person is dead, did he or she die recently enough to have a newspaper obituary—it often mentions the date of birth—or long enough ago to be in a volume of *Who Was Who* or the *Dictionary of National Biography?* Never assume that information that you know is necessarily common knowledge; it needs to be specified.

*Go straight to the index.*

Most reference books are arranged in alphabetical order but, if not, they should have an index. Some indexes may seem inadequate, but have you used the right key word? A good index should refer you from the one not used. For example, some will use carpentry and ignore woodwork as an entry. Others will ignore both and go straight to the object to be made or repaired. If there is no index, turn first to the contents page, as in some books the index is at the front rather than the back.

*Is it important to be up to date?*

Most books have the date of publication on the back of the title page. Is the answer given one which may be surpassed or superseded? Despite some instant publishing, when dealing with statistics most books have a built in obsolescence. There is a cut off date when the text goes to the printer and the up-dating must wait for the next edition. Some current events are too recent to be found in books at all, although well documented at the time in newspapers and magazines (see below).

*If in doubt, re-check your answer.*

If the answer is of importance, try not to depend on one source. Mistakes can occur in print or in transcribing. Sometimes it is necessary to check another source for verification or to obtain another point of view. In all cases you should . . .

*Note your source.*

Even if you think you will remember, always note where you find your information, preferably next to the answer, or in a card file or book where it can be easily found. Note the title, author, publisher and date of publication as well as the page number. Nothing is more annoying than having to undertake the same search twice.

## RESEARCHING A SUBJECT

Reference has already been made to Ann Hoffmann's book for detail, but Kipling's six honest serving men can still be the basis for any subject: What? Why? When? How? Where? Who? cover aspects of most enquiries. The starting point depends on the writer's personal knowledge of the subject. Where it is unfamiliar always start from the general and go on to the particular. An article in an encyclopedia can fill in the background and often recommend bibliographies or other references. If an article in the *Encyclopaedia Britannica* is too detailed or too complex, try *The World Book*. The latter may be in the children's library, but because it has to appeal to a wider readership, the text and illustrations are clearer. Avoid a detailed book on the subject until you need it; it may tell you more than you want to know.

The following sources are suggestions as sources of information, but not all will be relevant to your subject.

**Reference Libraries.** Use the largest one in your vicinity for encylopedias, specialised reference books, annuals and for back numbers of newspapers and periodicals. Ask for *Walford's Guide to Reference Material*. The three volumes list the standard reference works of subjects, most of which should be available for consultation.

**Lending Libraries.** Find the class number of the books you want, and see what is available.

**Special Libraries.** *The Aslib Directory of Information Sources in the United Kingdom* should be available in your reference library. It gives details of special libraries of industries, organisations and societies.

**Catalogues, bibliographies and subject guides.** Some libraries publish their catalogues, but this is becoming less frequent. There is a series of subject catalogues to the British Library (formerly the British Museum Library) up to 1975 and the *British National Bibliography* updates this (*see* COMPILING A BIBLIOGRAPHY below).

**Newspapers and bibliographies.** There is a monthly index to *The Times*, cumulated annually, which often provides the date of an event. The index also includes the *The Times Supplements*. For periodical articles, begin with the *British Humanities Index*, and, if necessary, check also the specialist indexes and abstracting journals such as *Current Technology Index*. Your public library can often locate runs of periodicals and magazines, and the interloan service can obtain specific periodical articles if you have the details. *Profile*, an on line index to quality newspapers is the most up to date available, but retrospective only to 1985 and few libraries have the facility as yet.

## COMPILING A BIBLIOGRAPHY

Checking what books are already available may reveal both the range of titles already in print and the potential market for your work. If yours is to be the tenth book on the subject published in the last two years, saturation point may be near. On the other hand, if you know the books and believe you can do better, or have evolved a different approach, you can mention this in a covering letter to a potential publisher. A quick way to evaluate what is available is by checking the shelves of a public library or bookstore, but it should be remembered that in a library, many of the best books will be on loan. This practice also makes one aware of publishers' interests.

A more comprehensive and systematic list of recent books can be compiled by consulting the *British National Bibliography*, a cumulating list based on the copyright books in the British Library, with advance notice (up to three months) of new books through the Cataloguing in Publication scheme. The arrangement is by the Dewey Decimal Classification used in all public libraries. Other subject lists are less satisfactory to consult. The British Museum (now British Library) has a series of subject indexes up to 1975, and many British books are included in the American *Cumulative Book Index* (1928 on). *British Books in Print* is predominantly an author-title list, but does index some books under the key word of a subtitle; as its name implies, out of print books are excluded.

Facilities now exist to obtain a bibliography on any subject by using one of the computer data banks based on the British Library, the Library of Congress or commercial firms. The difficulties are expense (£25.00 per hour) and, at the time of going to press, some initial teething problems. The Book Information Service of Book Trust (formerly the National Book League) will compile booklists and bibliographies at a charge currently of £6.50 an hour to Friends and £10.00 to others. The address is Book Information Service, Book Trust, Book House, 45 East Hill, London SW18 2QZ.

## OBTAINING BOOKS

**Books in print.** In 1988 56,514 different books were published in the United Kingdom alone, joining the many thousands of other titles still in print from previous years. The number of books available means that the chances of finding a copy of what you want on your bookseller's shelf, when you want it, may be slim. But if it is in print it can be ordered for you, although delivery times vary with each publisher. Most large bookshops and libraries now have the monthly microfiche editions of *British Books in Print* giving details of author, publisher, price, number of pages and international standard book number (ISBN). The latter is often useful for speeding the order.

**Out of print books** present more difficulty. Generally the older the book, the more difficult it may be to obtain. Such books are no longer available from the publishers, who retain only a file copy, all other stocks having been sold. Therefore unless you are lucky enough to find an unsold copy on a bookseller's shelves, it must be sought in the second-hand market or through a library loan. There are many specialist second-hand and antiquarian booksellers, and a number of directories listing them and their interests. The most well known are *Sheppard's Book Dealers in the British Isles*, now published by Europa, and Peter Marcan's *Directory of Specialist Book Dealers in the United Kingdom*. Copies of these should be in your local reference library. Many advertise in *Book and Magazine Collector*, a monthly magazine, which has an extensive 'wants' column.

**Public libraries** should be able to obtain books for you, whether or not they are in print, either from their own stock, from other libraries in the system or through the interloan scheme. This operates through the British Lending Library, but all requests must go through your library as you cannot apply direct. Your local library tickets may sometimes be used in other libraries, but different issuing systems have discouraged this in recent years.

## A WRITER'S REFERENCE BOOKSHELF

However good and accessible a public library may be, there are some books required for constant or instant consultation, which should be within easy reach of the desk or typewriter. The choice of title may vary, but the following list is offered as suggestions for a core collection.

1. **Dictionaries.** With the use of word processor packages, a dictionary is no longer quite so essential for spelling checks, although still needed to clarify definitions and meanings. A book is often easier to consult, and portable. The complete *Oxford English Dictionary* is not, and although the definitive work, neither the full nor the compact edition with its magnifying glass, nor the two volume *Shorter Oxford Dictionary* is easy to handle for quick reference, so a one volume dictionary is more practical. The number of new words and meanings coming into vogue suggests a replacement every five years or so, or supplementing your choice by a good paperback edition. If you use an old copy, you will be surprised by the improved format and readability of the new editions.

The most popular one volume dictionaries are the *Concise Oxford Dictionary* (7th ed. 1982, £9.50–80,000 definitions), *Chambers' Twentieth Century Dictionary* (4th ed. 1983, £15.95–150,000 entries, appealing to crossword addicts), *The Collins English Dictionary* (£14.50–96,000 entries). Recommended paperback dictionaries are *Oxford Paperback Dictionary* (1983, £3.95–50,000 entries) or the

*Penguin English Dictionary* (n.e. 1986, £4.95–80,000 entries). If you write for the American market, it is advisable also to have an American dictionary to check variant spellings and meanings. The equivalent of the Oxford family of dictionaries is Webster's, the most popular one volume edition being *Webster's New Collegiate Dictionary* (Merriam U.S., 1983, £24.00–175,000 entries).

2. **Roget's Thesaurus.** When the exact word or meaning eludes you, the thesaurus may help clear a mental block. There are many versions of Roget available, both in hardback and paperback, including a revision by E. M. Kirkpatrick (Longman, 1987, £8.50), another edited by D. C. Browning (Dent, 1982, £10.50) and a paperback edition from Penguin (1984, £3.95).

3. **Grammar and English usage.** A wide choice is available but Fowler's *Modern English Usage* remains a standard work (2nd ed. revised Sir Ernest Gowers, Oxford U.P., £10.95 and £4.95 paperback). Many prefer Sir Ernest Gowers' *Complete Plain Words* (3rd ed. 1986 revised Sidney Greenbaum and Jane Whitcut, H.M.S.O., £5.50; Penguin 1987, £4.50). More recent works are *The Oxford Guide to English Language.* (Oxford U.P., 1984, £17.50 and £4.95) and *Bloomsbury Good Word Guide* (Bloomsbury, 1988, £13.95), and Michael Legat's *The Nuts and Bolts of Writing* (Hale, 1989, £9.95 and £4.95).

4. **Encyclopaedias and annuals.** Multi-volume encyclopaedias are both expensive and space consuming. They are best left for consultation at the nearest reference library, where the most up-to-date versions should be available, unless your need justifies ownership. Of the single volumes, *Pears Cyclopaedia* contains a surprising amount of general information and a new edition is issued annually (Pelham Books, 97th ed. 1988, £10.95). For those concerned with current affairs, the complete edition of *Whitaker's Almanack* has valuable statistics and information on government and countries, as well as many miscellaneous facts not found elsewhere. For annual replacement if constantly used.

5. **Atlases, gazetteers and road maps.** These also need replacing with updated editions from time to time. An old edition can be misleading with recent changes of placenames and metrication. The *The Times Atlas of the World* is the definitive work, but it is expensive and bulky for quick reference. The *The Times Concise Atlas of the World* (Times Books, 1986, £27.50) has the most comprehensive gazetteer-index. It is a little more manageable but still requires special shelving.

With the building of the M25 and other motorways, many existing road atlases of Britain may be out of date and need replacing. There are many paperback editions at 3 miles to 1 inch (1:190,080) for less than £5.00, but most detailed is *AZ Great Britain Road Atlas* (Geographers AZ, 1989, £4.95; 1:250,000) with 31,000 place names and 56 town maps. Hardbacks recommended by *Which* magazine are *AZ Great Britain Road Atlas* (1988, £11.95; 1:200,000) and *Ordnance Survey Touring Atlas of Great Britain* (1988, £15.00). The *Reader's Digest Driver's Atlas of the British Isles* (1988, £16.95) includes Ireland. For London and environs *Greater London Street Atlas* (AA/Geographia, 5th ed., 1987, £19.95) is a detailed 3.12 miles to 1 inch street map for the whole M25 area.

6. **Literary companions and dictionaries.** There are many to choose from, and frequency of consultation will determine whether all or some of the following are desirable. *Brewer's Dictionary of Phrase and Fable* (13th ed., Cassell, 1981, £13.95 and £6.95) avoids many distractions and diversions by settling queries, as does *The Oxford Companion to English Literature* (5th ed. edited by Margaret Drabble, Oxford U.P., 1985, £19.50). This new edition complements rather than replaces Sir Paul Harvey's earlier editions. Either can be used for checking an

author's work, but the definitive and exhaustive lists are to be found in the *New Cambridge Bibliography of English Literature*. At £80.00 per volume for the four volumes and £32.50 for the index volume it is very expensive.

7. **Books of quotations.** Once divorced from their text and unattributed, quotations are not easy to trace. This should be a warning to any writer or researcher to note author, title and page number to any item copied. Tracing quotations often needs resort to more than one collection, but the most popular anthologies are *The Oxford Dictionary of Quotations* (3rd ed., Oxford U.P., 1985, £22.50) and the *Penguin Dictionary of Quotations* (Penguin, 3rd ed. 1979, £3.95). The *Penguin Dictionary of Modern Quotations* (Penguin, 1980, £3.95), *The Twentieth Century Quotations* (Sphere, 1987, £4.99) and *Bloomsbury Dictionary of Quotations* (Bloomsbury, 1987, £14.95) contain more recent material.

8. **Biographical dictionaries.** *Pears Cyclopaedia* contains a brief but useful section, but for a fuller working tool the standard works are *Chambers' Biographical Dictionary* (Chambers, 1984, £25.00, paperback £15.00–15,000 entries) or the American-biased *Webster's Biographical Dictionary* (Merriam U.S., 1976, £21.00–150,000 entries). Frequency of consultation will determine whether you need a personal copy of *Who's Who* or the *Concise Dictionary of National Biography*, which are available in most libraries.

9. **Dates and anniversaries.** A brief guide to anniversaries is included in the Journalists' Calendar section of this book (see **Index**). *The Encyclopaedia of Dates and Events*, edited by L. C. Pascoe in the Teach Yourself series (Hodder, 1979, o.p.) and *Chambers' Dictionary of Dates* (Chambers, 1983, £4.95), both paperback, are the most used works.

10. **Working directories for writers.** A current copy of *Writers' & Artists' Yearbook* is essential, as recent moves and mergers have made so many publishers' details out of date. It is useful for very much more information besides that found in the first section. Browse through, or use the index, in spare moments to familiarise yourself with its contents for future reference.

Frequency of consultation will determine whether you also need *Willing's Press Guide* (annual, 1989, British Media Publications, £54.00) or *Benn's Media Directory* (Benn, 2 vols. 1989, £65.00 per volume), both very comprehensive in their coverage of British and overseas newspapers, magazines and other media information. *Cassell's Directory of Publishing* complements all the above, but gives more information about publishing personnel not found elsewhere.

## SOME BOOKS ABOUT WRITING AND THE BOOK TRADE

The book trade has changed considerably in the last ten years. The paperback explosion of the seventies appears to have settled down, but in turn we seem to be experiencing a bookshop chain development. In publishing, computerisation is beginning to affect many aspects and we are undergoing another period of mergers and takeovers of publishing companies large and small. Partly for that reason, much material in older books is inapplicable, although a few remain important for historical reasons. The following is a selection from recent publications. It does not include any of the many books on writing specific types of novels or articles which are best examined in a library or book shop before purchase.

Basil Blackwell Ltd. *Guide for Authors*. Blackwell, 1985, o.p. Useful 56-page pamphlet intended as a house guide; gives a resumé of book production stages with an appendix on preparing disc or tape manuscripts.

Bolt, David. *The Author's Handbook*. Piatkus Books, 1986. £7.95 & £3.95. Written to fill some of the gaps in the author's search for information.

Bonham-Carter, Victor. *Authors by Profession, volume 2: From the Copyright Act 1911 until the End of 1981*. Bodley Head, 1984, o.p.. Volume 1 published by the Society of Authors covered the history of authorship up to 1911; the present volume brings it closer to date.

Clark, Giles N. *Inside Book Publishing: a career builder's guide*. Blueprint, 1988. £12.95 and £6.95. Intended to give an overview to young publishers, it describes the processes and business of modern publishing.

Curwen, Peter. *The World Book Industry*. Euromonitor, 1986, £38.00. The only book attempting a world survey, but marred by a lack of index. To be dipped into rather than read.

Legat, Michael. *An Author's Guide to Publishing*. Robert Hale, 1982. £7.95 and £4.95. Assumes no experience of publishing, a useful, clear introduction with a glossary.

Legat, Michael. *Writing for Pleasure and Profit*. Robert Hale, 1986. £8.95 and £4.95. The best of the recent introductions to writing, covering novels, non-fiction and other topics briefly but clearly.

Mumby, F. A. *Publishing and Bookselling in the Twentieth Century*. Unwin Hyman, 6th ed. 1982. £12.95; paperback 1984. £8.95. Revised by Ian Norrie to include events up to 1970, this is the best historical survey.

Owen, Peter, editor. *Publishing—the Future*. Peter Owen, 1988. £6.95. A collection of articles by leading figures on various aspects of the book trade today.

# Journalists' Calendar
# 1990

## SELECTED ANNIVERSARIES

**JANUARY**

**1 1540 English History: Anne of Cleves,**
who had arrived in England in late
December 1539, met **King Henry VIII**
**for the first time.** They were married on
the 6th, and divorced in July. (See also
28th July 1540.)

**1660 British History: Samuel Pepys**
**recorded the first entry in his diary.** An
account of life in Restoration Britain,
1660–69.

**1960 African History: French Cameroon**
**became an independent Republic.** (British
territory of S. Cameroon incorporated in
1961.)

**2 1905** Birth of Sir **Michael Tippett,**
composer.

**1920** Birth of **Isaac Asimov,** American
scientist and prolific science fiction writer
(*I, Robot*).

**6 1840** Death of **Fanny Burney,** Mme
Frances D'Arblay, novelist, diarist,
intimate of Dr Johnson and his circle
(*Evelina*, novel.)

**8 1935** Birth of **Elvis Presley,** American
pop singer, actor and entertainer. (Died
1977.)

**1940 British History: WWII: Rationing**
**introduced in Britain;** butter, bacon and
sugar were the first commodities to be
affected.

**9 1890** Birth of Dr **Karl Capek,**
Czechoslovakian playwright and novelist.
Inventor of the neologism, Robot, in his
novel, *R.U.R.* (Rossum's Universal
Robots). (Died 1938.)

**10 1840 British History: The Penny Post**
**system came into operation in Britain.** (A
revolutionary reform of Britain's postal
system because it replaced a tariff system
based on distance by one based on the
mail's weight.)

**1920 World History: The League of**
**Nations came into being.** (Replaced in
1945 by the United Nations.)

**12 1950 Disaster:** British submarine,
*Truculent,* sank in the Thames with the

loss of over 60 lives, after colliding with
Swedish tanker, *Divina.*

**1960** Death of **Nevil Shute,** novelist (*A*
*Town Like Alice*).

**1970 African History: Biafra surrendered**
**and called for a ceasefire** and armistice
negotiations; 15th Gen. Gowon accepted
the breakaway state's unconditional
surrender, thus ending the bloody two-
and-a-half year civil war.

**14 1900 Opera: Premiere** of Puccini's *Tosca*
in Rome.

**15 1815** Death of **Emma, Lady Hamilton,**
Nelson's mistress. (Born 12th May 1765.)

**16 1920 American History: Prohibition came**
**into force in America.** (Repealed in
December 1933.)

**17 1820** Birth of **Anne Brontë,** novelist
(pseudonym Acton Bell) (*The Tenant of*
*Wildfell Hall*).

**18 1980** Death of **Cecil Beaton,**
photographer and designer.

**19 1915 British History: WWI: First air raid**
**on Britain.** Bombs dropped from a
Zeppelin on Great Yarmouth and King's
Lynn, Norfolk.

**20 1790** Death of **John Howard,**
philanthropist, social and penal reformer.

**1875** Death of **Jean Millet,** French
painter, chiefly known for his peasant
scenes.

**1900** Death of **John Ruskin,** art and
social critic.

**1900** Death of **Richard Doddridge**
**Blackmore,** novelist (*Lorna Doone*).

**1930** Birth of **Edwin 'Buzz' Aldrin,**
American astronaut and second man on
the moon. (See also 5th August 1930.)

**21 1905** Birth of **Christian Dior,** French
fashion designer. (Died 1957.)

**1940** Birth of **Jack Nicklaus,** American
golfer.

**1950** Death of **George Orwell,** writer and
novelist (pseudonym of Eric Arthur
Blair).

**24 1965** Death of Sir **Winston Churchill.**

**25 1540** Execution of St **Edmund Campion,** English Jesuit and martyr.

**1640** Death of **Robert Burton,** clergyman, scholar and author (*The Anatomy of Melancholy*, treatise on psychiatric disturbance).

**26 1925** Birth of **Paul Newman,** American film actor.

**1950 Asian History: India became an independent Republic** within the Commonwealth.

**29 1820** Death of King **George III.** During his reign Britain lost the American colonies but established her worldwide empire.

## FEBRUARY

**1 1790 American History: First meeting of the US Supreme Court.**

**1895** Birth of **John Ford,** American film director. (Died 1973.)

**1910 Crime: Dr Crippen murdered his wife, Cora.** Caught later with his lover, Ethel le Neve, as they fled to America. First criminal to be caught by means of trans-Atlantic radio communication. Returned to England and executed in November.

**1915** Birth of Sir **Stanley Matthews,** footballer.

**2 1650** Birth of **Nell Gwyn,** actress and mistress of Charles II.

**1970** Death of **Bertrand Russell,** philosopher/mathematician.

**3 1960 African History: Politics: Prime Minister Macmillan made his 'Wind of Change' speech** at Cape Town, South Africa.

**1980 BBC TV: First telecast of** *Newsnight.*

**4 1920** Birth of **Norman Wisdom,** actor.

**1945 World History: WWII: The Yalta Conference.** The second meeting of the Big Three, Roosevelt, Stalin and Churchill. The talks covered the Allies' policy for the final phase of the war and how the post-war world should be governed. Ended 11th. (See also 17th July 1945.)

**5 1840** Birth of **Hiram Stevens Maxim,** American inventor of the first automatic machine gun.

**1840** Birth of **John Boyd Dunlop,** Scottish surgeon and inventor of the pneumatic tyre.

**1920** Birth of **Frank Muir,** comedy writer and broadcaster.

**1920 Armed Forces: RAF College, Cranwell, opened.**

**6 1665** Birth of Queen **Anne,** the last Stuart monarch.

**1840 British and Imperial History: The Treaty of Waitangi concluded** between Britain and the Maori chiefs of New Zealand. In return for the protection of their rights the Maoris acknowledged British supremacy and provided for the annexation of New Zealand as a British colony.

**7 1940 BBC Radio: Bulgarian service began.**

**1945 World History: WWII:** The US 1st Army **captured the Bridge at Remagen** over the Rhine and began crossing the final natural barrier to the German heartland.

**8 1920** Birth of **Lana Turner,** American film actress.

**1925** Birth of **Jack Lemmon,** American film actor.

**9 1945** Birth of **Mia Farrow,** American film actress.

**10 1840 British History: Royal Family: Marriage of Queen Victoria and Prince Albert.**

**1890** Birth of **Boris Pasternak,** Soviet novelist. (OS: 29th January. Died 30th May 1960.)

**11 1800** Birth of **William Fox Talbot,** photographic pioneer.

**1920** Birth of **Farouk,** last King of Egypt. (Died 1965.)

**1940** Death of **John Buchan,** Scottish novelist (*The Thirty-Nine Steps*).

**11 1975 British History: Politics; Margaret Thatcher elected leader of the Conservative Party.**

**12 1690** Death of **Charles le Brun,** French painter and leading arbiter of taste in France during the last 30 years of Louis XIV.

**1935** Death of **Escoffier,** French chef ('The king of chefs and chef of kings').

**1950** Media: Formation of the **European Broadcasting Union (EBU).**

**13/14 1945 World History: WWII: The Bombing of Dresden.** The RAF and USAF carried out one of the most destructive and controversial bombing raids of the war. Most of the old city was destroyed and tens of thousands died in the firestorms which engulfed the city.

**1975 European History: Politics: Declaration by Turkish Cyprus of a separate state.**

14 **1975** Death of P(elham) G(renville) **Wodehouse,** novelist and playwright.

15 **1965** Death of Nat 'King' Cole, American singer and pianist (byname of Nathaniel Cole).

18 **1965 African History: Gambia gained independence.** (Became a Republic on 25th April 1970.)

19 **1910 Sport: Manchester United played their first football league game** at the new ground at **Old Trafford.** Beaten 4–3 by Liverpool.

**1940** Birth of 'Smokey' Robinson, American singer/songwriter and record producer.

**1960** Birth of Prince Andrew, The Duke of York, third child of The Queen and Prince Philip.

20 **1920** Death of Robert Peary, American Arctic explorer, first man to reach the North Pole.

21 **1965** Murder of Malcolm X (Malcolm Little), American Black Islamic militant.

23 **1905 Charity: The first Rotary Club founded** by Paul Harris, in Chicago, USA.

24 **1920 British History: Politics: Nancy Astor became the first woman to speak in the House of Commons.**

26 **1815 European History: Napoleon Bonaparte escaped from the Island of Elba.** (See also 18th June and 21st October.)

**1950** Death of Sir Harry Lauder, Scottish music hall and vaudeville entertainer.

28 **1975 Disaster: The Moorgate tube disaster.** Over 40 people killed in Britain's worst underground accident.

29 **1840** Birth of John Holland, American inventor, pioneer and designer of the first modern submarine.

**1960 Disaster:** 10–12,000 people killed when an earthquake and tidal wave destroyed the Moroccan town of Agadir.

**MARCH**

1 **1810** Birth of **Frederic Chopin,** Polish composer and pianist.

2 **1900** Birth of **Kurt Weill,** American composer. (Died 3rd April 1950.)

**1930** Death of D(avid) H(erbert) **Lawrence,** novelist.

3 **1920** Birth of **Ronald Searle,** artist, creator of St Trinian's schoolgirls.

4 **1890 Transport: The Forth railway bridge,** the longest in Britain, **officially opened.**

5 **1790** Death of **Flora Macdonald,** Scottish Jacobite heroine.

**1815** Death of **Franz Mesmer,** Austrian physician. Developed 'mesmerism', forerunner of hypnotism.

6 **1475** Birth of **Michelangelo,** Italian Renaissance painter.

**1900** Death of **Gottlieb Daimler,** pioneering German motor engineer.

7 **1930** Birth of **Anthony Armstrong-Jones,** the **Earl of Snowdon.**

9 **1890** Birth of Vyacheslav Molotov, Soviet politician, Stalin's Foreign Minister. (OS: 25th February. Died 1986.)

**1945 World History: WWII: USAF carried out one of the most destructive air attacks in history.** About 16 square miles, or 25%, of Tokyo destroyed and over 80,000 people killed in the bombing and subsequent firestorm, caused by the dropping of incendiary bombs and napalm on the largely wooden city. The attack set a new pattern for attacks and several other Japanese cities suffered similar fates. (Attack began on 9th and continued into the 10th.)

12 **1710** Birth of **Thomas Arne,** composer (*Rule Britannia*).

**1890** Birth of Vaslav **Nijinsky,** Soviet ballet dancer and choreographer. (OS: 28th February. Died 4th April 1950.)

13 **1930 Science: Astronomy: The discovery of the planet Pluto announced** by American astronomer Clyde Tombaugh.

16 **1940** Death of **Selma Lagerlof,** Swedish novelist, first woman to win the Nobel Prize for Literature (*The Wonderful Adventures of Nils*).

**1940** Birth of **Bernardo Bertolucci,** Italian film director.

18 **1905** Birth of **Robert Donat,** English film actor. (Died 1958.)

**1940 BBC Radio: Finnish service began.**

**1965 Science: The first space walk** performed by **Alexei Leonov** from a Voskhod 2 space capsule.

19 **1950** Death of **Edgar Rice Burroughs,** American novelist, creator of Tarzan.

21 **1960 African History: The Sharpeville Massacre:** S. African police shot and killed at least 70 Black demonstrators.

22 **1910** Birth of **Nicholas Monsarrat,** novelist (*The Cruel Sea*). (Died 1979.)

**1945 Middle East History: The Arab League formed.**

24 **1905** Death of **Jules Verne,** French novelist.

**1930** Birth of **Steve McQueen,** American film actor. (Died 7th November, 1980.)

25 **1975** Assassination of King **Faisal of Saudi Arabia,** by his nephew, Prince Museid.

**1980 Religion: Enthronement** of Dr **Robert Runcie** as 102nd **Archbishop of Canterbury.**

27 **1945 British History: WWII: The last V2 bomb landed in Britain** at Orpington, Kent. Since September 1944 over 1000 of the 'Vengeance' weapons had been launched against Britain.

**1980 Disaster: The Alexander Keilland,** an oil accommodation rig in the N. Sea, collapsed killing over 120 Norwegian and British workers.

29 **1970** Death of **Vera Brittan,** author (*Testament of Youth*).

**APRIL**

1 **1815** Birth of **Otto von Bismarck,** German statesman, founder and first Chancellor of the German Empire.

**1945 World History: WWII: US forces landed on Okinawa.** Secured on 21/22nd after a battle in which the Americans suffered the heaviest losses in any one single campaign against the Japanese. The capture of the island would provide a springboard for the invasion of the Japanese mainland by the Allies.

**1960 Science:** The USA launched the **world's first weather satellite,** *Tiros 1* (Television and Infra-Red Orbiting Satellite).

**1805** Birth of **Hans Christian Andersen,** Danish writer of fairy tales. (Died 4th August 1875.)

**1840** Birth of **Emile Zola,** French novelist.

3 **1925** Birth of **Tony Benn,** Labour politician.

4 **1970 BBC Radio:** *Week Ending* began.

5 **1900** Birth of **Spencer Tracey,** American film actor. (Died 1967.)

6 **1520** Death of **Raphael,** Italian Renaissance painter.

**1590** Death of Sir **Francis Walsingham,** courtier, diplomat and creator of Elizabeth I's secret service, the Queen's principal secretary for nearly 20 years.

**1890** Birth of **Anthony Fokker,** Dutch aircraft designer. Designed planes for the Germans during WWI after the Allies turned him down. (Died 1939.)

**1965 Science:** The USA launched the **world's first commercial communications satellite,** *Intelsat 1,* otherwise known as **Early Bird.** (NB: Telstar, launched in 1962, was the first commercially financed satellite. See also 12th August 1960.)

**1970 BBC Radio:** *Start the Week* began.

7 **1770** Birth of **William Wordsworth,** poet. (Died 23rd April 1850.)

**1920** Birth of **Ravi Shankar,** Indian sitarist and composer, founder of the National Orchestra of India.

9 **1940 World History: WWII: Germany invaded Denmark and Norway.**

**1940** Death of Mrs Patrick Campbell, actress and friend of George Bernard Shaw.

11 **1970 Science: Space exploration:** *Apollo 13* launched to the Moon; 13th/14th: attempt abandoned following an explosion on board the module; splashdown on 17th. Astronauts: Lovell, Maise and Swigert.

12 **1945** Death of President **Theodore Roosevelt,** American statesman.

13 **1945 World History: WWII: 'The Holocaust':** The Americans liberated the concentration camp at **Buchenwald.** (See also 15th and 29th.)

**1945 World History: WWII: Vienna captured by the Red Army** after it had entered the suburbs on 7th.

14 **1865 Assassination** of President **Abraham Lincoln** (died 15th) by John Wilkes Booth.

**1925 Birth of Rod Steiger,** American film actor.

15 **1945 World History: WWII: 'The Holocaust'** The British liberated the concentration camp of **Bergen Belsen.** (See also 13th and 29th.)

16 **1940 Birth of Queen Margrethe II of Denmark.**

17 **1790 Death of Benjamin Franklin,** American statesman and scientist.

18 **1980 African History:** At midnight the former British colony of Southern Rhodesia became the independent nation of **Zimbabwe.** (See also 11th November 1965.)

19 **1900 Birth of Richard Hughes,** novelist (*A High Wind in Jamaica*). (Died 1976.)

**1970 BBC Radio:** *Analysis* began.

21 **1910 Death of Mark Twain,** American novelist. (Born 30th November 1835.)

**1945 World History: WWII: The Battle of Berlin** began in earnest when the Soviets under Zhukov entered the city's suburbs.

**1960 Architecture: Brasilia inaugurated as the new capital of Brazil.**

22 **1915 World History: WWI: The first use of gas in warfare on the western front.** The Germans used chlorine gas against the Allies in the Second Battle of Ypres.

23 **1775 Birth of Joseph Turner,** painter.

**1915 Death of Rupert Brooke,** poet.

24 **1815 Birth of Anthony Trollope,** novelist.

25 **1915 World History: WWI: Opening of the Gallipoli campaign** with the first landing of Allied forces in Turkey.

28 **1945 Execution of Benito Mussolini,** Italian dictator, shot by partisans while trying to escape the country with his mistress.

29 **1895 Birth of Sir Malcolm Sargent,** conductor. (Died 1967.)

**1945 World History: WWII: 'The Holocaust':** The Americans liberated the concentration camp at **Dachau.** (See also 13th and 15th.)

30 **1945 Suicide of Adolf Hitler.**

**1975 Asian History: The Vietnam War ended** when S. Vietnam government surrendered unconditionally to N. Vietnam. The USA had evacuated its personnel from Saigon on 29th. (NB: Although two peace treaties had been signed in 1973 fighting had continued.)

MAY

1 **1700 Death of John Dryden,** poet and playwright.

2 **1860 Birth of Theodor Herzl,** Hungarian Jew, founder of Zionism.

3 **1960 The European Free Trade Association (EFTA) came into force.** (Convention signed November 1959.)

4 **1980 Death of Marshal Tito,** Yugoslavian statesman, founder of modern Yugoslavia.

5 **1980 British History: Terrorism: SAS stormed the Iranian Embassy** in London to free hostages held by Iranian militants.

6 **1910 Death of King Edward VII.**

**1915 Birth of Orson Welles,** American film actor, director, producer and writer. (Died 10th October 1985.)

**1960 British History: Royal family: Princess Margaret married Anthony Armstrong-Jones.**

7 **1840 Birth of Peter Tchaikovsky,** Russian composer. (OS: 25th April.)

**1890 Death of James Nasmyth,** Scottish engineer, inventor of the steam hammer.

**1915 World History: WWI:** The liner, *Lusitania* torpedoed by a German submarine off the coast of Ireland with the loss of nearly 1200 lives.

**1945 World History: WWII: The Nazis surrendered unconditionally to the Allies.** Surrender document signed by Chief of the German Staff, General Jodl, at Rheims, France.

8 **1945 World History: WWII: Victory in Europe (V.E.) Day.**

10 **1940 World History: WWII: The Nazis invaded the Netherlands, Belgium and Luxembourg.**
**Neville Chamberlain resigned as Prime Minister; Winston Churchill became head of the wartime Coalition Government.**

**11 1940 BBC Radio:·Hindi Service** began.

**12 1820** Birth of **Florence Nightingale,**
nurse founder of trained nursing as a
profession. (Died 13th August 1910.)

**13 1840** Birth of **Alphonse Daudet,** French
novelist.

**15 1740** Death of **Ephraim Chambers,**
encylopaedist. His work inspired the
great encyclopaedia of Diderot,
D'Alembert, et al.

**16 1905** Birth of **Henry Fonda,** American
film actor. (Died 1982.)

**17 1890 Media:** *Comic Cuts,* **the first comic
paper,** issued in London.

**1900 African History: Boer War:
Mafeking relieved by British forces** after
being under siege by the Boers since
October 1899.

**18 1920** Birth of Pope **John Paul II.**
Elected 1978.

**1980 Disaster: Eruption of Mt St
Helens,** America's only active volcano.
Nearly 100 people killed.

**22 1915 Disaster: Britain's worst railway
accident.** 227 people killed at Quintins
Hill, near Gretna Green.

**23 1960 Middle East History:** Israeli
government announced that **Adolf
Eichmann,** former high-ranking Nazi,
had been captured by the Israeli secret
service in Argentina and would be
brought to trial for his war crimes.
(Eichmann was subsequently tried and
executed, to date the only person to be
publicly executed in Israel.)

**24 1905** Birth of **Mikhail Sholokov,** Soviet
author (*Quiet Flows The Don*). (OS:
11th. Died 1984.)

**26 1940 World History: WWII: The
Dunkirk evacuation began.** By the end
of the following week over 300,000 men
had been evacuated to Britain.

**27 1840** Death of **Niccolo Paganini,** Italian
composer and violin virtuoso.

**28 1660** Birth of King **George I.**

**29 1630** Birth of King **Charles II.**

**1950 BBC Radio:** *The Archers* first
broadcast as a trial on the Midlands
Home Service; experiment ended 2nd
June. First national broadcast on 1st
January 1951.

**30 1640** Birth of **Peter Paul Rubens,**
Flemish painter.

**1960** Death of **Boris Pasternak,** Soviet
novelist. (See 10th February 1890.)

**31 1910 Imperial and African History:** The
Union of South Africa formed with the
uniting of Cape Province, Natal,
Transvaal and the Orange Free State.

**1930** Birth of **Clint Eastwood,**
American film actor.

**JUNE**

**2 1740** Birth of the **Marquis de Sade,**
Comte Donatien-Alphonse-Francois de
Sade, French soldier, writer and
libertine. His works on erotica gave rise
to the term Sadism.

**1840** Birth of **Thomas Hardy,** novelist
and poet.

**2 1940** Birth of ex-king **Constantine** of
Greece.

**3 1865** Birth of King **George V.**

**1925** Birth of **Tony Curtis,** American
film actor.

**4 1910** Birth of Sir **Christopher Cockerell,**
engineer, inventor of the hovercraft.

**1970 Pacific History: Tonga achieved
independence.**

**5 1905** Birth of **Jean Paul Sartre,** French
philosopher. (Died 15th April 1980.)

**1940 World History: WWII: Battle of
France began** with the invasion proper by
the Nazis. Armistice signed on 22nd; all
hostilities ended on 28th.

**1975 British History: Britain's first
National Referendum held** on whether to
join the EEC. Result 2–1 majority in
favour.

**7 1905 European History: Norway gained
independence from Sweden** when its
parliament declared the union
dissolved.

**1910** Birth of **Pietro Annigoni,** Italian
painter.

**1940** Birth of **Tom Jones,** Welsh singer.

**1970** Death of E(dward) M(organ)
**Forster,** novelist.

**1980** Death of **Henry Miller,** American
novelist (*Tropic of Capricorn* and
*Tropic of Cancer*).

**8 1810** Birth of **Robert Schumann,**
German composer.

**9 1870** Death of **Charles Dickens,** novelist.

**10 1940 World History: WWII: Italy
entered the war by declaring war on
Britain and France.**

**11 1910** Birth of **Jacques Cousteau,** French underwater explorer; inventor of the aqualung.

**14 1940 World History: WWII: Paris entered by the Germans;** France surrendered on 22nd.

**16 1890** Birth of **Stan Laurel,** of Laurel and Hardy fame. (Died 1965.)

**17 1900** Birth of **Martin Bormann,** Hitler's deputy.

**18 1815 European History: Napoleonic Wars: The Battle of Waterloo.**

**1920** Birth of **Ian Carmichael,** film and TV actor.

**1940 British and World History: WWII: Churchill made his famous 'We shall fight them on the beaches . . .' speech** in the House of Commons. Later on in the same day actor Norman Shelley impersonated the Prime Minister and gave the speech out over the radio.

**1970 British History: Edward Heath won the general election** and became Prime Minister. Defeated in 1974 by Harold Wilson.

**20 1905** Birth of **Lillian Hellman,** American novelist and playwright (*The Little Foxes*). (Died 1984.)

**21 1970 Sport: Tony Jacklin** became the **first Englishman** since Ted Ray in 1920 to win the **US Open Golf Championship.**

**22 1910** Birth of Sir **John Hunt,** leader of the British team which conquered Mt Everest.

**23 1940** Birth of **Adam Faith,** former pop singer and actor.

**1970 British History:** Brunel's *SS Great Britain,* the world's first all-metal sea-going vessel, returned to Bristol, England, for restoration in the Falkland Islands, where it had lain rusting since the last century.

**25 1950 World History: The Korean War began** when the North invaded the South. Armistice signed in 1953.

**26 1830** Death of King **George IV.**

**26 1945 World History: The UN Charter signed in San Francisco** by delegates of some 50 countries. UN formally came into existence on 24th October.

**29 1905 Transport: The Automobile Association (AA) established.**

**1960 BBC Television Centre opened.**

**30 1520 Assassination of Montezuma II,** ruler of the Aztecs during the invasion of Mexico by Cortes.

**1660** Death of **William Oughtred,** minister and mathematician, inventor of the slide rule.

**1960 African History: The Belgian Congo became independent as the Congo Republic.** (Name changed to Zaire in 1971.)

**1980 European History: Vigdis Einnbogadottir elected President of Iceland,** the first woman in the world to hold the post of President of a country. (See also 21st July 1960.)

JULY

**1 1690 British History: The Battle of the Boyne,** Ireland. William III defeated the Jacobites under James II.

**1960 African History: Ghana proclaimed itself an independent Republic** within the Commonwealth. **Somalia gained independence** as the Somali Republic.

**4 1840 British History:** The founding of the **Cunard Steamship Company** effectively took place with the sailing of its first vessel, *Britannia,* on its first journey from Liverpool to Halifax, Nova Scotia.

**6 1960** Death of **Aneurin Bevan,** Labour statesman, founder of the NHS.

**7 1860** Birth of **Gustav Mahler,** Austrian composer.

**1930** Death of Sir **Arthur Conan Doyle,** novelist.

**1940** Birth of **Ringo Starr,** the drummer of the Beatles pop group.

**7 1940 BBC Radio:** *Radio Newsreel* began.

**1965 BBC TV:** first telecast of *Tomorrow's World.*

**1970** Death of Sir **Allen Lane,** publisher, founder of the Penguin publishing company.

**8 1890** Birth of **Stanton Macdonald-Wright,** American expressionist painter. (Died 1973.)

**10 1900 French History: Transport: Metro,** the Paris underground railway, **opened.**

**1940 World History: WWII: The Vichy Government formed** after the collapse of France. On the following day Henri Pétain was made head of the puppet state.

**1940 World and British History: WWII: The Battle of Britain began** with the first heavy air attack by the Germans. It reached its climax in August and by the time it ended on 17th September, the RAF's victory had forced Hitler to postpone his planned invasion of Britain.

11 **1960 African History:** Following the mutiny of the Congo's national army and several days of violent unrest, Mr Tshombe, Prime Minister of the province of Katanga, proclaimed its independence from the Republic. Mr Lumumba, Prime Minister of the Congo, appealed to the UN for help. 14th/15th: The first UN troops arrived in the Congo.

12 **1705 Death of Titus Oates,** renegade Anglican priest and Protestant conspirator who fabricated a Catholic plot to assassinate Charles II (the Popish Plot 1678), which resulted in a short but violent reign of terror in London.

**1910 Death of Charles Rolls,** aviator and co-founder of the car firm, **Rolls Royce.**

13 **1930 Sport: The World Cup Football Competition instituted;** held in Uruguay and won by the host country.

**1940 British History: WWII:** The Cabinet decided on the formation of **Home Guard** (originally called the Local Defence Volunteers until Churchill coined the new name). 14th: National radio broadcast made calling for men to volunteer for the new organisation.

17 **1790 Death of Adam Smith,** Scottish political economist. Author of *Wealth of Nations.*

**1945 World History: WWII: The Potsdam Conference.** Third and last of the big war conferences. Roosevelt had died since the last meeting in Yalta – see 4th February 1945 – and Churchill had lost the General Election and been replaced by Clement Attlee; only Stalin remained of the original Big Three. It was already apparent that things had changed since Yalta. The USA and USSR implicitly recognised each other's superpower status and the new spheres of influence they would control in the post-war world.

21 **1890 Architecture: Battersea Bridge, London, opened.**

**1960 Asian History: Mrs Bandaranaike took office as Prime Minister of Ceylon** (Sri Lanka), the first woman in the world to hold such a position. (See also 30th June 1980.)

22 **1890 Birth of Rose Kennedy,** American, matriarch of the Kennedy family.

27 **1930 Birth of Shirley Williams,** politician.

**1980 Death of the Shah of Iran,** Mohammed Reza Pahlavi.

28 **1540 Execution of Thomas Cromwell,** Henry VIII's chief administrator. **Marriage of King Henry VIII to Catherine Howard,** his fifth wife. (See also 1st January 1540.)

**1750 Death of Johann Sebastian Bach,** German composer.

29 **1890 Death of Vincent van Gogh,** Dutch painter.

**1970 Death of Sir John Barbirolli,** conductor and cellist.

30 **1940 Birth of Sir Clive Sinclair,** industrialist.

**AUGUST**

1 **1930 Birth of Lionel Bart,** composer.

**1960 African History: Dahomey gained independence** from France. (Now known as the Republic of Benin.)

2 **1905 Birth of Myrna Loy,** American film actress.

**1980 European History: Terrorism:** Over 80 people killed in a right-wing terrorist attack on Bologna railway station. It was Italy's worst ever terrorist outrage.

3 **1920 Birth of P(hyllis) D(orothy) James,** novelist.

**1960 African History: Niger gained independence** from France.

4 **1265 English History: Battle of Evesham.** Simon de Montfort defeated and slain by Prince Edward (later Edward I), and the Barons' Rebellion crushed.

**1900 Birth of Queen Elizabeth, The Queen Mother.**

5 **1930 Birth of Neil Armstrong,** American astronaut and first man on the moon. (See 20th January 1930.)

**1960 African History: Upper Volta gained independence** from France. (Now known as Burkina Faso.)

6 **1660** Death of **Diego Velasquez,** Spanish painter.

**1890 American History: Crime: The electric chair used for the first time.** Victim: William Kemmler at Auburn Prison, New York.

**1945 World History: WWII: The first atomic bomb dropped** on the Japanese city of Hiroshima. The second bomb dropped on 9th on Nagasaki.

7 **1960 African History: Ivory Coast gained independence** from France.

8 **1900 Sport: The Davis Cup for tennis contested for the first time,** Massachusetts, USA. Ended on 10th with the USA beating Britain.

10 **1810** Birth of **Count Cavour,** Italian statesman, responsible for the unification of Italy. First Prime Minister of the new kingdom.

11 **1890** Death of **Cardinal Newman,** churchman and leader of the Oxford Movement. Later converted to Roman Catholicism and was made a cardinal.

**1960 African History: Chad gained independence** from France.

12 **1960 Science:** The USA launched the **world's first communications satellite,** *Echo 1.* (See also 6th April 1965.)

13 **1910** Death of **Florence Nightingale,** nurse. (Born 12th May 1820.)

**1960 African History: Central African Republic gained independence** from France.

14 **1840** Birth of **Richard Krafft-Ebing,** German neurologist and sexual psychologist.

**1945 World History: WWII: Japan surrendered to the Allies.**

15 **1890** Birth of **Jacques Ibert,** French composer. (Died 1962.)

**1945 World History: WWII: Victory in Japan (V.J.) Day.**

**1950** Birth of Princess **Anne, The Princess Royal.**

**1960 European History: Cyprus gained independence** from Britain. (Independence proclaimed at midnight.)

**1975 Assassination** of Sheikh Mujibar **Rahman** of Bangladesh, first Prime Minister and President of Bangladesh.

17 **1840** Birth of **Wilfrid Scawen Blunt,** poet.

**1930** Birth of **Ted Hughes,** poet laureate, 1984–

**1960 African History: Gabon gained independence** from France.

18 **1850** Death of **Honoré de Balzac,** French novelist.

20 **1940 British and World History: WWII: Battle of Britain: Churchill made his famous speech saluting the RAF:** 'Never in the field of human conflict was so much owed by so many to so few.'

**1940 Assassination of Leon Trotsky** in Mexico by Ramón Mercader.

21 **1930** Birth of Princess **Margaret.**

22 **1920** Birth of **Ray Bradbury,** prolific American fantasy novelist (*The Martian Chronicles*).

**1940** Death of Sir **Oliver Lodge,** physicist, pioneer of wireless telegraphy.

**1960 African History: Senegal proclaimed itself independent** when it seceded from the Federation of Mali, which had been granted independence from France earlier in the year.

23 **1305 Execution** in London by hanging, drawing and quartering of **William Wallace,** Scottish patriot.

**1540** Death of **Francisco Parmigianino,** Italian Mannerist painter of the High Renaissance.

**1690 British and Asian History: Calcutta founded** by Job Charnock as a trading post for the East India Co.

23 **1770 Suicide of Thomas Chatterton,** poet, precursor of the Romantic Movement. (Death immortalised in the painting by Henry Wallis.)

25 **1900** Death of **Friedrich Nietzsche,** German philosopher.

**1930** Birth of **Sean Connery.** Scottish film actor.

27 **1900** Birth of **Mother Teresa of Calcutta,** Albanian nun.

29 **1915** Birth of **Ingrid Bergman,** American film actress. (Died 1982.)

30 **1940** Death of Sir **Joseph John Thomson,** physicist, who discovered the electron.

31 **1980 European History: In Poland an agreement was signed** by Gdansk strikers, led by Lech Walesa, and the

Government to provide for the formation of **independent and free trade unions**.

## SEPTEMBER

**2 1910** Death of **Henri Rousseau,** French painter.

**1940 BBC Radio: Burmese service** began.

**1945 World History: End of World War II** with the formal unconditional surender by Japan on board the *USS Missouri*.

**3 590 Religion: St Gregory the Great consecrated Pope,** architect of the medieval papacy.

**4 1905** Birth of **Mary Renault** (born Mary Challans), novelist (*The King Must Die*). (Died 1983.)

**6 1970 Middle East History: Terrorism:** Arab terrorists hijacked 4 passenger planes: Swissair and TWA airliners flown to Jordon, a Pan Am jet flown to Cairo, where it was blown up on 7th and an El Al plane flown to Heathrow, London, where one of the terrorists, **Leila Khaled,** was arrested; 9th: a BOAC plane hijacked to Jordan and on 12th all three planes blown up. 30th: the remaining hostages were released by terrorists and Khaled flown to Egypt.

**7 1910** Death of **William Holman Hunt,** painter, one of the founders of the Pre-Raphaelite Brotherhood.

**1930** Birth of King **Baudouin of Belgium.**

**1940 British and World History: WWII: Opening of the London 'Blitz'** by German bombers. The heavy air raids continued until mid-1941, when the bombers were diverted to the Eastern Front.
**London Underground tube stations first used as air raid shelters** (continued until May 1945).

**9 1900** Birth of **James Hilton,** novelist (*Goodbye, Mr Chips*). (Died 1954.)

**10 1890** Birth of **Franz Werfel,** Jewish Czech/German poet, playwright and novelist (*The Song of Bernadette*). (Died 1945.)

**11 1915 British History: Women; The Women's Institute founded in Britain.** First branch in North Wales.

**1940 British History: WWII: Buckingham Palace bombed.**

**1950** Death of **Jan Smuts,** S. African statesman.

**1980 BBC Radio: Radio Norfolk opened.**

**12 1940 European Pre-History:** A group of French schoolboys accidently discovered the **painted pre-historic caves at Lascaux.**

**1960 British History: Transport:** (Voluntary) M.o.T. **tests on motor vehicles introduced in Britain.**

**13 1905** Birth of **Claudette Colbert,** American film actress.

**15 1890** Birth of Dame **Agatha Christie,** novelist. (Died 1976.)

**16 1620 American History: The Pilgrim Fathers set sail from Plymouth** (OS: 6th. See also 21st December.)

**16 1975 Pacific History: Papua New Guinea gained independence** from Australia.

**17 1940 World History: WWII: The German High Command** officially postponed **'Operation Sealion',** the invasion of Britain following the failure of the Luftwaffe to gain the necessary air supremacy in British skies.

**1980 Assassination** of **Anastasio Somoza,** ex-dictator of Nicaragua.

**18 1905** Birth of **Greta Garbo,** Swedish film actress.

**19 1905** Death of **Thomas Barnardo,** social reformer, founder of homes for destitute children. (Born 4th July 1845.)

**1960 British History: Transport:** Britain's **first traffic wardens** appeared on the streets of London.

**22 1960 African History: Mali proclaimed itself an independent republic** following the seceding of Senegal from the Federation of Mali in August. (See 22nd August 1960.)

**1980 Middle East History: The Gulf War Began** when Iraq invaded Iran over a territorial dispute. Ceasefire went into effect on 20th August 1988.

**20 1920** Birth of **Mickey Rooney,** American film actor.

**1940 British History: The George Cross instituted,** Britain's highest civilian award for acts of courage.

**27 1940 World History: WWII: Tripartite Pact signed** by Germany, Italy and

Japan. A 10-year military and economic pact designed to bring about a 'new order'. The pact became the foundation of the Axis partnership.

28 1970 Death of **Gamal Abdel Nasser,** Egyptian leader.

29 1810 Birth of **Elizabeth Gaskell,** novelist (*Cranford*).

1950 **BBC TV:** first telecast of *Come Dancing.*

## OCTOBER

1 1890 Birth of **Stanley Holloway,** actor. (Died 1982.)

1920 Birth of **Walter Matthau,** American film actor.

1960 **African History: Nigeria gained independence** from Britain.

2 1890 Birth of **Julius 'Groucho' Marx,** American film actor and comedian. (Died 1977.)

1950 **British History: Legal Aid became effective in Britain.**

3 1975 **European History: Terrorism: Dr Tiede Herrema,** Dutch industrialist, **kidnapped by the IRA** in Ireland. Released on 7th November after the security forces had surrounded the house he was being held in by Eddie Gallaher and Marion Coyle.

4 1965 **BBC Radio:** *The World at One* began.

5 1840 Birth of **John Addington Symonds,** poet, essayist and literary historian, biographer of Ben Jonson, Shelley and Walt Whitman.

1930 **Disaster: British Airship R101** crashed near Beauvais, France, killing 48 of the 54 passengers and crew.

7 1900 Birth of **Heinrich Himmler,** German Nazi leader. (Died 1945.)

9 1890 Birth of **Aimee Semple McPherson,** American evangelist. (Died 1944.)

1900 Birth of **Alastair Sim,** Scottish comedy film actor. (Died 1976.)

1940 Birth of **John Lennon,** singer/songwriter. (Murdered 8th December 1980.)

10 1930 Birth of **Harold Pinter,** playwright.

1970 **Pacific History: Fiji gained independence** from Britain.

11 1440 **British History: Eton College founded by Henry VI.**

13 1890 Birth of **Conrad Richter,** American novelist (*The Town*). (Died 1968.)

1905 Death of Sir **Henry Irving,** actor/manager, first in his profession to be knighted.

1925 Birth of **Margaret Thatcher.**

14 1890 Birth of **Dwight Eisenhower,** American military commander and statesman. (Died 1969.)

1940 Birth of **Cliff Richard,** singer.

1980 **Transport: Launch** by Rover of the **Mini Metro.**

15 1920 Birth of **Mario Puzo,** American novelist (*The Godfather*).

1970 **BBC Radio:** *You and Yours* began.

17 1915 Birth of **Arthur Miller,** American playwright.

1965 **BBC TV:** First telecast of *Call My Bluff.*

19 1920 Death of **John Reed,** American author (*Ten Days That Shook The World).*

20 1890 Death of Sir **Richard Burton,** explorer of Africa, author and translator of *The Arabian Nights*, the *Kama Sutra* and *The Perfumed Garden.*

1960 **British History: Old Bailey Trial** of D. H. Lawrence's *Lady Chatterley's Lover.* First prosecution under the Obscene Publications Act 1959. Sought by Penguin Books in order to have the book published in Britain. Ended on 2nd November with Penguin's acquittal.

21 1790 Birth of **Alphonse de Lamartine,** French poet and statesman.

1805 **European History: Napoleonic Wars: Battle of Trafalgar.**

1805 Death of Admiral **Lord Nelson.**

1815 **European History: Napoleon arrived at St Helena** to begin his exile. (Died there in 1821.)

1940 Birth of **Geoff Boycott,** cricketer.

1960 **British History: Armed forces: The Launch of Britain's first nuclear submarine,** *Dreadnought.*

23 1940 Birth of **Pele** (Edson Arantes do Nascimento), Brazilian footballer.

1950 Death of **Al Jolson,** American singer and entertainer.

24 1945 **World History: The United Nations formally came into existence. UN Day.** (See also 26th June 1945.)

25 1400 Death of **Geoffrey Chaucer,** poet and storyteller (*The Canterbury Tales*).

**1415 English and European History: Hundred Years' War: Battle of Agincourt.**

25 1760 Birth of King **George II.**

26 1440 **Execution of Gilles de Rais,** French nobleman and Constable of France, on charges of Satanism and child murder. His name later connected with the story of Bluebeard.

28 1940 **World History: WWII: Italy invaded Greece.** The invasion, prompted by Mussolini's desire for glory, was against the wishes of Nazi Germany, which did not want to open yet another new front and over-extend its resources. As it turned out, the Italians took on more than they could handle and had to turn to Germany for help to conquer Greece.

29 1740 Birth of **James Boswell,** Scottish lawyer and biographer of Samuel Johnson.

30 1920 Death of **Henri Dunant,** Swiss philanthropist, founder of the International Red Cross.

31 1620 Birth of **John Evelyn,** diarist and author.

**1960** Birth of Prince **Reza,** eldest son of the former Shah of Iran and Queen Farah. (See also 22nd July 1980.)

**NOVEMBER**

1 1960 **European History: Benelux Economic Union came into force** (signed 3rd February 1958). The first completely free international labour market.

2 1950 Death of **George Bernard Shaw,** playwright.

4 1740 Birth of **Augustus Toplady,** Hymn writer (*Rock of Ages*).

8 1890 Death of **Cesar Franck,** Belgian/French composer.

**1900** Birth of **Margaret Mitchell,** American novelist (*Gone With The Wind*). (Died 1949.)

**1960 American History: John F. Kennedy elected President of the USA,** the first Roman Catholic to hold the post.

9 1940 Death of **Neville Chamberlain,** politician.

1970 Death of **Charles de Gaulle,** French statesman. (Born 22nd November 1890.)

10 1975 **African History: Angola gained independence** from Portugal. (Declaration signed at midnight.)

11 1920 Birth of **Roy Jenkins,** statesman.

**1965 African History: Rhodesia declared UDI.** (See also 18th April 1980.)

**1975 Pacific History: Australia: Gough Whitlam's** Labour government dismissed from office by Gov. General, Sir John Kerr. Malcolm Fraser appointed to head a caretaker Liberal government.

**1980 BBC Radio: Radio Lincolnshire opened.**

12 1840 Birth of **Auguste Rodin,** French sculptor

13 1970 **Middle East History:** Lt. General **Hafez Al-Assad became Prime Minister of Syria** in a military coup. (Assumed the Presidency in February 1971.)

14 1540 Death of **Il Rosso,** also known as **Rosso Fiorentino,** Italian painter and decorator of the early Mannerist school. (Born Giovanni Battista di Jacopo.)

**1840** Birth of **Claude Monet,** French Impressionist painter.

**1900** Birth of **Aaron Copland,** American composer.

14/15 1940 **British History: WWII: Coventry Cathedral destroyed by the Germans** when they launched a massive air raid on the city in retaliation for the RAF's bombing of Munich on 8th.

15 1905 Birth of **Mantovani,** Italian conductor. (Died 1980.)

16 1960 Death of **Clark Gable,** American film actor.

17 1940 Death of **Eric Gill,** sculptor, engraver and typographer (*Prospero and Ariel,* Broadcasting House, London).

19 1600 Birth of King **Charles I.**

20 1945 **World History: The trials of leading Nazis began before the Nuremberg War Crimes Tribunal.**

**1980 Asian History: Mao's widow, Jiang Qing, leader of the 'Gang of Four', went on trial.**

21 1920 **British History: 'Bloody Sunday':** The IRA murdered 11 Englishmen

suspected of being intelligence agents; the auxiliary police force, known as the 'Black and Tans', took revenge the same day attacking spectators at a Dublin football match. 12 people were killed and 60 others wounded.

22 1890 Birth of **Charles de Gaulle,** French statesman. (Died 9th November 1970.)

1900 Death of Sir **Arthur Sullivan,** composer.

1975 **European History: Juan Carlos sworn in as Spain's King,** the first for 44 years.

25 1970 **Suicide** of **Yukio Mishima,** Japanese novelist.

28 1820 Birth of **Friedrich Engels,** German Socialist and associate of Karl Marx. (Died 5th August 1895.)

1905 **European History:** *Sinn Fein* founded in Dublin by Arthur Griffith.

1960 **African History: Mauritania gained independence** from France.

30 1900 Death of **Oscar Wilde,** Irish poet and playwright.

**DECEMBER**

1 1910 Death of **Alicia Markova,** prima ballerina.

2 1960 **Religion: Archbishop Fisher of Canterbury** made a historic visit to the Vatican, Rome, to meet Pope John XXIII, the first such visit for over 400 years.

3 1910 Death of **Mary Baker Eddy,** founder of the Christian Science Movement.

6 1980 **British History: Terrorism: The Balcome Street siege began,** with the IRA holding Mr and Mrs Matthews prisoners in their London flat. Ended on 12th with the terrorists surrendering to the security forces.

8 1890 Birth of **Bohuslav Martinu,** Czechoslovakian composer. (Died 1959.)

1980 **Murder** of **John Lennon,** singer/songwriter. (Born 9th October 1940.)

9 1960 **ITV** First telecast of Granada TV's *Coronation Street.*

15 1890 Death of Chief **Sitting Bull,** American Indian leader.

17 1770 Baptism of Ludwig van **Beethoven,** German composer.

18 1890 **British History: Transport: The world's first** *electric* **tube railway opened** between King William St. and Stockwell. Carriages were called 'padded cells', because they only had small slits for windows.

21 1620 **American History: The Pilgrim Fathers landed at Plymouth Rock,** Massachusetts. (OS: 11th. See 16th September.)

1940 Death of **F. Scott Fitzgerald,** American novelist.

25 1950 **British History: Crime: The Stone of Scone** or the Stone of Destiny, the Scottish Coronation Stone, **stolen from Westminster Abbey** by Scottish nationalists. Recovered in April 1951.

26 1890 Death of **Heinrich Schliemann,** German archaeologist, excavator of Troy and Mycenae. (Born 6th January 1820.)

27 1945 **World History: The International Monetary Fund (IMF) established.**

28 1940 **BBC Radio: Persian service** began.

1950 **British History: The Peak District designated as Britain's first National Park.**

29 1890 **American History: The Battle of Wounded Knee,** the last major conflict between American Indians and Government forces.

1890 Death of **Octave Feuillet,** French novelist and playwright.

# Typescripts

## PREPARATION

Many publishers refuse even to consider handwritten manuscripts. No publisher will accept them as final copy. If you cannot afford to have the whole script typed before acceptance, there are ways round the problem. See below under PRELIMINARY LETTER.

## NEATNESS

The first impression made on a publisher and a publisher's reader may be vital. They will try to discount the physical appearance of your typescript, but a tatty typescript covered with handwritten corrections, on different sizes of paper and with inadequate margins and spacing, will perhaps not receive benign consideration first thing on a Monday morning.

Even if you have followed the advice below and have a signed contract in your pocket, and the publisher is awaiting the final manuscript with impatience, there are other reasons for neatness. The publisher's copy editor needs a 'clean' manuscript in order to avoid spending an unnecessary amount of time on marking it up for the printer. The manuscript then has to go to a printer for setting. The typesetting keyboard operator is basically a copy typist, working a complicated and expensive set of equipment. He must be able to read your typescript quickly and accurately, and at the same time he must interpret a code of marks which the copy editor or designer will have made all over it.

## TYPING

Authors are increasingly using word processors for the advantages they have to offer over the traditional typewriter (see article **Word Processing**).

For ordinary typescripts, use the black ribbon. For plays, use red for names of characters, stage directions, etc., and black for dialogue. If a two-colour ribbon is not available use capitals for character names and underline stage directions in red by hand. Keep a fairly new ribbon in the typewriter so that it is black but not splodgy. Remember that typewriter maintenance is a tax-deductible expense!

The paper used should be uniform in size, preferably the standard size A4, which has replaced the old foolscap and quarto sizes. Neither flimsy paper nor very thick paper should be used. If in doubt, ask the stationer for a standard A4 typewriter paper. Use one side of the paper only. It is helpful but not essential if manuscripts are typed to a width of sixty characters per line. This makes it easier for printers and publishers to calculate the extent of a work and so—using copyfitting tables—to work out the space occupied when it is printed.

### Margins

Good margins are essential, especially on the left hand side. This enables the copy editor to include instructions to the printer. On A4 paper a left hand margin of 1½–2 inches allows sufficient space.

### Double Spacing

This is necessary if you are to make any corrections to the typescript, and there are always some improvements which you will want to make; they can only be made clear to the printer if there is space available between the lines. The copy editor too needs this extra space. Double spacing means a *full* line of space between two lines of copy—not half a line of space.

*Consistency*

Be as consistent as possible in your choice of variant spellings, use of subheadings, etc.

Authors who want to know more about the technicalities of preparing a manuscript for the printer should consult *Copy-Editing* by Judith Butcher, Cambridge University Press, Desk edition 1983, £25.00. Much of this is outside the author's scope, but dipping into this book will make him aware of points of style and consistency, particularly with reference to the use of inverted commas, roman and arabic numerals, italic and roman, rendering of foreign words, etc.

*Numbering*

Pages (or folios as publishers prefer to call them to distinguish them from the pages of the final book) should be numbered throughout. If you need to include an extra folio after, say, folio 27, call it 27a and write at the foot of folio 27: 'Folio 27a follows'. Then write at the foot of 27a: 'Folio 28 follows'. Don't do this too often or you will confuse and irritate your readers.

## CORRECTIONS TO TYPESCRIPT

Corrections to the final typescript should be kept to a minimum. Often the publisher's editor will want to suggest a few additional changes—this happens even to the best authors—and once all or some of these are included, the typescript may have become very messy. If the publisher then feels it is not in a fit state for the printer he may well ask you to have it retyped.

## BINDING

Printers prefer to handle each folio separately, so do not use a binder which will make this impossible. Ring binders are acceptable. Alternatively you can use a cardboard envelope folder. In this case it will help if you can clip the pages of each chapter together, but never staple them.

## PROTECTION OF TYPESCRIPTS

This can be achieved by placing a stiffer piece of paper at front and back. On the first folio of the typescript itself, give the title, your name and, most important of all, your address. It is worth including your address on the last page also, just in case the first folio becomes detached.

## SUBMISSION

The terms 'manuscript' and 'typescript' are interchangeable in present usage, though different editors may favour one or the other.

## CHOOSING YOUR PUBLISHER

It will save you time and postage if you check first that you are sending your typescript to a firm that will consider it. Publishers specialise. It is no use sending a work of romantic fiction to a firm that specialises in high-brow novels translated from obscure languages just because they are described in this book as fiction publishers. It is still less use to send it to a firm which publishes no fiction at all. The way to avoid the more obvious mistakes is to look in your library or bookshop for books which are in some way similar to yours, and find out who publishes them. Remember, though, that paperbacks are often editions of books published first in cased editions.

## PRELIMINARY LETTER

This again will save you time, money and probably frustration. The letter by itself will tell the publisher very little; what he or she would in most cases prefer to see is a brief preliminary letter together with a synopsis of the book and the first couple of chapters from it. From this material the publisher will be able to judge whether the book would perhaps fit the list, in which case you will be asked to send the complete manuscript. This is one way of avoiding paying a typing bill until it looks as though the investment in the manuscript may be worthwhile.

There is no point whatsoever in asking for a personal interview. The publisher will prefer to consider the manuscript on its own merits, and will not want to be influenced by a personal meeting.

## POSTAGE OF MANUSCRIPTS

Always send postage to cover the return of your manuscript or, if you prefer, explain that you will arrange to pick it up from the publisher's office. (Again, if your manuscript has been rejected the publisher will not be willing to discuss the reasons in person.)

Manuscripts are best sent by recorded delivery. Registered post is not recommended. You are unlikely to agree with the Post Office on the value of your lost manuscript, and if anyone does rob the mail, they head for the registered packets first. Recorded delivery is useful because you can check that the publisher has received the manuscript. Whether you send it first or second class depends entirely on how fast you want it to arrive. A properly packed parcel almost always arrives by either rate.

Packing is important. It is not enough to put the manuscript in an envelope. Padded bags are a good idea and are available in several sizes from many stationers.

At all costs, *keep a duplicate*, with all the latest changes to the text included on it.

## ESTIMATING

To estimate the length or *extent* of a manuscript, calculate the average number of words per page over, say, eight pages. Multiply the average by the number of pages in the manuscript, making allowances for half-pages at the end of chapters, etc.

## WHAT IS THE PUBLISHER DOING WITH YOUR MANUSCRIPT?

Whether or not the publisher finally accepts or rejects the manuscript, there is usually a considerable interval between submission and the publisher's decision. Most publishers acknowledge receipt of manuscript, and if you do not receive an acknowledgement it is advisable to check that the manuscript has arrived. Apart from that, it is not worth chasing the publisher for a quick decision: if pressed, the publisher will probably reject, purely because this is the safer decision.

You should hear from the publisher within about two months. During this time he will either have had the manuscript read 'in the house' or will have sent it to one or more advisers whose opinions he respects. Favourable readers' reports may mean that the publisher will immediately accept the manuscript, particularly if it fits easily into his current publishing programme.

On the other hand, a reader's report may be glowing, but the publisher may still hesitate. He knows he has a good book, but he wants to be sure he will be able to sell it. He is, after all, considering an investment of at least £5000 and frequently more. He may need time to obtain further opinions, and also to obtain estimates from printers, to judge whether the book could be produced at a reasonable price. The worst delays occur when the publisher is attracted to a manuscript but cannot see how he can publish it successfully.

If you have not had a decision after two months, write either a tactful letter saying 'I don't want to rush you, but . . . . .' or alternatively request an immediate decision and be prepared to start again with another publisher.

If your book is topical you have a right to a speedy decision, but it is as well to establish this early on.

## ILLUSTRATIONS

If illustrations form a large part of your proposed book and you expect to provide them yourself, then they should be included with the manuscript. If you are sending specimen pages you should include also some sample illustrations. This applies largely to children's picture books and to travel and technical books. It is prudent to send duplicate photographs, photocopies of line drawings and so on so that little harm is done if illustrations go astray.

In the case of a children's book, if you intend to illustrate it yourself, obviously one finished piece of artwork is essential, plus photocopies of roughs for the rest (one must bear in mind that the final artwork may have to be drawn to a particular size and the number of illustrations fixed according to the format chosen by the publisher). If you have written a children's story, or the text for a picture book, do *not* ask a friend to provide the illustrations. The publisher who likes your story may well not like your friend's artwork: you will have considerably lengthened the odds against the story being accepted. Of course this does not apply when an artist and author work closely together to develop an idea, but in that case it is best to start by finding a publisher who likes the artist's work before submitting the story.

Travel manuscripts should be accompanied by a sketch map to show the area you are writing about. The publisher will have an atlas in his reference shelves, but it may not have sufficient detail with which to follow your manuscript. Irreplaceable material should not be sent speculatively.

Many illustrated books these days have illustrations collected by the publishers. If your proposed book is to be illustrated, it is best to establish early on who is responsible for the illustration costs: an attractive royalty offer might be less attractive if you have to gather the pictures, obtain permission for use, and foot the bills.

## QUOTATIONS

It is normally the author's responsibility to obtain (and pay for) permission to quote written material which is still in copyright. Permission should always be sought from the publisher of the quoted work, not from the author. Fees for quotation vary enormously: for fashionable modern writers permission may be costly, but in other cases only a nominal fee of a few pounds is charged. There is no standard scale of fees. It is permissible to quote up to about 200 words for the purpose of criticism or review, but this does not apply to use in anthologies, nor does it apply to poetry. And it is a concession, not a right. Even though this is your area of responsibility, your publisher will be able to give you some advice.

## PROOF READING

There are many ways of producing books, especially with the advent of modern printing processes, but they all have certain points in common from the author's point of view, and it is as well to be forewarned.

As author you will see either one or two stages of proofs. Sometimes you will be shown the finalised copy of the typescript immediately before it goes to the printer. If so, this is really your last chance to make changes which will not tend to sour relations with your publisher! Take the opportunity to comb through the manuscript, and if there are changes which you suspect you will want to make in proof, make them now. (See also **Correcting Proofs.**)

## CORRECTIONS TO PROOFS

There was a time when authors could virtually rewrite their books in galley proof, and revise them again at page. Do not be seduced by biographies of Victorian writers into thinking this is the way the professional writer works!

Modern printing is highly mechanised, but corrections are time-consuming and may involve extensive handwork. This makes corrections far more costly than the original setting. You will probably have signed a contract undertaking to pay the cost of corrections (other than printer's errors) over say 10 per cent or 15 per cent of the cost of composition. This does not mean that you can change ten or fifteen lines in every hundred.

The cost of adding a comma at galley stage, in modern processes, is insignificant. But if you add a word in one line of a paragraph, it will probably mean resetting down to the end of the paragraph. If you add a word at page stage, and this results in the paragraph being longer, many pages may have to be adjusted by one line until the end of the chapter is reached. What to you seemed a simple improvement may take an hour's work on expensive equipment.

## STAGES OF PROOFS

Increasingly often only one stage of proofs is used in book production, and there is rarely any need for the author to see more than one stage. The proofs may be in several forms. Ask your editor how many stages of proofs you will see. It could be that you will be asked to check computer print-outs which bear no resemblance to the finished book but which do contain everything that will appear in that book!

*Galley proofs* hold columns of continuous text. They were originally a rough print taken from metal type. Modern typesetting methods most often produce proofs from a master print or direct from computer data by the Laserprint process.

*Page proofs* have been made up into pages, including page numbers, headlines, and so on. It is prohibitively expensive to make corrections at this stage, except to the printer's own errors.

It is worth noting that during the production of some books which have illustrations in the text, such as children's or 'coffee table' books, the editor or designer has to do a scissors and paste job to put the whole thing together. This may require some minor modifications to the text to make the final result come together happily.

# Screenplays for Films

## JEAN McCONNELL

Despite the old saying that the plot of the best movie can be written on a postcard, film companies do not actually welcome a plot on a postcard. Nor is it enough simply to send a story in narrative form. You should be prepared to write your idea into a full screenplay. In consequence, it is advisable to check as far as possible in case a company is already working on a similar idea and your efforts are likely to be wasted.

## LAYOUT

1. Use A4 size typing paper.
2. It is not necessary to put in elaborate camera directions. A shooting script will be made later. Your job is to write the master scenes, clearly broken down into each incident and location.
3. Your screenplay will tell your story in terms of visual action and dialogue spoken by your characters. If you intend it to be a full-length feature film, running about 1½ hours, your script will be about 100-130 pages long.
4. The general layout of a page of screenplay can be seen from the specimen page. The following points should be noted.
*(a)* Each scene should be numbered on the left and given a title which indicates whether the scene is an interior or an exterior, where it takes place, and the lighting conditions, i.e. Day or Night. The situation of each scene should be standardised; don't call your 'sitting room' a 'lounge' the next time you come to it, or people will think you mean a different place.
*(b)* Note that the dialogue is spaced out, with the qualifying directions such as '(frowning)' on a separate line, slightly inset from the dialogue. Double space each speech from the previous one.
*(c)* Always put the names of the characters in CAPITALS, except when they occur in the actual dialogue. Double space the stage directions from the dialogue, but single space the lines of the stage directions themselves.
*(d)* Leave at least a 1½ inch margin on the left hand and a reasonably wide right-hand margin. It is false economy to cram the page. You will, of course, type on one side of the sheet only.
*(e)* If you have to make a correction, cross it out neatly and type the whole section out again. But don't irritate your reader with too many corrections. Better to re-type the page.
*(f)* Only give the camera directions when you feel it to be essential. For instance, if you want to show something from a particular character's point of view, or if you think you need it to make a point, i.e. 'HARRY approaches the cliff edge and looks down. LONG SHOT—HARRY'S POINT OF VIEW. ALICE fully-clad is walking into the sea. CUT TO: CLOSE UP OF HARRY'S HORRIFIED FACE.' Note the camera directions are put in capital letters on a separate line, as in the specimen page.

## PREPARATION OF MANUSCRIPT

1. Make at least two copies, and never send your very last copy out to anyone. It will invariably be lost.

13  (continued)

She moves across the barn to the door, where she turns.

> ELIZABETH
> I still think the police ought to know.

She goes out. ALAN stands immobile until her
footsteps retreat, and then he sighs with relief.
He darts quickly to the large wine vat, climbs
up and begins heaving at the lid.

CUT TO:

14  EXT. FARMYARD  DAY

DONALD intercepts ELIZABETH as she crosses yard.

> DONALD
> What does he say?

> ELIZABETH
> Nothing.

> DONALD
> (frowning)

> Right! Now it's my turn.

He starts for the barn. ELIZABETH watches him
anxiously.

CUT TO:

15  INT.  BARN  DAY

Donald's shadow falls across the threshold.
He hesitates while his eyes get used to the gloom.

> DONALD
> Alan?

ALAN lets the lid of the vat fall and jumps down.
He stands quite still as DONALD crosses the barn
and stands staring at him. The two men are silent
a moment.

> DONALD
> (then, with realisation)
> You knew it was there, didn't you?

CLOSE SHOT — DONALD'S POINT OF VIEW
ALAN'S face is haggard.

> ALAN
> I hoped to God it wouldn't be.

2. The length of your manuscript will depend on whether you are submitting a feature film, a short film for children, say, or a documentary. But it is better to present a version which is too short rather than too long.

3. Prepare the title page in the same way as for a story or article to an editor, except that it is not necessary to state the number of words.

4. If you give a list of characters, do not suggest the actor or actress you would like to play it. This is a decision to be made elsewhere and relies on many factors about which you cannot know. Don't attach character sketches, as these should appear in the body of the screenplay.

5. Bind your screenplay, giving it a front and back cover, and securing the pages firmly.

## SUBMISSION

Attach a stamped, addressed envelope to your manuscript whether sending it through an agent or direct. But do remember that if film companies state that they will only consider material sent through an agent, they definitely mean it.

Most companies have Story Departments to which you should address your material. As Story Editors are very busy people, you can make their life easier by complying with the following rules.

1. If you have based your screenplay on someone else's published work you should make the fact clear in a covering letter, stating *(a)* that the material is no longer in copyright, or *(b)* that you yourself own the copyright, or at least an option on it, or *(c)* that you have not obtained the copyright but have reason to believe that there would be no difficulty in doing so.

2. Apart from a note of any relevant credits you may already possess, do not regale the Editor with your personal details, unless they bear a direct relation to the material submitted. For instance, if your story concerns a brain surgeon, then it would be relevant for the Editor to know that you actually are one. Otherwise, trust your work to stand on its own merit.

3. There is no need to mention if your work has been turned down by other companies, however regretfully. The comments of others will not influence a Story Editor one way or the other.

4. Don't pester the company if you don't get a reply, or even an acknowledgement, for some weeks. Most companies will formally acknowledge receipt and then leave you in limbo for at least six weeks. However, after a passage of three months or more, a brief letter asking politely what has happened is in order. A telephone call is unlikely to be helpful. It is possible the company may have liked your work enough to have sent it to America, or to be getting further readers' opinions on it. This all takes time. If they don't like it, you will certainly get it back in due course.

5. Accept that this is really a tough market; for this there are at least three reasons. One, films cost so much to make these days that the decision to go ahead is only taken after a great many important factors have been satisfied and an even greater number of important people are happy about it. Two, the number of films made is small in relation to, say, books published or TV plays produced. Three, writing a screenplay calls for knowledge and appreciation of the technicalities of film-making, as well as the ability to combine dialogue, action and pictures, visualising the story throughout in the language of the cinema.

6. Try to get an agent. A good agent will give you a fair opinion of your work. If he thinks it worthwhile, then he is the one who will know the particular film company to whom he can sell it.

(A list of agents who handle film material will be found at the end of the section on **Scripts for theatre, radio, tv and film.**)

# Writing for Television

BILL CRAIG
*Past-President of The Writers' Guild of Great Britain*

"Television drama" is a generic term which covers several varied and specialist areas of writing for the domestic screen. Since each differs from the others in terms of requirements and rewards and since each is definable in copyright terms, let's start by identifying them.

The television play is a one-off creation of a single mind and talent and absolutely the property of its author. As a form it is the vehicle for the talents of newest and least-experienced writers in the medium and also for those who are held in the highest regard. It is (for practical reasons) the traditional point of entry for the tyro. There has been some reduction in the number of plays produced annually but the BBC and certain ITV companies are still in the market for 30, 60 and 90 minute slot-length works. If the bad news is that they get several thousand unsolicited manuscripts every year, the good news is that they are all read. No script-unit will risk missing out on an undiscovered genius.

The same observations (with some modification) would apply to the original series or serial: that is, a multi-part work of sole authorship and of finite length. They tend to be written by established television writers who have a proven ability to go the necessary distance, but a new writer with an attractive idea can come in through this door.

What's the procedure? Invest some time and talent and write the play. A commission on a synopsis is unlikely without some evidence that you can write interesting action, dialogue and characters. With the finite series/serial—write the first episode and synopsise the rest.

The situation-comedy is the most highly-paid area of television writing--and understandably so. It calls for a quirky and idiosyncratic mind, and its overriding imperative—to make the viewer laugh—subordinates all of the other dramatic tools to this end. If it's difficult to play Beethoven's *Ninth* on a one-stringed fiddle, then it's Hell to do it for a run of six episodes. The sit-com is unique in screen drama in so far as most of them are played before live studio audiences. Once upon a time, they were constructed round individual comedians. Some still are, but for several years now the practice has been to cast according to the script with actors who can play comedy. And that's not a bad thing, is it?

Again, this form is an original in copyright terms, though dual authorships are not uncommon. A synopsis is pretty useless (ever tried to explain a joke?), so write the pilot-script and briefly indicate where you can go with other episodes.

We now come to a significant point of departure and go into those areas where the copyright is split with another party.

First, the drama-series: *Bergerac, Boon, Casualty,* et al. These are definable as a series of original and self-contained scripts using the same characters and backgrounds throughout. The format—that is, the characters and general ambience—will be owned or leased by the production organisation. They represent a substantial part of television drama, but it is rare for a writer without previous screen experience to be commissioned to write for them. It is quite pointless to submit a speculative script or synopsis: the series you are seeing now was recorded months ago.

The daily or bi-weekly serial (*Coronation Street, Brookside, Take the High Road, Emmerdale Farm*) will occasionally try out new writers, but theproduction pressures on reliability and deadline delivery dates don't allow for too many risks to be taken outside what is usually an established and pretty permanent writing team.

Dramatisation and Adaptation are terms which are interchanged in an ignorantly casual manner; they are not the same thing. A dramatisation is the conversion of a prose-work to a screenplay. An adaptation is a similar conversion of a dramatic work. The difference is considerable, and the screen credit should reflect this fact.

There has been a great increase in the number of dramatisations made from novels. Again, these are usually written by writers with a track record in television, but occasionally the author of the book to be dramatised will be approached to write the screenplay. If you don't come under either of those headings, then you probably wouldn't get very far by simply suggesting that you'd like to dramatise this or that novel. Adaptations are usually "in-house" works.

All of this leaves uncovered an odd and often lucrative area—the format. It is possible to sell an idea for a series without ever having written a script. But make sure that your submission is as detailed as it possibly can be in terms of background, main characters and development. Doing it the simple way in this instance can mean finding out that fifty other people have had the same simple idea. And selling an idea carries no guarantee that you'll be asked to write the scripts.

Script layout and presentation. Use A4. Type it or have it typed. Blank margin about four inches on the left hand side. Directions and character names in capitals, dialogue in capitals and lower case, double spaced. Don't go mad with directions; keep them functional and indicative. Don't be intimidated by camera directions; use them only when they make a dramatic point you want to get across.

Number and head the scenes thus: 1. INT. JOE'S ROOM. DAY

Avoid nonsense action directions such as "Her inner resilience manifests itself in a way reminiscent of the wind howling across her native moors". If you mean she's from Yorkshire, just say it.

There are several books on the subject of layout and technique. Two which come to mind are *Writing for Television* by Malcolm Hulke (Black) and *The Way to Write for Television* by Eric Paice (Elm Tree Books). *Writing for the BBC* (BBC Books) could be money well-spent.

Given success to your efforts, you will be contracted under the terms of the relevant agreement between the British Broadcasting Corporation or the Independent Television Companies Association and the Writers' Guild of Great Britain, 430 Edgware Road, London W2 1EH. The Guild has sole bargaining rights in the television drama rates, its agreements are complex and comprehensive and several of the rights and benefits contained in them are available to Guild members only.

Payments are made in stages: BBC—half on commission, half on acceptance; ITCA—half on commission, a quarter on delivery, a quarter on acceptance.

The foregoing comments apply mainly to programmes produced by the British Broadcasting Corporation or the ITV companies. The increasingly-important independent production sector should not, however, be ignored, since many of their productions are primarily intended for television screening.

These programmes are made by either entirely independent production organisations or subsidiaries of the ITV companies (e.g. *Minder*, Euston Films/Thames Television.)

Generally speaking, the scripts are laid out in film format (see **Screenplays for Films**) although some, since they produce on tape, might prefer the television format. The procedures described above for submitting unsolicited work should be observed.

Contracts should conform to the terms laid down by the agreement between the Writers' Guild of Great Britain and the British Film and Television Producers Association/Independent Programme Producers Association. Again, the Agreement is comprehensive and covers all forms and aspects of screen drama. Payment is made in four stages: treatment, first draft, second draft and principal photography. Further exploitation is also covered.

Further useful information and addresses may be found in a booklet called *Contacts*. The 1989–90 edition is available, price £4.65 including postage, from *The Spotlight*, 7 Leicester Place, London WC2H 7BP.

# Word Processing
## A Guide for Authors

RANDALL McMULLAN

If you use a typewriter then you have already compromised the "purity" of your writing technique, and the typewriter is a rather unfriendly aid to writing. You realise this every time you get to the end of a page and wish that you could alter the first sentence. Only those who use pencil and rubber can claim to be untainted by mechanical help, and their technique is rather similar to that of a word processor.

Using a word processor simply makes writing better, or faster, or both. In short: you create, check and change your text on a screen before printing it out as "hard copy" on paper. It is now so easy to revise your text that you leap from a reluctance to retype into Proust-like problems of how to stop revising. Indeed, once text has been stored in a word processor it need not be keyed again, even by the typesetter, and the same material can be used again or easily adapted for other uses. For example, this article is certainly new and original—yet fragments of this text have been keyed before.

## EQUIPMENT

The associations of word processors with computers and computer jargon are not helpful, but they can be lived with. Most of us learn to drive a car with no great interest in what makes it work but, when we have to, we put up with the technicalities and the jargon of cars to make them run. Word processors are actually computers or "hardware" for which the word processing set of instructions is just one of the available "software" programs. The same computer can also run other programs, such as those which organise databases of information or do accounts. This other ability may not interest you, but it is there anyway.

### Hardware

The type of computer which runs a word processor is called a microcomputer or desktop computer, and it usually includes the keyboard, the computer "box", and the screen ("VDU" or "monitor"). In earlier years there was a gulf of price and ability between word processors on a home computer and an office computer. Standards have now merged, and the word processing facilities on a £500 word processor are often equivalent to those that cost £5,000 ten years ago, or perhaps £20,000 fifteen years ago. Let's assume that, as an author, you are seeking sensibly priced word processing equipment which conforms to modern office standards.

### Software

The word processing software is usually bought separately and the computer is neutral about which word processing program you use. However, word processors do have "personalities" in the way that they implement features. Some packages, and their reviewers, are biased towards the daily demands of office work, while other packages are better at making heavy revisions to a long manuscript, for example.

Choosing from a series of "menus" or "icons" on screen is helpful to new or casual users, but when you are proficient it is quicker to use a package which responds to commands given at the keyboard. Standardisation with other people is usually more important than some special feature that you end up never using. The popularity of the principal word processors has resulted in the availability of additional programs, such as those for indexing and desktop publishing, which can be purchased separately if and when you need them.

*Printers*

The word processor printer receives electronic signals from the storage disk along a cable. These signals cause the printer to reproduce the text that you have composed on screen. The same text can be printed out in different styles and on different printers. Printers do a lot of work so need to be robust and fast. While they may not need to produce perfect-looking print, good print is now quite possible with cheap, fast printers.

Authors are unlikely to buy equipment that does not include a keyboard and they sometimes wonder whether they can link a typewriter to a word processor. This is sometimes possible with an electronic typewriter but such a typewriter is likely to wear out under heavy workloads. It is usually better to keep your type-writer separate from your word processing equipment. Cheaper prices make it reasonable to have both—and to have several types of printer if necessary. Despite rumours of paperless "electronic offices", you will probably find that word processing generates satisfying amounts of paper—it is so easy to make drafts and duplicates. Although at first you might be impressed by the way that a printer automatically "types" a page, you will soon tire of feeding single sheets into the printer.

Dot-matrix printers are cheap, quiet and can produce changes of print style and size without stopping. New models offer both fast, "dotty" styles and slower, near-letter-quality (NLQ) styles where the dot structure is barely noticeable. Dot-matrix printers generally use continuous paper with perforated "tractor" margins, but they will also print single sheets. Daisy-wheel printers are slow but can give the sharp carbon ribbon quality of the best typewriters. They tend to be noisy, and automatic paper feed is usually more expensive.

Laser printers have an internal mechanism like a photocopier and they can, with the right software and a lot of learning, produce different sizes and styles of print, like a typesetter. Laser printers also produce plain text with satisfying speed and quietness. Inkjet printers can give similar effects to laser printers and cost about half the price.

## BUYING

*Stay with the crowd*

This guideline will allow you to avoid technicalities of word processing equipment including some contained in this article. Staying with the herd will probably save you money and never leave you in isolation. When working alone you want help to be quick and cheap, and plenty of advice on the most common makes of word processing equipment is available from books, magazines, friends and dealers. Don't agonise about choices too much and don't wait for next month's machine—you'll wait for ever. The trend is to standardise on established systems and, although costs do drift downwards, your word processor could already be earning money.

*What to buy*

IBM originally set the "standard" for the modern desktop personal computer with models called the "PC", "XT", and "AT". These computers were made and sold in modular form so that different parts, such as screens or circuit cards, could easily be added or swapped. Other manufacturers soon produced IBM-compatible machines using the same format, often with better features and always with lower prices. Amstrad is one brand of compatible that is easily found in High Street stores, while many other good "clones" are available at reasonable prices.

Apple Macintosh desktop computers are less widespread than IBM-compatible models and they use different formats, which means that you can't easily swap disks or move work files between machines. The Macintosh is admired for its system of screen help and for its compact "designer" styling. Unfortunately, this compact design means that there is little competition for Apple and prices are kept high.

Something like 400 different types of word processing software have been made available for the IBM PC and its many compatibles, but only half a dozen are widely used for professional purposes. WordStar Professional, Word Perfect and Word are good for general use, while Displaywrite, WordStar 2000 and Multi-Mate are tuned towards heavy-duty office use. All modern word processing packages are competent and they share about 80 per cent of the same features.

## Where to buy

Your best method of purchasing computer goods often relates to how you personally buy an item like a TV. You might go to a well-known departmental store and arrange for the TV to be delivered and installed, or you might bring it home in an unopened box from a warehouse and set it up yourself. It is common to buy computer equipment by mail order from reputable discount warehouses; buy a monthy magazine like *Personal Computer World* and read it for the advertisements as well as for the articles. Otherwise choose a dealer in a convenient location and negotiate a suitable package of price and help. Don't expect too much help – you don't get driving lessons with a car, and the dealer's profit margins are usually less than those of a motor dealer.

## Reliability

A computer and printer are much more reliable than, say, a video recorder. Electronics are most likely to develop faults within the first few weeks, so it is a good idea to keep equipment running for long periods at first. Many dealers will simply replace box for box if there is an early fault. Service contracts at 10 per cent of cost per annum are not usually worthwhile for people without office budgets. Computers are now so much cheaper that it might be more economical to buy two computers if the prospect of a breakdown really worries you. One of the advantages of using popular makes of word processing hardware and software is that you can take your disk to a friend or dealer and make an emergency printout. As a general rule, you should often save your work onto disk—once per page at the least.

## Costs

Initially you can buy all the equipment you need for £500 to £1000, so don't overspend, especially on your first machine. It's surprising how many authors, not usually an affluent lot, try to spend more than they need to. It is easy to enhance your equipment at a later stage, and you often need to have used it for a year or so before you can make a sensible decision as to whether extra features will benefit your particular type of work. If you have money left over, then consider buying a portable machine which supplements your main machine; or just go on holiday!

## TECHNICALITIES

### Keyboard

The feel of a keyboard is a matter of personal choice and of construction. A keyboard made by IBM can cost more than a complete home computer, but it is considered worth it by some people. In general, good keyboards are constructed with springs beneath each key, while cheaper keyboards are constructed with buttons resting on a rubber membrane. A computer keyboard is laid out in the same "QWERTY" pattern as a typewriter, thank goodness. There are the usual Shift keys which you hold down to produce upper-case letters and there are extra keys, such as the Control and Alt keys which can also produce special effects when they are held down in combination with the other keys. Computer keyboards have also acquired extra keys such as a duplicate set of numeral keys, a set of arrow keys to move about the screen, and "function" keys which change from program to program.

### Monitor

The monitor or VDU (visual display unit) is the TV-like screen which displays your text. Electronically the monitor works like a TV, but it has a higher resolution in order to display the standard 80 characters across the screen. It is rare, and expensive, to have a monitor which can display the full length of an A4 page on screen, but it is easy to pan the screen over your text when it is displayed on a standard-sized screen.

A colour monitor does not give as sharp or as fine an image as a monochrome monitor unless you invest in high-resolution equipment which tends to cost as much again as a complete computer. A monochrome monitor is usually the best choice for word processing, unless you have a special need for colour graphics. Monochrome monitors are available in shades of green or amber, and the best choice seems to be a matter of fashion rather than health. There is continuing investigation and debate about possible health hazards due to glare or radiation from VDUs.

### Microprocessor chips

If you open up the main computer box you probably won't be able to identify the microprocessor, which is technically at the heart of matters. It is one of many small black plastic rectangles attached to a circuit board at the base of the box. The central microprocessor chip can be described in terms of its speed and its capacity to handle 8 bits, 16 bits or 32 bits of information at a time. These ratings have an effect on the ability of the computer to change graphics on the screen but little effect on word processing, and your computer may be rather bored as it waits for your keystrokes. Unless you have other types of computing to do there may be little merit in purchasing faster and dearer machines. Indeed there are cost advantages in the use of older and slower types of microprocessor such as those used in the Amstrad PCW models.

### Memory

The main memory of a computer is the RAM (Random Access Memory) into which the word processor instructions are loaded. The typical size of this RAM has been increasing over the years as memory gets cheaper and programs offer more features, such as spelling checkers, which use the RAM.

### Disk drives

The current generation of desktop computers lose their memory when switched off—you may well know the feeling—so programs such as the word processor are stored on magnetic disks, and so are your work files. The disks work like a cross between a gramophone record and a tape recorder. "Floppy" disks (which may actually be quite rigid) are slid into the drive mechanism, which then spins the disk and magnetically "writes" and "reads" the magnetic data on the surface of the disk.

"Hard" disks, also called fixed drives, have 30 to 100 times the capacity of a single floppy disk, and they are a permanent part of the computer unit. Because programs and work files are left in the hard disk you have very fast access to large amounts of data. But data must be carefully organised and frequently "backed-up" by copying the data onto floppy disks which are then kept in a safe place. Hard disks are not usually a prime requirement for writers, and they can always be fitted to your computer later if you have the need; they have become temptingly cheap in recent years.

Authors worry whether their masterpieces can all be stored onto a single disk, but disk capacity, in kilobytes, has little to do with size of text. Indeed, there are many reasons why nearly all writing is best handled and stored as separate "files" of data, usually no longer than a chapter. Even if a single work is organised as many files over several disks you can still do continuous printing, numbering or searching. If necessary, you can happily work with just one floppy disk drive as it is still possible to duplicate disks using a single drive.

*Disk formats*

Despite some agreement about operating systems in computers, they can have incompatible disk sizes and formats. Even when computers use the same type of blank disk, the material stored by one computer cannot always be read by a machine which uses a different format. Weariness with this type of stupidity was a major reason why people accepted the IBM format for 5.25-inch disks and made it an effective standard. Having written something on one machine you can easily slide your floppy disk into any of the millions of other PC-type machines around the world.

IBM themselves have moved on to other floppy disk formats, of which the major one is the more compact 3.5-inch disk, a size which is particularly convenient for portable computers. There is a gradual movement towards the smaller disk format, but the 5.25-inch standard is also going to exist for a long time. The modularity of the PC-type of machine means that, when the time comes, it is relatively easy and cheap to install another drive type.

The Amstrad PCW series of word processors use a special disk size which is (almost) unique to Amstrad. These machines are so numerous that they form a standard of their own and, because there are a large number of Amstrad users, it is relatively easy to have data transferred from the Amstrad format to other formats.

*Operating system*

The control and "housekeeping" of a desktop computer is handled by a special program called the Disk Operating System or DOS. On PC-type computers this operating system is grippingly titled MS-DOS or PC-DOS. You needn't care about the operating system while you are writing within the word processor but you will need to use the operating system for some chores, such as making copies of files or disks. The method of driving the operating system ranges from typing a command like DELETE to pointing at little screen images (icons) of wastepaper bins.

## WRITING

A word processor should lead to new habits of creating and editing text. The "insert" action of word processors is rather different from the "overwrite" action of typewriters, as when you enter new text on the screen the word processor pushes the existing words apart to make room for the new material. Although confusing at first, this "sweep forward" effect is a useful way of keeping old work in view before you adapt or delete it.

On a typewriter it is important to fix mistakes as you make them and to compose the correct layout right from the first line, but with a word processor it is usually more efficient to enter all the text in one pass and to correct errors or change layout in later passes. It is sometimes easier to quickly re-type a wrong word and then delete the incorrect version with a single keystroke; or you can let your spelling checker work for you.

Modern word processors are WYSIWYG (What You See Is What You Get) which means that the layout shown on screen is the same as that produced on the paper. Even so, it is often more convenient and accurate to check your work from a paper printout rather than from the screen. Such drafts may be single-spaced and perhaps printed in "dotty" mode. You can then reformat the same text to double-spacing for your final manuscript. Do remember to use a dark new ribbon, or set the printer to double-strike, so that publishers can read and photocopy with ease.

Don't be worried by the hearsay about the "difficulty" of learning these techniques of word processing—if it was really that difficult then how could all those other people manage it? The mental investment of learning to "drive" a word processing package is small compared to the benefits which result. Once you have started word processing you probably won't return to your typewriter.

# Correcting Proofs

*The following notes and table are extracted from BS 5261: Part 2: 1976 and are reproduced by permission of the British Standards Institution, 2 Park Street, London, W1A 2BS, from whom copies of the complete Standard may be obtained.*

## NOTES ON COPY PREPARATION AND PROOF CORRECTION

The marks to be used for marking-up copy for composition and for the correction of printers' proofs shall be as shown in table 1.

The marks in table 1 are classified in three groups as follows.

(a) Group A: general.

(b) Group B: deletion, insertion, and substitution.

(c) Group C: positioning and spacing.

Each item in table 1 is given a simple alpha-numeric serial number denoting the classification group to which it belongs and its position within the group.

The marks have been drawn keeping the shapes as simple as possible and using sizes which relate to normal practice. The shapes of the marks should be followed exactly by all who make use of them.

For each marking-up or proof correction instruction a distinct mark is to be made:

(a) in the text: to indicate the exact place to which the instruction refers;

(b) in the margin: to signify or amplify the meaning of the instruction.

It should be noted that some instructions have combined textual and marginal mark.

Where a number of instructions occur in one line, the marginal marks are to be divided between the left and right margins where possible, the order being from left to right in both margins.

Specification details, comments, and instructions may be written on the copy or proof to complement the textual and marginal marks. Such written matter is to be clearly distinguishable from the copy and from any corrections made to the proof. Normally this is done by encircling the matter and/or by the appropriate use of colour (see below).

Proof corrections shall be made in coloured ink thus:

(a) printer's literal errors marked by the printer for correction: green;

(b) printer's literal errors marked by the customer and his agents for correction: red;

(c) alterations and instructions made by the customer and his agents: black or dark blue.

### Table 1. Classified list of marks

NOTE. The letters M and P in the notes column indicate marks for marking-up copy and for correcting proofs respectively.

**Group A General**

| Number | Instruction | Textual mark | Marginal mark | Notes |
|--------|-------------|--------------|---------------|-------|
| A1 | Correction is concluded | None | / | P<br>Make after each correction |
| A2 | Leave unchanged | ------ <br>under characters to remain | (✓) | M P |
| A3 | Remove extraneous marks | Encircle marks to be removed | ✗ | P<br>e.g. film or paper edges visible between lines on bromide or diazo proofs |
| A3.1 | Push down risen spacing material | Encircle blemish | ⊥ | P |
| A4 | Refer to appropriate authority anything of doubtful accuracy | Encircle word(s) affected | (?) | P |

**Group B Deletion, insertion and substitution**

| B1 | Insert in text the matter indicated in the margin | ⋏ | New matter followed by ⋏ | M P<br>Identical to B2 |
|----|---------------------------------------------------|---|--------------------------|------------------------|
| B2 | Insert additional matter identified by a letter in a diamond | ⋏ | ⋏<br>Followed by for example ◇A | M P<br>The relevant section of the copy should be supplied with the corresponding encircled letter marked on it e.g. ◇A |
| B3 | Delete | / through character(s)<br>or ⊢⊣ through words to be deleted | ∂ | M P |
| B4 | Delete and close up | ⌢/ through character<br>or ⊢⊣ through characters e.g. charac̃ter charǎacter | ∂ | M P |

**Table 1** *(continued)*

| Number | Instruction | Textual mark | Marginal mark | Notes |
|---|---|---|---|---|
| B5 | Substitute character or substitute part of one or more word(s) | / through character or ⊢——⊣ through word(s) | New character or new word(s) | M P |
| B6 | Wrong fount. Replace by character(s) of correct fount | Encircle character(s) to be changed | ⊗ | P |
| B6.1 | Change damaged character(s) | Encircle character(s) to be changed | ✕ | P This mark is identical to A3 |
| B7 | Set in or change to italic | ——— under character(s) to be set or changed | ⊔ | M P Where space does not permit textual marks encircle the affected area instead |
| B8 | Set in or change to capital letters | ═══ under character(s) to be set or changed | ≡ | |
| B9 | Set in or change to small capital letters | ═══ under character(s) to be set or changed | = | |
| B9.1 | Set in or change to capital letters for initial letters and small capital letters for the rest of the words | ≡ under initial letters and ═══ under rest of the word(s) | ≡ | |
| B10 | Set in or change to bold type | ∿∿∿ under character(s) to be set or changed | ∿ | |
| B11 | Set in or change to bold italic type | ∿∿∿ under character(s) to be set or changed | ⊔∿ | |
| B12 | Change capital letters to lower case letters | Encircle character(s) to be changed | ≢ | P For use when B5 is inappropriate |

**Table 1** *(continued)*

| Number | Instruction | Textual mark | Marginal mark | Notes |
|---|---|---|---|---|
| B12.1 | Change small capital letters to lower case letters | Encircle character(s) to be changed | ≠ | P<br>For use when B5 is inappropriate |
| B13 | Change italic to upright type | Encircle character(s) to be changed | ⊔ | P |
| B14 | Invert type | Encircle character to be inverted | ◠ | P |
| B15 | Substitute or insert character in 'superior' position | / through character<br>or<br>⅄ where required | ⌐ under character<br>e.g. ² | P |
| B16 | Substitute or insert character in 'inferior' position | / through character<br>or<br>⅄ where required | ∟ over character<br>e.g. /₂ | P |
| B17 | Substitute ligature e.g. ffi for separate letters | ├──────┤ through characters affected | ⌣<br>e.g. ffi | P |
| B17.1 | Substitute separate letters for ligature | ├──────┤ | Write out separate letters | P |
| B18 | Substitute or insert full stop or decimal point | / through character<br>or<br>⅄ where required | ⊙ | M P |
| B18.1 | Substitute or insert colon | / through character<br>or<br>⅄ where required | ⊙ | M P |
| B18.2 | Substitute or insert semi-colon | / through character<br>or<br>⅄ where required | ; | M P |

**Table 1** *(continued)*

| Number | Instruction | Textual mark | Marginal mark | Notes |
|--------|-------------|--------------|---------------|-------|
| B18.3 | Substitute or insert comma | / through character<br><br>or<br><br>⋀ where required | 〉 | M P |
| B18.4 | Substitute or insert apostrophe | / through character<br><br>or<br><br>⋀ where required | ⁊ | M P |
| B18.5 | Substitute or insert single quotation marks | / through character<br><br>or<br><br>⋀ where required | ⁊ and/or ⁊ | M P |
| B18.6 | Substitute or insert double quotation marks | / through character<br><br>or<br><br>⋀ where required | ⁊ and/or ⁊ | M P |
| B19 | Substitute or insert ellipsis | / through character<br><br>or<br><br>⋀ where required | • • • | M P |
| B20 | Substitute or insert leader dots | / through character<br><br>or<br><br>⋀ where required | ⊙⋯ | M P<br>Give the measure of the leader when necessary |
| B21 | Substitute or insert hyphen | / through character<br><br>or<br><br>⋀ where required | ⊢⊣ | M P |
| B22 | Substitute or insert rule | / through character<br><br>⋀ where required | ⊢⊣ | M P<br>Give the size of the rule in the marginal mark e.g.<br><br>⊢1 em⊣  ⊢4 mm⊣ |

**Table 1** *(continued)*

| Number | Instruction | Textual mark | Marginal mark | Notes |
|--------|-------------|--------------|---------------|-------|
| B23 | Substitute or insert oblique | / through character<br><br>or<br><br>∧ where required | Ⓘ | M P |

**Group C  Positioning and spacing**

| Number | Instruction | Textual mark | Marginal mark | Notes |
|--------|-------------|--------------|---------------|-------|
| C1 | Start new paragraph | | | M P |
| C2 | Run on (no new paragraph) | | | M P |
| C3 | Transpose characters or words | between characters or words, numbered when necessary | | M P |
| C4 | Transpose a number of characters or words | **3**  **2**  **1**<br>\|  \|  \| | 123 | M P<br>To be used when the sequence cannot be clearly indicated by the use of C3. The vertical strokes are made through the characters or words to be transposed and numbered in the correct sequence |
| C5 | Transpose lines | | | M P |
| C6 | Transpose a number of lines | | ——— 3<br>——— 2<br>——— 1 | P<br>To be used when the sequence cannot be clearly indicated by C5. Rules extend from the margin into the text with each line to be transposed numbered in the correct sequence |
| C7 | Centre | ⌐enclosing matter to be centred⌐ | [ ] | M P |
| C8 | Indent | | | P<br>Give the amount of the indent in the marginal mark |

**Table 1** *(continued)*

| Number | Instruction | Textual mark | Marginal mark | Notes |
|--------|-------------|--------------|---------------|-------|
| C9 | Cancel indent | | | P |
| C10 | Set line justified to specified measure | and/or | | P<br>Give the exact dimensions when necessary |
| C11 | Set column justified to specified measure | | | M P<br>Give the exact dimensions when necessary |
| C12 | Move matter specified distance to the right | enclosing matter to be moved to the right | | P<br>Give the exact dimensions when necessary |
| C13 | Move matter specified distance to the left | enclosing matter to be moved to the left | | P<br>Give the exact dimensions when necessary |
| C14 | Take over character(s), word(s) or line to next line, column or page | | | P<br>The textual mark surrounds the matter to be taken over and extends into the margin |
| C15 | Take back character(s), word(s), or line to previous line, column or page | | | P<br>The textual mark surrounds the matter to be taken back and extends into the margin |
| C16 | Raise matter | over matter to be raised<br>under matter to be raised | | P<br>Give the exact dimensions when necessary. (Use C28 for insertion of space between lines or paragraphs in text) |
| C17 | Lower matter | over matter to be lowered<br>under matter to be lowered | | P<br>Give the exact dimensions when necessary. (Use C29 for reduction of space between lines or paragraphs in text) |
| C18 | Move matter to position indicated | Enclose matter to be moved and indicate new position | | P<br>Give the exact dimensions when necessary |

**Table 1** *(continued)*

| Number | Instruction | Textual mark | Marginal mark | Notes |
|---|---|---|---|---|
| C19 | Correct vertical alignment | | | P |
| C20 | Correct horizontal alignment | Single line above and below misaligned matter<br><br>e.g.<br><br>mi<sub>s</sub>aligned | | P<br>The marginal mark is placed level with the head and foot of the relevant line |
| C21 | Close up. Delete space between characters or words | linking ⌒⌣ characters | | M P |
| C22 | Insert space between characters | \|<br><br>between characters affected | | M P<br>Give the size of the space to be inserted when necessary |
| C23 | Insert space between words | ⅄<br><br>between words affected | | M P<br>Give the size of the space to be inserted when necessary |
| C24 | Reduce space between characters | \|<br><br>between characters affected | | M P<br>Give the amount by which the space is to be reduced when necessary |
| C25 | Reduce space between words | ⋀<br><br>between words affected | | M P<br>Give amount by which the space is to be reduced when necessary |
| C26 | Make space appear equal between characters or words | \|<br><br>between characters or words affected | | M P |
| C27 | Close up to normal interline spacing | ( each side of column linking lines ) | | M P<br>The textual marks extend into the margin |

At the sign of the red pale

The Life and Work of William Caxton, by H W Larken

[An Extract]

Few people, even in the field of printing, have any clear conception of what William Caxton did or, indeed, of what he was. Much of this lack of knowledge is due to the absence of information that can be counted as factual and the consequent tendency to vague generalisation.

Though it is well known that Caxton was born in the county of Kent, there is no information as to the precise place. In his prologue to the *History of Troy*, William Caxton wrote 'for in France I was never and was born and learned my English in Kent in the Weald where I doubt not is spoken as broad and rude English as in any place of England.' During the fifteenth century there were a great number of Flemish cloth weavers in Kent; most of them had come to England at the instigation of Edward III with the object of teaching their craft to the English. So successful was this venture that the English cloth trade flourished and the agents who sold the cloth (the mercers) became very wealthy people. There have b There have been many speculations concerning the origin of the Caxton family and much research has been carried out. It is assumed often that Caxton's family must have been connected with the wool trade in order to have secured his apprenticeship to an influential merchant.

W. Blyth Crotch (Prologues and Epilogues of William Caxton) suggests that the origin of the name Caxton (of which there are several variations in spelling) may be traced to Cambridgeshire but notes that many writers have suggested that Caxton was connected with a family at Hadlow or alternatively a family in Canterbury.

Of the Canterbury connection a William Caxton became freeman of the City in 1431 and William Pratt, a mercer who was the printer's friend, was born there. H. R. Plomer suggests that Pratt and Caxton might possibly have been schoolboys together, perhaps at the school St. Alphege. In this parish there lived a John Caxton who used as his mark three cakes over a barrel (or I tun) and who is mentioned in an inscription on a monument in the church of St. Alphege.

In 1941, Alan Keen (an authority on manuscripts) secured some documents concerning Caxton; these are now in the BRITISH MUSEUM. Discovered in the library of Earl Winterton at Shillinglee Park by Richard Holworthy, the documents cover the period 1420 to 1467. One of Winterton's ancestors purchased the manor of West Wratting from a family named Caxton, the property being situated in the Weald of Kent.

There is also record of a property mentioning Philip Caxton and his wife Dennis who had two sons, Philip (born in 1413) and William.

Particularly interesting in these documents is one recording that Philip Caxton junior sold the manor of Little Wratting to John Christemasse of London in 1436 the deed having been witnessed by two aldermen, one of whom was Robert Large, the printer's employer. Further, in 1439 the other son, William Caxton, conveyed his rights in the manor Bluntes Hall at Little Wratting to John Christemasse, and an indenture of 1457 concerning this property mentions one William Caxton alias Causton. It is an interesting coincidence to note that the lord of the manor of Little Wratting was the father of Margaret, Duchess of Burgundy.

In 1420, a Thomas Caxton of Tenterden witnessed the will of a fellow townsman; he owned property in Kent and appears to have been a person of some importance.

[1] See 'William Caxton'.

(A) attached to Christchurch Monastery in the parish of

## AT THE SIGN OF THE RED PALE

The Life and Work of William Caxton, *by H W Larken*

### An Extract

FEW PEOPLE, even in the field of printing, have any clear conception of what William Caxton did or, indeed, of what he was. Much of this lack of knowledge is due to the absence of information that can be counted as factual and the consequent tendency to vague generalisation.

Though it is well known that Caxton was born in the county of Kent, there is no information as to the precise place. In his prologue to the *History of Troy*, William Caxton wrote '. . . for in France I was never and was born and learned my English in Kent in the Weald where I doubt not is spoken as broad and rude English as in any place of England.'

During the fifteenth century there were a great number of Flemish cloth weavers in Kent; most of them had come to England at the instigation of Edward III with the object of teaching their craft to the English. So successful was this venture that the English cloth trade flourished and the agents who sold the cloth (the mercers) became very wealthy people.

There have been many speculations concerning the origin of the Caxton family and much research has been carried out. It is often assumed that Caxton's family must have been connected with the wool trade in order to have secured his apprenticeship to an influential merchant.

W. Blyth Crotch (*Prologues and Epilogues of William Caxton*) suggests that the origin of the name Caxton (of which there are several variations in spelling) may be traced to Cambridgeshire but notes that many writers have suggested that Caxton was connected with a family at Hadlow or alternatively a family in Canterbury.

Of the Canterbury connection: a William Caxton became freeman of the City in 1431 and William Pratt, a mercer who was the printer's friend, was born there. H. R. Plomer[1] suggests that Pratt and Caxton might possibly have been schoolboys together, perhaps at the school attached to Christchurch Monastery in the parish of St. Alphege. In this parish there lived a John Caxton who used as his mark three cakes over a barrel (or tun) and who is mentioned in an inscription on a monument in the church of St. Alphege.

In 1941, Alan Keen (an authority on manuscripts) secured some documents concerning Caxton; these are now in the British Museum. Discovered in the library of Earl Winterton at Shillinglee Park by Richard Holworthy, the documents cover the period 1420 to 1467. One of Winterton's ancestors purchased the manor of West Wratting from a family named Caxton, the property being situated in the Weald of Kent. There is also record of a property mentioning Philip Caxton and his wife Dennis who had two sons, Philip (born in 1413) and William.

Particularly interesting in these documents is one recording that Philip Caxton junior sold the manor of Little Wratting to John Christemasse of London in 1436—the deed having been witnessed by two aldermen, one of whom was Robert Large, the printer's employer. Further, in 1439, the other son, William Caxton, conveyed his rights in the manor Bluntes Hall at Little Wratting to John Christemasse, and an indenture of 1457 concerning this property mentions one William Caxton alias Causton. It is an interesting coincidence to note that the lord of the manor of Little Wratting was the father of Margaret, Duchess of Burgundy.

In 1420, a Thomas Caxton of Tenterden witnessed the will of a fellow townsman; he owned property in Kent and appears to have been a person of some importance.

[1] See 'William Caxton'.

**Table 1** *(continued)*

| Number | Instruction | Textual mark | Marginal mark | Notes |
|--------|-------------|--------------|---------------|-------|
| C28 | Insert space between lines or paragraphs | or | | M P The marginal mark extends between the lines of text. Give the size of the space to be inserted when necessary |
| C29 | Reduce space between lines or paragraphs | or | | M P The marginal mark extends between the lines of text. Give the amount by which the space is to be reduced when necessary |

# Editorial, Literary and Production Services

The following list of specialists offer a wide variety of services to writers (both new and established), to publishers, journalists and others. Services include advice on MSS, editing and book production, indexing, translation, research, writing, marketing and publicity.

**Academic File (Centre for Near East, Asia and Africa Research Limited)** (1985), Ground Floor, 172 Castelnau, London SW13 9DH    *tel* 01-741 5878    *telex* 940 12777 Near G    *fax* 01-741 5671. *Directors:* Sajid Rizvi, Shirley Rizvi. Research, advisory and consultancy services related to politics, economics (oil, etc.) and societies of the Middle East, Asia and North Africa: editing, editorial assessment, art and design and desk-top publishing.

**Academic Projects/Research Factors (Features & Editorial Services)**, 84 Rupert Street, Norwich NR2 2AT    *tel* (0603) 615416/620301. *Editors:* Dr. Dennis Chaplin, Laura Ashworth. Features, backgrounders, research briefs for press and broadcasting. Subjects include: defence, politics, technology, medicine, economics, finance, business, marketing, PR, advertising. Also: press releases, promotorials, special feature projects, ghosted books/features, book editing, typing, word processing, house journals, speeches, magazine/newspaper editing/design/typesetting (desktop).

**Airplay** (1988), P.O. Box 175, Bath BA1 2FX    *tel* (0225) 743782/318335. Consists of a major radio-drama producer, mainstream actors and editors with access to full stereo recording studio facilities for the production of pilot tapes for new musicals, screen and teleplays and stage plays. This fusion means that Airplay can offer very favourable terms. Full details by return.

**Anvil Editorial Associates** (1966), Lleifior, Malltraeth, Bodorgan, Anglesey, Gwynedd LL62 5AF    *tel* Bodorgan (0407) 840688    *fax* (0407) 840180. *Director:* Dr H. Bernard-Smith. Comprehensive editorial service, including editing, indexing, copyediting, and proof-reading. Planning, preparation, writing and editing of books, house journals, company histories, reports, brochures, promotional literature, pamphlets and scripts. Full MS service using justifying and multi-pitch electronic typewriters and word processors.

**Appleround Associates** (1983), 1 Newburgh Street, London W1V 1LH    *tel* 01-734 0881 and 01-937 6106. *Director:* Caroline Hobhouse. General editorial services ranging from complete co-published books, through provision of camera-ready, to consultancy. Preliminary enquiry, with S.A.E. essential.

**Arioma Editorial Services.** Gloucester House, High Street, Borth, Dyfed SY24 5HZ    *tel* (0970) 871 296. *Partners:* Moira Smith, Patrick Smith. Research, co-writing, ghost-writing, indexing; manuscripts prepared for monographs. *Speciality:* military aviation history.

**Authors' Advice Line** (1988), 12 Hadleigh Gardens, Boyatt Wood, Eastleigh, Hampshire SO5 4NP    *tel* (0703) 612232. *Directors:* J. Evans, L. Bruce, B. J. Rolfe. Critical evaluation and advice on publishing potential of manuscripts, specializing in romantic and historical fiction. Blurbs, typing.

**Authors' Advisory Service** (1972), 21 Campden Grove, Kensington, London W8 4JG    *tel* 01-937 5583. All typescripts professionally evaluated in depth and edited by long-established publishers' reader specialising in constructive advice to new writers and with wide experience of current literary requirements. Critic and reader for literary awards. Lecture service on the craft and technique of writing for publication.

**Authors in Science Consultancy** (1987), Sally Crawford, 112 Great Titchfield Street, London W1P 7AJ    *tel* 01-637 1759. Experienced medical editor, publishers' reader and health writer offers advice (including writing courses for scientists) and general editing service for non-fiction authors new and established who know their subject: medical science/nutrition/health/psychology and who wish to write for the general reader.

**Authors' Research Services** (1966), Richard Wright, 32 Oak Village, London NW5 4QN    *tel* 01-485 4836. Offers comprehensive research service to writers, academics and business people world-wide, including fact checking, bibliographical references and document supply. Specializes in English history, social sciences, business.

**Benn's Media Information Service** (BEMIS), established 1978 in association with *Benn's Media Directory*, Benn Business Information Services Ltd., P.O. Box 20, Sovereign Way, Tonbridge, Kent TN9 1RQ    *tel* (0732) 362666    *telex* 95454    *fax* (0732) 770483. Primarily—but not exclusively—an updating service for subscribers to *Benn's Media Directory*. Spot enquiries by post or telephone regarding the Press or broadcasting media—either in the UK or elsewhere in the world—answered by return, normally without charge. Enquiries needing in-depth research (current or historical) individually costed before the work is undertaken.

**Beswick Writing Services** (1988), Francis Beswick, 19 Haig Road, Stretford, Greater Manchester M32 0DS    *tel* 061-865 1259. Manuscript criticism/advice (non-fiction specialist), proof-reading, editorial revision. Particular interests: educational, religious, philosophical, academic, ecology.

**Book Production Consultants** (1973), 47 Norfolk Street, Cambridge CB1 2LE    *tel* (0223) 352790    *telex* 818405    *fax* (0223) 460718. *Directors:* A. P. Littlechild, C. S. Walsh. Complete book production service: editing, designing, illustrating, translating, indexing, artwork; production management of printing and binding. For books, journals, manuals, reports, diaries, promotional products.

**Bookwatch Ltd.** (1982), 7-up, Sycamore Place, Hill Avenue, Amersham, Bucks HP6 5BG    *tel* (0494) 728232    *fax* (0494) 726966. *Directors:* Peter Harland, Jennifer Harland. Market research, bestseller lists, syndicated reviews, features. Publishers of *Books in the Media*, weekly for booksellers and librarians.

**Harriet Bridgeman and Elizabeth Drury,** 19 Chepstow Road, London W2 5BP    *tel* 01-229 7420/727 4065    *fax* 01-792 8509. Editors; specialists in fine art book production and design.

**Brooke Associates (Manchester) Ltd** (1979, incorporated 1987), Faulkner House, 45 Station Road, Urmston, Manchester M31 1JG.    *tel* 061-746 8140 (061-748 6768 outside office hours)    *telex* 265871 Monref G, quoting ref. 72 Mag 20263    *fax* 061-746 8132. Research, editing and contract writing. Specializes in business, management, tourism, history, biography, social science.

**Mrs. D. Buckmaster** (1966), 51 Chatsworth Road, Torquay TQ1 3BJ    *tel* (0803) 294663. General editing of MSS, specialising in traditional themes in religious, metaphysical and esoteric subjects. Also success and inspirational books or articles.

**Bucks Literary Services** (1983), 73 Vicarage Road, Marsworth, Nr Tring, Herts HP23 4LU  *tel* Cheddington (0296) 668630. *Partners:* J. L. N. Stobbs, A. M. B. Stobbs. Authors' advisory, editorial and research service; typing.

**Causeway Resources** (1989), 8 The Causeway, Teddington, Middlesex TW11 0HE  *tel* 01-943 3290. *Director:* Keith Skinner. Historical and contemporary research, specialising in family and social history; biography; theatre, cinema and television; criminal and police history.

**Central Office of Information,** Hercules Road, London SE1 7DU  *tel* 01-928 2345. Commissions feature articles on British affairs for publication in overseas newspapers, magazines and trade press.

**Christmas Archives** (1978), Wassail House, 64 Severn Road, Cardiff CF1 9EA  *tel* (0222) 341120  *fax* (0222) 340038. All aspects of Christmas, graphic design, folklore, custom, folk art and religious celebration; greeting cards, books, magazines, photographs.

**Joseph F. Clarke** (1977), 37 Grafton Way, London W1P 5LA. Bibliographical and literary research.

**Judy Corbett, Freelance Researches** (1987), Dolbelidr, Trefnant, St. Asaph, Clwyd LL17 0BB.  *tel* (074 574) 659. Offers comprehensive research and typing service covering all topics including genealogy.

**Ingrid Cranfield** (1972), 16 Myddelton Gardens, Winchmore Hill, London N21 2PA  *tel* 01-360 2433. Non-fiction research, advisory and editorial services for authors and media, including critical assessment, rewriting, proof reading, copy editing, writing of marketing copy, indexing, interviews and transcripts. Special interests: geography, travel, exploration, adventure (own archives), language, education, youth training. Translations from German and French.

**Creative Comics,** Denis Gifford, 80 Silverdale, Sydenham, London SE26  *tel* 01-699 7725. Specialises in strip cartoons and comics for both adults and children, custom-tailored to clients' requirements. Everything from jokes, puzzles, and single strips to serials and complete comics, books, supplements, and give-aways.

**Margaret Crush** (1980), Moonfleet, Burney Road, West Humble, Dorking, Surrey RH5 6AU  *tel* (0306) 884347. Editing, copy editing, writing, rewriting, proof reading for publishers, especially illustrated books and children's books.

**Meg and Stephen Davies,** 31 Egerton Road, Ashton, Preston, Lancs PR2 1AJ  *tel* (0772) 725120. Indexing to general and post-graduate level in the arts and humanities. Can offer indexes on PC disk. Also proof-reading and copy editing. Registered Indexer with Society of Indexers since 1971.

**DD Editorial Services** (1983), Gosford House, Gosford Road, Beccles, Suffolk NR34 9QX  *tel* (0502) 717735. *Partners:* D. Derbyshire, J. Nicholls. Proof reading, copy editing, indexing, index repagination, compilation of diaries.

**Andrew Duncan** (1986), 19 Rainham Road, London NW10 5DL  *tel* 01-969 8332. A professional researcher working in historical and contemporary sources.

**Editorial/Visual Research** (1973), Angela Murphy, 21 Leamington Road Villas, London W11 1HS  *tel* 01-727 4920. Comprehensive research service including historical, literary, film and picture research for writers, publishers, film and television companies. Services also include copy-writing, editing, and travel and feature writing.

**Dr Martin Edwards** (1985), Rose Cottage, 68 Greenhill Road, Sandford, Avon BS19 5PB   *tel* (0934) 852470. Specialist editorial and research service in the medico-scientific field: including copy-editing, co-editorial/-authorship, proof reading, abstracting and conference productions. Special interest in the improvement of foreign texts.

**Brian J. Ford,** Rothay House, 6 Mayfield Road, Eastrea, Cambridgeshire PE7 2AY   *tel.* (0733) 350888. Scientist and adviser on scientific matters; author, producer/director scientific films and programmes in addition to editor/contributor to many leading books and journals. Has hosted many leading BBC television and radio programmes, and overseas documentaries.

**Freelance Editorial Services** (1975), Bill Houston, B.SC., DIP.LIB., M.PHIL., 45 Bridge Street, Musselburgh, Midlothian EH21 6AA   *tel* 031-665 7825. Editing, proof reading, indexing, abstracting, translations, bibliographies; particularly scientific and medical.

**Freelance Press Services** (1967), 5-9 Bexley Square, Manchester M3 6DB   *tel* 061-832 5079. A Market Research Department for the freelance writer and photographer. Issues a monthly Market News service the *Freelance Market News*; £18.50 p.a. A good rate of pay made for news of editorial requirements. (Small amounts are credited until a worthwhile payment is reached.) Agents for the U.K. for the books of the American Writer Inc. and Writers Digest, including *The Writers Handbook*; also the American *Writers Market*. Writers' market guides for Canada and Australia.

**Jean Gay** (1965), April Cottage, Hatch Lane, Tisbury, Salisbury, Wilts SP3 6NT.   *tel* (0747) 871201. *Director:* Mrs. Jean Ayres-Gay. Copy-editing, proof reading, indexing, index-refolioing.

**Geoslides,** 4 Christian Fields, London SW16 3JZ   *tel* 01-764 6292. Visual aid production services: slide packs; filmstrips; colour to monochrome processing; packaging. Photo library. Commission photography. Specialist work for educational publishing. Audio tape production.

**C. N. Gilmore** (1987), 19B St Michael's Road, Bedford MK40 2LY.   *tel* (0234) 261853. Sub-editing, copy-editing, slush-pile reading, reviewing. Will also collaborate. Undertakes work in all scholarly and academic fields as well as fiction and practical writing.

**Guildford Reading Services** (1978), 1 The Crescent, Guildford, Surrey GU2 6AL   *tel* 504325. *Director:* B. V. Varney. Proof reading, press revision, copy preparation, sub-editing.

**Hambleside Group** (1976) incorporating Hambleside Publishers, 13 Southgate Street, Winchester, Hampshire SO23 9DZ.   *tel* (0962) 840088   *telex* 477357 Hamble G   *fax* (0962) 840144. *Directors:* D. R. Yellop, R. A. Jeffery, R. C. Yale, D. K. Sleap. Graphic art design, editorial and copy preparation, magazine publication, promotional literature and sport.

**John Hassell** (1973), Mayfield House, Clench, Marlborough, Wiltshire SN8 4NT   *tel* Marlborough 810 384. *Director:* John Hassell. Advisory and editorial work for authors.

**Bernard Hawton,** 137 Park Road, Chandler's Ford, Hampshire SO5 1HT   *tel* (0703) 267400. Proof reading.

**Historica Consultancy** (1986), 8-9 The Incline, Coalport, Telford, Shropshire TF8 7HR,   *tel* (0952) 584043. Historical consultants for drama, documentary and fiction.

**Historical Newspaper Loan Service** (1972), 8 Monks Avenue, New Barnet, Herts EN5 1DB *tel* 01-440 3159. *Proprietor:* John Frost. Headline stories from 40,000 British and overseas newspapers reporting major events since 1850.

**Holland-Ford Associates (Robert),** 103 Lydyett Lane, Barnton, Northwich, Cheshire CW8 4JT *tel* (0606) 76960. *Director:* Robert Holland-Ford. Impresarios, Concert/Lecture Agents.

**Rosemary Horstmann,** 43 Westcombe Park Road, Blackheath, London SE3 7QZ *tel* 01-853 4706. Broadcasting scripts evaluated. General consultancy on editorial and marketing matters. Tuition in interviewing and tape-recording, lectures, writing workshops. Send sae for brochure.

**Icon Communications** (1984), 31 Wells Road, Nottingham NG3 3AP. *tel* (0602) 505499. *Partners:* Carole Baker, B.A., Charles Mansfield. Writers' workshops. Postal courses in applied stylistics, narratology and semiotics for improving writing style. Word processor sales and training to RSA exam level. Desk top publishing sales, advice and training for authors. Transfer of LocoScript documents to PC systems for laser printing. DTP packages for the PCW. Publishers of SEAM English Academy Monographs. User Guides and Operators' Manuals. Open learning courses in communications and *English for Industry.*

**Indexers, Society of,** 16 Green Road, Birchington, Kent CT7 9JZ (see **Societies** and **Article** for further details).

**Indexing Specialists** (1965), 202 Church Road, Hove, East Sussex BN3 2DJ *tel* (0273) 23309 *fax* (0273) 208278. *Director:* Richard Raper, B.SC., DTA. Indexes for books, journals and reference publications on professional, scientific and general subjects. *Consultancy:* high-tech indexes and their design.

**Ken Jackson** (1985), 30 The Boundary, Langton Green, Tunbridge Wells, Kent TN3 0YB *tel* (0892) 545198. Commissioning, copy-editing, proof-reading, indexing, particularly of technical or religious manuscripts.

**Sara Kerruish Literary Agency** (1985), Fuaran, Coldwell End, Youlgreave, Derbyshire DE4 1UY. *tel* (0629) 636731. Editing, copy editing, proof reading, indexing.

**Keys Editorial and Research Services** (1986), 17B Roseangle, Dundee DD1 4LP *tel* (0382) 22429. Editing, research, proof reading, translation from Portuguese. Special interests: teaching English as a foreign or second language.

**Laserbacks** (1987), Ann Kritzinger Ltd, 11 Rosemont Road, London NW3 6NG *tel* 01-341 7650. *Directors:* Ann Kritzinger (Chairman), Kim Spanoghe (Technical), Peta Knaggs (Text Editor). Fast high-tech production of cost-effective short-run books for self-publishers, from typescript (or disk) to bound copies (optional proprietary hardback binding kit for DIY).

**Leeds Postcards (Northern Trading Co-operative Ltd.)** (1979), P.O. Box 84, Leeds, W. Yorkshire LS1 4HA *tel* (0532) 468649. *Directors:* Richard Honey, Christine Hankinson, Richard Scott, Stephen Edwards. Publishing, printing and distribution service for artists, campaigns and unions, specialising in postcards and greeting cards.

**Library Research Agency** (1974), Burberry, Devon Road, Salcombe, Devon TQ8 8HJ *tel* (0548 84) 2769. *Directors:* D. J. Langford, M.A., B. Langford. Research and information service for writers, journalists, artists, businessmen from libraries, archives, museums, record offices and newspapers in UK and Europe. Sources may be in English, French, German, Russian, Serbo-Croat, Bulgarian.

**London Media Workshops** (1978), 101 King's Drive, Gravesend, Kent DA12 5BQ   *tel* (0474) 564676. *Booking Secretary:* Linda Forbes. Short courses run by top working professionals in writing for radio, television, video and the press.

**Betty Low,** 71 Ravenslea Road, London SW12 8SL   *tel* 01-673 3239. Editing, copy-editing, proof-reading, writing (reports, jacket blurbs, etc.) and research. Speciality: Economics and business books.

**Duncan McAra** (1988), 30 Craighall Crescent, Edinburgh EH6 4RZ   *tel* 031-552 1558. Consultancy on all aspects of general trade publishing; editing; proof correction; reading, assessing and placing typescripts with suitable publishers. Main subjects include art, architecture, archaeology, biography, film, military and travel.

**Sally McCann** (1987), 18 Devonshire Drive, Alderley Edge, Cheshire SK9 7HT   *tel* (0625) 584260. Freelance editing, author liaison and proofing of non-fiction works (especially academic and educational) in the arts, social sciences and humanities.

**McText** (1986), Denmill, Tough, By Alford, Aberdeenshire AB3 8EP   *tel* (0336) 2582. *Partners:* K. and Duncan McArdle. Editing, proof reading, copywriting for: ads and promotion, brochures, catalogues, DTP (incl. production), house journals, manuals. French, German translation.

**MADES** (Malham Administrative, Design and Editorial Services) (1977), Sheila Malham, The Post Office, High Street, Aldeburgh, Suffolk IP15 5AA   *tel* (0728) 452755   *fax* (0728) 453909. Design, print and editorial services; typing.

**Manuscript Appraisals** (1984), 95 Bramble Road, Eastwood, Leigh-on-Sea, Essex SS9 5HA.   *tel* (04022) 20414. *Proprietor:* Raymond J. Price. *Consultants:* N. L. Price, m.b.i.m., Mary Hunt, William J. Ling. An independent appraisal of authors' MSS (fiction and non-fiction, but no poetry) with full editorial guidance and advice. Proof reading if required. Interested in the work of new writers.

**Marlinoak Ltd** (1984), Anbrian House, St. Mary's Street, Worcester WR1 1HA   *tel* (0905) 24626. *Directors:* Alan L. Billing, m.b.i.m., Hazel J. Billing, j.p., b.a., dip. ed. Preparation of scripts, plays, books. MS service, ghostwriting, translation, proof reading, research undertaken. Full secretarial facilities.

**Morley Adams, Ltd.** (1917), 131 Aldersgate Street, London EC1A 4JA   *tel* 01-600 4502. *Directors:* V. G. R. Lucas, M. J. Gay, W. J. M. Grimshaw, R. Simpson. Specialists in the production of crosswords and other puzzles, quizzes, etc. Experts in handling advertisers' competitions.

**Elizabeth Murray** (1975), 3 Gower Mews Mansions, Gower Mews, London WC1E 6HR   *tel* 01-636 3761. Literary, biographical, historical research for authors, radio, theatre and television.

**Andrew Nash** (1981), 15 Cedar Road, Farnborough, Hampshire GU14 7AU   *tel* (0252) 514466. Non-fiction. Writing, rewriting and editing including joint authorship with subject specialists. Reworking of books, leaflets, etc., to chosen reading level. Rewriting of specialist and technical material in plain English. For texts thus written or edited, preparation of artwork brief, glossary, and/or index. Also copy-editing and proof-reading. Member of the Society of Authors.

**Paul Nash** (1979), Rhandir Isaf, Croesaubach, Oswestry, Shropshire SY10 9BG   *tel* (0691) 652650. Indexing of technical publications; proof reading. Registered indexer with Society of Indexers.

**Paul H. Niekirk** (1976), 40 Rectory Avenue, High Wycombe, Buckinghamshire HP13 6HW  *tel* (0494) 27200. Text editing for works of reference and professional and management publications, particularly texts on law. Freelance writing. Editorial consultancy and training. Marketing consultancy and research.

**Northern Writers Advisory Services** (1986), 77 Marford Crescent, Sale, Cheshire M33 4DN  *tel* 061-969 1573. *Proprietor:* Jill Groves. Offers word processing, copy editing, proof-reading and desk-top publishing to small publishers, societies and authors.

**Northgate Training** (1978), Scarborough House, 29 James Street West, Bath, Avon BA1 2BT  *tel* (0225) 339733. *Directors:* M. R. Lynch, J. M. Bayley. Editorial services for education and training, including writing and design of educational resources (audio-visual aids, games, booklets) and of management games and training packs. Specialising in distance and open learning training packages.

**Oriental Languages Bureau,** Lakshmi Building, Sir P. Mehta Road, Fort, Bombay 400 001, India  *tel* 2861258  *telegraphic address* Orientclip. *Partner:* Rajan K. Shah. Undertakes translations and printing in all Indian languages and a few foreign languages.

**Ormrod Research Services** (1982), Weeping Birch, Burwash, East Sussex TN19 7HG  *tel* (0435) 882541. Comprehensive research service; literary, historical, academic, biographical, commercial. Critical reading with report, editing, indexing, proof reading, ghosting.

**Oxprint** (1974), Aristotle House, Aristotle Lane, Oxford OX2 6TR  *tel* (0865) 512331  *fax* (0865) 512408. *Directors:* Per Saugman, John Webb (Managing), I. W. Goodgame, F.C.A. Editorial, design, typesetting, illustrating scientific, educational and general books. Specialists in taking complete projects from start to finish. Desktop and bureau facilities now available thus widening our services into company design and commercial literature.

**Pageant Publishing** (1978), 5 Turners Wood, London NW11 6TD  *tel* 01-455 3703  *fax* 01-209 0726. *Director:* Gillian Page. Consultancy on all aspects of academic publishing: publication of academic journals.

**Geoffrey D. Palmer** (1987), 47 Burton Fields Road, Stamford Bridge, York YO4 1JJ  *tel* (0759) 72874. Editorial and production services, including STM and general copy editing, artwork editing, proof-reading and indexing. Specialising in mathematics, ecology, engineering, geography and geology. Other interests include: architecture, Green issues, road and rail transport history and policy. Word processing facilities.

**Margaret Parker,** 17 North Street, Norton St Philip, Bath, Avon BA3 6LE. *tel* (037 387) 616. Experienced university press editor offers copy-editing and proof-reading services to publishers or academics in non-technical subjects (monographs or journal articles).

**Penman Literary Service, The** (1950), 175 Pall Mall, Leigh-on-Sea, Essex SS9 1RE  *tel* (0702) 74438. Preparation of authors' MSS. for submission, from typing, with any necessary attention to punctuation, spelling and general layout, to full revision and re-typing if requested. Charges depend upon work recommended and/or desired in the particular case.

**Christopher Pick,** 41 Chestnut Road, London SE27 9EZ  *tel* 01-761 2585. Writer, publishing consultant, editor. Author and editor of non-fiction books and articles for all popular markets. Special interests: travel, heritage/history and current affairs. Non-fiction title and series planning and development projects undertaken; re-writing, but only for publishers on already contracted manuscripts.

**Picture Research Agency,** Pat Hodgson, Jasmine Cottage, Spring Grove Road, Richmond, Surrey TW10 6EH     *tel* 01-940 5986. Illustrations found for books, films and television. Written research also undertaken particularly on historical subjects, including photographic and film history. Small picture library.

**Keith Povey Editorial Services** (1980), North Burrow, Bratton Clovelly, Okehampton, Devon EX20 4BJ.     *tel* (083 787) 296     *fax* (083 787) 369. Copy-editing, indexing, proof-reading, publisher/author liaison.

**Prefis Ltd** (Book Machine) (1982), 64 Baldock Street, Ware, Herts SG12 9DT     *tel and fax* (0920) 465890. *Director:* Paul Procter B.A., Originator of a word-processing and page-make-up system (the **Book Machine**) specifically designed for the author, publisher's editor and designer, and the typesetter, running on standard IBM compatible microcomputers.

**Press Editorial Syndicate** (1964), 27A Arterberry Road, Wimbledon, London SW20 8AF     *tel* 01-947 5482     *telegraphic address* Bakerbook, London. *Director:* W. Howard Baker. Specialist editorial services for book publishers.

**Victoria Ramsay,** (1981), Abbots Rest, Chilbolton, Stockbridge, Hants SO20 6BE.     *tel* (0264) 860251. Freelance editing, copy-editing and proof-reading; non-fiction research and writing of promotional literature and pamphlets. Any non-scientific subject undertaken. Special interests include cookery, education, travel, African and Caribbean works and works in translation from French.

**Research Ireland** (1985), Pamela Bradley, Fair View, Kindlestown Hill, Delgany, Co. Wicklow, Ireland.     *tel.* 01-874034. Research service for writers, specialising in Irish history, biography, genealogy.

**S. Ribeiro,** 42 West Heath Court, North End Road, London NW11 7RG. *tel* 01-458 9082. Creative writing tutor will edit, re-write and typeset for individuals or publishers. No fee for an initial review. Individual and small group writing tutorials by arrangement. Wide interests and experience include work on the short story; poetry; full-length novels and autobiography; literary and academic articles. Sound background in British-American usage.

**Rich Research** (1978), 1 Bradby House, Carlton Hill, St. John's Wood, London NW8 9XE     *tel* 01-624 7755. *Director:* Diane Rich. Professional picture research and fee negotiation. Illustrations found for books, films, television; advertising agencies; and exhibitions. Fast access to world-wide sources.

**Anton Rippon Press Services,** 20 Chain Lane, Mickleover, Derby DE3 5AJ     *tel* (0332) 512379/384235     *fax* (0332) 292755. Writer and researcher on historical, sociological and sporting topics. Features, programmes, brochures produced, ghost writing.

**Vernon Robinson Editorial Services,** (1973), 114 Blinco Grove, Cambridge CB1 4TT     *tel* (0223) 244414. Copy-editing and proof reading of all educational books. Competitive rates. Specialise: science, maths, engineering, economics, computer science, biology, etc.

**Roger Smithells Ltd., Editorial Services,** Garth Cottage, 26 High Street, Buriton, Petersfield, Hampshire GU31 5RX     *tel* (0730) 62369. Journalistic specialists in everything relating to travel and holidays; newspaper and magazine articles; TV and radio scripts; compilers of travel books.

**Roth-Mills** (1974), 22 Quarry High Street, Oxford OX3 8JT    *tel* (0865) 60088. *Directors:* Ernest Roth, Sonya Mills. Publishers' editorial service, copy-editing, anglicising, proof-reading, non-technical translation from French, German and Italian. Full word processing facilities.

**Paul Sample Editorial Services**, 45 St Mark's Road, Salisbury, Wiltshire SP1 3AY    *tel* (0722) 412464. Full range of editorial services, from freelance news and feature writing through to editorial consultancy, design, layout, proof-reading and print liaison.

**Sarratt Information Services** (1986), Willow View House, 52 Church Lane, Sarratt, Hertfordshire WD3 6HL.    *tel* 01-422 4384. *Directors:* D. M. Brandl, M.I. INF.SCI., G. H. Kay, B.SC., C.ENG., M.I.CHEM., E.M.B.C.S., A. C. Rickard, B.A., M.I.INF.SCI., H. Nermut, A.I.INF.SCI. Research, bibliographies compiled, references checked, indexes compiled, translations, abstracting, data entry.

**Science Unit,** Rothay House, 6 Mayfield Road, Eastrea, Cambridgeshire PE7 2AY    *tel.* (0733) 350888. Independent scientific consultancy specialising in microscopical matters. Advises on programmes and publications in general scientific field. Activities are world-wide, with publications in many overseas and foreign-language editions.

**Scriptmate** (1985), 11 Rosemont Road, London NW3 6NG    *tel* 01-341 7650. Ann Kritzinger (Managing). Reports and revision suggestions given on unpublished work in the fields of fiction, non-fiction and drama by team of 80 specialist readers.

**Mrs Ellen Seager,** Baytrees, Burnham Road, Little Bookham, Surrey    *tel* (0372) 58746. Critical assessment of fiction and non-fiction work with helpful direction, tuition and advice. Creative writing tutor. Ghost writing. Publishing and market information.

**Seminar Cassettes Ltd.** (1973), Drake Educational Associates, St. Fagans Road, Fairwater, Cardiff CF5 3AE.    *tel* (0222) 560333    *fax* (0222) 554909. Spoken word cassettes on current affairs, psychology, metaphysics, ecology and interviews with literary and artistic figures. Widely used in English language teaching and in universities, polytechnics, school libraries and bookshops as unique and authentic source material.

**Christine Shuttleworth** (1981), Flat 1, 25 St Stephen's Avenue, London W12 8JB. *tel* 01-749 8797. Indexing (with MACREX program), copy-editing, proof reading, non-technical translation from German. Registered Indexer and Council member, Society of Indexers; member, Society of Freelance Editors and Proof-readers.

**Robert and Jane Songhurst** (1976), 3 Yew Tree Cottages, Grange Lane, Sandling, near Maidstone, Kent ME14 3BY    *tel* Maidstone 57635. Literary consultants, authors' works advised upon (fees by agreement), literary and historical research, feature writing, reviewing, editing.

**Strand Editorial Services,** (1974) 8 Holmwood Avenue, South Croydon, Surrey CR2 9HY.    *tel* 01-657 1247. *Joint Principals:* Derek and Irene Bradley. Providing a comprehensive service to publishers, editorial departments, and public relations and advertising agencies at any stage in the production process.

**Tamar Literary Services** (1988), 18 Barton Close, Landrake, Saltash, Cornwall PL12 5BA    *tel* (0752) 851 451. *Director:* Dr Brian Gee. General editing and research for authors and publishers (non-fiction). Specialist editing, indexing, and photographic research undertaken in scientific fields (particularly history of science and science education). Word processing (MS WORD/-

SPELLCHECK) facilities available for authors who wish for assistance with final copy on disc.

**Hans Tasiemka Archives** (1950), 80 Temple Fortune Lane, London NW11 7TU    *tel* 01-455 2485.    *fax* 01-455 0231. *Proprietor:* Mrs. Edda Tasiemka. Comprehensive newspaper cuttings library from 1850's to the present day on all subjects for writers, publishers, picture researchers, film and TV companies.

**Lyn M. Taylor,** 1 Eglinton Crescent, Edinburgh EH12 5DH    *tel* 031-225 6152. Comprehensive editorial service. Copy-editing and proof reading in all subjects. Specialising in scientific and medical.

**Teague Sands Literary Services (TSLS)** (1987), 364A Radford Road, Nottingham NG7 5EQ.    *tel* (0602) 704620/(0954) 51546. *Partners:* Cheryl Teague, Kenneth Roy Steven Sands. Offers services in editing, proof-reading, manuscript appraisal, copywriting, design and print.

**Technidraught** (Cartography) (1984), 3 Rayleigh Road, Basingstoke, Hampshire RG21 1TJ    *tel* (0256) 28186. *Partners:* P. J. Corcoran, Rosemary Corcoran. Cartographic design and draughting service for publishers and authors, research and editing facilities, specializing in academic, education, travel and related fields.

**Tecmedia Ltd.** (1972), 5 Granby Street, Loughborough LE11 3DU    *tel* (0509) 230248    *telex* 341995 ref. 214. *Directors:* M. J. Potter, J. D. Baxter. Specialists in the design, development and production of mixed media training packages.

**Hilary Thomas** (1974), 27 Grasvenor Avenue, Barnet, Herts EN5 2BY    *tel* 01-440 5662. Genealogical, literary and historical research.

**3 & 5 Promotion** (1985), 5 Church Street, Harston, Cambridge CB2 5NP    *tel* (0223) 871028. *Proprietor:* Rosemary Dooley. Publicity services for publishers, specialising in music, academic humanities, health care, travel.

**Carolina Tucker,** B.A., A.L.A. (1986), Ford Cottage, Lymore Valley, Milford-on-Sea, Nr. Lymington, Hants SO41 0TW    *tel* (0202) 472380, (0590) 42441 (evening). MSS reading and evaluation for publishers. Advisory and editorial service for authors. Full revision and re-typing of MSS if required.

**John Vickers,** 27 Shorrolds Road, London SW6 7TR    *tel* 01-385 5774. Archives of British Theatre photographs by John Vickers, from 1938-1974.

**Gordon R. Wainwright,** 22 Hawes Court, Sunderland SR6 8NU    *tel* 091-548 9342. Criticism, advice, revision and all other editorial work for publishers and authors, especially those concerned with educational books. Public relations and publicity. Preparation, planning, editing, writing and publication of books, pamphlets, house journals, company histories, brochures, reports, promotional literature, etc. Articles on education and training matters supplied to newspapers, journals and magazines. Training in report writing, rapid reading and non-verbal communication. Lecture service. Consultancy service in all aspects of communication. Travel writing assignments undertaken.

**Dr. Roger Whiting,** M.A., D.LITT., F.R.HIST.S., M.J.I. (1971), 15 Lansdown Parade, Cheltenham, Gloucestershire GL50 2LH    *tel* (0242) 235677. Member of the Society of Authors and Institute of Journalists (Travel Specialists' Group). Writing, re-writing, consulting and research on historical, religious and travel material. Travel writing assignments and lecture engagements on historical, religious and travel subjects undertaken.

**Joan Wilkins Associates,** 54 Church Street, Tisbury, Salisbury, Wilts SP3 6NH. *tel* Tisbury (0747) 870490. Comprehensive editorial (editing, sub editing, indexing, proof reading) and preparation of reports. Word processing. Conference services include recording, verbatim reporting and tape transcribing. Rates on application.

**Rita Winter, Translation and Editorial Services** (1988), Kilrubie, Eddleston, Peeblesshire, Scotland EH45 8QS *tel* (07213) 353. Ex-academic librarian offers comprehensive editorial service including: proof-reading, copy editing, research, typing, indexing and index repagination. Also reading service/critical assessment of Dutch texts and translations from/into Dutch. Special interests: biographies, travel, leisure, art, literature, geography, anthropology.

**Della Woodman** (1973), Unit 9, OJ's Industrial Park, Claybank Road, Portsmouth, Hants PO3 5NH. *tel* (0705) 694493. *Proprietors:* Mrs. D. Emmerson, N. Emmerson. Typesetting, paste-up, camera-ready artwork, design and preparation of books to print stage, illustration, proof-reading, indexing, general editing and research services.

**Worts-Power Associates** (1983), 48 Kings Road, Long Ditton, Surrey KT6 5JF *tel* 01-398 7723 *fax* 01-398 8723. *Directors:* Kim Worts, Shelley Power. Represents freelance publishing workers; supplies book production and design, editors, copyeditors, proof readers, indexers.

**Richard M. Wright** (1977), 32 Oak Village, London NW5 4QN *tel* 01-485 4836. Indexing, copy-editing, proof reading, specialising in economics, business, education, social sciences.

**Write Line Critical Service** (1988), 130 Morton Way, Southgate, London N14 7AL *tel* 01-886 1329. Criticism and assessment of poetry, fiction (including short stories) and general articles. Suggestions for revision/development of work, advice about publication outlets. Special interest: poetry.

**Writerlink Ltd** (1984), Bolsover House, 5 Clipstone Street, London W1P 7EB *tel* 01-323 4323. *Directors:* Charles Dawes, John Hare, John Bennett, Sally Cartwright. Expert individual advice given to authors by a team of readers widely experienced in publishing.

**Hans Zell Associates, Publishing Consultants** (1987), 11 Richmond Road, P.O. Box 56, Oxford OX1 3EL. *tel* (0865) 511428/(0993) 775235 *telex* 94012872 Zell G *fax* (0865) 310183 (Zell). *Partners:* Hans M. Zell, Lady Jay. Consultancies, project evaluations, market assessments, feasibility studies, research and surveys, funding proposals, freelance editorial work, commissioning, journals management, exhibition services. Specializes in services to publishers and the book community in Third World countries and provides specific expertise in these areas.

# Indexing

The Society of Indexers maintains a Register of members whose practical competence in compiling indexes has been tested and approved by its Assessors. Introductions are freely available to authors, publishers and others responsible for commissioning indexes by contacting the Society's Registrar, Mrs. E. Wallis, 25 Leyborne Park, Kew Gardens, Surrey, TW9 3HB  *tel* 01-940 4771.

In addition, there are some 200 general and specialist indexers listed in the Society's annual booklet *Indexers Available*, which is obtainable by sending a SAE (at least 6½ x 8½) to the *Secretary*, 16 Green Road, Birchington, Kent, CT7 9JZ.

For other details of the Society of Indexers, see the entry under **Societies, Associations and Clubs.**

# Translation

The role of the translator in enabling literature to pass beyond its national frontiers is receiving growing recognition. In view of the general increase of activity in this field, it is not surprising that many people with literary interests and a knowledge of languages should think of adopting free-lance translating as a full- or part-time occupation. Some advice may be usefully given to such would-be translators.

The first difficulty the beginner will encounter is the unwillingness of publishers to entrust a translation to anyone who has not already established a reputation for sound work. The least the publisher will demand before commissioning a translation is a fairly lengthy specimen of the applicant's work, even if unpublished. The publisher cannot be expected to pay for a specimen sent in by a translator seeking work. If, on the other hand, a publisher specifically asks for a lengthy specimen of a commissioned book the firm will usually pay for this specimen at the current rate. Perhaps the best way the would-be translator can begin is to select some book of the type which he feels competent and anxious to translate, ascertain from the foreign author or publisher that the English-language rights are still free, translate a substantial section of the book and then submit the book and his specimen translation to an appropriate publisher. If he is extremely lucky, this may result in a commission to translate the book. More probably, however—since publishers are generally very well informed about foreign books likely to interest them and rarely open to a chance introduction—the publisher will reject the book as such. But if he is favourably impressed by the translation, he may very possibly commission some other book of a similar nature which he already has in mind.

In this connection it is important to stress that the translator should confine himself to subjects of which he possesses an expert knowledge. In the case of non-fiction, he may have to cope with technical expressions not to be found in the dictionary and disaster may ensue if he is not fully conversant with the subject. The translation of fiction, on the other hand, demands different skills (e.g. in the writing of dialogue) and the translator would be wise to ask himself whether he possesses these skills before taking steps to secure work of this nature.

Having obtained a commission to translate a book, the translator will be faced with the question of fees. These vary considerably from publisher to publisher but for the commoner European languages they should range from £30.00 upwards per thousand words. Translators should be able to obtain, in addition to the initial fee, a royalty of 2½%. However, some publishers will consent to pay royalties of this nature, if at all, only on second editions and reprints. In the past it was common practice for a translator to assign his copyright to the publisher outright, but this is no longer the rule. Most reputable publishers will now sign agreements specifying the rights they require in the translation and leaving the copyright in the translator's hands. In the case of plays a proportion of the author's royalties (up to 50%) is the usual method of payment.

Advice regarding fees, copyright, Public Lending Right and other matters may be obtained from the Translators Association of the Society of Authors (see **Societies, Associations and Clubs**).

Technical translators are catered for by the Institute of Translation and Interpreting (see **Societies, Associations and Clubs**). Annual prizes are awarded for translations from the German, the Italian and the French languages (see **Literary Prizes and Awards**).

# Press-cutting Agencies

## UNITED KINGDOM

In the following section it should be noted that no agency can check every periodical, local paper, etc., and that some agencies cover more than others. Special attention should be given to the time limit specified by certain agencies.

**Contemporary Music Press Bureau** (1982), 46 Grange Road, Orpington, Kent BR6 8EA   *tel* (0689) 51811. Music press articles from 1970; specialises in pop, rock, soul, jazz, reggae. *Subscription:* £15 search fee, cuttings free.

**Durrant's Press Cuttings Ltd** (1880), 103 Whitecross Street, London EC1Y 8QT   *tel* 01-588 3671   *fax* 01-374 8171. *Directors:* A. M. Kennedy, T. W. Lorenzen. Press cutting service for publishers and art galleries from a guaranteed comprehensive reading list. *Subscription rates:* from £92.

**International Press-Cutting Bureau** (1920), 224-236 Walworth Road, London SE17 1JE   *tel* 01-708 2113   *fax* 01-701 4489   *telegraphic address* Adverburo, London, SE1. *Subscription rates:* on application. *Representatives:* Brussels, Copenhagen, Geneva, Madrid, Milan, Paris, Lisbon, Stockholm, Berlin, Helsinki, The Hague.

**Newsclip** (incorporating **Apcut Ltd.**), St. Marks Studios, Chillingworth Road, London N7 8QJ   *tel* 01-609 0018   *fax* 01-609 5729. *Subscription rates:* on application.

**Press Information (Scotland), Ltd.,** Virginia House, 62 Virginia Street, Glasgow G1 1TX   *tel* 041-552 6767. Comprehensive Scottish cuttings service. *Subscription rates:* on application.

**Romeike & Curtice Ltd.** (1852), Hale House, 290-296 Green Lanes, London N13 5TP   *tel* 01-882 0155   *telex* 896462 Inform G   *fax* 01-882 6716. *Directors:* Paul J. Morgan, Stephen D. George, Shelagh A. Smith. Provides a media monitoring service to over 5500 clients in different industries, covering more than 2500 newspapers and magazines as well as national radio and TV. *Subscription rates:* £27.50 per month and £0.50 per clipping. Minimum contract: 3 months.

**We Find It Press Clippings,** 3 Timbey Park, Belfast, N. Ireland BT7 3BT   *tel* (0232) 646008. Northern Ireland press coverage; fast, up-to-date, accurate feedback. Rates on application.

## *Overseas*

### AUSTRALIA

**Australian Press Cuttings Agency,** 11-15 Albert Street, Richmond 3121, Victoria   *tel* 4298388   *fax* 4299229. $65 per month and 60c. per cutting.

### CANADA

**Canadian Press Clipping Services,** 4601 Yonge Street, North York, Ontario M2N 5L9   *tel* 416-221-1660   *fax* 416-221-8401.

## INDIA

**International Clipping Service,** Lakshmi Building, Sir P. Mehta Road, Fort, Bombay, 1    *tel* 2861258    *telegraphic address* Orientclip. *Partner:* Rajan K. Shah. Supplies Press Cuttings of news, editorials, articles, advertisements, press releases, etc., from all India papers. Undertakes compilation of statistical reports on competitive press advertising pertaining to all products.

## NEW ZEALAND

**Chong Press Clippings Bureau,** P.O. Box 13330, Onehunga, Auckland    *tel* 640 463    *fax* 667-607. All New Zealand newspapers and most magazines covered, any selected topic, $18 per week plus 55 cents per clipping.

## SOUTH AFRICA

**S.A. Press Cutting Agency,** 52/57 Mitrie House, 110 Stanger Street, Durban 4001, Natal    *tel* 370403    *fax* DBN-374-307. English and Afrikaans newspapers and trade journals from Zambia to the Cape. *Minimum rates:* R.80.00 per 100 cuttings plus reading fee R.20.00 per month plus postage.

## SPAIN

**Express Mail** (1961), Apartado 14762, 28080 Madrid    *tel* 881 58 23. Comprehensive Spanish and Portuguese cuttings service. Individual attention. Undertakes full investigations.

## UNITED STATES OF AMERICA

**Burrelle's Press Clipping Service** (1888), 75 East Northfield Avenue, Livingston, New Jersey 07039    *tel* 201-992-6600.

**Luce Press Clippings, Inc.,** 420 Lexington Avenue, New York, N.Y. 10170    *tel* 212-889-6711.

**New England Newsclip Agency, Inc.,** 5 Auburn Street, P.O. Box 9128, Framingham, Mass. 01701-9128    *tel* 508-879 4460    *fax* 508-620-1719.

**Reviews on File,** Walton, N.Y. 13856    *tel* 607-865-4226. *Owner:* Dorothy M. Brandt. Back clippings on authors.

# Government Offices and Public Services

Enquiries, accompanied by a stamped addressed envelope, should be sent to the Public Relations Officer.

**Agriculture, Fisheries and Food, Ministry of,** Whitehall Place, London SW1A 2HH   *tel* 01-270 3000   *telex* 01-889351   *fax* 01-270 8125.

**Ancient and Historical Monuments of Scotland, Royal Commission on,** 54 Melville Street, Edinburgh EH3 7HF   *tel* 031-225 5994.

**Ancient and Historical Monuments in Wales, Royal Commission on,** Edleston House, Queens Road, Aberystwyth, Dyfed SY23 2HP   *tel* Aberystwyth (0970) 624381-2.

**Arts Council of Great Britain,** 105 Piccadilly, London W1V 0AU   *tel* 01-629 9495   *fax* 355 4389.

**Australia, High Commissioner for Commonwealth of,** Australia House, Strand, London WC2B 4LA   *tel* 01-379 4334   *telex* 27565   *fax* 01-240 5333.

**Barbados High Commission,** 1 Great Russell Street, London WC1B 3NH   *tel* 01-631 4975   *telex* 262081 Barcom G.

**Bodleian Library,** Oxford OX1 3BG   *tel* (0865) 277000   *telex* 83565   *fax* 277182.

**Botswana High Commission,** 6 Stratford Place, London W1N 9AE   *tel* 01-499 0031.

**British Broadcasting Corporation,** Broadcasting House, London W1A 1AA   *tel* 01-580 4468.

**British Coal,** Hobart House, Grosvenor Place, London SW1X 7AE   *tel* 01-235 2020   *telex* 882161 CBHOB G   *fax* 01-235 2020, ext: 34848.

**British Council, The,** 10 Spring Gardens, London SW1A 2BN   *tel* 01-930 8466.

**British Film Institute,** 21 Stephen Street, London W1P 1PL   *tel* 01-255 1444   *telex* 27624 Bfildng   *fax* 01-436 7950.

**British Library, The,** 2 Sheraton Street, London W1V 4BH   *tel* 01-636 1544.

**British Library,** Document Supply Centre, Boston Spa, Wetherby West Yorkshire LS23 7BQ   *tel* Boston Spa (0937) 843434   *telex* 557381   *fax* 0937 546333.

**British Library Newspaper Library,** Colindale Avenue, London NW9 5HE   *tel* 01-323 7353.

**British Museum,** Great Russell Street, London WC1B 3DG   *tel* 01-636 1555   *fax* 01-323 8480.

**British Railways Board,** Euston House, 24 Eversholt Street, P.O. Box 100, London NW1 1DZ   *tel* 01-928 5151   *telex* 299431 Brhqln G   *fax* 01-922 6994.

**BSI,** *Enquiries:* Linford Wood, Milton Keynes, Bucks MK14 6LE   *tel* (0908) 221166. *Head Office:* 2 Park Street, London W1A 2BS   *tel* 01-629 9000.

**British Tourist Authority/English Tourist Board,** Thames Tower, Black's Road, London W6 9EL   *tel* 01-846 9000   *telex* 21231   *fax* 01-563 0302.

**Broadcasting Standards Council,** 7 The Sanctuary, London SW1P 3JS   *tel* 01-233 0544   *fax* 01-233 0397.

**Cable Authority,** Gillingham House, 38-44 Gillingham Street, London SW1V 1HU.   *tel* 01-821 6161   *fax* 01-821 5835.

**Cadw,** Welsh Historic Monuments, Brunel House, 2 Fitzalan Road, Cardiff CF2 1UY   *tel* (0222) 465511.

**Canadian High Commission,** Cultural Affairs Section, Canada House, Trafalgar Square, London SW1Y 5BJ   *tel* 01-629 9492, ext. 246   *telex* 261592 Cdaldn   *fax* 01-491 3968.

**Central Electricity Generating Board,** Sudbury House, 15 Newgate Street, London EC1A 7AU   *tel* 01-634 5111   *telex* 883141   *fax* 01-634 5811.

**Central Office of Information,** Hercules Road, London SE1 7DU   *tel* 01-928 2345. In the UK conducts press, television, radio and poster advertising; produces booklets, leaflets, films, radio and television material, exhibitions and other visual material. For the Foreign and Commonwealth Office supplies British information posts overseas with press, radio and television material, publications, reference services, films, exhibitions and display and reading-room material.

**College of Arms or Heralds' College,** Queen Victoria Street, London EC4V 4BT   *tel* 01-248 2762.

**Commonwealth Institute,** Kensington High Street, London W8 6NQ   *tel* 01-603 4535. 24-hour recorded information 01-602 3257. Permanent exhibitions on over 40 Commonwealth countries. Temporary thematic and visual arts exhibitions. Full educational programme for all ages. Range of holiday events. Public Information Centre. Educational Resource Centre for use by teachers and youth workers. Theatre. Compix commercial picture library and mail order publications service. Room hire facilities.

**Copyright Receipt Office, The,** The British Library, 2 Sheraton Street, London W1V 4BH   *tel* 01-323 7180/7185   *telex* 21462   *fax* 01-323 7039.

**Countryside Commission,** John Dower House, Crescent Place, Cheltenham, Gloucestershire GL50 3RA   *tel* (0242) 521381   *fax* (0242) 584270/224962.

**Countryside Commission for Scotland,** Battleby, Redgorton, Perth PH1 3EW   *tel* (0738) 27921, ext. 203   *fax* (0738) 30583.

**Court of the Lord Lyon,** HM New Register House, Edinburgh EH1 3YT   *tel* 031-556 7255.

**Cyprus High Commission,** 93 Park Street, London W1Y 4ET   *tel* 01-499 8272   *telex* 263343   *fax* 01-491 0691

**Data Protection Registrar,** Office of the Data Protection Registrar, Springfield House, Water Lane, Wilmslow, Cheshire SK9 5AX   *tel Enquiries:* (0625) 535777; *Administration:* (0625) 535711   *telex* 265871 Mon ref G (quote ref. CKK 057)   *telecom gold* 74: CKK 057   *fax* 0625 524510.

**Defence, Ministry of,** Main Building, Whitehall, London SW1A 2HB   *tel* 01-218 9000.

**Design Council, The,** 28 Haymarket, London SW1Y 4SU   *tel* 01-839 8000   *telex* 8812963   *fax* 01-925 2130.

**Education and Science, Department of,** Elizabeth House, York Road, London SE1 7PH   *tel* 01-934 9000.

**Electricity Council,** 30 Millbank, London SW1P 4RD    *tel* 01-834 2333    *telex* 23385 and 261130.

**Employment, Department of,** Information Division, Caxton House, Tothill Street, London SW1H 9NF    *tel* 01-273 3000. *Public enquiries:* 01-273 6969.

**Energy, Department of,** 1 Palace Street, London SW1E 5HE    *tel* 01-238 3042    *telex* 918777.

**English Heritage,** Fortress House, 23 Savile Row, London W1X 2HE    *tel* 01-734 6010    *telex* 892091 Hbmcfh G.

**Environment, Department of the,** 2 Marsham Street, London SW1P 3EB    *tel* 01-276 3000.

**Fair Trading, Office of,** Field House, 15-25 Bream's Buildings, London EC4A 1PR.    *tel* 01-242 2858    *telex* 269009 Oftring G    *fax* 01-269 8800.

**Foreign and Commonwealth Office,** King Charles Street, London SW1A 2AH    *tel* 01-270 3000    *telex* 287711 (a/b Prdrme G).

**Forestry Commission,** 231 Corstorphine Road, Edinburgh EH12 7AT    *tel* 031-334 0303    *fax* 031-334 3047.

**Gambia High Commission,** 57 Kensington Court, London W8 5DG    *tel* 01-937 6316.

**General Register Office,** now part of the **Office of Population Censuses and Surveys,** *q.v.*

**Ghana, High Commission for,** 13 Belgrave Square, London SW1X 8PR    *tel* 01-235 4142--5.

**Guyana High Commission,** 3 Palace Court, Bayswater Road, London W2 4LP    *tel* 01-229 7684--8.

**Hayward Gallery,** South Bank Centre, Belvedere Road, London SE1 8XZ    *tel* 01-928 3144.

**Health, Department of,** Richmond House, 79 Whitehall, London SW1A 2NS    *tel* 01-210 3000.

**Historic Buildings & Monuments, Scotland,** 20 Brandon Street, Edinburgh EH3 5RA    *tel* 031-244 3107.

**Historical Manuscripts, Royal Commission on,** Quality House, Quality Court, Chancery Lane, London WC2A 1HP    *tel* 01-242 1198    *fax* 01-831 3550.

**Historical Monuments of England, Royal Commission on the,** Fortress House, 23 Savile Row, London W1X 2JQ    *tel* 01-734 6010    *fax* 01-494 3998.

**Home Office,** Queen Anne's Gate, London SW1H 9AT    *tel* 01-273 3000. *Public Relations Branch:* Director of Information Services: B. L. Mower.

**Independent Broadcasting Authority,** 70 Brompton Road, London SW3 1EY    *tel* 01-584 7011    *fax* 01-589 5533.

**India, High Commission of, Press & Information Wing,** India House, Aldwych, London WC2B 4NA    *tel* 01-836 8484, ext. 147, 286.

**Inland Revenue, Board of,** Somerset House, London WC2R 1LB.    *tel* 01-438 6420.

**Ireland, Embassy of,** 17 Grosvenor Place, London SW1X 7HR    *tel* 01-235 2171    *telex* 916104 Iverna G    *fax* 01-245 6961.

**Jamaican High Commission,** 1-2 Prince Consort Road, London SW7 2BZ    *tel* 01-823 9911    *telex* 263304 Jamcom G    *fax* 01-589 5154.

**Kenya High Commission,** 24-25 New Bond Street, London W1Y 9HD    *tel* 01-636 2371/5.

**Lesotho, High Commission of the Kingdom of,** 10 Collingham Road, London SW5 0NR    *tel* 01-373 8581-2.

**London Museum**—see **Museum of London.**

**London Records Office, Corporation of City of,** Guildhall, London EC2P 2EJ    *tel* 01-260 1251.

**London Regional Transport,** 55 Broadway, London SW1H 0BD    *tel* 01-222 5600.

**Malawi High Commission,** 33 Grosvenor Street, London W1X 0DE    *tel* 01-491 4172--7.

**Malaysian High Commission,** 45 Belgrave Square, London SW1X 8QT    *tel* 01-235 8033    *telex* 262550    *fax* 235 5161.

**Malta High Commission,** 16 Kensington Square, London W8 5HH    *tel* 01-938 1712-6    *telex* 261102 Mlt Ldn G    *fax* 01-937 8664.

**Mauritius High Commission,** 32--3 Elvaston Place, London SW7 5NW    *tel* 01-581 0294.

**Museum of London,** London Wall, London EC2Y 5HN    *tel* 01-600 3699    *fax* 01-600 1058. Amalgamating the collections of the London Museum and the Guildhall Museum.

**Museum of Mankind** (Ethnography Department of the British Museum), 6 Burlington Gardens, London W1X 2EX    *tel* 01-323 8043 (information).

**National Economic Development Office,** Millbank Tower, Millbank, London SW1P 4QX    *tel* 01-217 4000    *fax* 01-821 1099.

**National Maritime Museum,** Greenwich, London SE10 9NF, including the Old Royal Observatory    *tel* 01-858 4422.

**National Savings, Department for,** Marketing and Information Division, Charles House, 375 Kensington High Street, London W14 8SD    *tel* 01-605 9432/9438    *fax* 01-605 9446.

**National Trust for Scotland, The,** 5 Charlotte Square, Edinburgh EH2 4DU    *tel* 031-226 5922    *fax* 031-315 2103.

**Natural Environment Research Council,** Polaris House, North Star Avenue, Swindon SN2 1EU    *tel* Swindon (0793) 411500.

**Natural History Museum,** Cromwell Road, London SW7 5BD    *tel* 01-938 9123.

**New Zealand, High Commissioner for,** New Zealand House, Haymarket, London SW1Y 4TQ    *tel* 01-930 8422    *telex* 24368    *fax* 839 4580.

**Nigeria High Commission,** Nigeria House, 9 Northumberland Avenue, London WC2N 5BX    *tel* 01-839 1244.

**Northern Ireland Office,** Whitehall, London SW1A 2AZ.    *tel* 01-210 3000. Also Stormont House, Belfast BT4 3ST    *tel* (0232) 63255.

**Northern Ireland Tourist Board,** River House, 48 High Street, Belfast BT1 2DS    *tel* Belfast (0232) 231221    *telex* 748087    *fax* 240960. *Press only:* (0232) 235906.

**Office of Population Censuses and Surveys,** St. Catherines House, 10 Kingsway, London WC2B 6JP    *tel* 01-242 0262.

**Patent Office** (Department of Trade and Industry), State House, 66-71 High Holborn, London WC1R 4TP  *tel* 01-831 2525. *Copyright Enquiries:* 01-829 6145. *Marketing and Publicity Unit:* 01-829 6512. *Sales Branch* (for information retrieval services), Patent Office, Block C, Station Square House, St. Mary Cray, Orpington, Kent BR5 3RD  *tel* Orpington (0689) 32111.

**PLR Office,** Bayheath House, Prince Regent Street, Stockton-on-Tees, Cleveland TS18 1DF  *tel* (0642) 604699. Address enquiries to The Registrar of Public Lending Right.

**Post Office Headquarters,** 33 Grosvenor Place, London SW1X 1PX  *tel* 01-235 8000.

**Public Record Office,** *Modern Departmental Records:* Ruskin Avenue, Kew, Richmond, Surrey TW9 4DU  *tel* 01-876 3444. *Medieval, Early Modern and Legal Records* and the *Census Returns:* Chancery Lane, London WC2A 1LR  *tel* 01-876 3444  *fax* Kew 878 8905, Chancery Lane 878 7231.

**Public Trust Office,** Stewart House, 24 Kingsway, London WC2B 6JX  *tel* 01-269 7000  *fax* 01-831 0060.

**Racial Equality, Commission for,** Elliot House, 10--12 Allington Street, London SW1E 5EH  *tel* 01-828 7022  *fax* 01-630 7605.

**Regional Arts Associations, Council of (CORAA),** Litton Lodge, 13A Clifton Road, Winchester, Hants SO22 5BP  *tel* (0962) 51063.

**Royal Mint,** Llantrisant, Pontyclun, Mid-Glamorgan CF7 8YT  *tel* Llantrisant 222111 and 7 Grosvenor Gardens, London SW1W 0BH  *tel* 01-828 8724--8.

**Science and Engineering Research Council,** Polaris House, North Star Avenue, Swindon SN2 1ET  *tel* (0793) 411000.

**Science Museum,** South Kensington, London SW7 2DD  *tel* 01-938 8000. *Enquiries: Information Office* 01-938 8080/8008. *Press Office* 01-938 8181.

**Scotland, National Library of,** George IV Bridge, Edinburgh EH1 1EW  *tel* 031-226 4531  *telex* 72638 Nlsedi G  *fax* 031-226 4531 ext 2305.

**Scottish Information Office,** New St. Andrew's House, Edinburgh EH1 3TD  *tel* 031-244 4950, and Dover House, Whitehall, London SW1A 2AU  *tel* 01-270 6744.

**Scottish Office,** Dover House, Whitehall, London SW1A 2AU  *tel* 01-270 6755.

**Scottish Record Office,** HM General Register House, Edinburgh EH1 3YY  *tel* 031-556 6585.

**Scottish Tourist Board,** 23 Ravelston Terrace, Edinburgh EH4 3EU  *tel* 031-332 2433  *telex* 72272  *fax* 031-343 1513.

**Serpentine Gallery,** Kensington Gardens, London W2 3XA  *tel* 01-402 6075/0343  *fax* 01-402 4103. *Recorded information:* 01-723 9072.

**Sierra Leone, High Commissioner for,** 33 Portland Place, London W1N 3AG  *tel* 01-636 6483-5.

**Singapore High Commission,** 2 Wilton Crescent, London SW1X 8RW  *tel* 01-235 8315  *telex* 262564 Shciuk G  *fax* 01-2456583.

**Social Security, Department of,** Richmond House, 79 Whitehall, London SW1A 2NS  *tel* 01-210 3000. *Overseas Branch:* Central Office, Long Benton, Newcastle-upon-Tyne NE98 1YX  *tel* 091-285711.

**South Africa, Republic of,** South African Embassy, Trafalgar Square, London WC2N 5DP  *tel* 01-930 4488.

**Sri Lanka, High Commission for the Democratic Socialist Republic of,** 13 Hyde Park Gardens, London W2 2LU   *tel* 01-262 1841   *fax* 262 7970.

**Stationery Office, Her Majesty's,** St. Crispins, Duke Street, Norwich NR3 1PD   *tel* (0603) 622211.

**Swaziland High Commission,** 58 Pont Street, London SW1X 0AE   *tel* 01-581 4976   *telex* 28853   *fax* 01-5895332.

**Tanzania High Commission,** 43 Hertford Street, London W1Y 8DB   *tel* 01-499 8951.

**Trade and Industry, Department of,** 1-19 Victoria Street, London SW1H 0ET   *tel* 01-215 5000   *telex* 8811074. *Enterprise Initiative* (0800) 500 200. *Europe Open for Business* 01-200 1992   *fax* 01-215 3979.

**Transport, Department of,** 2 Marsham Street, London SW1P 3EB   *tel* 01-212 3434.

**Treasury, HM,** Treasury Chambers, Parliament Street, London SW1P 3AG   *tel* 01-270 3000.

**Trinidad and Tobago High Commission,** 42 Belgrave Square, London SW1X 8NT   *tel* 01-245 9351.

**Trinity House, London,** Tower Hill, London EC3N 4DH   *tel* 01-480 6601   *telex* 884300   *fax* 01-480 7662. The General Lighthouse Authority for England, Wales and the Channel Islands, a Charitable Organisation for the relief of Mariners and a Deep Sea Pilotage Authority.

**United Kingdom Atomic Energy Authority,** 11 Charles II Street, London SW1Y 4QP   *tel* 01-930 5454   *telex* 22565   *fax* 01-930 5454 ext 517/274.

**Victoria and Albert Museum,** South Kensington, London SW7 2RL   *tel* 01-938 8500   *telex* 268831 Vicart G   *fax* 01-938 8341.

**Wales, The National Library of,** Aberystwyth, Dyfed SY23 3BU   *tel* (0970) 623816   *telex* 35165   *fax* (0970) 615709.

**Wales Tourist Board,** Brunel House, 2 Fitzalan Road, Cardiff CF2 1UY   *tel* (0222) 499909   *telex* 497269   *fax* (0222) 485031.

**Wellington Museum,** Apsley House, 149 Piccadilly, Hyde Park Corner, London W1V 9FA   *tel* 01-499 5676. Closed Mondays.

**Welsh Office,** Gwydyr House, Whitehall, London SW1A 2ER   *tel* 01-270 0567   *fax* 01-270 0570 and Cathays Park, Cardiff, CF1 3NQ   *tel* (0222) 825111   *fax* (0222) 823036.

**West India Committee (The Caribbean),** Commonwealth House, 18 Northumberland Avenue, London WC2N 5RA   *tel* 01-976 1493   *fax* 01-976 1541.

**Zambia High Commission,** 2 Palace Gate, Kensington, London W8 5NG   *tel* 01-589 6655   *telex* 263544.

In *Whitaker's Almanack* will be found names and addresses of many other public bodies.

---

See also the **Picture research** section.

# Societies and prizes

## Societies, Associations and Clubs

**Academi Gymreig Yr.** *President:* Prof. J. E. Caerwyn Williams; *Chairman:* R. Geraint Gruffydd; *Treasurer:* Prof. Dafydd Jenkins; *Administrator:* Angharad Dafis, 3rd Floor, Mount Stuart House, Mount Stuart Square, The Docks, Cardiff CF1 6DQ *tel* (0222) 492064. The Society was founded in 1959 to promote creative writing in the Welsh language. Existing members elect new members on the basis of their contribution to Welsh literature or criticism. The society publishes a literary magazine, *Taliesin*, books on Welsh literature, and translations of modern European classics into Welsh. It is currently engaged in the production of a new English/Welsh Dictionary. The society's activities are open to all.

**Academi Gymreig, Yr: English Language Section.** *President:* Ronald Mathias; *Chairman:* Gillian Clarke; *Administrator:* Kevin Thomas, 3rd Floor, Mount Stuart House, Mount Stuart Square, The Docks, Cardiff CF1 6DQ *tel* (0222) 492025. This section was founded in 1968 to provide a meeting-point for writers in the English language who are of Welsh origin and/or take Wales as a main theme of their work. Membership at present is by invitation and members pay an annual subscription. Associate Membership is open to all interested individuals or organisations. Although it is an autonomous body, members of the English Language Section co-operate with members of the parent body for joint conferences and similar activities.

**Agricultural Journalists, Guild of,** c/o Pharo Communications, Forum House, 41-51 Brighton Road, Redhill, Surrey RH1 6YS *tel* (0737) 767631. *President:* Derek Watson; *Chairman:* Stephen Howe; *Hon. General Secretary:* Don Gomery. Established to promote a high standard among journalists who specialise in agricultural matters and to assist them to increase their sources of information and technical knowledge. Membership is open to those earning their livelihood wholly or mainly from agricultural journalism.

**American Correspondents in London, Association of,** *President:* Gilbert Lew-thwaite, c/o *Baltimore Sun*, 14 Gough Square, Fleet Street, London EC4A 3DE *tel* 01-353 3531 *fax* 01-353 5331.

**American Publishers, Association of, Inc.** (1970), *President:* Nicholas A. Veliotes. *Executive Vice President:* Thomas D. McKee, 220 East 23rd Street, New York, N.Y. 10010 *tel* 212-689-8920 *fax* 212-696 0131. A confederation of more than 300 member houses which is the major voice of the publishing industry in the United States. Members drawn from all regions of the country publish the great majority of printed materials sold to American schools, colleges and libraries, bookstores, and by direct mail to homes. Their basic products comprise books in the categories of school and college textbooks, general trade, reference, religious, technical, professional, scientific, and medical—both hard cover and paperback. They also publish scholarly journals, and produce a range of educational materials including computer software, classroom periodicals, maps, globes, films and filmstrips, audio and video tapes, records, cassettes, slides, transparencies, and test materials.

**Art and Design, National Society for Education in** (1888), 7A High Street, Corsham, Wiltshire SN13 0ES *tel* (0249) 714825 *fax* (0249) 716138. *General Secretary:* John Steers, N.D.D., A.T.C., D.A.E. A professional association of principals and lecturers in colleges and schools of art and of specialist art, craft and design teachers in other schools and colleges. Has representatives on National and Regional Committees which are the concern of those engaged in Art and Design Education. Publishes *Journal of Art and Design Education* (3 p.a.).

**Artists, Federation of British,** 17 Carlton House Terrace, London SW1Y 5BD *tel* 01-930 6844. *Chief Executive:* Oliver Warman, R.B.A. Administers 9 major National Art Societies at The Mall Galleries, The Mall, London, SW1.

**Artists, International Guild of,** Ralston House, 41 Lister Street, Riverside Gardens, Ilkley, W. Yorkshire LS29 9ET *tel* (0943) 609075. *Director:* Leslie Simpson, F.R.S.A. The guild offers to artists a service and insight into the opportunities in the art world as well as help with art problems and exhibition. *Membership:* £15.

**Arts** (1863), 40 Dover Street, London W1X 3RB *tel* 01-499 8581. *Secretary:* Christopher Miers. *Subs:* £300. For men and women connected with or interested in the arts.

**Arts Council of the Bailiwick of Guernsey** (1981), c/o Les Merriennes, St Martins, Guernsey, C.I. *tel* (0481) 36811. *Secretary:* Jennifer Seth-Smith. Co-ordinates the organisations under the council's umbrella, presents artistic events, sponsors reports, aims to bring about the creation of an arts centre in Guernsey and to encourage all the arts in Guernsey, Alderney and Sark. *Membership fee:* £5, under 18 £2.

**Arts Council of Great Britain,** 105 Piccadilly, London W1V 0AU *tel* 01-629 9495. *Chairman:* Peter Palumbo; *Secretary-General:* Luke Rittner. To develop and improve the knowledge, understanding and practice of the arts, and to increase their accessibility to the public throughout Great Britain. The arts with which the Council is mainly concerned are dance and mime, drama, literature, music and opera, and the visual arts, including photography and arts films.

**Asian Affairs, Royal Society for,** (1901), 2 Belgrave Square, London SW1X 8PJ *tel* 01-235 5122. *President:* The Lord Denman, C.B.E., M.C., T.D.; *Chairman of Council:* Sir Michael Wilford, G.C.M.G.; *Secretary:* Miss M. FitzSimons. For the study of all Asia past and present. Fortnightly lectures etc. Library. *Publication: Asian Affairs*, three times a year, free to members. *Editor:* R. A. Longmire. *Subscription:* £32.00 London members, £25 members more than 60 miles from London, £22.00 overseas members, £5.00 junior (under 21), £50 affiliated.

**Aslib,** The Association for Information Management, (1924), Information House, 26-27 Boswell Street, London WC1N 3JZ *tel* 01-430 2671 *telex* 23667 *fax* 01-430 0514. An association which promotes the effective management and use of information in industry, central and local government, education and the professions. It provides publications, training, independent advice and recruitment services to those in the information sector. For particulars of membership apply: The Director.

**Assistant Librarians, Association of** (1895), c/o The Library Association, 7 Ridgmount Street, London WC1E 7AE (Group of the Library Association, *qv.*). *President:* Martin Stone, B.A., A.L.A. *Hon. Secretary:* Avril E. Johnston, M.A, DIP. LIB, A.L.A. Publish library text books and bibliographical aids.

**Australia, Children's Book Council of,** *National Executive:* P.O. Box 420, Dickson, A.C.T. 2602. The Council, a non-profit organization, exists to encourage reading among children of all ages, to promote better writing, illustration and book production, and to encourage the sharing of literature. *Reading Time*, the official journal of the Council, is published 4 times a year. *Subscription:* $20.00. Entries for awards for 1989 and 1990 should be forwarded to Box 202, Sandy Bay, Tasmania 7005.

**Australia Council,** Northside Gardens, 168 Walker Street, North Sydney, New South Wales 2059, Australia   *tel* (02) 923 3333. *Chairperson:* Professor Donald Horne, A.O.
The Australia Council is a statutory authority which provides a broad range of support for the arts in Australia. Established in 1968 as The Australian Council for the Arts (supporting mainly the performing arts), it was restructured in 1973 to embrace music, theatre, film/radio/television, literature, visual arts, crafts, Aboriginal arts and community arts. (In June 1976 the activities of the film/radio/television board were transferred to the Australian Film Commission.) In March 1975, by Act of Parliament, the Australia Council was established as an independent authority.
The Council is involved in the administration of grants, public information services, policy development, research, international activities, and advisory services to many other organisations including government bodies. A wide range of projects and activities, both individual and group, receive Australia Council funds. Support includes grants made to enable artists to study, and living allowances to permit others (notably writers) to 'buy time' to follow their creative pursuits. Some of the major initiatives of the Council in past years, include: negotiation with international bodies for the touring of exhibitions, a Public Lending Right scheme for Australian authors; copyright protection; moral rights for artists; art and working life; women in the arts; Arts Law Centre; a Provident Fund for performers; Artist-in-Residence schemes at tertiary institutions, and increased employment for Australian artists in all fields. Australia Council publications include information booklets, directories, research reports, newsletters, program reviews and an Annual Report.
**Literature Board, The,** Australia Council, P.O. Box 302, North Sydney, New South Wales 2059. Because of its size and isolation and the competition its literature meets from other English speaking countries, Australia has always needed to subsidise writing of creative and cultural significance. The Literature Board, one of the Boards of the Australia Council, was created in 1973, taking over the duties of the earlier Commonwealth Literary Fund, established in 1908.
The Board's chief objective is the support of the writing of all forms of creative literature—novels, short stories, poetry, plays, biographies, history and works on the humanities. The Board also assists with the publication of literary magazines and periodicals. It has a publishing subsidies scheme and it initiates and supports projects of many kinds designed to promote Australian literature both within Australia and abroad.
About two-thirds of the Board's expenditure in recent years has gone to writers

in the form of direct grants including Fellowships and Writers' Project Grants (living allowances), and Emeritus Fellowships. Category A Fellowships (valued at $31,000 per year) are living allowances to assist published writers of substantial achievement to complete a major project or projects. Category B Fellowships (valued at $22,000 per year) are living allowances for developing writers of potential who may or may not have had a work published or performed. Writers' Project Grants (maximum value $10,000) are to assist writers to meet living expenses while writing a particular literary work. Emeritus Fellowships are paid at varying rates to senior writers of distinction.

**Australia, The Library Association of,** 376 Jones Street, Ultimo, Sydney, N.S.W. 2007    *tel* 692 9233    *fax* (02) 692 0687. *Director:* Sue Kosse. The Association is an Australia-wide organisation incorporated by Royal Charter in 1963 with c. 7,500 members, of whom c. 5,500 are professional members. The objects of the Association are to promote, and improve the services of libraries and other information agencies; to improve the standard of library and information personnel and foster their professional interests. It publishes the *Australian Library Journal* four times a year, and the newsletter *Incite* twenty-one times a year, as well as a range of specialist publications to cater for the interests of members in different types of libraries. The governing body of the Association is the General Council.

**Australian Book Publishers Association,** 161 Clarence Street, Sydney, N.S.W. 2000    *tel* (02) 29 5422    *fax* 02-262 1631. The Association aims to foster original and licensed publishing in Australia, to help improve the Australian book industry as a whole. There are over 150 member firms.

**Australian Society of Authors, The,** 22 Alfred Street, Milsons Point, N.S.W. 2061    *tel* 92-7235    *fax* (02) 929 2212. *President:* Colin Thiele, *Executive Officer:* Gail Cork, *Chairman:* Tom Keneally.

**Australian Writers' Guild Ltd** (1962), 60/60A Kellett Street, Kings Cross, NSW 2011    *tel* 357 7888    *fax* 357 7776. *Executive Officer:* Angela Wales. A trade union and professional association dedicated to promoting and protecting the professional interests of writers for stage, screen, television and radio. *Subscription:* full members: entrance fee $130, annual fee $130–$500 dependent on income from writing; associate members: entrance fee $65, annual fee $66.

**Authors** (1891) (at the Arts Club). 40 Dover Street, London W1X 3RB    *tel* 01-499 8581. *Secretary:* Huldine Ridgway. *Subscription:* £300.

**Authors' Agents, The Association of** (1974), 20 John Street, London WC1N 2DR    *tel* 01-405 6774. *President:* Gill Coleridge; *Secretary:* Linda Shaughnessy; *Treasurer:* Vivien Green. Maintains a code of professional practice to which all members of the association commit themselves; holds regular meetings to discuss matters of common professional interest; and provides a vehicle for representing the view of authors' agents in discussion of matters of common interest with other professional bodies.

**Authors' Guild of Ireland, Ltd.,** 282 Swords Road, Dublin 9    *tel* 375974. *Directors:* John K. Lyons, Mrs. Iseult McGuinness. A society for the protection of copyright owned and managed, on a non-profit basis, by Full Members who must be owners of copyright in literary or dramatic works by reason of authorship, or who are the personal successors of such authors. Agents for the control of performing rights and collection of royalties in Ireland. *Secretary:* Tom Mooney.

**Authors League of America, Inc, The** (1912), 234 West 44th Street, New York, N.Y. 10036    *tel* 1-212-391 9198    *fax* 1-212-869 8237. A national membership organization to promote the professional interest of authors and dramatists, procure satisfactory copyright legislation and treaties, guard freedom of expression, and support fair tax treatment for writers.

**Authors' Licensing and Collecting Society Limited (ALCS),** 7 Ridgmount Street, London WC1E 7AE   *tel* 01-255 2034. *President:* Lord Willis. Independent, non-profit-making collecting society for the collective administration of literary rights in the spheres of reprography, lending right, off-air recording and cable television. Membership, £5.75 annually, open to authors, successor membership to authors' heirs. See **ALCS** Article.

**Authors' Representatives, Inc., Society of** (1928), Ten Astor Place, 3rd Floor, New York, N.Y. 10003   *tel* 212-353-3709.

**Authors, The Society of,** 84 Drayton Gardens, London SW10 9SB   *tel* 01-373 6642. *President:* Sir Victor Pritchett, K.B.E.; *General Secretary:* Mark Le Fanu. The Society was founded in 1884 by Sir Walter Besant with the object of representing, assisting, and protecting authors. It is a limited company and an independent trade union. The Society's scope has been continuously extended; specialist associations have been created for translators, broadcasters, educational, medical, technical and children's writers (details will be found elsewhere in this issue). Members are entitled to legal as well as general advice in connection with the marketing of their work, their contracts, their choice of a publisher, etc., and also to have litigation in which their work may involve them conducted by the Society and at the Society's expense provided the Committee of Management is satisfied that the member's case is sound in law and that the proceedings are justified. Annual Subscription: £50 (£45 by direct debit). Full particulars of membership from the Society's offices. (See article: **The Society of Authors.**)

**Aviation Artists, The Guild of** (incorporating the Society of Aviation Artists), The Bondway Business Centre, 71 Bondway, Vauxhall Cross, London SW8 1SQ   *tel* 01-735 0634. *President:* Michael Turner, P.G.AV.A.; *Secretary:* Mrs. Yvonne Bonham. A guild of artists formed in 1971 to promote all forms of aviation art through the organisation of exhibitions and meetings. Annual open exhibition in June/July in London. £1000 prize for "The Aviation Painting of the Year". Quarterly members' journal. Entrance fee £25. Associates £25. Members £30 (by invitation). Non-exhibiting friends £15.

**BAPLA (British Association of Picture Libraries and Agencies)** (1975). *Administrator:* Sal Shuel, BAPLA, 13 Woodberry Crescent, London N10 1PJ   *tel* 01-883 2531   *fax* 01-883 9215. BAPLA is a trade association formed to promote fair and honest trading within the profession, and between members and their clients. To this end it published a Code of Professional Standards and Fair Practice and a set of Recommended Terms and Conditions for the Submission and Reproduction of Photographs. BAPLA makes a constant effort to promote the fact that photographs, prints, drawings, have a copyright and that this copyright has a commercial value, that if any picture has the impact to promote a product, sell a book, it also has a market value for being so used. Publishes an annual Directory of Members and a quarterly Journal.

**E. F. Benson Society, The** (1984), 88 Tollington Park, London N4 3RA   *tel* 01-272 3375. *Secretary:* Allan Downend. To promote interest in E. F. Benson and the Benson family. Publishes twice-yearly journal *The Dodo*. The society arranges two literary evenings a year and an annual outing. *Annual subscription:* £5.00 single; £6.00 couple; £10 overseas.

**E. F. Benson: The Tilling Society** (1982), Martello Bookshop, 26 High Street, Rye, East Sussex TN31 7JJ  *tel* (0797) 222242. *Secretaries:* Cynthia and Tony Reavell. To bring together enthusiasts for E. F. Benson and his Mapp & Lucia novels. News and information is exchanged through two annual newsletters. Annual gathering in Rye. *Annual subscription:* £5, overseas £7.

**Bibliographical Society** (1892), British Library, Humanities and Social Sciences, Great Russell Street, London WC1B 3DG. *President:* R. C. Alston; *Hon. Secretary:* Mrs. M. M. Foot. Acquisition and dissemination of information upon subjects connected with historical bibliography.

**Blackpool Art Society, The** (1884). *President:* Norman Piper; *Hon. Secretary:* Jack Tebay, 17 Leeds Road, Blackpool FY1 4HQ  *tel* (0253) 33986. *Studio:* Wilkinson Avenue, off Woodland Grove, Blackpool. Summer and Autumn exhibition (members' work only). Studio meetings, practical, lectures, etc., out-of-door sketching.

**Book Development Council,** see **Publishers Association.**

**Book House Ireland** (1983), 65 Middle Abbey Street, Dublin 1  *tel* 730108. *Administrator:* Cecily Golden. Represents Clé: The Irish Book Publishers' Association and The Booksellers' Association of Great Britain and Ireland (Irish Branch); provides a joint secretariat for both associations; book trade information and resource centre, produces regular newsletters, runs courses, has function rooms, a library and co-ordinates trade and social events for the Irish book industry.

**Book Marketing Council,** see **Publishers Association.**

**Book Packagers Association** (1985), 147-149 Gloucester Terrace, London W2 6DX  *tel* 01-723 7328. *Secretary:* Rosemary Pettit. To represent the interests of book packagers; to exchange information; to provide services such as standard contracts and meeting facilities at book fairs.

**Book Trust,** (formerly **National Book League**). Book House, 45 East Hill, Wandsworth, London SW18 2QZ  *tel* 01-870 9055  *fax* 874-4790. Founded in 1925 as the National Book Council, and incorporated as an educational charity. The name and the constitution of the National Book League were changed in September 1986 and it is now known as **Book Trust**. *Patron:* HRH Prince Philip, Duke of Edinburgh; *Chairman:* Peter Bagnall; *Chief Executive:* Keith McWilliams. The Book Trust's principal aim is to foster the growth of a wider and more discriminating interest in books. The membership now exceeds 4,000. Among the Trust's services to its members are a lending library of books about books, and the use of the Book Information Service and the Children's Books Library, part of the Children's Book Foundation, which holds a reference collection of the last 24 months of children's publications and provides an information service for queries about children's books. Book lists on many subjects are published. The Trust organises touring exhibitions which are shown in many parts of the country. It also takes part in research projects and administers many literary prizes, including the £20,000 Booker Prize; also The School Bookshop Association. The headquarters is a meeting-place for members. The Trust produces a quarterly newsletter, *Booknews*, circulated to members. Membership is open to all. Annual subscription £25.00. Special facilities and subscriptions for libraries, schools and other corporate bodies. Full details from the Publicity Officer.

**Books Across the Sea,** The English-Speaking Union of the Commonwealth, Dartmouth House, 37 Charles Street, London W1X 8AB *tel* 01-493 3328. The English Speaking Union of the United States, 16 East 69th Street, New York, N.Y. 10021. World voluntary organisation devoted to the promotion of international understanding and friendship. Exchanges books with its corresponding BAS Committees in New York, Australia, Canada and New Zealand. The books exchanged are selected to reflect the life and culture of each country and the best of its recent publishing and writing. The books are circulated among members and accredited borrowers, bulk loans are made to affiliated schools and public libraries. New selections are announced by bulletin, *The Ambassador Booklist.*

**Booksellers Association of Great Britain and Ireland** (1895), 154 Buckingham Palace Road, London SW1W 9TZ *tel* 01-730 8214. *Director:* T. E. Godfray. To protect and promote the interests of booksellers engaged in selling new books.

**Botanical Artists, Society of** (1985), Burwood Gallery, Union Street, Wells, Somerset BA5 2PU *tel* (0749) 74472 (during exhibitions 01-222 2723). *Founder President:* Suzanne Lucas; *Hon. Treasurer:* Pamela Davis; *Hon. Secretary:* Christine Hart-Davies; *Executive Secretary:* Mrs. S. M. Burton. The society's aims are to honour and strive to continue in the great tradition of talent, beauty and infinite care apparent in the art of botanical painting through the ages. An exhibition is held in March each year at the Westminster Gallery, Westminster Central Hall, Storey's Gate, London SW1H 9NU. Artists who use more recent techniques in style and interpretation are welcome, and non-members may submit work. Information from the Executive Secretary. *Membership fee:* £20.00.

**British Academy,** 20-21 Cornwall Terrace, London NW1 4QP *tel* 01-487 5966 *telex* 263194. *President:* Dr A. J. P. Kenny; *Foreign Secretary:* Professor J. B. Trapp; *Treasurer:* Dr E. A. Wrigley; *Secretary:* P. W. H. Brown.

**British Amateur Press Association** (1890), 78 Tennyson Road, Stratford, London E15 4DR. To promote the fellowship of writers, artists, editors, printers, publishers and other craftsmen/women, and to encourage them to contribute to, edit, print or publish, as a hobby, magazines and literary works produced by letterpress and other processes.

**British American Arts Association (UK),** 49 Wellington Street, London WC2E 7BN *tel* 01-379 7755 *fax* 01-240 3354. *Director:* Jennifer Williams. Acts as an information service and clearing house for exchange between Britain and the United States in all the arts fields—literature, poetry, theatre, dance, music, visual arts. Counsels artists, administrators, organizations and sponsors on opportunities to promote, perform, show and tour their work; does not run programmes or give funds.

**British Artists, Royal Society of,** 17 Carlton House Terrace, London SW1Y 5BD *tel* 01-930 6844. *President:* Tom Coates, R.O.I., R.W.S., R.P., N.E.A.C.; *Keeper:* Leslie Worth, V.P.R.W.S. Incorporated by Royal Charter for the purpose of encouraging the study and practice of the arts of painting, sculpture and architectural designs. Annual Open Exhibition at the Mall Galleries, The Mall, London SW1.

**British Association of Industrial Editors, The** (1949). 3 Locks Yard, High Street, Sevenoaks, Kent TN13 1LT *tel* (0732) 459331 *fax* (0732) 455905. The objects include development of the qualifications of those engaged in the management, editing and production of internal corporate communications media. BAIE defines internal corporate communications to include such audiences as shareholders, customers, clients, agents and suppliers, as well as employees. Membership is open to men and women engaged in, or who have a valid interest in, corporate communications.

**British Copyright Council, The,** Copyright House, 29-33 Berners Street, London W1P 4AA. *Chairman:* Maureen Duffy, *Vice Chairmen:* Anne Bolt, Juri Gabriel, Graham Whettam; *Secretary:* Geoffrey Adams; *Treasurer:*Charles Clark. Its purposes are to defend and foster the true principles of creators' copyright and their acceptance throughout the world, to bring together bodies representing all who are interested in the protection of such copyright, and to keep watch on any legal or other changes which may require an amendment of the law.

**British Council, The,** 10 Spring Gardens, London SW1A 2BN *tel* 01-930 8466 *telex* 8952201 Bricon G *fax* 01-839 6347. *Chairman:* Sir David Orr, M.C., LL.D; *Director General:* Richard Francis. The British Council promotes Britain abroad. It provides access to British ideas, talents and experience in education and training, books and periodicals, the English language, the arts, the sciences and technology.

The Council is represented in more than eighty countries. Around the world the Council runs 138 offices, 116 libraries and 52 English language schools and employs 1,600 staff in its London headquarters and in university towns in England, Scotland, Wales and Northern Ireland.

The Council's lending and reference libraries throughout the world cater for the serious reader and act as show-cases for the latest British publications. They vary in size from small reference collections and information centres to comprehensive libraries equipped with reference works, on-line facilities and a selection of British periodicals. Bibliographies of British books on special subjects are prepared on request.

Working in close collaboration with book trade associations, and in particular the Book Development Council (International Division of the Publishers Association), the British Council organises book and electronic publishing exhibitions for showing overseas. These exhibitions range from small specialist displays of 100 or so titles to a big trade exhibit of 3,000 titles representing 500 British publishers which is mounted annually at Frankfurt.

The Council publications include *British Book News*, a monthly guide to forthcoming books published in Britain. It also publishes a series of literary bibliographies and *Contemporary Writers*, a series of pamphlets on British writers of today. The Council has also produced several series of recordings including *Commonwealth Writers*, interviews of leading writers speaking about their work; *Critics on Criticism*, critics discussing major current approaches to the study of English literature; and *Recorded Interviews*, leading British novelists and dramatists describing their major works and careers as writers. A catalogue of publications, covering the arts, books, libraries and publishing, education and training, English language teaching and information for and about overseas students, is available on request.

The Council acts as the agent of the Overseas Development Administration for two schemes of book aid for developing countries: the Books Presentation Programme under which books are presented to institutional libraries; and the English Language Book Society (ELBS) Scheme which subsidises the production of tertiary level textbooks for sale in specified countries at greatly reduced prices.

In 1988/89 the Council also supported over 1,000 events in the visul arts, film and television, drama, dance and music, ranging from the classical to the contemporary.

The Council is an authority on teaching English as a second or foreign language and gives advice and information on curriculum, methodology, materials and testing through its English Language and Literature Division. It also promotes British literature overseas through writers' tours, academic visits, seminars and exhibitions.

Further information about the work of the British Council is available from the Press and Information Department at the headquarters in London or from British Council offices and libraries overseas.

**British Directory Publishers, Association of,** Imperial House, 17 Kingsway, London WC2B 6UN. *Correspondence* to 147-149 Gloucester Terrace, London W2 6DX. *Chairman:* A. M. W. Graham. To provide for the exchange of information between members on the technical, commercial and management problems arising in Directory Publishing. Maintains code of Professional Practice.

**British Film Institute,** 21 Stephen Street, London W1P 1PL *tel* 01-255 1444 *telex* 27624. *Director:* Wilf Stevenson.

The general object of the British Film Institute is "to encourage the development of the art of the film, to promote its use as a record of contemporary life and manners, to foster study and appreciation of it from these points of view, to foster study and appreciation of film for television and television programmes generally, to encourage the best use of television". Its divisions include the National Film Archive and the National Film Theatre on the South Bank. The Institute has also helped to set up 40 Film Theatres outside London. Through its Information Service, its *Monthly Film Bulletin* (which gives credit and reviews of every feature film released in Britain), its quarterly *Sight and Sound*, and its Education Department it provides materials and services for film and television education. The BFI Library contains Britain's largest collection of printed material relating to film and television, open to BFI members only. The annual subscription for Members £15.75 including *Sight and Sound*, and NFT programme (post free), or £26.50 including *Sight and Sound, Monthly Film Bulletin* and programme (post free). Associateship (National Film Theatre) (London) £10.25 (including programme post free), £7.50 to full-time students at recognised education establishments, £7.00 to Senior Citizens.

**British Institute of Professional Photography,** Amwell End, Ware, Herts SG12 9HN *tel* Ware (0920) 464011. (Founded 1901, Incorporated 1921.) *Principal Objects:* Professional Qualifying Association; to represent all who practise photography as a profession in any field; to improve the quality of photography; establish recognised examination qualifications and a high standard of conduct; to safeguard the interests of the public and the profession. *Membership:* approx. 3500. Admission can be obtained either via the Institute's examinations, or by submission of work and other information to the appropriate examining board. Fellows, Associates and Licentiates are entitled to the designation Incorporated Photographer or Incorporated Photographic Technician. *Meetings:* The Institute organises numerous meetings and conferences in various parts of the country throughout the year. *Publications:* a monthly journal, *The Photographer* and an annual Register of Members and *guide to buyers of photography*, plus various pamphlets and leaflets on professional photography.

**British Kinematograph, Sound and Television Society** (founded 1931. Incorporated 1946), 547-549 Victoria House, Vernon Place, London WC1B

4DJ   *tel* 01-242 8400. *Secretary:* R. B. Mobsby. Aims to encourage technical and scientific progress in the industries of its title. Publishes technical information, arranges international conferences and exhibitions, lectures and demonstrations, and encourages the exchange of ideas. Monthly journal *Image Technology*.

**British Science Fiction Association, Ltd., The** (1958). *President:* Arthur C. Clarke; *Membership Secretary:* Jo Raine, 33 Thornville Road, Hartlepool, Cleveland TS26 8EW. For authors, publishers, booksellers and readers of science fiction, fantasy and allied genres. Publishes informal magazine, *Matrix*, of news and information, *Focus*, an amateur writers' magazine, and critical magazine, *Vector* (all enquiries to membership secretary).

**British Science Writers, Association of,** c/o British Association for the Advancement of Science, Fortress House, 23 Savile Row, London W1X 1AB   *tel* 01-494 3326. *Chairman:* Tom Wilkie; *Secretary:* Dr Peter Briggs. An association of science writers, editors, and radio, film, and television producers concerned with the presentation and communication of science, technology and medicine. Its aims are to improve the standard of science writing and to assist its members in their work. Activities include visits to research establishments, luncheon meetings for those concerned with scientific policy, and receptions for scientific attachés and Parliamentarians.

**British Sculptors, Royal Society of,** 108 Old Brompton Road, London SW7 3RA   *tel* 01-373 5554. *President:* John Ravera; *Hon. Treasurer:* Philomena Davis; *Secretary:* Maureen O'Connor. Aims to promote and advance the Art of Sculpture. Informs and advises its members on professional matters; provides an advisory service to the general public.

**British Theatre Association** (1919), The British Theatre Library, Cranbourn Mansions, Cranbourn Street, London WC2H 7AG *tel* 01-734 1664. *Administrator:* Ron Haddon. The British Theatre Library holds one of the largest collections of plays in the world and its Reference Section provides a uniquely comprehensive research facility. An extensive programme of training in theatre skills. *Drama* magazine published quarterly.

**Broadcasting Group, The Society of Authors** (1979), 84 Drayton Gardens, London SW10 9SB   *tel* 01-373 6642. A specialist unit within the framework of the Society of Authors exclusively concerned with the interests and special problems of radio and television writers.

**Brontë Society, The,** Brontë Parsonage, Haworth, nr. Keighley, W. Yorkshire BD22 8DR   *tel* Haworth (0535) 42323. *President:* Lord Briggs of Lewes, M.A.,B.SC., F.B.A. *Chairman of the Council:* Arthur Hartley, *Hon. Secretary:* Eunice Skirrow, J.P. *Hon. Editor:* Mark Seaward, PH.D., D.SC. Examination, preservation, illustration of the memoirs and literary remains of the Brontë family; exhibitions of MSS. and other subjects. Publishes: *The Transactions of the Brontë Society* (bi-annual) and *60 Treasures*.

**Browning Society, The** (1881, refounded 1969), 9 Lakenheath, Southgate, London N14 4RJ   *tel* 01-886 2277. *Secretary:* Roy E. Bolton. The aim of the society is to widen the appreciation and understanding of the lives and poetry of Robert Browning and Elizabeth Barrett Browning and other Victorian writers and poets. *Membership fee:* £10.

**Byron Society (International)** (1971), Byron House, 6 Gertrude Street, London SW10 0JN   *tel* 01-352 5112. *Hon. Director:* Mrs. Elma Dangerfield, O.B.E. To promote research into the life and works of Lord Byron by seminars, discussions, lectures and readings. Publishes *The Byron Journal* (annual). *Subscription:* £10.00 p.a.

**Cable Television Association** (1934), 50 Frith Street, London W1V 5TE  *tel* 01-437 0549/0983. *Director:* Richard Woollam. The trade body representing the interests of companies involved in the provision of cable television in the United Kingdom. Associate membership open to individuals.

**Caldecott, Randolph, Society** (1983). *Secretary:* Kenn Oultram, Clatterwick Hall, Little Leigh, Northwich, Cheshire CW8 4RJ  *tel* (0606) 891303 (office hours). To encourage an interest in the life and works of Randolph Caldecott, the Victorian artist, illustrator and sculptor. Meetings: London, Chester. *Subscription:* £5.00-£8.00 p.a.

**Canada, Periodical Writers Association of** (1976), 24 Ryerson Avenue, Toronto, Ontario M5T 2P3  *tel* 416-868 6913  *fax* 416-860 0826. To protect and promote the interests of periodical writers in Canada.

**Canada, The Writers' Union of,** The Writers' Centre, 24 Ryerson Avenue, Toronto, Ontario M5T 2P3  *tel* 416-868 6914  *fax* 416-860 0826. *Chair:* Gregory M. Cook.

**Canadian Authors' Association,** 121 Avenue Road, Suite 104, Toronto, Ontario M5R 2G3  *tel* 416-926 8084. *President:* Mary Dawe.

**Canadian Book Publishers' Council.** Consists of 41 educational and trade publishers; maintains offices at 45 Charles Street East, 7th Floor, Toronto, Ontario M4Y 1S2  *tel* 416-964 7231  *fax* 416-964 2701. Interested in advancing the cause of the publishing business by co-operative effort and encouragement of high standards of workmanship and service. Co-operates with other organisations interested in the promotion and distribution of books. Canadian Book Publishers' Council has three divisions, the School Group concerned with primary and secondary school instructional materials, the College Group concerned with post-secondary materials, and the Trade Group concerned with general interest adult and children's books. *Executive Director:* Jacqueline Hushion.

**Canadian Periodical Publishers' Association** (1973), 2 Stewart Street, Toronto, Ontario M5V 1H6  *tel* 416-362-2546  *fax* 416-362 2547. *Executive Director:* Catherine Keachie. A trade association representing members' interests to provincial and federal governments, and providing services to Canadian magazines, including retail distribution. Resource centre for information about Canadian magazines.

**Canadian Poets, League of** (1966), 24 Ryerson Avenue, Toronto, Ontario M5T 2P3 Canada  *tel* 416-363 5047. *Executive Director:* Angela Rebeiro; *Executive Assistant:* Dolores Ricketts. To promote the interests of poets and to advance Canadian poetry in Canada and abroad.

**Canadian Publishers, Association of** (1976—formerly Independent Publishers Association 1971), 260 King Street East, Toronto, Ontario M5A 1K3  *tel* 416-361 1408  *fax* 416-361 0643. *Executive Director:* Hamish Cameron. Represents the interests of Canadian publishers in Canada and abroad; facilitates the exchange of information and professional expertise among its members.

**(Daresbury) Lewis Carroll Society** (1970), *Secretary:* Kenn Oultram, Clatterwick Hall, Little Leigh, Northwich, Cheshire CW8 4RJ  *tel* (0606) 891303 (office hours). To encourage an interest in the life and works of Lewis

Carroll, author of *Alice's Adventures*. Meetings at Carroll's birth village (Daresbury). *Subscription:* £3.00–£5.00 p.a.

**Lewis Carroll Society, The,** (1969), 7 Avondale, 109 Truro Road, Wood Green, London N22 4DP. *Secretary:* Mrs Catherine Richards. To promote interest in Charles Dodgson's life and works and to encourage research. Activities include regular meetings and publication of *Jabberwocky* quarterly and newsletter *Bandersnatch*. *Annual subscription:* ordinary £8.00 ($15.00); institutions £10.00 ($18.00); students and retired £5.00 ($10.00).

**Cartoonists Club of Great Britain.** *Secretary:* Charles Sinclair, 2 Camden Hill, Tunbridge Wells, Kent TN2 4TH *tel* (0892) 28938. Aims to encourage social contact between members and endeavour to promote the professional standing and prestige of cartoonists. *Annual sub.:* New members £15; Full members £15, Associate £15.

**Catholic Writers Guild,** *Hon. Secretary:* 1 Leopold Road, London W5 3PB *tel* 01-992 3954. For Catholic writers, journalists and those working in public relations and broadcasting. Monthly meetings. *Subscription:* £5.00 p.a.

**Chartered Society of Designers, The,** *Director:* Patricia Rees Cummings, 29 Bedford Square, London WC1B 3EG *tel* 01-631 1510 *fax* 01-580 2338. The leading professional body for designers. It represents 10,000 designers in 15 categories under the main sections of product design, fashion and textiles, interiors, graphics, design management and education. Provides a range of services to members including an information service; advice on legal, employment and other professional issues; access to a debt collection service; etc. Members can use the club facilities available at the Society's headquarters. Organises an extensive programme of events and professional training courses. Concerned with standards of competence, professional conduct and integrity in the design profession; the establishment of high standards in design education; and representation of the profession's interests in government and on official bodies. The Society's Code of Conduct is included in **Law and Regulations**.

**Chesterton Society, The** (1974), 179 Spring Lane, Hemel Hempstead, Herts HP1 3RD *tel* (0442) 61828. *Secretary:* P. M. S. Pinto. To promote interest in the life and work of Chesterton and those associated with him or influenced by his writings. *Subscription:* £10 p.a., includes journal *The Chesterton Review* (Q.) and newsletters.

**Children's Writers Group,** 84 Drayton Gardens, London SW10 9SB *tel* 01-373 6642. *Secretary:* Diana Shine. A subsidiary organisation for writers of children's books, who are members of the Society of Authors.

**Cinematograph, Television & Allied Technicians Writers' Section, Association of** (1946), 111 Wardour Street, London W1V 4AY *tel* 01-437 8506 *fax* 01-437 8268. *National Organiser:* Bob Hamilton; *General Secretary:* Alan Sapper. To defend the interests of writers in film, television and radio. By virtue of its industrial strength, ACTT is able to help its writer members to secure favourable terms and conditions. In cases of disputes with employers, ACTT can intervene in order to ensure an equitable settlement. Its specialised production agreement with the BFTPA lays down minimum terms for writers working in the documentary area.

**John Clare Society, The** (1981), Tudor Court, 86 Glinton Road, Helpston, Peterborough PE6 7DQ *tel* (0733) 252485. Promotes a wider appreciation of the life and works of the poet John Clare. *Subscription:* £5.00 p.a.

**Classical Association.** *Secretary (Branches):* Miss H. M. Jones, 20 Lowestoft Road, Watford WD2 5AX. *Secretary (Council):* Dr M. Schofield, St John's College, Cambridge CB2 1TP.

**William Cobbett Society, The** (1976), *Secretary:* R. F. Hatt, Combe Wood, Burnt Hill Way, Boundstone, Farnham, Surrey GU10 4RN    *tel* (0252) 3543. To make the life and work of William Cobbett better known. *Subscription:* £5.00 p.a.

**Comann Leabhraichean, An,** (Gaelic Books Council), (1968), Department of Celtic, University of Glasgow, Glasgow G12 8QQ    *tel* 041-339 8855, ext. 5190. *Chairman:* Professor Derick S. Thomson. Stimulates Scottish Gaelic publishing by awarding publication grants for new books, commissioning authors, setting literary competitions and providing editorial services and general assistance to writers and readers. Also publishes a catalogue of all Scottish Gaelic books in print and a magazine of book news. Runs a mobile bookselling service in the Highlands and Islands of Scotland and supports, and sometimes organises, literary evenings. Enquiries to the Editorial Officer.

**Comedy Writers Association of Great Britain** (1981), 24 Daresbury Road, Chorlton-cum-Hardy, Manchester M21 1WA    *tel* 061-881 9266. *Vice-Chairman:* John Brown. The aim of the association is to develop and promote comedy writing in a professional and friendly way. *Membership:* £30 p.a.

**Comics Enthusiasts, The Association of,** (1978). *Founder:* Denis Gifford, 80 Silverdale, Sydenham, London SE26 4SJ. A society for those interested in comics and strip cartoons from both the collecting and professional angles. *Comic Cuts,* the society's journal (8 p.a.). Annual membership £5; specimen issue £1.

**Commonwealth Press Union** (1909), Studio House, 184 Fleet Street, London EC4A 2DU    *tel* 01-242 1056    *telex* 936565 Cpulon    *fax* 01-831 4923. Organisation of newspapers, periodicals, news agencies throughout the Commonwealth.

**Composers' Guild of Great Britain, The,** 34 Hanway Street, London W1P 9DE    *tel* 01-436 0007. The Composers' Guild was created in June 1945 under the aegis of The Incorporated Society of Authors, Playwrights, and Composers. In 1948 it was formed into an independent body under the title of The Composers' Guild of Great Britain. Its function is to represent and protect the interests of composers of music in this country and to advise and assist its members on problems connected with their work. *Annual subscription:* £20.00, Associate membership £15.00. Further particulars obtained from the General Secretary of the Guild.

**Confédération Internationale des Sociétés d'Auteurs et Compositeurs,** 11 Rue Keppler, 75116 Paris, France    *tel* 47-20-59-37    *telex* 649940 Cisac F    *telegraphic address* Interauteurs, Paris.

**Joseph Conrad Society (U.K.), The** (1973). *Chairman:* Mrs. Juliet McLauchlan; *President:* Dr. Wit Tarnawski; *Vice-President:* Philip Conrad; *Secretaries:* S. Tyley and R. G. Hampson, The English Dept., Royal Holloway and Bedford New College, Egham Hill, Egham, Surrey TW20 0EX. Maintains close and friendly links with the Conrad family. Activities include an Annual Gathering, with lectures and discussions; publication of the *Conradian* and a series of pamphlets; and maintenance of a study centre in London.

**Contemporary Arts, Institute of,** The Mall, London SW1Y 5AH   *tel* 01-930 3647. A centre which aims at encouraging collaboration between the various arts, the promotion of experimental work and the mutual interchange of ideas. Exhibitions, theatre, music, dance, poetry, lectures, cinema and discussions, all play a part in the programme.

**Copyright Licensing Agency Ltd., The** (1983), 33-34 Alfred Place, London WC1E 7DP   *tel* 01-436 5931   *fax* 01-436 3986. *Secretary:* Colin P. Hadley. Formed by the Authors' Licensing & Collecting Society (ALCS) and the Publishers Licensing Society (PLS) in 1982, CLA administers collectively photocopying and other copying rights that it is uneconomic for writers and publishers to administer for themselves. The Agency issues collective and transactional licences, and the fees it collects, after the deduction of its administration costs, are distributed every six months to authors and publishers via their respective societies. Since 1987 CLA has distributed £2.47m. See article in **Copyright** section.

**Crime Writers' Association** (1953), P.O. Box 172, Tring, Herts HP23 5LP. For professional writers of crime novels, short stories, plays for stage, television and sound radio, or of serious works on crime. Associate membership open to publishers, journalists, booksellers specialising in crime literature. Publishes *Red Herrings* monthly.

**Critics' Circle, The** (1913). *President:* Rodney Milnes; *Vice-President:* William Hall; *Hon. General Secretary:* Peter Hepple, 47 Bermondsey Street, London SE1 3XT   *tel* 01-403 1818. *Objects:* To promote the art of criticism, to uphold its integrity in practice, to foster and safeguard the professional interests of its members, to provide opportunities for social intercourse among them, and to support the advancement of the arts. Membership is by invitation of the Council. Such invitations are issued only to persons engaged professionally, regularly and substantially in the writing or broadcasting of criticism of drama, music, films, or ballet.

**Cromwell Association, The** (1935), *Press Liaison Officer:* B. Denton, 10 Melrose Avenue, off Bants Lane, Northampton NN5 5PB   *tel* (0604) 582516. Encourages the study of Oliver Cromwell and his times, holds academic lectures and meetings, publishes annual journal *Cromwelliana*, erects memorials at Cromwellian sites. *Subscription:* £10.00 p.a.

**Cyngor Llyfrau Cymraeg—see Welsh Books Council.**

**De Vere Society, The** (1986), Hertford College, Oxford OX1 3BW   *tel* (0865) 242209. *Secretary:* John Considine. The aim of the society is to seek and, if possible, to establish the truth concerning the authorship of the Shakespeare plays and poems and, in addition, to promote research into the family of de Vere, Earls of Oxford. *Membership fee:* U.K. £10, U.S. $30.

**Design and Artists Copyright Society Ltd** (1983), St. Mary's Clergy House, 2 Whitechurch Lane, London E1 7QR   *tel* 01-247 1650   *fax* 01-377 5855. *Chief Executive:* Richard Curwen; *Administrator:* Janet Tod. For the protection of British artists copyright and collection of copyright dues in the U.K. and throughout the world. DACS is part of the international network of copyright collecting societies for artists, and a member of the British Copyright Council and of C.I.S.A.C. Membership of DACS is open to any visual artist: painter, sculptor, printmaker, photographer, designer, craftsperson, etc and also the estate of an artist for 50 years after the artist's death. *Joining fee:* £17.25.

**Dickens Fellowship** (1902), *Headquarters:* The Dickens House, 48 Doughty Street, London WC1N 2LF *tel* 01-405 2127. *Hon. Secretary:* Alan Watts. House occupied by Dickens 1837-9. Membership rates and particulars on application. Publication: *The Dickensian.*

**Dorman (Sean) Manuscript Society** (1957), 4 Union Place, Fowey, Cornwall PL23 1BY. For mutual help among part-time writers in England, Scotland and Wales only. Circulating manuscript parcels affording constructive criticism, with Remarks Book. Special circulator for advanced writers. Technical discussion circulators. *Subscription:* £3.50 p.a. (after initial six months' trial period at £1.50).

**Early English Text Society** (1864), St. Peter's College, Oxford OX1 2DL. *Hon. Director:* Professor John Burrow; *Executive Secretary:* T. F. Hoad. To bring unprinted early English literature within the reach of students in sound texts. *Annual subscription:* £15.00.

**Edinburgh Bibliographical Society** (1890), c/o New College Library, Edinburgh EH1 2LU *tel* 031-225 8400, ext. 256. *Secretary:* M. C. T. Simpson; *Treasurer:* E. D. Yeo.

**Educational Publishers Council,** see **Publishers Association.**

**Educational Writers Group,** 84 Drayton Gardens, London SW10 9SB *tel* 01-373 6642. A specialist unit within the membership of The Society of Authors.

**Eighteen Nineties Society, The,** 17 Merton Hall Road, Wimbledon, London SW19 3PP. *President:* Brian Reade. *Chairman:* C. C. Gould. *Secretary:* Dr. G. Krishnamurti. Founded in 1963 as The Francis Thompson Society, it widened its scope in 1972 to embrace the entire artistic and literary scene of the eighteen-ninety decade. Its activities include exhibitions, lectures, poetry readings. Publishes biographies of neglected authors and artists of the period; also check lists, bibliographies, etc. Its Journal appears periodically, and includes biographical, bibliographical and critical articles and book reviews. The Journal is free to members, and is not for public sale. All correspondence to the *Hon. Secretary,* 97-D Brixton Road, London SW9 6EE.

**George Eliot Fellowship, The** (1930). *President:* Jonathan G. Ouvry. *Secretary:* Mrs. K. M. Adams, 71 Stepping Stones Road, Coventry CV5 8JT *tel* (0203) 592231. Promotes an interest in the life and work of George Eliot and helps to extend her influence. Monthly meetings are arranged and an annual magazine is produced. *Annual subscription:* £6.00.

**English Association,** The Vicarage, Priory Gardens, Bedford Park, London W4 1TT *tel* 01-995 4236. *Chairman:* Professor Martin Dodsworth; *Secretary:* Dr. Ruth Fairbanks-Joseph.

**English Speaking Board (International), Ltd.,** 32 Norwood Avenue, Southport, Merseyside PR9 7EG *tel* (0704) 231366. *President:* Christabel Burniston, M.B.E.; *Chairman:* Arthur Ridings. *Aim:* to foster all activities concerned with English speech. The Board conducts examinations and training courses for teachers and students where stress is on individual oral expression. The examination auditions include talks, prepared and unprepared. Examinations are also held for those engaged in technical or industrial concerns, and for those using English as an acquired language. Three times a year, in January, May and September, members receive the English Speaking Board Journal, *Spoken English.* Articles are invited by the editor on any special aspect of spoken English. Members can also purchase other publications at reduced rates. Individual membership £10 per annum. Residential summer conference held annually, July-August. A.G.M. in London in the spring.

**Fabian Society,** 11 Dartmouth Street, London SW1H 9BN  *tel* 01-222 8877  *fax* 01-976 7153.

**Fantasy Society, The British** (1971), 15 Stanley Road, Morden, Surrey SM4 5DE. *President:* Ramsay Campbell. *Secretary:* Di Wathen. The Society was formed for devotees of fantasy, horror, and related fields, in literature, art and the cinema. Publications include *British Fantasy Newsletter* (Quarterly) featuring news and reviews and 24 annual booklets; *Dark Horizons*; *Winter Chills*, an all-fiction publication; *Masters of Fantasy* on individual authors; and *Mystique*, containing fiction. There is a small-press library and an annual convention and fantasy awards sponsored by the Society. Membership fees are £10 per annum.

**Fine Art Trade Guild, The** (1910) incorporating The Printsellers Association (1847), 16-18 Empress Place, London SW6 1TT  *tel* 01-381 6616. *Clerk of the Guild:* John D. Mountford. For the promotion and improvement of all aspects of the Fine Art Trade.

**Folklore Society, The** (1878), c/o University College, Gower Street, London WC1E 6BT  *tel* 01-387 5894. *Hon. Secretary:* Marion Bowman. Collection, recording and study of folklore.

**Foreign Press Association in London** (1888). *President:* Reiner Gatermann, *Secretary:* Davina Crole. *Registered Office:* 11 Carlton House Terrace, London SW1Y 5AJ  *tel* 01-930 0445 and 8883. *Objects:* The promotion of the professional interests of its members. Membership open to overseas professional journalists, men or women, residing in the United Kingdom. Entrance fee, £103.50; annual subscription, £80.50.

**FPS (Free Painters & Sculptors),** 15 Buckingham Gate, London SW1E 6LB. *Secretary:* Philip Worth. *Trends* open bi-annual London Exhibition. Provincial Exhibitions for Members. Exhibits the work of progressive-minded artists, irrespective of their differing points of view; to provide opportunities for members to meet and discuss their work. Loggia Gallery and Sculpture Garden available for members to exhibit  *tel* 01-828 5963. (Weekdays 6-8 p.m., Sat. and Sun. 2-6 p.m.)

**Freelance Photographers, Bureau of** (1965), Focus House, 497 Green Lanes, London N13 4BP  *tel* 01-882 3315. *Head of Administration:* John Tracy. To help the freelance photographer by providing information on markets, and free advisory service. Membership fee £28.00 per annum.

**Gaelic Books Council—see Comann Leabhraichean, An**

**Gay Authors Workshop** (1978), Kathryn Byrd,BM Box 5700, London WC1N 3XX. To encourage writers who are lesbian or gay. Anthology in preparation. Quarterly newsletter. Membership £4.00; unwaged £2.00.

**Ghost Story Society, The** (1988), 2 Looe Road, Croxteth, Liverpool L11 6LJ  *tel* 051-546 2287. *Secretary:* Jeffrey A. Dempsey. Devoted mainly to supernatural fiction in the literary tradition of M. R. James, Walter de la Mare, Arthur Machen, Algernon Blackwood, etc. Thrice-yearly newsletter and annual journal, *All Hallows*. *Membership:* £5 (£6/$12 overseas).

**Graphic Fine Art, Society of** (1919), 9 Newburgh Street, London W1V 1LH. *President:* Mrs Lorna B. Kell. A fine art society holding an annual open exhibition. Criterion for membership is good drawing: drawings, line and wash, water colours and any of the forms of print making.

**Greeting Card and Calendar Association, The,** 6 Wimpole Street, London W1M 8AS  *tel* 01-637 7692  *telex* 21201  *fax* 01-436 3137. Publishes *Greetings* bi-monthly.

**Hakluyt Society** (1846), c/o The Map Library, The British Library, Great Russell Street, London WC1B 3DG  *tel* 025-125 4207. *President:* Sir Harold Smedley, K.C.M.G., M.B.E.; *Hon. Secretaries:* Mrs. Sarah Tyacke and T. E. Armstrong, M.A., PH.D. Publication of original narratives of voyages, travels, naval expeditions, and other geographical records.

**Thomas Hardy Society Ltd., The** (1967). *Secretary:* Mrs Kate N. Fowler, Park Farm, Tolpuddle, Dorchester, Dorset DT2 7HG  *tel* Puddletown (0305) 848651. *Subscription:* £9.00 (£12.00 overseas) p.a. Publishes *The Thomas Hardy Journal* (3 p.a.)

**Harleian Society** (1869), College of Arms, Queen Victoria Street, London EC4V 4BT. *Chairman:* J. Brooke-Little, C.V.O., M.A., F.S.A., Norroy and Ulster King of Arms. *Secretary:* P. Ll. Gwynn-Jones, M.A. Lancaster Herald of Arms. Instituted for transcribing, printing and publishing the heraldic visitations of Counties, Parish Registers and any manuscripts relating to genealogy, family history and heraldry.

**Heraldic Arts, Society of** (1987), 46 Reigate Road, Reigate, Surrey RH2 0QN  *tel* (0737) 242945. *Secretary:* John Ferguson, A.R.C.A., S.H.A., F.R.S.A. The objectives of the society are to serve the interests of heraldic artists, craftsmen, designers and writers, to provide a 'shop window' for their work, to obtain commissions on their behalf and to act as a forum for the exchange of information and ideas. The society also offers an information service to the public. Candidates for admission as members should be artists or craftsmen whose work comprises a substantial element of heraldry and is of a sufficiently high standard to satisfy the requirements of the society's advisory council. Associate membership is also available. *Membership:* £15 p.a.

**Sherlock Holmes Society of London, The** (1951). *President:* Frank A. Allen, F.P.S.; *Chairman:* Anthony D. Howlett, M.A., LL.B.; *Hon. Secretary:* Cdr. G. S. Stavert, M.B.E., M.A., R.N. (ret'd), 3 Outram Road, Southsea, Hants PO5 1QP  *tel* (0705) 812104. *Objects:* to bring together those who have a common interest as readers and students of the literature of Sherlock Holmes; to encourage the pursuit of knowledge of the public and private lives of Sherlock Holmes and Dr. Watson; to organize meetings and lectures for the discussion of these topics; to co-operate with other bodies at home and abroad that are in sympathy with the aims and activities of the Society. *Subscription,* including two issues of *The Sherlock Holmes Journal:* £9.00 p.a. within 50 miles of Baker Street, £7.50 p.a. outside this radius, overseas £9.00 or $20.00.

**Home Affairs Council** see **Publishers Association**.

**Hesketh Hubbard Art Society,** 17 Carlton House Terrace, London SW1Y 5BD  *tel* 01-930 6844. *President:* Dorothy King. Weekly drawing workshops open to all.

**Illustrators, The Association of** (1973), 1 Colville Place, London W1P 1HN  *tel* 01-636 4100. To further and promote better relationships between illustrators, agents and clients which will result in the raising of standards and through which individual illustrators can support the common good of illustrators as a whole. Gallery space available for hire. Membership open to all involved with illustration.

**Illustrators, Society of Architectural and Industrial** (1975), P.O. Box 22, Stroud, Gloucestershire GL5 3DH *tel* Brimscombe (0453) 882563. *Administrator:* Eric Monk. A professional body to represent all who practise architectural, industrial and technical illustration, including the related fields of model making and photography.

**Independent Literary Agents Association, Inc.**, c/o Ellen Levine Literary Agency, 432 Park Avenue South, Suite 1205, New York, N.Y. 10016 *tel* 212-899 0620.

**Independent Producers, The Association of** (1976), 17 Great Pulteney Street, London W1R 3DG *tel* 01-434 0181 *fax* 01-437 0086. *Chair:* Rosie Bunting; *Director:* Jane Williams. To encourage production of films and to broaden the base of finance and exhibition beyond that which is currently available for film-makers in the U.K. Membership is open to anyone active in the film and television industries. Information service, seminars, production workshops, producer magazine, annual handbook.

**Independent Programme Producers Association** (IPPA), 50-51 Berwick Street, London W1V 4RD *tel* 01-439 7034 *fax* 01-494 2700. *Contacts:* Paul Styles (Director)/John Woodward (Deputy Director). The trade association for British independent television producers. Services to members include an industrial relations unit (with the BFTPA), model contracts, publication of a regular journal and international directory, a seminar programme, negotiating and sponsorship advice services, a European producers' network, plus links with Commonwealth countries, and advice on all matters relating to independent production for television and satellite. IPPA has established trading guidelines with the BBC and ITV similiar to those previously agreed with Channel 4 and maintains an active lobby to ensure that the needs of the sector are heard by broadcasters and government.

**Independent Publishers Guild** (1962), 147-149 Gloucester Terrace, London W2 6DX *tel* 01-723 7328. Membership is open to publishing companies and packagers, associate membership to companies or individuals who have not yet published three books and supplier membership to companies or individuals (but not printers or binders) who are specialists in fields allied to publishing. Offers a forum for the exchange of ideas and information and represents the interests of its members. £30 or £35 p.a.

**Indexers, Society of.** Objects: (1) to improve the standard of indexing; (2) to maintain a Register of Indexers (for details see article: **Indexing**); (3) to act as an advisory body on the qualifications and remuneration of indexers; (4) to publish or communicate books, papers and notes on the subject of indexing; (5) to raise the status of indexers and to safeguard their interests; (6) to publish and run an open-learning indexing course, 'Training in Indexing'. Membership is open to those who are interested in indexing and all aspects of information retrieval. There is no entrance fee. *Annual Subscription:* £15.00. Copies of the Society's journal, *The Indexer*, are sent free to members. *Secretary:* Mrs H. C. Troughton, 16 Green Road, Birchington, Kent CT7 9JZ *tel* (0843) 41115.

**Indian Publishers', The Federation of,** Federation House, 18/1-C Institutional Area, J.N.U Road, New Delhi 110067 *tel* 654847.

**International Amateur Theatre Association,** *Secretariat:* 19 Abbey Park Road, Grimbsy DN32 0HJ *tel* (0472) 43424. To encourage, foster and promote exchanges of theatre; student, educational, adult, puppet theatre activities at international level. To organise international seminars, workshops, courses and conferences, and to collect and collate information of all types for international dissemination, and within the United Kingdom.

**International Songwriters & Composers, The Society of,** (1936), 12 Trewartha Road, Praa Sands, Penzance, Cornwall TR20 9ST *tel* (0736) 762826. *Secretary:* Carole Ann Jones. Gives advice to members on contractual and copyright matters; assists with protection of members rights; assists with analysis of members works; international collaboration register free to members; outlines requirements to record companies, publishers, artists. *Subscription:* £15 p.a. UK, £18 p.a. EEC, £20 p.a. overseas. Publishers of quarterly magazine, *Songwriting & Composing*.

**Irish Book Publishers Association,** Book House Ireland, 65 Middle Abbey Street, Dublin 1 *tel* 730108. *President:* Steve MacDonogh. *Administrator:* Cecily Golden.

**Irish Composers, Association of** (1969), Liberty Hall, Room 804, Dublin 1 *tel* 740070. *Secretary:* Fergus Johnston. To protect the rights of Irish composers and to foster and promote the writing of contemporary music in Ireland. *Annual subscription:* IR£15.

**Irish Playwrights, Society of** (1969), Liberty Hall, Room 804, Dublin 1 *tel* 740070. *Secretary:* Patricia Martin. To safeguard the rights of Irish playwrights and to foster and promote Irish playwriting. *Annual subscription:* IR£15.

**Richard Jefferies Society, The** (1950), 45 Kemerton Walk, Swindon, Wilts SN3 2EA *tel* (0793) 21512. *President:* Prof. W. J. Keith (Toronto). *Hon. Secretary:* Cyril Wright. Promotes interest in the life, works and associations of Richard Jefferies; helps to preserve buildings and memorials, and co-operates in the development of a Museum in his birthplace. Provides a service to students, lecturers, readers and writers. The Society arranges regular meetings in Swindon, and occasionally elsewhere. Outings and displays are organised. The membership is worldwide. *Annual subscription:* £3.00.

**Johnson Society, The,** Johnson Birthplace Museum, Breadmarket Street, Lichfield, Staffordshire WS13 6LG *tel* (0543) 264972. *Hon General Secretary:* Patricia A. Wilmot. To encourage the study of the life and works of Dr. Samuel Johnson; to preserve the memorials, associations, books, manuscripts, letters of Dr. Johnson and his contemporaries; preservation of his birthplace.

**Johnson Society of London** (1928). *President:* The Revd Dr. E. F. Carpenter, K.C.V.O.; *Secretary:* Miss Stella Pigrome, Round Chimney, Playden, Rye, East Sussex TN31 7UR *tel* Iden (079 78) 252. To study the life and works of Doctor Johnson, and to perpetuate his memory in the city of his adoption.

**Journalists, The Institute of,** Chris Underwood, F.J.I., Bill Todd, F.J.I. (*Joint General Secretaries*), Unit 2, Dock Offices, Surrey Quays Road, London SE16 2XL *tel* 01-252 1187 *fax* 232 2302. The senior organisation of the profession, founded in 1884 and incorporated by Royal Charter 1890. Men and women are equally eligible for Fellowship (F.J.I.) and Membership (M.J.I.). The Institute maintains an Employment Register and has accumulated funds for the assistance of members; offers free legal advice to members in matters relating to their professional activities and employment. A Free-lance Division links editors and publishers with free-lances. A directory and panel of free-lance writers on special subjects are available for the use of editorial publishers. There are also Special Sections for public relations officers, broadcasters, travel writers and motoring correspondents. Occasional contributors to the press may be eligible for election as Affiliates. Certificated as an independent trade union. *Subscriptions:* related to earnings, maximum £135.00; Affiliate £68.00.

**Keats-Shelley Memorial Association** (1903). *Chairman:* The Countess of Birkenhead; *Patron:* H.M. Queen Elizabeth the Queen Mother. *Hon. Secretary:* Leonora Collins, Flat 1, 33 Aberdeen Road, London N5 2UG   *tel* 01-354 3874. Occasional meetings; annual *Review* and progress reports. Supports house in Rome where John Keats died, and celebrates the poets Keats, Shelley, Byron, and Leigh Hunt. Subscription to "Friends of the Keats-Shelley Memorial," minimum £5.00 per annum.

**Kent and Sussex Poetry Society,** centre Tunbridge Wells, formed in 1946 to create a greater interest in Poetry. *President:* Laurence Lerner; *Chairman:* Isa Weidman; *Hon. Secretary:* Madeline Munro, Pendips, Furzefield Avenue, Speldhurst, Tunbridge Wells, Kent TN3 0LD   *tel* (0892) 863275. *Annual Subscription:* adults, £4.00; country members £2.00; students, £1.00. Well-known poets address the society, a Folio of members' work is produced and a full programme of recitals, discussions and readings is provided.

**Kipling Society, The,** *Hon. Secretary:* Norman Entract, 18 Northumberland Avenue, London WC2N 5BJ   *tel* 01-930 6733. *Aims:* To honour and extend the influence of Kipling, to assist in the study of Kipling's writings, to hold discussion-meetings, to publish a quarterly journal and to maintain a Kipling Reference Library. Membership details on application.

**Lancashire Authors' Association, The** (1909), "for writers or lovers of Lancashire literature and history." *President:* G. A. Wormleighton, M.B.E., F.C.A.; *General Secretary:* J. D. Cameron, M.B.E., Kings Fold, Pope Lane, Penwortham, Preston PR1 9JN   *tel* (0772) 742236. *Subscription:* £5.00 p.a. Publishes *The Record* (Q.).

**Lancashire Dialect Society, The** (1951). *Secretary:* Peter Wright, 30 Broadoak Road, Stockport, Cheshire SK7 3BL. Fosters the study of Northern dialects and their preservation in speech and writing. *Annual subscription:* £3.00. Journal and Newsletter published annually.

**Learned and Professional Society Publishers, The Association of** (1972). Aims to promote and develop the publishing activities of learned and professional organisations which produce journals and other publications. Membership is open to professional and learned societies and to individuals with publishing interests: details are available from the Secretary, Professor B. T. Donovan, 48 Kelsey Lane, Beckenham, Kent BR3 3NE   *tel* 01-658 0459.

**Library Association,** 7 Ridgmount Street, London WC1E 7AE   *tel* 01-636 7543   *telex* 21897 Laldn G   *fax* 01-436 7218. *President:* A. G. D. White, F.L.A., M.B.I.M.; *Chief Executive:* G. Cunningham, B.A., B.SC.(ECON). Founded in 1877 to promote bibliographical study and research and the better administration of libraries, and to unite all persons interested in library work. Conferences and meetings are held, publications issued and a library and information department maintained. The monthly journal,

*The Library Association Record*, is distributed free to all members. Subscription varies according to income.

**Limners, The Society of** (1986), 2 Glentrammon Close, Green Street Green, Orpington, Kent BR6 6DL   *tel* (0689) 51158. *Founder/President:* Elizabeth Davys Wood, P.S.L.M., S.W.A. The aim of the society is to promote an interest in miniature painting (in any medium), calligraphy and heraldry and encourage their development to a high standard. New members are elected after the submission of four works of acceptable standard and guidelines are provided for new artists. Members receive four newsletters a year and an annual exhibition is arranged. *Membership:* £10.

**Linguists, Institute of,** 24A Highbury Grove, London N5 2EA   *tel* 01-359 7445   *fax* 01-354 0202. To provide language qualifications. To encourage Government and industry to develop the use of modern languages and encourage recognition of the status of professional linguists in all occupations. To promote the exchange and dissemination of information on matters of concern to linguists.

**Literary Societies, Alliance of.** *Secretary:* H. W. Woodward, c/o Birmingham and Midland Institute, Margaret Street, Birmingham B3 3BS   *tel* 021-236 3591. An informal alliance of a number of Literary Societies formed to give mutual help in preserving particularly properties with literary associations.

**Literature, Royal Society of** (1823), 1 Hyde Park Gardens, London W2 2LT   *tel* 01-723 5104. Fellows and Members. Men and women. *Chairman of Council:* John Mortimer, Q.C., C.B.E., F.R.S.L.; *Secretary:* Mrs. P.M. Schute. For the advancement of literature by the holding of lectures, discussions, readings, and by publications. Administrators of the Dr. Richards' Fund and the Royal Society of Literature Award, under the W.H. Heinemann Bequest and the Winifred Holtby Memorial Prize.

**Little Presses, Association of** (1966), 89A Petherton Road, London N5 2QT   *tel* 01-226 2657. *Co-ordinator:* Bob Cobbing. A loosely knit association of individuals running little presses who have grouped together for mutual self-help, while retaining their right to operate autonomously. Membership fee: £7.50 p.a. Publications include: *Poetry and Little Press Information, Catalogue of Little Press Books in Print, Getting Your Poetry Published.*

**Little Theatre Guild of Great Britain.** *Secretary:* Ann Mattey, Flat 6, 34 Broadwater Down, Tunbridge Wells, Kent KT1 5NX   *tel* (0892) 34710. To promote close co-operation between Little Theatres, to maintain and further the highest standards in the art of theatre. Membership is confined to independent play producing organisations which control their own established theatres.

**Arthur Machen Society, The** (1986), 19 Cross Street, Caerleon, Gwent NP6 1AF   *tel* (0633) 422520. *Secretary:* Rita Tait. To honour the life and work of Arthur Machen. Provides a forum for the exchange of ideas and information and aims to bring Machen's work before a new generation of readers. Publishes twice-yearly journal *Avallaunius. Annual subscription:* £10.00; £15.00 libraries. Overseas, please enquire.

**Marine Artists, Royal Society of,** 17 Carlton House Terrace, London SW1Y 5BD   *tel* 01-930 6844. *President:* Terence Storey. To promote and encourage marine painting. Open Annual Exhibition.

**Master Photographers Association,** TMT House, 1 West Ruislip Station, Ickenham Road, Ruislip, Middlesex HA4 7DW   *tel* Ruislip 630876   *telex* 884

389 (TMTCo) *fax* (0895) 631219. To promote and protect professional photographers. *Subscription:* £57.89 a year. Members can qualify for awards of Licentiateship, Associateship and Fellowship.

**Mechanical-Copyright Protection Society Ltd. (MCPS),** Elgar House, 41 Streatham High Road, London SW16 1ER *tel* 01-769 4400 *telex* 946792 MCPS G *fax* 01-769 8792. *Managing Director:* R. W. Montgomery. See article in **Copyright** section.

**Media Society, The** (1973), *Secretary:* RodneyBennett-England, Church Cottage, East Rudham, Norfolk PE31 8QZ *tel* (048 522) 664. To promote and encourage independent research into the standards, performance, organisation and economics of the media and hold regular discussions, debates, etc. on subjects of topical interest and concern to print and broadcast journalists. *Subscriptions:* £15.00 p.a.

**Medical Journalists Association** (1966), 14 Hovendens, Sissinghurst, Kent TN17 2LA *tel* (0580) 713920. Formed by doctor-writers and journalist/ broadcasters specialising in medicine and the health services. Aims to improve the quality and practice of medical journalism. Administers major awards for medical journalism and broadcasting. £20.00 p.a. *Chairman:* Alan Massam. *Hon. Secretary:* Tony Thistlethwaite.

**Medical Writers Group,** 84 Drayton Gardens, London SW10 9SB *tel* 01-373 6642. *Secretary:* Jacqueline Granger-Taylor. A specialist unit within the membership of the Society of Authors.

**Miniature Painters, Sculptors and Gravers, Royal Society of** (1895), Westminster Gallery, Westminster Central Hall, London SW1H 9NH. *President:* Suzanne Lucas *tel* (0747) 860 311. Secretary: Pauline Gyles. Open Annual Exhibition: November.

**Miniaturists, The Hilliard Society of,** (1982), 15 Union Street, Wells, Somerset BA5 2PU *tel* (0749) 74472. *Secretary:* Mrs. S. M. Burton. To promote the art of miniature painting; annual exhibition and dinner; exchanges views through half-yearly newsletters; puts patrons in touch with artists.

**Miniaturists, Society of** (1895), *Director:* Leslie Simpson, Ralston House, 41 Lister Street, Riverside Gardens, Ilkley, West Yorkshire LS29 9ET *tel* (0943) 609075.

**William Morris Society** (1955), Kelmscott House, 26 Upper Mall, London W6 9TA *tel* 01-741 3735. *Secretary:* Peter Preston. To spread knowledge of the life, work and ideas of William Morris. Publishes a *Newsletter* (Q.), and a *Journal* (2 p.a.). Library and collections by appointment.

**Motoring Writers, The Guild of,** 2 Pembroke Villas, The Green, Richmond, Surrey TW9 1QF *tel* 01-940 6974. *Chief Executive:* Jean Peters. To raise the standard of motoring journalism. For writers, broadcasters, photographers on matters of motoring, but who are not connected with the motor industry.

**Music Publishers Association Ltd.** (1881), 7th Floor, Kingsway House, 103 Kingsway, London WC2B 6QX *tel* 01-831 7591 *fax* 01-242 0612. *Secretary:* P. J. Dadswell. The only trade organisation representing the U.K. music publishing industry; protects and promotes its members' interests in copyright, trade and related matters. A number of sub-committees and groups deal with particular interests. Details of subscriptions available on written request.

**Musical Association, The Royal,** Peter Owens, 135 Purves Road, London NW10 5TH  *tel* 01-960 5239.

**Musicians, Incorporated Society of,** 10 Stratford Place, London W1N 9AE  *tel* 01-629 4413. *President:* 1989: William Mathias, c.b.e.; *General Secretary:* David Padgett-Chandler. Representative body of professional musicians; its objects are the promotion of the art of music and maintenance of the honour and interests of the musical profession. *Subscription:* £52.00 p.a.

**Name Studies in Great Britain and Ireland, Council for,** *Chairman:* R. A. McKinley; *Hon. Secretary:* Miss Jennifer Scherr, 21 Caledonia Place, Bristol BS8 4DL. The advancement, promotion and support of research into the place-names and personal names of Great Britain and Ireland and related regions in respect of, i) the collection, documentation, and interpretation of such names, ii) the publication of the material and the results of such research, iii) the exchange of information between the various regions. Acts as a consultative body on Name Studies. Membership consists of representatives from relevant British and Irish organisations and a number of individual scholars elected by Council and usually domiciled in one of the relevant countries. Membership is by invitation, and members pay a small annual subscription. Publishes an annual newsletter, *Nomina*, which includes news of research in progress, publications, courses in name studies, reviews, short articles, notes and queries; edited by Dr. Alexander Rumble, Dept. of Palaeography, University of Manchester, Oxford Road, Manchester M13 9PL.

**National Graphical Association—see NGA 1982**

**National Poetry Foundation** (1981), 27 Mill Road, Fareham, Hants PO16 0TH  *tel* (0329) 822218. The aim of the foundation is to provide a truly national poetry organisation which in turn provides a worthwhile appraisal system, advice and information, magazine and discussion documents, all for a single low-cost fee, and to help poets have a book of their own poetry published at no additional cost, once they have sufficient poetry of a high enough standard.

**National Society of Painters, Sculptors & Printmakers** (1930), 122 Copse Hill, Wimbledon, London SW20 0NL. *President:* Denis Baxter. An annual exhibition representing all aspects of art for artists of every creed and outlook.

**National Union of Journalists.** Head Office: Acorn House, 314 Gray's Inn Road, London WC1X 8DP  *tel* 01-278 7916  *telex* 892384  *fax* 01-837 8143. A trade union for working journalists with 32,206 members and 176 branches throughout the U.K. and the Republic of Ireland, and in Paris, Brussels and Geneva. Its wages and conditions agreements cover the whole of the newspaper press, news agencies and broadcasting, the major part of periodical and book publishing, and a number of public relations departments and consultancies, information services and Prestel-Viewdata services. Administers disputes, unemployment, benevolent, and provident benefits. Official publications: *The Journalist, Freelance Directory, Freelance Fees Guide* and policy pamphlets.

**New English Art Club,** 17 Carlton House Terrace, London SW1Y 5BD  *tel* 01-930 6844. *Hon. Secretary:* William Bowyer, r.a., r.w.s., r.p. For persons interested in the art of painting, and the promotion of fine arts. Open Annual Exhibition at Mall Galleries.

**New Zealand Book Marketing Council,** Box 40086, Glenfield, Auckland    *tel* 444-7197. *Chairman:* L. Earney.

**New Zealand, Book Publishers Association of, Inc.,** Box 44146, Point Chevalier, Auckland 2    *tel* 892-533    *fax* ·Auckland 867369. *Director:* Gerard Reid; *President:* Bob Ross.

**New Zealand Copyright Council Inc.,** P.O. Box 5028, Wellington    *tel* 724430. *Chairman:* Bernard Darby. *Secretary:* Tony Chance.

**Newspaper Press Fund,** Dickens House, 35 Wathen Road, Dorking, Surrey RH4 1JY    *tel* Dorking (0306) 887511. *Secretary:* P.W. Evans. For the relief of hardship amongst member journalists, their widows, and dependants. Limited help is available for non-member journalists and their dependants.

**Newspaper Publishers Association, Ltd., The,** 34 Southwark Bridge Road, London SE1 9EU    *tel* 01-928 6928    *fax* 01-401 2428.

**Newspaper Society,** Bloomsbury House, Bloomsbury Square, 74-77 Great Russell Street, London WC1B 3DA    *tel* 01-636 7014. *Director:* Dugal Nisbet-Smith; *Secretary:* C. Gordon Page, A.C.I.S.

**NGA 1982,** National Graphical Association, Graphic House, 63-67 Bromham Road, Bedford MK40 2AG    *tel* (0234) 51521    *fax* 0234-270580.

**Painter-Etchers and Engravers, Royal Society of** (1880), Bankside Gallery, 48 Hopton Street, London SE1 9JH    *tel* 01-928 7521. *President:* H.N. Eccleston, O.B.E., R.W.S.. *Secretary:* Michael Spender. Spring Exhibition open to non-members; Autumn Exhibition for members only. Friends of the RE open to all those interested in artists' original printmaking. Particulars from the Secretary.

**Painters in Oils, Pastels and Acrylics, British Society of** (1988), Ralston House, 41 Lister Street, Riverside Gardens, Ilkley, W. Yorkshire LS29 9ET    *tel* (0943) 609075. *Director:* Leslie Simpson, F.R.S.A. The society promotes interest and encourages high quality in the work of painters in these media. Exhibitions open to all artists. *Membership:* £25.

**Painters in Water Colours, Royal Institute of** (1831), 17 Carlton House Terrace, London SW1Y 5BD    *tel* 01-930 6844. *President:* Ronald Maddox, F.C.S.D. Membership (R.I.) open to all. Annual Exhibition open to all artists.

**Pastel Society, The** (1899), 17 Carlton House Terrace, London SW1Y 5BD    *tel* 01-930 6844. *President:* John Blockley. Membership open to all. Pastel and drawings in pencil or chalk. Annual Exhibition open to all artists working in dry media.

**Mervyn Peake Society, The** (1975). *Hon. President:* Sebastian Peake; *Chairman:* John Watney; *Secretary:* Frank Surry, The Studio, 43 Bond Street, Ealing, London W5 5AS. Devoted to recording the life and works of Mervyn Peake. Publishes a journal and news letter. *Annual subscription:* £10 (U.K. and Europe): £8 for students; £12 all other countries.

**P.E.N., International.** A world association of writers. *International President:* Francis King, C.B.E. *International Secretary:* Alexandre Blokh, 38 King Street, London WC2E 8JT    *tel* 01-379 7939    *cables* Lonpenclub, London, WC2. *President of English Centre:* Lady Antonia Fraser. *General Secretary of English Centre:* Josephine Pullein-Thompson, M.B.E., 7 Dilke Street, London SW3 4JE    *tel* 01-352 6303.

   P.E.N. was founded in 1921 by C.A. Dawson Scott under the presidency of John Galsworthy, to promote friendship and understanding between writers and defend freedom of expression within and between all nations.

The initials P.E.N. stand for Poets, Playwrights, Editors, Essayists, Novelists—but membership is open to all writers of standing (including translators), whether men or women, without distinction of creed or race, who subscribe to these fundamental principles. P.E.N. takes no part in state or party politics; it has given care to, and raised funds for, refugee writers, and also administers the P.E.N. Writers In Prison Committee which works on behalf of writers imprisoned for exercising their right to freedom of expression, a right implicit in the P.E.N. Charter to which all members subscribe. The Translations Committee strives to promote the translations of works by writers in the lesser-known languages. International Congresses are held most years. The 50th Congress was held in Lugano in May 1987, and the 51st in Puerto Rico in December 1987.

Membership of the English Centre is £16.00 per annum for country members, £20.00 for London members. Associate membership is available for writers not yet eligible for full membership and persons connected with literature. Membership of any one Centre implies membership of all Centres, at present 86 autonomous Centres exist throughout the world. The English Centre has a programme of literary lectures, discussion, dinners and parties. A yearly *Writers' Day* is open to the public.

*Publications: The Pen* (English P.E.N. broadsheet); P.E.N. International (bi-lingual, Fr.-Eng., reviews of books in languages of limited currency; sponsored by UNESCO); *The Survival and Encouragement of Literature in Present Day Society* (Archive Press) 1979; News Bulletins published by various Centres; English Centre edited a series of annual anthologies of contemporary poetry; *New Poems*—1952-62; from 1965 the volume appeared biennially and from 1972 to 1977 annually. From 1978 to 1983 PEN and the Arts Council and Hutchinson combined to publish *New Poetry* and *New Stories* annually. From 1984, in partnership with Quartet Books, the English Centre publish prose and poetry anthologies, *P.E.N. New Fiction* and *P.E.N. New Poetry*, in alternate years.

**Penman Club, The,** 175 Pall Mall, Leigh-on-Sea, Essex SS9 1RE *tel* Southend 74438. *President:* Trevor J. Douglas. *General Secretary:* Leonard G. Stubbs, F.R.S.A. Literary Society for writers throughout the world, published and unpublished. Members in almost every country. Benefits of membership include criticism of all MSS. without additional charge. Marketing and general literary advice, also use of large writers' library. *Subscription:* £5.25 p.a. S.A.E. for Prospectus from the General Secretary.

**Performing Right Society, Ltd.** (1914), 29-33 Berners Street, London W1P 4AA *tel* 01-580 5544 *fax* 01-631 4138. See article in **Copyright** section.

**Periodical Publishers Association,** Imperial House, 15-19 Kingsway, London WC2B 6UN *tel* 01-379 6268. *Chief Executive:* Ian Locks.

**Personal Managers' Association, Ltd., The,** *Liaison Secretary:* Angela Adler, 1 Summer Road, East Molesey, Surrey KT8 9LX *tel* 01-398 9796. An association of Personal Managers in the theatre, film and entertainment world generally.

**Photographic Society, The Royal** (1853), The RPS National Centre of Photography, The Octagon, Milsom Street, Bath BA1 1DN *tel* (0225) 462841. Aims to promote the general advancement of photography and its applications. Publish *The Photographic Journal* monthly, £45.00 p.a., overseas £50.00 p.a. and *The Journal of Photographic Science,* bi-monthly £70.00 p.a., overseas £80.00.

**Playwrights Trust, New,** Whitechapel Library, 77 Whitechapel High Street, London E1 7OX *tel* 01-377 5429. *Director:* Susan Croft. Support and development organisation for playwrights and aspiring playwrights, and those interested in developing and producing new work. Services include script-reading. Workshops, writer/company Link Service. Issues *Newsletter* monthly and *Script Bulletin* bi-monthly. *Subscriptions:* £12.00 (waged), £6 (unwaged); £15.00 community organisations; £30.00 funded and commercial organisations.

**Playwrights Workshop** (1949). A meeting place where those people in the Manchester area interested in drama can meet to discuss playwriting in general and their own plays in particular. Details of places and times of meetings from *Hon. Secretary:* Robert Coupland, 22 Brown Street, Altrincham, Cheshire WA14 2EU *tel* 061-928 3095.

**Poetry Society, The** (1909) Incorporated, 21 Earls Court Square, London SW5 9DE *tel* 01-373 7861 and 2551. *Chairman:* Alan Brownjohn; *Director* and *General Secretary:* Belinda Walker; *Treasurer:* John Cotton. The Society is a national body entirely devoted to the encouragement of the art. It publishes *Poetry Review* quarterly, runs poetry readings, children's events, verse-speaking examinations and administers various prizes and competitions. It incorporates the National Poetry Secretariat which sponsors poetry readings. It houses a poetry bookshop.

**Portrait Painters, Royal Society of** (1891), 17 Carlton House Terrace, London SW1Y 5BD *tel* 01-930 6844. *President:* David Poole. Annual Exhibition when work may be submitted by non-members with a view to exhibition.

**Beatrix Potter Society** (1980), *Chairman:* Christopher Hanson-Smith; *Secretary:* Brian Riddle, 24 Warren Road, Wanstead, London E11 2NA. To promote the study and appreciation of the life and works of Beatrix Potter as author, artist, diarist, farmer and conservationist. *Subscription:* U.K. £5.00, overseas £12.00.

**Press Council, The** (1953), Independent. *Chairman:* Louis Blom-Cooper, Q.C.; *Director:* Kenneth Morgan, O.B.E., 1 Salisbury Square, London EC4Y 8AE *tel* 01-353 1248.

**Private Libraries Association** (1956), Ravelston, South View Road, Pinner, Middlesex HA5 3YD. *President:* Peter Eaton; *Hon. Editor:* David Chambers; *Hon. Secretary:* Frank Broomhead. *Subscriptions:* £16.00 per annum. International society of book collectors and private libraries. Publications include the quarterly *Private Library*, annual *Private Press Books*, and other books on book collecting.

**Publishers Association,** 19 Bedford Square, London WC1B 3HJ. Established 1896 *tel* 01-580 6321-5 and 7761; 323 1548 *telex* 267160 Pubass G *fax* 01-636 5375. *Chief Executive:* Clive Bradley; *Director of Administration:* Philip Flamank; *Director of Market Development:* Tony Read; *Director of Educational and Professional Publishing:* John Davies. Association of British publishers whose over-all membership represents some 258 members (embracing 600 companies, starred in the list of British Publishers given earlier in this book).

**Publishers Licensing Society Limited** (1981), 33–34 Alfred Place, London WC1E 7DP *tel* 01-436 5931 *fax* 01-436 3986. *Secretary:* Gervase E. Muller, Turpin Transactions Ltd., The Distribution Centre, Blackhorse Road, Letchworth, Herts, SG6 1HN *tel* (0462) 672555. The aims of the society are to exercise and enforce on behalf of publishers the rights of copyright and other rights of a similar nature, to authorise the granting of licences for, *inter alia*, the making of reprographic copies of copyright works, and to receive and distribute to the relevant publisher copyright proprietors the sums accruing from such licensed use.

**Radclyffe International Philosophical Association, The** (1955), BM-RIPhA, Old Gloucester Street, London WC1N 3XX. *President:* William Mann, F.R.I.Ph.A., *Secretary General:* John Khasseyan, F.R.I.Ph.A. *Objects:* To dignify those achievements which might otherwise escape formal recognition; to promote the interests and talent of its members; to encourage their good fellowship and to form a medium of exchange of ideas between members. *Entrance fee:* £10.00. *Subscription:* £15.00 (Fellows, Members and Associates). Published authors and artists usually enter at Fellowship level.

**Railway Artists, Guild of,** (1979). *Hon. Administrator:* F. P. Hodges, 45 Dickins Road, Warwick CV34 5NS *tel* (0926) 499246. To forge a link between artists depicting railway subjects and to give members a corporate identity; also stages railway art exhibitions.

**Regional Arts Associations.** RAAs are funded by the Arts Council, British Film Institute, Crafts Council and their constituent local authorities, as well as educational and private sources. They exist to promote and develop the arts in their regions.

With their grasp of regional needs and demands they are well equipped to provide a service of information, help and guidance to all kinds of arts organisations in their area, and in many cases can provide financial assistance. They can take the initiative in promoting activities themselves and in planning and co-ordinating regional tours.

Representatives of all the associations meet as the Council of Regional Arts Associations (CORAA), Litton Lodge, 13A Clifton Road, Winchester, Hampshire SO22 5BP *tel* (0962) 51063.

The subsidy responsibility for many activities in England and Wales has been transferred from the Arts Council of Great Britain to the Regional Arts Associations, but the Arts Council retains as direct beneficiaries a number of the larger organisations, including certain regional theatre companies and major festivals.

Annual Subscriptions for Full Membership (Organisations) and Associate Membership (Individuals) vary between the Associations and details may be obtained from the addresses listed below. Membership entitles one to the periodicals and broadsheets and to other benefits.

There are no regional arts associations in Scotland and all enquiries should be addressed to The Scottish Arts Council, 12 Manor Place, Edinburgh EH3 7DD *tel* 031-226 6051.

**East Midlands Arts** (1969), Mountfields House, Forest Road, Loughborough, Leicestershire LE11 3HU *tel* (0509) 218292 *fax* (0509) 262214. *Director:* John Buston. *Literature Officer:* Debbie Hicks. Derbyshire (excluding High Peak District), Leicestershire, Northamptonshire, Nottinghamshire. Also funds the Buckinghamshire Arts Association.

**Eastern Arts Association** (1971), Cherry Hinton Hall, Cherry Hinton Road, Cambridge CB1 4DW *tel* (0223) 215355. *Director:* Jeremy Newton. Specialist officers for each art form. Bedfordshire, Cambridgeshire, Essex, Hertfordshire, Norfolk and Suffolk.

**Greater London Arts** (1966), 9 White Lion Street, London N1 9PD *tel* 01-837 8808. *Director:* Trevor Vibert. The area of the 32 London Boroughs and the City of London.

**Lincolnshire and Humberside Arts** (1964), St Hugh's Newport, Lincoln LN1 3DN *tel* (0522) 533555. *Media and Cultural Industries Officer:* David Baker.

**Merseyside Arts** (1968), Graphic House, Duke Street, Liverpool L1 4JR *tel* 051-709 0671 *fax* 051-708 9034. *Director:* Peter Booth. Liverpool City Council, the district councils of Ellesmere Port & Neston, Halton, West Lancashire, the metropolitan boroughs of Knowsley, Sefton, St. Helens and Wirral and part of the counties of Cheshire and Lancashire.

**North Wales Arts Association** (1967), 10 Wellfield House, Bangor, Gwynedd LL57 1ER *tel* (0248) 353248 *fax* (0248) 351077. *Director:* D. Llion Williams, Clwyd, Gwynedd and District of Montgomery in the County of Powys.

**North West Arts** (1966), 12 Harter Street, Manchester M1 6HY *tel* 061-228 3062 *fax* 061-236 5361. *Director:* Josephine Burns. Greater Manchester, High Peak District of Derbyshire, Lancashire (except District of West Lancashire), Cheshire (except Ellesmere Port and Halton Districts). Publish monthly *The Artful Reporter*.

**Northern Arts** (1961), 9-10 Osborne Terrace, Newcastle-upon-Tyne NE2 1NZ *tel* 091-281 6334 *fax* 091-2818430. *Director:* Peter Stark. Cumbria, Cleveland, Tyne and Wear, Northumberland and Durham.

**South East Arts Association** (1973), 10 Mount Ephraim, Tunbridge Wells, Kent TN4 8AS *tel* (0892) 515210. *Director:* Christopher Cooper. Covers Kent, East Sussex and Surrey. Publishes arts magazine *Event* 10 times a year, as well as 'Support for the Arts' information pack for artists and arts organizations.

**South-east Wales Arts Association** (1973), Victoria Street, Cwmbran, Gwent NP44 3YT *tel* (063-33) 75075. *Director:* H.C.H. Perks. South Glamorgan, Mid-Glamorgan, Gwent, Districts of Radnor and Brecknock in the County of Powys, and the City of Cardiff.

**South West Arts** (1956), Bradninch Place, Gandy Street, Exeter, Devon EX4 3LS *tel* (0392) 218188 *fax* (0392) 413554. *Director:* Martin Rewcastle. Avon, Cornwall, Devon, Dorset (except Districts of Bournemouth, Christchurch and Poole), Gloucestershire, Somerset.

**Southern Arts** (1968), 19 Southgate Street, Winchester, Hants SO23 9DQ *tel* (0962) 55099. *Director:* Bill Dufton; *Literature Officer:* Jane Spiers. The arts development agency for Berkshire, Hampshire, Isle of Wight, Oxfordshire, West Sussex, Wiltshire, and Bournemouth, Christchurch and Poole, Districts of Dorset.

**West Midlands Arts** (1971), 82 Granville Street, Birmingham B1 2LH *tel* 021-631 3121 *fax* 021 643 7239. *Director:* Michael Elliott. County of Hereford and Worcester, West Midlands Metropolitan Area, Shropshire, Staffordshire, Warwickshire.

**West Wales (Association for the) Arts** (1971), Red Street, Carmarthen, Dyfed SA31 1QL *tel* (0267) 234248 *fax* (0267) 233084. *Director:* Carwyn Rogers. Dyfed and West Glamorgan.

**Yorkshire Arts** (1969), Glyde House, Glydegate, Bradford, West Yorkshire BD5 0BQ *tel* (0274) 723051 *fax* 0274-394919. North, South and West Yorkshire. Offers a range of awards and schemes to help writers and those who promote literary activity in the region. Provides grants to festivals, literary societies, poetry-reading groups, etc. Appoints short-term 'placements' for creative writers.

**Ridley Art Society** (1889), 69 Sterndale Road, London W14 0HU. *tel* 01-603 4371. *President:* Professor Carel Weight, R.A.; *Chairman:* Hermione Thornton-Lofthouse; *Hon. Secretary:* to be appointed. To promote excellence in the fine arts. An exhibition is held annually and members can submit four works.

**Romantic Novelists' Association The.** *Chairman:* Mrs Margaret Pemberton, 13 Manor Lane, Lewisham, London SE13 5QW    *tel* 01-852 5067. *Hon. Secretary:* Mrs Dorothy Entwistle, 20 First Avenue, Amersham, Bucks HP7 9BJ. To raise the prestige of Romantic Authorship. Open to romantic and historical novelists. See also under **Literary Awards.**

**Royal Academy of Arts,** Piccadilly, London W1V 0DS    *tel* 01-439 7438. Academicians (R.A.) and Associates (A.R.A.) are elected from the most distinguished artists in the United Kingdom. Major loan exhibitions throughout the year with the Annual Summer Exhibition, May to August. Also runs art schools for 80 students, mainly post-graduate, in painting and sculpture.

**Royal Birmingham Society of Artists,** 69A New Street, Birmingham B2 4DU    *tel* 021-643 3768. *President:* C. A. Sawbridge; *Hon. Secretary:* Tom Barker, R.B.S.A. The Society has its own galleries and rooms prominently placed in the city centre. Members (R.B.S.A.) and Associates (A.R.B.S.A.) are elected annually. There are two annual Spring Exhibitions open to all artists and an Autumn Exhibition of Members' and Associates' works. *Annual Subscription* (Friends of the R.B.S.A.): £5.00 entitles subscribers to season ticket for painting days, criticisms and lectures organised by the Society and to submit work for the Annual Friends' Exhibition in July. Further details from the Hon. Secretary.

**Royal Literary Fund, The,** 144 Temple Chambers, Temple Avenue, London EC4Y 0DT    *tel* 01-353 7150. *President:* Arthur Crook. *Secretary:* Fiona Clark. Founded in 1790, the Fund is the oldest and largest charity serving literature. The object of the Fund is to help writers and their families who face hardship. It does not offer grants to writers who can earn their living in other ways, nor does it provide financial support for writing projects. But it sustains authors who have for one reason or another fallen on hard times – illness, family misfortune, or sheer loss of writing form, all of which can afflict established authors and deprive them of that peace of mind so necessary for work.

Applicants must have published work of approved literary merit, which may include important contributions to periodicals. The literary claim of every new applicant must be accepted by the General Committee before the question of need can be considered.

The Fund has never received a subsidy from the Government nor has the Welfare State replaced its function. By working with Social Security and the resources at the disposal of the Prime Minister, notably the Civil List, it has come to the rescue of authors in a way that is beyond the scope of state assistance.

The Fund is supported by the investment of legacies, subscriptions and donations. The principal contributors are authors themselves, publishers and others in the book trade.

**Royal Society, The** (1660), 6 Carlton House Terrace, London SW1Y 5AG    *tel* 01-839 5561    *telex* 917876    *fax* 01-930 2170. *President:* Sir George Porter;

*Treasurer:* Professor R. W. K. Honeycombe, *Secretaries:* Professor B. K. Follett, Sir Francis Graham-Smith; *Foreign Secretary:* Professor M. A. Epstein C.B.E. Promotion of the natural sciences (pure and applied) through meetings, publications, grants and awards.

**Royal Society for the encouragement of Arts, Manufactures and Commerce (RSA)** (1754), 8 John Adam Street, London WC2N 6EZ *tel* 01-930 5115 *telex* 892351 *fax* 01-839 5805. *Chairman of Council:* Professor Charles Handy. *Secretary and Chief Executive:* Christopher Lucas. Annual lecture programme on wide range of subjects, monthly journal, library. RSA Examinations Board is a major examining body. The RSA's current work is indicated by its main committees: Arts, Manufactures and Commerce, Design, Education, Environment.

**Royal West of England Academy** (1844), Queens Road, Clifton, Bristol BS8 1PX *tel* (0272) 735129. *President:* Leonard Manasseh, O.B.E., R.A., P.R.W.A., F.R.I.B.A., A.A. (Dipl), F.C.S.D.; *Academy Secretary:* Jean McKinney. Aims to further the interests of practising painters and sculptors. Holds art exhibitions and is a meeting place for artists and their work.

**Ruskin Society of London, The** (1985), *Hon. Secretary:* Miss O. E. Madden, 351 Woodstock Road, Oxford OX2 7NX *tel* (0865) 515962. To promote literary and biographical interest in John Ruskin and his contemporaries. *Annual subscription:* £5.00.

**Dorothy L. Sayers Society, The** (1976), *Chairman:* Dr Barbara Reynolds. *Secretary:* Christopher J. Dean, Rose Cottage, Malthouse Lane, Hurstpierpoint, W. Sussex BN6 9JY *tel* (0273) 833444. To promote and encourage the study of the works of Dorothy L. Sayers; to collect relics and reminiscences about her and make them available to students and biographers, to hold an annual seminar, to publish proceedings and pamphlets and a bimonthly bulletin. *Annual subs.:* £5.00.

**Scientific and Technical Authors' Group,** 84 Drayton Gardens, London SW10 9SB *tel* 01-373 6642. A specialist unit within the membership of the Society of Authors.

**Scientific and Technical Communicators, The Institute of** (1972), 52 Odencroft Road, Britwell, Slough, Berks SL2 2BP *tel* (0753) 691562. *President:* Dennis Reeder, F.I.S.T.C.; *Secretary:* Alma Cook, M.I.S.T.C. A professional body for those engaged in the communication of scientific and technical information. *Objects:* to establish and maintain professional standards, to encourage and co-operate in professional training and to provide a source of information on, and to encourage research and development in, all aspects of scientific and technical communication. *The Communicator* is the official journal of the Institute, and is published 10 times per year.

**Scottish Academy, Royal** (1826), Princes Street, Edinburgh EH2 2EL *tel* 031-225 6671. *President:* Sir Anthony Wheeler, P.R.S.A.; *Secretary:* R. R. Steedman, R.S.A.; *Treasurer:* W.J.L. Baillie, R.S.A.; *Administrative Secretary:* W. T. Meikle. Academicians (R.S.A.) and Associates (A.R.S.A.) and non-members may exhibit in the Annual Exhibition of Painting, Sculpture and Architecture. Annual Exhibition dates approximately mid April to August, Festival Exhibition August/September. Other artists' societies' annual exhibitions, normally between October and January. Royal Scottish Academy Student Competition held in March.

**Scottish Arts,** 24 Rutland Square, Edinburgh EH1 2BW  *tel* 031-229 1076. *Honorary Secretary:* W. B. Logan  *tel* 031-229 8157. *Subs.:* Full £176.00, but various reductions. Art, literature, music.

**Scottish Arts Council,** 12 Manor Place, Edinburgh EH3 7DD. *Chairman:* Sir Alan Peacock; *Director:* Timothy Mason. Principal channel for government funding of the arts in Scotland, the Scottish Arts Council forms part of the Arts Council of Great Britain. It aims to develop and improve the knowledge, understanding and practice of the arts, and to increase their accessibility throughout Scotland. It offers about 1000 grants a year to professional artists and arts organisations concerned with the visual arts, drama, dance and mime, literature, music, festivals, traditional and ethnic arts and community arts.

**Scottish History Society** (1886), Department of Scottish History, St. Salvator's College, University of St. Andrews, Fife KY16 9AJ. *Hon. Secretary:* Norman Macdougall, PH.D. The Society exists to publish documents illustrating the history of Scotland.

**Scottish Newspaper Publishers' Association,** 48 Palmerston Place, Edinburgh EH12 5DE  *tel* 031-220 4353  *fax* 031-220 4344. *President:* Ralph C. M. Frost. *Director:* J. B. Raeburn, F.C.I.S. To promote and represent newspaper interests.

**Scottish Publishers Association** (1974), 25A South West Thistle Street Lane, Edinburgh EH2 1EW  *tel* 031-225 5795  *fax* 031-220 0377. *Director:* Lorraine Fannin. *Publicist:* Alison Harley. To assist Scottish publishers primarily in the publicity, promotion and marketing of their books.

**Screenwriters Workshop, London** (1983), 64 Church Crescent, London N10 3NE  *tel* 01-883 7218. Formed by a group of film and television writers to serve as a forum for contact, discussion and practical criticism. Membership open to anyone interested in writing for film and television, and to anyone working in these and related media. *Annual subscription:* £15. Send large sae for further details.

**Shakespearean Authorship Trust.** *Hon. Secretary:* Dr. D. W. Thomson Vessey, 26 Ouse Walk, Huntingdon, Cambridgeshire PE18 6QL. *Hon. Treasurer:* John Silberrad, Dryads' Hall, Woodbury Hill, Loughton, Essex IG10 1JB. *Aims:* The advancement of learning with particular reference to the social, political and literary history of England in the sixteenth century and the authorship of the plays and poems commonly attributed to William Shakespeare. *Annual Subscription:* £10.00. Subscribers receive copies of the Trust's publications, and are entitled to use its library.

**Shaw Society, The,** 6 Stanstead Grove, Catford, London SE6 4UD  *tel* 01-690 2325. *Secretary:* Barbara Smoker. Improvement and diffusion of knowledge of the life and works of Bernard Shaw and his circle. Meetings in London, annual festival at Ayot St. Lawrence; publication: *The Shavian.*

**Singapore Book Publishers' Association,** P.O. Box 846, Raffles City Post Office, Singapore 9117. *President:* Mr Charles Cher; *Hon. Secretary:* Mr N. T. S. Chopra.

**SLADE—Society of Lithographic Artists, Designers, Engravers & Process Workers—see NGA 1982.**

**Society of Authors—see Authors, The Society of.**

**Songwriters, Composers and Authors, British Academy of,** (1947), 34 Hanway Street, London W1P 9DE  *tel* 01-436 2261. *General Secretary:* Eileen Stow. To give advice and guidance to its songwriter members.

**South African Publishers Association,** P.O. Box 326, Howard Place 7450, South Africa  *tel* (021) 53-8907  *fax* (021) 534410.

**SPREd—Society of Picture Researchers and Editors,** BM Box 259, London WC1N 3XX  *tel* 01-404 5011. A professional organisation of picture researchers and picture editors. Operates a freelance register service—details from Miranda Smith  *tel* 01-539 5927. See article: **Picture Research.**

**Strip Illustration, Society of,** 7 Dilke Street, Chelsea, London SW3 4JE. Founded in 1977 by a group of professionals, the Society is open to artists, writers, editors, and anyone professionally concerned with comics, newspaper strips, and strip illustration. Monthly Newsletter, monthly meetings, and an annual convention.

**Sussex Playwrights' Club.** Founded in 1935. Members' plays are read by local actors before an audience of Club members. The Club from time to time sponsors productions of members' plays by local drama companies. Details: Hon. Secretary, Sussex Playwrights' Club, 2 Princes Avenue, Hove, East Sussex BN3 4GD.

**Syndicat de Conseils Littéraires Français,** c/o Agence Hoffman, 77 bd Saint-Michel, 75005 Paris  *tel* (1) 43-26-56-94  *telex* 203605 Aghoff  *fax* 43-26-34-07.

**Syndicat National de l'Edition** (the French publishers' association), 35 Rue Grégoire de Tours, 75279 Paris 06  *tel* 43-29-75-75  *telex* 270838 Lifran F  *fax* 43-25-35-01.

**Theatre Research, The Society for.** *Hon. Secretaries:* Derek Forbes and Senga Wallace Roche, c/o The Theatre Museum, 1E Tavistock Street, London WC2E 7PA. Publishes annual volumes and journal, *Theatre Notebook*, holds lectures, runs enquiry service and makes research grants annually.

**Theatre Writers' Union** (1976), Actors Centre, 4 Chenies Street, London WC1E 7EP  *tel* 01-631 3619. The Union's principles include the furthering of the interests of all writers working in the theatre, particularly the subsidised theatre; the negotiation of minimum terms contracts with representative organisations across the entire theatrical spectrum, the improvement of theatre writers' status and the protection of their rights; the encouragement of new writing in the theatre; the pressing for adequate expenditure on theatre writing by various funding bodies; the development of regional script centres, providing cheap photocopying facilities. Membership open to playwrights, performed or not yet performed, fee from £11.00 p.a.

**Edward Thomas Fellowship, The** (1980), 3 South Court, Halswell House, Goathurst, nr Bridgwater, Somerset TA5 2DH  *tel* (0278) 662856. *Hon. Secretary:* Richard N. Emeny. To perpetuate the memory of Edward Thomas, foster an interest in his life and work, to assist in the preservation of places associated with him and to arrange events which extend fellowship amongst his admirers. *Annual subscription:* £4.00.

**Francis Thompson Society, The,** now incorporated in **The Eighteen Nineties Society,** *qv*.

**Tolkien Society, The** (1969), *Secretary:* Debi Haigh-Hutchinson, 27 Barnbrough Street, Leeds, W. Yorks LS4 2QY  *tel* (0532) 740295. *Membership Secretary:* C. D. Oakey, Flat 5, 357 High Street, Cheltenham, Gloucestershire GL50 3HT	*tel* (0242) 577232. The society is dedicated to promoting research into and educating the public in the life and works of Professor J. R. R. Tolkien. *Subscription:* U.K. £15.00; surface (outside Europe) £15.50, Europe letter rate (including Eire) £16.50; airmail zone B (U.S.) £17.00, zone C (Australia) £18.00.

**Translation and Interpreting, The Institute of,** 318A Finchley Road, London NW3 5HT	*tel* 01-794 9931	*fax* 01-435 2105. All correspondence to be addressed to the *Secretary.* A professional association for translators and interpreters which restricts its qualified entry to those who have either passed translation or interpreting examinations in technical, scientific, commercial or social science fields, or can provide evidence of a similar degree of competence and experience gained by other specified means. Subscriber membership (non-qualified) and student membership are also possible. Details of members capable of handling particular language and subject combinations are available from the Institute office.

**Translators Association, The** (1958), 84 Drayton Gardens, London SW10 9SB	*tel* 01-373 6642. *Secretary:* Kate Pool. A specialist unit within the membership of the Society of Authors, exclusively concerned with the interests and special problems of writers who translate foreign literary or dramatic work into English for publication or performance in Great Britain or English-speaking countries overseas. Members are entitled to general and legal advice on all questions connected with the marketing of their work, such as rates of remuneration, contractual arrangements with publishers, editors, broadcasting organisations, etc. The annual subscription is £45 by direct debit, £50 by cheque and includes membership of the Society of Authors. Full particulars may be obtained from the offices of the Association.

**Travel Writers, The British Guild of,** *Hon. Secretary:* Gillian Thomas, 90 Corringway, London W5 3HA	*tel* 01-998 2223. Arranges meetings, discussions and visits for its members (who are all professional travel writers) to help them encourage the public's interest in travel.

**Trollope Society, The** (1987), 9A North Street, London SW4 0HN	*tel* 01-720 6789. *Chairman:* John Letts. The aim of the society is to produce the first ever complete edition of the novels of Anthony Trollope. *Membership fee:* ordinary (one year) £10.00, foundation (ten years) £70.00, life £100.

**Turner Society, The** (1975), B.C.M. Box Turner, London WC1N 3XX. *President:* Sir Hugh Casson, C.H., K.C.V.O., P.P.R.A.; *Chairman:* Eric Shanes. To foster a wider appreciation of all facets of Turner's work; to encourage exhibitions of his paintings, drawings and engravings. Publishes: *Turner Society News. Subscriptions:* £5; overseas: £5 (surface mail), £10 (airmail); corporate: £10.

**Typographic Designers, Society of,** *President:* David Playne, F.S.T.D., F.C.S.D.; *Chair:* Angela Reeves, F.S.T.D., F.C.S.D. *Hon. Secretary:* Mike Seaton, M.S.T.D., New Inn Lane, Avening, Tetbury, Glos. GL8 8NB. Founded in 1928, the Society has been recognised as the authoritative organisation for the typographic profession in the U.K. It advises and acts on matters of professional practice, provides a better understanding of the craft and the rapidly changing technology in the graphic industries by lectures, discussions and through the journal *Typographic* and the Newsletter. Typographic students are encouraged to first gain Licentiateship of the Society as the accepted yard stick by employers by an annual assessment of submitted work to a sponsored professional brief. The STD is a full member of

The International Council of Graphic Design Associations, ICOGRADA, which brings professionals together for a General Assembly, Congress and exhibition of work, every three years.

**United Society for Christian Literature** (1799), Robertson House, Leas Road, Guildford, Surrey GU1 4QW *tel* Guildford 577877. *President:* Lord Luke. *Chairman:* Alan Brown. *General Secretary:* Rev. Alec Gilmore, M.A., B.D. To aid Christian literature principally in the Third World and Eastern Europe.

**United Society of Artists,** 4 Frogmore Cottage, High Street, Watford, Herts WD1 2HX. *President:* Robert Hill, R.O.I., N.E.A.C. Membership by election on application. Annual exhibition open to all non-members.

**University, College and Professional Publishers Council,** see **Publishers Association.**

**Voice of the Listener** (1983), 101 King's Drive, Gravesend, Kent DA12 5BQ *tel* (0474) 564676. *Chairman:* Jocelyn Hay. *Administrative Secretary:* Karen Plummer. An independent association working to ensure the maintenance of high standards in broadcasting in the UK. Membership open to all concerned about the future of public service broadcasting.

**Edgar Wallace Society** (1969), 7 Devonshire Close, Amersham, Bucks HP6 5JG *tel* (0494) 72 5398. *Organiser:* John A. Hogan. To promote an interest in the life and work of Edgar Wallace through the *Crimson Circle* magazine (Q.). *Subscription:* £6.00 p.a.

**The Walmsley Society** (1985), 47 Westcroft, Leominster, Herefordshire HR6 8HF *tel* (0568) 611733. *Secretary:* Jack L. W. Hazell. *Treasurer and Membership Secretary:* Miss Jane Ellis, 152 Osmondthorpe Lane, Leeds, W. Yorkshire LS9 9EG. The society's aim is to promote and encourage an appreciation of the literary and artistic heritage left to us by Leo and J. Ulric Walmsley. Affiliated to the Alliance of Literary Societies.

**Watercolour Society, British** (1830), *Director:* Leslie Simpson, Ralston House, 41 Lister Street, Riverside Gardens, Ilkley, West Yorkshire LS29 9ET *tel* (0943) 609075.

**Watercolour Society, Royal** (founded 1804), Bankside Gallery, 48 Hopton Street, London SE1 9JH *tel* 01-928 7521. *President:* Charles Bartlett; *Secretary:* Michael Spender. Membership (R.W.S.) open to British and overseas artists. An election of Associates is held annually, and applications for the necessary forms and particulars should be addressed to the Secretary. Open Exhibition held in summer. Exhibitions: spring and autumn. Friends of the RWS open to all those interested in watercolour painting.

**Mary Webb Society** (1972), *Secretaries:* Mrs. H. M. Dormer, 6 Ragleth Road, Church Stretton, Shropshire SY6 7BN *tel* (0694) 722755 and Mrs. A. Parry, 4 Lythwood Road, Bayston Hill, Shrewsbury SY3 0LU *tel* Bayston Hill 2766. To further an interest in the life and works of Mary Webb by meetings, lectures and excursions.

**H. G. Wells Society, The** (1960), School of Literary and Media Studies, Polytechnic of North London, Prince of Wales Road, Kentish Town, London NW5 3LB *tel* 01-607 2789. *Secretary:* Christopher Rolfe. Promotion of an active interest in and encouragement of an appreciation of the life, work and thought of H. G. Wells. Publishes *The Wellsian* (annually) and *The Newsletter* (quarterly). *Subscription:* £5.00 per annum.

**Welsh Arts Council,** Museum Place, Cardiff CF1 3NX  *tel* (0222) 394711. *Chairman:* Mathew Prichard; *Director:* T. A. Owen. An autonomous committee of the Arts Council of Great Britain, the Welsh Arts Council shares that body's aims and has responsibility for implementation of the council's policies in Wales. Its seven departments are Music, Art, Literature, Drama, Craft, Film and Dance. It also runs the Oriel Bookshop and Gallery in Cardiff.

**Welsh Books Council/Cyngor Llyfrau Cymraeg,** Castell Brychan, Aberystwyth, Dyfed SY23 2JB  *tel* (0970) 624151  *fax* (0970) 625385. *Director:* Gwerfyl Pierce Jones. Founded in 1961 to encourage and increase the interest of the public in Welsh literature and to support authors of popular books in the Welsh language. With the establishment of Editorial, Design, Marketing and Wholesale Distribution Departments, the Council promotes all aspects of book production in Wales and provides a service for Welsh-language books and English-language books of Welsh interest. Also distributes the government grant for Welsh-language publications.

**West Country Writers' Association, The.** *President:* Christopher Fry, F.R.S.L.; *Chairman:* The Rev. Dr David Keep; *Hon. Secretary:* Dorothy Stiffe, 2 Thistleboon Drive, Swansea SA3 4HY  *tel* (0792) 360983. Founded in 1951 by Waveney Girvan for the purpose of fostering the love of literature in the West Country and to give authors an opportunity of meeting to exchange news and views. An Annual Week-end Congress is held in a West Country town and there are Regional Meetings. Newsletter (2 p.a.). Membership is open to published authors. *Annual Subscription:* £5.

**Wildlife Artists, Society of,** 17 Carlton House Terrace, London SW1Y 5BD  *tel* 01-930 6844. *President:* Robert Gillmor. To promote and encourage the art of Wildlife painting and sculpture. Open Annual Exhibition.

**Charles Williams Society** (1975), 26 Village Road, Finchley, London N3 1TL  *Secretary:* Mrs Gillian Lunn. To promote interest in Charles Williams' life and work and to make his writings more easily available.

**Henry Williamson Society, The** (1980), *Secretary:* John L. Homan. All correspondence to *Membership secretary:* Mrs Mary Heath, Longclose, Langtree, Torrington, North Devon EX38 8NR  *tel* (080 55) 200. Aims to encourage a wider readership and greater understanding of the literary heritage left by Henry Williamson. Two meetings annually; also weekend activities. Publishes journal twice yearly. *Annual subscriptions:* £8.00. Family, student and overseas rates available.

**Women Artists, Society of** (1855), Westminster Gallery, Westminster Central Hall, Storeys Gate, London SW1H 9NU. *President:* Barbara Tate. Annual Exhibition of painting, sculpture, etc. Open to all women.

**Women in Publishing** (1977), c/o J.Whitaker, 12 Dyott Street, London WC1A 1DF. Promotes the status of women within publishing; encourages networking and mutual support among women; provides a forum for the discussion of ideas, trends and subjects to women in the trade; offers practical training for career and personal development; supports and publicises women's achievements and successes. *Subscription:* £10.00 p.a.

**Women Writers and Journalists, Society of,** (1894), *Secretary:* Olive McDonald, 2 St. Lawrence Close, Edgware, Middlesex HA8 6RB  *tel* 01-952 1190. For women writers and artists. Lectures, monthly lunch-time meetings.

Free literary advice for members. *The Woman Journalist.* (3 p.a.) *Subscription:* Town £15.00; Country £12.00; Overseas £9.00.

**Worshipful Company of Musicians** (1500), 1 The Sanctuary, Westminster, London SW1P 3JT   *tel* 01-222 5381. *Clerk:* M. J. G. Fletcher.

**Worshipful Company of Stationers and Newspaper Makers** (1557), Stationers' Hall, London EC4M 7DD   *tel* 01-248 2934. *Master:* J. D. Ryman; *Clerk:* Captain P. Hames, R.N. One of the Livery Companies of the City of London. Connected with the printing, publishing, bookselling, newspaper and allied trades.

**Writers' Circles.** The *Directory of Writers' Circles*, containing addresses and telephone numbers of several hundred writers' circles, guilds, workshops and literary clubs through the UK, is published regularly by Laurence Pollinger Ltd. It is available from compiler/editor Jill Dick (£3.00 post free) at Oldacre, Horderns Park Road, Chapel-en-le-Frith, Derbyshire SK12 6SY.

**Writers' Guild of Great Britain, The,** 430 Edgware Road, London W2 1EH   *tel* 01-723 8074-5-6. See also **Article.**

**Yachting Journalists' Association,** (1973). *Secretary:* Steve Ancsell, The Glider Centre, Bishop's Waltham, Hampshire SO3 1DH   *tel* (0489) 896311   *fax* (0489) 892416. To further the interests of yachting journalists and boating. *Subscription:* £15.00 p.a.

**Yorkshire Dialect Society, The** (1897). The aims of the Society are to encourage interest in: (1) dialect speech; (2) the writing of dialect verse, prose and drama; (3) the publication and circulation of dialect literature and the performance of dialect plays; (4) the study of the origins and the history of dialect and kindred subjects—all dialects, not only of Yorkshire origin. *Annual subscription:* £2.50; life membership, £52.50. *Meetings:* the Society organises a number of meetings during the year—details from the Hon. Secretary. *Annual Publications: Transactions* and *The Summer Bulletin* free to members, list of other publications on request. *Hon. Secretary:* Stanley Ellis, School of English, The University, Leeds LS2 9JT.

**Young Publishers, Society of** (1949), 12 Dyott Street, London WC1A 1DF   *tel* 01-836 8911. The society provides a forum for younger people (under 35) in the trade, as well as an advisory service for prospective new entrants in publishing. *Membership Secretary:* Sally Choules, Booklink, St Chad's Court, 146B King's Cross Road, London WC1X 9DH   *tel* 1-837 1763.

**Francis Brett Young Society** (1979), *Secretary:* Mrs J. Pritchard, 52 Park Road, Hagley, Stourbridge, West Midlands DY9 0QF   *tel* (0562) 882973. To provide opportunities for members to meet, correspond, and to share the enjoyment of the author's works. Journal published twice yearly. *Annual subscription:* £3.00.

# The Society of Authors

The Society of Authors is an independent trade union, representing writers' interests in all aspects of the writing profession, including publishing, broadcasting, TV and films, theatre and translation. Founded over a hundred years ago by Walter Besant, the Society now has more than 4,000 members. It has a professional staff, responsible to a Management Committee of 12 authors and a Council (an advisory body meeting twice a year) consisting of 60 eminent writers. There are specialist groups within the Society to serve the particular needs of broadcasters, literary translators, educational writers, medical writers, children's writers, and scientific and technical writers. There are also regional groups representing Scotland, the North of Engand, and the Isle of Man.

## WHAT THE SOCIETY DOES FOR MEMBERS

Through its permanent staff (including a solicitor), the Society is able to give its members a comprehensive personal and professional service covering the business aspects of authorship, including:

providing information about agents, publishers, and others concerned with the book trade, journalism, broadcasting, and the performing arts;

advising on negotiations, including the individual vetting of contracts, clause by clause, and assessing their terms both financial and otherwise;

taking up complaints on behalf of members on any issue concerned with the business of authorship;

pursuing legal actions in respect of breach of contract, copyright infringement, and the non-payment of royalties and fees, when the risk and cost preclude individual action by a member and issues of general concern to the profession are at stake;

holding weekend conferences, seminars, meetings, and social occasions;

producing a comprehensive range of publications, free of charge to members, including the Society's quarterly journal, *The Author*, and *Quick Guides* covering many aspects of the profession such as: copyright, publishing contracts, libel, income tax, VAT, authors' agents, permissions, and the protection of titles. The Society also publishes a model book contract, a model translator/publisher agreement, *Guidelines for Educational Writers, Guidelines for Medical Writers*, and *Sell Your Writing*. Members concerned with radio and television receive *Broadcasting* regularly, and translators are sent *Translators News*.

*Members have access to:*

the Retirement Benefit Scheme,

Group Medical Insurance Schemes with both BUPA and the Bristol Contributory Welfare Association,

the Pension Fund (which offers discretionary pensions to a number of members),

the Contingency Fund (which provides financial relief for authors or their dependents in sudden financial difficulties),

automatic free membership of the Authors' Licensing and Collecting Society,

books and stationery at special rates,

membership of the Royal Over-Seas League at a discount,

use of the Society's photocopying machine at special rates.

The Society frequently secures improved conditions and better returns for members. It is common for members to report that, through the help and facilities offered, they have saved more, and sometimes substantially more, than their annual subscriptions (which are an allowable expense against income tax).

## WHAT THE SOCIETY DOES FOR AUTHORS IN GENERAL

The Society lobbies Members of Parliament, Ministers, and Government Departments on all issues of concern to writers. Recent issues have included the establishment and funding of Public Lending Right, the threat of VAT on books, and changes to copyright legislation. Concessions have also been obtained under various Finance Acts.

The Society litigates in matters of importance to authors. For example, the Society backed Andrew Boyle when he won his appeal against the Inland Revenue's attempt to tax the Whitbread Award. It backed a number of members in proceedings against the BBC and Desmond Wilcox in connection with the publication of a book, *The Explorers*, and also in a High Court action over copyright infringment by *Coles Notes*.

The Society campaigns for better terms for writers. With the Writers' Guild, it has negotiated agreements with BBC Publications, Faber & Faber, Century Hutchinson, Bloomsbury, Headline, Hodder & Stoughton and Methuen London. Other publishers are now being approached, and the campaign is active. The translators' section of the Society has also drawn up a minimum terms agreement for translators which has been adopted by Faber & Faber, and has been used on an individual basis by a number of other publishers.

The Society is recognised by the BBC for the purpose of negotiating rates for writers' contributions to radio drama, talks and features, as well as for the broadcasting of published material. It was instrumental in setting up the Authors' Licensing and Collecting Society (ALCS), which collects and distributes fees from reprography and other methods whereby copyright material is exploited without direct payment to the originators.

The Society keeps in close touch with the Arts Council of Great Britain, the Association of Authors' Agents, the British Council, the Broadcasting and Entertainment Trades Alliance, the Institute of Translation and Interpreting, the Minister for the Arts, the National Union of Journalists, the Publishers Association, and the Writers' Guild of Great Britain.

The Society is a member of the Congress of European Writers Organisations, the British Copyright Council, the National Book Committee, the Radio and Television Safeguards Committee, and the International Confederation of Societies of Authors and Composers (CISAC).

## AWARDS ADMINISTERED BY THE SOCIETY

Two travel awards—The Somerset Maugham Awards and the Travelling Scholarships.

Two prizes for novels—The Betty Trask Awards and the McKitterick Prize.

Two poetry awards—The Eric Gregory Awards and the Cholmondeley Award.

The Tom-Gallon Award for short story writers.

The Crompton Bequest for aiding financially the publication of selected original work.

The Authors' Foundation and Kathleen Blundell Trust, which are endowed with wide powers to support literary and artistic effort and research.

The Margaret Rhondda Award for women journalists.

The Scott Moncrieff Prize for translations from French.

The Schlegel-Tieck Prize for translations from German.

The John Florio Prize for translations from Italian.
The Roger Machell Prize for a book on the performing arts.
The Francis Head Bequest for assisting authors who, through physical mishap, are temporarily unable to maintain themselves or their families.

## HOW TO JOIN

There are two categories of membership (admission to each being at the discretion of the Committee of Management):

*Full Membership*—those authors who have had a full-length work published, broadcast or performed commercially in the U.K. or have an established reputation in another medium.

*Associate Membership*—those authors who have had a full-length work accepted for publication, but not yet published; and those authors who have had occasional items broadcast or performed, or translations, articles, illustrations or short stories published.

Associate members pay the same annual subscription and are entitled to the same benefits as full members. The owner or administrator of a deceased author's copyrights can become a member on behalf of the author's estate.

The Annual Subscription (which is tax deductible under Schedule D) for full or associate membership of the Society is £50 (£45 by direct debit), and there are special joint membership terms for husband and wife. Authors under 35, who are not yet earning a significant income from their writing, may apply for membership at a lower subscription of £32.

Further information from The Society of Authors, 84 Drayton Gardens, London, SW10 9SB    *tel* 01-373 6642.

## IN CONCLUSION

"When we begin working, we are so poor and so busy that we have neither the time nor the means to defend ourselves against the commercial organisations which exploit us. When we become famous, we become famous suddenly, passing at one bound from the state in which we are, as I have said, too poor to fight our own battles, to a state in which our time is so valuable that it is not worth our while wasting any of it on lawsuits and bad debts. We all, eminent and obscure alike, need the Authors' Society. We all owe it a share of our time, our means, our influence": *Bernard Shaw*

# The Writers' Guild of Great Britain

The Writers' Guild of Great Britain is the writers' trade union, affiliated to the TUC, and representing writers' interests in film, radio, television, theatre and publishing. Formed in 1959 as the Screenwriters' Guild, the union gradually extended into all areas of freelance writing activity and copyright protection. In 1974 when book authors and stage dramatists became eligible for membership substantial numbers joined, and their interests are now strongly represented on the Executive Council. Apart from necessary dealings with Government and policies on legislative matters affecting writers, the Guild is, by constitution, non-political, has no involvement with any political party, and pays no political levy. The Guild employs a permanent secretariat and staff and is administered by an Executive Council of twenty-nine members. There are also Regional Committees representing Scotland, Wales, the North and West of England.

The Guild comprises practising professional writers in all media, united in common concern for one another and regulating the conditions under which they work.

## WHAT IT DOES

The Guild gives help and advice to individual members on any aspect of their business life, including contracts, agents, publishers, television companies and fees. Also in:

### Television

The Guild has national agreements with the BBC and the commercial companies regulating minimum fees and going rates, copyright licence, credit terms and conditions for television plays, series and serials, dramatisations and adaptations. One of the most important achievements in recent years has been the establishment of pension rights for Guild members only. Both the BBC and the Independent Television Association pay an additional 7.5% of the going rate on the understanding that the Guild member pays 5% of his or her fee. The Guild Pension Fund amounts to well over one million pounds at present.

In 1985, a comprehensive agreement was negotiated with the BBC to cover cable sales; in addition a special agreement was negotiated to cover the very successful twice-weekly serial *EastEnders*.

Most children's and educational drama has been similarly protected within the above industrial agreements. However, there are certain areas which the Guild will be reviewing with a view to making further agreements.

During 1989, the Guild concluded agreements to cover videograms with both the Independent Television Association and the BBC. A Format Agreement and a Light Entertainment Agreement were also made with the BBC in 1989. The Guild has not as yet concluded an agreement for light entertainment with ITA, but has every intention of doing so.

### Film

On March 11th 1985, an important agreement was signed with the two producer organisations: the British Film and Television Producers Association and the Independent Programme Producers Association. For the first time, there exists an industrial agreement which covers both independent television productions and independent film productions. Pension fund contributions have been negotiated for Guild members in the same way as for the BBC and the ITV.

At the end of 1987, the Guild gave notice that it wished to re-negotiate the agreement. Detailed proposals for new rates and changes in certain of the conditions were put to the producer bodies in 1988. The Guild hopes to conclude a new agreement in 1989. The Guild is concerned to see that its members are protected in the independent field, particularly in the light of proposals that both the BBC and the independent channels should now take up to 25% of their programming from the independent sector.

## Radio

The Guild has fought for and obtained a standard agreement with the BBC, establishing a fee structure which is annually reviewed. The current agreement includes a Code of Practice which is important for establishing good working conditions for the writer working for the BBC. In December 1985 the BBC agreed to extend the pension scheme already established for television writers to include radio writers. It was also agreed that all radio writers would be entitled to at least one attendance payment as of right. Again this brings the radio agreements more into line with the television agreements.

The independent radio companies do very little drama and so far no major independent network radio company has signed an agreement with the Guild. Nevertheless, with the advent of an independent network this could change. As and when plans are announced the Guild will make appropriate approaches and proposals to the independent network.

## Books

The Guild fought long, hard and successfully for the loans-based Public Lending Right to re-imburse authors for books lent in libraries. This is now law and the Guild is constantly in touch with the Registrar of the scheme which is administered from offices in Stockton-on-Tees.

The Guild together with its sister union, the Society of Authors, has drawn up a draft Minimum Terms Book Agreement which has been widely circulated amongst publishers. In 1984, the unions achieved a significant breakthrough by signing agreements with two major publishers; negotiations were also opened with other publishers. The publishing agreements will, it is hoped, improve the relationship between writer and publisher and help to clarify what the writer might reasonably expect from the exploitation of copyright in works written by him or her.

Agreements have now been signed with Hamish Hamilton Ltd., W. H. Allen and Co. PLC, Journeyman Press Ltd., BBC Books, Faber and Faber Ltd., Century Hutchinson Ltd., Headline Book Publishing PLC, Bloomsbury Publishing Ltd., Hodder and Stoughton Ltd. and Methuen London. Negotiations are currently taking place with other leading publishers.

## Theatre

In 1979, the Guild with its fellow union, the Theatre Writers' Union, negotiated the first ever industrial agreement for theatre writers. The Theatre National Committee Agreement covers the Royal Shakespeare Company, the National Theatre Company and the English Stage Company. A major revision of the agreement has been undertaken, and it is hoped that negotiations will be concluded, with new rates and improved conditions.

On 2nd June 1986, a new agreement was signed with the Theatrical Management Association. That agreement covers some 95 provincial theatres.

In 1989, after some four years of negotiation, an agreement was concluded between the Guild and Theatre Writers Union and the Independent Theatre Council, which represents some 200 of the smaller and fringe theatres.

*Miscellaneous*

The Guild is in constant touch with Government and national institutions wherever and whenever the interests of writers are in question or are being discussed. In 1988, the Guild hosted a lunch at the House of Lords, under the auspices of its Honorary Life President, Lord Willis of Chislehurst, with a view to achieving a lobby which will represent writers' interests. A similar cross-party lobby involving also the Guild's fellow arts unions, Equity and the Musicians Union, was held in the House of Commons in January 1989. The Guild and its fellow unions believe that it is important to keep in constant touch with all parties to ensure that the various arts forms they represent are properly cared for.

Amongst matters dealt with recently are the Gerald Howarth Private Member's Bill which proposed changes in the law on obscenity. Effectively, the Bill as it stood would have been a straitjacket on the writing professions, including as it did draconian measures for censuring the work of writers. The Guild had worked with other organisations to deal with a similar Bill which had been introduced by Winston Churchill in 1985. As one Bill disappears, so another takes its place. The Guild was very much involved in trying to have the dreadful Clause 28 of the Local Government Bill deleted. Unfortunately, the campaign to rid the Bill of the clause was unsuccessful, but the Guild, along with other institutions, continues to fight for freedom of expression.

Proposals for changes in the law on copyright were published in a draft Bill in August 1987. The Guild along with other organisations made important submissions on behalf of the Guild and writers in general. The new Bill was published in 1989. Moral rights have been granted to writers for the first time.

Working with federations of other unions, that is the Federation of Film Unions, the Federation of Theatre Unions and the Federation of Broadcasting Unions, the Guild makes its views known to Government bodies on a broader basis. It is constantly in touch with the Arts Council of Great Britain, the Library Campaign and other national bodies.

Perhaps one of the closest working relationships the Guild has established is with its fellow arts unions, Equity and the Musicians Union. The three unions have agreed to work much more closely together where they share a common interest. Representatives of the three governing bodies meet on a quarterly basis. Other meetings are held if thought necessary.

Regular Craft Meetings are held by all the Guild's specialist committees. Each section (television and film, radio, theatre, books and women's) holds some four craft meetings per annum. This gives Guild members the opportunity of meeting those who control, work within, or affect the sphere of writing within which they work. Through its craft meetings the Guild has established a new relationship with the British Academy of Film and Television Arts.

Internationally, the Guild plays a leading role in the International Affiliation of Writers' Guilds, which includes the American Guilds East and West, the Canadian Guilds (French and English) and the Australian and New Zealand Guilds. When it is possible to make common cause, then the Guilds act accordingly. The Writers' Guild of Great Britain was responsible for establishing an association between the Affiliation and the Banff Television Festival in 1986. The writers' contribution was such a great success that the Banff Television Festival have asked the British Guild to continue its association with the event.

The Guild takes a leading role in the European Writers' Congress. In 1987, the conference was held in Segovia in Spain. There a paper, jointly prepared by the Writers' Guild of Great Britain and the Swedish Writers Union, on the question of Public Lending Right, was adopted as the official policy of European countries from Iceland to Greece. The Writers' Guild also took a leading role in the discussion of minimum terms publishing agreements. In 1989 the conference was held in Frebourg in Switzerland. The Writers' Guild was very much involved in helping to organize the agenda and the general structure of the conference.

The Guild in its day to day work takes up problems on behalf of individual members, gives advice on contracts, and helps with any problems which affect the lives of its members as professional writers.

The monthly Newsletter, edited by Patrick Campbell, keeps members in touch with current work and negotiations. The magazine carries articles, letters, and reports written by members and the General Secretary.

## MEMBERSHIP

Membership is by a points system. One major piece of work (a full-length book, an hour-long television or radio play, a feature film, etc.) entitles the author to full membership; lesser work helps to accumulate enough points for full membership, while temporary membership may be enjoyed in the meantime. Importantly, a previously unpublished, broadcast or performed writer can apply for membership when he or she receives his or her first contract. The Guild's advice before signature can often be vital. Affiliate membership is enjoyed by agents and publishers.

The minimum subscription is £50 plus 1% of that part of an author's income earned from professional writing sources in the previous calendar year.

Temporary members can join the Guild during their first year for a minimum subscription of £30. In succeeding years, at current rates, it is £50.

## IN CONCLUSION

The writer is an isolated individual in a world in which individual voices are not always heard. The Guild brings together those individual writers in order to make common cause in respect of those many vitally important matters which are susceptible to influence only from the position of collective strength which the Guild enjoys. The writer properly cherishes his or her individuality; it will not be lost within a union run by other writers.

The Writers' Guild of Great Britain, 430 Edgware Road, London, W2 1EH *tel* 01-723 8074. *General Secretary:* Walter J. Jeffrey.

# Literary Prizes and Awards

In the past year many special awards and prizes have been offered for novels, short stories and works of non-fiction. Details of these awards, as they are offered, will be found in such journals as *The Author*. Book Trust (*qv.*) publish a useful *Guide to Literary Prizes, Grants and Awards* (£3.25 including postage). The number of permanent literary prizes in Great Britain is small compared with America, where there are scores of literary awards.

### J. R. Ackerley Prize for Autobiography

This £500 prize, first awarded in 1982, is given annually for an outstanding work of literary autobiography written in English and published during the previous year by an author of British nationality. Books are nominated by the judges. Information from P.E.N., 7 Dilke Street, Chelsea, London SW3 4JE   *tel* 01-352 6303.

### The Age Australian Book of the Year Award

Founded in 1974, this annual award of two prizes of $3000 each is given, one to a work of imaginative writing, the other to a non-fiction work. Authors must be Australian by birth or naturalisation. Publishers only must submit books (maximum two works of imaginative writing and/or three works of non-fiction). Details from the Literary Editor, *The Age*, 250 Spencer Street, Melbourne, Victoria, Australia 3000.

### Air Canada Award

Given annually to a Canadian writer, in any genre, who is younger than 30 and shows promise. Nominations by governing executive of any CAA Branch or other writers' organization. Administered by the Canadian Authors Association. Award is two tickets to any destination served by the airline. Further details from the CAA, 121 Avenue Road, Suite 104, Toronto, Ontario M5R 2G3   *tel* 416-926 8084.

### The Alexander Prize

Candidates for the Alexander Prize, who must either be under the age of 35 or have been registered for a higher degree within the last three years, may choose their own subject for an Essay, but they must submit their choice for approval to the Literary Director, Royal Historical Society, University College London, Gower Street, London WC1E 6BT   *tel* 01-387 7532.

### The Hans Christian Andersen Medals

The Hans Christian Andersen Medals are awarded every two years to an author and an illustrator who by the outstanding value of their work are judged to have made a lasting contribution to literature for children and young people. Details from International Board on Books for Young People, British Section, Book Trust, Book House, 45 East Hill, London SW18 2QZ   *tel* 01-870 9055.

### Angel Literary Award

Prizes of £1000 and £500 are awarded annually to writers living and working in East Anglia. One prize is given for a work of fiction and one for non-fiction. Further details from Caroline Gough, Angel Hotel, Angel Hill, Bury St. Edmunds, Suffolk IP33 1LT   *tel* (0284) 753926   *fax* (0284) 750092.

### Arts Council of Great Britain

*Writers' Awards*

The Arts Council awards bursaries to writers whose work is of outstanding quality. In 1989–90 five bursaries will be awarded to three novelists, one writer of short stories and one biographer. The closing date for applications is 30 November each year. Details are available from July onwards from the Literature Department, Arts Council of Great Britain, 105 Piccadilly, London W1V 0AU  *tel* 01-629 9495.

## The Arts Council/An Chomhairle Ealaíon, Ireland
*Bursaries for Creative Writers*
In 1989 awards totalling IR£30,000 were offered to creative writers of poetry, fiction and drama to enable them to concentrate on or complete writing projects. At least the same amount will be distributed in 1990.
*Denis Devlin Memorial Award for Poetry*
This award, value approximately IR£1300, is made triennially for the best book of poetry in the English language by an Irish citizen published in the preceding three years. The next award will be made in 1992.
*Macaulay Fellowship*
Fellowships, value IR£4,000, are awarded once every three years to writers under 30 years of age (or in exceptional circumstances under 35 years) in order to help them to further their liberal education and careers. The cycle of awards is: Literature (1990), Visual Arts (1991), Music (1992).
*The Marten Toonder Award*
This award is given to an artist of recognised and established achievement on a rotating cycle as follows: Visual Arts (1990), Music (1991), Literature (1992). Candidates must be Irish-born (Northern Ireland is included). Value IR£3,000.
*Prize for Poetry in Irish*
This is Ireland's major award to Irish-language poetry; it is given triennially for the best book of Irish-language poetry published in the preceding three years. The next award will be made in 1992. Value IR£1,300.
*Travel Grants*
Creative artists (including writers) may apply at any time of the year for assistance with travel grants to attend seminars, conferences, workshops, etc. Applications are assessed four times each year.
Further details may be obtained from The Arts Council (An Chomhairle Ealáion), 70 Merrion Square, Dublin 2  *tel* (01) 611 840  *fax* 761 302.

## Arvon Foundation International Poetry Competition
This competition, founded in 1980, is awarded biennially for previously unpublished poems written in English. First prize £5,000 plus other cash prizes. Full details from Arvon Foundation Poetry Competition, Kilnhurst, Kilnhurst Road, Todmorden, Lancashire 0L14 6AX.

## Authors' Club First Novel Award
The award was instituted in 1954 by Lawrence Meynell and is made to the author of the most promising first novel published in the United Kingdom during each year. The award takes the form of a silver mounted and inscribed quill plus £200 and is presented to the winner at a dinner held in the Club at 40 Dover Street, London W1X 3RB. Entries for the award (one from each publisher) are accepted during October and November and must be full length novels—short stories are not eligible.

## Authors' Club Sir Banister Fletcher Award
The late Sir Banister Fletcher, who was President of the Authors' Club for many years, left the Authors' Club a sum of money to be held upon trust: "to apply the income thereof in or towards the provision of an annual prize for the book on architecture or the arts most deserving." The Committee of the Club present a prize of £200 at a dinner held in the Club. Details from the Authors' Club, 40 Dover Street, London W1X 3RB.

## Authors' Club Nelson Hurst & Marsh Biography Award

This is a major new national biography prize of £3000 plus a trophy to be presented every two years. It was introduced for the years 1985–86. Entries must be serious biographies written by British authors and published in the U.K. Details from the Authors' Club, 40 Dover Street, London W1X 3RB.

## The Authors' Foundation

The Foundation, which was founded in 1984 to mark the centenary of the Society of Authors, provides grants to authors for specific projects which have been commissioned by a British publisher. The aim is to provide funding (in addition to a proper advance) for research, travel or other necessary expenditure. Grants are available to novelists as well as writers of non-fiction.

Application should be in the form of a letter sent to the Authors' Foundation at the Society of Authors, giving reasons for the application (including information about the basic terms of the publishing contract). The closing date for applications is 30 June.

The Phoenix Trust has been merged with the Foundation, which hopes to provide grants totalling at least £35,000 in 1990, helped by support from the Arts Council and Mrs Isobel Dalziel.

## Verity Bargate Award

This award, founded in 1983, is given annually to a new play suitable for production at the Soho Poly Theatre. The winning play will be published by Methuen and the writer will receive a prize of £1,000. The play may also receive a production at the Soho Poly. Details from Soho Poly Theatre, 16 Riding House Street, London W1P 7PD. Please send sae for details.

## The Alice Hunt Bartlett Prize

The Poetry Society prize of £500 is awarded annually to the author of a volume of poetry comprising not less than 20 poems or 400 lines published in English and presented in triplicate to the Society's library in the year of publication. The closing date in each year is 28th February. The award is for a first collection of poetry. In the event of the poems being translations into English the prize is divided equally between the author and the translator.

## H. E. Bates Short Story Competition

This annual prize is awarded for a short story—maximum length 2000 words—to anyone resident in Great Britain. The first prize is for £100, other prizes to a total value of £150. Further details from Tourist Information Centre, 21 St. Giles Street, Northampton NN1 1JA   *tel* (0604) 22677.

## The Samuel Beckett Award

Founded in 1983, this award is open to residents of the United Kingdom and the Republic of Ireland. Two prizes of £1500 each are awarded annually, one for a stage play and one for a television play. Plays entered must be the first full-length work by the entrant professionally performed in the United Kingdom or the Republic of Ireland, and adaptations or translations are not eligible. Two non-returnable typed scripts must be submitted. The judges, who change yearly, reserve the right to call in entries at their own discretion, to vary these provisions in ways consistent with the aims of the award and to withhold the award. Further information available from Frank Pike, Faber and Faber, 3 Queen Square, London WC1N 3AU   *tel* 01-278 6881.

## The David Berry Prize

Candidates for the David Berry Prize of £100 may select any subject dealing with Scottish History within the reigns of James I to James VI inclusive, provided such subject has been previously submitted to and approved by the

Council of the Royal Historical Society, University College London, Gower Street, London WC1E 6BT *tel* 01-387 7532.

## The James Tait Black Memorial Prizes

The James Tait Black Memorial Prizes, founded in memory of a partner in the publishing house of A. and C. Black Ltd., were instituted in 1918 and since 1979 have been supplemented by the Scottish Arts Council. Two prizes, of £1,500 each are awarded annually: one for the best biography or work of that nature, the other for the best novel, published during the calendar year. The prize winners are announced normally in the February following the year of the awards. The adjudicator is the Professor of English Literature in the University of Edinburgh.

Publishers are invited to submit a copy of any biography, or work of fiction that in their judgement may merit consideration for the award. Copies should be sent to the Department of English Literature, David Hume Tower, George Square, Edinburgh EH8 9JX, marked "James Tait Black Prize". They should be submitted as early as possible, with a note of the exact date of publication. Co-operation on this point is essential to the work of the adjudicator.

By the terms of the bequest, and by tradition, eligible novels and biographies are those written in English, originating with a British publisher, and first published in Britain in the year of the award; but technical publication else-where, simultaneously or even a little earlier, does not disqualify. Both prizes may go to the same author; but neither to the same author a second time.

## The Kathleen Blundell Trust

The late Miss Kathleen Blundell (who died in 1985) generously left the bulk of her estate to establish a charitable trust for the benefit and encouragement of young writers. The Trust, established in 1987, provides awards to writers under the age of 40 to assist them with their next book. Applications should be in the form of a letter sent to the Kathleen Blundell Trust at the Society of Authors, giving reasons for the application (including information about the basic terms of the publishing contract). The application must be accompanied by a copy of the author's latest book and the author's work must 'contribute to the greater understanding of existing social and economic organisation'. The closing date for applications is 30 June.

## The Boardman Tasker Prize

This annual prize of £1,000, founded in 1983, is given for a work of fiction, non-fiction or poetry, the central theme of which is concerned with the mountain environment. Authors of any nationality are eligible but the work must be published or distributed in the United Kingdom. Further details from Mrs. Dorothy Boardman, 56 St. Michael's Avenue, Bramhall, Stockport, Cheshire SK7 2PL.

## The Booker Prize

This annual prize for fiction of £20,000 is sponsored by Booker plc, and administered by Book Trust. The prize is awarded to the best novel in the opinion of the judges, published each year. The Prize is open to novels written in English by citizens of the British Commonwealth, Republic of Ireland, Pakistan, Bangladesh and South Africa and published for the first time in the U.K. by a British publisher. Entries are to be submitted only by U.K. publishers who may each submit not more than three novels with scheduled publication dates between 1 October of the previous year and 30 September of the current year, but the judges may also ask for other eligible novels to be submitted to them. In addition, publishers may submit eligible titles by authors who are previous Booker Prize winners. Entry forms and further information are available from the Publicity Officer, Book Trust, Book House, 45 East Hill, London SW18 2QZ *tel* 01-870 9055.

## Katharine Briggs Folklore Award

An award of £50 and an engraved goblet is given annually for a book in English, having its first original and initial publication in the U.K., which has made the most distinguished contribution to folklore studies. The term folklore studies is interpreted broadly to include all aspects of traditional and popular culture, narrative, belief, customs and folk arts. Details from the Publicity Officer, The Folklore Society, University College London, Gower Street, London WC1E 6BT *tel* 01-387 5894.

## The British Academy Research Awards

These are made annually (in the case of Learned Societies or group research applications) and quarterly (in the case of individual applications) to scholars conducting advanced academic research in the humanities and normally resident in the U.K. The main headings under which an application would be eligible are: (*a*) Travel and maintenance expenses in connection with an approved programme of research; (*b*) Archaeology fieldwork; (*c*) Costs of preparation of research for publication; (*d*) In special cases, aid to the publication of research. Successful applicants are normally expected to publish the results within two years. Details and application forms from The British Academy, 20-21 Cornwall Terrace, London NW1 4QP.

## The British Film Institute Book Award

Founded in 1984, this annual prize is given for any book, biography, reference work, collected essays, etc., on film or television which advances the public's understanding of those media. Details from Wayne Drew, Press Officer, British Film Institute, 21 Stephen Street, London W1P 1PL *tel* 01-255 1444.

## Canadian Authors Association Literary Awards

The awards consist of a silver medal and $5000 and apply in (i) fiction, (ii) non-fiction, (iii) poetry, (iv) drama (for any medium). These annual awards are to honour writing that achieves literary excellence without sacrificing popular appeal and are given to works by Canadian authors. Further details from the Canadian Authors Association, 121 Avenue Road, Suite 104, Toronto, Ontario M5R 2G3 *tel* 416-926 8084.

## Children's Book Award

Founded in 1980 by The Federation of Children's Book Groups this award is given annually to authors of works of fiction for children published in the United Kingdom. Children participate in the judging of the award. "Pick of the Year" booklist is published in conjunction with the award. Details from Jenny Blanch, 30 Senneleys Park Road, Northfield, Birmingham B31 1AL *tel* (021) 427 4860.

## Children's Book of the Year Awards

The Children's Book Council of Australia makes annual awards in three sections: (1) Book of the Year: Older Readers (for literary merit, quality of production and appeal to readers over 10 years of age); (2) Book of the Year: Younger Readers (criteria as above, plus appeal to newly independent readers, approxiamtely 7–10 years of age); (3) Picture Book of the Year (for readers of any age, with special consideration of the quality and unity of text and illustration). The Council may select up to one winner and two honour books in each category. In all three categories, winners receive cash award of $6000 and a Book Council Medal while honour book nominees receive $2000 and a certificate. Prize money is donated by the council's major sponsor, Myer

(Australia). Information from Children's Book Council of Australia (Inc.), P.O. Box 202, Sandy Bay, Tasmania 7005.

## Cholmondeley Awards

In 1965, the Dowager Marchioness of Cholmondeley established these non-competitive awards, for which submissions are not required, for the benefit and encouragement of poets of any age, sex or nationality. In 1988 the total value of the awards was £6,000. The scheme is administered by the Society of Authors.

## Collins Biennial Religious Book Award

This £2000 prize was founded in 1969 to commemorate the 150th Anniversary of the founding of Wm. Collins Sons & Co. Ltd. It is given biennially to a living citizen of the United Kingdom, the Commonwealth, the Republic of Ireland, and South Africa for a book which in the judges' opinion has made the most distinguished contribution to the relevance of Christianity in the modern world. Details from Lesley Walmsley, Wm. Collins PLC, 8 Grafton Street, London W1X 3LA   *tel* 01-493 7070.

## Commonwealth Writers Prize

Established in 1987 by the Commonwealth Foundation, the award is for the best work of fiction written in English by a citizen of the Commonwealth and published in the year prior to the award. First prize of £10,000, four prizes of £1,000 each to the regional winners and £1,000 for the runner-up to the winner. Details and entry form from Commonwealth Foundation, Marlborough House, Pall Mall London SW1Y 5HY   *tel* 01-930 3783.

## The Constable Trophy

A biennial competition supported by the five Northern based Regional Arts Associations for fiction writers living in the North of England (Northern Arts, North-West Arts, Yorkshire Arts, Lincolnshire and Humberside Arts, Merseyside Arts) for a previously unpublished novel. The winning entry will receive a prize of £1,000 and a silver cup and will be considered for publication by Constable & Co. Ltd., as may up to two runners-up. The winning novel may also receive an advance of £1,000 against royalties on publication. Full details from The Literature Department, Northern Arts, 10 Osborne Terrace, Newcastle upon Tyne NE2 1NZ.

## Thomas Cook Travel Book Awards

Awards are given annually in three categories to encourage the art of travel writing. (*a*) Travel Books award value £7500, (*b*) Guide Books, £2500. (*c*) Best Illustrated Travel Book, £1000. Books written in English and published in the current year are eligible. Details may be obtained from Book Trust, Book House, 45 East Hill, London SW18 2QZ   *tel* 01-870 9055.

## The Duff Cooper Memorial Prize

Friends and admirers of Duff Cooper, first Viscount Norwich (1890-1954), contributed a sum of money which has been invested in a Trust Fund. The interest is devoted to an annual prize for a literary work in the field of biography, history, politics or poetry published in English or French during the previous twenty-four months. There are two permanent judges (the present Lord Norwich, and the Warden of New College, Oxford) and three others who change every five years. All communications should be sent to the Viscount Norwich, 24 Blomfield Road, London W9 1AD.

## The Rose Mary Crawshay Prizes

One or more Rose Mary Crawshay prizes are awarded each year. The Prizes, which were originally founded by Rose Mary Crawshay in 1888, are awarded to women of any nationality who, in the judgement of the Council of the British Academy, have written or published within three calendar years next preceding the date of the award an historical or critical work of sufficient value on any subject connected with English literature, preference being given to a work regarding Byron, Shelley, or Keats.

## CWA Cartier Diamond Dagger Award
This award was first given in 1986 and is for outstanding contribution to the genre. Nominations not required. It is sponsored by Cartier in conjunction with the Crime Writers' Association, P.O. Box 172, Tring, Herts HP23 5LP.

## CWA John Creasey Memorial Award
The award was founded in 1973 following the death of John Creasey, to commemorate his foundation of the Crime Writers' Association. It is given annually, for the best crime novel by a previously unpublished author, by the Crime Writers' Association. Nominations by publishers only. P.O. Box 172, Tring, Herts HP23 5LP.

## CWA Gold Dagger Award and Silver Dagger Award
Founded in 1955 and awarded annually for a crime novel published in the United Kingdom. Nominations by publishers only. The panel of 5 judges are reviewers of crime fiction. Given by the Crime Writers' Association, P.O. Box 172, Tring, Herts HP23 5LP.

## CWA Gold Dagger Award for Non-Fiction
Founded in 1977 and awarded annually for a non-fiction crime book to an author published in the United Kingdom. Nominations by publishers only. Chosen by four judges of different professions. Given by the Crime Writers' Association, P.O. Box 172, Tring, Herts HP23 5LP.

## CWA Silver Dagger Award—for details see under CWA Gold Dagger Award.

## Deloitte-Bookseller Award
Founded in 1987 and sponsored jointly by Deloitte Haskins & Sells and *The Bookseller*, this £1000 prize is awarded annually for the best cover design for any book (hardback or paperback) in any category published in the previous year. The award is open to all U.K.-based designers and design teams and entries may be submitted either by publishers or by designers. Entry forms are available from January to March from Victoria Pugh, The Media Group, Deloitte Haskins & Sells, P.O. Box 207, 128 Queen Victoria Street, London EC4P 4JX  *tel* 01-248 3913.

## The Isaac Deutscher Memorial Prize
This prize of £100 was founded in 1968 and is awarded each year to the author of an essay or full-scale work, published or in manuscript, in recognition of outstanding research and writing in the Marxist tradition of Isaac Deutscher. Material should be submitted before 1st May of the current year to The Isaac Deutscher Memorial Prize, c/o Gerhard Wilke, 75 St. Gabriels Road, London NW2 4DU  *tel* 01-450 0469.

## Dillons Commonwealth Poetry Prize
An annual prize totalling £11,000 sponsored by Dillons the Bookstore and comprising £5000 for the best published poet: £2000 for the best first-time published poet: £1000 each for individual world Commonwealth awards. Extra £2500 fund for sponsored readings by winners. Open to all published Commonwealth poets, including U.K. Entries in non-English officially recognised languages accepted with translation. Closing date is 31st December. Details from the Poetry Prize Administrator, Commonwealth Institute, Kensington High Street, London W8 6NQ  *tel* 01-603 4535, ext. 263.

**The Earthworm Award**
The Earthworm Award was set up by Friends of the Earth to promote and reward environmental awareness and sensitivity in literature for children of all ages. The award is given in June each year for children's books, both fact and fiction, published in the United Kingdom in the twelve months preceding the award. There is a first prize of £1000 and prizes of £250 each for three runners-up. The Earthworm Award has been sponsored by the Save and Prosper Educational Trust. Applications to The Arts for the Earth, Friends of the Earth, 26–28 Underwood Street, London N1 7JQ  *tel* 01-253 3553/490 1555.

**The European Poetry Translation Prize**
Founded in 1983 a prize of £500 is given every two years for a published volume of poetry which has been translated into English from a European language. It is administered by the Poetry Society, 21 Earls Court Road, London SW5 9DE.

**Christopher Ewart-Biggs Memorial Prize**
This Prize of £4000 is awarded once every two years to the writer, of any nationality, whose work contributes most, in the opinion of the judges, to peace and understanding in Ireland; to closer ties between the peoples of Britain and Ireland; or to co-operation between the partners of the European Community. Eligible works must be published during the two years to 31 December 1990 and can be written in either English or French. Entry forms are available from Secretary, Memorial Prize, 31 Radnor Walk, London SW3 4BP  *tel* 01-352 4275.

**The Geoffrey Faber Memorial Prize**
As a memorial to the founder and first Chairman of the firm, Messrs. Faber & Faber Limited established in 1963 the Geoffrey Faber Memorial Prize.
The Prize of £1,000 is awarded annually: and it is given, in alternate years, for a volume of verse and for a volume of prose fiction. It is given to that volume of verse or prose fiction first published originally in this country during the two years preceding the year in which the award is given which is, in the opinion of the judges, of the greatest literary merit.
To be eligible for the prize the volume of verse or prose fiction must be by a writer who is: (*a*) not more than 40 years old at the date of publication of the book; (*b*) a citizen of the United Kingdom and Colonies, of any other Commonwealth state, of the Republic of Ireland or of the Republic of South Africa.
There are three judges who are reviewers of poetry or of fiction as the case may be; and they are nominated each year by the editors or literary editors of newspapers and magazines which regularly publish such reviews.
Messrs. Faber & Faber invite nominations from such editors and literary editors. No submissions for the prize are to be made.

**The Eleanor Farjeon Award**
In 1965 the Children's Book Circle instituted an annual award to be given for distinguished services to children's books and to be known as the Eleanor Farjeon Award in memory of the much-loved children's writer. A prize of (minimum) £750 may be given to a librarian, teacher, author, artist, publisher, reviewer, television producer or any other person working with or for children through books. The award is sponsored by Books for Children.

**Prudence Farmer Poetry Prize**
This poetry prize was founded in 1974 and is awarded annually for the best poem printed during the previous year in the *New Statesman & Society*, Foun-

dation House, Perseverance Works, 38 Kingsland Road, London E2 8DQ  *tel* 01-739 3211  *telex* 28449  *fax* 01-739 9307.

**The Fawcett Book Prize**
This annual award of £500, which was founded in 1982, is given to "the book which does most to illuminate women's position in society today". The prize, which is given for fiction and non-fiction books in alternate years, is awarded in May, and the deadline for applications is 31st December. Books published in Great Britain and the Commonwealth during the previous two years are eligible. Details from the Joint General Secretary, The Fawcett Society, 46 Harleyford Road, London SE11 5AY  *tel* 01-587 1287.

**The Kathleen Fidler Award**
An annual award of £1000 is given to an author of any age or nationality for an unpublished novel for the 8-12 age range, which must be the author's first attempt for this age range. Details from Book Trust Scotland, 15a Lynedoch Street, Glasgow G3 6EF  *tel* 041-332 0391.

**The John Florio Prize**
This prize was established in 1963 for the best translation into English of a twentieth century Italian work of literary merit and general interest published by a British publisher during the preceding two years. It is awarded under the auspices of the Italian Institute and the British-Italian Society, and named after John Florio. Details from the Secretary, The Translators Association, 84 Drayton Gardens, London SW10 9SB.

**E. M. Forster Award**
The distinguished English author, E. M. Forster, bequeathed the American publication rights and royalties of his posthumous novel *Maurice* to Christopher Isherwood, who transferred them to the American Academy and Institute of Arts and Letters (633 West 155th Street, New York, N.Y. 10032), for the establishment of an E. M. Forster Award, to be given from time to time to an English writer for a stay in the United States. Applications for this award are not accepted.

**Glaxo Prize for Medical Writing**
Thanks to the generosity of Glaxo Laboratories Ltd., who have taken over the funding of this prize from Astra Pharmaceuticals Ltd., the Medical Writers Group of the Society of Authors is offering two prizes of £750 each for an illustrated book and for a textbook. The closing date for entries, which must be submitted by publishers, is 30 June. Details from the Secretary, MWG, 84 Drayton Gardens, London SW10 9SB.

**Goodman Fielder Wattie Book Award**
This annual award, sponsored by Goodman Fielder Wattie Ltd. since 1967, is run by the Book Publishers Association of New Zealand, and is given for the best book taking into account writing and illustration, design and production, and impact on the community. Authors must be New Zealanders or resident in New Zealand. It is New Zealand's major literary award; 1st prize $17,000, 2nd $8,000, 3rd $4,000. Details from Goodman Fielder Wattie Award, Box 44146, Auckland 2.

**E. C. Gregory Trust Fund**
A number of substantial awards are made annually from this Fund for the encouragement of young poets who can show that they are likely to benefit from an opportunity to give more time to writing. A candidate for an Award must: (*a*) be a British subject by birth but *not* a national of Eire or any of the British dominions or colonies and be ordinarily resident in the United Kingdom

or Northern Ireland; (b) be under the age of thirty at 31st March in the year of the Award (i.e. the year following submission); (c) submit for the consideration of the Judges a published or unpublished work of belles-lettres, poetry or drama poems (not more than 30 poems). Entries for the Award should be sent not later than 31st October to the Society of Authors, 84 Drayton Gardens, London SW10 9SB.

## Guardian Award for Children's Fiction
The *Guardian*'s annual prize of £500 for an outstanding work of fiction for children by a British or Commonwealth writer, instituted in 1967. Further details from Stephanie Nettell, 24 Weymouth Street, London W1N 3FA  *tel* 01-580 3479.

## The Hawthornden Prize
The Hawthornden Prize, for which books do not have to be specially submitted, is awarded annually to the author of what, in the opinion of the Committee, is the best work of imaginative literature published during the preceding calendar year by a British author under forty-one years of age. It was founded by the late Miss Alice Warrender in 1919 and is administered by Hawthornden Castle International Retreat for Writers, Hawthornden Castle, Lasswade, Midlothian, Scotland EH18 1EG.

## The Felicia Hemans Prize for Lyrical Poetry
The Felicia Hemans Prize of books or money is awarded annually for a lyrical poem, the subject of which may be chosen by the competitor. Open to past and present members and students of the University of Liverpool only. The prize shall not be awarded more than once to the same competitor. Poems, endorsed "Hemans Prize", must be sent in to the Registrar, The University of Liverpool, P.O. Box 147, Liverpool L69 3BX  *tel* 051-794 2000, on or before May 1st. Competitors may submit either published or unpublished verse, but no competitor may submit more than one poem.

## David Higham Prize for Fiction
This prize of £1000 which was founded in 1975 is awarded annually to a citizen of the British Commonwealth, Republic of Ireland, South Africa or Pakistan for a first novel or book of short stories written in English and published during the current year. Entry forms are available from Book Trust, Book House, 45 East Hill, London SW18 2QZ  *tel* 01-870 9055. Publishers only may submit books.

## Historical Novel Prize
The prize, value £5,000, was founded in 1977 in memory of Georgette Heyer and is awarded annually for an outstanding full-length previously unpublished historical novel. Details from: The Bodley Head, 32 Bedford Square, London, WC1B 3EL or Transworld Publishers, Century House, 61-63 Uxbridge Road, London W5 5SA.

## The Calvin and Rose G. Hoffman Memorial Prize for Distinguished Publication on Christopher Marlowe
This annual prize of not less than £5000 is awarded to the best work, published or unpublished, that examines the life and works of Christopher Marlowe or the relationship between the works of Marlowe and Shakespeare. The adjudicator is Dr Stanley Wells of the Shakespeare Institute in Stratford-upon-Avon. The closing date for entries is 1 September, and the competition is open to all. Applications to The Headmaster, The King's School, Canterbury CT1 2ES  *tel* (0227) 475501.

## Winifred Holtby Memorial Prize

The prize will be for the best regional novel of the year written in the English language. The writer must be of British or Irish nationality, or a citizen of the Commonwealth. Translations, unless made by the author himself of his own work, are not eligible for consideration. If in any year it is considered that no regional novel is of sufficient merit the prize may be awarded to an author, qualified as aforesaid, of a literary work of non-fiction or poetry, concerning a regional subject.

Publishers may submit novels published during the current year to The Royal Society of Literature, 1 Hyde Park Gardens, London W2 2LT.

## International Poetry Competition

Prizes totalling £1000 are awarded biennially for the best three poems. Open to anyone over sixteen writing in English. Details from the Greenwich Festival, 151 Powis Street, London SE18 6JL    *tel* 01-317 8687    *fax* 01-316 5009.

## Sir Peter Kent Conservation Book Prize

Established in 1987, the European Year of the Environment, for the best book on environmental issues published in the UK in the 2 years ending 31 December.The theme varies each year. The award is worth £1,500 and is sponsored by BP Exploration Limited. Details and entry form from Book Trust, Book House, 45 East Hill, London    *tel.* 01-870 9055.

## King George's Fund for Sailors Book of the Sea Award

This £1000 award is sponsored by Pusser's Rum and goes annually to the best non-fiction book which contributes most to the knowledge and/or enjoyment of those who love the sea. A second award of £250 may be given at the discretion of the judges. Books must have been published in, or have first gone on sale in, the UK, during the year in question, and awards are presented at the Earl's Court Boat Show the following January. Five copies of entries should be sent to KGFS, 1 Chesham Street, London SW1X 8NF    *tel* 01-235 2884.

## The Martin Luther King Memorial Prize

A prize of £100 is awarded for a literary work reflecting the ideals to which Dr. Martin Luther King dedicated his life: viz. a novel or non-fiction book, poetry collection, essay, play, TV, radio or motion picture script, first published or performed in the United Kingdom during the calendar year preceding the date of the award. Details from John Brunner, c/o NatWest Bank, 7 Fore Street, Chard, Somerset TA20 1PJ. No enquiries answered without s.a.e.

## The Library Association Besterman Medal

The Library Association Besterman Medal is awarded annually for an outstanding bibliography or guide to the literature first published in the United Kingdom during the preceding year. Recommendations for the award are invited from members of the Library Association, who are asked to submit a preliminary list of not more than three titles. The following are among the criteria which will be taken into consideration in making the award: (i) the authority of the work and the quality and kind of the articles or entries; (ii) the accessibility and arrangement of the information; (iii) the scope and coverage; (iv) the quality of the indexing; (v) the adequacy of the references; (vi) the up-to-dateness of the information; (vii) the physical presentation; (viii) the originality of the work.

## The Library Association Carnegie Medal

The Library Association Carnegie Medal is awarded annually for an outstanding book for children written in English and receiving its first publication in the United Kingdom during the preceding year. It was instituted by the Library Association, whose work owes so much to the benefactors of the Carnegie

Trust, to commemorate the centenary of Andrew Carnegie's birth in 1835. Recommendations for the award are made by members of the Library Association and the decision rests with a Panel of the Youth Libraries Group. Consideration is given not only to the literary quality and suitability of the work, but also to the type, paper, illustrations and binding. It should be added that the award is not necessarily restricted to books of an imaginative nature.

## The Library Association Kate Greenaway Medal

The Kate Greenaway Medal is intended to recognise the importance of illustrations in children's books. It is awarded to the artist, who, in the opinion of the Library Association, has produced the most distinguished work in the illustration of children's books first published in the United Kingdom during the preceding year. Books intended for younger as well as older children are included and reproduction will be taken into account. Recommendations are invited from members of the Library Association who are asked to submit a preliminary list of not more than three titles.

## The Library Association McColvin Medal

The Library Association McColvin Medal is awarded annually for an outstanding reference book first published in the United Kingdom during the preceding year. The following types of book are eligible for consideration: (i) encyclopedias, general and special; (ii) dictionaries, general and special; (iii) biographical dictionaries; (iv) annuals, yearbooks and directories; (v) handbooks and compendia of data; (vi) atlases. Recommendations for the award are invited from members of the Library Association, who are asked to submit a preliminary list of not more than three titles. The following are among criteria which will be taken into consideration in making an award; (i) the authority of the work and the quality and kind of the articles or entries; (ii) the accessibility and arrangement of the information; (iii) the scope and coverage; (iv) the style; (v) the relevance and quality of the illustrations; (vi) the quality of the indexing; (vii) the adequacy of the bibliographies and references; (viii) the up-to-dateness of the information; (ix) the physical presentation; (x) the originality of the work.

## The Library Association Wheatley Medal

The Library Association Wheatley Medal is awarded annually for an outstanding index published during the preceding three years. Printed indexes to any type of publication may be submitted for consideration. Recommendations for the award are invited from members of the L.A. and the Society of Indexers, publishers and others. The final selection is made by a committee consisting of representatives of the L.A. Cataloguing and Indexing Group and the Society of Indexers, with power to co-opt. The award is made to the compiler of the winning index to a work which must have been published in the United Kingdom.

## LWT Plays on Stage Competition

The competition is open to drama companies, repertory companies, producing managements and producing theatres in the United Kingdom who are professional and have a track record of at least 180 performances during the previous two years. Three prizes with a total value of £48,000 are awarded each spring for the best production proposals. Information from LWT Plays on Stage, London Weekend Television, South Bank Television Centre, London SE1 9LT   *tel* 01-261 3196.

## The Sir William Lyons Award

The Lyons Award of £500 is to encourage young people in automotive journalism, including broadcasting, and to foster interest in motoring and the motor industry through these media. It is awarded to any person of British nationality resident in the United Kingdom under the age of 22 and consists of writing two essays and an interview with the Award Committee. Further details from the Chief Executive, Jean Peters, 2 Pembroke Villas, The Green, Richmond, Surrey TW9 1QF.

**Roger Machell Prize**
An annual award of £2,000 (sponsored by Hamish Hamilton) for a book on the performing arts, including music, ballet, the theatre, film or television. Work submitted must be in the English language and the work of one author, of over 50,000 words, to have been first published in the UK. Closing date for entries 30 November. Full details from the Society of Authors, 84 Drayton Gardens, London SW10 9SB.

**The McKitterick Prize**
This annual award of £5,000 was endowed by the late Tom McKitterick for first novels by authors over the age of 40. The closing date for entries is 31 December and the award is open to first published novels and unpublished typescripts. Full details from the Society of Authors, 84 Drayton Gardens, London SW10 9SB.

**The Enid McLeod Literary Prize**
This annual prize of £100 is given for a full-length work of literature which contributes most to Franco-British understanding. It must be written in English by a citizen of the U.K., British Commonwealth, the Republic of Ireland, Pakistan, Bangladesh, or South Africa, and first published in the U.K. Further details from the Secretary, Franco-British Society, Room 636, Linen Hall, 162-168 Regent Street, London W1R 5TB *tel* 01-734 0815.

**The Macmillan Prize for a Children's Picture Book**
Three prizes of £500 (1st), £300 (2nd) and £100 (3rd) are awarded annually for children's book illustrations by art students in higher education establishments in the United Kingdom. Applications to Publicity Manager, Macmillan Children's Books, 18-21 Cavaye Place, London SW10 9PG *tel* 01-373 6070.

**Macmillan Silver Pen Award for Fiction**
This award of £500 founded in 1969 and sponsored by Macmillan since 1986 is given annually for an outstanding novel written in English and published during the previous year by an author of British nationality. Books are nominated by members of the P.E.N. Executive Committee. Information from P.E.N., 7 Dilke Street, Chelsea, London SW3 4JE *tel* 01-352 6303.

**Arthur Markham Memorial Prize**
A prize for a short story, essay or poems on a given subject is offered annually as a memorial to the late Sir Arthur Markham. Candidates must be manual workers in or about a coal mine, or have been injured when so employed. Full details can be obtained from The Registrar and Secretary, The University, Sheffield S10 2TN.

**Kurt Maschler Emil Award**
An annual prize of £1,000 was founded in 1982 and is given to a British author/artist or one resident in Britain for more than ten years. It is given for a children's book in which text and illustrations are of excellence and enhance and balance each other. Details from Book Trust, Book House, 45 East Hill, London SW18 2QZ *tel* 01-870 9055.

**The Somerset Maugham Trust Fund**
The purpose of these annual awards, totalling about £15,000, is to encourage young writers to travel, to acquaint themselves with the manners and customs

of foreign countries, and, by widening their own experience, to extend both the basis and the influence of contemporary English literature. Mr. Maugham urged that in the selection of prize-winners, originality and promise should be the touchstones: he did not wish the judges to "play for safety" in their choice. A candidate for the award must be a British subject by birth and ordinarily resident in the United Kingdom or Northern Ireland. He or she must, at the time of the award, be under thirty-five years of age, and must submit a published literary work in volume form in the English language, of which he or she is the sole author. The term "literary work" includes poetry, fiction, criticism, history and biography, belles-lettres, or philosophy, but does not include a dramatic work. A candidate who wins an award must undertake to spend not less than three months outside Great Britain and Ireland, and to devote the prize to the expenses of this sojourn.

Any questions relating to the terms of the award should be addressed to The Society of Authors, 84 Drayton Gardens, London SW10 9SB, to which candidates should send the literary work they wish to submit for an award. Three copies of one published work (which are non-returnable) should be submitted by a candidate, and it must be accompanied by a statement of his or her age, place of birth, and other published works.

The closing date for the submission of books to be considered is December 31st.

### The Vicky Metcalf Awards for Short-Fiction and a Body of Work

These awards are given annually to Canadian writers to stimulate writing for children. $2,000 for a Body of Work; $1,000 for a Short story; $1,000 to the responsible editor if published in a Canadian journal or anthology. Details from Canadian Authors Association, 121 Avenue Road, Suite 104, Toronto, Ontario M5R 2G3   *tel* (416) 926-8084.

### MIND Book of the Year—the Allen Lane Award

This £1,000 award, inaugurated in memory of Sir Allen Lane in 1981, is given to the author of any book published in the current year which outstandingly furthers, in the opinion of the judges, public understanding of the prevention, causes, treatment or experience of mental illness or mental handicap. The award is administered by MIND, the National Association for Mental Health. Further details from Christine Shaw, MIND, 22 Harley Street, London W1N 2ED   *tel* 01-637 0741.

### The Mother Goose Award

The award, sponsored by Books for Children, is open to all artists having published a first major book for children during the previous year. Only books first published in Britain will be considered and this includes co-productions where the illustration originated in Britain. The award is presented annually at Easter and is in the form of a bronze egg together with a cheque for £1000. Recommendations for the award are invited from publishers and should be sent to each panel member. Full details and names and addresses of the panel members from Sally Grindley, Books for Children, Park House, Dollar Street, Cirencester, Glos. GL7 2AN.

### Shiva Naipaul Memorial Prize

This annual prize of £1,000 was founded in 1985, and is given to an English language writer of any nationality under the age of 35 for an essay of not more than 4,000 words describing a visit to a foreign place or people. Details from *The Spectator*, 56 Doughty Street, London WC1N 2LL.

## National Book Awards

Books written by U.S. citizens and published by U.S. publishers are eligible for this annual prize of $10,000 in each of two categories: fiction and non-fiction. Runners-up in each category will receive $1,000. Books are entered by publishers by July 15th each year. Details from National Book Awards, 155 Bank Street, Studio 1002d, New York, N.Y. 10014.

## National Book Council Awards for Australian Literature

These awards, sponsored by *The Book Printer*, are a feature of Australian Book Week, held annually. They are for books of the highest literary merit which make an outstanding contribution to Australian literature and consist of the NBC Gold Banjo Award ($10,000) and the NBC Silver Banjo Award ($7500), which must be for a book in a different category from that winning the NBC Gold Banjo Award. A new prize inaugurated in 1988 and sponsored by Qantas is the National Book Council/Qantas New Writer's Award, which can be awarded to a writer under the age of 35 or for the first published book of a writer of any age. Details from the Awards Secretary, 1st floor, 302 Lygon Street, Carlton, Victoria, Australia 3053 *tel* (03) 347 5855.

## National Poetry Competition

Now established as the major annual poetry competition in Britain. Prizes of £2,000, £1,000, £500, 5 of £100, 10 of £50. Entry fees of £2.00 per poem, maximum entry of 10 poems, length of each poem not to exceed 40 lines. Details and entry forms from National Poetry Competition, National Poetry Centre, 21 Earls Court Square, London SW5 9DE.

## The NCR Book Award for Non Fiction

An annual award founded in 1987 and sponsored by NCR Limited to stimulate more interest in non-fiction writing and publishing in the U.K. The award carries a prize of £25,000, currently the highest award available in the U.K. Additionally, £1,500 goes to the other three shortlisted authors. The award is run in co-operation with the Publishers Publicity Circle. Applications welcomed from publishers. Details from The Administrator, NCR Book Award, 206 Marylebone Road, London NW1 6LY *tel* 01-725 8246 *telex* 263931 *fax* 01-724 6519.

## Airey Neave Research Fellowships

The Airey Neave Trust promotes research in the form of fellowships for a carefully selected group of individuals who are at an early stage of their careers. The aim is to help outstanding young scholars to carry out projects in centres of excellence with a proved record of research in which the necessary experience and facilities can be found. The theme is national and international law and human freedom. Details from the Secretary, The Airey Neave Trust, House of Commons, London SW1A 0AA.

## John Newbery Medal

This annual prize which was founded in 1922 is given for children's literature to a citizen or resident of the U.S.A. The judges are 15 members of the Association for Library Service to Children (ALSC), a division of the American Library Association (committee members change annually) and the prize is given to the author of the most distinguished contribution to American literature for children published in the U.S. during the preceding year. Further details from ALSC, The American Library Association, 50 East Huron Street, Chicago, Illinois 60611.

## The Nobel Prize

The Nobel Prize in Literature is one of the awards stipulated in the will of the late Alfred Nobel, the Swedish scientist who invented dynamite. The awarding authority is the Swedish Academy, Källargränd 4, S-111 29 Stockholm, Sweden. No direct application for a prize will, however, be taken into consideration. For authors writing in English it was bestowed upon Rudyard Kipling in 1907, upon W. B. Yeats in 1923, upon George Bernard Shaw in 1925, upon Sinclair Lewis in 1930, upon John Galsworthy in 1932, upon Eugene O'Neill in 1936, upon Pearl Buck in 1938, upon T.S. Eliot in 1948, upon William Faulkner in 1949, upon Bertrand Russell in 1950, upon Sir Winston Churchill in 1953, upon Ernest Hemingway in 1954, upon John Steinbeck in 1962, upon Samuel Beckett in 1969, upon Patrick White in 1973, upon Saul Bellow in 1976, upon William Golding in 1983, upon Wole Soyinka in 1986 and upon Joseph Brodsky in 1987. The Nobel Prizes are understood to be worth about £280,000 each. They number five (*a*) Physics, (*b*) Chemistry, (*c*) Physiology or Medicine, (*d*) Literature, and (*e*) Promotion of Peace.

**The Noma Award for Publishing in Africa**
Established in 1979, this annual book prize of $5,000 is available to African writers and scholars whose work is published in Africa. The principal aim of the Award is to encourage publication of works by African writers and scholars in Africa. The prize is given to the author of an outstanding new book published (during the preceding twelve months) by a publisher domiciled on the African continent or its offshore islands, in any of these three categories: (i) scholarly or academic, (ii) books for children, (iii) literature and creative writing, including fiction, drama, and poetry. Any original work in any of the indigenous or official languages of Africa is eligible for consideration. Full details from The African Book Publishing Record, P.O. Box 56, Oxford OX1 3EL   *tel* (0865) 511428   *telex* 94012872 Zell G.

**Odd Fellows (Manchester Unity) Social Concern Annual Book Awards**
A prize worth £2000 is awarded for the book, or pamphlet of not less than 10,000 words, in an area of social concern (to be specified each year). Entries must be published in the current year; must be written by citizens of Britain, the Commonwealth, Republic of Ireland, Pakistan or South Africa; and must first have appeared in English. Entry forms are available from Book Trust, Book House, 45 East Hill, London SW18 2QZ   *tel* 01-870 9055.

**Oppenheim-John Downes Memorial Trust**
Awards, varying from £50 to £1500 depending on need, from this Trust Fund are given each December to deserving artists of any kind including writers, musicians, artists who are unable through poverty to effectively pursue their vocation. Applicants must be over 30 years of age and of British birth. Full details and Application for an Award form from the Trust, c/o 36 Whitefriars Street, London EC4Y 8BH, enclosing s.a.e.

**Catherine Pakenham Memorial Award**
Young women journalists (over 18 and under 30 years of age), resident in Britain, are eligible for this annual award which was founded in 1970 in memory of Lady Catherine Pakenham. The award of £500 is given for an article or TV or radio script (not a short story). Applications for entry forms should be sent to the Literary Editor, *The Evening Standard*, Northcliffe House, 2 Derry Street, London W8 5EE (an enclosed s.a.e. essential), after 1 September.

**Parents Magazine Best Book for Babies Award**
An annual award of £1000 for the best book for the under-fours—babies and toddlers. Eligible books must be published in the year ending 31 May, in the United Kingdom. A shortlist of ten books is chosen in February and the winner presentation is in May. Details and entry form from the Book Trust, Book House, 45 East Hill, London SW18 2QZ   *tel* 01-870 9055.

**The Pascall Prize**
Founded in 1987, this prize of $25,000 (Australian) is awarded every two years to an individual who has achieved excellence in Australian creative writing in a body of published, performed or broadcast work on any subject. The work must be predominantly in English and produced by a person who is Australian-born, is resident in Australia or has lived a substantial portion of his or her life in Australia. Nominations to The Geraldine Pascall Foundation, Level 4, 67 Castlereagh Street, Sydney, NSW 2000, Australia  *tel* (02) 231 4888  *fax* (02) 221 8201.

**Peterloo Poets Open Poetry Competition**
Founded in 1986 this annual competition sponsored by Marks & Spencer offers for 1990 a first prize of £1000 and five other prizes totalling £1600 (including a special prize of £500 for Afro-Caribbeans resident in the UK). Closing date for entries is 1 February 1990. Full details and rules of entry from Peterloo Poets, 2 Kelly Gardens, Calstock, Cornwall PL18 9SA.

**The Portico Prize**
Founded in 1985, this annual prize of £1,500 is awarded for a work of general interest and literary merit set wholly or mainly in the North West of England (Lancashire, Manchester, Liverpool, High Peak of Derbyshire, Cheshire and Cumbria). Information from the Portico Library, 57 Mosley Street, Manchester M2 3HY  *tel* 061-236 6785.

**Radio Times Drama Awards**
Founded in 1973 and now given biennially, these Awards, totalling at present £15,000, are given for an original play for radio and also for television. Full details in *Radio Times* in January 1990.

**Radio Times Radio Comedy Awards**
Founded in 1985 and now given biennially, these Awards, totalling at present £5,000, are given for an original 30 minute radio comedy script with the potential to become a series. Full details in *Radio Times* in January 1991.

**FAW Barbara Ramsden Award**
The award was founded by public subscription in 1971 to honour Barbara Ramsden, M.B.E., a publisher's editor of distinction. This major Australian literary award for quality writing is made each year on literary merit as a published book to both author and then in symbolic recognition of the importance of the publishing process to the publisher's editor. The winners are each presented with a plaque specially designed by Andor Meszaros. There is no restriction of category and more than one work may be submitted. The award is administered by the Victorian Fellowship of Victorian Writers, of which Barbara Ramsden was a treasurer of long standing. Details of this award and other national awards (all of which open in October each year and close 31 December), organised by the largest administrator of literary awards in Australia, from The Secretary, Victorian Fellowship of Australian Writers, 1/317 Barkers Road, Kew, Victoria 3101  *tel* 03-817 5243.

**Trevor Reese Memorial Prize**
Founded in 1979, a prize of £500 is given every two years for an historical monograph on Imperial or Commonwealth history. Details from The Director, Institute of Commonwealth Studies, 27-28 Russell Square, London WC1B 5DS.

**The Margaret Rhondda Award**
This award, first made in July 1968 on the tenth anniversary of Lady Rhondda's death, and afterwards every three years, is given to a woman writer as a grant-

in-aid towards the expenses of a research project in journalism. It is given to women journalists in recognition of the service which they give to the public through journalism. Closing date for next award December 31st, 1989. Further details from The Society of Authors, 84 Drayton Gardens, London SW10 9SB.

### The John Llewellyn Rhys Memorial Prize

The prize of £500, inaugurated by the late Mrs. Rhys in memory of her husband who was killed in 1940, is offered annually to the author of the most promising literary work of any kind published for the first time during the current year. The author must be a citizen of this country or the Commonwealth, and not have passed his or her 35th birthday by the date of the publication of the work submitted. Entry forms and further information are available from the John Llewellyn Rhys Memorial Prize, c/o Book Trust, Book House, 45 East Hill, London SW18 2QZ  *tel* 01-870 9055. Publishers only may submit books.

### The Rogers Prize

This prize of the value of £100 will be offered by the Senate, for an essay or dissertation on the subject of Advance in Surgery or Medicine. The Prize is open to all persons whose names appear on the Medical Register of the United Kingdom. The essay or dissertation must be submitted to the Secretary to the Scholarships Committee, University of London, Senate House, London WC1E 7HU (from whom further particulars may be obtained) not later than 30th June.

### Romantic Novelists' Association Award

The annual award of £5000 (sponsored by the Boots Company plc) for the best romantic novel of the year is open to non-members as well as members of the Romantic Novelists' Association. Novels must be published between January 1st and December 31st of year of entry. Two copies of the novel required. The Netta Muskett Award is for unpublished writers in the romantic novel field who must join the Association as probationary members. MSS. entered for this award must be specially written for it. No Award will be made unless a MS. is accepted for publication through the Association. Details from the Hon. Secretary, Mrs Dorothy Entwistle, 20 First Avenue, Amersham, Bucks HP7 9BJ.

### The Rooney Prize for Irish Literature

The Rooney Prize was set up in 1976 to encourage young Irish writing talent to persevere. The sum of IR £3000 is awarded annually to a different individual, who must be Irish, published in either Irish or English and under 40 years of age. The prize is non-competitive and there is no application procedure or entry form. Information from J. A. Sherwin, Strathin Enterprises Limited, Strathin, Templecarrig, Delgany, Co. Wicklow, Irish Republic.

### The Royal Society of Literature Award under the W. H. Heinemann Bequest

The purpose of this foundation is to encourage the production of literary works of real worth. The prize shall be deemed a reward for actual achievement. Works in any branch of literature may be submitted by their publishers to the verdict of the Royal Society of Literature which shall be final and without appeal. Prose fiction shall not be excluded from competition, but the Testator's intention is primarily to reward less remunerative classes of literature: poetry, criticism, biography, history, etc. Any work originally written in the English language shall be eligible. The recipient of a Prize shall not again be eligible for five years.

### Runciman Award

Established in 1985 by the Anglo-Hellenic League for a literary work wholly, or mainly, about Greece. The £1000 prize is sponsored by the Onassis Foundation and to be eligible a work must be published in its first English edition in the U.K. Details from Book Trust, Book House, 45 East Hill, London SW18 2QZ  *tel* 01-870 9055.

## The Schlegel-Tieck Prize
This prize was established in 1964 under the auspices of the Society of Authors and its Translators Association to be awarded annually for the best translation published by a British publisher during the previous year. Only translations of German twentieth-century works of literary merit and general interest will be considered. The work should be entered by the publisher and not the individual translator. Details may be obtained from the Secretary, The Translators Association, 84 Drayton Gardens, London SW10 9SB.

## The Science Book Prizes
These prizes, established in 1987 by the Committee on the Public Understanding of Science and sponsored by the Science Museum, are awarded annually to the authors of popular, non-fiction science and technology books written in English and published in the UK during the previous year that are judged to contribute most to the public understanding of science. Two prizes of £1000 each are awarded, one for books written primarily for those under 16 and the other for books with a general readership; publishers may enter up to five books in either category. Entries may cover any aspect of science and technology, including biography and history, but books published as educational textbooks or for professional or specialist audiences are not eligible. The author of a prize-winning book will be ineligible for another Science Book Prize for three years following the award. Details from COPUS, c/o The Royal Society, 6 Carlton House Terrace, London SW1Y 5AG  *tel* 01-839 5561  *fax* 01-930 2170.

## The Scott Moncrieff Prize
This prize was established in 1964 under the auspices of the Society of Authors and its Translators Association to be awarded annually for the best translation published by a British publisher during the previous year. Only translations of French twentieth century works of literary merit and general interest will be considered. The work should be entered by the publisher and not the individual translator. Details from the Secretary, The Translators Association, 84 Drayton Gardens, London SW10 9SB.

## Scottish Arts Council Awards
A limited number of Book Awards, value £750 each, are made each year by the Scottish Arts Council to published books of literary merit written by Scots or writers resident in Scotland. These awards are for new writing as well as for work by established authors (applications from publishers). Writers' bursaries are awarded twice a year to writers resident in Scotland who display professional standing and a record of publication. Applications from writers should be supported by an appropriate reference. Details of both schemes from the Literature Department. The Scottish Arts Council, 19 Charlotte Square, Edinburgh EH2 4DF  *tel* 031-226 6051.

## The Signal Poetry for Children Award
A prize of £100 is given annually for an outstanding book of poetry published for children in Britain and the Commonwealth during the previous year, whether single poet or anthology and regardless of country of original publication. Articles about the winning book are published in *Signal* each May. Not open to unpublished work. Further details from The Thimble Press, Lockwood, Station Road, South Woodchester, Stroud, Glos GL5 5EQ.

### The André Simon Memorial Fund Book Awards

Two prizes of £1500 each have been awarded annually since 1977 to the authors of a book on food and a book on drink respectively. Applications to Tessa Hayward, 61 Church Street, Isleworth, Middx TW7 6BE  *tel* 01-560 6662.

### Ally Sloper Award

Founded in 1976, this is an annual award which is presented at the annual convention of British strip/comic artists, and is given to veteran strip cartoonists only, for work in newspapers and comics. The award is given by Denis Gifford on behalf of the Association of Comic Enthusiasts. Full details are available from 80 Silverdale, Sydenham, London SE26 4SJ.

### Smarties Prize

Established in 1985 to encourage high standards and stimulate interest in books for children of primary school age. Two prizes of £1000; £8000 for overall winner. Eligible books must be published in the 12 months ending 31 October of the year of presentation and be written in English by a citizen of the U.K., or an author resident in the U.K., and published in the U.K. Prize is sponsored by Rowntree Mackintosh Confectionery. Details from Book Trust, Book House, 45 East Hill, London SW18 2QZ  *tel* 01-870 9055.

### The W. H. Smith Annual Literary Award

A prize of £10,000 is awarded annually to a Commonwealth author (including a citizen of the United Kingdom) whose book, written in English and published in the United Kingdom, within 12 months ending on December 31st preceding the date of the Award, in the opinion of the judges makes the most outstanding contribution to literature. Submissions are not accepted; the judges make their decision independently. Further details are available from W. H. Smith & Son Ltd., Strand House, 7 Holbein Place, London SW1W 8NR  *tel* 01-730 1200 ext. 5458.

### W. H. Smith Illustration Awards

These annual awards are given to practising book and magazine illustrators, for work first published in Great Britain in the twelve months preceding the judging of the award. Book covers, illustrations of a purely technical nature and photographs together with works produced as limited editions are excluded. Cover illustrations to magazines are eligible. Enquiries to The National Art Library, Victoria and Albert Museum, South Kensington, London SW7 2RL, or the Book Trust, Book House, 45 East Hill, Wandsworth, London SW18 2QZ.

### Southern Arts Literature Prize

The £1000 prize is awarded annually for a published novel, poetry, or literary non-fiction to writers living within the Southern Arts region. Details from The Literature Officer, Southern Arts, 19 Southgate Street, Winchester, Hants SO23 9DQ  *tel* (0962) 55099.

### The Spectator Young Writer Awards

The competition asks promising young writers to write an article of fewer than 2000 words on a subject of their choice suitable for publication in *The Spectator*. It is open to young people under 25 whether or not they are in higher education. The first prize consists of an award of £1000 in cash and books plus publication of the article in *The Spectator* and a writing contract, and there are additional prizes in cash and books of £1000 (2nd) and £500 (3rd). Information from *The Spectator*, 56 Doughty Street, London WC1N 2LL  *tel* 01-405 1706  *telex* 27124.

## Winifred Mary Stanford Prize

The prize was founded in 1977 by Mr. Leonard Cutts in memory of his wife who died in 1976. The prize of £1000 is awarded biennially and is open to any book published in the U.K. in the English language which has been inspired in some way by the Christian faith, written by a man or woman 50 years of age or under at the date of publication. The subject of the book may be from a wide range, including poetry, fiction, biography, autobiography, biblical exposition, religious experience and witness. Books must have been published in the two years prior to the award which is made at Easter. Literary merit will be a prime factor in selection. Submission by publishers only to the Secretary to the Judges, Winifred Mary Stanford Prize, c/o Hodder & Stoughton, 47 Bedford Square, London WC1B 3DP *tel* 01-636 9851.

## Sunday Express Book of the Year Award

A prize of £20,000 is awarded annually to the author of an outstanding, new work of fiction, including short stories, which is first published in English in Britain. No entries are accepted from authors or publishers. Nominations are made by a panel. Details from the *Sunday Express*, 245 Blackfriars Road, London SE1 9UX.

## E. Reginald Taylor Essay Competition

A prize of £100, in memory of the late E. Reginald Taylor, F.S.A., is awarded annually for the best unpublished essay submitted during the year. The essay, not exceeding 7500 words, should show *original research* on a subject of archaeological, art-historical or antiquarian interest within the period from the Roman era to A.D. 1830. The successful competitor may be invited to read the essay before the Association and the essay may be published in the *Journal* of the Association if approved by the Editorial Committee.

Competitors are advised to notify the Hon. Editor in advance of the intended subject of their work. The essay should be submitted not later than 31st December to the Hon. Editor, Dr. Martin Henig, British Archaeological Association, Institute of Archaeology, 36 Beaumont Street, Oxford OX1 2PG.

## The Dylan Thomas Award

This annual award of £1000 was established in 1983 to honour the contribution made to English letters by Dylan Thomas and to encourage writers working in two literary genres in which Dylan Thomas's work is justly celebrated—poetry and short-story writing. The award is made in alternate years for poetry and short stories and is open to writers throughout the U.K. Full details of the rules obtainable from The Dylan Thomas Award, The Poetry Society, 21 Earls Court Square, London SW5 9DE *tel* 01-373 7861/2.

## Time-Life Silver Pen Award for Non-Fiction

This award of £1000 founded in 1969 and sponsored by *Time-Life* since 1986 is given annually for an outstanding work of non-fiction written in English and published during the previous year by an author of British nationality. Books are nominated by members of the P.E.N. Executive Committee. Information from P.E.N., 7 Dilke Street, Chelsea, London SW3 4JE *tel* 01-352 6303.

## The Times Educational Supplement Information Book Awards

There are two annual awards of £500 to the authors of the best information books—one for children up to the age of 9, the other for children aged 10-16. The books must be published in Britain or the Commonwealth. Details from the Times Educational Supplement, Priory House, St. John's Lane, London EC1M 4BX *tel* 01-253 3000 *telex* 24460 Ttsupp *fax* 01-608 1599.

**The Times Educational Supplement Schoolbook Award**
£500 is given for the best school textbook. The age range and subject area vary from year to year. Details from the Times Educational Supplement, Priory House, St John's Lane, London EC1M 4BX *tel* 01-253 3000 *telex* 24460 Ttsupp *fax* 01-608 1599.

**The Tom-Gallon Trust**
This Trust was founded by the late Miss Nellie Tom-Gallon and is administered by the Society of Authors. An award is made biennially from this Fund to fiction writers of limited means who have had at least one short story accepted for publication. An award of £500 will be made in 1989. Authors wishing to enter should send to the Secretary, Society of Authors, 84 Drayton Gardens, SW10 9SB: (i) a list of their already published fiction, giving the name of the publisher or periodical in each case and the approximate date of publication; (ii) one published short story; (iii) a brief statement of their financial position; (iv) an undertaking that they intend to devote a substantial amount of time to the writing of fiction as soon as they are financially able to do so; (v) a stamped addressed envelope for the return of the work submitted. Closing date for next award 20th September 1990.

**The Betty Trask Awards**
The Betty Trask Awards are for the benefit of young authors under 35 and are given on the strength of a first novel (published or unpublished) of a romantic or traditional, rather than experimental nature. They stem from a generous bequest by the late Miss Betty Trask (who died in 1983) and are administered by the Society of Authors. It is expected that prizes totalling at least £20,000 will be presented each year. The winners are required to use the money for a period or periods of foreign travel. Full details of the conditions of entry can be obtained from the Society of Authors, 84 Drayton Gardens, London SW10 9SB.

**The Travelling Scholarship**
This is a non-competitive award, for which submissions are not required (see article: **The Society of Authors**).

**The TSB Peninsula Prize**
Founded in 1987, this annual prize is awarded for the best unpublished novel to come out of the South and West of England. It is organized through Wheaton Publishers Ltd, supported by South West Arts and generously sponsored by TSB. The author of the winning entry will receive a £1500 cash award from TSB, publication of the novel in hardback, plus a £1000 advance on royalties, a specially commissioned trophy and a leatherbound copy of the book. Details from The Administrator, TSB Peninsula Prize, Hennock Road, Exeter, Devon EX2 8RP *tel* (0392) 74121.

**The Dorothy Tutin Award**
This award of a carriage clock, donated by Johnathon Clifford, was founded in 1980, and is presented to the person who it is felt has done the most to encourage the writing and love of poetry in the U.K. Details from Johnathon Clifford, 27 Mill Road, Fareham, Hants PO16 0TH *tel* (0329) 822218.

**UEA Writing Fellowship**
Funded by the University and by the Eastern Arts Association, this Fellowship is offered annually, to be held in the School of English and American Studies at the University of East Anglia for the Summer Term.
The duties of the Fellowship will be discussed at interview. It will be assumed that one activity will be the pursuit of the Fellow's own writing. In addition, the Fellow will be expected to take part in some of the following activities: (a)

contributing to the teaching of a formal course in creative writing; (b) running a regular writers' workshop on an informal extra-curricular basis; (c) being available for a specified period each week to advise individual students engaged in writing; (d) giving an introductory lecture or reading at the beginning of the Fellowship; (e) organizing one or two literary events involving other writers invited from outside the University; (f) making some contribution to the cultural and artistic life of the region (by, for instance, a public lecture or reading). The salary for the Fellowship will be £2500 plus free flat. Applications for the Fellowship should be lodged with the Administrative Secretary, University of East Anglia, Norwich NR4 7TJ by 1st October of each year.

## Wandsworth London Writers Competition
The competition is open to writers of 16 years and over who live, work or study in the Greater London Area. Awards are made periodically in three classes, Poetry, Short Story and Play, the prizes totalling £775 in each class. Entries must be previously unpublished work. The award is sponsored by the Greater London Arts Association, and the judging is under the chairmanship of Martyn Goff, former Chief Executive of Book Trust. Further details from Assistant Director of Leisure and Amenity Services (Libraries, Museum and Arts), Wandsworth Town Hall, High Street, London SW18 2PU.

## The Welsh Arts Council's Awards to Writers
Prizes of £1,000 each are awarded to the authors of books published during the previous calendar year which, in the Literature Committee's opinion, are of exceptional literary merit. Bursaries and enabling grants totalling £40,000 are awarded annually to authors writing in both Welsh and English. The Council also organizes competitions from time to time. For further details of the Welsh Arts Council's policies, write to the Literature Department, Welsh Arts Council, Museum Place, Cardiff CF1 3NX    *tel* (0222) 394711.

## Whitbread Literary Awards
Awards to be judged in two stages and offering a total of £27,500 prize money open to five categories: Novel, First Novel, Children's Novel, Biography/Autobiography, Poetry. The winner in each category will receive a Whitbread Nomination Award of £1,500. The five nominations will go forward to be judged for the Whitbread Book of the Year. The overall winner receives £21,500 (£20,000 plus £1,500 Nomination Award). Writers must have lived in Great Britain and Ireland for three or more years. Submissions only from publishers. Closing date for entries: 1 August. Further details may be obtained from The Booksellers Association, 154 Buckingham Palace Road, London SW1W 9TZ    *tel* 01-730 8214.

## The Whitfield Prize
The Whitfield Prize (value £1000) is offered in the spring of each year for the best work on English or Welsh history by an author under 40 published in the United Kingdom in the preceding calendar year. Three non-returnable copies of a book eligible for the competition should be submitted by the author or the publisher before 31 December to the Executive Secretary, Royal Historical Society, University College London, Gower Street, London WC1E 6BT    *tel* 01-387 7532.

## John Whiting Award
Founded in 1965, this prize of £4,000 is given annually. Eligible to apply are any writers who have received during the previous two calendar years an award through the Arts Council new theatre writing schemes, or who have had a premier production by a theatre company in receipt of an annual subsidy.

Details from the Drama Director, Arts Council of Great Britain, 105 Piccadilly, London W1V 0AU    *tel* 01-629 9495.

## H. H. Wingate Prizes

Awarded to the books which best stimulate an interest in and awareness of Jewish concern among a wider reading public. The two categories: fiction and non fiction. Books must be published in English and authors normally resident in the UK, Israel, the British Commonwealth, South Africa, Pakistan or Republic of Ireland are eligible. The awards are each of £2,000 and are awarded annually in December. Details from Norman Morris, Balfour Diamond Jubilee Trust, Balfour House, 741 High Road, London N12.

## Wolfson Literary Awards for History

The awards were established in 1972 to pay tribute to a lifetime's contributions to the study of history and also to encourage the writing of scholarly history for the general public. No application is necessary, but further details from M. Paisner, Messrs. Paisner & Co., Bouverie House, 154 Fleet Street, London EC4.

## Yorkshire Post Literary Awards

A prize of £1,000 is awarded for the Book of the Year and a prize of £800 for the Best First Work each year. Also annual awards of £800 each are made for works which in the opinion of the Panel of Judges have made the greatest contribution to the understanding and appreciation of Music and Art. Nominations are only accepted from publishers and should arrive (together with one copy of the book) by 15th December in the case of main prizes, by 16th January in the case of the Art and Music Awards. Correspondence to Secretary of the Book Awards, Yorkshire Post Newspapers Ltd., P.O. Box 168, Wellington Street, Leeds LS1 1RF    *tel* (0532) 432701 ext. 1512.

# Index

# THE NEW LONDON TELEPHONE CODES

The **Index** precedes these telephone codes.

## THE NEW LONDON TELEPHONE CODES
for use Inside as well as Outside the London telephone area

The 01 London exchanges are being split into two areas from 6 May 1990. Local calls within one of these areas will be dialled as before. Between the two areas, or from outside the London telephone area, it will be necessary to include the 071 or 081 code. The following British Telecom list is here at the end of the 1990 edition for ease of reference.

| exch-ange no. | new code no. | exch-ange no. | new code no. | exch-ange no. | new code no. | exch-ange no. | new code no. | exch-ange no. | new code no. | exch-ange no. | new code no. |
|---|---|---|---|---|---|---|---|---|---|---|---|
| 200 | 081 | 235 | 071 | 265 | 071 | 299 | 081 | 332 | 081 | 366 | 081 |
| 202 | 081 | 236 | 071 | 266 | 071 | 300 | 081 | 335 | 081 | 367 | 081 |
| 203 | 081 | 237 | 071 | 267 | 071 | 301 | 081 | 336 | 081 | 368 | 081 |
| 204 | 081 | 238 | 071 | 268 | 071 | 302 | 081 | 337 | 081 | 370 | 071 |
| 205 | 081 | 239 | 071 | 269 | 071 | 303 | 081 | 339 | 081 | 371 | 071 |
| 206 | 081 | 240 | 071 | 270 | 071 | 304 | 081 | 340 | 081 | 372 | 071 |
| 207 | 081 | 241 | 071 | 271 | 071 | 305 | 081 | 341 | 081 | 373 | 071 |
| 208 | 081 | 242 | 071 | 272 | 071 | 308 | 081 | 342 | 081 | 374 | 071 |
| 209 | 081 | 243 | 071 | 273 | 071 | 309 | 081 | 343 | 081 | 375 | 071 |
| 210 | 071 | 244 | 071 | 274 | 071 | 310 | 081 | 345 | 081 | 376 | 071 |
| 214 | 071 | 245 | 071 | 276 | 071 | 311 | 081 | 346 | 081 | 377 | 071 |
| 215 | 071 | 246 | 071 | 277 | 071 | 312 | 081 | 347 | 081 | 378 | 071 |
| 217 | 071 | 247 | 071 | 278 | 071 | 313 | 081 | 348 | 081 | 379 | 071 |
| 218 | 071 | 248 | 071 | 279 | 071 | 314 | 081 | 349 | 081 | 380 | 071 |
| 219 | 071 | 249 | 071 | 280 | 071 | 316 | 081 | 350 | 071 | 381 | 071 |
| 220 | 071 | 250 | 071 | 281 | 071 | 317 | 081 | 351 | 071 | 382 | 071 |
| 221 | 071 | 251 | 071 | 283 | 071 | 318 | 081 | 352 | 071 | 383 | 071 |
| 222 | 071 | 252 | 071 | 284 | 071 | 319 | 081 | 353 | 071 | 384 | 071 |
| 223 | 071 | 253 | 071 | 286 | 071 | 320 | 071 | 354 | 071 | 385 | 071 |
| 224 | 071 | 254 | 071 | 287 | 071 | 321 | 071 | 355 | 071 | 386 | 071 |
| 225 | 071 | 255 | 071 | 288 | 071 | 322 | 071 | 356 | 071 | 387 | 071 |
| 226 | 071 | 256 | 071 | 289 | 071 | 323 | 071 | 357 | 071 | 388 | 071 |
| 227 | 071 | 257 | 071 | 290 | 081 | 324 | 071 | 358 | 071 | 389 | 071 |
| 228 | 071 | 258 | 071 | 291 | 081 | 325 | 071 | 359 | 071 | 390 | 081 |
| 229 | 071 | 259 | 071 | 293 | 081 | 326 | 071 | 360 | 081 | 391 | 081 |
| 230 | 071 | 260 | 071 | 294 | 081 | 327 | 071 | 361 | 081 | 392 | 081 |
| 231 | 071 | 261 | 071 | 295 | 081 | 328 | 071 | 363 | 081 | 393 | 081 |
| 232 | 071 | 262 | 071 | 297 | 081 | 329 | 071 | 364 | 081 | 394 | 081 |
| 233 | 071 | 263 | 071 | 298 | 081 | 330 | 081 | 365 | 081 | 397 | 081 |
| 234 | 071 | | | | | | | | | | |

| exch-ange no. | new code no. | exch-ange no. | new code no. | exch-ange no. | new code no. | exch-ange no. | new code no. | exch-ange no. | new code no. | exch-ange no. | new code no. |
|---|---|---|---|---|---|---|---|---|---|---|---|
| 398 | 081 | 449 | 081 | 494 | 071 | 543 | 081 | 586 | 071 | 636 | 071 |
| 399 | 081 | 450 | 081 | 495 | 071 | 544 | 081 | 587 | 071 | 637 | 071 |
| 400 | 071 | 451 | 081 | 496 | 071 | 545 | 081 | 588 | 071 | 638 | 071 |
| 401 | 071 | 452 | 081 | 497 | 071 | 546 | 081 | 589 | 071 | 639 | 071 |
| 402 | 071 | 453 | 081 | 498 | 071 | 547 | 081 | 590 | 081 | 640 | 081 |
| 403 | 071 | 455 | 081 | 499 | 071 | 549 | 081 | 591 | 081 | 641 | 081 |
| 404 | 071 | 456 | 081 | 500 | 081 | 550 | 081 | 592 | 081 | 642 | 081 |
| 405 | 071 | 458 | 081 | 501 | 081 | 551 | 081 | 593 | 081 | 643 | 081 |
| 406 | 071 | 459 | 081 | 502 | 081 | 552 | 081 | 594 | 081 | 644 | 081 |
| 407 | 071 | 460 | 081 | 504 | 081 | 553 | 081 | 595 | 081 | 645 | 081 |
| 408 | 071 | 461 | 081 | 505 | 081 | 554 | 081 | 597 | 081 | 646 | 081 |
| 409 | 071 | 462 | 081 | 506 | 081 | 555 | 081 | 598 | 081 | 647 | 081 |
| 420 | 081 | 463 | 081 | 507 | 081 | 556 | 081 | 599 | 081 | 648 | 081 |
| 421 | 081 | 464 | 081 | 508 | 081 | 558 | 081 | 600 | 071 | 650 | 081 |
| 422 | 081 | 466 | 081 | 509 | 081 | 559 | 081 | 601 | 071 | 651 | 081 |
| 423 | 081 | 467 | 081 | 511 | 071 | 560 | 081 | 602 | 071 | 653 | 081 |
| 424 | 081 | 468 | 081 | 512 | 071 | 561 | 081 | 603 | 071 | 654 | 081 |
| 426 | 081 | 469 | 081 | 514 | 081 | 562 | 081 | 604 | 071 | 655 | 081 |
| 427 | 081 | 470 | 081 | 515 | 071 | 563 | 081 | 605 | 071 | 656 | 081 |
| 428 | 081 | 471 | 081 | 517 | 081 | 564 | 081 | 606 | 071 | 657 | 081 |
| 429 | 081 | 472 | 081 | 518 | 081 | 566 | 081 | 607 | 071 | 658 | 081 |
| 430 | 071 | 473 | 071 | 519 | 081 | 567 | 081 | 608 | 071 | 659 | 081 |
| 431 | 071 | 474 | 071 | 520 | 081 | 568 | 081 | 609 | 071 | 660 | 081 |
| 432 | 071 | 475 | 081 | 521 | 081 | 569 | 081 | 618 | 071 | 661 | 081 |
| 433 | 071 | 476 | 071 | 523 | 081 | 570 | 081 | 620 | 071 | 663 | 081 |
| 434 | 071 | 478 | 081 | 524 | 081 | 571 | 081 | 621 | 071 | 664 | 081 |
| 435 | 071 | 480 | 071 | 526 | 081 | 572 | 081 | 622 | 071 | 665 | 081 |
| 436 | 071 | 481 | 071 | 527 | 081 | 573 | 081 | 623 | 071 | 666 | 081 |
| 437 | 071 | 482 | 071 | 529 | 081 | 574 | 081 | 624 | 071 | 667 | 081 |
| 438 | 071 | 483 | 071 | 530 | 081 | 575 | 081 | 625 | 071 | 668 | 081 |
| 439 | 071 | 484 | 071 | 531 | 081 | 576 | 081 | 626 | 071 | 669 | 081 |
| 440 | 081 | 485 | 071 | 532 | 081 | 577 | 081 | 627 | 071 | 670 | 081 |
| 441 | 081 | 486 | 071 | 533 | 081 | 578 | 081 | 628 | 071 | 671 | 081 |
| 442 | 081 | 487 | 071 | 534 | 081 | 579 | 081 | 629 | 071 | 672 | 081 |
| 443 | 081 | 488 | 071 | 536 | 081 | 580 | 071 | 630 | 071 | 673 | 081 |
| 444 | 081 | 489 | 071 | 537 | 071 | 581 | 071 | 631 | 071 | 674 | 081 |
| 445 | 081 | 490 | 071 | 538 | 071 | 582 | 071 | 632 | 071 | 675 | 081 |
| 446 | 081 | 491 | 071 | 539 | 081 | 583 | 071 | 633 | 071 | 676 | 081 |
| 447 | 081 | 492 | 071 | 540 | 081 | 584 | 071 | 634 | 071 | 677 | 081 |
| 448 | 081 | 493 | 071 | 541 | 081 | 585 | 071 | 635 | 071 | 678 | 081 |
| | | | | 542 | 081 | | | | | | |

| exch-ange no. | new code no. | exch-ange no. | new code no. | exch-ange no. | new code no. | exch-ange no. | new code no. | exch-ange no. | new code no. | exch-ange no. | new code no. |
|---|---|---|---|---|---|---|---|---|---|---|---|
| 679 | 081 | 731 | 071 | 778 | 081 | 839 | 071 | 888 | 081 | 944 | 081 |
| 680 | 081 | 732 | 071 | 780 | 081 | 840 | 081 | 889 | 081 | 946 | 081 |
| 681 | 081 | 733 | 071 | 783 | 081 | 841 | 081 | 890 | 081 | 947 | 081 |
| 682 | 081 | 734 | 071 | 785 | 081 | 842 | 081 | 891 | 081 | 948 | 081 |
| 683 | 081 | 735 | 071 | 786 | 081 | 843 | 081 | 892 | 081 | 949 | 081 |
| 684 | 081 | 736 | 071 | 788 | 081 | 844 | 081 | 893 | 081 | 950 | 081 |
| 685 | 081 | 737 | 071 | 789 | 081 | 845 | 081 | 894 | 081 | 951 | 081 |
| 686 | 081 | 738 | 071 | 790 | 071 | 846 | 081 | 897 | 081 | 952 | 081 |
| 687 | 081 | 739 | 071 | 791 | 071 | 847 | 081 | 898 | 081 | 953 | 081 |
| 688 | 081 | 740 | 081 | 792 | 071 | 848 | 081 | 900 | 081 | 954 | 081 |
| 689 | 081 | 741 | 081 | 793 | 071 | 850 | 081 | 902 | 081 | 958 | 081 |
| 690 | 081 | 742 | 081 | 794 | 071 | 851 | 081 | 903 | 081 | 959 | 081 |
| 691 | 081 | 743 | 081 | 796 | 071 | 852 | 081 | 904 | 081 | 960 | 081 |
| 692 | 081 | 744 | 081 | 798 | 071 | 853 | 081 | 905 | 081 | 961 | 081 |
| 693 | 081 | 745 | 081 | 799 | 071 | 854 | 081 | 906 | 081 | 963 | 081 |
| 694 | 081 | 746 | 081 | 800 | 081 | 855 | 081 | 907 | 081 | 964 | 081 |
| 695 | 081 | 747 | 081 | 801 | 081 | 856 | 081 | 908 | 081 | 965 | 081 |
| 697 | 081 | 748 | 081 | 802 | 081 | 857 | 081 | 909 | 081 | 968 | 081 |
| 698 | 081 | 749 | 081 | 803 | 081 | 858 | 081 | 920 | 071 | 969 | 081 |
| 699 | 081 | 750 | 081 | 804 | 081 | 859 | 081 | 921 | 071 | 974 | 081 |
| 700 | 071 | 751 | 081 | 805 | 081 | 861 | 081 | 922 | 071 | 976 | 071 |
| 701 | 071 | 752 | 081 | 806 | 081 | 863 | 081 | 923 | 071 | 977 | 081 |
| 702 | 071 | 754 | 081 | 807 | 081 | 864 | 081 | 924 | 071 | 978 | 071 |
| 703 | 071 | 755 | 081 | 808 | 081 | 866 | 081 | 925 | 071 | 979 | 081 |
| 704 | 071 | 756 | 081 | 809 | 081 | 868 | 081 | 927 | 071 | 980 | 081 |
| 706 | 071 | 758 | 081 | 820 | 071 | 869 | 081 | 928 | 071 | 981 | 081 |
| 707 | 071 | 759 | 081 | 821 | 071 | 870 | 081 | 929 | 071 | 983 | 081 |
| 708 | 071 | 760 | 081 | 822 | 071 | 871 | 081 | 930 | 071 | 984 | 081 |
| 709 | 071 | 761 | 081 | 823 | 071 | 874 | 081 | 931 | 071 | 985 | 081 |
| 720 | 071 | 763 | 081 | 824 | 071 | 875 | 081 | 932 | 071 | 986 | 081 |
| 721 | 071 | 764 | 081 | 826 | 071 | 876 | 081 | 933 | 071 | 987 | 071 |
| 722 | 071 | 766 | 081 | 828 | 071 | 877 | 081 | 934 | 071 | 988 | 081 |
| 723 | 071 | 767 | 081 | 829 | 071 | 878 | 081 | 935 | 071 | 989 | 081 |
| 724 | 071 | 768 | 081 | 831 | 071 | 879 | 081 | 936 | 071 | 991 | 081 |
| 725 | 071 | 769 | 081 | 832 | 071 | 881 | 081 | 937 | 071 | 992 | 081 |
| 726 | 071 | 770 | 081 | 833 | 071 | 882 | 081 | 938 | 071 | 993 | 081 |
| 727 | 071 | 771 | 081 | 834 | 071 | 883 | 081 | 940 | 081 | 994 | 081 |
| 728 | 071 | 773 | 081 | 835 | 071 | 884 | 081 | 941 | 081 | 995 | 081 |
| 729 | 071 | 776 | 081 | 836 | 071 | 885 | 081 | 942 | 081 | 997 | 081 |
| 730 | 071 | 777 | 081 | 837 | 071 | 886 | 081 | 943 | 081 | 998 | 081 |